THE CELL
IN DEVELOPMENT AND HEREDITY

THE MACMILLAN COMPANY
NEW YORK · CHICAGO
DALLAS · ATLANTA · SAN FRANCISCO
LONDON · MANILA

IN CANADA
BRETT-MACMILLAN LTD.
GALT, ONTARIO

THE CELL

IN

DEVELOPMENT AND HEREDITY

BY

EDMUND B. WILSON

DA COSTA PROFESSOR OF ZOÖLOGY, COLUMBIA UNIVERSITY

THIRD EDITION

WITH CORRECTIONS

" Natura nusquam magis est tota quam in minimis "

PLINY

New York

THE MACMILLAN COMPANY

Seventh Printing

SET UP AND ELECTROTYPED BY J. S. CUSHING CO.
PRINTED IN THE UNITED STATES OF AMERICA

To the Memory

OF

THEODOR BOVERI

PREFACE TO THE FIRST EDITION

THIS volume is the outcome of a course of lectures, delivered at Columbia University in the winter of 1892–93, in which I endeavored to give to an audience of general university students some account of recent advances in cellular biology, and more especially to trace the steps by which the problems of evolution have been reduced to problems of the cell. It was my first intention to publish these lectures in a simple and general form, in the hope of showing to wider circles how the varied and apparently heterogeneous cell-researches of the past twenty years have grown together in a coherent group, at the heart of which are a few elementary phenomena, and how these phenomena, easily intelligible even to those having no special knowledge of the subject, are related to the problems of development. Such a treatment was facilitated by the appearance, in 1893, of Oscar Hertwig's invaluable book on the cell, which brought together, in a form well designed for the use of special students, many of the more important results of modern cell-research. I am glad to acknowledge my debt to Hertwig's book; but it is proper to state that the present volume was fully sketched in its main outlines at the time the *Zelle und Gewebe* appeared. Its completion was, however, long delayed by investigations which I undertook in order to re-examine the history of the centrosomes in the fertilization of the egg,— a subject which had been thrown into such confusion by Fol's extraordinary account of the "Quadrille of Centres" in echinoderms that it seemed for a time impossible to form any definite conception of the cell in its relation to inheritance. By a fortunate coincidence the same task was independently undertaken, nearly at the same time, by several other investigators. The concordant results of these researches led to a decisive overthrow of Fol's conclusions, and the way was thus cleared for a return to the earlier and juster views founded by Hertwig, Strasburger, and Van Beneden, and so lucidly and forcibly developed by Boveri.

The rapid advance of discovery in the meantime has made it seem desirable to amplify the original plan of the work, in order to render it useful to students as well as to more general readers; and to this end it has been found necessary to go over a considerable part of the ground already so well covered by Hertwig.[1] This book does not, however, in any manner aim to

---

[1] Henneguy's *Leçons sur la cellule* is received, too late for further notice, as this volume is going through the press.

be a treatise on general histology, or to give an exhaustive account of the cell. It has rather been my endeavor to consider, within moderate limits, those features of the cell that seem more important and suggestive to the student of development, and in some measure to trace the steps by which our present knowledge has been acquired. A work thus limited necessarily shows many gaps; and some of these, especially on the botanical side, are, I fear, but too obvious. On its historical side, too, the subject could be traced only in its main outlines, and to many investigators of whose results I have made use it has been impossible to do full justice.

To the purely speculative side of the subject I do not desire to add more than is necessary to define some of the problems still to be solved; for I am mindful of Blumenbach's remark that while Drelincourt rejected two hundred and sixty-two "groundless hypotheses" of development, "nothing is more certain than that Drelincourt's own theory formed the two hundred and sixty-third." [1] I have no wish to add another to this list. And yet, even in a field where standpoints are so rapidly shifting and existing views are still so widely opposed, the conclusions of the individual observer may have a certain value if they point the way to further investigation of the facts. In this spirit I have endeavored to examine some of the more important existing views, to trace them to their sources, and in some measure to give a critical estimate of their present standing, in the hope of finding suggestion for further research.

Every writer on the cell must find himself under a heavy obligation to the works of Van Beneden, Oscar Hertwig, Flemming, Strasburger, and Boveri; and to the last-named author I have a special sense of gratitude. I am much indebted to my former student, Mr. A. P. Mathews, for calling my attention to the importance of the recent work of physiological chemists in its bearing on the problems of synthetic metabolism. The views developed in Chapter VII. have been considerably influenced by his suggestions, and this subject will be more fully treated by him in a forthcoming work; but I have endeavored as far as possible to avoid anticipating his own special conclusions. Among many others to whom I am indebted for kindly suggestion and advice, I must particularly mention my ever helpful friend, Professor Henry F. Osborn, and Professors J. E. Humphrey, T. H. Morgan, and F. S. Lee.

In copying so great a number of figures from the papers of other investigators, I must make a virtue of necessity. Many of the facts could not possibly have been illustrated by new figures equal in value to those of special workers in the various branches of cytological research, even had the necessary material and time been available. But, apart from this, mod-

_____
[1] Allen Thomson.

ern cytology extends over so much debatable ground that no general work of permanent value can be written that does not aim at an objective historical treatment of the subject; and I believe that to this end the results of investigators should as far as practicable be set forth by means of their original figures. Those for which no acknowledgment is made are original or taken from my own earlier papers.

The arrangement of the literature lists is as follows. A general list of all the works referred to in the text is given at the end of the book (p. 449). These are arranged in alphabetical order, and are referred to in the text by name and date, according to Mark's convenient system. In order, however, to indicate to students the more important references and partially to classify them, a short separate list is given at the end of each chapter. The chapter-lists include only a few selections from the general list, comprising especially works of a general character and those in which reviews of the special literature may be found.

E. B. W.

Columbia University, New York,
    July, 1896.

PREFACE TO THE THIRD EDITION

I MUCH appreciate the kind indulgence accorded to this work even in later years when it had become in many respects urgently in need of reconstruction. I now offer a third edition, rewritten throughout and much enlarged, with the following comment.

The first edition, planned in the early nineties and published in 1896, attempted to outline a new and rapidly growing subject which, in spite of many difficulties of detail, already showed broader bearings of remarkable general interest. Nearly thirty years have since gone by, in the course of which cellular biology has expanded in ever widening circles. Its general interest has grown correspondingly; but so, also, have its technical complexities and difficulties. To attempt a revision of the work at this day strictly along the original lines, and in equally brief form, would therefore have been impracticable, even were it desirable.

The year 1900, in which the second edition appeared, is memorable for the rediscovery of Mendel's long forgotten laws of heredity. This event opened a new era in the course of which the whole subject of the cell in relation to heredity and development has been made over. Cytology was from the beginning closely affiliated with anatomy, histology and embryology, and hardly less closely with general physiology and genetics. Since 1900 its coöperation with these subjects, and with cell-physiology, biophysics and biochemistry, has been one of the most striking features in the biological progress of our time; and the study of the cell has thus become so diversified that no single work could possibly cover more than a small portion of it.

It is with good reason. therefore, that in recent years extended general treatises on cellular bioiogy have largely gone out of fashion in favor of more circumscribed works dealing with particular aspects of the subject, and thus making possible a more intensive treatment. Since 1900 many admirable works of this type, and some of broader scope, have appeared, and much has thus been gained in the way of thorough and critical analysis; nevertheless I have ventured to think that the need of a work of somewhat more synthetic type has not disappeared.

No work written with such an aim can escape shortcomings in many directions, nor can it fail to be largely colored by individual bias. Every writer must treat the subject from the standpoint given by those fields of work in which he is most at home; and at best he can only try to indicate a few of the points of contact between those fields and others. I have desired to hold fast as far as possible to the general plan followed in the original work. Now, as then, I have written frankly from the standpoint of a zoölogical student of cytology and embryology, without pretence of competence to touch on other fields in more than an incidental way; and, as before, while always holding in view the needs of technical students and teachers of the subject, I have tried not wholly to lose sight of the interests of more general readers.

The work has grown to large proportions, but so has the subject; and the latter fact must be my apology for the necessarily scant treatment accorded to many important topics. I much regret this as affecting the botanical side of the subject; for in principle, botanical and zoölogical cytology are inseparable, though often in practice treated as distinct. My shortcomings in this direction are, however, more than compensated by Professor Sharp's excellent *Introduction to Cytology*, which appeared in 1921, written primarily from the standpoint of a botanist. The coöperative *General Cytology*, written by a group of biologists under the editorship of E. V. Cowdry (*University of Chicago Press*, 1924), did not appear until nearly the whole of the present work was already in type, and too late for more than the insertion of a few references to it.

I would especially emphasize the fact that it has not been possible to list or refer to the whole vast literature of the subject. For the most part the literature-lists include only works cited in the text or of interest for other particular reasons; and the same is true of the terms included in the glossary. At the end of each chapter, as in the first edition, will be found a short selected list of titles relating especially to its subject-matter, comprising for the most part works of more comprehensive scope or containing useful reviews of the literature. More abbreviated references to these will be found also in the final general literature-list.

I am indebted to the authorities of the Cambridge Press for permission to copy Figs. 285, D, F; 287, 290 and 385; to the Yale Press for use of the electrotypes of Figs. 1, 28, 45-47, 53, 68, 69, 172, 173, 186, 348, 459, 509, 513, 514, 520, and 523; to Professor T. H. Morgan for use of the drawing for Fig. 444; to Professor Martin Heidenhain for permission to reproduce Fig. 52, taken from his great work *Plasma und Zelle;* and to a large number of investigators from whose works other figures have been copied. Acknowledgment for all such figures is made in the legends. Those for which no acknowledgment is made are original or taken from earlier works by the writer.

Especial acknowledgments are due to Mabel T. Hedge, Helen E. Fernald, and Helen Daniels (Mrs. D. B. Young) for their artistic and conscientious work in the preparation of illustrations and for much other aid; and also to Alice E. Sheppard and Martha L. Clark (Mrs. W. W. Bennett).

E. B. W.

COLUMBIA UNIVERSITY, NEW YORK,
        December, 1924.

TABLE OF CONTENTS

CHAPTER II

CELL DIVISION

CHAPTER III

REPRODUCTION AND THE LIFE CYCLE

CHAPTER VI

Maturation and Reduction. Meiosis

CHAPTER IX

Some Problems of Cell-Organization

CHAPTER X

Chromosomes and Sex

CHAPTER XI

MORPHOLOGICAL PROBLEMS OF THE CHROMOSOMES

CHAPTER XII

Heredity and the Chromosomes

CHAPTER XIII

Growth, Cell-Division and Development

CHAPTER XIV

DEVELOPMENT AND HEREDITY

LIST OF FIGURES

INTRODUCTION

CHAPTER I

CHAPTER II

CHAPTER III

CHAPTER IV

CHAPTER V

LIST OF FIGURES

CHAPTER VI

CHAPTER VII

CHAPTER VIII

CHAPTER IX

CHAPTER X

CHAPTER XI

CHAPTER XII

CHAPTER XIII

CHAPTER XIV

THE CELL
IN DEVELOPMENT AND HEREDITY

THE CELL

INTRODUCTION

"Every animal appears as a sum of vital units, each of which bears in itself the complete characteristics of life."   VIRCHOW.[1]

Among the milestones of modern scientific progress the cell-theory of Schleiden and Schwann, enunciated in 1838–39, stands forth as one of the commanding landmarks of the nineteenth century. Its importance is not to be judged by its original form; as first outlined it was but a rude sketch, in many respects faulty and distorted. Its announcement nevertheless marked a turning point in the advance of biology, opening a new point of view for the study of living organisms, and revealing the outlines of a fundamental common plan of organization that underlies their endless external diversity. The cell-theory thus became a perennial source of fruitful researches which down to our own day have continued to press forward into always expanding fields of discovery. Long ago it became evident that the key to every biological problem must finally be sought in the cell; for every living organism is, or at some time has been, a cell. Applied by Goodsir, Virchow and their successors to the analysis of organic functions, the cell-theory opened far-reaching new vistas of progress in physiology and pathology and revolutionized our views of vital action, in health and in disease. It was the guide of Remak, Nägeli, Kölliker, and other immediate followers of Schleiden and Schwann, in those pioneer microscopical researches which ultimately demonstrated that cell-division constitutes the central phenomenon in organic reproduction, genetic continuity and heredity. Thirty years later it was the cell-theory that cleared the way for a remarkable group of investigators, including Fol, Auerbach, Bütschli, O. Hertwig, Van Beneden, Flemming, Strasburger and Carnoy, who laid the foundations for the new science of cytology and solved at last the ancient riddle of the fertilization of the egg and the beginnings of the individual life. Followed up especially by Boveri and his successors these researches provided the basis for a detailed analysis of heredity and development that stands among the most remarkable achievements of our time. Every field of biological research has been illuminated by the cell-theory. In respect to the range and diver-

[1] *Cellularpathologie*, 1858, p. 12.

I

sity of the phenomena which it has brought under a single point of view it is
surpassed by no other of the great generalizations of biology, and equaled
only by the theory of organic evolution. By force of habit we still continue
to speak of the cell "theory" but it is a theory only in name. In substance it
is a comprehensive general statement of fact and as such stands to-day
beside the evolution-theory among the foundation-stones of modern biology.

The cell-theory and the evolution-theory are now closely affiliated; but
the historian of biology is struck by the fact that for a long time they did
not come within hailing distance of each other. The theory of evolution
originally grew out of the study of natural history and took definite shape
long before the finer structure of living bodies was made known. A century
ago, in the time of Lamarck and Cuvier, naturalists had but the vaguest
notions concerning the finer details of internal organization. They were
mainly concerned with more obvious characters of living things; with forms,
colors, habits, distribution; with gross anatomy, organogeny and morphological classification. Long afterwards it was in the main the study of such
characters that led to the Darwinian revolution. The study of cells and
their activities seemed at first to have little connection with all this. The
convergence between the study of cells (cytology) and that of heredity and
evolution (genetics) was set on foot more than forty years after Schleiden
and Schwann, and it is still in the full tide of its advance.

In tracing the main outlines of this movement we may conveniently
divide the history of the subject since Schleiden and Schwann into three
periods. The first, from 1840 to 1870, was a time of foundation, during
which the fundamental outlines of the cell-theory were marked out and the
principles of genetic continuity became more clearly defined. The second,
extending from 1870 to 1900, included a development of cytology and
cellular embryology which gave more definite form to our general ideas
concerning the physical basis of heredity and the mechanism of development. The third period, opening with the rediscovery of Mendel's laws of
heredity in 1900, includes those modern and more searching inquiries into
the mechanism of sex and heredity which find their fullest expression in the
so-called chromosome-theory of heredity. These periods are separated by
no sharply drawn boundaries; they are but different phases of a single
movement. We approach it by a statement of the most elementary facts
from which it proceeded.[1]

[1] Schleiden and Schwann are universally and rightly recognized as the founders of the cell-theory;
but like every other great generalization it was preceded by a long series of earlier investigations, beginning with the memorable microscopical studies of Leeuwenhoek, Malpighi, Grew and Hooke in
the latter half of the seventeenth century.

Wolff, in the *Theoria generationis* (1759), clearly recognized the "spheres" and "vesicles" com-
posing the embryonic parts both of animals and of plants, though he did not grasp their real nature
or mode of origin. His conclusions were developed by Mirbel, Sprengel and Treviranus early in the

In all higher plants and animals the body may be resolved into a vast assemblage of extremely minute structural units, known as *cells* out of which, or their products, every part is built (Figs. 1, 2). The substance of the skin, of

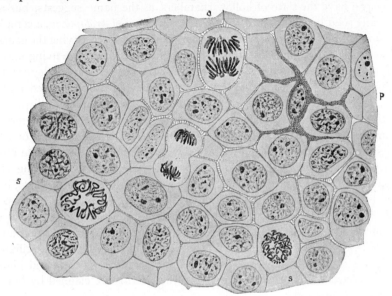

Fig. 1.—A small portion of the epidermis of a larval salamander (*Amblystoma*) seen in a slightly oblique tangential section, enlarged about 550 diameters. Most of the cells, polygonal in form, are in the so-called "resting" or vegetative (non-mitotic) state; but several are undergoing division (mitosis). Near *s* and *s* are spireme stages of mitosis, near *a* a middle anaphase, and near the center a late anaphase. Near *p* is a branching, granular pigment-cell that has crept up from below, forcing its way between the epidermal cells. Note the delicate plasma-bridges (plasmodesms) by which the latter are in many places connected. (This figure is combined from three separate camera drawings.)

the brain, of the blood, the bones, muscles or of any tissue, is shown by the microscope to be composed of innumerable minute bodies, as if it were a colony or congeries of organisms more elementary than itself (*cf.* p. 101).

nineteenth century; and nearly at the same time Oken (1805) foreshadowed the cell-theory in the form that it assumed with Schleiden and Schwann. His conception of "Bläschen" and of "Urschleim" was, however, hardly more than a lucky guess. A still closer approximation to the truth, prior to Schleiden and Schwann, appears in the works of Meyen, von Mohl, Raspail and Dutrochet and others. "The cells of plants," writes Meyen in 1830, "appear either singly, so that each one forms a single individual, as in the case of some algæ and fungi, or they are united together in greater or smaller masses to constitute a more highly organized plant. Even in this case each cell forms an independent, isolated whole; it nourishes itself, it builds itself up, and elaborates the raw nutrient materials which it takes up, into very different substances and materials." (Quoted from O. Hertwig, *The Cell*, English Trans., p. 3.) This passage might almost have been written at the present day. Such statements, however, were insufficiently based, and served only to pave the way for the real founders of the cell-theory.

Among other immediate predecessors or contemporaries of Schleiden and Schwann should be especially mentioned: Robert Brown, who discovered the cell-nucleus (1831, published in 1833);

By the early botanists these bodies were casually designated as "cells" (Robert Hooke, 1665), and this name was ultimately adopted by nearly all observers. It was an unlucky term; for later studies proved that cells do not in general have the form of hollow chambers, as the name suggests, but are typically solid bodies. The cell is largely composed of *protoplasm*, a complex mixture of substances, commonly of viscid consistency, and having the general properties of a colloidal system. Early recognized as the active living part of the organism, and later (1868) happily characterized by Huxley as the "physical basis of life," protoplasm is now universally recognized as the immediate substratum of all forms of vital activity.[1] Endlessly diversified in the details of their form and structure cells possess a characteristic common type of organization and may be treated as elementary organic units out of which and their products the body is built. In higher animals and plants (*Metazoa, Metaphyta*) the body is *multicellular*, consisting of a great number of such units, while in the lowest organisms or *Protista*, it is unicellular, consisting of but a single cell (Fig. 3). All such organisms, of which a multitude are known, are of microscopic size. They display a wonderful diversity of structural and physiological type. Some are plants (desmids, diatoms, bacteria, etc.), others animals (rhizopods, ciliates) while in still others (flagellates) the boundary between animals and plants becomes hard to define, so that many of these forms are claimed by botanists and zoölogists alike.

Both structurally and physiologically the multicellular organism suggests an aggregate or colony of unicellular ones; whether this be literally true or not the analysis of biological phenomena is made definite and effective by the conception that the cell constitutes a primary organic unit both of

Dujardin, who emphasized the physiological importance of protoplasm ("sarcode") in Protista; Purkinje, Valentin, Johannes Müller, Henle, Unger, Nägeli and the early investigators of protoplasm enumerated beyond. The significance of Schleiden's and Schwann's work lies in the thorough and comprehensive way in which the problem was studied, the philosophic breadth with which the conclusions were developed, and the far-reaching influence which they thus exercised upon subsequent research. In this respect it is hardly too much to compare the *Mikroskopische Untersuchungen* with the *Origin of Species*.

More detailed accounts of the history of research during this period will be found in the works mentioned at the end of this Introduction, especially those of Heidenhain and O. Hertwig. See also Gerould ('22).

[1] The word protoplasm is due to Purkinje (1840) who applied it to the formative substance of the animal embryo and compared it with the "granular material" of the cambium in plants. It was afterwards independently used by H. von Mohl (1846) to designate the contents of the plant-cell. The fundamental significance of protoplasm in the cells of higher organisms, its identity with the "sarcode" (Dujardin) of Protista, and its essential similarity in animals and plants were gradually made known by numerous researches between 1840 and 1870. Among the most important of these were the classical works of De Bary and of Max Schultze; but beside them stand many others of high interest, in particular those of Unger, von Mohl, and Cohn among botanists, and of Virchow, Kölliker and Beale among zoölogists. These early works have been reviewed by many writers. Accounts of them, with literature lists, will be found in the works cited in the preceding footnote.

structure and of action.[1] In the unicellular body all the vital activities are performed by one such unit. In the multicellular plant or animal each function, and hence the life of the organism as a whole, has at its root a multitude of cell-activities. The more complex life of the higher plant or animal arises through the specialization of the cells, this way or that, for the better performance of particular functions; hence that "physiological division of labor" which, as in organized human society, leads to higher

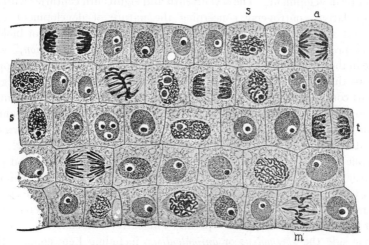

Fig. 2.—Group of cells from the meristem or embryonic tissue of the growing root-tip of the onion, as seen in longitudinal section. Like the preceding figure this is combined from a number of separate camera drawings, several stages of mitosis having been brought together. At *a, a* are seen anaphase-figures, at *s, s* spiremes, at *m* a metaphase, and at *t* an early telophase.

functional efficiency. On such considerations was based the famous comparison of the multicellular body to a "cell-state," due especially to Virchow (1858) though foreshadowed by Schwann and other early writers, and later elaborated by Milne Edwards, Haeckel and many others. This conception of the multicellular organism brought about a revolution in the prevailing views of vital action, and gave as great an impetus to physiology and pathology as to morphology. As we now can see, it requires some qualification, especially as applied to the phenomena of growth; but the conviction of its essential truth has survived all criticism, and as measured by its continued fruitfulness, it still stands among the most important generalizations of modern biology.

---

[1] *Cf.* p. 101. "It is to the cell that the study of every bodily function sooner or later drives us. In the muscle-cell lies the problem of the heart-beat and that of muscular contraction; in the gland-cell reside the causes of secretion; in the epithelial cell, in the white blood-cell, lies the problem of the absorption of food, and the secrets of the mind are hidden in the ganglion-cell." (Verworn, *Allgemeine Physiologie*, p. 53, 1895.)

Equally momentous was the influence of the cell-theory on embryology, where it first was brought to bear upon the problem of heredity. Prior to the cell-theory all attempts to comprehend the mechanism of development and heredity had been futile. Aristotle, it is true, and long afterwards Harvey (1651), had firmly grasped the principle of epigenesis or progressive new-formation in development: but neither of these great embryologists had the smallest real conception of the nature of the germ or of the mechanism of its development. The seventeenth and eighteenth centuries witnessed a speculative controversy concerning the nature of development which constitutes one of the most picturesque episodes in the history of biology.[1] It was precipitated by the doctrine of *preformation* or *"evolution,"* which arose in the latter part of the seventeenth century. This assumed, in opposition to the teaching of Aristotle and Harvey, that the germ-cell (egg or sperm) contains an embryo fully formed in miniature, as the bud contains the flower or the chrysalis the butterfly. Development is merely the unfolding or "evolution" of a preëxisting germ; inheritance the handing down from parent to child of an infinitesimal reproduction of its own body. This doctrine was advocated by some of the most eminent naturalists and physiologists of the time. One group of these writers considered the preformed germ to be borne by the sperm and to be introduced by it into the egg; another that it is from the first contained within the egg and is merely awakened to its development by the sperm. Thus arose two contending schools, on one side the *spermatists* or *animalculists*, including Leuwenhoek, Hartsoeker, Boerhave and Leibnitz, on the other the *ovists*, among whom were numbered Swammerdam, Malpighi, Haller and above all Bonnet. By this eminent French naturalist (1720–1793) the theory of preformation was consistently worked out to its logical limit in the theory of *encasement*, the embryo itself being conceived as containing eggs including embryos for the next generation, these other eggs and embryos in turn, and so on *ad infinitum* like an unending series of boxes, one within another; hence the term *"emboîtement."* This conclusion, evidently, was but a logical *tour de force*, hardly to be taken seriously, as Bonnet himself in the end frankly admitted; its mere statement, indeed, carries its own refutation. The controversy was in fact wholly futile, for spermatists and ovists alike received their *coup de grâce* through the work of Caspar Friederich Wolff (1759), who brought forward a renewed and masterly demonstration that the fertilized egg does not at the beginning contain any preformed germ but gives rise to the embryo little by little by the progressive production of new parts previously non-existent as such. Biologists therefore gradually returned

---

[1] A fuller account of this will be found in O. Hertwig, *Lehrbuch der Entwicklungsgeschichte*, 9te Aufl. 1910. See also Whitman ('94a, '94b).

to the views of the fathers of embryology, and in the end universally accepted the fact that development, in its external aspects at least, is not a

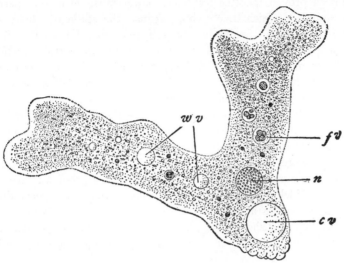

Fig. 3.—*Amœba Proteus*, an animal consisting of a single naked cell, × 280. (From Sedgwick and Wilson's Biology.)
   n. The nucleus; *w. v.* Water-vacuoles; *c. v.* Contractile vacuole; *f. v.* Food-vacuole.

process of "evolution" or unfolding but one of progressive new-formation, or *epigenesis*.[1]

This result provided the foundation for modern embryology; but for nearly a century after Wolff the actual nature of the egg and the mechanism of its development remained in the dark. The way towards a solution of the mystery was first opened by the proof that *the egg is a single cell*, like other kinds of cells in every essential respect. This fact had been recognized by Schwann, but was not at first generally accepted. Its demonstration by Gegenbaur (1861) and many later observers constituted the first solid advance towards a true view of heredity, making manifest the wonderful fact that a single cell may contain within its microscopic compass the total heritage of even the most complex adult individual. So far as the egg is concerned the problem of heredity thus took on perfectly definite shape; but in respect to paternal inheritance the mystery remained as impenetrable as before. It was soon to be dispelled. Since the time of Leeuwenhoek (1677) it had been known that the sperm or fertilizing fluid contains innumerable minute bodies, endowed with the power of active movement, and therefore regarded by the early observers as parasitic animalcules or

[1] A critical analysis of Wolff's remarkable work is given by Wheeler ('98) and by O. Hertwig ('10).

ınfusoria—hence the term *spermatozoa* (sperm-animals) by which the sperms
are still often called.   As long ago as 1786, however, the experiments of
Spallanzani proved that the fertilizing power must lie in the sperms, not
in the liquid in which they swim, because the spermatic fluid loses its
power when filtered.   Spallanzani himself, it is true, did not thus interpret
his results, but concluded, strangely enough, that the fertilizing effect was
due to the seminal fluid in which the sperms swim.[1]   The correct conclusion
seems first to have been drawn by Prévost and Dumas (1824), who in addition to repeating Spallanzani's experiments performed many others demonstrating that "The prolific principle resides in the spermatic animalcules."[2]
Shortly after the appearance of Schwann's great work Kölliker demonstrated
(1841) that the sperms arise by the transformation of cells in the testis; obviously, therefore, they are not parasites but, like the ovum, form a part
of the parent organism.   In 1865, finally, the final proof was attained by
Schweigger-Seidel and La Valette St. George that the sperm does not
consist of a nucleus alone, as Kölliker believed, but contains also cytoplasm.   It was thus shown to be, like the egg, a single cell, peculiarly modified in structure and of extreme minuteness, yet morphologically equivalent
to other cells.[3]

One all-important point remained undetermined, namely, the history of
the sperm in fertilization.   In the time of Schleiden and Schwann it was
supposed by some leading observers that the sperm might affect the egg
merely by contact-action or by carrying to it a catalytic agent (Kölliker,
Bischoff); and it was for a time believed, even by such observers as Bütschli, Van Beneden and Strasburger, that the sperm completely disintegrates as it enters the egg or fuses with its surface-layer.[4]   On the other hand,
an important group of observers had conjectured that the sperm must
actually penetrate the egg, though unable to demonstrate the fact with
certainty.   This view, long ago adopted by Leeuwenhoek, Hartsoeker and
other "spermatists," was reasserted by Prévost and Dumas (1824), and
later by other observers (1840–1855) who observed the presence of sperms
inside the egg-membrane (Barry, Meissner, Keber) or in contact with the
egg.   Newport (1854) seems first to have actually described the entrance
of the sperm (in the frog), and in the following year it was also described
by Pringsheim in the green alga *Œdogonium*.   The first demonstrative
evidence of the fact, with a full and detailed account of the process of pene-

[1] See F. R. Lillie ('16, '19).
[2] Cited from Lillie.
[3] The discovery of the sperm is often accredited to Ludwig Hamm, described as a pupil of Leeuwenhoek (1677), but he seems to have done no more than call the attention of Leeuwenhoek to the
subject.   Hartsoeker afterward claimed the merit of having seen them as early as 1674 (Allan Thomson) but his observations were not made known until after those of Leeuwenhoek.
[4] See O. Hertwig ('17, p. 31).

tration, was however given by Fol (1879) in the sea-urchin egg, while at the same time it was described in lower plants by Schmitz. In the meantime O. Hertwig ('75) had traced the fate of the sperm within the egg; and while he had not actually seen the process of penetration his work left no doubt of the fundamental fact that fertilization is accomplished by a single sperm that enters the egg.

We retrace our steps in order to consider earlier investigations on the origin of cells. In this all-important question is involved the central problem of development and heredity, as gradually became clear in the course of the first two decades after Schleiden and Schwann. Several earlier observers had observed the origin of cells by the division of preëxisting cells, in particular the botanists, Brogniart (1827), Meyen (1830), Mirbel (1835) and von Mohl (1835); and this mode of cell-formation was also recognized in limited measure by the authors of the cell theory, though only with considerable hesitation. Its fundamental significance was obscured for a time by the erroneous conclusion of Schleiden and Schwann that cells most commonly arise *de novo* by a process of "free cell-formation," new cells making their appearance by crystallizing, as it were, out of a continuous and formless matrix or "cytoblastema." The problems thus raised engaged the efforts of investigators more and more seriously in the period between 1840 and 1860,[1] under the lead especially of Unger, von Mohl and Nägeli on the botanical side, and of Kölliker, Remak and Virchow, on the zoölogical. In the end the long series of investigations set on foot at this time overturned the theory of free cell-formation, and finally established the conclusion that every cell arises by the division of a preëxisting cell, and in no other way. This conclusion (as Heidenhain has pointed out) was clearly stated already by Kölliker in his classical work on the embryology of cephalopods (1844) and extended by him to both plants and animals; but this observer later admitted the occurrence also of free cell-formation. The universality of cell-division was first definitely maintained by Remak and by Virchow whose celebrated aphorism *omnis cellula e cellula* (1855)[2] has become a household word in every modern laboratory. Echoes of free cell-formation, it is true, have now and then continued to be heard, even down to our own day, but have always been a product of error. To-day, therefore, we may with complete confidence repeat Remak's remark (1852) that the origin of cells *de novo* is no more credible than the spontaneous generation of life.

It is here that the full significance of the cell-theory for heredity and

[1] For accounts of the early literature see Remak (1855), Flemming (1882), Sachs (1890). A more recent detailed and critical review is given in Heider ('00).
[2] *Arch. für Path. Anat.* VIII, p. 23.

development first dawns upon us. If the cells of the body always arise by division of preëxisting cells, all must be descended by division from the original germ-cell as their common ancestor; and such is the observed fact. The first step in development consists in the division of the egg into two cells, which then divide in turn to form four, eight, sixteen and so on in more or less regular progression (Fig. 4). Step by step the egg thus splits up into a multitude of cells which build up the body of the embryo, and finally of the adult. This process, known as the *cleavage* or *segmentation*

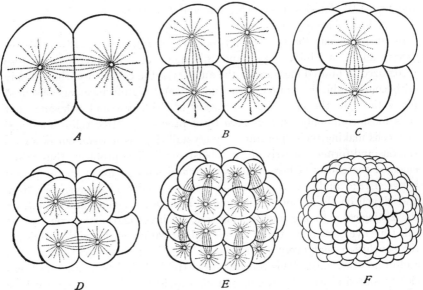

Fig. 4.—Cleavage of the ovum in the holothurian *Synapta* (slightly schematized). [After SE-LENKA.]
A–E. Successive cleavages to the 32-cell stage. F. Blastula of 128 cells.

of the egg, was observed long before its meaning was understood. It seems to have been first definitely described by Prévost and Dumas (1824) in the case of the frog's egg, though earlier observers had seen it; but at that time neither the egg nor its descendants were known to be cells. Its true meaning was first fully deciphered by Kölliker and Remak in the first decade after Schleiden and Schwann, though important contributions in the same direction were made at that time by Bergmann, Bischoff, Martin Goodsir and Barry. This critical point once made clear, the dominating signifi-cance of cell-division in the history of life began to stand forth in its true proportions. It became manifest that cleavage is but an infinitesimal part of a greater series of cell-divisions that has no assignable limits in the past or future.   The germ-cell arises by division of a cell preëxisting in the body of the parent, and in its turn divides to form the body of the offspring and also new germ-cells for coming generations; and so on without end. Embryologists thus arrived at the conception, vividly set forth by Virchow in 1858,[1] of an unbroken series of cell-divisions that extends backwards from our own day throughout the entire past history of life.   So far as we know, life under existing conditions never arises *de novo*.   It is a *continuum*, a never-ending stream of protoplasm in the form of cells, maintained by assimilation, growth and division.   The individual is but a passing eddy in the flow which vanishes and leaves no trace, while the general stream of life goes forwards.

Heredity thus appears as a consequence of the genetic continuity of cells by division, and the germ-cells constitute its physical basis.   With this result before us we may formulate the problem of development with greater precision. If the egg contains no preformed embryo, what does it transmit?   Such was the question which, in the seventies and eighties of the last century, first brought the cell-theory to closer quarters with the problems of heredity and development.   Among many speculative attempts to answer it we here refer only to Darwin's celebrated hypothesis of pangenesis (1868) which assumed the germ-cells to be reservoirs of minute germs or "gemmules," originally thrown off by the cells of the body or soma, later transported to the germ-cells and there held in reserve.   During the development of the embryo the gemmules were supposed to determine the production of (or actually to develop into) somatic cells like those from which they arose. Darwin thus assumed (in accordance with a notion even now widely prevalent) that the parent literally transmits its characters to the offspring, and thus sought to explain the heredity of "acquired" or "somatogenic" characters, at that time generally accepted as a fact.   Pangenesis was, however, a purely speculative construction, devoid of any actual basis of observed fact.   It received no support from later experimental tests by Galton and others.   It was therefore gradually abandoned,[2] leaving the internal cell-mechanism of heredity as hidden as before.

The early eighties brought forth certain theoretical writings which grew out of cytological researches then in progress and in consequence of which the whole problem took on a different aspect.   In 1883 appeared the first

[1] See quotation from Virchow's *Cellularpathologie*, at p. 114.

[2] Darwin's theory must not be confused with the "intracellular pangenesis" of De Vries (1889), which, though modeled upon Darwin's conception, differed wholly from it in respect to heredity. De Vries accepted Darwin's fundamental conception of gemmules (which he calls *pangens*) as minute organized units, capable of independent growth and division, and responsible for particular heredity qualities; but denied the transportal of pangens from cell to cell, and hence from somatic to germ-cells.   This view, subsequently adopted by many other writers, received an elaborate theoretical development in Weismann's well-known work on the *Germ Plasm* (1885).

of Weismann's memorable series of essays which did so much to illuminate the problem of heredity and to bring it into closer relations with microscopical research. The way for Weismann's main conclusion was prepared by Nussbaum (1880), who emphasized the genetic continuity of the germ-cells from generation to generation, urging that during development the fertilized egg divides to produce on the one hand the cell-material of the individual body, on the other the cells by which the characters of the species are maintained.[1] From this as a starting point Weismann's analysis led him to a bold challenge of the entire Lamarckian principle on which Darwin's theory of pangenesis had been based. "I do not propose to treat of the whole problem of heredity, but only of a certain aspect of it,—the transmission of acquired characters, which has been hitherto assumed to occur. In taking this course I may say that it was impossible to avoid going back to the foundation of all phenomena of heredity, and to determine the substance with which they must be connected. In my opinion this can only be the substance of the germ-cells; and this substance transfers its hereditary tendencies from generation to generation, at first unchanged, and always uninfluenced in any corresponding manner by that which happens during the life of the individual which bears it. If these views be correct, all our ideas upon the transformation of species require thorough modification, for the whole principle of evolution by means of exercise (use and disuse) as professed by Lamarck, and accepted in some cases by Darwin, entirely collapses" (Essays, 1885).

Nussbaum and Weismann thus held, in opposition to the prevailing view, that the child does not inherit its characters from the parental *body*, but from the *germ-cell*, and the latter in turn does not owe its characteristics to the body which bears it, but to its *descent from a preëxisting germ-cell of the same kind* (Fig. 5); so far as heredity is concerned the body is merely a carrier of germ-cells, held in trust for coming generations. Thus regarded, the individual appears as an evanescent by-product; it is but an incident,— almost, we might say, an accident.[2] So far as the species is concerned the germ-cells alone are of consequence, for they alone live on, carrying with them, as it were, the traditions of the race from which they have sprung, and handing them on in turn to generations still unborn. To the layman this often appears as a paradox, and even among biologists it long remained a subject of controversy. Time has demonstrated, however, that it simplifies and illuminates the whole problem in remarkable degree and, for the present at least, offers the only intelligible conception of heredity. Upon it is

[1] See quotation at p. 256.
[2] "It has, I believe, been often remarked that a hen is only an egg's way of making another egg" (Samuel Butler).

founded the whole modern science of genetics, and it has given a powerful impetus to the study of cytology and embryology, lending new interest to the study of the germ-cells and their transformations during development. These problems, obviously, are inseparable from the cytological problems offered by cells in general. We now therefore return to those remarkable researches, on the internal organization of cells, the structure of protoplasm

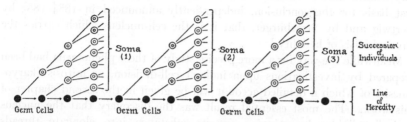

Fig. 5.—Diagram illustrating the Nussbaum-Weismann theory of heredity. In each generation the germ-cell (black) gives rise on the one hand to the body or soma, on the other to new germ-cells. The line of heredity is thus seen to be always through the germ-cells, not through the soma.

and nucleus, and the mechanism of cell-division and fertilization, which mark the opening of the second period in the history of our subject.

It is here that we see cytology first emerging from the earlier histology and embryology. The advance guard of the movement was led by Schneider ('73), Fol ('73, '75, '79), Bütschli ('73, '76) and Auerbach ('74), soon reënforced by O. Hertwig ('75–'78), Van Beneden ('75, '76), Strasburger ('75–'79) and Flemming ('79, '82). During the eighties it gained full headway under the leadership especially of Van Beneden, Flemming, Strasburger and Boveri whose cytological observations on the germ-cells were closely affiliated with the theoretical writings of Nägeli, Weismann, O. Hertwig, Strasburger, Roux and DeVries (p. 14). We can at this point barely mention the most important of the advances of this period.

One of the most fundamental of the discoveries of the time was Oscar Hertwig's demonstration of the fate of the sperm within the egg (1875). Other observers had paved the way by showing that, at the time of fertilization, the egg contains *two nuclei* that fuse together or become closely associated before development begins.[1] Hertwig, in his work of 1875 and subsequently ('77, '78, '84, etc.), paralleled and supplemented by that of Fol ('77, '79) demonstrated in the eggs of the sea-urchin (*Toxopneustes lividus*) that *one of these nuclei belongs to the egg, while the other is derived from the sperm.* This result was soon extended to the fertilization of higher

[1] An exhaustive review of the earlier literature will be found in Fol ('79) Mark ('81) and Flemming ('82). See also Rabl ('15), O. Hertwig ('17), and F. R. Lillie ('19).

plants by Strasburger ('77) and ultimately by many observers to higher organisms generally. *In every case an essential phenomenon of normal fertilization is the union or close association of a sperm-nucleus, of paternal origin, with an egg-nucleus, of maternal origin, to form the primary nucleus of the embryo. This nucleus, known as the cleavage- or segmentation-nucleus, gives rise by division to all the nuclei of the body; hence every nucleus of the child may contain nuclear substance derived from both parents;* and this gave the first basis for the conclusion, independently announced in 1884–1885 by Hertwig and by Strasburger, that it is the cell-nucleus which carries the physical basis of heredity.[1]

Meanwhile the way for a more precise study of these phenomena had been prepared by investigations upon indirect cell-division, or mitosis (karyo-kinesis) of which a detailed account will be given in the second chapter of this work. The most essential result was the discovery that the nucleus typically divides by spinning out its substance into elongate threads (spireme) which *split lengthwise*, shorten and thicken to form *chromosomes*. Many observers contributed to this discovery and its development, foremost among them Flemming ('82) and Strasburger ('80, '82), who showed that the phenomena are fundamentally similar in animals and plants. This was followed by the final proof, brought forward by Van Beneden ('83) and by Heuser ('84) that in plants and animals alike the longitudinal halves of each split chromosome separate from each other and pass into the two respective daughter-nuclei. The nucleus, therefore, does not undergo a mere mass-division but a meristic division of its entire substance. The great theoretic interest of this fact was indicated by Wilhelm Roux (1883), while almost at the same moment Nägeli (1884) developed his interesting theory of the *idioplasm*, a hypothetical substance assumed to be present in every cell and possessing specific properties by virtue of which the hered-itary characters of the species are determined. By Hertwig and Stras-burger this conception and that of Roux were blended in a single and coherent theory by the assumption that the *idioplasm is identical with the nuclear substance or chromatin.*

The cytological discoveries of this period reached their climax in the splendid researches of Edouard Van Beneden ('83–'84, '87) on the history of the nuclei during the fertilization of the egg of the nematode *Ascaris megalocephala*, which demonstrated that *the chromosomes of the offspring are derived in equal numbers from the nuclei of the two conjugating germ-cells, and hence equally from the two parents.* This fundamental discovery opened

[1] The more modern form of this conclusion is outlined elsewhere (*cf.* p. 916). Haeckel expressed the same thought as early as 1866; but this was no more than a lucky guess. "The internal nucleus provides for the transmission of hereditary characters, the external plasma on the other hand for accommodations or adaptations to the external world" (*Gen. Morph.*, pp. 287–289).

remarkable new possibilities for the detailed analysis of the nuclear organization and the cytological study of heredity and development. Weismann instantly grasped its importance and was the first to emphasize its far-reaching significance. To him, therefore, above all others, belongs the credit for having placed the keystone between the study of cytology and that of heredity, thus finally bringing the cell-theory and the evolution-theory into organic connection.

The subsequent history of cytology in its relation to genetics can only be rightly apprehended in the light of other lines of inquiry that were initiated during this period. One of these, a logical sequel to the pioneer studies of Kölliker, Remak, and Hofmeister, was the foundation of cellular embryology through the work of C. O. Whitman on the early development of leeches (1878), of Rabl on that of snails (1879), and that of Van Beneden and Julin on ascidians (1884). These researches demonstrated that the cleavage of the ovum, in some animals at least, is a perfectly ordered process, in which every individual cell in the early stages of development may possess a definite morphological value in the building of the body. This led in later years to numerous studies in cell-lineage devoted to the task of tracing out the formation of the embryonic body cell by cell; while efforts to test these results of observation by means of experiment created experimental embryology. In the latter field, the early leaders were especially Pflüger, Roux, Chabry and Driesch (1883–92); but the earlier work of Newport (1854–55), should also here be mentioned. Nearly at the same time, O. and R. Hertwig (1886–89) initiated experimental studies on the chemical environment of the egg and the conditions of artificial hybridization which had an important influence upon the later course of cellular biology. In later years, these studies were followed by many fruitful experimental researches on the chemical physiology of the germ-cells and their development; among the most interesting of the results was Loeb's discovery (1899) that the unfertilized egg may experimentally be caused to develop by purely chemical or physical stimulus, without the action of a sperm-cell ("artificial parthenogenesis"). The Hertwigs' studies likewise led to experimental researches on hybridization and merogony, particularly by Boveri, which yielded results fundamentally important to our conceptions of the internal mechanism of development, and contributed in an important way to the development of experimental cytology.

The third period in the history of our subject opened in 1900 with the rediscovery of Mendel's long forgotten laws of heredity (1865) by the independent work of DeVries, Correns and Tschermak. This momentous discovery produced an effect almost as far reaching in cytology as in genetics because of the remarkable new questions that it raised concerning the maturation of the germ-cells. The fact had long been recognized that every sexually produced organism is of double or *diploid* hereditary constitution, a condition obviously traceable to its origin from a zygote formed by the union of two germ-cells (gametes) respectively of maternal and paternal origin. Mendel and his successors brought forward specific experimental proof that the zygote and its product (*i. e.*, the diploid organism) unites in itself two corresponding sets of qualities ("factors," "units," "genes," etc.), likewise of maternal and paternal origin respectively, while the gametes are of single or *haploid* constitution, containing but a single such set of qualities. This result, evidently, is exactly parallel to Van Beneden's earlier discovery that the gametes contain a single or haploid group of chromosomes, which is made double or diploid by the act of fertilization. More especially, Mendel found in hybrids that in the case of any pair of corresponding or homologous qualities (such as two colors, C and c) in respect to which the parents differ, half the gametes of the hybrid receive one member of this pair (C) and half the other (c). This is the essential fact (segregation) at the basis of Mendel's first "law"; and, as Mendel clearly perceived, it can only mean that at some period in the history of the gametes the two members of each such pair are separated or disjoined so as to pass into different gametes. Mendel found, finally, that different pairs of qualities (Aa, Bb, Cc) behave independently of one another during segregation, (independent or free assortment) so that all possible recombinations of them may appear in the gametes and zygotes (Figs. 102, 105).

These fundamental discoveries resulted from purely genetic experiments having no direct reference to the cytological problems involved. In the meantime, however, cytologists had independently demonstrated that the general history of the chromosomes during the life-cycle runs so exactly parallel to that of the Mendelian phenomena that both may in large degree be formulated in the same terms. This was first clearly set forth by Sutton (1902–03) and by DeVries ('03), who offered the first complete demonstration that the behavior of the chromosomes may offer a mechanical (or at least mechanistic) explanation of Mendel's laws.[1] Taken together these advances marked the advent of a new era in both cytology and genetics and opened the way for many new lines of progress. Prominent among them were investigations on the determination of sex and the phenomena of linkage which demonstrated that both are in conformity with Mendel's laws. That sex-determination is connected with the chromosomes was suggested by McClung (1901–02) and established by the direct observations of Stevens

---

[1] Important data necessary for this conclusion had already been brought forward, especially by Montgomery, Boveri, and Guyer, and the cytological explanation of Mendel's laws was indicated nearly at the same time by Boveri and by Cannon (see p. 926).

and of Wilson in 1905. In respect to linkage, numerous researches, especially by Morgan and his followers, have demonstrated that the hereditary units are linked together in groups equal in number to the chromosomes. Followed out in great detail and in many directions these researches have removed every doubt concerning the intimate connection of the chromosomes with the determination of development generally, and have provided a remarkably effective means for the detailed analysis of the intricate and puzzling problems of genetics.

The determinative action of the nucleus in development was thus finally placed beyond doubt, but probably no investigator would to-day maintain that the nucleus or the chromosomes are the sole agents of heredity. On the contrary, both cytological and experimental research have clearly demonstrated that the protoplasm (cytoplasm) plays an important part in development. This has been directly proved on the cytological side by experiments on the development of egg-fragments by Boveri, Driesch, Fischel and later investigators, while indirectly the same conclusion is indicated by genetic experiments on the part of Correns, Toyama and others. With reference to this problem much interest has been aroused in recent years by cytological studies on the *mitochondria* or *chondriosomes*, cytoplasmic structural elements now widely believed to play an important part in the chemical activities of cells and perhaps also in differentiation; by some authors, accordingly (Benda, Meves) they have been regarded as representing a mechanism of "cytoplasmic heredity" comparable in importance with that represented by the chromosomes. This view, still very far from substantiation, remains a subject of controversy and must be taken with proper scepticism; but in spite of its doubtful status it should be kept clearly in view in all cytological discussions of these problems. To some extent, perhaps, our conclusions concerning the chromosomes have thus far been more definite and frutiful because we are able to follow their history more readily.

The present work has been written by a student of embryology and cytology, with especial reference to the cell considered as the physical basis of heredity and development. It is plain that any treatment of this subject must be based on our knowledge of cells generally, but neither can we, on the other hand, go very far into the minutiæ of histology, cell-physiology, biophysics and biochemistry. The order of treatment has been determined by practical rather than by strictly logical considerations. The first two chapters offer a general elementary sketch of cell-structure and cell-division, the third a preliminary outline of the phenomena of reproduction and of the life-cycle as related to the physiological problems of syngamy. The morphological aspects of these problems are treated in some detail in the succeeding chapters, the fourth considering the structure and origin of the gametes, the fifth their union in syngamy or fertilization, and the sixth their maturation and the phenomena of meiosis or the reduction and segregation of the chromosomes. The seventh chapter offers a brief outline of the related phenomena displayed in the sexual processes of lower organisms, where we may seek for indications of their historical origin.

These seven chapters offer a general foundation for the study of more specific problems of cytology and genetics, and of the more general ones involved in the phenomena of development. The eighth chapter includes a brief outline of certain chemical and physiological cell-phenomena that are of importance for the subsequent analysis; the ninth an account of some general problems and theories of cell-organization.

The tenth chapter deals with the cytological basis of sex-production and serves as an introduction to the eleventh and twelfth chapters which give some account of the organization and individuality of the chromosomes and their relation to various specific problems of genetics and to heredity in general. The last two chapters deal with the cell in development, considering some of the problems of cleavage, localization and differentiation from the standpoint of the cytologist, together with an outline of current theories of development and heredity.

LITERATURE.   INTRODUCTION.[1]

(See also Literature I, II, V, XIII, XIV, etc.)

Auerbach, L., '74. Organologische Studien. *Breslau.*
Beale, L. S., '61. On the Structure of the Simple Tissues of the Human Body: *London.*
Boveri, Th., '87–'90. Zellenstudien, I–III (see General List).
Carnoy, J. B., '84. La biologie cellulaire: *Lierre.*
Delage, Yves, '03. La structure de protoplasm, les théories sur l'hérédité et les grandes problèmes de la biologie générale: *Schleicher, Paris,* 2nd Ed.
Flemming, W., '82. Zellsubstanz, Kern und Zelltheilung: *Leipzig.*
Id., '79–'82. Beiträge zur Kenntnis der Zelle, etc.: (See II).
Fol, H., '79. Recherches sur la fécondation et la commencement de l'hénogénie: *Mém. Soc. phys. et d'Hist. Nat. Genève.,* XXVI.
Gerould, J. H., '22. The Dawn of the Cell-Theory: *S. M.,* XIV.
Grew, Nehemiah, 1682. The Anatomy of Plants: *London.*
Haecker, V.,'99. Praxis und Lehre der Zellen- und Befructungs-lehre: *Jena.*
Haecker, V., '11. Allgemeine Vererbungslehre: *Vieweg, Braunschweig.*

---

[1] The list includes for the most part earlier works or more recent ones in which the earlier literature is reviewed. For explanation of the abbreviations, see p. 1145. Compare general literature list at the end.

For additional earlier works see especially the historical introductory chapters in Heidenhain's *Plasma und Zelle* ('07, '11), O. Hertwig's *Handbuch der Entwicklungslehre* ('06), the same author's *Allgemeine Biologie,* 5th ed. ('20), Lillie's *Problems of Fertilization* ('19) and Sharp's *Introduction to Cytology* ('21).

Harvey, Wm., 1651. Exercitationes de Generatione Animalium: *London;* Trans. in Sydenham Soc., X, '47.

Heidenhain, M., '07. '11. Plasma und Zelle I, II: *Fischer, Jena.*

Henle, J., 1841. Allegemeine Anatomie: *Leipzig.*

Henneguy, L. F., '03. Leçons sur la Cellule: *2nd Ed. Schleicher, Paris.*

Hertwig, O., '75, '77, '78 (see V).
  '84. Das Problem der Befruchtung und der Isotropie des Eies, eine Theorie der Verebung: *J. Z.*, XVIII.
  '93, '98. Die Zelle und die Gewebe: *Fischer, Jena.*
  '01, '06. Die Entwicklungslehre im 16 bis 18 Jahrhundert: *Handb. der vergleichenden experimentellen Entwicklungslehre der Wirbeltierre*, I, 1, 1, *Fischer, Jena.*
  '17. Documente zur Geschichte der Zeugungslehre, etc., *A. M. A.*, XL.
  '20. Allgemeine Biologie, 5te Auflage: *Fischer, Jena.*

Hertwig, O. and R., '87. Ueber den Befruchtungs- und Theilungsvorgang des thierischen Eies unter den Einfluss äusserer Agentien: *J. Z., N. F.*, XIII.

Hofmeister, '67. Lehre von der Planzenzelle: *Leipzig.*

Hooke, Robt., 1665. Mikrographia, or some physiological Descriptions on minute Bodies by magnifying Glasses: *London.*

Huxley, T. H., '53. Review of the Cell-theory: *Brit. and Foreign Med. Chir. Review*, XII.

V. Kölliker, A., '85. Die Bedeutung der Zellkerne für die Vorgänge der Veverbung: *Z. W. Z.*, XLII.

Lillie, F. R., '19. Problems of Fertilization: *Univ. Chi. Press.*

Locy, W. A., '15. Biology and its Makers: 3rd Ed., *New York.*

Malpighi, M., 1675. Anatome Plantarum.

Mark, E. L., '81. Maturation, Fecundation and Segmentation of *Limax campestris: Bull. Mus. Comp. Zoöl. Harvard*, VI.

Nägeli, C., 84. Mechanisch-physiologische Theorie der Abstammungslehre: *München u. Leipzig*, '84.

Prévost and **Dumas**, 1824. Nouvelle théorie de la génération: *A. S. N.*, 1.

Rabl, C., '06. (See XIV.)
  '15. Edouard Van Beneden, etc.: *A. M. A.*, LXXXVIII.

Remak, R., '50-'55. Untersuchungen über die Entwicklung der Wirbelthiere: *Berlin.*

Sachs, J., '90. History of Botany: Trans. *Oxford.*

Schleiden, M. J., '38. Beiträge sur Phytogenesis: *Müller's Archiv.* Trans. in *Sydenham Soc.*, XII, London, '47.

Schwann, Th., '39. Mikroscopische Untersuchungen über die Uebereinstimmung in der Struktur und dem Wachsthum der Thiere und Pflanzen: *Berlin.* Trans. in *Sydenham Soc.*, XII, London, '47.

Strasburger, E., '75, '08. Zellbildung und Zelltheilung: 1st and 3rd Ed., *Jena.*
  '84. Neue Untersuchungen über den Befruchtungsvorgang, etc.: *Jena.*
  '07. Die Ontogenie der Zelle seit 1875: *P. R. B.*
  '10. The Minute Structure of Cells in Relation to Inheritance: In *Darwin and Modern Science.*

Tyson, James, '78. The Cell Doctrine: *Philadelphia.*

Van Beneden, E., '83,-'84. Recherches sur la maturation de l'œuf, la fécondation et la division cellulaire: *A. B..* IV (dated 1883, issued 1884. See Rabl, '15).

Virchow, R., '58. (See also '55). Die Cellularpathologie in ihrer Begründung auf physiologische und pathologische Gewebelehre: *Berlin.*

Waldeyer, W., 88. Ueber Karyokinese und ihre Beziehung zu den Befruchtungsvorgängen: *A. M. A.,* XXXII (trans. in *Q. J.,* XXX).

Weismann, A., '82–'88. Essays on Heredity, 1st and 2nd series: Trans. Oxford, '89, '92, '04. The Evolution Theory (Trans. by Thomson): *London.*

Wheeler, W. M., '98. Caspar Friedrich Wolff and the Theoria Generationis: *W. H. L.*

Whitman, C. O., '78. The Embryology of *Clepsine: Q. J.,* XVIII.
    '94. (a) Evolution and Epigenesis: (b) Bonnet's Theory of Evolution: *Woods Hole Biol. Lect.,* 1894.

Wilson, E. B., '96, '00. The Cell in Development and Inheritance, 1st and 2nd Editions: *Macmillan, New York.*
    '09. The Cell in Relation to Heredity and Evolution: In *Fifty Years of Darwinism: N. Y.*

Wolff, Caspar Friedrich, 1759. Theoria Generationis.

CHAPTER I

GENERAL MORPHOLOGY OF THE CELL

"We have seen that all organisms are composed of essentially like parts, namely, of cells; that these cells are formed and grow in accordance with essentially the same laws; hence, that these processes must everywhere result from the operation of the same forces."

SCHWANN.[1]

Schwann first gave clear expression to the fundamental conception that beneath unending diversity of form and function all cells conform to a common morphological and physiological type. Like Schleiden, it is true, he failed to grasp the real nature of the cell, considering the protoplasmic cell-contents as of minor importance; nevertheless the essential truth of his sweeping generalization was established by later investigation on an ever widening basis. Even to-day we cannot frame an adequate brief definition of the cell; but fortunately such a definition is unnecessary. In practice we need no more than the simple formula put forward long ago by Leydig and Max Schultze, and still in everyday use. The cell, according to this definition, *is a mass of protoplasm* (in modern terminology the *cytosome*) *containing a nucleus;* and to this may be added Schultze's statement that *both nucleus and cytosome,* arise *by division of the corresponding elements of a preëxisting cell.*[2] This definition must not be taken in too formal or narrow a sense. Like most other definitions in natural science it must be allowed a certain flexibility, but in respect to essential accuracy the old definition remains to-day unshaken by the advances of half a century.

The general sketch of the cell here offered is but a bare outline. Many of the topics touched upon will be more critically discussed in later chapters.

I. GENERAL SKETCH. INTRODUCTORY

The early writers applied the term "protoplasm" [3] to the substance of the cell-body or cytosome in contradistinction to that of the nucleus; and the word (often shortened to *plasma*) is still commonly used in the same sense by modern writers. Later it acquired a broader significance, often

---

[1] *Untersuchungen*, 1839, p. 227.

[2] Leydig, *Lehrbuch der Histologie,* 1857, p. 9; Schultze, *Arch. Anat. u Phys.* 1861, p. 11.

[3] This word, nearly equivalent, etymologically and in meaning, to the "Urschleim" of Oken (1801), was first employed by Purkinje (1840) to designate the formative material of the animal embryo, and later applied by Mohl to the contents of plant cells. Beale (1870) proposed the appropriate word *bioplasm* as a substitute for protoplasm, but this has never come into general use.

being applied to the cell-substance as a whole, including the nucleus. In the interest of greater precision, therefore, Strasburger ('82) proposed to designate the substance of the cytosome as *cytoplasm* and that of the nucleus as *nucleoplasm* (better *karyoplasm*), both being included under the more general term "protoplasm." This terminology has been widely adopted, and we shall continue to use it; nevertheless, when we speak of "protoplasm" we commonly have in mind the earlier use of the word, *i. e.,* as equivalent to "cytoplasm."

Cytosome and nucleus taken together form a living unit or protoplasmic system that is often spoken of as the *protoplast* (Hanstein) or sometimes as the *energid* (Sachs). Externally the cytosome is bounded by a thin, peripheral, clear, protoplasmic film of different consistency, the *plasma-membrane* (sometimes called the *ectoplast*), and it may also be surrounded by non-protoplasmic walls or "true membranes" of varied nature which in the tissues form partitions between contiguous cells. In both plants and animals, however, the cell-walls are often traversed by fine strands of protoplasm (plasma-bridges, or plasmodesms) by means of which a direct protoplasmic continuity is maintained between the protoplasts. In plants, as a rule, the cell-walls are harder, thicker and more conspicuous than in animals, and to this circumstance the unlucky term "cell" owes its origin. For the walls of such tissues, when viewed in section, give an appearance like that of a honeycomb often in the older tissues emphasized by death and disappearance of the protoplast so as to leave only the lifeless walls; hence the term "cell," first employed by botanists of the seventeenth century.[1] Here, too, was the source of the erroneous view of Schleiden and Schwann that the cell-wall is the most important part of the cell. The living protoplasm of the cytosome was at first overlooked or regarded as a waste-product. The researches of Dujardin, De Bary, Cohn, Max Schultze and many others long since showed, however, that most living cells are not hollow but solid bodies, and that in many cases—for example, the cells of blood and lymph or various *Protista*,—they are naked masses of protoplasm. Thus it was proved that neither the vesicular form nor the presence of a surrounding wall is an essential character of the cell and that the *cell-contents, i. e.,* the cytosome and nucleus, must be the seat of vital activity. The term "cell" thus became a biological misnomer. In the older cells of plants, it is true, the cytosome itself often becomes sac-like through the appearance of watery vacuoles which enlarge and finally fuse to form a single large central vacuole, surrounded by a thin peripheral

---

[1] As first employed by Robert Hooke (1665) the word was used to designate the minute cavities separated by solid walls, observed in cork, a tissue which he described as made up of "little boxes or cells distinct from one another."

layer (the "primordial utricle" of earlier botanists), though often traversed also by anastomosing strands of protoplasm. In such cases the living protoplasm does indeed assume the form of a hollow chamber; but this is

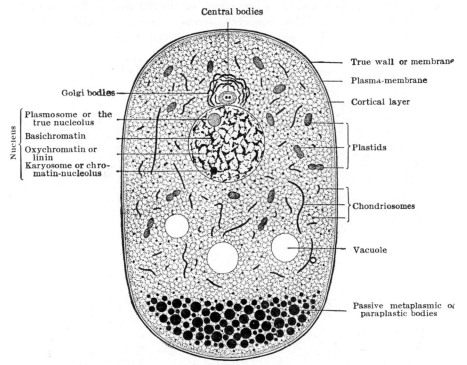

Central bodies

True wall or membrane

Plasma-membrane

Golgi bodies

Cortical layer

Plasmosome or the true nucleolus

Basichromatin

Nucleus

Oxychromatin or linin

Karyosome or chromatin-nucleolus

Plastids

Chondriosomes

Vacuole

Passive metaplasmic or paraplastic bodies

Fig. 6.—General diagram of a cell. Its cytoplasmic basis is shown as a granular meshwork or framework in which are suspended various differentiatied granules, fibrillæ and other formed components.

of secondary origin and significance. In their young and less differentiated condition these same cells are solid, like those of animals generally.

The nucleus (Figs. 6 and 8)[1] is typically of definite, rounded form, and often contains one or more smaller *nucleoli*. In all ordinary cases the nucleus is single, but in some cells two or more nuclei are present. Examples of cells that are constantly binucleate are offered by the sporophytic generation of the rusts and certain other fungi (Fig. 309), by the ciliate Infusoria generally, and by certain of the rhizopods (*e. g., Arcella, Amœba diploidea*) (Fig. 296), flagellates (*Giardia,* Fig. 43) and Sporozoa. In the so-called *polymorphic* nuclei, *e. g.,* in some forms of leucocytes or in the giant-cells

---

[1] The nucleus was seen by Fontana in 1781, but was emphasized as a characteristic element of the cell by Meyen (1826), and especially by Robert Brown in 1831.

of the bone-marrow (Figs. 10 and 34) the nucleus consists of a nest or group of more or less separate vesicles or sacculations. In other cases several or many separate nuclei lie scattered in a common protoplasmic mass; such a structure is known as a *syncytium*, or (in the case of Protista) a *plasmodium*. This condition frequently occurs among the Radiolaria and other rhizopods and is characteristic of the so-called "non-cellular" fungi

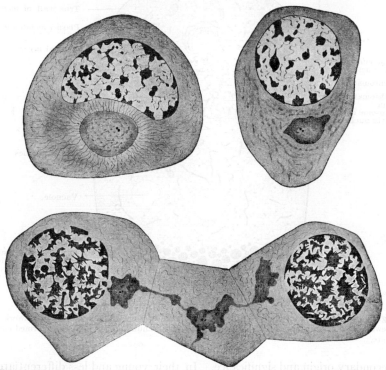

Fig. 7.—Spermatogonia of the salamander (MEVES). Above, two cells showing large nuclei, with linin-threads and scattered chromatin-granules; in each cell a centrosome or idiozome with two centrioles. Below, three contiguous spermatogonia, showing chromatin-reticulum, centriole, and spindle-remnants.

such as *Mucor* and other Phycomycetes, and algæ such as *Caulerpa* or *Vaucheria* (cœnocytes).

The nucleus was long supposed to be absent in some of the Protista; and for such forms, Haeckel set up a group of so-called *Monera*, in which the body was supposed to be no more than a minute and homogeneous mass of protoplasm. Later a similar view was held in regard to the Bacteria and Cyanophyceæ. With the improvements of cytological technique and the general advance of protistology this conception was progressively restricted and at last abandoned by nearly all investigators. Some of the "Monera" were found to possess single nuclei of the ordinary type; others to be multinucleate, with many small nuclei; still others to contain numerous minute *chromidia* in the form of granules, clumps or net-like formations scattered through the protoplasm and forming a diffuse or "distributed" nucleus, or nuclear system. Such chromidial formations appear to be not uncommon in lower plants and animals including certain Bacteria, Cyanophyceæ, rhizopods, flagellates and even ciliates (Figs. 14, 32). Identification of the chromidial substance as of nuclear nature or as "chromatin" rests in part on its staining-reactions and resistance to peptic digestion (p. 643); and the chromidial granules have been asserted to multiply by division (Fig. 32). Such evidence is in itself by no means conclusive, but the case seems to be established decisively in some species by the fact that at certain stages of the life-history true individualized nuclei may be formed by aggregation or growth of the chromidial granules and may later in their turn give off such granules or break down into them (Fig. 343). The conviction has thus become general among protistologists and cytologists that even among the simplest of known organisms the cell always contains nuclear substance ("chromatin" or a related substance), whether in the form of an individualized nucleus or of a scattered nuclear system. Whether the latter can be called a "nucleus" or not is a question of definition. In principle, however, there seems to be no present justification for admitting the existence of "Monera" in Haeckel's sense.[1]

It is therefore highly probable that a chemical and morphological differentiation of the active cell-substance into cytoplasmic and nuclear components is characteristic of all cells *as they now exist* and is necessary to their continued life. This result, primarily based on morphological grounds, is strikingly borne out by physiological experiments on living cells. A fragment of a cell deprived of its nucleus may for a considerable time live and manifest the power of coördinated movement (*e. g.*, in ciliates or rhizopods, p. 657); but it has lost the power of assimilation, growth and repair, and sooner or later dies. The operations of destructive metabolism may continue for a considerable time in the absence of a nucleus; those of constructive metabolism quickly cease with its removal. Strong ground is thus given for the conclusion that the nuclear substance plays some part in the constructive and formative processes of the cell; and this is one of many reasons why the nucleus has come to be widely regarded as a primary factor in growth, development and heredity. There is reason, therefore, to believe that the differentiation of the active cell-substance into cytosome and nucleus is in some manner and degree an expression of

[1] *Cf.* Doflein, '16.

the dual process of metabolism, constructive and destructive, that lies at the basis of all life.

In addition to the nucleus, the cytosome often contains a structure known as the *central apparatus* or *microcentrum* of which the most essential

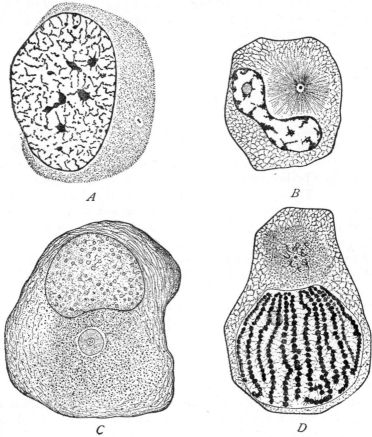

A   *B*

C   *D*

Fig. 8.—Various cells showing cytosome, nucleus, and central bodies. *A*, from peritoneal epithelium of the salamander-larva; two central bodies (centrioles) at the right; nucleus showing netknots (FLEMMING); *B*, Spermatogonium of frog, aster containing one centriole, nucleus with a single plasmosome (HERMANN); *C*, Spinal ganglion-cell of frog, sphere near the center, containing a single centrosome with several centrioles (LENHOSSÉK); *D*, spermatocyte of *Proteus*, nucleus in the spireme-stage, granular sphere (idiozome) containing a centriole and rod-shaped Golgi-bodies ("pseudo-chromosomes") (HERMANN).

component is the central body (*centrosome, centriole*) about which as a center arise the *asters* that form a conspicuous feature of many forms of mitotic cell-division (p. 144). The central body possesses in many cases the power of growth and division and retains its morphological identity

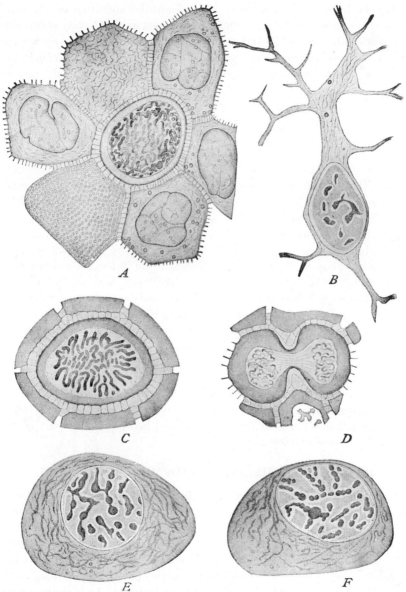

Fig. 9.—Living cells of salamander-larva (FLEMMING). *A*, group of epidermal cells at different foci; the central cell with nucleus in the spireme-stage; *B*, connective tissue-cell; *C*, epidermal cell in early mitosis (segmented spireme) surrounded by protoplasmic bridges; *D*, dividing cell; *E*, *F*, cartilage-cells with cytoplasmic fibrillæ or chondrioconts.

during the interkinesis or vegetative (non-mitotic) condition of the cell [1] (when it is commonly double). Out of these facts grew the early conclusion of Van Beneden and of Boveri that the central body, like the nucleus, is a permanent and autonomous component of the cell; and Boveri concluded, because of its important rôle in cell-division, that the central body may be regarded as the "dynamic center" of the cell. While there is much to support these conclusions in the case of higher animals they still lack an adequate basis of fact. Though central bodies are present in many lower plants (thallophytes), they seem to be absent in the higher forms; while experimental and cytological evidence has prominently raised the question whether, even in higher animals, they may not under certain conditions be formed *de novo* from the protoplasmic substance (p. 684). The presence of central bodies cannot, therefore, safely be made part of the definition of a cell; and the same is true in respect to various other cell-components, such as the chondriosomes and Golgi-bodies, despite their wide occurrence.

The old definition of Leydig and Schultze, therefore, still holds its own. Since cells are commonly solid bodies nothing could be less appropriate than to call them "cells," and many attempts have been made to find a better name. Beale ('70) long since proposed the word *bioplasm* as a substitute for "protoplasm," at the same time suggesting the appropriate term *bioplast* to designate the living part of the cell (protoplasm and nucleus). This is exactly equivalent to Hanstein's "protoplast" [2] or Sachs's "energid" [3] and seems a better term; but none of these words has thus far become generally current, though Hanstein's term is increasingly used, especially by botanical writers. The word "cell" has indeed become so firmly established, largely because of its convenient brevity, that all efforts to replace it by a better one have failed. Probably, therefore, it must be accepted as part of the established nomenclature of science.

II. THE CYTOSOME AND ITS FORMED COMPONENTS

The cell is a complex living system containing many differentiated structural components which will henceforward be referred to as *formed bodies*. Some of these are found only in the nucleus (nucleoli of various types, etc.), others only in the cytosome (chondriosomes, Golgi-bodies), still others in either nucleus or cytosome (central bodies or division-centers). The cytoplasmic components, vary endlessly in nature, origin and function, and it is difficult to classify them logically. Only those of more general occurrence and significance will here be considered.

---

[1] Often erroneously spoken of as the "resting cell."
[2] Hanstein, *Das Protoplasma*, 1880.
[3] Sachs, J., *Flora*, 1892.

1. The Central Bodies, Central Apparatus, Microcentrum

The general term *central body* is applied to a structure which forms the focus of the aster or astral system during mitotic cell-division, and hence is often spoken of as the *division-center*. In many cases this body persists during the vegetative or "resting" period of the cell, and is handed on by division to the daughter-cells without loss of its identity; hence the above-mentioned view of Van Beneden and of Boveri that the central body may be a permanent or autonomous cell-organ which always arises from a pre-

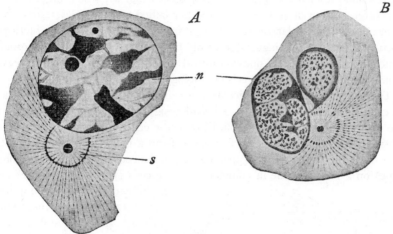

Fig. 10.—Leucocytes of the salamander (HEIDENHAIN). *A*, cell with a single nucleus containing a very coarse network of chromatin and two nucleoli (plasmosomes); *s*, permanent aster, its center occupied by two central bodies surrounded by a microsome-ring; *B*, similar cell, with double nucleus; the smaller dark masses in the latter are oxychromatin-granules (linin), the larger masses are basichromatin.

existing body of the same kind. This conclusion probably went too far; but there is no doubt that the central body often has such an origin.[1]

Van Beneden and Boveri also adopted the hypothesis that the central bodies are of general if not universal occurrence; but this view has not been sustained by later research (p. 150). They are of widespread occurrence in the cells of higher animals and occur in those of many lower plants. On the other hand, with exception of the blepharoplasts (p. 387) they seem to be absent in case of the cells of higher plants (cormophytes) generally. In the resting or vegetative state of the cell the central body is most frequently double, and typically lies in the cytosome; but in some cases it is intra-nuclear.[2] In the former case the two bodies often lie near the nucleus but may be far removed from it. In epithelial cells generally they commonly

[1] See p. 680.　　　　[2] Exceptionally in Metazoa, commonly in Protista (p. 204).

lie towards the free surface and often very near it, as is typically seen in columnar cells (Fig. 42).

The central bodies and associated structures often form a rather complicated apparatus conveniently designated as the *central apparatus* or *microcentrum*. Its most constant and essential component is the *centriole*, a minute granule or rod, often double, in some cases lying naked in the cytoplasm, more often surrounded by a cytoplasmic investment of various degrees of complexity. In some cases the latter is a rather definite, small rounded spheroid, the *centrosome* (Fig. 8); when larger (Fig. 7) it is often spoken of as the *sphere* (earlier called *attraction-sphere* or *centrosphere*) or in particular cases as the *periplast* or *idiozome*.[1] In practice it is often difficult to distinguish certainly between centriole and centrosome; hence the convenient and non-committal term "central body" which leaves open the question as to its precise homology in any particular case.[2]

The central bodies, in particular the centrioles, are undoubtedly organs of cell-division; but they have a broader significance than this. Even in the vegetative or non-mitotic condition of the cell the central body is sometimes surrounded by radiating fibrillæ to form a more or less definite aster or astral sphere, as is shown conspicuously in leucocytes (Fig. 10) and sometimes on a smaller scale in connective-tissue cells (Fig. 8); sometimes also in the early stages of the animal oöcyte (surrounding the "yolk-nucleus," p. 339), and even in nerve-cells. An interesting example of this is described by Del Rio Hortega ('15) in the cells of Purkinje, where a pair of centrioles, apparently always present, is surrounded by conspicuous, irregularly radiating wavy fibrillæ to form an aster-like body. These cells, so far as known, are not capable of division. The function of the astral formations in these various cases is unknown; but it may possibly be connected with the fact that in the vegetative or non-mitotic phase of the cell the central apparatus often forms a focus about which are aggregated certain of the other formed elements, such as the Golgi-bodies and chondriosomes (p. 329); and in the

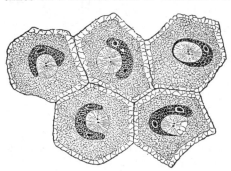

Fig. 11.—Group of cells from the pharyngeal epithelium of the tunicate *Salpa*, showing the radiate sphere and central body lying in a nuclear bay (BALLOWITZ).

---

[1] For a more critical account see p. 672.

[2] See especially Flemming, '91a, Meves, '02, Boveri, '00, etc. The word "centrosome" has been widely employed especially in the botanical literature as a general term for central body; but this is undesirable. See p. 673.

earlier stages of the animal egg it seems typically to form the original center of the yolk-formation (p. 339). In the early stages of maturation of the germ-cells the central bodies lie at or near that pole of the nucleus towards which the nuclear threads are polarized (Fig. 149), and hence may play a part, if only indirectly, in the conjugation of the spireme-threads during synapsis (p. 550). Again, in the formation of the motile sperms of both plants and animals in many cases the centriole plays the part of a basal body or *blepharoplast*, from which grows forth the axial filament of a flagellum or cilium; [1] and the same seems to be the case also in the flagellated cells of sponges and in many flagellated protista. In some cases, however, the blepharoplasts are quite separate from the centrioles; and it is probable that the centriole may be composed of two closely associated components which may appear as separate bodies. In any case the facts enumerated above show clearly that the central bodies are concerned in many cell-activities that have no immediate connection with cell-division.

2. The Cytoplasmic Granules

Granules are among the most characteristic, widespread and varied of the cytoplasmic formed bodies and have attracted the close attention of cytologists from an early period. They are commonly suspended in a clear, apparently homogeneous and more or less viscid ground-substance or *hyaloplasm*. They vary widely in size, number, staining-reactions, mode of origin and physiological significance, and in many of these respects often show periodic changes correlated with the cyclical activities of the cell, as is typically shown in gland-cells (p. 37). The smallest of the granules graduate down to the limits of true microscopical vision, and the ultra-microscope (p. 33) makes it certain that granules still smaller lie beyond those limits (p. 61). In some cells the cytosome is closely crowded with granules, *e. g.*, the yolk-granules of the animal ovum; in others (as in ectoplasm of many Protozoa), they are so small or few as to be nearly or quite invisible. Such protoplasm is commonly spoken of as "hyaline," because of its glass-like transparency and apparent homogeneity. The larger granules (for instance yolk-granules) vary widely in physical consistency, sometimes being solid or semi-solid bodies, in other cases liquid drops which may readily fuse together when brought into contact.[2] It is probable that similar differences exist among the more minute granules, perhaps among those that are of ultra-microscopical size, and that these too may be either of solid or liquid nature.

[1] In some of these cases the centriole has the form of a rod or V (p. 357).
[2] *Cf.* Wilson, '99.

The classification and terminology of the granules is a difficult matter, involving many disputed questions of fact and of theoretic interpretation. Many of them are relatively passive bodies which belong to the "metaplasmic" or "paraplastic" products of the active protoplasm; examples of these are starch-grains, yolk-granules, and minute drops of fatty or watery liquid. Some kinds of granules, however, such as the various forms of plastids, the centrioles, perhaps also the mitochondria and Golgi-bodies (pp. 45, 48) belong to the more active elements of the protoplasm and in some cases (plastids, centrioles) are self-perpetuating by growth and division.

The structural relation of the granules to other formed elements in the protoplasm (such as fibrillæ, astral rays, alveolar structures, etc.) has given rise to much controversy. When fibrillar formations are present the larger granules and many of the smaller ones are independent of the fibrillæ, i. e., they are *inter-filar* in position. An important group of observers, however (Flemming, Van Beneden, Heidenhain, Altmann, Retzius, and in a measure Benda), have described the protoplasmic fibrillæ as containing small "intra-filar" granules, more or less definitely aligned in linear series so as to give the fibrilla an appearance of segmentation. A similar conclusion, as will later appear (p. 906) is still more strongly suggested in case of the spireme threads that appear in the nucleus of the cell at the time of cell-division (p. 121).

No claim of logical consistency can by made for the following grouping of the granules. It is offered only as a convenient way of defining certain features of the current terminology.[1]

a. Microsomes. This term, at present of only vague and hardly definable meaning, is significant only in the light of its history. By its author (Hanstein, 1880), it was applied to the granules in general, as seen in living protoplasm, in contradistinction to the clear, homogeneous ground-substance or *hyaloplasm* in which they lie, and in this sense it was used by many observers of living protoplasm. In the meantime the word came into general use as applied to the smaller granules seen in fixed (coagulated) and stained preparations, and in particular those supposed to belong to the active protoplasm as distinguished from passive "metaplasmic" storage-granules. More precise subsequent studies showed that these small granules are of various specific types which came to be designated by special names, such as "chromidia," mitochondria," etc. The meaning of the original word "microsome" was thus progressively narrowed until it became a non-committal term, applied to any small granules that could not readily be assigned

---

[1] A valuable discussion of the granules is given in Heidenhain's great work, *Plasma und Zelle*, ('07, '11), and in Arnold's book on *Plamastrukturen* ('14). See also Schlater ('11), Retzius ('14), Schreiner ('16) and Meves ('18).

to a place in a more specific category. In this vague sense the word is still commonly employed, usually with more or less of a tacit assumption that microsomes form a constant and characteristic component of the active protoplasm. It was apparently with this in mind that some writers proposed to restrict the term to "true" or "intra-filar" microsomes, that form an integral part of the so-called "cytomitome" or cytoplasmic fibrillar system,[1] as was earlier described by Van Beneden, Altmann and many others (Fig. 23). This, however, hardly seems justified by the history of the term, while many observers have also described the "microsomes" that are scattered along the fibrillæ (e. g., astral rays) as adherent to them rather than forming an integral part of their substance. In point of fact, however, the word is commonly employed in a looser and broader sense, as above indicated.

The granules called microsomes are of small size and in many cases graduate down to a minuteness lying at the furthest limits of microscopical vision.[2] They show variable staining-reactions, being in some cases strongly basophilic (p. 87), in other cases oxyphilic, and they appear to be of proteid nature; but their extreme minuteness makes difficult the decision of this question. They have been assumed by some observers to be persistent structural elements, multiplying by fission (cf. the "mitochondria"); by others to be derived from the nucleus (cf. "chromidia"); by still others to form de novo out of the apparently homogeneous hyaloplasm in which they lie, or by the growth of ultra microscopical particles suspended in it. [3] The difficulties here encountered are increased by the fact that minute granules of this type may readily be produced as artificial coagulation-products of an originally homogeneous medium, such as filtered egg-albumin or a solution of albumose. All studies of the granules based on fixed and stained sections must therefore guard against this source of error.

---

[1] See Heidenhain ('07, p. 476); also Retzius ('14).

[2] Microscopical measurements are usually given in *microns*, or thousandths of a millimeter ($1\mu = .001$ mm.). Dimensions of still smaller order are given in sub-microns or millionths of a millimeter ($1\mu\mu = .001\mu = .000001$ mm.). The lower limit of microscopical vision in the ordinary sense of the term (i. e., the limit of resolving power, or capacity to differentiate between two separate objects) was shown by Abbe to be between 200 and 400 $\mu\mu$, a limit fixed by the wave length of light, which in the visible spectrum lies approximately between 450 $\mu\mu$ and 760 $\mu\mu$. Particles lying nearer together than half this distance cannot be distinguished as separate bodies; or, to state the matter differently, particles less than about 200 $\mu\mu$ in diameter cannot be seen as such, since they form no true image, and this may be taken as the practical working limit of the ordinary microscope under the most favorable conditions. (See Barnard, '19.) Particles of these dimensions are said to be ultra-microscopic. Though such particles are invisible as such, their presence may readily be detected by means of the ultra-microscope (cf. p. 720) which makes visible the diffraction-images produced by powerful reflected light. By this method it is said that particles as small as 5 $\mu\mu$ in diameter can be distinguished (Hatschek). High powers of the ordinary microscope, as usually employed (e. g., the oil-immersion apochromatic objective of 1.5 mm. with compensation lenses 6–12, Zeiss) give good definition up to 2500–3000 diameters or somewhat higher, but beyond this point, more is lost in definition and illumination than is gained in enlargement.

[3] P. 74. Altmann ('94), Wilson ('99, '23), Heidenhain ('07, '11), etc.

Evidently, the term "microsome," despite its historical priority, has now no definite or generally accepted meaning. It is no more than a convenient synonym for the non-committal phrase "small granule." As such it may often be used with advantage in a purely provisional descriptive sense, provided that it carry no implication as to the specific nature of the bodies thus designated.

b. Mitochondria. Many of the granules now designated by this name were described as "microsomes" by the earlier observers—the term "mitochondria" was indeed first applied by Benda ('98) to granules in the sperm-forming cells that were long ago described as "cytomicrosomes" by La Valette St. George ('86). Since identified as a specific type of granules that occur in nearly all kinds of cells, they have been brought into especial prominence in recent years through the researches of Benda, Meves, Duesberg, Regaud, Guilliermond and others who have ascribed to them an important rôle in histogenesis and heredity. Since they belong to the more general category of the *chondriosomes*, which are considered under another heading (p. 45), they will here be only briefly mentioned. These granules are typically of rather small size, but sometimes very minute, and show the cytological characters (solubilities, staining reactions, etc.) of the chondriosomes generally (p. 45). They are typically separate, being scattered separately through the protoplasm, but according to Benda and a few other observers they may sometimes become aligned in linear series to form fibrillæ known as *chondriomites* (Fig. 12). One of their characteristics appears to be a great plasticity of form; they may elongate to form homogeneous rods or even fibrillæ (*chondrioconts*, p. 46) while the latter may in turn break up into granules, as observed in cultures of living cells *in vitro*. Gradations between the extreme forms are also commonly seen in sections.

In dividing cells the mitochondria are not in or attached to the astral rays but lie between them, and they do not extend into the spindle, though they may closely surround it. They possess remarkable powers of multiplication, and by some observers (Benda, Meves, Duesberg) are believed to be self-perpetuating by division; this conclusion still rests, however, on insufficient evidence. Their possible physiological significance is considered beyond (p. 47).

c. Chromidia or Chromioles. By this term have been designated minute basophilic granules supposed to be derived originally from the nucleus, or (as in various bacteria, rhizopods and flagellates) to form a scattered or distributed nucleus. Much confusion still exists in regard to the relation between them and the mitochondria and other forms of granules. At one time the term "chromidia" was applied in a loose way to many kinds of basophilic granules in the cytosome with the implication that they are composed of "chromatin" and are presumably of nuclear origin.   Later researches proved that in case of the Metazoa many of the granules formerly

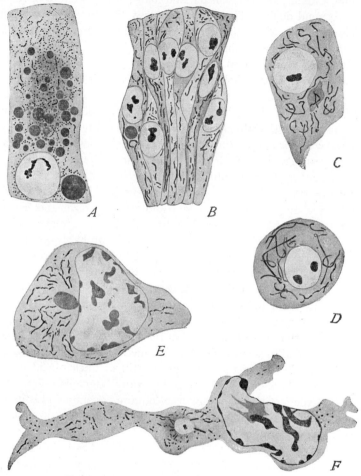

Fig. 12.—Chondriosomes in embryonic cells (MEVES).

A, entoderm-cell, chick of 27 hrs., mitochondria and chondriomites; *B*, group of cells from medullary tube; *C*, cartilage-cell, chick-embryo; *D*, embryonic erythrocyte, chick; *E*, leucocyte, salamander-larva; *F*, wandering cell of same.

described as "chromidia" are mitochondria and have no direct connection with the nucleus, while others are of doubtful origin.   It has now become clear that the term chromidia should be strictly reserved for granules known to be of nuclear origin (or to represent a scattered nucleus); and it is at present an open question whether chromidia as thus defined exist in the cells of higher organisms (p. 700).

The case is different in the Protista, where the researches of R. Hertwig, Schaudinn, Calkins, Dobell, Schaxel, and many others seem to have placed the facts beyond doubt. These granules show the same general reactions as basichromatin (p. 88), staining intensely with basic dyes such as safranin, gentian violet, or hematoxylin, resisting peptic-hydrochloric digestion, and being attacked by nuclease (p. 644). The only certain test of their nature lies, however, in their morphological history, *i. e.*, their derivation from the nucleus or their aggregation to form a nucleus, as is seen in some of the bacteria, rhizopods and flagellates. A further discussion of these granules and their relation to the mitochondria is given in Chapter IX.

d. Metachromatic or Volutin-Granules. The granules thus called are of general interest because of their close general similarity to chromidia, with which they may readily be confused in such groups as the bacteria or blue-green algæ in which the nature of the nucleus has long been in dispute (p. 83). They are of spherical form and variable size, and are found in the protoplasm of many lower organisms (bacteria, spirochætes, cyanophyceæ, various protozoa, fungi and algæ) and probably exist also in higher forms. They are characterized especially by their strong affinity, in fixed material, for various blue or violet basic tar-colors, in particular methylene blue, but also toluidin blue, gentian violet, thionin, etc., in which they commonly stain red or bluish red (hence the term metachromatic). In this respect they are stated to differ from chromidia;[1] nevertheless their basophilic character suggests a chemical relation with chromatin, and they have been regarded by some writers as a stage in its formation. A. Meyer concluded that they consist like basichromatin of nucleic acid combined with an organic base, a view accepted by many later observers. This is supported by the fact that a phosphorus-containing compound is necessary for their development, and Van Herwerden has proved that a nucleic acid compound, readily obtainable from normal yeast, cannot be obtained from volutin-free cultures.[2] On the other hand, it has been shown cytologically by Guilliermond, Dobell and others that the metachromatic granules may coexist in the same cell with a formed nucleus (*e. g.*, in the yeasts), or with chromidial granules. Some writers have therefore concluded that the metachromatic granules are of different nature from chromidia, and presumably represent reserve-material which has no morphological connection with the nucleus. In bacteria they do not take part in the spore-formation (Guilliermond, '08), nor is there other evidence of their morpho-

---

[1] See especially Meyer ('04, '08), Dobell ('11), Guilliermond ('08, '12), Van Herwerden ('17).
[2] See Reichenow ('16), Van Herwerden ('17).

logical connection with a nucleus. In the blue-green algæ, on the other hand, they enter into the formation of the central body or "karyoplast," and by some recent writers have been regarded as forerunners of the chromioles or chromatin-granules of more highly evolved types of nuclei.[1]

e. Secretory Granules. These granules are of widespread if not universal occurrence in secreting cells whether aggregated to form glands or scattered

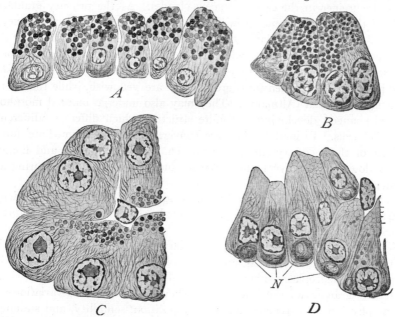

Fig. 13.—Cells of the pancreas in Amphibia (MATHEWS).
A–C, Necturus; D, Rana.
A, B, two stages of the "loaded" cell, showing zymogen-granules in the peripheral and fibrillar structures in the basal part of the cell; C, cells after discharge of the granule-material and invasion of the entire cell by fibrillæ; in D, portions of the fibrillar material are clumped to form the so-called "mitosome," "paranucleus" or Nebenkern," probably an artifact.

among other kinds of cells; they are of plastic and transitory nature, sooner or later disintegrating or dissolving to form an important part of the secretion. The constituent thus produced is often an enzyme, as in glands generally, but may be another substance, such as mucin, or fat. The secretory granules vary widely in size, chemical composition, physical consistency, staining-reactions and internal structure in different kinds of secretory cells, and also during the cycle of activity in the same individual. In their earliest stages these granules are very minute, and have been described by many observers as graduating down to the limits of visibility (E. Müller,

[1] See Acton, '14, Baumgärtel, '20.

Altmann, Heidenhain, etc.). At this time they are hardly to be distinguished from the "microsomes" of undifferentiated protoplasm and show similar staining-reactions. As will later appear, however, many of the more recent observers have concluded that these granules are derived from mito-chondria (Altmann, Meves, Regaud, etc.) or from Golgi-bodies (Nassonov. Bowen); still others believe them to arise from extruded fragments of nu-cleoli (Schreiner in the case of mucous glands). As the primary granules enlarge they often become crowded together so as to produce a honey-comb-like or "pseudalveolar" structure (p. 72) of the protoplasm (Fig. 13). Meanwhile they commonly undergo marked changes of staining-reaction; in the parotid, for example, they stain at first intensely red in acid fuchsin and picric acid, but when fully grown they are yellowish, while the inter-granular net is red (Altmann). They may also undergo marked morpho-logical changes, developing a definite structure which differs in different kinds of cells. Ultimately they are converted into the immediate fore-runner of the secretory product (zymogen, mucinogen, etc.) and finally break down, or dissolve to form the product itself, thus disappearing as individualized bodies.[1]

f. Storage-Granules and other Forms. Under this heading we may briefly refer to a great variety of granules commonly characterized as "metaplas-mic," "paraplasmic," "paraplastic" or "ergastic," since in their fully developed forms they are clearly secondary products of the protoplasmic activity. Examples of these are grains of starch or glycogen, the yolk-granules or deutoplasm-spheres of the animal egg, fat-drops, or the char-acteristic granules of the leucocytes. They show very wide variations of form, physical consistency, chemical composition, solubility, and staining-reactions. Logically they can hardly be distinguished from the secretory granules; for, like the latter they are specific protoplasmic products tem-porarily stored in the cell in the form of discrete bodies destined sooner or later to distintegrate or dissolve, their products often playing a most important part in the life of the organism.

The question of their nature and origin is too large to be taken up *in extenso* at this point. Some of them, such as the starch-grains, are definitely known to be products of plastids (p. 43). Others involve precisely the same problems as those raised by the secretory granules. Fat, for example, is laid down in the protoplasm in the form of small droplets which grow and may coalesce to form larger drops. By the earlier observers the smallest droplets were believed to be laid down by the general protoplasm in the

---

[1] Heidenhain divides the history of the granule during the secretory cycle into two periods: first a constructive or progressive one during which it grows and assumes its specific character: and sec-ond, a degressive or histolytic one in which its substance is transformed into the secretory product and the granule as such finally degenerates ('07, p. 383).

form of vacuoles that might appear at any point. Since the researches of Altmann, however, the opinion has gained ground that fat-synthesis is localized in cytoplasmic corpuscles or granules; but this is not yet decisively demonstrated. In the case of plants these corpuscles have been regarded by some observers as special forms of plastids ("elaioplasts"), analogous to the starch-forming amyloplasts (Wakker, '88); but this too has been disputed. In the case of animals an important group of observers, headed by Arnold ('07, '13, '14, etc.) have followed the lead of Altmann, consider-

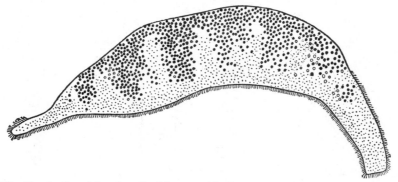

Fig. 14.—A ciliate infusorian, *Trachelocerca*, with chromidial nucleus consisting of scattered chromatin-granules (GRUBER).

ing fat-droplets as products of minute "lipoid granules" which are connected by intermediate conditions with granules which do not show fat-reactions (marked blackening in osmic acid, etc.) and are nearly similar to the protoplasmic "microsomes." These granules have been identified with mitochondria by many modern students of these bodies (Fauré-Fremiet, Dubreuil, etc.) On the other hand, Schreiner, a very competent observer, has recently produced evidence ('15, '16) that the lipoid granules are derived from fragments of *nucleoli* that have been extruded from the nucleus.

Similar uncertainty still hangs over the origin of many other forms of the granules included under this heading, for example, the yolk-spheres or the various forms of granules found in the leucocytes. The former either arise directly from, or are formed in close connection with, a mass of minute granules, at first closely associated with the nucleus and regarded by earlier observers as chromidia extruded from it. It is now generally agreed that these granules are cytoplasmic mitochondria, and strong evidence has been produced that from them arise the yolk-spheres or deutoplasm-granules (Henneguy, Van der Stricht, Loyez, Van Durme, Hirschler, etc.); but here again the evidence is not yet decisive (p. 341).

g. Pigment Granules. Cell-pigments may be diffuse, but most commonly appear in the form of separate and often closely crowded small granules of fairly uniform size. The fact is well-established that some forms of pigment are produced by specific forms of plastids (chlorophyll by the chloroplasts, anthocyanin by the chromoplasts), but it is not yet known whether the

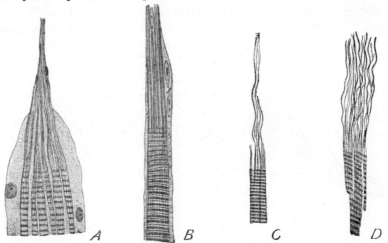

Fig. 15.—Preparations of striated muscle-cells to show longitudinal fibrillæ and their supposed direct connection with those of tendon (O. SCHULTZE).

same is true of pigments generally. A number of modern observers have found[1] that some kinds of pigment-granules arise by the direct transformation of mitochondria or at least arise under their influence. The nature and origin of the pigment-granules thus raises the same general question as that of the secretory or the storage-granules.

3. Fibrillæ

Like the granules, the cytoplasmic fibrillæ are among the most widespread and important components of the cell-substance, and by a prominent school of cytologists, headed by Flemming, have been regarded as an essential feature of the protoplasmic structure (p. 63). They are of many kinds and of varied physiological significance. Among the most familiar forms are the *myofibrils* and *neurofibrils*, characteristic of muscle-cells and nerve-cells respectively. In the striated muscle the myofibrils (Fig. 15) have a complicated structure the precise nature of which has long been a subject of debate.[2] In the nerve-cell they form a more open, net-like structure from which fibrillæ pass out into the axis-cylinder process

[1] See, for example, Meves ('11), Ciaccio ('11), Schridde ('13) on hæmoglobin; also Asvadovra ('13), Prenant ('13) and Duesberg ('15).

[2] For a critical review see Heidenhain's *Plasma und Zelle*, II.

(Fig. 16). Fibrillæ form a widespread and often conspicuous feature of gland-cells (Fig. 13), where they have been assumed by some writers to play an important rôle in secretion (production of the secretory granules) and have been designated as *ergastoplasmic* fibrillæ (Bouin); here as elsewhere, however, their functional significance is still far from clear. Fibrillæ form a conspicuous feature in many forms of epithelia, in particular the columnar epithelia, where the fibrillæ, often closely crowded, commonly run parallel to the long axis of the cell (Figs. 17, 18) in some cases also forming net-like structures.[1] These epitheliofibrillæ have been conjectured to be intra-cellular nerve-endings (neurofibrils), motor elements, analogous to myofibrils, paths of nutritive transportal, etc. The greater number of

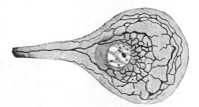

Fig. 16.—Unipolar nerve-cell of earthworm stained with gold chloride, showing neurofibrils and axis-cylinder (Szüts).

writers have, however, accepted the conclusion of Nussbaum, Kromayer, Heidenhain ('99) and many others that they are of the nature of supporting or skeletal structures, hence the term *tonofibrillæ* (Heidenhain). This conclusion receives fresh support from the recent work of Del Rio, cited above, which shows that these fibrillæ stain differently from both chondriosomes and neurofibrils and are morphologically distinct from them. In the superficial cells of stratified epithelia the fibrillæ commonly run transversely (parallel to the surface) and it is an interesting fact, observed by a number of earlier histologists and recently confirmed by Del Rio, that many of them traverse the inter-cellular plasma-bridges and thus pass from one cell to another (Fig. 41, *cf*. p. 104).

Other forms of fibrillæ are exemplified by the basal filaments, rhizoplasts, or ciliary roots of flagellated or ciliated cells; perhaps by the so-called spindle-fibers and astral rays in the mitotic figure; and those forms of chondriosomes known as chondrioconts. An especial interest attaches to the latter, which are found in nearly all kinds of cells, because of the conclusion of Benda, Meves and others that they represent the most primitive type of fibrillæ from which in the course of histogenesis arise directly many if not all of the more differentiated forms, such as myofibrils, neurofibrils or glandular fibrils. This view, as will be later shown, is still insufficiently based and must await the test of further inquiry.

[1] The epitheliofibrillæ have been studied by many observers, especially by M. Heidenhain ('99) and more recently by Del Rio-Hortega ('17), who has obtained very striking pictures by the use of Achúcarro's method (tannin-silver impregnation) and offers a valuable discussion of the subject. Preparations made in my laboratory by J. Nonidez show that Del Rio's remarkable figures do not exaggerate the clearness and brilliancy of the preparations.

Many of the forms of fibrillæ mentioned above have been regarded as artifacts or in some cases as optical illusions (Bütschli); and the question here raised remains to a considerable extent unsettled. For example, it is still by no means certain that the archiplasmic fibrillæ (spindle-fibers and

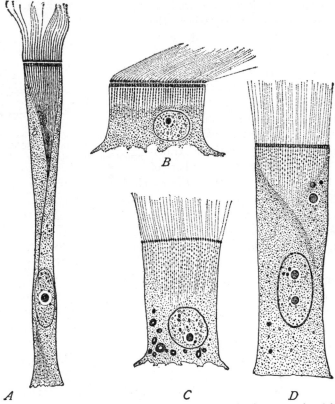

Fig. 17.—Ciliated cells, showing cytoplasmic fibrillæ terminating in a zone of peripheral basal bodies to which the cilia are attached (ENGELMANN).

A, from intestinal epithelium of *Anodonta; B*, from gill of *Anodonta*, *C*, *D*, intestinal epithelium of *Cyclas*.

astral rays) actually preëxist in the living protoplasm; and it has been shown that these and certain other forms of fibrillæ may be closely simulated by the coagulation of homogeneous colloidal solutions, such as filtered egg-albumin or solutions of albumose (p. 65). On the other hand, some kinds of fibrillæ, such as the chondrioconts may clearly be seen in living protoplasm, as was long since shown by Flemming ('82) and confirmed by many more recent observers. The actual existence of fibrillæ as preformed structural components of the protoplasmic substance can therefore not be doubted. [1]

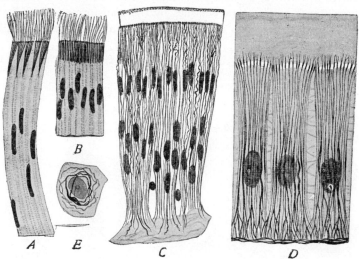

Fig. 18.—Protoplasmic fibrillæ of epithelial cells as demonstrated by the Achúcarro-Del-Rio method of gold-silver impregnation (DEL RIO).

A, B, columnar cells, intestinal epithelium of the mollusk *Tapes,* showing basal granules (blepharoplasts, trichoplasts) and basal rods (rhizoplasts); *C,* œsophageal epithelium of *Lumbricus,* with longitudinal fibrillæ; *D,* bucco-pharyngeal epithelium of the snail *Aplysia; E,* cell from the deeper epidermis of the toad *Pelobates.* [2]

4. Plastids

These bodies, especially characteristic of the cells of plants, are of general interest because they possess in many cases the power of independent growth and division, and many competent observers have accepted the probability that they arise in no other way. They are usually bodies of definite form, exclusively cytoplasmic, and vary widely in number, form and size; in some cases they are single or few in number (many algæ), in others very numerous (chloroplasts of higher plants generally); they are commonly rounded in form, but may be band-shaped, lobed or irregular. Physiologically they are localized areas of specific chemical transformation, producing characteristic products, such as starch, pigment of various kinds and perhaps fat, and are classified accordingly.

In their least differentiated condition they are small, colorless bodies, known as (1) *leucoplasts,* especially abundant in embryonic tissues but also found in differentiated cells. From the embryonic leucoplasts (themselves possibly derived from chondriosomes),[3] arise various other forms of

[1] *Cf.* p. 64.
[2] These figures do not exaggerate the clearness with which the fibrillæ appear.
[3] See p. 709.

plastids, as differentiation proceeds. In some cases they remain colorless, but enlarge to form (2) *amyloplasts*, which act as centers for the formation of reserve starch in the storage-tissues by the transformation of dissolved carbohydrates (glucose) into solid starch-grains. In other cases the plastid

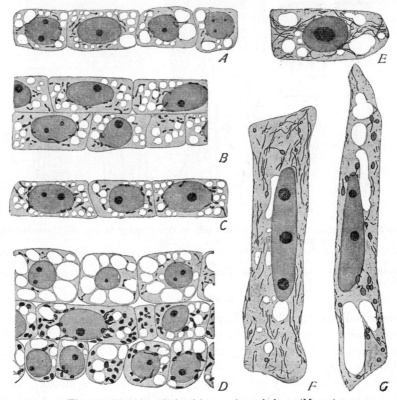

Fig. 19.—Plastids and chondriosomes in seed-plants (MEVES).

A, embryonic cells from young leaf-bud of *Tradescantia*, showing chondriosomes (in black); B, cells from meristem at base of older leaf; C, D, from same leaf, nearer the tip, showing supposed stages of division of the chondriosomes and their transformation into chloroplasts; E, embryonic cell from aërial roots of *Chlorophytum*, showing chondrioconts; F, G, older cells of same, showing formation of starch-grains in the chondrioconts.

develops pigment and becomes a *chromoplast* or *chromatophore*. The most important of these physiologically are (3) the *chloroplasts* or chlorophyll-bodies which are centers for the new formation of starch by photosynthesis (Fig. 19). The so-called stigma or "eye-spot" of various flagellates, zoö-spores and plant gametes, a light-sensitive organella, has been regarded by some authors as a special type of chromoplast; and some authors have also regarded as plastids the *pyrenoids*, localized bodies imbedded in the chromoplasts of green algæ, and serving as localized centers of starch-formation.

Besides the undoubted forms of plastids at least two other types of plastid-like bodies have been recognized by some observers. These are: (4) the *tonoplasts* which, according to DeVries, give rise to the vacuoles, the walls of which they form, and (5) the *elaioplasts*, regarded by Wakker (1888) and his followers as plastids which act as centers of fat-formation. The plastid nature of these two types is, however, somewhat uncertain.

The classical work of Schimper (1881–85) and of A. Meyer (1883) led them to the conclusion that plastids are never formed *de novo* but always by the growth and division of preëxisting plastids and ultimately from the minute undifferentiated leucoplasts of the germ-cells. They were thus conceived as having a persistent individuality and conforming to the general law of genetic continuity, like cells, nuclei or chromosomes (p. 828). The fact is now generally admitted that differentiated forms of plastids, in particular the chloroplasts, multiply in this manner; and in some lower plants the plastids are known to divide regularly at each cell-division (*e. g.*, in *Zygnema*, or *Anthoceros*).[1] No general agreement has, however, yet been reached as to whether plastids may not also arise *de novo* in the cytoplasm.[2] In this respect they are in the same case as the chondriosomes and the Golgi-bodies described below. In recent years strong evidence has been brought forward to show that plastids are of the same nature as chondriosomes (Levitsky, Guilliermond, Meves, etc.) and are actually derived from them in the course of early development (p. 709).

5. Chondriosomes [3]

These bodies, or their products, are among the most characteristic of the formed components of the cytosome and are known to occur in nearly all kinds of cells, among both plants and animals, and everywhere showing the same general characters. They have attracted much attention in recent

---

[1] Davis (99), 'Kursanow ('11), Scherrer ('14).

[2] *Cf.* Harper ('19).

[3] The term "chondriosome" was suggested by Benda ('04) and brought into more general use by Meves ('08). Meves also suggested the word *chondrioma* to designate the entire chondriosome-content of the cell; but this term, though sometimes convenient, has not been widely employed. Cowdry ('19, '16, and earlier) has urged the desirability of replacing the term "chondriosomes" by the earlier one "mitochondria" (Benda), employed in a more general sense, so as to apply to all the forms later called "chondriosomes." The word mitochondria (thread-granules) seems, however, both etymologically and historically to be most appropriately applied to the granules as such, rather than to other forms which they may assume. Meves ('10) proposed to replace these various terms by new ones containing the component "plasto" (*plastos*, form) because of the important part supposed to be played by the chondriosomes in histogenesis; hence, *plastosomes*, *plastochondria*, *plastoconts*. Many more special terms, such as *chondrioplasts*, *chromochondria*, *myochondria*, etc., are found in the literature. See Glossary; consult also the useful table of terms given by Cowdry ('18).

years because of the questions raised by Altmann, Benda, Meves and their followers concerning their possible significance in histogenesis and heredity; but opinion concerning them is still in a very unsettled state. Morphologically they appear in the form of small granules (*mitochondria*), rods or filaments (*chondrioconts*) and other bodies, many of which were observed by the earlier observers of protoplasm and described under the name of "granules," "microsomes," protoplasmic fibrillæ or "fila," "nebenkerns," etc. In a sense, therefore, we are here dealing with new names for old things.[1]   More recent studies have shown that they consist of a specific material, showing definite cytological and michrochemical characters but morphologically highly plastic, so that it may appear under many forms, which are probably to be regarded as only different phases of the same material. The most common of these are separate mitochondria and chondrioconts, both of which may often be observed in the same cell (Fig. 12); and all gradations between them may be observed in sections.   Less frequently the mitochondria are aligned in linear series to form *chondriomites;* while in special cases the chondriosomes may enlarge or aggregate to form more massive bodies, spheroidal *chondriospheres* (Fig. 168), or even may give rise to a single body, such as the "nebenkern" of the sperm-forming cells (Figs. 164, 174) or the ring-shaped chrondriosome-body of *Centrurus* (Fig. 169). These bodies often show a differentiation into a more deeply staining cortical and a lightly staining central or medullary substance, which in the sperm-forming cells may give rise to complicated structural patterns (p. 372). All such more complicated forms seem, however, to be secondary and specialized formations which arise primarily from minute scattered granules, rods or threads.

According to M. R. and W. H. Lewis ('14, '15), the chondriosomes as seen in cultures of living cells *in vitro* are almost never at rest, often changing their shape from moment to moment, and also undergoing rapid changes of position. The various morphological forms are readily transformed one into another. In the living cell "granules may be seen to fuse into rows or chains, and these to elongate into threads "; and these are said in turn to anastomose with each other and may give rise to a complicated network which in turn may again break down into threads, rods, loops, and rings.[2] The threads or chondrioconts are, however, stated to arise more commonly by the stretching out of single granules; and it should be added that few other observers have found the threads anastomosing to form networks. These observations, together with the evidence offered by fixed preparations, leave no doubt of the plasticity and polymorphic character of the chondriosomes; though the possibility should be kept in mind that some of the

[1] See Retzius, '14.   [2] '14, p. 331.

changes seen in living cultures may be due to slightly abnormal conditions under which the cells are placed.

The physico-chemical nature of chondriosomes has been the object of numerous researches [1] which indicate that their principal chemical components are phospholipoid and albuminous substances, thus resembling chemically the phosphatids, of which lecithin is an example; and we here find some indication of their reactions to fixing and staining agents. They are soluble in various degrees in dilute acetic acid, ether, acetone, alcohol and other fat-solvents; hence the fact that they are often imperfectly fixed or even destroyed by many of the ordinary fixing agents containing acetic acid, and were often overlooked until a more appropriate technique had been devised.[2] They often darken more or less in osmic acid, though less so than the Golgi-elements, to which they appear to be somewhat related chemically (p. 48). In sections they are stained by various dyes, of which those most frequently employed are iron hæmatoxylin, crystal violet (Benda's alizarin-crystal-violet method) and acid-fuchsin (Altmann's acid-fuchsin picric acid or Bensley's acid-fuchsin methyl-green). In the living state they are stained characteristically by weak solutions of Janus green B. As in the case of so many other cell-components, however, their identification rests less upon their microchemical reactions than on their morphological history.

The broader theoretical interest of the chondriosomes as possibly persistent and autonomous cell-components, which has been urged by Altmann, Benda, Meves, Duesberg, Guilliermond and many others,[3] will be more fully considered later. They play an important part in the formation of the germ-cells (p. 369); during cell-division they are distributed with approximate equality to the daughter-cells (*chondriokinesis*, p. 163). An important group of observers have ascribed to them the powers of independent growth and division, and consider them as of fundamental importance for the process of histogenesis (p. 706), forming the source from which arise many of the more specific cell-components, including the plastids, various forms of fibrillæ, such as the neurofibrils and myofibrils, and a great variety of granules, such as secretory and storage-granules, yolk, fat, pigment, etc. In this direction the chondriosome-theory comes into close relation with the granule-theory of protoplasm as developed by Altmann and his followers (p. 74).

---

[1] See especially Regaud ('08), Fauré-Fremiet ('10), Löwschin ('13). Also the general reviews of Kingsbury ('12), Duesberg ('12), E. V. Cowdry ('16, '18), N. H. Cowdry ('17), Guilliermond ('14, etc.).

[2] *E. g.*, Benda's fluid (Flemming's with very little acetic or none, or those of Altmann, Bensley, Regaud and Champy. See Cowdry, *op. cit.* Also Gatenby in Lee ('21).

[3] See Benda ('03), Meves ('07, '08, '18, etc.), Duesberg ('07, '19, etc.), Guilliermond ('14, etc.).

Little is certainly known as yet concerning their specific physiological meaning. Because of their important rôle in the formation of the sperm-tail Benda conjectured that they may be contractile and perform motor functions; but this has found little or no support, nor has the later sugges-tions of Koltzoff ('06, '09) that they are in the nature of skeletal or support-ing structures. Kingsbury ('12) and Mayer, Rathery and Schaffer ('14) seek to connect them with the respiratory functions; but this view also lacks definite support, though it has been favorably regarded by some authors. More promising is the view of Regaud ('09a, '10), who considers the chondrio-somes as centers of specific chemical action, like the plastids, which serve to extract, elaborate and fix definite chemical constituents of the protoplasm, hence the term *electosomes*. This view, a modification of that of Benda and Meves, is based on observations which have seemed to show, as above stated, that the mitochondria may actually give rise to other intra-cellular structures of specific type. To this subject we shall later return in a more general discussion of the theoretical significance of the chondriosomes.[1]

6. Golgi-apparatus, Golgi-bodies, Dictyosomes. (" Internal Reticular Apparatus " of Golgi. " Canalicular System " or " Trophospongium " of Holmgren)

By these various names are designated a group of cell-components, as yet imperfectly known, which show some points of resemblance to the chondriosomes though morphologically quite distinct from them. Like the chondriosomes the Golgi-elements are in considerable degree polymorphic, though always consisting, apparently, of the same specific material. Like the chondriosomes they blacken with osmic acid, but much more intensely; and they show somewhat similar solubilities, being readily attacked by dilute acetic acid and other lipoid-solvents, so that they are often de-stroyed or imperfectly fixed by reagents containing these ingredients. In these respects they, like the chondriosomes, behave somewhat like lecithin-compounds and may possibly be composed of lecithalbumin (Weigl, '12). The best methods for their demonstration consist in fixation by reagents containing little or no acetic acid and impregnation by metallic silver or osmium,[2] by which they are usually well differentiated from the chondrio-somes. Their identification depends, however, mainly on morphological evidence, which shows them to be quite distinct from the chondriosomes or

---

[1] Chapter IX.

[2] *E. g.*, Golgi's silver-method following formol-arsenious acid, or that of Cajal following formol-uranium-nitrate; the method of Kopsch consists simply in prolonged treatment by osmic acid, without other staining. In all these cases the Golgi-elements appear intensely black; but this treat-ment alone will not always differentiate them from the chondriosomes.

other formed elements, so that they must be considered as specific cell-components *sui generis*.

The Golgi apparatus is of very wide distribution among the cells of higher animals and is known in the Protozoa [1] everywhere showing the same

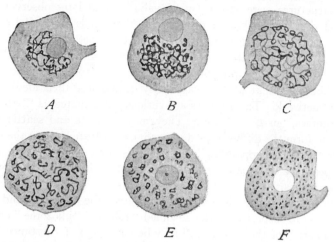

Fig. 20.—Variations of the Golgi-apparatus in nerve-cells, spinal ganglia of young cat (*A, C, D, F*) and rabbit (*B*) (CAJAL).
A–C, reticular type; *D–F*, scattered or diffuse type.

general characters; and there is reason to believe that the same may be true of plant cells though considerable doubt concerning this still exists. It appears in two principal forms, the *localized* and the *diffuse*, which may be converted into one another in changing phases of cell-activity and are therefore to be regarded as merely different phases of the same structural element. In its localized form, as first described by Golgi ('98) in nerve-cells of the spinal ganglia of vertebrates, it commonly gives the appearance of a localized net-like structure, composed of more or less contorted and varicose fibrils, which appear intensely black after silver impregnation or prolonged treatment by osmic acid. This structure Golgi called the *internal reticular apparatus*, a name afterwards widely employed, though in some cases no longer appropriate. In the younger cells and often in the older ones it lies most commonly at one side of the nucleus, but in certain cases may completely surround it (Figs. 20, 21). In the epithelial tissues generally (including the glands) the apparatus typically lies on the side towards the lumen—a fact of much interest in connection with its supposed functions in secretion (p. 52). In the localized form, later observers found

[1] In gregarines, Hirschler ('14), King and Gatenby ('23).

the Golgi-apparatus with many variants, in many other kinds of cells,[1] including the germ-cells (spermatogonia, oöcytes, spermatocytes) though described under other names such as "archoplasmic loops" (Hermann, '91) or "pseudo-chromosomes" forming the "central capsule" (Heidenhain, '00). These structures were shown by Sjövall ('06) and later observers [2] to be identical with the Golgi-apparatus of the tissue-cells and to be quite distinct from the chondriosomes (with which they were formerly confused). It seems to be well established that in many cases the Golgi "net" is built up from originally separate bodies,—lamelliform, rod-like, banana-shaped or the like—and that in such cases they do not lose their identity in the so-called network. These bodies are variously designated as "batonettes," "dictyosomes," or *Golgi-bodies*. They may separate and scatter through the cell to form the diffuse type and again concentrate to form the localized type or "reticular apparatus"; and there is some evidence that the net-like appearance may be an artifact produced by imperfect fixation of the separate bodies.

In its localized phase it commonly surrounds the centrioles and there is some reason to suspect that the so-called "sphere," "idiozome" or "archiplasm-sphere" of the resting cell may be composed of substance that belongs to the Golgi-apparatus (p. 361).[3] This relation to the central bodies was first clearly seen in case of the germ-cells ("pseudo-chromosomes" of Heidenhain, '00) and in epithelial cells of Descemet's membrane ("centrophormium" of Ballowitz, '98, '00) and was later described in many other cases, including the nerve-cells, epithelial cells of various kinds, gland-cells, cartilage-cells, the primordial germ-cells, spermatogonia, spermatocytes and oöcytes. [4] The Golgi-apparatus is not to be confused with the chondriosomes, which likewise may be aggregated about the central bodies but lie more peripherally and often show no definite grouping about the centers (Figs. 22, 149).

The localized type of Golgi-apparatus is connected by many intergradations with the diffuse. Even in the nerve-cells of vertebrates, as shown by Cajal ('08, '14) and other observers the structure shows wide variations, the reticulum often breaking up into separate islands or even into separate rods or granules scattered through the cell (Figs. 20–22). On the other hand, in the nerve-cells of gasteropods (Weigl) and Crustacea (Poluscynski) the apparatus is said to be permanently diffuse, appearing in the form of

[1] For reviews and literature-lists see especially Duesberg ('12, '14, '20), Nussbaum ('13), Pappenheimer ('16), Hirschler ('17, '19), Gatenby ('16, '17, '18, '19), Nassonov ('23).

[2] See especially Weigl ('12), Hirschler, Gatenby (*op. cit.*), Bowen ('20, '21).

[3] See Bowen, '20, '22.

[4] See Sjövall ('06), Barinetti ('12), Pensa ('13), Weigl ('12), Terni ('14), Cajal ('14), Berenberg-Gossler ('13), Hirschler ('18, '19), Duesberg ('20), etc.; also the earlier works of Hermann and Heidenhain.

granules, curved rods (batonettes) plates, or ring-like bodies scattered at random through the cell. Such diffuse forms have now been found in many kinds of cells, either as a permanent condition or one that is incidental to other cell-activities. The most interesting of these cases are found in embryonic cells and during the mitotic division of the tissue-cells. In later stages of development (birds, mammals) as shown by the work of Golgi, Sjövall, Marcora and others,[1] the Golgi-apparatus is of localized and net-

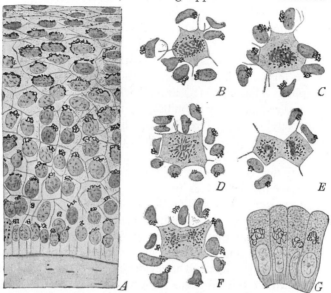

Fig. 21.—Golgi-apparatus and dictyokinesis in epithelial cells, Golgi-method. (*A–F* from DEINEKA; *G*, from BERGEN).

A, vertical section, epidermis of the horse; *B–E*, successive stages of division (dictyokinesis) from Descemet's membrane, new-born cat; *G*, columnar epithelial cells, prostate of dog.

like type; but it was observed by Fañanas ('12) that in early stages of the hen's egg (44 hours and later) it appears in the form of separate, scattered rod-like bodies, which only in later stages of development become aggregated to form a localized net at one side of the nucleus. This is confirmed by the more recent independent work of Hirschler ('18) and Gatenby ('19) on pulmonates (*Lymnœa*). Both observers have found the Golgi-elements in the cleavage-stages and as late as the gastrula in the form of separate, scattered bodies, quite distinct from the chondriosomes in form and staining-reactions (Fig. 347).

In the diffuse type the Golgi-bodies proper are readily distinguishable after a suitable technique by their intense blackening after osmic or silver

---

[1] Review in Hirschler, '18.

impregnation. In some cases, however, and possibly in all, each of these bodies (batonette, etc.) is accompanied by a small spheroid of clear, non-staining substance to which it is closely applied (hence perhaps its curved form). Gatenby calls this an "archoplasm-sphere," and regards it as the same substance as that of the sphere surrounding the central bodies in the localized type, a view supported especially by the history of the Golgi-elements in the sperm-forming cells (p. 364). There is, however, little ground for calling this material by the vague term "archoplasm," and none for supposing it to have any connection with the substance of the division-figure. Preferably, therefore, it may be called simply the "sphere-substance." Recent studies have prominently raised the possibility that this substance forms an integral part of the Golgi-body, and that the large clear sphere (idiozome, etc.) around which the Golgi-apparatus lies when in the localized form may be built up by the aggregation of the smaller spheres accompanying the scattered Golgi-bodies of the diffuse type (p. 361).[1]

These facts seem to show that the localized form is to be regarded as a secondary condition. Additional ground for this conclusion is offered by the history of the Golgi-bodies in the sperm-forming cells, and also by their behavior during mitosis (p. 165).

Concerning the functional significance of the Golgi-elements even less is known than in case of the chondriosomes. The important fact has recently been made clear that they play an important part in the formation of the acrosome during spermatogenesis [2] and perhaps also contribute to that of the middle-piece. The evidence that the Golgi-apparatus may be concerned in the processes of secretion will be considered later (p. 715).

A considerable group of observers, headed by Holmgren ('99, '00 and later), have considered the Golgi-apparatus in its localized or net-like form as a system of intracellular canals filled with fluid which after coagulation and impregnation with silver or osmium appear as solid filaments.[3] Thus arose the term "canalicular system," first applied to the Golgi-apparatus by Holmgren and adopted by many later writers as synonymous with the latter term. Holmgren concluded further that this system arises from ingrowths of the surrounding cells ("trophocytes") which become vacuolated and are finally transformed into canaliculi, forming a hollow network that still communicates with the exterior. Owing to the supposed trophic functions of

[1] See Gatenby ('19), Ludford and Gatenby ('21), Bowen ('20, '22).

[2] *Cf.* p. 381. See Sjövall ('06), Perroncito ('10), Weigl ('12), Cataneo ('14) and especially Hirschler ('19), Gatenby ('17–'19), Bowen ('20, '22), Gatenby and Woodger ('21), Ludford and Gatenby ('21).

[3] Duesberg ('12, '14) gives a valuable review and discussion of this problem, with literature-lists. See also Cajal ('14) and Pappenheimer ('16).

these ingrowths the Golgi-net was designated as a "trophospongium." The terms "Golgi-apparatus," "canalicular system" and "trophospongium" were thus employed for a time as synonyms for the same structure even by observers who differed more or less concerning its nature and

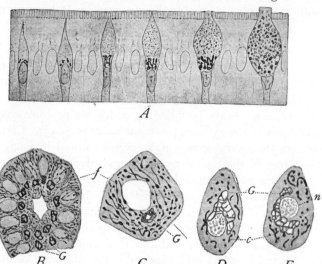

Fig. 22.—The Golgi-apparatus in various cells (*A–C* from CAJAL, *D, E*, from PENSA).

A (slightly schematized) progressive functional changes in goblet-cells from the intestinal epithelium of mammal; *B*, pancreas-cells, showing both Golgi-apparatus (*G*) and chondrioconts (*f*); *C*, the same more enlarged; *D, E*, cartilage cells, showing Golgi-reticulum (*G*) and chondriosomes (*c*).

origin. It now seems probable, as emphasized especially by Duesberg, that two quite distinct structures were confused in this usage, one the Golgi-apparatus proper, the other a system of trabeculæ or fibrils formed as ingrowths from the surrounding cells. Such ingrowths, forming a true "trophospongium" seem to have been clearly demonstrated in a number of cases, in particular by Nussbaum ('13) and by Ross ('15) in nerve-cells; but these and other observers are now agreed that this structure is quite distinct from the Golgi-apparatus. Some competent observers (Cajal, Bensley, Cowdry) have adopted Holmgren's conclusion that the Golgi-net represents the coagulated, lipoid-containing contents of a system of intracellular canaliculi, but have found no evidence of its connection with the exterior or of its derivation from "trophocytes" or other surrounding cells.

An external origin of the Golgi-apparatus seems to be quite excluded by its behavior during mitosis and also by the behavior of the scattered, or diffuse Golgi-bodies in the early embryonic cells. In such cases the Golgi-bodies can at most be regarded as vacuoles or their coagulated contents, which at no time have any connection with the exterior. It is, however, difficult thus to regard the scattered Golgi-bodies as vacuoles (or their contents) in view of their shape and other peculiarities; and it seems more natural to consider them as definite bodies, solid or semi-solid, that have no connection with the trophocyte-ingrowths observed by Holmgren and Nussbaum.[1]

7. Vacuoles

Vacuoles are found in many kinds of cells, conspicuously developed especially in the tissue-cells of higher plants generally and in many of the Protista. They are in general spheroidal cavities containing a watery liquid, and probably always bounded by a delicate protoplasmic limiting film comparable with the external plasma-membrane (p. 55). Certain forms of vacuoles (in the swarm-spores of lower plants, and in many Protists) possess the power of rhythmical pulsation and play an important part in excretion. In some cases vacuoles have the power of division, and for this and other reasons have been considered as products of special forms of plastids (*tonoplasts* of De Vries). Some authors have gone so far as to conclude that vacuoles (or tonoplasts) arise only by the division of preëxisting vacuoles,[2] but it seems unlikely that this is of general validity. In many Protozoa, for example, solid food is digested in the interior of vacuoles which may be seen to form *de novo* during the ingestion of food. The power of division, therefore, is probably confined to certain special forms of vacuoles.

The prominence of vacuoles in the cells of higher plants as contrasted with those of animals has earlier been indicated. In higher animals, generally, vacuoles are either wanting or inconspicuous; in many of the Protista (ciliates, rhizopods), on the other hand, they are often developed to such an extent as to give the whole protoplasm a foam-like or pseudo-alveolar structure (p. 72). If, as above suggested, the canalicular system of Holmgren may be comparable to a vacuolar system, the latter would be of more general occurrence in lower animals than has generally been supposed.

8. The Cell-membrane or Wall

All kinds of cells are probably limited externally by some kind of membrane, though this is not always evident to the eye. Animal cells are in general characterized by a relatively slight development of the membrane,

---

[1] For further facts concerning the Golgi-apparatus see p. 714. Bensley ('10) has concluded that in plant-cells the "canalicular apparatus" is represented by the vacuoles, at first forming an intricate closed network of fine canals, quite comparable to the Golgi-apparatus of animal cells. This view, which has been supported by Guilliermond, recalls a suggestion of Cajal's that the canalicular system (Golgi-apparatus) in the cells of higher animals may be comparable to the contractile vacuole with its associated drainage-canals in ciliates.

[2] DeVries, '85, Went, '88.

which is often so thin and delicate that the cells appear to the eye naked, and in many cases were formerly so described. The plant-cell, on the other hand, commonly shows sharply marked and often very thick walls, to which circumstance indeed the cell owes its name (p. 22). This difference is, however, a superficial one arising from the existence of two widely different types of cell-membrane, one of which is common to all types of cells while the other varies widely in the extent of its development and is often absent. There are, respectively, the plasma-membrane [1] and the cell-wall proper, sometimes referred to as the "true membrane." The first of these belongs to the protoplast proper and forms part of the cytoplasm. The second lies outside the cytosome, in some cases separated from it by a considerable space, and is generally regarded as a non-protoplasmic or metaplasmic product of the cytoplasm, though in many cases it possesses, like protoplasmic structures, the power of growth by intussusception. By many writers the term "cell-wall" is reserved exclusively for membranes of this type.

As now commonly employed the term plasma-membrane designates a thin peripheral surface-film or limiting layer of cytoplasm, differing in physical consistency from the underlying substance, but often indistinguishable cytologically. Its presence is demonstrated by experiments on plasmolysis, the penetration of various dyes and the like, which prove this layer to have the properties of a semi-permeable membrane and one which plays a most important part in regulating the exchanges of the cell with its environment, and in the stimulation of the protoplasmic activities.[2] Secondly the existence of the plasma-membrane is more directly established by the so-called "micro-dissection" or "micro-vivisection" method due to Barber and Kite and developed particularly by Chambers.[3] Experiments by this method prove that the plasma-membrane or surface-film of protoplasm is of firm or even tough consistency, in some cases highly elastic, and offers considerable resistance to mechanical injury. A similar membrane is formed about the protoplasmic vacuoles, and also about naked masses of protoplasm produced by cutting, tearing, or shaking cells to pieces.

Modern studies on the plasma-membrane indicate that it is comparable

[1] Also called ectoplasm, ectoplast, Hautschicht, Plasmahaut, etc. See Glossary.
[2] See R. S. Lillie, '09, '13, '14, '20, '24.
[3] See Barber ('14), Kite ('12, '13), Chambers ('17, '19, '24), Seifriz ('18). These operations are performed on living cells suspended in hanging drops (of sea-water, blood-serum or other appropriate normal fluid) by means of the "micro-dissection-needle" devised by Barber. Such needles are made by drawing out small glass rods to an extremely fine point and can be used to puncture, cut, tear or displace the living cell-substance under high powers of the microscope. Their use by the observers mentioned has afforded important data concerning the physical nature of the cell-substance. Accurate control of these operations is made possible by a number of simple mechanical appliances readily attached to the stage of the microscope. See Barber ('14) and, for fuller accounts, Chambers ('15, '17).

physically to the surface-layer or film that tends to form at the free surfaces (or the interfaces) of non-living colloidal systems; and on this basis
many interesting experiments and hypotheses have been put forward in
attempts to show how the osmotic phenomena of the cell are controlled by
changes in the permeability of this layer [1] and how this may play a part in
cell-division and fertilization (pp. 191, 410). It has been plausibly argued
by Overton, Loeb and others that the plasma-membrane owes some of its
characteristic properties to its richness in lipoid substances (hence the effect
of fat-solvents in artificial parthenogenesis, etc.). Others have urged the
emulsoid nature of the plasma-membrane and the variations of viscosity
owing to the inversion of phases (Clowes), or the degree of dispersion of the
suspended phase; [2] but the questions raised by these inquiries lie outside
the scope of this work.

The outer or true membrane, often wholly wanting, shows a very
wide diversity of development, chemical composition and other characters.
It is typically exemplified by the cellulose walls of plant-cells or the cuticular
membranes often formed on the free surfaces of epithelial cells in animals.
In free (solitary) cells the true membrane forms a distinct surrounding envelope.   In the tissues the membranes form intercellular partitions or
walls between the cell-bodies, often consisting of several layers.   The cell-
bodies may become widely separated by continued growth of the inter-
cellular substance, so that in extreme cases (e. g., in cartilage) they lie scattered in a non-living "matrix."

The structure of the wall may be studied to greatest advantage in the
higher plants, where its origin and nature have occupied the close attention of many eminent botanists. Some of these, impressed with its growth
by intussusception, have considered it to be "living," or at least to arise by a
direct transformation of the peripheral protoplasm (Wiesner, Molisch,
Haberlandt and at first Strasburger, etc.). At present the earlier view of
Mohl and Nägeli is generally accepted that it is a secretion-product of the
protoplasm, either at the periphery of the cell or in the interior of the cell-
plate (p. 159). In the higher plants generally it usually shows a central
layer (the middle lamella or primary wall) the presence of which is traceable to the method of cleavage by cell-plate formation. To this layer,
composed of pectose (a carbohydrate) succeed on either side "secondary"
and often "tertiary" layers, laid down upon the middle lamella after its
formation and largely composed of cellulose. These layers, as they grow
older, often undergo a variety of chemical and physical changes, including
the deposit in them of other organic or inorganic substances, and a great

[1] See for instance Bancroft ('13, '14), Clowes ('16a, '16b), Loeb ('13), R. S. Lillie (*op. cit.*).
[2] Lloyd ('16), Spaeth ('16), Free ('18). See Sharp ('21).

variety of sculpturing, pitting and the like on their surfaces. In animal cells much less is known of the true walls, owing to their greater delicacy and often their lack of visible structure. Many of them (including the inter-cellular substances generally) are nitrogenous bodies, such as keratin or chitin; but as in the case of plants they sometimes become impregnated with inorganic deposits, such as silica, lime-salts, etc. Owing to their different mode of formation (*i. e.*, by secretion from the external surface instead of by cell-plate formation) animal membranes do not show a middle lamella; and though in exceptional cases they may become greatly thickened, they do not in general show the distinction between primary, secondary and tertiary walls.

III. PROTOPLASM. ITS COMPOSITION AND STRUCTURE

The structure of protoplasm has always offered a problem of primary interest to students of the cell; for it seemed that we might expect here to gain some insight into the mechanism of the protoplasmic activities. This was early urged by the eminent physiologist Brücke (1861), who argued that the activities of cells demand for their explanation the assumption of a fundamental organization or architecture of protoplasm as distinguished from its merely chemical or physical properties.[1] It seemed a reasonable hope that at least some of the features of such an organization might appear in a visible structure of the protoplasm; and this has led to pro-longed cytological study of the problem. If this hope has thus far had a rather meager fulfillment, the problem still retains a fundamental interest and attempts to solve it have played a very important part in the advance-ment of our actual knowledge of the cell. It is necessary to approach the subject by some preliminary discussion of our use of terms.

1. Terminology

Max Schultze, Kühne, DeBary, Hanstein and other earlier observers of protoplasm (cytoplasm) described it as a clear substance, having the general properties of a viscid liquid, and containing granules. They thus recognized in rudimentary fashion the fact that protoplasm is not a homogeneous or single substance but a mixture of different components; and this conclusion has constantly gained in weight with the advance of later researches both on the chemistry of the cell-substance and on the visible forms which it may assume. Many of the visible cell-components (such as various forms of granules and fibrillæ) differ markedly in different kinds of cells and often seem to be of secondary origin, arising in the course of differentiation, or coming and going with different phases of the cell-activities. Some of these

[1] See quotation at p. 632.

secondary elements, such as starch-grains or fat-drops, behave like inert and lifeless bodies; and this fact led to the conception of a fundamental living protoplasm as distinguished from its "non-living" products. Lionel Beale (1861) drew a sharp distinction between the primary, "formative," "germinal" or "living" matter of the cell (afterwards called *bioplasm*), and the "formed material," maintaining that "the changes which more especially distinguish living structures from lifeless matter take place in the substance that I have termed *germinal matter*, and in this alone." [1] Van Beneden (1870) distinguished, in case of the animal egg, an active "protoplasm," and a passive "deutoplasm," consisting of storage products in the form of yolk. Hanstein (1880) in like manner contrasted the active, living protoplasm with the passive or lifeless *metaplasm* to which it may secondarily give rise; while Sachs (1892, 1895) distinguished the living *energid* (active protoplasm and nucleus) from the passive *energid-products* (metaplasm). Already in Beale's work, however, appears a further distinction between "formed material" and "secondary deposits," the latter being considered as wholly passive products of the formed material: as examples of such deposits he gives the starch-grains and fat-drops. This distinction, though not very logically carried out, foreshadowed later attempts to find a more adequate classification of the cell-components. For instance Kupffer (1896) recognized in addition to the active protoplasm of the energid two types of formed material or energid-products, the active or *dynamoplastic* (such as *myofibrillæ* or *neurofibrillæ*) and the passive or *paraplastic* (metaplasmic of Hanstein). Arthur Meyer similarly grouped the cell-components into three classes, as follows: [2]

a. *Protoplasmatic:* comprising the primary and most active elements, represented by the undifferentiated or fundamental cell-substance, the nucleus, the plastids, and perhaps the centrioles, all of which possess the powers of growth and self-perpetuation and arise by division of preëxisting elements of the same kind.

b. *Alloplasmatic:* (= dynamoplastic of Kupffer), assumed to be secondary products of differentiation of the protoplasm, and not self-perpetuating, but performing active functions. Examples of such structures were considered to be cilia, flagella, myofibrillæ, neurofibrillæ, astral rays and spindle-fibers. Meyer included here also the "tonoplasts" of DeVries, or vacuolar walls.

c. *Ergastic:* (= paraplastic, metaplastic) relatively passive secondary products of differentiation, in the form of "inclusions" (starch-grains, fat-drops, etc.) or external secretions (intercellular substances), all of which are often spoken of as "lifeless."

[1] Q. J., 1862, p. 80.
[2] See Meyer, '96, '12. Certain modifications of Meyer's categories have been here added.

No attempt is here made to identify a living "protoplasm" as such or to distinguish between "living" and "non-living" cell-components. Life is treated as a property of the cell-system as a whole, the components of that system differing only in the degree and manner of their activity.   In this respect Meyer's views are quite in agreement with those earlier expressed by Hanstein, Flemming,[1] Kölliker, O. Hertwig and other leading students of the subject, and the same view of the matter has been adopted by many modern physiologists and biochemists who regard the cell as essentially a complex colloidal system.[2]

Logically, no doubt, this is correct; and from a purely physiological point of view is perhaps the only possible mode of treatment.   The cytologist, however, finds it convenient to distinguish, as did Beale, between a primary undifferentiated substance that is common to all kinds of cells and the formed components that may appear within it.   The former substance is probably to be identified with the *hyaloplasm* or clear ground-substance in which the differentiated protoplasmic elements are suspended.   Many of the latter have been spoken of, even by recent writers, as protoplasmic "inclusions"—obviously an inappropriate term in view of the fact that they may play an essential part in the cell-activities.   We shall therefore call them *formed bodies* [3] without attempting to distinguish at this point between "living" and "non-living" cell-components, or between "formed material" and "secondary deposits."

2. Chemical and Physical Properties of Protoplasm

Chemically considered, protoplasm is a complex mixture, comprising especially *proteins* and their many derivatives; the *lipoids* or fatty bodies; *carbohydrates;* and *inorganic salts*, together with a large amount of associated water.   In these respects the protoplasm of animals and plants shows a general similarity, though the relative proportions of the protoplasmic components varies widely in different organisms and even in different physiological states of the same species.   The earlier work on protoplasm emphasized the protoplasmic resemblances between plants and animals and laid especial weight on the importance of the proteins in both.

---

[1] "The moment we enter upon the question as to whether this substance or that is still to be called protoplasm or is no longer such, we are treading on uncertain ground, simply for the reason that no man can definitely say *what protoplasm is*. . . . That which lives is, in my view, the entire body of the cell " (Flemming, '82, pp. 78, 81).

[2] *Cf.* pp. 633, 635. "We cannot, without gross misuse of terms, speak of the cell life as being associated with any particular type of molecule. Its life is the expression of a particular dynamic equilibrium which obtains in a polyphasic system. Certain of the phases may be separated . . . but life, as we instructively define it, is a property of the cell as a whole, because it depends upon the organization of processes, upon the equilibrium displayed by the totality of the coexisting phases." (F. G. Hopkins, '13, p. 213).

[3] This is taken from Beale, but used in a somewhat broader sense.

More recent studies have shown, however, that marked chemical differences in this respect exist between the two groups, at least in higher forms, the carbohydrates being much more prominent in the protoplasm of plants, while the proteins and lipoids predominate in that of animals.[1]

Physically, protoplasm displays the properties of a complex colloidal system and commonly behaves as a viscous liquid. As such a liquid protoplasm was described by all the earlier investigators such as Dujardin, Schultze, Kühne and DeBary. These observers, and their followers, using relatively low powers of the microscope, described living protoplasm as consisting of a clear, homogeneous, viscid ground-substance or *hyaloplasm* containing suspended granules or *microsomes* [2] of various sizes, and often also vacuoles filled with a watery liquid. Bütschli (1878), working largely on living Protozoa, where the vacuoles are often very small and closely crowded, suggested that protoplasm has a foam-like or "alveolar" structure, similar to that of an emulsion; and he afterwards ('92) developed this conception into a general theory of protoplasmic structure, which, as will later be seen, is quite in harmony with more modern views concerning the colloidal properties of protoplasm.

The viscous liquid nature of protoplasm is patent in cells which display flowing movements of the living protoplasm, as in cyclosis or in the formation of pseudopodia. Free cells, when in a state of rest, tend towards the spheroidal form, while actively irregular cells such as *Amœba* or leucocytes generally become spheroidal upon electric shock. Living fragments of protoplasm, produced by shaking or cutting cells to pieces, generally round up to a spheroidal shape. Watery vacuoles in protoplasm are typically spheroidal; and they often move freely through the protoplasmic substance, as may also the cell-nucleus, plastids, granules, yolk-spheres and other formed bodies. Cells originally separate may completely fuse to form a single body, a process which occurs naturally in the conjugation of gametes and may be artificially induced in case of the eggs of sea-urchins and other animals (p. 972). There is strong evidence that during cell division the astral rays, possibly even the spindle-fibers, are lines of protoplasmic flow; while vortical and other movements of the peripheral protoplasm also may be observed at this time (pp. 192, 198).

Numerous researches in recent years have, however, proved that the protoplasmic viscosity varies widely in different kinds of cells and even in different physiological states of the same cell, and that it may sometimes reach a point at which the protoplasm passes over temporarily into a jelly-like or semi-solid condition. Such solidifications and liquefactions may occur

----

[1] See MacDougal, '20.   [2] These terms are due to Hanstein, 1880.

in living protoplasm as reversible processes which play an important part in the life of the cell (p. 197).

In its more liquid condition protoplasm (or rather the apparently homogeneous ground-substance or *hyaloplasm*) shows many of the properties of a watery colloidal solution, consisting of a continuous, watery, more liquid substance in which are suspended a multitude of very minute and often ultra-microscopic particles or droplets, electrically charged and in some cases (as demonstrated by the ultra-microscope) in active Brownian movement.[1] This movement is of course only possible in a liquid medium, and is much retarded, or ceases, when the viscosity of the medium increases beyond a certain point. In most cases the movement is not shown by the *visible* granules of living protoplasm, thus indicating a considerable degree of viscosity in the protoplasmic substance; but active Brownian movements of the visible granules are seen as soon as the protoplasm liquefies after death. The occurrence of such movements in living protoplasm seems, it is true, to be authenticated in a few cases;[2] but, as was long since pointed out by Flemming, who observed the dance of minute fat-drops in living cartilage-cells ('82, p. 50), it is not easy to exclude the possibility that such granules may lie in watery vacuoles in the protoplasm or that a submortem liquefaction is in progress. In the cytoplasm of the sea-urchin egg during its more liquid phase no Brownian movement of the microsomes is seen in the living object;[3] but when the protoplasm is killed by crushing or tearing active Brownian movements appear, while the alveolar spheres or macrosomes swell and disappear (Chambers).[4] On the other hand, the ultra-microscope (p. 33) reveals the existence in the ground-substance or hyaloplasm of living cells particles that lie beyond the reach of the ordinary microscope, which often are seen to be in active Brownian movement.[5] According to Gaidukov the movements of these particles cease upon death of the cell, which he ascribes to a post-mortem rigor or coagulation; and he also showed that in the protoplasm of *Vallisneria* an active Brownian movement of the particles is seen under the ultra-microscope (dark ground

---

[1] This movement, so called after its discoverer, Robert Brown (1828), is a rapid trembling movement of minute particles suspended in a liquid medium, readily seen in an aqueous suspension of finely powdered gamboge, carmine or lampblack. Its cause is now generally referred to bombardments of the suspended particles or granules by the molecules of the liquid in which they are suspended. Other things equal, the amplitude of the vibrations is inversely proportional to the size of the granules, and the smaller ones may have a slow and irregular, but very considerable, movement of translation. For an account of this subject see Bayliss, *Principles of General Physiology* ('15), and the work of Perrin ('10) there cited.

[2] See F. R. Lillie, '06.

[3] Wilson, '99, Chambers, '17.

[4] More or less complete dissolution of the macrosomes also often takes place on fixation of the cytoplasm by certain agents such as acetic or picric acid; hence the difficulty of proper fixation of alveolar protoplasm by many reagents containing a high percentage of such substances.

[5] See Gaidukov, '10. Mainesco, '12. Price, '14, Bayliss, '20, etc.

illumination) so long as the protoplasm is moving. When the latter movement ceases locally the Brownian movements likewise cease, but reappear
just before the protoplasmic movement is resumed. This means, of course,
that the viscosity of the protoplasm increases during rest and decreases
during movement. Somewhat similarly, Bayliss ('20) shows that in the
ectoplasm of a living *Amœba*, so long as the protoplasm is moving, the
minute particles made visible by dark ground illumination show an active
Brownian movement, but this ceases at once when the protoplasm is electrically stimulated, to be resumed when the stimulation ceases and the protoplasmic flow reappears. With a stronger stimulus the protoplasm is killed
and the Brownian movements cease at once, not to be renewed until the
protoplasm liquefies during *post-mortem* changes. These changes, manifestly, demonstrate the variations in degree of viscosity associated with
protoplasmic movement; and as Bayliss points out, they are quite analogous to the cessation and reappearance of the Brownian movements of
minute suspended solid particles in a solution of gelatin alternately
cooled and warmed.

Wide variations in the physical consistency of the protoplasmic substance
have been demonstrated by micro-dissection studies on living cells and
also by the use of the centrifuge.[1] According to Kite the protoplasm of
epithelial cells or of nerve-cells shows such a degree of rigidity that it may
be cut to pieces which undergo little or no change of form. The living
substance of the muscle-cell is also fairly solid but more viscous and highly
elastic, so that it may be drawn out into long threads which when released
almost regain their previous shape. On the other hand, in the "resting
state" or interkinesis of many cells—such as egg-cells (echinoderms, nemertines), sperm-forming cells, or Protozoa generally—the protoplasm
has the properties of a viscid liquid bounded by a plasma-membrane that
is of much more solid consistency. During the mitotic activities of these
cells Heilbrunn and Chambers have shown that a large part of the protoplasm temporarily undergoes a process of solidification or gelation, returning to the more liquid state at the close of division (p. 197). The variations in viscosity displayed by protoplasm are evidently comparable
with those seen in emulsoid colloidal substances, and when in its more
solid condition protoplasm may be analogous to the "gel" or solidified
state of colloidal substances generally. The problems here encountered
are, however, of great complexity. The larger particles suspended in the
hyaloplasm undoubtedly vary widely in physical consistency, being in
many cases more solid "granules," in other cases more liquid "drops";

---

[1] Barber, '11, '14; Kite, '12, '13; Kite and Chambers. '12; Chambers, '14, '15, '17, '18. etc.; Heilbrunn, '15, '17; Seifriz '18, '20.

but obviously it is difficult to draw any definite boundary line between these two extremes. The hyaloplasm or ground-substance in which these bodies lie is often of more liquid nature and has generally been held to be comparable to an "emulsoid"[1] containing ultra-microscopical suspended drops (in contradistinction to a "suspensoid" in which the dispersed particles are solid); but the grounds for such a conclusion seem inadequate. In any case, when speaking of the protoplasmic viscosity in general, we refer to the properties of the whole protoplasmic complex rather than to any of its particular components.

The behavior of the cell-substance as a whole may be greatly affected by the nature and amount of its formed components since these may be scanty or abundant, and of all degrees of viscosity from liquid watery drops to solid granules or even crystals. The nature of the inorganic salts present also has an important effect on the protoplasmic consistency.[2]

3. Fibrillar Theories of Protoplasm

The results of the earliest accurate cytological studies of protoplasm are embodied in the fibrillar theories, which sought the fundamental structure in delicate fibrillæ, either separate or forming a connected network, traversing a homogeneous ground-substance (Fig. 23). These theories are especially associated with the names of Heitzmann, Klein, Leydig, Flemming, Carnoy, Van Beneden, Retzius and, at a later period, Boveri, Watasé, Heidenhain and Ballowitz. Most of these writers regarded the fibrillæ as fundamental structural components of the cell-substance, ascribing to them a leading rôle in the protoplasmic activities; and even Flemming, who clearly recognized that life belongs to the cell-system as a whole (p. 59), considered it a probable hypothesis " that the essential energies on which life depends have their seat in the fibrillæ."[3]

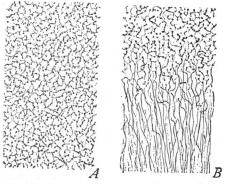

Fig. 23.—Reticular structure (probably a coagulation-product) in fixed and stained section of early blastomere of segmenting fish-egg (*Coregonus*). In *B* are shown the outer extremities of astral rays from a large aster lying below.

The early fibrillar theories of protoplasm arose through a shifting of the center of interest from studies on living protoplasm to those on fixed and stained material, a change largely due to the rapid development of

[1] See Kite, '13.   [2] Clowes (16), etc. See also Seifriz ('21).   [3] '82, p. 80.

cytological technique between 1870 and 1890. To this development, undeniably, we owe the discovery and elucidation of some of the most fundamental phenomena of the cell; but we now see that the results were in some respects misleading, and that some of the ablest observers fell into error because of a failure to distinguish between the structure of *living* protoplasm and that of the artificial coagula presented by sections. This applies particularly to the net-like formations; for, although these may perhaps really exist in some forms of living protoplasm (p. 40) they may also readily be produced in homogeneous colloidal solutions, *e. g.*, of albumin and gelatin, when coagulated by the ordinary cytological fixing solutions (p. 65). [1] As observations in this field multiplied, fibrillar conceptions of protoplasm grouped themselves into two general views, which may be designated as the *reticular* and the *filar* theories of protoplasm. By advocates of the reticular theory, such as Heitzmann, Kupffer ('75), Leydig ('67), Klein ('78), Van Beneden ('83), Carnoy ('85) and their followers, the fibrillæ were assumed to form a fine, continuous network or reticulum, extending throughout the cell and even from cell to cell (Heitzmann). On the other hand, Flemming ('82), and later advocates of the filar theory, such as Heidenhain and Ballowitz, believed the fibrillæ to be in general unbranched and discontinuous. The correctness of this view, up to a certain point, was from the first made evident by Flemming's demonstration that such separate fibrillæ may readily be seen in the living cells of cartilage and some other tissues (Fig. 9); and this has been fully confirmed by the later observations of Meves ('10), Fauré-Fremiet, ('10) Lewis and Robertson ('16), and others.

Under the influence of these views arose special terminologies differing more or less with different observers. The fibrillar threadwork was variously designated as the *protoplasm* (Kupffer), *spongioplasm* (Leydig), *reticulum* (Carnoy, Van Beneden), *filar substance* or *mitome* (Flemming); the clear intermediate substance as the *paraplasm* (Kupffer), *hyaloplasm* (Leydig), *cell-sap* or *enchylema* (Carnoy), *interfilar substance* or *paramitome* (Flemming). All these observers were substantially agreed that minute granules or *microsomes* are often scattered along the threads or collected at the nodes of the network. By Heitzmann (1873) the reticulum was believed to be continuous throughout the body, the cells being only local areas within it, and the nuclei local areas of concentration within the cells. The whole body was thus conceived as a continuous protoplasmic unit. Muscle-fibers, nerve-fibers, and the like were conceived to be special local modifications of the general network. A similar conception was by later writers applied

---

[1] Among the earliest observers to describe fibrillar structures in protoplasm were Frommann ('65, '67, '73), Heitzmann ('73), Arnold ('65), and Kupffer ('75).

to the astral and spindle formations in mitotic cell-division, which were assumed to arise by local regrouping of the preëxisting threadwork about the centrioles or division-centers (Klein, Van Beneden, Heidenhain); and by assuming these fibrillæ to be contractile or in a state of elastic tension attempts were made to offer a mechanical explanation of the division of both the nucleus and cell-body (p. 178).

4. Coagulation Phenomena

In the meantime, doubts arose in regard to the reticular and other fibrillar formations in protoplasm. From the first, Bütschli's studies on living protoplasm had led him to a different conception of the protoplasmic framework, while Flemming ('82) and later Berthold ('86), Schwarz ('87) Bütschli ('92) and A. Fischer ('94) had called attention to the danger of confusing

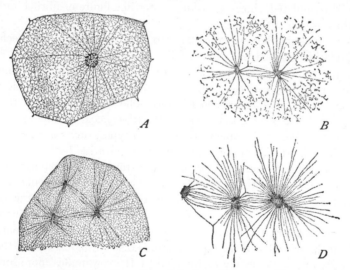

Fig. 24.—Coagulation-artifacts imitating cell-structures (FISCHER).

A, dead pith-cell impregnated with 5% albumin and 2.5% hæmoglobin and fixed in 1% osmic acid; *B*, 2% serum-albumin fixed in Flemming's fluid; *C*, 5% albumose solution in 5% gelatin, fixed in 1% osmic acid and 1% acetic; *D*, 2.5% albumose solution fixed in 1% osmic acid.

coagulation-artifacts with the normal structural elements. In 1899 the importance of this subject was brought to general attention particularly by the work of Hardy and of A. Fischer; and one can only agree with Hardy's opinion that it is "one of the most remarkable facts in the history of biological science that the urgency and priority of this question should have appealed to so few minds." [1] The studies of these observers proved that

[1] '99, p. 160.

the artificial coagulation of homogeneous solutions of albumose, gelatin, egg-albumin, peptone and similar substances may give rise to beautiful net-like or alveolar formations and even to close *simulacra* of astral rays and spindle-formations. Fischer, after impregnating dead and empty pith-cells with albumose solution, and fixing, sectioning and staining by the most approved cytological methods, obtained startling imitations of normal cells, showing fine protoplasmic networks, while about solid particles (such as the dead remains of nuclei) the fibrillæ assume an aster-like disposition and between them give rise to spindles (Fig. 24). The amphiaster was likewise imitated by Bütschli ('98) in gelatin solution containing air-bubbles, suddenly coagulated while hot, astral rays being formed about the bubbles and spindle-like formations between them. Hardy in like manner showed that a film of albumin, weighted in the middle with a drop of mercury and coagulated, shows a striking, aster-like figure of fibrillæ radiating from the position of the weight.

It is not possible here to enter far into the intricacies of the mechanism of coagulation-phenomena. The studies of Fischer and of Hardy proved that when colloidal solutions like white of egg or gelatin are coagulated (an irreversible process) by fixing agents, such as sublimate, osmic vapor, or alcohol, there is a separation of more solid substances from the more liquid, in such a manner as to form a comparatively coarse framework readily visible to the eye. This framework is of two types, each with many variations, which depend upon the nature and concentration both of the fixative and of the colloidal solution, and to some extent also on temperature and other attendant conditions. These two types, the spongelike and the vesicular, closely correspond respectively to the reticular and the alveolar structures in protoplasm. In the first case the more solid portions form a sponge-like network the interstices of which are occupied by a continuous liquid; in the second case the liquid phase is discontinuous, taking the form of separate drops completely surrounded by the continuous more solid portions.

The sponge-like type appears, for example, in an aqueous 13% solution of egg-albumin when coagulated by various fixatives, the more solid framework forming a fine, regular sponge-like net, with spheroidal granules at the nodes, the diameter of the meshes being least upon fixation by osmic vapor (0.5–0.7μ) and greatest with corrosive sublimate (1.7μ), as shown in Fig. 25. A corresponding difference is seen in protoplasm when fixed by the same two methods. With higher concentrations of albumin the nodal granules are much enlarged and closely crowded; with lower concentrations the net becomes irregular, discontinuous and finally appears as a flaky precipitate, or in the form of fine separate granules.

With gelatin-solutions the results are still more varied. In solutions of
7% to 15% coagulated by formalin an open net is produced, and the same
effect appears in solutions of less than 5% coagulated by alcohol or sublimate. If, however, the same stronger solutions be fixed by alcohol or
sublimate vesicular or alveolar structure appears, consisting of separate
droplets, each completely surrounded by more solid and continuous walls.
The diameter of these vesicles is inversely proportional to the concentration

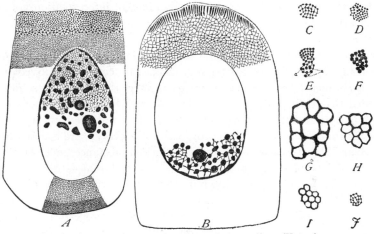

Fig. 25.—Coagulated cells and coagulation-artifacts (HARDY).

A, B, epithelial cells, gut of *Oniscus*, *A*, fixed with osmic vapor, *B*, with mercuric bichloride; *C–F*,
coagulated egg-albumin; *C*, 13% solids, sublimate; *D*, the same, potassium sulphocyanate; *E*, 30%
solids, with included carmine-grains (*a, a*), sublimate; *F*, 60% solids, sublimate; *G–J*, coagulated
gelatin fixed with sublimate; *G*, 10% solids; *H*, 25% solids; *I*, 50% solids; *J*, 4% solids.

of the solution; after sublimate fixation they range from 7μ (10% gelatin
solution) down to 2.5μ (50% gelatin), as shown in Fig. 25. With 4% gelatin solution, however, a network appears with meshes $\pm 2\mu$ in diameter.
These experiments show how readily reticulated and alveolar formations may be transformed into each other as a result of fixation, the
more liquid matter appearing in one case as a continuous substance filling
the interstices of a solid sponge-like network, in the other in the form of
separate and discontinuous drops with the solid matter forming a continuous honeycomb structure between them.

We are thus made to realize that the results of fixation do not in themselves necessarily give us any information concerning the structure of the
original system. We cannot wonder, therefore, that the works of Bütschli,
Hardy, Fischer and their predecessors set in motion a pronounced wave of
scepticism on the part of cytologists and physiologists concerning the
existence of reticular and filar formations in protoplasm, and even led

to a practical denial by some writers that the meshworks or frameworks seen in fixed material have any significance beyond that of coagulation-products. Though this conclusion went too far it served a most useful purpose by putting cytologists on their guard against sources of error in their technique and in reviving interest in the study of living protoplasm.

5. The Alveolar or Foam-Theory of Protoplasm

From the first Bütschli placed a wholly different interpretation upon the protoplasmic meshwork, whether observed in living protoplasm or in the artificial coagulum.   Already in his early work (1878) he expressed the opinion that in the Protozoa a gradual transition exists "from protoplasm in which appear simple scattered vacuoles to completely alveolar or, *what is the same thing, reticular protoplasm*, where the alveoli are so densely crowded that their protoplasmic walls take on a honeycomb arrangement, which in optical section appears reticular." This was the germ of Bütschli's later conclusion (1892) that protoplasm has everywhere a foam-like or "alveolar " structure, consisting of two principal substances, one continuous and commonly of higher viscosity, and a second that is discontinuous, appearing in the form of separate but often closely crowded *alveolar spheres* suspended in the continuous substance. Both substances were considered by Bütschli as viscid liquids of different physical properties forming an emulsion-like mixture. Later researches have shown, that the viscosity of this mixture varies greatly in different phases of the cell-activities (p. 60), and also that the alveolar spheres or " macrosomes " may in some cases approach the solid state, so as appropriately to be described as "granules." [1] These spheres were commonly spoken of by Bütschli as *alveoli*, though strictly speaking this term applies to the cavities which they fill.

Among the alveolar spheres, likewise suspended in the continuous substance, are numerous minute granules or *microsomes*, fairly uniform in size but to some extent intermingled with smaller ones which graduate down to the limit of microscopical vision (Figs. 26, 27). The microsomes are sharply distinct from the larger spheres or macrosomes in size, staining reactions and sometimes in color [2] even in the living protoplasm. In the eggs of echinoderms, tunicates and other animals the microsomes are rather strongly basophilic and have been regarded by some observers as "chromidia."   Van Herwerden ('13) has shown that, like basichromatin, they are readily dissolved by nuclease; but there is little evidence of their derivation from the nucleus.

In many objects, the alveolar spheres are closely pressed together so as to become angular in form, while the interalveolar substance is reduced

[1] *Cf.* Wilson, '99.   [2] *E. g.*, in *Ophiura*, Wilson, '99.

to thin walls or lamellæ between them, as often in an artificial emulsion. Thus arises a foam-like or honeycomb structure in which the microsomes

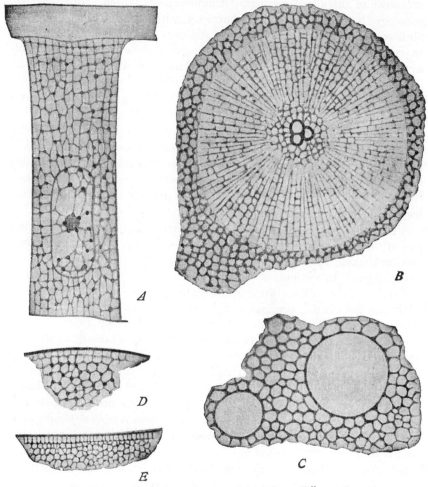

Fig. 26.—Alveolar or foam-structure of protoplasm. (BÜTSCHLI.).

A, epidermal cell of the earthworm; *B*, aster and central bodies from sea-urchin egg; *C*, intra-capsular protoplasm of a radiolarian (*Thalassicolla*) with vacuoles; *D*, peripheral cytoplasm of sea-urchin egg; *E*, artificial emulsion of olive-oil, sodium chloride, and water.

tend to collect at the angles where two or more of the lamellæ meet, and which in optical section gives the appearance of a net-like framework or reticulum (Fig. 26).

This general account has been confirmed by many later observers [1] who

[1] *E. g.*, by Erlanger ('96), G. F. Andrews ('97), Rhumbler ('98), Wilson ('99), etc.

have simplified the terminology by applying the old word *hyaloplasm* to the continuous or "interalveolar" substance and *enchylema* to the discontinuous substance of the alveolar spheres (Rhumbler, '98, Wilson, '00). The terminology is thus brought into harmony with that employed for the fibrillar conceptions of protoplasm, and for this reason will hereafter be employed in this work.[1] The microsomes show a tendency to collect at the angles or nodes where two or more of the hyaloplasmic lamellæ meet.

All this was closely imitated by Bütschli ('92) in artificial oil-emulsions in which the part of the hyaloplasm is played by thickened olive oil, that of the enchylema by drops of soapy solutions of mineral salts (*e. g.*, NaCl), and that of the microsomes by particles of soot or carmine suspended in the oil. The artificial alveolar structure thus prepared shows a startling resemblance to that of living protoplasm, which is heightened by the fact that drops of the mixture suspended in water undergo changes of form that may even simulate amœboid movements.

A critical comparison of alveolar protoplasm as seen in the living object and in fixed and stained sections is highly instructive. In the former case (sea-urchin egg) the outlines of the alveolar spheres are readily seen in the living object. In sections, on the other hand, even after the best fixation and staining, the outlines of the spheres are often no longer visible as such (owing to the clearing process), and the eye perceives only a meshwork of microsomes containing crowded clear cavities or alveoli (Figs. 27, 28). With less perfect fixation the alveolar spheres break up or run together in various degrees while the hyaloplasm coagulates in the form of a more cr less continuous network (Wilson, '99). It seems certain that many of the so-called reticular formations in protoplasm, as described by earlier observers, arise in this way. A study of such preparations makes it clear that *the "reticulum" is composed of the continuous substance or hyaloplasm*, while the so-called ground-substance, cell-sap or inter-filar substance corresponds to the alveolar substance.

Bütschli considered that the longitudinal "striation" or "fibrillation" seen in muscle-fibers or nerve-fibers, is merely an alveolar structure drawn out into elongated and parallel meshes, while the asters and spindles seen in mitosis were in like manner interpreted as temporary radial configurations of a similar alveolar structure about the division-centers (Fig. 26).

---

[1] Leydig (1883) used the word "hyaloplasm" in the contrary sense, applying it to the "ground-substance" (nuclear sap, enchylema, or inter-filar substance) as distinguished from the "spongioplasm" or substance of the network or fibrillar formation. Though this usage has been employed even by some recent writers (*e. g.*, Conklin '17) it seems to the author to be out of harmony with the general historical development of the subject as affected by Bütschli's theory, and to introduce needless confusion.

Both appearances were successfully imitated in the artificial emulsion; and Bütschli also produced very striking amphiastral figures by coagulating hot gelatin containing scattered air bubbles. About the latter conspicuous asters are formed while adjoining bubbles become connected by conspicuous

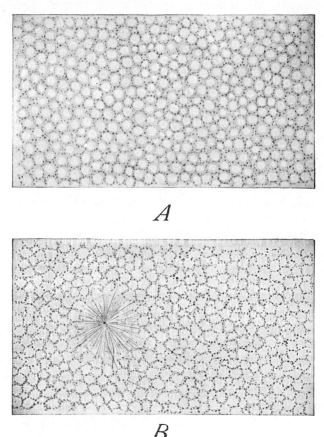

A

B

Fig. 27.—Structure of protoplasm.

A, alveolar structure, living protoplasm of the starfish *Asterias* showing alveolar spheres (mega-somes) and microsomes; *B*, the same after fixation (sublimate-acetic), a small sperm-aster and central body towards the left.

spindles. Bütschli also brought forward evidence that protoplasm which appears to be quite hyaline or homogeneous may nevertheless possess an alveolar structure that is invisible because of the extreme tenuity of the inter-alveolar walls.

Bütschli was careful to distinguish between the "primary" or "funda-

mental " alveolar structure and the "secondary " or derived structures
that may arise through the appearance of larger vacuoles or other inclusions
in the protoplasm. In the former, which he considers to be a universal
characteristic of protoplasm, the alveoli are not more than 1.5–2.0 microns in diameter. All coarser structures arising through the deposit of
larger drops, or granules ("pseudalveolar structures " of Reinke) are of
secondary origin and inconstant occurrence. Bütschli offers evidence in
later experimental studies ('98, etc.), that the meshworks seen in coagulated
colloids, especially in gelatin, are often not true networks but alveolar
formations which he compares directly with the gel phase of the colloids
(cf. p. 66).

6. Critique of Bütschli's Theory

There can now be no doubt that protoplasm exhibits in many cases the
structure described by Bütschli; but even his strongest supporters are now
convinced that he, like many another reformer, pushed his conclusions too
far. In the first place, the evidence that true fibrillar formations exist in
protoplasm has become irresistible.[1] This conclusion rests in part upon the
extreme clearness with which such formations can be demonstrated, for
instance, in nerve-cells (Bethe, Apathy, Cajal, Dogiel, etc.), or columnar
epithelial cells (Heidenhain, Del Rio, etc.); in part on histogenetic studies,
particularly on muscle-cells, in which the formation and growth of the
fibrillar formations, step by step, has been minutely studied (e. g., Heidenhain, '99, Godlewski, '01, Duesberg, '09). Again, recent studies on chondriosomes have most clearly demonstrated the existence in nearly all kinds
of cells of those specific forms of fibrillæ known as chondrioconts, and have
given ground for the conclusion that from them some of the more specialized
types of fibrils (myofibrillæ, etc.) may be derived (p. 707). The chondrioconts were long since seen in the living cells of cartilage and other tissues
by Flemming ('82), and undoubtedly form an important part of the filar
formation or "mitome," as described by him.[2]

The existence of fibrillæ in the protoplasmic substances is by no means
incompatible with the alveolar theory and many observers have urged that
both types of structure may coexist side by side. Strasburger, for example
('92), whose views have been followed by many botanists, considers the
cytoplasm to consist in general of two physiologically different plasms
which differ characteristically both in structure and in function, one being
an especially nutritive or vegetative trophoplasm, typically alveolar in
structure, the other a more active kinoplasm especially concerned with

[1] See especially Heidenhain's great work on Plasma und Zelle ('07, '11), in which these formations
are exhaustively treated.
[2] See Meves '10 b.

movement (cilia, etc.), cell-division and irritability, and typically fibrillar in structure ("filar plasm" as distinguished from "alveolar plasm").[1]

In the second place, it is more than doubtful whether Bütschli's "finer" or "true" alveolar structure is a primary or universal characteristic of protoplasm; and whether it is logically separable from the coarser or "secondary" structure ("pseudo-alveolar structure" of Reinke). In the sea-urchin eggs, a classical example of the alveolar structure, it may very

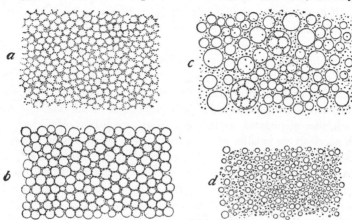

Fig. 28.—*a*, protoplasm of the egg of the sea-urchin (*Toxopneustes*) in section showing mesh-work of microsomes; *b*, protoplasm from a living starfish egg (*Asterias*) showing alveolar spheres with microsomes scattered between them; *c*, the same in a dying condition after crushing the egg: alveolar spheres fusing to form larger spheres; *d*, protoplasm from a young ovarian egg of the same (all the figures magnified 1200 diameters).

clearly be seen, both in the living material, and in sections, that this structure is of secondary origin (Wilson, '99.) The very young ova consist largely of hyaline protoplasm or hyaloplasm, with only a few scattered "granules." Step by step as the egg grows the granules increase in number and the alveolar spheres emerge into view, at first very minute and scattered, later growing more numerous and larger until they crowd together to form the alveolar structure as described by Bütschli; though in the forms studied by the author the alveolar spheres do not flatten together to the extent figured by him. The observations of the writer also showed that the "microsomes," like the alveolar spheres, may be liquid drops; and also, in conformity with the earlier conclusion of G. F. Andrews (1897), that the "continuous" or interalveolar walls may themselves show a still finer alveolization down to the limits of microscopical vision.

Comparative studies show that it is practically impossible to draw any clear or logical line of distinction between the "true" or "fundamental"

[1] *Cf.* p. 633.

alveolar structure and the coarser "secondary" (pseudo-alveolar). Such facts point to the conclusion, that "we are probably justified in regarding the continuous substance (*i. e.*, the hyaloplasm) as the most constant and active element, and that which forms the fundamental basis of the system, transforming itself into granules, drops, fibrillæ or networks" [1] in different phases of its activity. This opinion is in principle shared by Heidenhain ('07), Conklin ('12) and others.[2]

Bütschli's conception of protoplasmic structure is essentially that of a complex colloidal system. The genesis of the alveolar structure in the ovarian egg, as above described, leads us to conclude that it is similar in type to the invisible structure of a colloidal solution or suspension. The combined cytological and physico-chemical evidence thus seems to justify the conclusion that in protoplasm, as in other colloidal systems, the discontinuous phase (or phases) may show all degrees of dispersion from very large molecular aggregates (as in the coarser "pseudalveolar" formations, through successively smaller ones down to ultra-microscopical "particles," molecules and ions.[3] We may thus conceive Bütschli's structure as arising in the hyaloplasm either by growth or by successive aggregations of particles which ultimately become visible in the form of suspended granules, microsomes and alveolar spheres or macrosomes. If this be correct the visible alveolar structure differs from that of the apparently homogeneous hyaloplasm only in degree, and a consistent view of the whole series of phenomena is attained. For the cytologist, however, it is essential to keep always in view the fact that artificial preparations are coagulation-products which may depart more or less widely from the conditions existing in life.

7. The Granule Theory of Protoplasm

We may here briefly consider a speculative conception of protoplasm which, though long discredited, still offers many interesting suggestions for the general problems of cell-organization. It was suggested by several earlier observers [4] that the protoplasmic granules might be regarded as organic units ("plastidules," etc.) which build up the cell somewhat as cells build up the multicellular body; and this speculation was at least brought within the range of possibility by the remarkable studies of Schimper ('85) on the plastids of plant-cells, which showed that these bodies independently grow and divide, like symbiotic organisms within the cell,

[1] Wilson, '00, p. 50.
[2] *Cf.* Heidenhain, 1907, p. 489.
[3] *Cf.* Bayliss. "There is no hard and fast line to be drawn between matter in pieces visible to the naked eye, down through ultra-microscopical particles to molecules." *The Nature of Enzyme Action*, p. 201, 1911.
[4] Henle ('41), Béchamp and Estor ('60), Maggi ('78).

and that in higher plants the plastids of the adult tissue-cells arise in this manner from minute plastids present in large numbers in the embryonic cells and even in the egg. The granule-theory first appears in clearly defined form, and based on more extended observation, in the works of Altmann ('86, '90, '94) and underwent further systematic development by J. Arnold, Schlater, Rohde, St. Hilaire, C. Schneider, and many others including Benda, Meves, and other leaders in the modern theory of the chrondriosomes (pp. 47, 717).

Altmann, making use of a special technique,[1] was able to demonstrate fuchsinophilous (red-staining) granules in many kinds of cells, often nearly

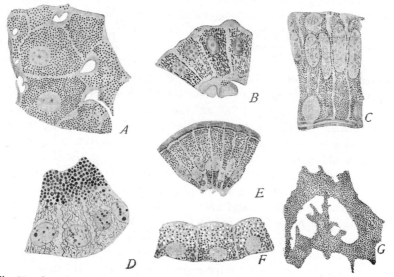

Fig. 23.—Granular structures as figured by Altmann after various modes of fixation and staining by acid fuchsin and picric acid. Many of these are now known to be mitochondria (ALTMANN).

A, liver of the mouse; B, tubules of mesonephros, embryo chick; C, intestinal epithelium of frog; D, pancreas of *Triton*, showing secretory granules and fibrillæ; E, epithelium of intestinal villus, cat; F, Harderian gland, rabbit; G, small portion of pigment-cell with pigment-granules, salamander larva.

uniform in size, and in many cases so closely crowded as almost to constitute an alveolar structure like that of Bütschli (Fig. 29). These granules were regarded by Altmann as "elementary organisms" ("bioblasts," "cytoblasts") or their products, which live in a homogeneous basis or groundsubstance. He pointed out the analogy between such a structure and that

---

[1] Fixation by potassium bichromate and osmic acid; staining with acid fuchsin and picric acid, by which the granules are stained intensely red. This method has been developed by Meves, Bensley and other more modern students of the mitochondria.

of a bacterial zoögloea, further suggesting that the granules might in some cases even live separately in the form of minute microörganisms of the *Micrococcus* type. The granules were assumed to arise only by the growth and division of preëxisting granules—*omne granulum e granulo* (1890)— after the fashion of plastids; and Altmann regarded them as the essential living units of protoplasm out of which every living part of the cell is built. [1] Admitting that many of these granules (secretory granules, etc.) belong to the passive or metaplasmic elements, Altmann regarded such granules as products of originally living granules or bioblasts. This is quite analogous to the formation of non-living products by entire cells and, as will be seen, is nearly akin to more recent views concerning the chondriosomes. Altmann did not hesitate to push his conception beyond the visible structure of protoplasm into that which lies beyond the reach of the microscope; but this side of the question may better be considered at a later point (p. 717). His conclusions were insecurely based, and at first gained few adherents, in part because of their too speculative character, in part because of his failure to distinguish sufficiently between structures that preëxist in the living cell and those that are products of the coagulating effect of fixing agents. Continued studies on the protoplasmic granules, especially as seen in *vivo*, nevertheless led many competent observers to a somewhat more favorable judgment concerning the essential features of his theory, though it still remains a subject of controversy. [2] It is now generally admitted that many forms of granules play an active and important part in the protoplasmic activities and are not to be regarded as merely coagulation-artifacts, or metaplasmic products. The main controversial questions relate to their morphological nature and origin. A prominent place in the study of this question has been taken by J. Arnold ('79, '07, '14, etc.) who believes that the so-called "inter-granular substance" of earlier writers (hyaloplasm) is largely made up of very minute but still visible granules or "*plasmosomes*" and fibrillæ ("*plasmomites*") by the enlargement of which may be derived many of the larger formed elements; and a somewhat similar view is advocated by Heidenhain ('11) who follows Altmann in the conclusion that the smallest visible granules (plasmosomes) may themselves arise by enlargement of still smaller invisible metastructural bodies. To this question we shall later return (p. 717). Here we only draw attention to the prominence recently given to the granule-theory by the researches of Benda, Meves and their followers, who have urged the identity

---

[1] "Protoplasm may be defined as a colony of bioblasts, the individual elements of which are grouped like those of a zoögloea or in filamentary chains, and held together by an indifferent substance." Altmann, '94, p. 140.

[2] Literature especially in Heidenhain ('11) and J. Arnold ('14). See also earlier works of Arnold ('08, '00, '07b, '13a, etc.), Schlater ('95, '03, '11), Rohde ('14, etc.).

of the mitochondria (p. 47) with Altmann's granules and ascribed to them a position of fundamental importance in the cell-activities.

Leaving all theory aside, Altmann's objective description of the structure of protoplasm to a certain extent approaches that of Bütschli as modified by G. F. Andrews and the author, save that the "granules" were assumed to be of more solid consistency than the alveolar spheres or the microsomes (pp. 72, 73). The recent experimental studies of Kite and others on living protoplasm gives considerable reason to regard the alveolar spheres as of rather firm consistency, even in the echinoderm egg (one of Bütschli's principal objects); while a number of observers have actually described them as "granules." The physical consistency of the granules or drops seems, however, a matter of secondary importance in view of the readiness with which the protoplasmic colloids may undergo changes of physical consistency (*cf.* p. 60). In another direction Altmann's theory comes into relations with the filar theory of Flemming; for Altmann held that the granules might grow out into rods or fibrillæ or produce such structures by a process of linear alignment; and this is borne out by recent studies on the chondriosomes, as will later be explained. Whatever be its points of weakness on the physiological and theoretical side, therefore, the granule-theory opens the way to a reconciliation between opposing views on protoplasmic structure so widely divergent as at first sight to offer a total and fundamental contradiction; [1] while the contradiction between it and the colloidal nature of the cell-substance is I believe wholly illusory.

Summary on Protoplasmic Structure

Up to the present time no single theory of protoplasmic structure has commanded general acceptance, and it is more than doubtful whether any universal formula for this structure can be given. We are driven by a hundred reasons to conclude that protoplasm has an organization that is perfectly definite, but it is one that finds visible expression in a protean variety of structures, and we are not in a position to regard any of these as universally diagnostic of the living substance. As far as *visible* structure is concerned no satisfactory distinction, practical or logical, in the opinion of the author, can be drawn between a "primary" or "fundamental" structure, and a secondary one. The fundamental structure of protoplasm lies beyond the present limits of microscopical vision and hence still remains a matter of inference and hypothesis. Probably the only element of protoplasm that will be admitted by all cytologists to be omnipresent is the "homogeneous" hyaloplasm, which offers to the eye no visible structure. Almost always, however, protoplasm exhibits a visible structure owing to

---

[1] See especially Meves ('10b).

the presence in the hyaloplasm of alveolar, reticular, fibrillar or granular formations; but these vary widely in different kinds of cells, at different periods of development, and in different phases of physiological activity.

We are not in a position to characterize any of these elements as "living" in contradistinction to "lifeless" constituents of the protoplasm. Nevertheless, there is reason to conclude that of all the cell-constituents the "structureless" hyaloplasm is the most constant and most active; and may perhaps be regarded as forming the fundamental basis of the protoplasmic system from which directly or indirectly, all other elements take their origin. Such a view, it is true, does not yet command the acceptance of many cytologists, yet it involves a minimal amount of theory and is fully in harmony with those physicochemical studies that have proved the cell-substance to have in many cases the properties of a colloidal system. This conclusion, it is true, throws us back upon the assumption of a "meta-structure" in protoplasm that lies beyond the present limits of microscopical vision; but in this respect the biologist is perhaps in no worse case than the chemist or the physicist.[1]

IV. THE NUCLEUS

As seen in the living cell the nucleus most commonly appears as a clear, rounded, sac-like body bounded by a delicate membrane and often showing no visible structure save for the presence within it of one or more smaller rounded bodies, *the nucleoli*. After coagulation by fixing agents, the nucleus offers a much more complicated appearance, containing in addition to the nucleoli a net-like framework (Fig. 6) in which are suspended granules or irregular clumps composed of a substance that stains intensely with certain dyes (in particular the basic coal tar colors such as methyl-green or safranin), and hence from the time of Flemming (1879) has been widely known as *chromatin*.

The form of the nucleus is on the whole singularly constant as compared with that of the cytosome, and shows little correlation with the latter; but it is a familiar fact that long cells, such as muscle-cells, columnar epithelial cells (Figs. 17, 42) or certain forms of parenchyma, usually have more or less elongated nuclei. Typically rounded and with an even contour, it may in certain cases become irregular and has often been observed, in particular cases, to undergo slow amœboid changes of form in the living cell, *e. g.*, in cartilage-cells, leucocytes, or animal ova. Nuclei of irregular or amœboid form are frequent in cells characterized by very active metabolism, in which case the nuclei are often not only of large size but show a marked

[1] Further evidence on this question will be presented later. (See p. 717.)

further increase of surface by the formation of lobes, sacculations, or even, in extreme cases, of complex branches ramifying through the cell. An extreme example of this is offered by the spinning glands of certain insect-larvæ (Lepidoptera, Trichoptera) in which the nucleus, originally spheroidal, finally assumes a labyrinthine appearance with convolutions occupying a large area in the cell (Figs. 31, 34). In other cases the nucleus shows deep infoldings or incisions and sometimes even tubular ingrowths of membrane forming intra-nuclear canaliculi; and it has been shown that such infoldings may unfold or evaginate, thus increasing the nuclear size.[1]

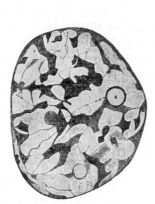 

Fig. 30.—Two nuclei from the crypts of Lieberkühn in the salamander (HEIDENHAIN).

The character of the chromatin-network (basichromatin) is accurately shown. The left nucleus contains three plasmosomes or true nucleoli; the right, one. A few fine linin-threads are seen in the left nucleus running off from the chromatin-masses. The clear spaces are occupied by the ground-substance or nuclear sap.

In certain types of cells the surface of the nucleus may also be increased by its breaking up into more or less separate vesicles or karyomerites, thus forming "polymorphic" nuclei or nuclear nests. Nuclei of this type are in some instances morphological multiples resulting from a process of true nuclear division without cytoplasmic division (e. g., in case of the ring-nuclei of giant-cells, Fig. 34, or of certain kinds of leucocytes). More commonly, perhaps, the karyomerites are partial structures due to incomplete union of the chromosomes after cell-division or to amitotic fragmentation of the nucleus (p. 221). Such facts add to the evidence that active exchanges of material between nucleus and cytosome take place in metabolism. In respect to the relative volumes of nucleus and cytosome each type of cell tends towards a certain norm, the *karyoplasmic* ratio (R. Hertwig) (p. 727).

[1] See Champy, '13, Champy and Carleton, '21.

The nuclear substance, considered as a whole, is of colloidal nature like the cytoplasm, and varies widely in physical consistency. In some cases (*e. g.*, in sea-urchin eggs) its substance as a whole shows the properties of a liquid, while the membrane by which it is bounded is very viscous and tough. This is shown by the quick and complete collapse of the nucleus when crushed or cut, while the membrane may remain nearly intact (Kite, '13). That the interior mass of the nucleus often is liquid is proved in several other ways. Nuclei may readily fuse together, either within the cell (as in the fertilization of the egg) or outside the cell when isolated in the fresh condition, as observed by Albrecht ('99). Chambers ('16) has more recently shown that the nucleus of the egg (in sea-urchins) may be cut in two, with the micro-dissection needle, and that the fragments will round up to form spheroidal droplets which will again fuse to form a single normal nucleus. After such an operation the egg is stated still to be capable of normal fertilization and cleavage. Nevertheless the consistency of the nuclear substance as a whole often shows a high degree of viscosity, as shown by the usual absence of Brownian movement and also by microdissection. Kite, for instance, found in some Protozoa (*Amœba, Paramœcium*), and in certain metazoan tissue-cells (muscle, epidermis) that the nuclear substance was of firmer consistency like that of a "gel," though not a very solid one.

In fixed preparations the nuclear substance is of course in the main an artificial and semi-solid coagulum. How far the nuclear framework that it contains corresponds to the conditions preëxisting in life is a difficult question. Very often no trace of the framework is seen before coagulation sets in; and this has led to a sceptical attitude concerning it on the part of some observers. On the other hand, living nuclei sometimes show certain well-marked structures in addition to the nucleoli. Flemming ('76–'82) clearly demonstrated this in epithelial cells, cartilage-cells, connective-tissue-cells and leucocytes, showing that the coarser features of the framework are distinctly visible in life, and that they conform closely in form and extent to those that appear in fixed material; and although these observations were later disputed (see especially Tellyesnicky, '05) they have since been confirmed by a number of competent observers. [1] As a rule the only portions of the framework visible in life are the clumps or net-knots of basichromatin, and it is still rather uncertain how far the finer framework may not be a coagulation-effect. Gross ('17) found that some types of living nuclei show in addition to true nucleoli only numerous small granules or microsomes (salivary glands of *Lymnæa*, germinal vesicle of *Anodonta* and *Unio*). In other types, including the epithelial cells of salamander larvæ

[1] See Heidenhain ('07), p. 113.

(Flemming's original object) the living nuclei show in addition to such granules very distinct net-knots. In both cases (as earlier described by F. R. Lillie, '06, in the eggs of *Chætopterus*) the small granules ("microsomes") are said to show active Brownian movements, a fact used by Gross as an argument against the existence of a nuclear network in life. On the other hand, Lundegårdh ('12) figures and describes the living nuclei in root-tips

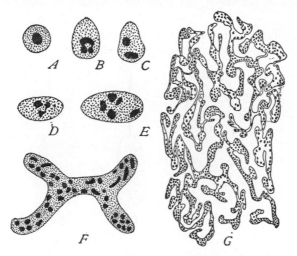

Fig. 31.—Nuclei of spinning glands in the insect *Platyphylax* (VORHIES).

A–F, young nuclei, showing multiplication of nucleoli and beginning of branching; *G*, mature labyrinthine nucleus with numerous nucleoli.

of *Allium* and *Vicia* as filled with small bodies which he considers as "drops" crowded together to form a "granular-alveolar" structure, but also, he insists, anastomosing to form a net-like framework. Such an account seems rather contradictory unless the "drops" be at least semi-solid. [1] The strongest evidence of the preëxistence of some kind of nuclear framework is, however, the gradual formation from it, during mitosis of the spireme-thread, a process long since observed in the living object by both Flemming and Strasburger and since repeatedly traced out with minute care by many observers (Fig. 52). It seems certain that this thread is formed from the more solid portion of the nuclear substance (including the net-knots) and that the apparent absence of structure so often observed in living nuclei is deceptive, being due to a lack of differences of refractive index sufficient to make the formed components of the nucleus visible. It must be confessed, however, that we are not yet in a position to state precisely the rela-

[1] Bütschli long since pointed out the unstable character of a liquid or even viscid network. *Cf.* p. 68.

tion between the preëxisting nuclear framework of the living nucleus and the net-like structure seen in sections.

A. GENERAL STRUCTURE

In a general way we may distinguish (a) *vesicular*, (b) *massive*, and (c) *chromidial* or *scattered* nuclei; but these are connected by many transitional forms.

The most common type of nucleus is the vesicular, which is of general occurrence in the tissue-cells of most multicellular animals and plants and

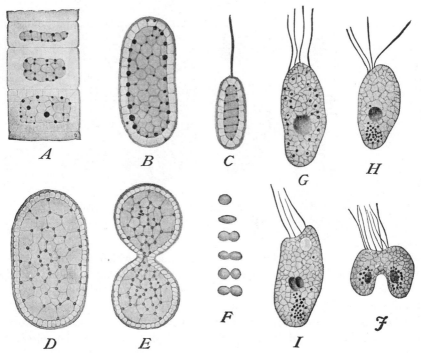

Fig. 32.—Forms of Cyanophyceæ, Bacteria, and Flagellates with chromidial nuclei (*A–C*, Bütschli; *D–F*, Schewiakoff; *G–J*, Calkins).

A, *Oscillaria*; *B*, *Chromatium*; *C*, *Bacterium lineola*; *D*, *Achromatium*; *E*, the same in division; *F*, supposed stages of fission of the granules; *G*, *Tetramitus*, with central sphere and scattered granules; *H*, aggregation of the granules; *I*, division of the sphere; *J*, fission of the cell.

is also frequent among the Protista. The nucleus of this type is usually if not always bounded by a definite wall or membrane, and contains a sponge-like framework of which the most conspicuous element is the so-called "*chromatin.*" Among Protozoa nuclei of this type often contain a more or less massive central body, the *endosome*, or *karyosome*—sometimes several such—in which all or some of the chromatin may be concentrated; and within it may be contained a still smaller centriole (Figs. 87, 88).[1]

Massive nuclei occur typically in the male germ-cells of animals generally and of many lower plants. Such nuclei usually appear homogeneous and stain with great intensity in basic dyes; but this condition is connected with the more usual one by transitional forms. Nuclei of this type, or approximating to it, are common also among Protista, for example, in the ciliates generally; but in most of the latter forms suitable staining reveals the presence of a very fine chromatic framework. The chromidial nuclei (Figs. 14, 32, 33) are represented by small granules (chromidia or chromioles) or larger irregular clumps of chromatin or a related substance, scattered through the protoplasm without forming a single individualized body.[2] Such a condition can be called a "nucleus" only as a matter of convenience, since this term properly applies only to cases in which the nuclear substance is aggregated to form an individualized body. A permanent chromidial condition of the nucleus is unknown among true multicellular organisms, and exists only in certain special cases among the Protista of which the best determined seem to occur in certain rhizopods, ciliates, bacteria and blue-green algæ. Considerable doubt still exists in regard to these cases, owing to the present lack of any decisive microchemical tests for "chromatin."[3] These doubts are, however, in large measure removed by morphological evidence which shows that in some species the scattered chromidia become aggregated to form a nucleus-like body in preparation for spore-formation (bacteria), division or conjugation. Similar evidence is afforded by those cases in which the scattered or chromidial nucleus is a temporary formation, derived by the breaking down of an ordinary nucleus (or by elimination of chromatin from it) and destined to reform such a nucleus (or nuclei), as has been described in some rhizopods (*Arcella*, Fig. 342, *Arachnula*, Fig. 343). An interesting problem is offered by the blue-green algæ (Cyanophyceæ) a group in which the presence or absence of a nucleus has long been a subject of debate.[4] Most students of this group have found evidence of a more or less diffuse condition of the nuclear substance in the form of scattered, deeply staining granules of "chromatin," "metachromatin" (volutin) or a related substance which, however, show a tendency to collect in the central region of the cytosome.

[1] By some writers this type of nucleus is characterized as a "karyosome-nucleus" in contradistinction to the vesicular type.

[2] *Cf.* p. 700.

[3] *Cf.* pp. 644, 650.

[4] For literature see especially Bütschli ('02), Olive ('05), Guilliermond ('05, '06), Fischer ('05), Gardner ('06), Zacharias ('07), Acton ('14), Baumgärtel ('20).

Thus arises a more or less definite "central body" (Bütschli) or "centroplasm" (Fischer) which by most recent observers is considered as a primi-

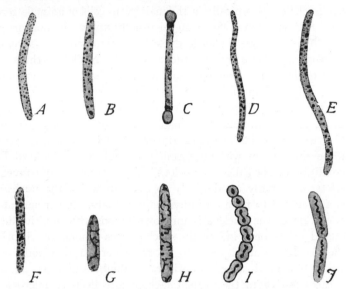

Fig. 33.—Nuclei in Bacteria (DOBELL).

A–C, bacilli of *flexilis* type, with chromidial nuclei, spore-formation in *C; D–F*, bacilli of similar type from a different host; *G, H, Bacillus saccobranchi*, with irregular type of nucleus; *I*, chain of Cocci with massive nuclei, some dividing; *J*, bacillus of *spirogyra* type, with spiral filamentary nucleus, just after division.

tive type of nucleus, though in many cases not bounded by any definite limiting membrane.[1]

B. THE NUCLEAR COMPONENTS

The vesicular nucleus, as seen in sections, usually shows four distinct components, namely: an inclosing wall or membrane; a nuclear framework usually described as a network or reticulum, though by some observers regarded as an alveolar structure; the *nuclear sap, enchylema*, or *ground-substance* which occupies the interstices of the framework; and one or more *nucleoli*, massive and usually rounded bodies suspended in the framework.

---

[1] In the Chroöcoccaceæ, a very primitive group of algæ, Acton ('14), has produced evidence that different species show intergradations between an almost undifferentiated or scattered condition of the nucleus ("metachromatic granules") and their definite aggregation to form a central nucleus which divides into two (amitotically) prior to division of the cytosome.

1. The Nuclear Membrane

This is a delicate but usually well-defined film which often stains but slightly with cytological dyes, and sometimes can hardly be differentiated from the surrounding cytoplasm, thus resembling the wall of a vacuole; in some cases, however, it approaches the nuclear framework ("chromatin") in staining-capacity. As will be shown in Chapter II, the nuclear membrane seems in some cases to be formed from the surrounding cytoplasm, a fact which led Strasburger to regard it as analogous to the outer cell-membrane and to designate it accordingly as the "inner cell-membrane." In animal cells, however, there are cases in which the nuclear membrane seems beyond a doubt to be derived from the nucleus (chromosomes).

It has long been disputed whether the membrane is continuous or interrupted, and even whether it has any existence as a separate structure. The earliest observers considered it as a definite and continuous structure; and this view is now rather generally accepted as the correct one.[1] Somewhat later the nucleus was conceived as being only a localized area in a structural framework common to the protoplast as a whole, the nuclear membrane being no more than a denser region of the same structure;[2] and a similar view has been advocated even by some recent observers, some of whom have gone so far as to deny the existence of a nuclear membrane as a definite structure[3] regarding it as only the optical section of the peripheral zone of the nuclear framework where it comes into connection with that of the cytoplasm. The studies of Kite and Chambers on living cells by means of the micro-dissection needle seem, however, to leave no doubt of the reality of the nuclear membrane and also show that it is in some cases of very tough and resistant nature.[4]

2. The Nuclear Framework

Most of the earlier observers considered the framework (Figs. 30, 36, etc.) to be a net-like or sponge-like reticulum; and this is still the view of most cytologists. A considerable number of more recent observers, however (Haecker, Reinke, Waldeyer), have followed Bütschli in the conclusion that the framework is an alveolar structure, analogous to that so often seen in the cytoplasm, though often of different character. The mode of formation of the nucleus leads to the conclusion that both types of structure may coexist in the same nucleus; for after cell-division the framework is often produced by a process that involves not only a vacuolization of the individual chromosomes but also a formation of branches by which

[1] *Cf.* Heidenhain ('07), p. 132.
[2] See for instance, Heitzmann ('83), Van Beneden ('83–'84), Wilson ('96, '99).
[3] See Stauffacher ('10), Derschau ('11).
[4] Kite ('13), Chambers ('18b, '21b, etc.).

different chromosomes become connected to form a network (p. 135). In its earlier stages, therefore, the nucleus is a network of alveolized chromosomes (Fig. 55). In later stages it becomes difficult to distinguish between

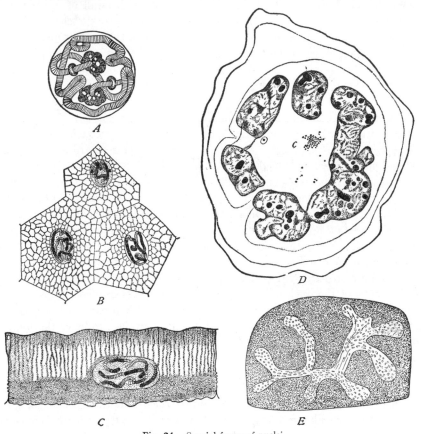

Fig. 34.—Special forms of nuclei.

A, permanent spireme-nucleus, salivary gland of *Chironomus* larva. Chromatin in a single thread, composed of chromatin-discs (chromomeres), terminating at each end in a true nucleolus or plasmosome (BALBIANI); *B*, permanent spireme-nuclei, intestinal epithelium of dipterous larva *Ptychoptera* (VAN GEHUCHTEN); *C*, the same, side view; *D*, polymorphic ring-nucleus, giant-cell of bone-marrow of the rabbit; *c*, a group of centrioles (HEIDENHAIN; *E*, branching nucleus, spinning gland of butterfly-larva (*Pieris*) (KORSCHELT).

the two types of structure and it seems very probable that in many cases the alveolar walls may break down in greater or less degree, so that the whole structure forms a sponge-like reticulum. It is, however, possible that a true alveolar structure may sometimes persist even in the mature nucleus.

The difficulties of determining this question with certainty are much increased by the fact that the character of the nuclear framework is often markedly affected by the nature of the fixatives employed.[1] When due allowance is made for this, however, it is certain that great variations in the nature of the framework exist in different kinds of cells, and the finer and closer the meshwork the greater the difficulty of determining its nature.

In fixed material, especially as viewed under relatively low magnification, the nuclei commonly appear deeply stained after treatment by certain dyes, such as carmine, hæmatoxylin, methyl-green, or gentian violet, while the cytoplasm remains relatively pale. Such dyes, accordingly, are often designated as "nuclear dyes," in contradistinction to the "plasma-dyes" which stain especially the cytoplasmic substance;[2] examples of the latter are offered by eosin, acid fuchsin, orange G or light green. It was shown by Ehrlich (1870–80) and his successors that the nuclear dyes in general, and in particular, the anilin dyes or coal-tar colors, are "basic," the plasma-dyes "acidic"[3] and it is convenient, accordingly, to designate the various cell-components as *basophilic* and *oxyphilic* according to their tendency to take up the basic or the acidic dyes. On what this tendency depends—whether on chemical affinity, on physical processes of adsorption, or on both—need not here be considered (p. 645).

The earlier cytologists, employing for the study of the nucleus mainly the basic or nuclear dyes (especially carmine, hæmatoxylin, and later safranin and gentian violet) observed that in fixed material, and after certain technical manipulation, only certain components of the nucleus were stained by these dyes. To the substance thus stained Flemming (1880) gave the name of *chromatin*, to that which stains slightly or retains the color feebly upon extraction (by acids, etc.) *achromatin*. "Chromatin," as thus defined, was considered by Flemming to be composed wholly or in part of the chemical substance "nuclein" (p. 642) and to form the more conspicuous part of the nuclear framework and also certain types of nucleoli.[4] Under the conception of "achromatin" Flemming included all the remaining nuclear substance except the enchylema. Strasburger ('82) and Carnoy ('84) recognized that the framework itself appears to consist of two constituents, namely, a continuous "achromatic" basis, and of more or less discontinuous granules or clumps of "chromatin" suspended in it (Figs. 35, 36). The first of these was found to be oxyphilic and was accordingly designated by

[1] See Lundegårdh, '12.

[2] The cytoplasm often contains various formed elements (granules, fibrillæ, etc.) that may likewise be deeply stained by the "nuclear" dyes. The term "plasma-dyes," therefore, only denotes their predominant effect on the cytoplasm considered as a whole.

[3] For further explanation of these terms see p. 646.

[4] See '82, p. 375.

Strasburger as *nucleohyaloplasm*, by Carnoy as the *plasmatic network* (composed of "*plastin*") and later by Schwarz ('87) as *linin*, a term still in common use. To the foregoing differences may be added the fact that "chromatin" as thus defined shows a high degree of resistance to hydro-

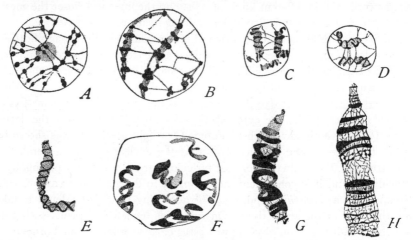

Fig. 35.—Nuclear structure in the salivary glands of larvæ of the fly *Chironomus* (ALVERDES).

A, B, younger nuclei, with reticulum, linin and basichromatin; *C, D, E*, origin of the basichromatic spirals; *F, G, H*, later stages, transformation of the spirals into disc-like bodies.

chloric-pepsin digestion, while the oxyphilic "linin" is less resistant in varying degree (pp. 643, 644).

Though this terminology is still in common use it involves us in many difficulties. It was found that the framework often undergoes great changes of staining-capacity in different phases of the cell-cycle and may even completely lose its affinity for the basic dyes, becoming purely oxyphilic, like linin or the general cytoplasm. Striking examples of this are offered by the egg-nucleus during the growth-period in many species of animals (p. 350); and this formerly led some observers to the illogical conclusion that the "chromatin" may completely disappear from the nucleus, and to the still more illogical inference that the nucleus, therefore, cannot be regarded as containing the basis of heredity. On the other hand, linin or "plastin" may readily be stained by acidic dyes; so that by using both a basic and an acidic dye of different colors both "chromatin" and "linin" may thus be strongly stained but in different colors. Obviously, therefore, "linin" or "plastin" is no less chromatic than chromatin. The dilemma thus arising was happily escaped by Heidenhain ('90, '07) who proposed to designate the basophilic and oxyphilic stainable nuclear materials respectively as *basichromatin* ("chromatin" of Flemming) and *oxychromatin*, concluding further (in harmony with an earlier suggestion of Van Beneden's) [1] that the two substances may be only different conditions of a single substance determined by comparatively slight chemical changes—e. g., by varying ratios between the percentage of nucleic acid and protein in the chromatin-substance.[2] A simple explanation is thus offered of the marked variations of staining capacity exhibited by the nuclear meshwork in different cells or in different physiological phases of the same cell; and it also escapes the supposed consequences of the disappearance of "chromatin" from the nucleus referred to above.

Many doubtful points nevertheless still remain. Heidenhain, following the lines marked out by Flemming, Strasburger and Van Beneden and other earlier observers, considers that both basichromatin and oxychromatin appear in the form of minute granules or chromioles and that both kinds of granules are suspended in a non-stainable, homogeneous substance or matrix, to which substance alone Heidenhain applies the term *linin*. The meaning of the latter term is thus greatly restricted, for it seems probable that as originally employed by Carnoy, Schwarz and their followers the "linin" or "plastin" included also much of what is now called oxychromatin. It is, however, far from certain that these granules have a persistent identity, and it is often difficult to distinguish them from mere artifacts produced by the coagulation of the reagents. We should not, however, take too sceptical an attitude towards this question, since as above stated there are cases in which granules or other formed components in the nuclear substance are clearly visible in life. One of the best of these is offered by the remarkable "spireme-nuclei" of the salivary gland-cells in Diptera long since described by Balbiani, Carnoy and other observers and more recently studied carefully by Alverdes ('12). In this case the more solid part of the nucleus appears in the form of a long convoluted thread with a nucleolus attached to each end (Figs. 34, 35). Even in the living cell this thread is seen to be composed of denser disk-like bodies suspended in a clearer basis; and in fixed preparations these bodies are found to be strongly basophilic, while the lighter substance ("linin" or "plastin") is oxyphilic.

It is extremely probable, therefore, that an analogous differentiation between basichromatin and oxychromatin exists even in nuclei where no trace of such a structure appears *in vivo*. The need of caution in this direction is, however, indicated by many facts. As every experienced cytologist knows, the character of the framework, the *apparent* number and size of the included basichromatin-masses, and the relative proportions of basophilic and oxyphilic materials, are materially affected both by the use of mordants, and by the subsequent manipulation of the dyes employed. Thoroughly con-

[1] '83–'84, p. 583, etc.   [2] See Chapter VIII, p. 652.

sistent results are indeed only reached after employment of a standard fixative and by simultaneous use of basic and acidic dyes in a mixture standardized in respect to their relative concentrations and the degree of acidification (as in the Biondi-Ehrlich mixture, p. 650). Even in this case, we are employing a method which, however carefully controlled, involves a certain arbitrarily chosen standard of performance difficult to control by other methods.

Such considerations led Lundegårdh ('10) to propose that the term "chromatin" be replaced by "karyotin" (caryotin), the substance thus designated appearing in either a basichromatic or an oxyphilic phase. This proposal has much to recommend it; nevertheless in the writer's view it is preferable to retain the older term "chromatin" provided we apply it to the whole stainable substance of the nucleus, whether basophilic or oxyphilic, and clearly recognize that basichromatin and oxychromatin are but passing phases, more or less marked and enduring, of one fundamental substance.

The physiological meaning of the changes of the nuclear framework in configuration and in staining reactions is imperfectly known. Very often

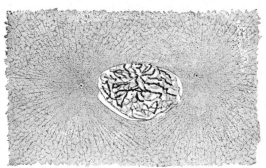

Fig. 36.—Prophase-nucleus, cleavage-blastomere of the whitefish *Coregonus*. Early chromosomes (segmented spireme), linin, central bodies and growing asters.

the nuclei of cells that are undergoing active metabolic changes, such as gland-cells or nurse-cells, contain a large amount of basophilic material and stain vigorously in basic dyes. In old and relatively passive cells, such as those of the epidermis, the reverse condition often exists. On the other hand, the fact is no less striking that in some of the most pronounced examples of actively growing cells the nuclear framework undergoes a marked diminution of its basophilic character. This appears in extreme form in the nucleus (germinal vesicle) of the egg-cell during the period of its most rapid growth in various animals (*e. g.*, in many insects, elasmobranchs and amphibians), and may even lead to a total disappearance of basophily (p. 351).

A similar diminution or loss of basophily has been observed also in the ova of plants and in the early blastomeres of the segmenting egg.

3. The Nucleoli [1]

The nucleoli are still imperfectly understood. There seem to be some forms of nuclei in which nucleoli are entirely absent; but in the nuclei of higher organisms, one or a few such bodies are almost invariably present and in extreme cases may be numbered by hundreds (p. 269). Morphologically considered the nucleoli show so many differences of form, staining-capacity and behavior as to render their classification difficult. Provisionally they may conveniently be grouped in two general classes which we shall designate as (1) *plasmosomes* or *true nucleoli,* and (2) *karyosomes* or *chromatin-nucleoli.*[2]

a. Plasmosomes. These bodies (Figs. 30, 267, 268) as their name indicates, are or tend to be oxyphilic (like the cytoplasm generally) while the karyosomes are basophilic in various degrees; but this distinction cannot be very logically carried out. In many combinations of basic and acid dyes, for example safranin and light-green or hæmatoxylin and eosin, the plasmosomes are sharply stained by the acidic dye; but in Flemming's triple mixture (safranin-gentian-orange) they stain characteristically with the basic safranin, though less intensely than the chromosomes; furthermore, their staining reaction is often markedly affected by the mode of fixation. Beyond this, the staining-reactions of these nucleoli often vary materially at different periods in the history of the nucleus; so that the same nucleolus may be at one time oxyphilic and at another time basophilic. It thus becomes probable that the varying staining reactions of the nucleoli are to a certain extent analogous to those of the chromatin of the nuclear framework, and may likewise be due to corresponding variations in chemical conditions. Such considerations formerly led to the view [3] that the nucleoli consist essentially of a basis of oxyphilic "plastin" or the like ("pyrenin" of Schwarz) which when impregnated with a basophilic "chromatin" becomes a basophilic or chromatin-nucleolus, and that the varying conditions of staining-reaction and digestibility are due to varying proportions and distribution of these two components. It is, however, more in accordance with present conceptions concerning the relations between basichromatin and oxychromatin to think of these varying reactions as due to different phases of a single original substance which may assume the

[1] For an exhaustive review of the earlier literature of this subject, see Montgomery, '98; of the later, Ludford, '22.

[2] This distinction is based on that of Flemming ('82) who designated these respective classes as "true nucleoli" (or simply "nucleoli") and "net-knots." The terms plasmosome and karyosome are due to Ogata ('83).

[3] R. Hertwig ('98), Farmer ('07), Reed ('14), etc.

basophilic or the oxyphilic condition according to changes in its chemical composition, *e. g.*, to varying ratios between the nucleic acid and the protein components (p. 652). This would equally well explain the fact that in general the oxyphilic nucleoli are readily attacked by pepsin-hydrochloric (Zacharias) while basophilic nucleoli (or nuclear components) are more resistant in various degrees (Jörgenssen, '13, etc.); but there are conspicuous exceptions to this—*e. g.*, the peripheral nucleoli of Amphibia (*Salamandra*).[1]

It is clear from the foregoing that it is often difficult to identify the plasmosomes by their micro-chemical reactions alone, though in "typical"

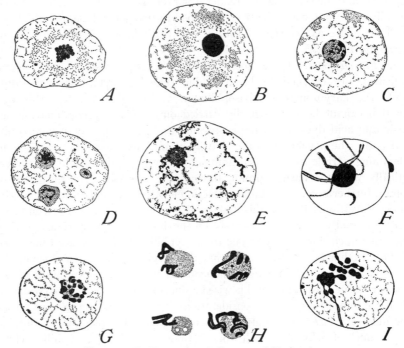

Fig. 37.—The Karyosphere in Insects and Myriapods.
(*A–E*, from Blackman; *F–I*, from Browne.)
A, earlier and *B*, later stage of spermatocytes in *Lithobius*; *C*, *D*, karyospheres showing both basichromatin and nucleolar substance; *E*, escape of chromosomes from karyosphere, *Scolopendra*; *F*, early spermatocyte of the hemipter *Notonecta*; *G*, later stage; *H*, escape of chromosomes leaving plasmosome-remnant; *I*, formation of the chromosomes.

cases they are readily recognizable by the use of double stains. In a broader sense their identity can only be fully established *by their morphological history;* for these nucleoli do not contribute directly (*i. e.*, as formed elements) to the formation of the chromosomes (p. 141). For the rest, it

[1] See p. 270.

may be said that the plasmosomes most commonly appear as sharply defined, rounded and rather highly refractive bodies, not directly connected with the general framework of the nucleus in which they are suspended. Physically they appear like liquid drops; and that they are at least semi-liquid is indicated by the forms which they assume when flattened out against the nuclear membrane, or against other nucleoli, both of which conditions are sometimes seen in the nuclei of the auxocytes in both sexes. Sometimes they are of irregular shape and undergo active changes of form in living cells.[1] As a rule they are devoid of a distinct limiting membrane; though in some cases they are surrounded by a basophilic envelope.

b. The karyosomes (Ogata), or chromatin-nucleoli (Montgomery). The bodies thus called are intensely basophilic, like basichromatin, and show the same high degree of resistance to peptic-hydrochloric digestion. They contrast sharply with the true nucleoli or plasmosomes in the fact that they contribute directly to the formation of the chromosomes, during cell-division. They are of at least three well-marked types, as follows:

Net-knots, as originally distinguished by Flemming, of more or less irregular form, often variable in size and number, and typically in direct continuity with the nuclear framework, of which they seem to be no more than thickened nodes (Fig. 8). They differ only in degree from the small granules or clumps of basichromatin, and like the latter give up their substance to the spireme-threads and chromosomes in the early stages of mitosis (p. 141). A transition to chromatin-nucleoli of more definite type is, however, given by the "prochromosomes" which are of similar general type, but are of constant number, equal to that of the chromosomes (Overton, Rosenberg, etc.) and are believed by many good observers to be converted directly into chromosomes or at least to serve as centers for their formation (p. 901).

Chromosome-nucleoli, known with certainty only in the nuclei of the gamete-producing cells (auxocytes and sometimes in the gonia, p. 759). These are sharply defined, usually spheroidal, and not continuous with the general framework. They represent either single chromosomes, or a small group of chromosomes, which persist in a condensed and rounded form during the "resting" or vegetative phase of the nucleus. They are best known in case of the sex-chromosomes, which are in general characterized by this behavior during the growth-period of the spermatocytes in many animals (Figs. 266, 267).

Karyospheres. These nucleoli, equivalent to the "*nucléoles-noyaux*" of Carnoy, are spheroidal bodies (Figs. 37, 109) commonly of large size

---

[1] Balbiani ('64); see Montgomery ('98).

which at certain stages contain all, or nearly all, the basichromatin in the nucleus (*e. g.*, the nucleolus of *Spirogyra*, or that of the spermatocytes of certain insects and myriapods) and from them arise the entire group of chromosomes (or many of them) in mitosis. Among the Protozoa, especially in rhizopods, the nucleus often contains a very large body of this type, commonly called by protozoölogists the "karyosome," which is described in some cases as giving rise to all of the chromosomes in mitosis, in others to only a part of them. In these cases the karyosome plays the part also of a central body or division-center, thus giving a possible transition to intra-nuclear central bodies (p. 204). For this reason, among others, it seems doubtful whether these bodies are closely comparable to the karyosomes of multicellular forms.

c. *Amphinucleoli.* Plasmosomes and karyosomes frequently coexist in the same nucleus, sometimes quite separate, in other cases closely associated to form a double nucleolus or *amphinucleolus*; the latter are commonly seen in the eggs of various mollusks, annelids and arthropods (Fig. 108), and in the spermatocytes of insects. In many of these cases the chromosome-nucleolus is often in its earlier stages attached to a plasmosome, though afterwards separating from it (Fig. 267). In some cases one or more chromosome-nucleoli are imbedded in a large plasmosome; in others all the chromosomes, in the form of closely crowded chromosome-nuclei, appear to be imbedded in a plasmosome to form a karyosphere (Fig. 37); and it is possible that all karyospheres are of this nature.

The origin of the nucleoli is still to a considerable extent in doubt; but the evidence is accumulating that all forms of them may be directly derived from the chromosomes. This is obviously the case with the various forms of chromatin-nucleoli, the origin of which has in many cases been traced step by step, especially in the case of chromosome-nucleoli (p. 759). In case of the plasmosomes the facts are not so evident; but here, too, there is reason to conclude that these nucleoli may arise by a direct transformation of a portion of the chromatin thread.[1] The questions here involved are hardly separable from those next to be considered.

d. *Functions of the Nucleoli.* The physiological meaning of the nucleoli still remains one of the most obscure questions of cytology. In case of the chromatin-nucleoli or karyosomes no great difficulties are encountered. In one form or another they are localized reservoirs of basichromatin, though we do not know why they should assume a compact form in an apparently inactive condition. Concerning the true nucleoli or plasmosomes we are still for the most part confined to indirect evidence and conjecture. In the later prophases of mitosis these nucleoli most commonly

[1] See Carothers ('13), Wenrich ('16, '17).

disappear, often previously becoming reduced in size or under going fragmentation. In some cases they are cast out bodily into the cytosome at the time the nuclear membrane disappears and there sooner or later degenerate, though sometimes persisting for a long time.[1] From this fact arose the view of Haecker, later held by many others, that the plasmosomes are accumulations of waste-products or by-products of the nuclear action, derived from the chromatin either by direct transformation of its substance, or as chemical cleavage-products or secretions (nuclear secretion-hypothesis). On the other hand, many cytologists, from the time of Flemming ('82, '91) have considered the nucleoli generally as centers for the storage or elaboration of substances such as "linin," "plastin" or "chromatin," destined to play some definite part in the later operations of the nucleus ("transportation-hypothesis of Haecker").[2]

This view is obviously correct as applied to the karyosomes. Flemming regarded the plasmosomes, likewise, as somehow concerned in the storage of "nuclein" or chromatin, or of materials necessary for the production of these substances. Strasburger ('98, '94, etc.), regarded the true nucleoli as storehouses of "kinoplasm," or material from which the spindle-fibers are formed during mitosis. There is, however, little definite evidence in support of this, while it is opposed by the fact, later to be described, that in animal cells perfect spindles and asters may be formed, one after another in regular succession, in the entire absence of nuclei (p. 176). More serious attention is demanded by the fact, especially striking during the growth-period of the oöcytes of many animals, that at the period when the chromosomes and the nuclear framework have become completely oxyphilic the nucleoli (which appear to be morphologically plasmosomes) are often intensely basophilic (pp. 270, 353).[3] This suggests that the nucleoli may in such cases be storehouses of nucleic acid to be drawn upon at a later period when the chromosomes are resuming their basophilic character. This, however, is purely hypothetical.

Observations have begun to accumulate in favor of the conclusion that the true nucleoli may be concerned in the secretory processes of the cell. Many earlier observers described a discharge of nucleolar fragments, or even of entire nucleoli, into the cytosome; and more recently a number of observers have found that such nucleolar material may give rise to various kinds of secretory products or storage-bodies. A conspicuous case of this is offered by the formation of yolk-spheres in oögenesis (p. 345). In the

---

[1] See Haecker (92, '93), Karsten ('93), Wheeler ('97), etc.

[2] See, for instance, Flemming ('82, '91), Went ('87), O. Hertwig ('93), Rhumbler ('93, '00), Carnoy and Le Brun ('97, '98), Lubosch ('02). For general and critical reviews see Haecker ('95, '99) Strasburger ('95, etc.), Montgomery ('99), Nemec ('10), Jörgenssen ('13), Buchner ('18).

[3] On this point see especially Jörgenssen ('13), also Maréchal ('06).

tissue-cells the extrusion of nucleolar fragments has been described by many observers,[1] several of whom believe they have traced to this source the origin of various formed bodies in the cytoplasm such as fat-drops and mucin-bodies (Schreiner, '15, '16) albuminous granules (Nakahara, '17, '18) and other products. To the writer none of these cases yet seems to be satisfactorily demonstrated, and the question is a most difficult one to be settled by studies on fixed material alone. Until the facts have been decisively demonstrated by the study of living cells judgment on these cases should be suspended. Nevertheless the observations in question prominently raise the question whether the nucleolus may not play a more active and important part in cell-metabolism than most writers have hitherto assumed.

4. The Enchylema, Ground-substance or Nuclear Sap

This has commonly been regarded as a structureless and non-stainable liquid, but the studies of Kite ('13) and Chambers ('14, etc.) show that this substance is in some cases of much firmer consistency than was formerly supposed. Heidenhain's important studies, already referred to, have shown that the spaces occupied by the enchylema may be much more restricted than appears after staining by a single "nuclear" or basic dye; for upon staining also with an acidic dye the spaces are often found to be occupied in greater or less degree by oxychromatin granules, and the meshwork thus appears to be correspondingly extended at the expense of the enchylema. The material thus brought into view is, however, often readily seen without use of the acidic dyes. It is very difficult, perhaps impossible, to determine how far these granules preëxist in life and how far are only coagulation-products of the enchylema. Zacharias ('02, etc.) has shown in various plant-cells, that in the early prophases of division, when the chromosomes are visible in fresh cells, a granular or net-like substance is immediately brought into view upon treatment by alcohol, HCl, and other coagulating agents. This material is dissolved by peptic digestion, while the basichromatin remains undigested. It seems probable that this material is in part thrown down from the enchylema or ground-substance; but it perhaps corresponds in part also to the linin and oxychromatin in Heidenhain's sense. This subject calls for further elucidation.

5. Other Structures

The nucleus may contain still other formed elements of less constant occurrence, of which the best known is the intra-nuclear division-center,

---

[1] See Lukjanow ('87), Montgomery ('98), Walker and Embleton ('08), Walker and Tozer ('09), etc.

or "nucleolo-centrosome," which plays the part of a central body during mitosis. This is very rare among higher forms; a classical case is the intra-nuclear center of the spermatocytes in *Ascaris megalocephala univalens*, discovered by Brauer (Fig. 323). In Protozoa such intra-nuclear centers are of common occurrence in flagellates (Fig. 88) and rhizopods (Fig. 87). The relation of these bodies to the extra-nuclear centers and to the blepharo-blasts will be considered elsewhere (p. 690).

Other and less familiar intra-nucleolar bodies include small deeply stain-ing granules or *nucleolini*, which have been described by many observers.[1] Carleton ('20) has recently produced evidence that certain types of these bodies may divide regularly in mitosis, the products being distributed regu-larly to the daughter-nuclei, while the nucleoli themselves disintegrate. Possibly, therefore, they may serve as centers for formation of the nucleoli; but nothing is known of their significance. Besides the foregoing may be mentioned intra-nuclear rodlets or straight axial fibrillæ (distinct from the nuclear framework) that have been found in the nuclei of some kinds of sperm-cells by Retzius, Champy and others and also in the red corpuscles of birds.[2] They are of unknown significance.

V. QUANTITATIVE RELATIONS OF NUCLEI, CELLS AND CELL-AGGREGATES

1. Cell-size and Body-size

All cells are subject to considerable fluctuations of size; nevertheless, within rather wide limits of variability the size of cells, like that of the body they may build, may be regarded as a specific constant. This is true alike of multicellular and unicellular organisms. An interesting example of the latter case is offered by the ciliate *Paramœcium caudatum*, a species in which Jennings ('08, '11) found it possible to isolate at least eight different races or strains which differ characteristically in size and breed true. Though each of these races is subject to considerable fluctuation the mean or norm is constant, the largest form being about five times the length of the smallest (Fig. 38). The smallest visible cells (Fig. 39) probably occur among the bacteria, some of which (*Cocci*) lie almost at the limit of microscopical vi-sion; but it is not impossible that still smaller cells exist, that cannot be seen even with the highest powers of the microscope. At the other extreme, so far as linear dimensions go, are probably those nerve-cells and their branches which innervate the extremities of the large mammals. Such neurons may attain a length of several feet. In volume, the upper existing

---

[1] See Montgomery ('98b).   [2] See Champy and Carleton ('21).

limit of magnitude is probably attained by the huge eggs of certain birds and sharks, and some of the extinct forms are known to have been larger

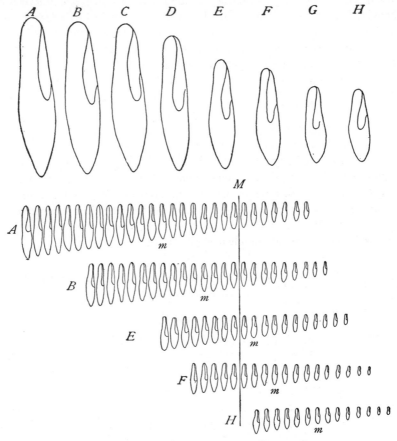

Fig. 38.—Eight races of *Paramœcium* (JENNINGS).

Upper row, diagram showing the relative mean size of races A–H. Below, diagrams of races *A, B, E, F,* and *H* (less highly magnified), to show range of fluctuation within each race. The mean size of each race indicated at *m*, that of the whole eight races indicated by vertical line *M*.

still. Among modern birds the largest egg-cell is that of the ostrich. Externally this egg is in round numbers about 6 inches in length, while the yolk (which alone represents the egg-cell) has a mean diameter of about 80 mm. or a little more than 3 inches.[1] The egg-shell of the extinct giant

[1] This is my own measurement of a fresh, unincubated egg. Measurements of the egg of the great shark, *Chlamydoselache,* from an alcoholic specimen in the Columbia museum, give a slightly higher value. For photographs, side by side, of the eggs of the hen, the ostrich, the extinct moa of New Zealand, and *Æpyornis,* see Lucas, *Animals of the Past,* Fig. 20.

bird *Æpyornis*, from New Zealand, measures about 13 inches in length; from which (assuming yolk and shell to have had the same relative proportions as in the ostrich) the diameter of the yolk should have been approximately 7 inches. If we estimate the diameter of the ostrich egg-cell (yolk) as 75 mm. and that of the smallest visible *Coccus* as .001 m. the ratio of their linear dimensions is as 75,000:1 and that of their volumes as $(75,000)^3:1$.

Such a difference is of the same order as that between a sphere of one inch in diameter and one of more than a mile, or between a sphere 500 feet in diameter and the earth.

The size of cells is to a certain extent characteristic of larger groups; for instance, amphibians in general have much larger cells than reptiles, birds or mammals; gymnosperms larger cells than angiosperms, and monocotyledonous plants larger ones than dicotyledonous. In a measure these differences are correlated with the rate of activity, so that it is almost proverbial among cytologists that relatively sluggish and clumsy animals, such as Orthoptera or urodeles are more likely to afford large and favorable cells for study than active ones such as Hymenoptera, Diptera or birds.

Like the size of cells, the size of the multicellular body is, within a certain range of variation, a specific constant, and in some cases follows the laws of Mendelian heredity, as shown by Mendel's familiar experiments on short and tall races of peas. The factors by which body-size is determined are of at least three widely different types.

(1) In a large class of cases, including both plants and animals, it has been demonstrated that within the species individuals of different size do not differ noticeably in respect to the size of their constituent cells, but only in respect to their number. This was first determined in plants by Amelung ('93) and by Strasburger ('93). Rabl ('99) found the cells of the crystalline lens to be nearly constant in size but variable in number, the size of the lens varying accordingly. Boveri ('04) found that epithelial cells and bone corpuscles from human dwarfs and giants are of the same size as in normal individuals. Conklin ('96, '12, '13), in an extended study of

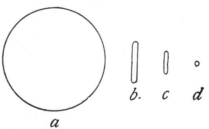

Fig. 39.—Comparative size of very small cells.
a, human erythrocyte or red blood-corpuscle ($6\,\mu$); *b*, typhoid bacillus ($2.4 \times 0.5\ \mu$); *c*, influenza bacillus ($0.5 \times 0.2\ \mu$); *d*, germ of poliomyelitis of Flexner and Noguchi (0.15–$0.3\ \mu$). (From Jordan's *General Bacteriology*, excepting *d*).

snails of the genus *Crepidula*, found a similar relation between different species. The size of an average male of *C. fornicata* is about 125 times that of an average male of *C. convexa;* in *C. plana* the size of an average female is about 15 times that of a dwarf female. In all these the size of the tissue-cells is in general nearly the same,[1] and the great differences of body-size are wholly due to variations in the number of cells. This does not apply to the sex-cells (ova) of different species, which differ widely in size. Within the same species, however, the ova are nearly of the same size but differ in number in individuals of different size, just as in case of the tissue-cells.

(2) The foregoing cases include only indefinite variations or fluctuations within the species. A second and quite different kind of giantism results from an increase in the size of cells without corresponding increase in their number. Typical of this class are certain of the so-called *gigas* races or species of such plants as *Œnothera* or *Primula*, in which the cells are distinctly larger than those of the normal types, though with a considerable range of variation. In the most typical cases this involves a corresponding increase of body-size, though sometimes this is seen only in certain parts.[2] In giants of this type the nuclei are correspondingly increased in size, and in most cases are tetraploid, *i. e.*, divide with twice the usual or diploid number of chromosomes (p. 728). It has been proved experimentally that the increased cell-size in certain of these cases is due to the increased nuclear size, which in turn is due to the doubled number of chromosomes. A classical case is offered by the experimental results of Gerassimoff ('02) on the fresh-water alga, *Spirogyra*. By exposing the normal forms to lowered temperature, and in certain other ways, it was found that mitotic division may be so modified that although the chromosomes divide the daughter-nuclei do not separate normally and cytoplasmic division fails. Binucleate cells are thus produced, the two nuclei either remaining separate or fusing into one, which then grows to twice the normal size. In either of these cases the doubling of the nuclear mass is followed by growth of the cytosome to double the normal volume; and by the continued division of such cells are produced giant filaments which may be reared to maturity, produce gametes of double the normal size, and conjugate to produce correspondingly enlarged zygotes (Fig. 313).

In this case the number of chromosomes is not certainly known; but there can be no doubt that it is doubled, so that the giant races may be called tetraploid. Certain tetraploid giant forms of *Œnothera*, *Primula* and *Solanum* (p. 728) are known to have arisen as sudden mutations from species of normal size and diploid chromosome-number. It is practically certain that they have been produced by a process of similar type; and this is known to be the case also in tetraploid mosses and sea-urchins experimentally produced by the Marchals and by Boveri (p. 729).

(3) In the foregoing cases, the chromosomes of the tetraploid forms, so

---

[1] Ganglion-cells and muscle-cells are said to form an exception.   [2] See p. 731.

far as they have been examined, appear to be of the same size as in the normal or diploid forms; and since their number has been doubled the total mass of "chromatin" is also double the normal. In a third class may be included cases of giantism which cannot be included in either of the first two, the most striking of which are *gigas*-forms having the normal or diploid chromosome-number. Examples of these are certain mutants of *Primula sinensis* (Gregory,'09), and of *Œnothera Lamarckiana* (Stomps, '16, '19), both belonging to genera in which tetraploid *gigas*-forms also are known; and similar diploid giants were found by Stomps in *Narcissus*. Beside these cases may be placed the curious one of *Primula kewensis*, a tetraploid mutant of hybrid origin, which is tetraploid and has larger cells and nuclei than the parent forms, but in which the chromosomes are but half the typical size. In this case increased size of nuclei and cells (in the approximate ratio 5:4) seems to have occurred without any increase in chromatin-mass (Farmer and Digby, '07).

From all this it is clear that the quantitative relations of chromosomes, nuclei, cytosomes and cell-aggregates offer a complex problem, and one that is incompletely solved. Nevertheless the undoubted causal relation between nuclear volume and cytoplasmic growth (*i. e.*, the *karyoplasmic ratio* of R. Hertwig) is a fact of great theoretical interest.[1]

VI. THE CELL IN RELATION TO THE MULTICELLULAR BODY

The body, we are accustomed to say, is built up of cells or their products (p. 3). In what sense do we use this phrase, and what is the morphological and physiological relation of the cells to the body which they form? These questions first arose with Schwann, who offered an admirably lucid discussion of the facts so far as known to him (1840). It was his conclusion that the cell should be regarded as a primary organic unit or elementary organism. The life of the higher organism, in his view, is essentially a composite. Each cell has its independent existence or individuality; and "the whole organism subsists only by means of the reciprocal action of the single elementary parts." [2] This conclusion took on new significance with the conclusion of Siebold (1845) that in the Protista or lowest forms of life the whole body consists of but a single cell; for this suggested the view that the multicellular body of higher forms is equivalent to an assemblage or colony of one-celled individuals; and from this grew the further conception that the multicellular organism may be regarded as a "cell-state" the one-celled members of which have undergone a physiological division of labor.[3]

[1] For further discussion see p. 727.
[2] *Untersuchungen*, Eng. Trans., Sydenham Soc., p. 181.
[3] A considerable group of modern authorities have sought the origin of Metazoa in syncytial or multinucleate rather than actually colonial forms (Jhering, A. Sedgwick, Delage).

Elaborated especially by Milne-Edwards, Virchow and Haeckel, this conclusion offered a simple and natural point of attack for the problems of cytology, embryology, and physiology, and revolutionized the problems of organic individuality. Its value as a means of biological analysis needs no
other demonstration than the immense advances that it made possible.
Inevitably in practice we treat cells as distinct, though closely coördinated,
elementary organisms or organic units; and although some writers have
questioned the validity of this procedure (p. 103) it nevertheless remains an
indispensable means of analysis.

That cells are elementary organisms, having a high degree of independence, is an obvious fact in case of the Protista and of the germ-cells of all
higher organisms. It is hardly less obvious in case of the blood-corpuscles,
the wandering leucocytes and other separate cells in the multinuclear body.
It is certain also, as will later be shown (p. 1031), that in certain of the lower
multicellular types, including even such forms as sponges, hydroids and
polyps, a highly differentiated multicellular body may be built up by the
aggregation of cells previously more or less completely separate. Further,
it has been shown by Harrison, Burrows, M. R. and W. Lewis, and others
that small groups of muscle-cells, epithelia, connective-tissue-cells, embryonic nerve-cells and others, may be removed from the body and kept
alive in suitable cultivation media *in vitro*, where they may continue to
grow and multiply for long periods, in some cases for several years (p. 234)
without loss of their specific character. Again, it has long been known that
in some of the higher plants, such as *Marchantia, Begonia*, or *Torenia*, a very
small fragment of the body, perhaps even a single cell, may give rise to a
complete plant.

All this tends to support the conclusion that fundamentally the cell
possesses in itself the complete apparatus of life, and to this extent tends to
sustain Schwann's general conception. On the other hand, it is obvious that
under normal conditions the physiological autonomy of the tissue-cells is
in considerable degree merged into the life of the organism considered as a
whole. This is due to a process of integration and differentiation through
which the tissue-cell often comes to appear as no more than a localized area
of specific activity, provided it is true with the complete apparatus of cell-
life and even capable of independent action within certain limits, but still
remaining a part and not a whole. This conclusion is most clearly brought
out by the phenomena of growth and development, which seem to show that
the multicellular body arises by the splitting up of a unicellular germ without impairment of the individuality of the organism as a whole (p. 1029).
From this point of view the apparently composite character of the individual
may be conceived as due to a secondary distribution of its energies among

localized centers of action.   This, however, is not subversive (as some writers
have assumed) of our fundamental conception of the cell-state.   It is paralleled by the integration and division of labor seen in such organisms as the
Pennatulaceæ (*e. g.*, *Renilla*) or the Siphonophora which are undoubtedly
colonies of simpler individuals yet display a high degree of individuality
considered as wholes.   We shall therefore proceed upon the assumption, if
only as a practical method, that the multicellular organism in general is
comparable, to an assemblage of Protista which have undergone a high
degree of integration and differentiation so as to constitute essentially a
cell-state.[1]

From any point of view the physiological and structural interrelations
of the tissue-cells remains a fundamentally important question.   Apart

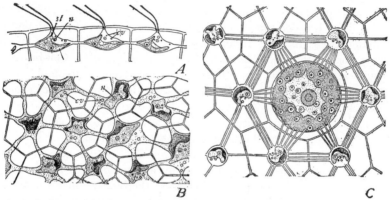

Fig. 40.—Protoplasmic cell-connections (plasmodesms), in *Volvox*, somewhat schematized
(JANET).

A, *V. globator*, in vertical optical section; *B*, in surface view, showing broad bridges; *C*, *V. aureus*,
gonidium, connected with surrounding vegetative cells by fine bridges; *cp.*, chloroplast, *cv*, contractile vacuoles; *p*, pyrenoid, *st*, stigma.

from the nervous mechanism and that provided by the soluble enzymes,
hormones and other chemical substances,[2] it is probable that an important
part in the coördination of the cell-activities is played by direct protoplasmic connections between cells ("cell-bridges," "plasmodesms").   Heitzmann long since (1873) held that even when distinct cell-walls are formed
they are still traversed by strands of protoplasm by means of which the

---

[1] This view has been vigorously assailed by many writers, especially by those who have emphasized
the conception of the "organism as a whole." See, for instance, Whitman ('88, '93), A. Sedgwick
('94), Dobell ('11), Child ('15) and especially Ritter ('19). Such criticisms seem to ignore the probable historical origin of multicellular from unicellular organisms, as well as the fundamental general
similarity between the protistan cell and that of the metazoön or metaphyte, both in structure and
mode of origin.

[2] See Cunningham ('21), Adami ('17), etc.

protoplasts remain in protoplasmic continuity. The whole body was thus conceived by him as a more or less continuous mass, the cells being no more than nodal points in a general network of protoplasm. This interesting conception, at first received with extreme scepticism, has met with considerable support from later observation. Direct protoplasmic cell-connections have long been known in colonial Protista, and in various simple algæ and fungi. A striking example is seen in *Volvox*, where the small somatic cells are connected both with one another and with the gonidia or germ-cells (Fig. 40); and more or less similar cell-connections are often seen in colonial flagellates, ciliates and other Protozoa. In multicellular organisms cell-bridges have been demonstrated in many forms. Their existence in the sieve-tubes of higher plants has long been known, and the researches of Tangl, Gardiner, Kienitz-Gerloff and their successors demonstrated their existence in many other tissues.[1] In lower plants, the protoplasmic bridges may be either broader strands (*e. g.*, in *Volvex globator*, and in red algæ) or fine filaments (*V. aureus*). In higher plants they are typically very fine and delicate fibrils, often invisible until after suitable staining. Cell-bridges of this type may be solitary, or scattered, or grouped together in bundles at the bottom of pits in the cell-wall where they pierce the pit-membrane or middle lamella of the wall.

In animal tissues the existence of both cell-anastomoses and of inter-cellular bridges is now well established for many kinds of cells. In certain forms of connective tissue-cells and cartilage-cells, also the bone-corpuscles, the scattered cells are often connected by anastomoses to form more or less net-like very delicate strands traversing the inter-cellular substance.

Plasmodesms or cell-bridges are of general occurrence in the epithelial tissues, where they were first observed in epidermal "spine-cells" ("Stachel-zellen") and supposed to be spine-like processes from the membrane or cell-periphery (M. Schultze, 1864). Later studies by many observers, (Ranvier, Renaut, Pfitzner, Schridde, Kromayer, Cajal, etc.) proved these structures to be protoplasmic inter-cellular bridges, and further showed that they are traversed by fibrillæ, which may be followed from one cell to another and even through several cells (Fig. 41). The plasma-bridges have since been found in the columnar epithelia generally.[2] Further, it has been shown by a considerable number of observers that the germ-cells in both animals and plants may be connected with the surrounding somatic cells (follicle

[1] Tangl ('79–'81), Gardiner '88, (98, '00), Keinitz-Gerloff ('91,'02), A. Meyer (96, '02), Kühle ('00), etc. Critical reviews with literature, in Kienitz-Gerloff, Strasburger ('01), and Davis ('05). See also Hill ('00, '01).

[2] Literature in Flemming ('95, '97), Heidenhain ('07, '11), Studnicka ('98, '09, '13), O. Hertwig ('12). It is probable that the plasma-bridges described in smooth muscle-cells belong to the interstitial connective tissue and may be shrinkage-products (Heidenhain).

cells, etc.) by protoplasmic bridges (Fig. 156).[1] Plasma-bridges have also been described in the case of embryonic cells of many types and considerable evidence has been produced to show that they may here play an important part in maintaining the unity of the organism.

The facts thus briefly reviewed have led some important modern writers to accept Heitzmann's general conclusion almost in its entirety. A. Meyer,

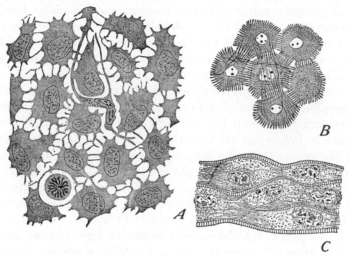

Fig. 41.—Intercellular bridges (plasmodesms), in animal tissues (A, FLEMMING; B, RIO-HORTEGA; C, IDE).

A, epithelium of the gill-lamellæ of salamander-larva, deeper layers in horizontal view; B, cells from the mucous membrane of a nasal polypus, fibrillæ traversing the inter-cellular bridges; C, human cancer-cells.

for example, expresses the opinion that both the plant and the animal individual is a continuous mass of protoplasm that forms a morphological unit whether it appear in the form of a single cell, a multinucleated cell, or a system of cells.[2] Sachs concluded, more specifically, that "The multicellular plant differs from the unicellular only in that in the one case the protoplasm is traversed by numerous sieve-like or lattice-like plates, while in the other these plates are absent." [3] Adam Sedgwick ('94) endeavored to show that in *Peripatus*, in lower vertebrates, and presumably in animals generally the embryonic cells are in general in direct continuity, the entire body being up to a late stage a continuous syncytium. This conclusion is in harmony with that reached by many experimental

[1] See, for example, Dendy ('88), (sponges), Retzius ('89), (mammals), Goroschankin ('83), (cycads), A. Meyer ('96), (Volvox), Ikeno ('98), (cycads).

[2] '96, p. 212. *Cf.* the views of Hanstein, Strasburger, Russow and others there cited.

[3] Cited from O. Hertwig, '12, p. 491.

embryologists (Wilson, '93, Hammar, '96, '97, etc.) and by some of the ablest students of normal development, such as Rauber ('83), Whitman ('93), and many later writers.

By the earlier botanical observers it was supposed that in the case of plants the plasma-bridges were a consequence of incomplete division and they were even conjectured to be direct derivatives of the spindle-fibers of previous mitoses (Tangl, Russow, and especially Gardiner). Later observers, however, such as Kienitz-Gerloff and Strasburger ('01) opposed this view, so far as the fine fibrils or "plasmodesms" of higher forms are concerned, though admitting that broader connections (as, for instance, in various algæ) may thus arise. The finer bridges are of secondary origin and penetrate the cell-wall secondarily; and it would seem that in some cases the protoplasmic outgrowths from opposite sides of the wall only approach each other closely but without actually uniting. A. Meyer ('96) has shown in *Volvox* that the cell-bridges are formed anew after division; and in like manner Flemming has observed that when the wandering cells or leucocytes creep about among the epithelial cells of the epidermis (of laval salamanders) they rupture the plasma-bridges, which are then formed anew behind them.[1] In harmony with this are the interesting observations of G. F. Andrews ('97) and E. A. Andrews ('98a, b) who have seen the living blastomeres of echinoderm and nemertine eggs spinning numerous delicate protoplasmic filaments which establish secondary connections between the blastomeres subsequent to their separation by division and may even traverse the blastocoele so as to connect widely separated cells.

VII. THE POLARITY AND SYMMETRY OF CELLS

Polarity and symmetry are among the most interesting features of the cell for the student of development;[2] for the polarity of the adult body is modeled on that of the ovum, which in its turn is but a particular case of a phenomenon seen in many other kinds of cells, among both unicellular and multicellular organisms. Fundamentally both the nature and the origin of polarity are unknown (p. 108). We know only its visible expression, which in most cases is both structural and functional, appearing on the one hand in a polarized grouping of the cell-components, on the other in differences of functional or metabolic activity with respect to the axis thus marked off. Which of these (if either) is the more fundamental is an open question, belonging to that ancient and probably barren problem as to

---

[1] '95, pp. 10–11, '97, p. 261.

[2] The polarity of the animal egg was first made known by von Baer (1834) and further investigated by Remak (1805-55). It was recognized in other forms of cells by Van Beneden ('83, '87) and Rabl ('85, '89).

whether structure or function came first in the order of nature (p. 670). So far as external appearances go it must be said that structural polarity would seem in general to be of secondary origin, of which the egg offers a conspicuous example (p. 1023); but critical consideration of such cases leaves us in doubt as to the underlying aspects of this problem.

Functional polarity in the form of a polarized localization of function is a familiar phenomenon in higher organisms but one that is not easy to investigate apart from the structural dispositions by which it is usually accompanied or preceded. It is strikingly shown in the phenomena of regeneration in plants where, as shown especially by "Vöchting ('85, '92, etc.) even very small pieces (e. g., in *Marchantia*) retain their original polarity, the new apical region being formed typically from or near to the most apical region of the piece; and since these pieces may be very small, Vöchting concluded that every cell is probably polarized in the same sense and may give rise to a complete plant. A similar polarization in relation to regeneration has been observed in various animals, particularly in coelenterates, planarians and annelids, though not in pieces so small; [1] but it has been shown that under certain conditions the direction of polarity may here be experimentally reversed (heteromorphosis). The phemonena of grafting, both in plants and animals, likewise emphasize the physiological polarity of fragments of the organism.

In the case of single cells physiological polarity is seen in the polarized metabolic activities of the germ-cells, gland-cells, many kinds of epithelial cells, the nerve-cells and others in which these activities are more or less clearly expressed by changes, periodic or permanent, in the cell-substance. This was clearly recognized by Remak whose terms "vegetative" and "animal," applied to the poles of the animal ovum, obviously imply a characteristic difference of metabolic activity between them. Child ('11–'16) has recently emphasized the general importance of "metabolic gradients " as an expression (if not the actual cause) of functional polarity, which in his view may sometimes be merely a graded difference in the rate of metabolism in the direction of the axis (though it may often be more than this). In support of this he has proved experimentally, by a study of susceptibility to the action of poisons and narcotics, that such gradients undoubtedly exist in the direction of the main axes, both in organisms as a whole and in individual cells.

Interesting possibilities for the further analysis of physiological polarity are opened by recent experiments. It has been shown that in hydroids the oral region is electronegative as compared with the basal; [2] and also

---

[1] See especially Morgan ('01), Loeb ('02), Child ('15).
[2] Mathews ('04), Hyman and Bellamy (22), Lund ('23).

that axial differences of electrical potential similar in type, though different in detail, exist in other animals; [1] and Lund has demonstrated that in the alga *Fucus* the polarity of the eggs shows a distinct orientation with respect to the electric field. Hyman and Bellamy (*op. cit.*) emphasize the fact that in the various cases studied by them the electrical gradients closely correspond with the metabolic, levels of high metabolic rate being electronegative to those of lower.

Structural polarity may appear either in the external form of the cell or in a polarized grouping of the various cell-components about an ideal *organic axis* or *cell-axis*. In the cells of higher animals generally, as was first indicated by Van Beneden ('83), the cell-axis is most commonly indicated by the position of the central bodies with reference to the nucleus, the axis passing through the center of both (Fig. 42), while both nucleus and central apparatus are often eccentric towards one or the other pole. This conception was developed by Rabl ('85) who considered that the nucleus likewise shows a polarity corresponding with the cell-axis as thus determined (p. 829). It was carried still further by Heidenhain ('94–'96, etc.) who considered the centers as forming the insertion of persistent astral rays or "organic radii" which extend throughout the cell and by their conditions of tension determine the position and movements of the nucleus and the succession of division-planes in the cell. This particular conception, however, has received little support from later investigation (p. 180).

The cell-polarity as marked out by nucleus and central bodies is often emphasized both by the external form of the cell and by many other of its structural features. The Golgi-bodies, and sometimes also the chondriosomes, are often grouped about the centers or oriented with respect to them (p. 50). In epithelial cells generally the centers, usually double in the form of a "diplosome," typically lie towards the free surface, often almost at the periphery, thus marking an axis that is vertical to the surface (Fig. 42). In the direction of this axis the cell is often elongated (as in the columnar epithelia), and the basal and peripheral regions of the cytosome as thus marked often show conspicuous differences of metabolic activity accompanied by corresponding morphological differentiations. This is shown with especial clearness in many forms of gland-cells (pancreas, salivary glands), in columnar ciliated cells, and above all in the germ-cells, in all of which the structural polarity is often manifested by a conspicuous stratification or polarized grouping of formed elements such as granules, yolk-spheres, pigment and the like. This grouping does not, however, in itself constitute the basis of polarity, as has been demonstrated by centrifuging eggs and

---

[1] In ctenophores the electronegativity is greatest at the aboral pole; in platodes and annelids both ends are electronegative to the middle. (*Cf.* Morgan and Diman '04.)

other cells by which these bodies may be caused to undergo marked dislocation without displacing the axis itself, as is shown by the later history
of the cell (p. 1089).[1] Both nucleus and centers likewise, may be displaced, either by centrifuging or by mechanical pressure; and both may
move extensively through the cytoplasm under normal conditions, without
changing the cell-polarity, as we see, for example, during the fertilization and
cleavage of the egg (p. 425). Polarity, finally, appears in many forms of
plant-cells in which central bodies are absent or are represented by much

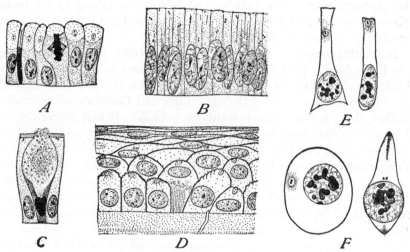

Fig. 42.—Central bodies (centrioles), in epithelial and other cells (A–D, ZIMMERMANN; E,
HEIDENHAIN and COHN; F, HEIDENHAIN).

A, from gastric glands of man; dead cell at the left. B, uterine epithelium, man; C, from human
duodenum; goblet-cell, with centriole in the middle; D, corneal epithelium of monkey; E, epithelial cells from mesoblast-somites, embryo duck; F, red blood-corpuscles from the duck-embryo.
The centrioles are double in nearly all cases.

larger and less clearly defined structures, e. g., in the somatic cells of *Isoëtes*
or in the synaptic stages of the sporocytes of *Marsilia* and *Equisetum* (Marquette, '07).

All this has led many observers to the conclusion that the fundamental
basis of polarity must be sought in the continuous and apparently homogeneous hyaloplasm of the egg ("ground-substance" of Lillie, "spongioplasm" of Conklin).[2] In harmony with this is the fact that in many ova

---

[1] Gurwitsch ('08), Lyon ('07), Lillie ('08, '09), Morgan ('08, '00), Boveri ('10), Morgan and
Spooner ('00), Conklin ('10, '12, '16, '17) and others.

[2] "Polarity is not a result of the position of the nucleus or of any configuration of granules. It
must depend upon some configuration or heterogeneous physical or chemical properties of the ground-
substance established early in the history of the egg, and which is not essentially disturbed by centrifuging " (Lillie, '09).

the polarized grouping of pigment, yolk and the like is visibly attained by a secondary process of segregation, often not effected until near the time of maturation and fertilization, but conforming to a preëxisting axis marked by the point of attachment of the egg, the position of the micropyle, the eccentricity of the nucleus, or by other characters (p. 1094). It is also in harmony with the earlier conclusion of Driesch ('96, '98), based on displacement of the nuclei and centers by mechanical pressure and on the development of egg-fragments, that the position of the nuclei and centers is non-essential, and that polarity and bilaterality belong to the protoplasmic substance as such (hyaloplasm) irrespective of the formed elements that it may contain (p. 1019).[1]

Interesting questions are thus raised concerning the organization of the hyaloplasm. Both Driesch and Boveri argued in favor of a "polar-bilateral orientation" of the ultimate protoplasmic particles that make up the "intimate structure" of the egg. Lillie and Conklin alike concluded, further, that the hyaloplasm is relatively solid, i. e., in high degree viscous. Lillie at first ('06) held the view, based on the Brownian movements of the microsomes (p. 61), that the hyaloplasm is a "fluid medium," but later ('09) concluded that it is "finely organized" and that the flowing movements that it seems to perform are an illusion produced by movements of the granules through it. Conklin considers the hyaloplasm as forming a framework of "spongioplasm" traversing a more fluid substance, in which the granules, etc., are suspended, and through the elasticity and contractility of which are determined the positions of all the included structures (nucleus, central bodies, granules, etc.) and their return to their normal positions after artificial displacement.[2]

Accepting the general conclusions thus indicated we can readily understand how the various inclusions and other intracellular structures may be shifted about without changing the direction of the cell-axis. We may also see how the cell-axis itself, persistent as it is when once established, may originally be laid down in this direction or that by an epigenetic process; and here, probably, we find the most reasonable interpretation of the fact that the direction of the axis is so often correlated with the relation of the cell to its immediate environment (as in columnar epithelial cells or the ovarian egg).

Van Beneden expressed the opinion that bilateral symmetry is likewise a widespread if not universal phenomenon among cells, at least in bilateral animals. This, however, has received little support from later researches.

---

[1] On this point see especially Boveri, '01.

[2] An interesting light is thrown upon these results by the work of Heilbrunn and Chambers on the changes of viscosity during mitosis (pp. 197, 1092).

Among Protista, it is true, there are certain forms (ciliates, flagellates and some of the unicellular plants) that are more or less distinctly bilateral; in some cases showing differentiated axes which have the same general relation to the environment and the movements of the individual as in higher forms (Fig. 43). It is also true that the eggs of insects and cephalo-

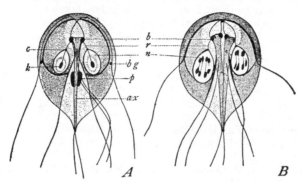

Fig. 43.—A bilateral, binucleate flagellate, *Giardia muris*, showing flagella and basal apparatus (Kofoid and Christiansen).

A, in the ordinary vegetative state, *B* in mitosis, the axostyle and blepharoplasts double.

ax, axostyle; *b*, blepharoplasts; *bg*, basal granules; *k*, karyosome; *n*, nucleus; *p*, parabasal body; *r*, rhizoplast.

pods and the sperms of some species of animals are bilateral, both in form and in structure (pp. 276, 374). A certain amount of support for considering the cells of columnar epithelium as bilateral structures was found by Heidenhain ('99). Nevertheless it must be said that there is little ground for regarding bilaterality as characteristic of cells generally; and as applied to the somatic cells Van Beneden's conclusion wears a somewhat transcendental aspect.

LITERATURE I

(See also VIII, XII, etc. For abbreviations see p. 1145).

Agar, W. E., '20. Cytology with special Reference to the Metazoan Nucleus: *Macmillan and Co., London.*

Altmann, R., '90, '94. Die Elementarorganismen und ihre Beziehungen zu den Zellen: *Leipzig.*

Arnold, J., '13. Das Plasma der somatischen Zellen im Lichte der Plasmosomen-Granulalehre und der Mitochondrienforschung: *A. A.,* XLIII. '14 (IX).

Bechold, H., '12 (VIII).

Beer, R., '04. On the Present Position of Cell-wall Research: *N. P.,* III.

Benda, C., '03. Die Mitochondria: *E. A. E.,* XII. '14. Die Bedeutung der Zelleibstruktur für die Pathologie: *Ver. d. Deutsch. Path. Ges.*

Bergh, R. S., '94. Vorlesungen über die Zelle und die einfachen Geweben: *Wiesbaden.*

Blackman, F. F., '12.   The Plasmic Membrane and its Organization: *N. P.*

Bruel, L., '13.   Zelle und Zellteilung (Zoologisch): *H. Nw.,* X, *Fischer, Jena.*

Buchner, P., '15.   Prakticum der Zellenlehre: *Bornträger, Berlin.*

Bütschli, O., '92, '94.   Untersuchungen über mikroscopische Schäume und das Protoplasma: *Leipzig.*   (Eng. Trans., E. A. Minchin, London.)
   '98.   Untersuchungen über Strukturen, etc.: *Leipzig.*

Cajal, S. R., '15.   Algunas variaciones, etc., del aparato reticular de Golgi: *Trab. Lab. Invest. Biol. Madrid,* XII.

Chambers, R.   Microdissection Studies, I ('17), *A. J. P.,* XLIII; II ('17[b]), *J. E. Z.,* XXIII; III ('21) *B. B.,* XLI; and other papers; '24.   The Physical Structure of Protoplasm, etc.   In General Cytology, *Chicago.*

Conklin, E. G., '12.   Cell-size and Nuclear Size: *J. E. Z.,* XII.

Cowdry, E. V., '18.   The Mitochondrial Constituents of Protoplasm: *P. C. I.,* 271.
   '16.   The General Functional Significance of Mitochondria: *A. J. A.,* 19; '24.   Mitochondria, Golgi Apparatus and Chromidial Substance: In General Cytology, *Chicago.*

Cowdry, N. H., '17.   A Comparison of the Mitochondria in Plant and Animal Cells: *B. B.,* XXXIII.

Cowdry, Chambers, Conklin and others, '24.   General Cytology, *Chicago.*

Dahlgren and **Kepner,**'08.   Principles of Animal Histology: *New York.*

Davis, B. M., '04 –'05.   Studies on the Plant Cell. I–VIII, *A. N.,* XXXVIII–XXXIX.

Delage, Yves, '03.   (Int.)

Doncaster, L., '20. An Introduction to the Study of Cytology: *Cambridge Univ. Press.*

Duesberg, J., '12. Plastosomes, "Apparato reticularo interno," und Chromidial-apparat: *E. A. E.,* 20.
   '20 (see IV).
   '14.   Trophospongien und Golgischer Binnapparat: *V. A. G.,* XLVI.

Fauré-Fremiet, '10 [IV].

Fischer, A., '99.   Fixierung, Färbung und Bau des Protoplasmas: *Fischer, Jena.*

Flemming, W., '82.   (Int.)

Gatenby, J. B., '19.   The Identification of Intracellular Elements: *J. R. M. S.,* '19.

Guilliermond, M. A., '14.   État actuel de la question de l'évolution, etc., des mitochondries: *Rev. Gén. Bot.,* XXVI.

Gurwitsch, A., '04.   Morphologie und Biologie der Zelle: *Jena.*
   '13.   Vorlesungen über allgemeine Histologie: *Fischer, Jena.*

Häcker, V., '99.   (Int.)

Hanstein, J., ' 80.   Das Protoplasma als Träger der pflänzlichen und thierischen Lebensverrichtungen: *Heidelberg.*

Hardy, W. B., '99.   Structure of Cell-Protoplasm: *J. P.,* XXIV.
   '13.   Note on Differences in electrical Potential in the living Cell: *J. P.,* 47.

Harper, R. A., '19.   The Structure of Protoplasm: *A. J. B.,* 6.

Heidenhain, M., '07. '11.   (Int.)

Henneguy, F., '03.   (Int.)

Hertwig, O., '98.   (Int.)

Huxley, T. H., '68.   The Physical Basis of Life: *Collected Essays*

Jordan, H. E., and **Ferguson, '16.** Textbook of Histology: *N. Y., Appleton and Co.*

Jost, L., '07, '13. Lectures in Plant Physiology, 1st Ed., *Eng. Trans., Clarendon Press;* 3rd Ed., *Fischer, Jena.*

Kite, G. L., '13. Studies on the Physical Properties of Protoplasm: *A. J. P.,* XXXII.

Koernicke, M., '04. Der heutige Stand der pflänzlichen Zellforschung: *B. d. deutsch. Bot. Ges.,* XXI, 1.

Küster, E., '13. Zelle und Zellteilung (Botanisch): *H. Nw., Fischer, Jena.*

Leydig, Fr., '54. Lehrbuch der Histologie des Menschen und der Thiere: *Frankfurt.*

Lillie, R. S., '13. The Physiology of Cell-division, V: *J. E. Z.,* XV.
'14. The general physico-chemical Conditions of Stimulation in living Organisms: *P. S. M.,* June.

Lundegårdh, H., '12. Fixierung, Färbung und Nomenklatur der Kernstrukturen: *A. M. A.*

Maurer, F., '15. Grundzüge der vergleichenden Gewebelehre: *Reineke, Leipzig.*

Meves, Fr., '17. Historisch-kritische Untersuchungen über die Plastosomen der Pflanzenzellen: *A. M. A.,* LXXXIX, I.
'18ª. Die Plastosomentheorie der Vererbung: *A. M. A.,* XCII.

Meyer, A., '20. Morphologische und Physiologische Analyse der Zelle: *Jena.*

Montgomery, T. H., '98ᵇ. Comparative Cytological Studies, with especial reference to the Morphology of the Nucleolus: *J. M.,* XV.: 2.

Mottier, D. M., '21. On certain Plastids, etc., *A. B.,* XXV.

Prenant, Bouin, Maillard, '04. Traité d'histologie. I Cytologie générale et speciale: *Paris.*

Retzius, G., '14. Was sind die Plastosomen?: *A. M. A.,* LXXXIV.

Rohde, E., '14. Zelle und Gewebe in neuem Licht: *Vortr. u. Aufs. über Entwick-Mech.,* H., 20.

Schafer, E. A., '12. Textbook of Microscopic Anatomy: *London, Longmans Green & Co.*

Schaffer, J., '20. Vorlesungen über Histologie und Histogenese: *Leipzig.*

Schimper, A. F. W.,' 85. Untersuchungen über die Chlorophyllkörper, etc.: *Z. W. B.,* XVI.

Schmidt, E. W., '12. Pflänzliche Mitochondrien: *P. R. B.,* IV.

Schneider, K. C., '02. Lehrbuch der vergleichenden Histologie der Tiere: *Jena.*

Sharp, L. W., '21. An Introduction to Cytology: *McGraw-Hill, New York.*

Strasburger, '98. Die Pflänzlichen Zellhäute: *J. W. B.,* XXXI.

Strasburger, E., '03. Text-book of Botany (Strasburger, Noll, Schenk, and Schimper). 2nd Eng. Edition from 5th German Edition.

Verworn, M., '13, '15. Zellphysiologie: *H. Nw., X., Fischer, Jena.*

Walker and **Tozer, '09.** History and Functions of the Nucleoli, etc.: *Q. J. Exp. Phys.,* II.

Wilson, E. B., '99. On Protoplasmic Structure, etc.: *J. M.,* XV. suppl.
'23. The Physical Basis of Life: *Sci.,* LVII, 1471.

CHAPTER II

CELL–DIVISION

"Where a cell exists there must have been a preëxisting cell, just as the animal arises only from an animal and the plant only from a plant. The principle is thus established, even though the strict proof has not yet been produced for every detail, that throughout the whole series of living forms, whether entire animal or plant organisms, or their component parts, there rules an eternal law of *continuous development*."

VIRCHOW.[1]

It is now sixty years since Virchow first adequately stated the principle of genetic continuity of cells by division, which was destined to form the rallying point for all future conceptions of heredity and development. Only a minute fraction of the vast field of cytology and embryology had then been examined, and Virchow's celebrated aphorism *omnis cellula e cellula* [2] was too far in advance of his time to appear in its true proportions. As years passed, it gradually became evident that this terse phrase embodies one of the most important generalizations of modern science. The advance of cytological research still continues day by day to add fresh weight to the demonstration that cells have no other mode of origin than by the division of preëxisting cells. [3] In this respect a fundamental likeness exists between unicellular organisms, the tissue-cells of higher plants and animals, and the germ-cells from which the higher organisms take their origin. Upon cell-division, therefore, depends not alone heredity but the very continuity of life.

The division of cells was probably first seen in the segmentation of the animal egg (Prévost and Dumas, 1824), and soon afterwards in the lower plants by several botanists; [4] but its significance was not fully recognized until after the promulgation of the cell-theory, as a result especially of the work of Kölliker, Remak and Virchow. During the first two decades following Schleiden and Schwann these observers, together with the botanists Mohl, Nägeli and others, were accumulating the proof that cells arise only by the division of preëxisting cells and that the authors of the cell-theory fell into error when they accepted the independent origin of cells

[1] *Cellularpathologie*, p. 25, 1858.
[2] *Cf*. Introduction, p. 11.
[3] Division may be equal (fission), unequal (gemmation or budding) or endogenous (usually multiple).
[4] Brogniart, Meyen, Mirbel, Mohl, 1827–1835.

out of a formative blastema.[1]   The mechanism of cell-division was not precisely investigated until long afterward, but Remak and Kölliker showed that the process involves a division of both the nucleus and the cytosome. Remak believed it to be of simple type (Fig. 44) and to proceed from the center outwards, the nucleolus dividing first, next the nucleus and finally the cytosome ("Remak's scheme"); and this was for a time widely accepted, though on wholly insufficient grounds. In the meantime, however, observations were accumulating to show that cell-division is by no means so simple an operation as this.

Among both plants and animals many cases were found, prior to the seventies, in which the nucleus was lost to view at the onset of cell-division while at the same

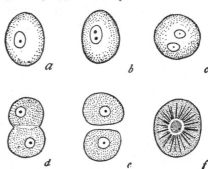

Fig. 44.—Direct division of blood-cells in the embryo chick, illustrating Remak's scheme (RE-MAK).

a–e, successive stages of division; *f*, cell dividing by mitosis.

time star-shaped radiations (asters) were often observed in the protoplasm.[2]   These observations, first made especially upon the polar divisions and early cleavages in living animal eggs, led to the conclusion that the nucleus actually disappears at this time by a process of "karyolysis" (Auerbach), to be subsequently formed *de novo* in the daughter-cells; and this was for a short time held even by such observers as Kölliker, Bütschli, Fol, Strasburger and Van Beneden.   As soon as the phenomena were examined by means of fixing and staining reagents (acetic and osmic acids, carmine), it was found that the seeming disappearance of the nucleus is illusory, being only the result of a profound transformation of its substance; and that this process, together with the appearance of astral radiations in the cytosome, belong to a mode of nuclear division far more complicated than Remak's traditional scheme.   In the end it became evident that nuclear division is of two widely different types, which came to be known as *direct* and *indirect* (Flemming, '79).   In the direct and simpler type the

[1] See Introduction, p. 9. For an early historical review of this period see Remak's *Untersuchungen ueber die Entwicklung der Wirbelthiere*, 1855, pp. 164–180. For later reviews see Tyson on the *Cell Doctrine* ('78), Sachs' *Geschichte der Botanik* ('90), Heidenhain's *Plasma und Zelle* (1907) and O. Hertwig's *Generelle Biologie*, 5th ed. ('20). As Heidenhain points out, Kölliker in his celebrated work, *Entwicklungsgeschichte der Cephalopoden* (1844), stated the essential doctrine expressed by Virchow in the phrase *omnis cellula e cellula*.

[2] Such radiations were figured by Remak himself (Fig. 44) and described or figured by other early observers, including von Baer, Virchow, Derbés, and Kowalewsky. They were first carefully studied by Fol ('73–'76) in the eggs of medusæ, and mollusks, and by Auerbach ('74) in those of nematodes.

nucleus, like the cell-body, undergoes a simple mass-division into two parts. In the indirect and more complex type, the nucleus is not destroyed, but is spun out into long threads which *split lengthwise* so that every portion is exactly divided between the daughter-nuclei. Before the separation of their longitudinal halves these threads shorten, and thicken to form more condensed bodies known as *chromosomes* (so named by Waldeyer because of their intense staining-capacity). The products of their fission (daughter-chromosomes) separate, and pass to opposite poles; and from the two groups of daughter-chromosomes are rebuilt two corresponding daughter-nuclei which by reason of the preceding processes are exact duplicates of each other and of the mother-nucleus. In this operation we now recognize one of the most fundamental mechanisms of heredity (p. 667).

By Schleicher (1878) this process was called *karyokinesis*, a term still widely employed for cell-division of this type. Flemming (1882) proposed the more appropriate term *mitosis*, in allusion to the characteristic thread-formation, while the direct mode of division was called *amitosis;* and this usage gradually became firmly established.[1] Strictly speaking, all these terms refer to division of the nucleus, but by an extension of meaning they are often applied to cell-division as a whole. It is often convenient to employ the term *cytokinesis* (Whitman, 1887) to designate the associated changes taking place in the cytoplasmic cell-body, though in practice it is sometimes difficult to draw any definite line of distinction between the nuclear and the cytoplasmic activities, *e. g.*, in the formation of the spindle. Cytokinesis includes not only the division of the cytosome as a whole but also the orderly distribution of smaller elements within it, such as the chondriosomes or the Golgi-bodies; and these processes have received corresponding names (*chondriokinesis, dictyokinesis*). The processes of cell-division as a whole may therefore be conveniently, if not quite logically, grouped as follows:

I. *Mitosis* (indirect division).
   1. *Karyokinesis* (the nuclear transformation).
   2. *Cytokinesis* (the cytoplasmic changes).
     a. Cleavage or Division of the Cytosome.
     b. Meristic division or distribution. Chondriokinesis (chondriosomes), *dictyokinesis* (Golgi-bodies), etc.
II. *Amitosis.*

Amitotic division was regarded by Remak and his immediate followers as the typical mode. Modern research has, however, demonstrated that it is a relatively rare and secondary process, often unaccompanied by division of

---

[1] Other terms are *karyodieresis, cytodieresis* (Henneguy), *kinesis*, and *akinesis* (Fol, Carnoy), but these are less generally used.

the cell-body, and especially frequent in highly specialized cells, or such as are in the early stages of degeneration; for instance, in glandular epithelia or in the cells of transitory embryonic envelopes. Some writers have maintained that nuclei which once have thus divided have undergone a fatal derangement that renders them incapable of long-continued multiplication, but this view can only be maintained in a qualified sense (p. 222). In any case it is a fact that in all the higher and in many of the lower forms of life mitosis is the usual and typical mode. We may therefore justly regard it as the basic phenomenon that underlies Virchow's "eternal law of continuous development."

I. GENERAL OUTLINE OF MITOSIS

In the course of mitotic division the nucleus usually disappears from view as an individualized body, while in its place appears a complicated structure known as the *mitotic* or *karyokinetic* figure, or, more simply, the *division-figure*. We may distinguish in this structure (Figs. 46, 49, etc.) a *chromatic* and an *achromatic figure*, of which the former is derived solely from the nucleus, the latter often from both nucleus and cytoplasm. The chromatic figure consists of the *chromosomes*, which are most often rod-shaped or V-shaped bodies, originally threads, formed by a transformation of the network of the vegetative nucleus, and staining with great intensity in the "nuclear" or basic dyes. The most constant feature of the achromatic figure as seen in sections is a fibrillar *spindle*, around or in which lie the chromosomes, while in a large class of cases at or near each of its poles is a central body, often double, surrounded by a star-shaped *aster*. When such asters are present the achromatic figure is called an *amphiaster*. This structure is colored only slightly by nuclear dyes and shows on the whole the staining qualities of the cytoplasm. In all higher plants and animals the formation and division of the chromosomes seem to take place essentially in the same way. In the Protista, on the other hand, exist various simpler types of mitosis in some of which it is questionable whether chromosomes are formed in the same sense as in higher forms (p. 210).

In respect to the achromatic figure, two general types may be distinguished, the *amphiastral* and the *anastral*. In the former true asters are present at the spindle-poles, characterized by their definite and sharply focussed astral rays and by the presence of well-marked central bodies at their foci (Fig. 49). Such amphiasters are typical of the mitoses of higher animals generally (though there are some exceptions), are of common occurrence among the thallophytes (Fig. 84), and are found in some Protista (Figs. 85, 90). In the anastral type (Fig. 65, etc.) true asters are wanting and often central bodies also. In many of these forms, it is true, fibrillæ radiate in more or less irregular fashion from the spindle-poles;[1] but they are not sharply focussed at the spindle-poles, nor are definite central bodies present. Anastral spindles are characteristic of the vegetative mitoses in higher plants

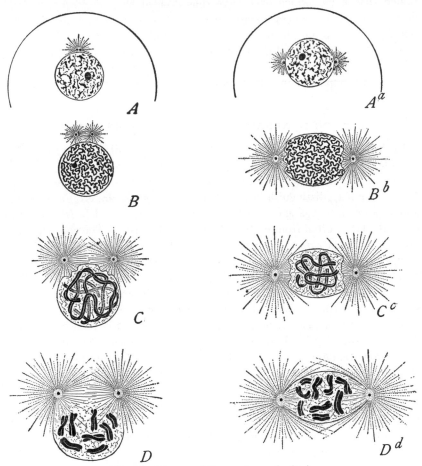

Fig. 45.—Diagram of the prophases of mitosis.

A–D, "Type A," (*Ascaris*); A^a–D^d, Type B (sea-urchin).

A, vegetative nucleus; B, fine spireme; C, coarse spireme; D, late prophase with chromosomes, spindles forming.

(cormophytes) generally, and occur also in the maturation-mitoses of certain animal ova and in many Protista. It now seems nearly certain that in the higher forms the absence of asters has resulted from a secondary sim-

---

[1] An excellent photograph of such a case is given by Timberlake ('oo, Fig. 2), from a dividing pollen-mother-cell of the larch, *Larix*, in which the equatorial crossing of the rays is clearly shown.

plification of the mitotic apparatus. In Protista, on the other hand, many of the anastral forms may represent a primitive condition (p. 213).

Both spindle and asters as seen in sections ordinarily show a beautiful fibrillar structure, consisting of delicate and closely crowded filaments which radiate from the spindle-poles, the astral rays spreading in all directions as they thread their way through the proto-plasmic meshwork, and finally branching out in it to lose themselves insensibly. The central body, at the center of the aster (and hence near the pole of the spindle) varies greatly in structure in different kinds of cells and at different stages of development. In its simplest form it is a very minute, intensely staining *centriole*, which is frequently double; and surrounding this may often be distinguished a larger *centrosome* (also called the *centrosphere* or *periplast*), from which the astral rays proceed. When the asters are absent (as in higher plants) centrioles and centrosomes, according to most observers, are also absent. The relations between centriole and centrosome have been the subject of controversy, and both these terms have become somewhat ambiguous. We shall find it convenient to employ the more vague term *central body* (which is historically the older) or *division-center*, without prejudicing the question as to its exact homology in any particular case.[1]

The chromosomes undergo their final division at the equator of the spindle, the daughter-chromosomes then separating and proceeding in opposite directions along the spindle nearly or quite to the

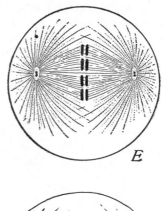

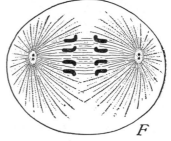

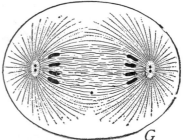

Fig. 46.—Diagram of the middle phases of mitosis.

E, metaphase; *F, G,* earlier and later anaphases.

poles where each daughter-group of chromosomes gives rise by a complicated process of "reconstruction" to a new nucleus. While this latter process is

[1] See p. 672.

going on the whole cell divides through the equatorial plane of the spindle, so that each daughter-cell contains a daughter-nucleus. At the close of the process the spindle usually disappears and often also the aster; but the central body (centriole), now usually divided into two, frequently persists in the vegetative cell (p. 29), and the same is sometimes the case with the remains of the spindle ("spindle-remnant" or *mitosome*).

Though every detail of mitosis varies more or less widely in different

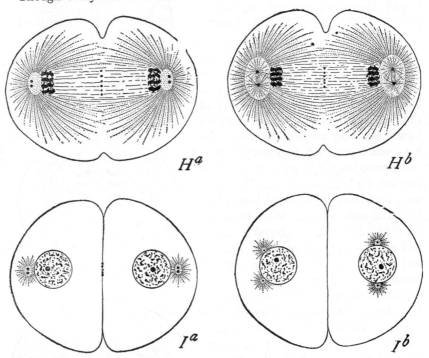

Fig. **47.**—Diagram of closing phases of mitosis. H^a and I^a, "Type A"; H^b and I^b, "Type B"; I^b showing two slightly different conditions in the interphase.

forms of cells the process always displays a typical succession of general phases or stages, as follows: [1]

(1) The *prophases*, in which the mitotic figure is formed and the chromosomes become longitudinally split (Figs. 45, 48, etc.).

(2) The *metaphase*, in which the longitudinally divided chromosomes take up a position in the equatorial plane of the spindle to constitute the equatorial plate or metaphase-group. In some cases they lie around the periphery of the spindle, in others within its substance (Figs. 46, 49).

[1] These terms were proposed by Strasburger. 1884

(3) The *anaphases*, in which the daughter-halves of each longitudinally split chromosome separate, thus giving rise to two sister-groups which pass to opposite poles of the spindle (Figs. 46, 58).

To these terms may be added a fourth, due to Heidenhain (1894), namely,

(4) The *telophases*, in which the daughter-nuclei are reconstructed from the two groups of daughter-chromosomes, and division of the cell-body takes place (Figs. 47, 50). Mitotic nuclear division is, however, not always followed by cell-division. The nucleus may divide, even many times, without cleavage of the cytosome, thus giving rise to multinucleate cells (syncytia or plasmodia). This is of comparatively rare occurrence in higher organisms, though common in lower ones.

The history of the chromatic figure and that of the achromatic are to a considerable extent experimentally separable; for example, a complete amphiaster may be formed in a mass of protoplasm deprived of a nucleus, and conversely a considerable part of the transformation of the nucleus may go forward without the formation of a spindle, possibly without the formation of asters (p. 168). For the purposes of a preliminary account, therefore, we may conveniently treat the history of the chromatic and the achromatic figures as if they were separate, though closely parallel processes. In such a preliminary description many critical questions must be passed over until the general outlines of the phenomena have been made clear.

II. KARYOKINESIS.   GENERAL HISTORY OF THE CHROMOSOMES

1. The Prophases

The essential feature of the early prophase is a gradual transformation of the nuclear framework into a thread or *spireme*, sometimes apparently continuous, more frequently segmented into separate pieces, which from an early period is longitudinally double, consisting of two exactly similar halves. The result of this process is remarkably constant throughout nearly all higher plants and animals, but its details vary considerably. In this respect there are two main types of spireme-formation in one of which the threads arise by a direct and gradual transformation of the nuclear framework, while in the other the process is preceded by a condensation of the framework into localized areas each of which resolves itself into a single thread. Even closely related forms, particularly among the higher plants, may differ markedly in this respect.[1] The first of these is exemplified by that classical object the epithelial cells of larval salamanders, which have been minutely examined by many observers (Fig. 52); and the same mode of spireme-formation appears in the presynaptic spireme of these

---

[1] See for instance Litardière ('21) on mitosis in ferns. Compare also the presynaptic spireme-formation in plants and animals, Chap. VI.

animals (p. 540) and has been described in many plants. In this case the nuclear framework becomes finer and more thread-like, becomes more basophilic and transforms itself into fine and closely convoluted threads which from an early period show here and there a longitudinal cleft and ultimately become longitudinally double.[1] (Fig. 53).

By the earlier observers the spireme was believed to be at first a single, continuous thread; and such in fact it appears to be in some cases, later segmenting transversely to form the separate chromosomes. Examples of this are offered by the somatic and meiotic prophases of *Carex* (Stout, '12) or by the spermatogonial prophases of *Ascaris* as described by Brauer (Fig. 53). In many cases, however, the chromosomes are undoubtedly separate from the very beginning of the spireme-formation. One of the best demonstrations of this is given by the cleavage-cells of *Ascaris* where, as was first described by Van Beneden and Boveri, the free ends of the separate spireme-threads may readily be detected, since they lie from the beginning in separate, pouch-like pockets of the nucleus (Figs. 416–418). A similar conclusion is indicated by many other facts which indicate that a continuous primary spireme is an exceptional occurrence and has only a secondary significance.

In the second type of spireme-formation the process begins by a drawing together of the nuclear framework into localized tracts or areas. At first these have an alveolar or net-like structure, and they may remain in this condition until the thread-formation.[2] The condensation may, however, proceed further, thus giving rise to more massive bodies or chromatin-blocks in which the net-like structure is hardly visible.[3] In such cases these bodies have often been called "prochromosomes" (p. 901). It was supposed by some earlier observers that these more massive bodies might in some cases be directly converted into the chromosomes, but it is now certain that in most cases each mass resolves itself into a fine, convoluted, zigzag or irregularly coiled thread which then unravels or uncoils (Figs. 421, 422) to form a single spireme-thread.[4] In case of the more solid, prochromosome-like bodies this process gives the aspect of a mere regrouping of the original substance,[5] and the coiled appearance is more striking. In case of the alveolized bodies the thread as

---

[1] The very early duality of the spireme-threads was first emphasized by Flemming and Strasburger (1882–1884). See p. 138.

[2] See Grégoire and Wygaerts, '03, '04, Grégoire, '06, Davis, '08, Sharp, '13, '20, Litardière, '21, Martens, '22, Overton '22, etc.

[3] Especially in the meiotic prophases of many animals (p. 538); but sometimes also in the somatic prophases, *e. g.*, in *Triton*, Janssens, '01.

[4] *Cf. merokinesis*, p. 895.

[5] See Janssens ('01), Bonnevie ('08–'11), Vejdovský ('11), Wilson ('12), etc. For the theoretical interest of these facts, see p. 899.

described by Grégoire, Sharp and Litardière is an irregular zigzag (Fig. 55) which is formed by the partial breaking down of the alveolar walls and

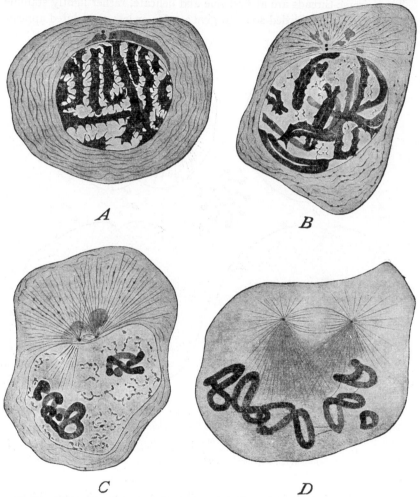

Fig. 48.—The prophases of mitosis (heterotypical form) in primary spermatocytes of *Salamandra* (MEVES).

A, early segmented spireme; two centrioles outside the nucleus in the remains of the sphere or idiozome; *B*, longitudinal doubling of the spireme, appearance of the astral rays, disintegration of the sphere; *C*, early amphiaster and central spindle; *D*, chromosomes in the form of rings, nuclear membrane disappeared, amphiaster enlarging, mantle-fibers developing.

coalescence of the vacuoles, while the remaining substance takes on the form of a continuous irregular thread. The two cases do not seem to differ in principle. In either case the result as usually described is a fine single thread, which usually retains for some time a more or less wavy course. In this type, the spireme seems always to be segmented from the beginning.

The spireme-threads are at first fine and delicate, rather lightly staining in basic dyes, and crowded so as to give a more or less convoluted appear-

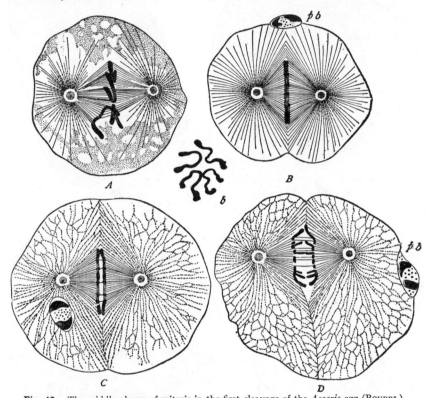

Fig. 49.—The middle phases of mitosis in the first cleavage of the *Ascaris* egg (Boveri.)

A, Closing prophase, the equatorial plate forming; *B*, metaphase; equatorial plate established; *b*, the equatorial plate, viewed *en face*, showing the four chromosomes; *C*, early anaphase; divergence of the daughter-chromosomes (polar body at one side); *D*, later anaphase; *p*, *b* second polar body.

ance, thus forming the *fine spireme*. The threads now shorten, thicken, assume a more open arrangement, and stain more intensely, thus forming the "open" or "coarse" spireme the threads of which are directly converted into the metaphase-chromosomes.

Neither the time at which the longitudinal duality of the spireme-threads appears nor its mode of origin have yet been certainly determined. Most observers have considered that the spireme-thread in the earliest prophases is longitudinally single and that it actually splits lengthwise at a slightly later stage, but both these conclusions are still a matter of dispute.   A large number of observers, beginning with Balbiani ('76) and Pfitzner ('81) have described the thread as containing a linear series of smaller bodies or *chromomeres* which divide by fission and thus initiate the splitting of the whole thread (p. 908). Others have considered the chromomeres as accidental or at least non-significant bodies;[1] but the most recent and accurate studies on the subject give very strong reason to reject such a view (p. 909).   By some observers the so-called splitting is regarded as comparable to the changes seen in the telophase (p. 133) and as arising through the appearance in the thread of a series of axial vacuoles which subsequently fuse.   The two

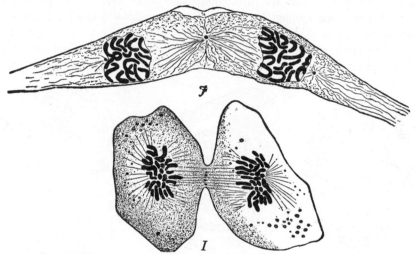

Fig. 50.—Final phases (telophases) of mitosis in salamander cells (FLEMMING).

I, epithelial cell from the lung; chromosomes at the poles of the spindle, the cell-body dividing; granules of the "mid-body" or *Zwischenkörper* at the equator of the disappearing spindle; *F*, connective tissue-cell (lung) immediately after division; daughter-nuclei reforming, mid-body a single granule in the middle of the remains of the spindle.

opposing conceptions are united by Müller ('12) who believes that the thread splits first between adjacent chromomeres (forming the "vacuoles"), the division of the chromomeres following (Fig. 54).[2]

A second group of observers believe the spireme-threads to be longitudinally double from their first appearance, and consider this condition as resulting from a doubling (by splitting or otherwise) that has occurred either during the vegetative stage of the nucleus or still earlier, during the preceding telophases or anaphases; to the writer, however, the evidence for

[1] See Grégoire and Wygaerts ('03), Grégoire ('06, '07), Mano ('04), Maréchal ('04, '07,) Stomps ('10), Lundegårdh ('12), Sharp ('13), etc.
[2] *Cf.* p. 99.

this seems insufficient (p. 139). During the middle prophases the longitudinal split often becomes obscured by close apposition of the longitudinal halves, but always comes clearly into view in the final stages. A noteworthy peculiarity of the spireme sometimes seen is a twisting of the longitudinal halves about each other to form a *strepsinema;* but this is much less common in the somatic mitoses than in meiosis (p. 544). After definite formation of the chromosomes the nuclear membrane usually disappears and the chromosomes, together with the remains of the linin network and enchylema, are set free in the protoplasm while the chromosomes take up their position in the equatorial plane of the spindle. In some cases the nuclear membrane persists throughout the whole process of mitosis, a condition common among the Protista, and sometimes occurring in higher forms.

Since a large part of the nuclear substance may enter into the formation of the spireme-thread, it seems certain that both oxychromatin (linin) and

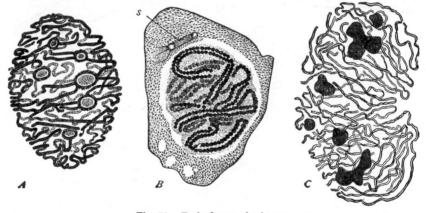

Fig. 51.—Early figures of spiremes.

A, from the endosperm of the lily, showing true nucleoli (FLEMMING); *B*, spermatocyte of salamander; segmented double spireme-thread (diplotene) composed of chromomeres; central bodies and central spindle at *s* (HERMANN); *C*, early spireme-thread completely split, with six nucleolar fragments. Endosperm of *Fritillaria* (FLEMMING).

basichromatin (if these be distinct substances) contribute to the chromosomes; and this is borne out by numerous observations showing that two corresponding substances may often be differentiated in the chromosomes (p. 896). In this respect, however, the chromosomes seem to differ widely in different species and at different periods. In many cases they appear quite homogeneous and intensely basichromatic; in others they seem to consist of a series of basichromatic chromomeres (Figs. 8, 427, 428) suspended in a more lightly staining or even oxychromatic linin or plastin;

in still other cases they have during the prophases a very loose texture and are but slightly basophilic, or even oxyphilic (*e. g.*, in the oöcyte-nucleus (p. 350). It seems certain also that in some cases a considerable part of the linin-network is converted into spindle-fibers or astral rays (p. 148).

2. The Metaphase

At full metaphase the chromosomes typically lie nearly in a single plane at the equator of the spindle, forming the so-called *equatorial plate* (Figs. 46E, 49). In some cases, of which the epidermal cells of larval sala-manders offer a classical example, they are arranged in ring-like fashion around the spindle; and this has very often been figured as the typical case. In point of fact this condition is exceptional; and in most cases the chromosomes actually lie in the spindle, the equatorial plate extending completely through it in the equatorial plane. At this time the chromo-somes are plainly double (or quickly become so), always placed with the division-plane lying in the equatorial plane and attached to the spindle-fibers in such a manner that the longitudinal halves of each chromosome are connected by one or more fibers with opposite spindle-poles (Figs. 49C, D). Their basophilic staining-capacity has now reached its climax; and in sections properly stained they are often the most conspicuous objects in the cell.

a. Forms and Arrangements of the Chromosomes. The metaphase-chro-mosomes show a great diversity of form in different species of plants and animals and often show marked individual differences of form and size in the same cell (Fig. 394). In a general way their number, size and form are characteristic of the species, though within a limited range variations occur. In part, their form is determined by their degree of condensation, which varies widely in different species, in part by their mode of attach-ment to the spindle, in part by other conditions. In many cases they still retain more or less the form of threads; in others they shorten and thicken to form short rods, sometimes even spheroidal bodies, in which all traces of the original thread-like condition have been lost. To a certain extent these conditions are characteristic of different groups; in arthropods, for example, they are commonly more rounded, in urodeles more thread-like. Nearly related groups may vary in this respect; among insects, for example, the chromosomes are in general more elongated in Orthoptera or Diptera (Figs. 396, 413), shorter and more rounded in Odonata, Coleoptera and Hemiptera (Figs. 354, 366). Many exceptions to this could, however, be mentioned.

In the case of thread-like or rod-shaped chromosomes their trans-verse diameter is on the whole fairly constant, and the size-differences which they may display are in the main due to differences of length; but

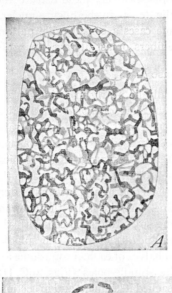
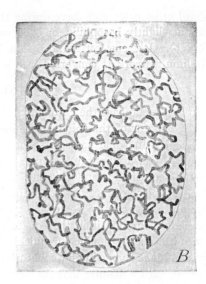

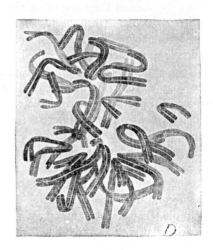

Fig. 52.—Prophases of mitosis in epithelial cells of the salamander accurately represented (HEIDENHAIN).

A, first stages of spireme-formation; *B*, fine spireme, duality here and there apparent; *C*, coarse, segmented spireme; *D*, chromosomes ready to go on the spindle, longitudinally split.

(In *A–C* the spireme-threads are still connected by fine "achromatic" bridges, not shown in the figure, so that the whole structure is still in a net-like condition though the spireme is evident.)

many exceptions to this are known (p. 834). When the size-differences are conspicuous the smaller chromosomes often tend to lie towards the center of the group (Fig. 394); but conspicuous exceptions to this exist. There is also a tendency for chromosomes of the same size to lie side-by-

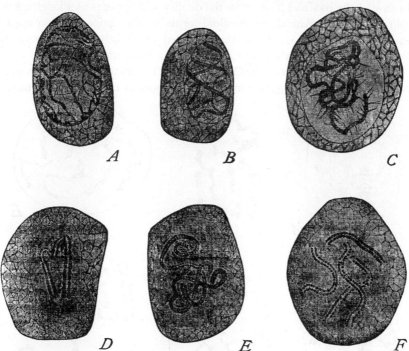

Fig. 53.—Formation of chromosomes and early splitting of the chromatin-granules in spermatogonia of *Ascaris megalocephala*, var. *bivalens* (BRAUER).

A, very early prophase; granules of the nuclear reticulum already divided; *B*, spireme; the continuous chromatin-thread split throughout; *C*, later spireme; *D*, shortening of the thread; *E*, spireme-thread divided into two parts; *F*, spireme-thread segmented into four split chromosomes.

side in pairs. A conspicuous example of this is offered in the Diptera, where all the chromosomes, as a rule, are plainly paired (Fig. 396). In most cases, however, the paired grouping is not clearly evident, or is demonstrably absent (p. 837).[1]

In respect to their form we may distinguish in the somatic mitoses three principal types of chromosomes, connected by various intermediate forms:

(1) Straight rods or threads, which arise directly by shortening of the spireme-threads.

(2) Loops, V's or hook-forms, derived from the rods by a flexure at the middle point or near one end.

[1] For the theoretical interest of these facts. see p. 575.

(3) Ovoidal or spheroidal forms, which arise by extreme shortening of the threads.[1]

All of these forms are double owing to the presence of a cleft or split that may be traced back to the original longitudinal split of the spireme-threads. In case of the rod- and loop-forms the duality still appears as a longitudinal split; but in the ovoidal or spheroidal forms, it often appears as an apparently transverse constriction (the so-called dumb-bell forms), owing to the great shortening which the chromosomes have undergone.

b. Spindle-Attachments of the Chromosomes. The metaphase-chromosomes, considered individually, show marked differences in respect to their modes

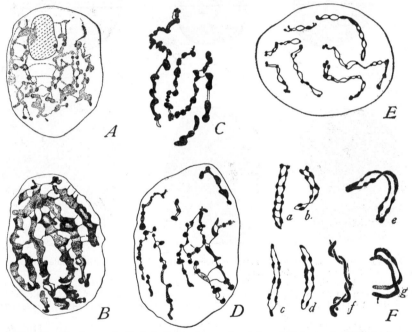

Fig. 54.—Prophases of mitosis in the meristem of root-tips of *Naias marina* (MÜLLER).

A, beginning of the band-like concentration of the nuclear framework; *B*, later stage; *C*, evolution of the chrommeres, *D*, early spireme; *E*, early stage of the splitting; *F*, later stages; *a–d*, fission of the chromomeres, *f–g* later stages, twisting of the halves.

of attachment to the spindle-fibers; and both their form and their history during the anaphases are profoundly influenced thereby. Recent studies have led to the remarkable conclusion that the mode of attachment is approximately constant for each particular chromosome and that it is inherited from generation to generation (p. 834). Attachment of the chro-

[1] In the maturation-mitoses occur many other forms, such as rings, crosses and tetrads, which will be considered in Chapter VI.

mosome to the spindle is commonly limited to a small area, and is of two general types, namely: (1) *terminal* or *telomitic* and (2) *non-terminal* or *atelomitic*, being in the former case at one end, and in the latter at some other point or points. Non-terminal attachment may be at the middle point (*median*) or at an intermediate point (*submedian, sub-terminal*). All gradations exist between these various cases; the attachment is sometimes not localized but extends along the whole length of the chromosome (*lateral* attachment). These various attachments show a very definite correlation with the form of the chromosomes (Fig. 56) sometimes evident in the prophases, commonly in the metaphase, and always in the anaphases; with terminal attachment the chromosome is rod-shaped; with median or sub-median usually V-shaped or loop-shaped; with sub-terminal hook-shaped or J-shaped. This correlation becomes more evident when we consider

3. The Anaphases

There is reason to conclude that the metaphase is a condition of relative stability in which the mitotic figure often remains for a considerable time. [1]

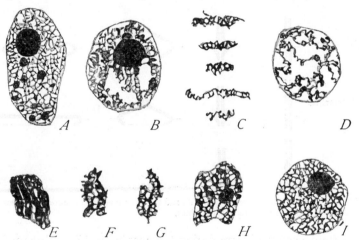

Fig. 55.—Prophases and telophases of mitosis, root-tips of the bean, *Vicia faba* (SHARP).

A, resting nucleus; *B*, early prophase; *C*, early prophase-chromosomes, unravelling of the spireme; *D*, early split spireme; *E*, *F*, telophases, vacuolization and branching; *G*, details of same; *H*, young nucleus.

The anaphases, on the other hand, are passed through rapidly and represent a phase of great activity, during which the daughter-halves of each chromosome move apart and proceed to opposite poles of the spindle. As they separate, their characteristic forms, in so far as they are correlated

[1] A striking example of this is offered in the polar mitoses of many eggs (p. 404).

with their modes of attachment, become more pronounced and often undergo very definite changes. All these appearances, as shown in the diagram (Fig. 56) are explained by the simple fact that whatever be the mode of attachment, the *daughter-chromosomes always begin to separate at the point of attachment* and move as if dragged towards the poles by traction of the spindle-fibers. In the simplest cases, shown by V-shaped chromosomes and by the lateral types of attachment, the chromosomes undergo

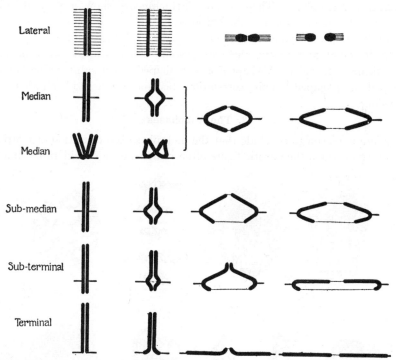

Fig. 56.—Types of chromosome-attachments and their results during the somatic mitoses. The spindle-fiber attachments indicated by fine lines.

no important change of form during the anaphases. The V-shaped chromosome, for example, is attached by its apex (median) and divides into two daughter-V's which move apart progressively from the apex towards the free ends, at which points they finally break apart. This condition is commonly seen in the anaphase-figures of growing root-tips of plants (Figs. 56, 57), or the epithelial cells of salamander-larvæ, both common demonstration-objects in the laboratory. Sometimes this appearance is modified by the approximation of the limbs of the daughter-V's until they have the appearance of double rods lying parallel to the spindle. The case is essentially the same with asymmetrical V's (sub-median attachment) or J-shaped chromosomes (sub-terminal) which differ from symmetrical V's only in the unequal length of the two limbs.

Rod-shaped chromosomes show more striking variations, since they may have any form of attachment. When this is median the daughter-rods are transformed during the early anaphases into V's because the middle point of each longitudinal half is drawn polewards while the ends still remain united (Figs. 56, 57). The double rod thus gives rise to a $\diamond$-shaped figure, which breaks apart into daughter V's exactly as in the case of chromosomes that are originally V-shaped. If attachment be sub-median or sub-terminal the daughter-chromosomes are correspondingly drawn out into unequal V's, J's, or hooks (Fig. 56).

With a terminal attachment the two halves of the rod first draw apart from the attached end to form Y-shaped or T-shaped figures and by a continuation of the process come to lie in a straight line along the spindle while still connected at one end. At this point, they finally break apart to form two daughter-rods, lying end to end and parallel to the axis of the spindle (Fig. 58). As seen during the early anaphase this mode of division might readily be mistaken for a transverse division of the rod; and for such it was in fact mistaken by some of the early observers before the importance of the mode of attachment had been recognized.

4. The Telophases

The preceding phases of mitosis are fundamentally important for a study of the mechanics of division. Those which now ensue are equally so for broader questions, including above all the individuality of the chromosomes and the theoretic interpretation of meiosis (pp. 561, 890).

a. Reconstruction of the Daughter-Nuclei. In the final anaphase the chromosomes, often closely crowded together, lie at the extreme end of the spindle (Fig. 50), and in some cases even pass beyond it so as to lie actually within the substance of the centroplasm (*i. e.*, inside the centrosome, Figs. 58, 322). Each daughter-group of chromosomes now gives rise to an ordinary nucleus by a process of "reconstruction"; and during the earlier part of this period the entire cell divides into two across the equator of the spindle. Three principal modes of nuclear reconstruction have been described, as follows:

The simplest and rarest type is by the formation of *chromosomal vesicles*, or *karyomeres*, a process long ago described by Bütschli and Fol in the blastomeres of segmenting eggs and since observed in embryonic cells of many species. In this process each chromosome is converted into a

small vesicle exactly like a minute nucleus, the whole group then fusing
together progressively so as to form first an irregular, chambered structure and finally a single nucleus (Figs. 58, 419). From the outer wall
of this, apparently, arises the nuclear membrane, while the inner walls
of the vesicles break down irregularly to form the nuclear network. The
nucleus thus formed is at first small, irregular in outline, and stains lightly.
It then rapidly enlarges, becomes spheroidal, and the staining capacity
of the network increases. A somewhat similar mode of reconstruction

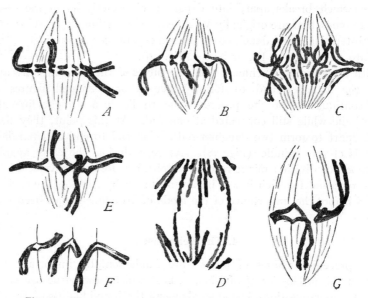

Fig. 57.—Chromosome attachments in mitosis in root-tips (Grégoire).
A–D, Galtonia, terminal attachments; *E, F, Allium,* terminal median, sub-median; *G, Trillium,*
sub-terminal, intermediate.

has been described by Sutton, McClung and many others in the spermatogonial divisions of the Orthoptera (Fig. 361). Both in this case and in
the cleavage of the ovum, where the divisions rapidly succeed one another,
the karyomeres sometimes fail to fuse or fuse but incompletely (Fig. 95),
thus giving rise to irregularly lobed "polymorphic nuclei," or nests of
more or less separate karyomeres, which might readily be mistaken for
stages of amitotic division.[1]

A second and more frequent mode of reconstruction, described in many
kinds of cells in both animals and plants, involves a twofold process including a branching of the chromosomes by which they give rise to an irregular

[1] See for instance, Beckwith, '14 (hydroids), Richards '17 (teleosts).

network, and also the development within them oi numerous vacuoles which enlarge, crowd together and finally seem to break down more or less so as to form an internal netlike structure. The nucleus thus becomes, in the phrase of Grégoire, a "network of networks," in which the boundaries of the original chromosomes can no longer be distinguished (Fig. 55). In the meantime

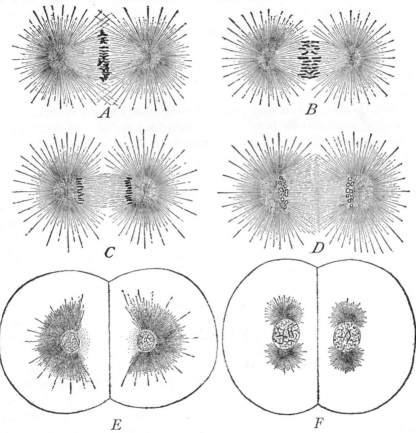

Fig. 58.—The later stages of mitosis in the egg of the sea-urchin, *Toxopneustes* (*A–D*, ✕1000; *E–F*, ✕500).

the nucleus becomes surrounded by a membrane the origin of which is difficult to determine precisely. By the earlier observers, the chromosome-group was believed to become surrounded by a "nuclear vacuole" containing karyolymph or enchylema and bounded by a membrane, formed from the cytoplasm. The nucleus would thus seem to have a double origin, the chromatin, linin and part of the enchylema being formed directly from the chromosomes, the membrane and the remaining portion of the enchylema from the surrounding cytoplasm. Strasburger and his followers were thus led to consider the nuclear membrane as essentially a cytoplasmic structure and to designate it as the "inner cell-wall." More recent studies, emphasizing the telophasic vacuolization of the chromosomes, indicate that the membrane is formed by the outer walls of vacuoles that appear in the peripheral regions of the chromosomes, or outside them; and it thus becomes a difficult question whether the membrane is formed from the surrounding cytoplasm, or from the periphery of the chromosomes, as appears to be the case in the first type of reconstruction. Perhaps both processes may take place, as often seems to be the case with the formation of spindle-fibers (p. 148).

Both the telophasic branching and the vacuolization were recognized by the early observers; for instance, Van Beneden ('83–'84, '87) described a sponge-like vacuolization of the chromosomes in *Ascaris*, while the branching was emphasized by many observers, including especially Rabl ('89) and Boveri ('87, etc.), who built on this basis the hypothesis of the individuality and genetic continuity of the chromosomes. "In the objects which I have studied . . . (these phenomena) . . . seem to me to admit of no other interpretation than that the daughter-chromosomes pass over into a network by sending forth branches; and that each new chromosome arises through the contraction of a particular region of this network. A highly important corollary to this is given by the evidence afforded by various forms of nuclei that each region of the network derived from a chromosome draws together again to form a chromosome again" (Boveri, '07, p. 232). The vacuolization has been emphasized by Grégoire and his followers, and has recently been studied with especial care by Sharp in seed-plants, by Litardière, in ferns, and by other observers.[1]

A third type of reconstruction, described by a few observers is by the formation of a *chromonema*,[2] a delicately coiled, convoluted or zigzag thread formed within the late anaphase- or telophase-chromosomes, which is said to uncoil or unravel and branch to form the reticulum; but this appearance, as described especially by Bonnevie in *Ascaris*, *Amphiuma*, and *Allium* and by Vejdovský in *Ascaris* and in certain Orthoptera (Fig. 59) has been variously interpreted. According to Vejdovský the chromonema lies in an achromatic basis by the swelling and liquefaction of which arises the enchy-

[1] See Grégoire and Wygaerts ('03), Kowalski ('04), Berghs ('04), Grégoire ('06), etc., De Smet ('14), Sharp ('13, '20), Litardière ('21). Some observers have found the vacuoles appearing already in the anaphases (Merriman, '04, Nemec, '10, Lundegårdh, '10, 12b) or even in the metaphase (Grégoire and Wygaerts, '03). Most of these observers have accepted the telophasic branching of the chromosomes; but this is questioned by Overton ('22).

[2] Bonnevie ('08, '11), Schneider ('10), Dehorne ('11), Vejdovský ('12), Brunelli ('10, '14), Bolles Lee ('11), Martens ('22).

lema or nuclear sap, while the nuclear membrane is formed from its periphery and the nuclear framework from the chromonema itself.[1] Most recent observers, especially among botanists [2] have failed to find evidence of a definite spiral in the telophase-chromosomes and have considered the so-

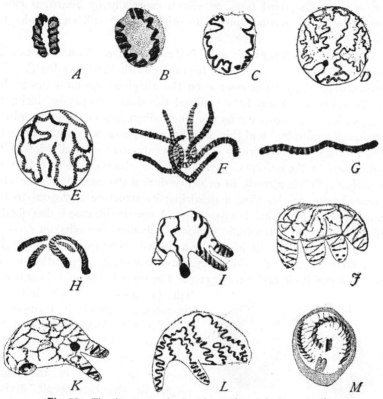

Fig. 59.—The chromonema in *Ascaris megalocephala* (VEJDOVSKÝ).

A, B, chromosomes from early gamete-nuclei; *C, D,* uncoiling of the thread; *E,* formation of new chromonema within the thread; *F,* late prophase-chromosomes; *G,* metaphase-chromosome; *H,* anaphase-chromosome with chromonema; *I,* telophase; *J,* "resting" stage; *K, L,* prophases; *M,* supposed spiral structure of bivalent chromosomes in prophase of spermatocyte-division in the grasshopper *Decticus.*

called chromonema as an illusion due to the vacuolization of elongate telophase-chromosomes which causes the more solid portions to appear as an irregular spiral or zigzag. The author's observations, especially on the spermatogonial divisions of Orthoptera, point to the same conclusion, although in these same cells (*Phrynotettix*, etc.) the contorted spiriform *prophase*-chromonema is very clearly seen (Wilson, '12).

[1] See p. 896.   [2] See especially the works of Grégoire, Sharp and Litardière.

The foregoing types of reconstruction, different in aspect as they are, are closely related. The first or karyomere type represents an extreme form of vacuolization with little or no branching, the second type a vacuolization of different character and complicated by the branching of the chromosomes. The third type, as shown especially by Sharp, is closely connected with the second, but in its original form still awaits adequate confirmation.

  b. *The so-called Anaphasic or Telophasic Duality*. As above stated, a considerable number of observers, beginning with Van Beneden ('83–'84) have described the telophase- or even the anaphase-chromosomes as longitudinally double. Many have believed this duality to persist during the resting-nuclei and to reappear as the longitudinal split of the early spireme in the ensuing mitosis; [1] and this conception has even been applied to some of the Protozoa in an effort to explain the apparent cross-division of the chromosomes in these forms (p. 212). Some observers believe that the anaphasic "split" is already in evidence during the metaphase, the chromosomes having at this time a quadripartite structure analogous to that seen in the heterotypic division (p. 509).[2] A remarkable case is described by Taylor ('22) in the heterotypic division (pollen-mother-cells) of *Gasteria*. As is the rule with this division, the anaphasic chromosomes are longitudinally double here, with widely separated halves, in preparation for the following homeotypic division (p. 519). The remarkable point is that each half-chromosome (or at least the chromomeres which it contains) is itself at first longitudinally double and later (early telophase) longitudinally quadripartite. This may possibly mean that in the closing phases of the heterotypic division preparation has already been made, not alone for the succeeding homeotypic division but also for an additional division, which later takes place in the pollen-grain (p. 496). This latter conclusion, however, has not yet been demonstrated.

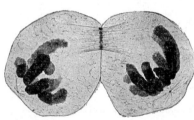

Fig. 60.—Telokinesis in spermatogonial division of the grasshopper *Rhomaleum*.

  On the other hand, a considerable group of observers have considered the so-called telophasic split as an illusion due to the vacuolization of the

---

[1] See Hof ('98), Farmer and Shove ('05), Bonnevie ('08, etc.), Meves ('07), Lundegårdh ('10, '12), Digby ('10, '14, '19), Farmer and Digby ('10), Brunelli ('10), Granier and Boule ('11), Frazer and Snell ('11), Bolles Lee ('11), Schneider ('10), Dehorne ('11), Frazer ('14), Schüstow ('13), Reed ('14), etc.
[2] Merriman ('04), Nawaschin ('10), in the root-tips of plants, Bonnevie ('08) in the eggs of *Ascaris*. See also Sands ('22).

chromosomes at this time.[1] Some advocates of the telophasic split (Lunde-gårdh, Schüstow, Frazer and Snell, etc.) endeavored to reconcile the contra-diction by assuming the telophasic vacuolization to result in a complete longitudinal division, as described by other observers in the prophasic splitting (p. 125). This, however, has been contradicted by some of the most careful recent studies both of the telophases and the prophases, which seem clearly to demonstrate that the telophasic vacuoles are often not in an axial series but quite irregularly disposed (Sharp), and that the pro-phase-threads are not double but single and subsequently split lengthwise.[2] The work of Sharp, Kuwada and Litardière shows clearly that in the prophases of various plants the fine prophase-spireme is formed from al-veolized bands very similar to the alveolized telophase-chromosomes; and that by the confluence of the vacuoles and partial breaking down of their walls arises a single irregular zigzag thread, which later splits length-wise. This is in accordance with many other observations on the formation of the prophase-spirals in animal mitoses referred to above.

Martens ('22) in a study of *Paris,* has endeavored to harmonize the con-flicting interpretations by the conclusion that the anaphasic and telophasic duality, though real, is not the forerunner of the future prophasic split This observer describes an anaphasic and telophasic chromonema, similar in principle to that of Bonnevie and Vejdovský but less regular, the sub-stance of which is said to concentrate at the periphery and thus produce a transitory appearance of duality, which, however, later disappears (Fig. 420). In the prophases the chromonema reappears as a single zigzag thread, as described by other observers; but this is asserted *not to split lengthwise* but again to concentrate on both sides of the chromosome until the latter becomes longitudinally double. This account confirms the ac-counts of those who consider the prophasic split to arise already in the preceding anaphases, but also contradicts observers who, like Sharp, Li-tardière, the writer and others, believe the prophase chromonema to split lengthwise. The contradictions here arising must await further study.[3]

c. Telokinesis. Under this name Heidenhain ('94) characterized certain movements of the mitotic figure, or its remains, that often take place during the later telophases soon after cleavage of the cytosome, and may conven-iently be considered here, though they affect particularly the cytoplasmic el-ements. They involve two principal events, both of which seem to vary widely in different kinds of cells and apparently may fail to take place in

---

[1] This point is urged by Grégoire, Lundegårdh ('10, 12), Sharp ('13, '20), de Smet ('14), Sakamura ('14), and others, more recently by Litardière ('21), and by Kuwada ('21) whose observations were made in my laboratory. My own observations on Orthoptera indicate the same conclusion.

[2] See especially Wilson, '12, Sharp, '13, Litardière, '21, Kuwada, '21.

[3] *Cf.* p. 896.

some cases. One is a rotation of the daughter-chromosome-groups towards
one side of the spindle accompanied by a corresponding movement of the
centers and often also by a more or less pronounced bending of the spindle
at its middle point (Fig. 60). In extreme cases the spindle is thus flexed almost into the form of a V or U and the nuclear axes form a more or less
wide angle with one another or may even become nearly parallel. In the
latter case the nuclei have rotated through nearly 90°, and the central bodies,

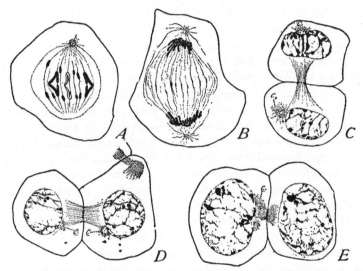

Fig. 61.—Telokinetic movements of the centers in the spermatogonia of the beetle *Blaps*
(Nonidez).
  A, metaphase; *B*, late anaphase; *C*, late telophase; *D, E*, still later stages, telokinetic movement
completed.

originally at opposite sides of the nuclei, have come to lie nearly side by
side. In their more pronounced forms these processes are often well seen in
the cleavage of the ovum (Fig. 62), and also in the early spermatids prior to
the differentiation of the sperm. In both these cases, further, the nuclei
often separate more or less from the spindle so as to lie beside it instead of
at its ends (Fig. 167).

   Secondly, the centrioles often perform at this time certain definite movements by which their original relation to the nucleus is greatly changed.
One is a separation of the two halves of each centriole (each of which becomes double during the metaphase or anaphase) and their migration to
opposite poles of the nucleus 90° away from their original position (Figs.
322, 327). This is clearly a preparation for the next division following
and might appropriately be reckoned as a prophasic event. In another

type of telokinetic movement, both centrioles, still closely associated, migrate around the periphery of the nucleus until they may come to lie at a position on the spindle side of the nucleus (instead of opposite to it) and nearly 180° away from their original position (Figs. 61, 278). The meaning of this remarkable process is quite unknown.

5. History of the Nucleoli

The history of the nucleoli in mitosis, as in the vegetative or interphasic nucleus, still involves many obscure points. In the prophases the chromatin-nucleoli undoubtedly contribute directly, in one way or another, to the formation of the chromosomes. The smaller net-knots seem to be drawn directly into the spireme-threads; larger blocks, in the form of pro-chromosomes or the like (p. 899) may be resolved into contorted or coiled threads which then unravel or uncoil to form spireme-threads (Fig. 421). The chromosome-nucleoli, characteristic of the auxocytes (though sometimes found in other cells), are usually likewise drawn out more or less before their longitudinal fission though in some cases this is but slight (p. 761). Karyospheres differentiate into a closely crowded group of basichromatic chromosomes, often imbedded in a more lightly staining or oxychromatic matrix from which the chromosomes break away or escape into the nuclear cavity (Fig. 37). The matrix may thus be left behind in the form of a plasmosome, while the chromosomes may undergo a considerable process of extension before condensing into their final form. A good example of this is offered by the spermatocytes of *Notonecta* (Browne, '13).

True nucleoli or plasmosomes are not known to make any direct morphological contribution to the chromosome-formation. They often persist with only slight change while the spireme forms and in the later stages rapidly diminish in size, fragment and disappear; but there are a few cases in which the plasmosome, or a considerable residue of it, is cast out bodily after completion of the mitotic figure. It is possible, nevertheless, as earlier indicated (p. 95), that these nucleoli may be storehouses of material that is given off in a soluble form and may play some part in the mitotic transformation. We may here again recall the possibility that in their basophilic condition these nucleoli may have stored up some substance, such as nucleic acid, that has been given off from the chromosomes (which have in consequence decreased in basophily) and is given back to them during their increase in basophily in the later prophases. This, however, is a mere conjecture.[1]

---

[1] The best examples of such changes are offered by the growing oöcytes (p. 354); others are seen in *Zygnema* according to Escoyez ('07) and van Wisselingh ('14) or in *Marsilia* according to Strasburger ('07) and Berghs ('09).

In the telophases the plasmosomes reappear, often very early, in the form of drop-like spheres which commonly flow together to form larger spheroids. Their exact source is still doubtful. Until recently most ob-

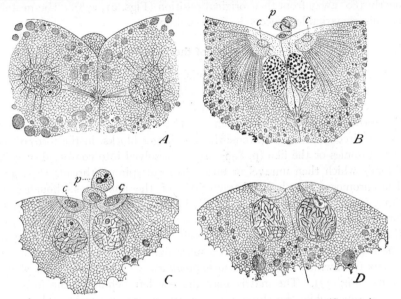

Fig. 62.—Telokinesis in the first cleavage of the gasteropod *Crepidula* (Conklin).

c, "centrosome"; *p*, polocytes; *s*, sphere-substance.

A, initial bending of the spindle; *B*, spindle bent into a *V*, nuclei almost in contact; centers above, near the surface; *C*, interphase, after disappearance of the spindle; *D*, early prophase of second cleavage, division of the daughter-centers and formation of the daughter-amphiasters.

servers have found them arising independently of the nuclear framework and apparently *de novo* (see, however, p. 911).

III. CYTOKINESIS. GENERAL HISTORY OF THE ACHROMATIC FIGURE

A. The Amphiastral Type

The amphiaster may be thought of as two astral systems which jointly give rise to the spindle that lies between them; and the spindle is perhaps comparable to a specially modified group of astral rays, but this is not entirely certain. The spindle is superficially similar to the spindle-shaped area found between the poles in the magnetic or electrostatic field, but it is more than doubtful whether the two cases are really analogous. As viewed in the living object the asters appear as radiating tracts of hyaloplasm, defined by a radial disposition of the alveolar spheres (macrosomes) and microsomes about the centers.   The spindle appears as merely a clear fusiform area between the asters, containing no alveolar spheres, and most commonly showing no trace of spindle-fibers.[1] The question is thus prominently raised as to whether the fibrillar structure of the amphiaster, as seen in sections, may not be a coagulation artifact; and, as has earlier been indicated, the experiments especially of Bütschli, Hardy and Fischer have in fact demonstrated that fine fibrillar aster-like and spindle-like structures (Fig. 24) may be produced by coagulating agents in artificial emulsions, or even in homogeneous colloidal solutions (p. 65).

As seen in sections both asters and spindle are in most cases undoubtedly composed of very distinct fibrillæ, those of the spindle often more sharply marked than astral rays.   Both sets of fibrillæ anastomose to some extent, but in well-fixed material this is as a rule hardly noticeable in the spindle until after the metaphase has been passed.   The astral rays are unbranched centrally but branch out distally into the protoplasmic framework and are lost to view, though often extending nearly to the periphery of the cell. In many cases the fibrillæ of both spindle and asters seem to consist of a homogeneous basis along which or in which are scattered microsomes; and some writers, for instance Van Beneden, have described the fibrillæ as actually built up as linear series of microsomes.

1. The Spindle

By the earlier observers, such as Van Beneden ('83, '87) and Boveri ('88) the metaphase-spindle was regarded as consisting of two cone-shaped, half-spindles placed base-to-base and separated by the equatorial plate of chromosomes.   Subsequently it became evident that, in many cases at least, the spindle consists of two kinds of fibers; and these have been supposed to differ widely in functional significance.   One of these includes *half-spindle* fibers, extending from the poles to the chromosomes, as just indicated; these, which are probably concerned in some manner with the movements of the chromosomes towards the poles, are called *traction-fibers*, or *chromosomal fibers*.   Secondly, the spindle contains *continuous fibers* which extend without interruption from pole to pole and sometimes constitute a *central spindle* about which the chromosomes are grouped in a ring, attached on either side to the traction-fibers, in this case called, because of their position, "mantle fibers" (Figs. 48, 247).   More frequently the two sets of fibers are mingled, and no central spindle can be distinguished. In such cases the chromosomes do not surround the spindle but lie in its substance.

[1] *E. g.*, in echinoderm eggs, Wilson, '99, '01. So-called spindle-fibers may sometimes be seen in the unfixed object (*e. g.*, in the spermatocyte-divisions of insects) but it is doubtful whether this may not be due to a sub-mortem change.

During the anaphases the two diverging groups of daughter-chromosomes are connected by a set of *connecting-fibers* or *interzonal-fibers* ("Verbin-dungsfasern," "filaments réunissants") which now form the equatorial region of the spindle (Figs. 46, 58). By the early observers these were believed to be spun out from the chromosomes as the latter drew apart, and hence to differ wholly in nature and origin from the true spindle-fibers; some recent observations seem to give this at least partial support. Many cytologists, however, have accepted the conclusion of Hermann ('91) that the connecting fibers are in the main identical with the continuous fibers which are exposed to view as the chromosomes draw apart. The interzonal region of the spindle is at first more or less convex in outline, but as the anaphases advance its boundaries become straighter and in the later anaphases and early telophase nearly parallel, while the connecting fibers become less crowded, more contorted, more granular in structure, and their anastomoses are more readily seen. In many cases they develop, during the early telophase, a series of deeply staining thickenings in the equatorial plane, forming the *cell-plate* or *mid-body*. This structure is conspicuous in the anastral forms of mitosis in the cells of higher plants, where it plays an important part in the division of the cell-body (p. 159). In the amphiastral types (animals generally) the mid-body is less developed and often rudimentary, being represented by only a few granules (Figs. 50, 60).

2. The Asters

The configuration of the astral formations, most conspicuously shown in embryonic cells, varies markedly in different phases of mitosis. In the very small asters of early stages, the rays are straight, simple and relatively few. With advancing development they rapidly elongate in all directions, increase in number, and in many cases those of the two asters intersect so as to *cross one another* at a decided angle in the equatorial region outside the spindle. This condition, of great interest for all general theories of mitosis (p. 186), is often seen in the metaphase or even earlier (Figs. 48, 205) and may persist until the late anaphase or even the early telophase. Sooner or later, however, the crossing of the rays disappears by a readjustment during which those from the two asters curve more and more towards one another and often seem to join in the equatorial plane so as to be continuous from pole to pole, even in the region outside the spindle. This condition is most perfectly seen in the living object during the early telophase just at the time when the cell-constriction appears, when the karykinetic field sometimes closely resembles the polarized mag-netic or electrostatic field, the astral rays and spindle fibers following a course nearly similar to that of the lines of force.   This configuration is, however, but temporary and is quickly lost as the constriction cuts through the spindle (Wilson, 'o1c).

The asters are typically equal, in which case the whole karyokinetic figure is perfectly symmetrical with respect to both chromatic and achromatic elements and cell-division is also equal.   The asters are, however, often unequal; and this is always accompanied by a correspondingly unequal division of the protoplasmic cell-body, *though the chromosomes divide equally as before.*   In some of these cases the asters only become unequal when the spindle takes up an eccentric position, thus diminishing the field of action of the more peripherally placed aster (*e. g.,* in the polar divisions of the egg, Figs. 183, 189).   In a few cases, however, the inequality seems to appear almost from the beginning and before the peripheral movement of the spindle occurs, as shown by Lillie ('12) in the first cleavage of the *Nereis egg* (Fig. 470).   In either case we find here additional evidence that the asters are directly concerned with division of the cytoplasmic cell-body (p. 175).

An exceptional feature of the asters is a very distinct spiral twisting of the rays.   Such spiral asters were first made known by Mark ('81) in case of the second polar spindles in the egg of the slug, *Limax;* and they have since been described in various other animals of widely separated groups, including echinoderms, nemertines, mollusks, annelids and vertebrates. Conklin ('02) ascribes the origin of spiral asters to vortical protoplasmic currents; and this is borne out by the more recent work of Painter [1] ('16), who concludes that the spiral asters probably are formed as a result of rotational shiftings of the aster subsequent to its formation in the typical manner.

3. The Central Bodies

The intricate questions involved in the relation between centriole, centrosome, aster and spindle, here indicated in only a general way, will be considered more critically at a later point (p. 672).   The centriole, always very minute and sometimes almost at the limit of microscopical vision, stains intensely with certain dyes (such as iron hæmatoxylin or crystal violet).   In the earliest stages of the asters it is most commonly single but sooner or later divides into two, a process which commonly takes place not later than the metaphase and sometimes even earlier (Figs. 322, 328).   In the very young aster the astral rays seem to be given off directly from the centriole.   Later the centriole is seen to be surrounded by a mass of *centroplasm* which usually forms a definite body generally known as the *centrosome* (Boveri) a term which has gradually displaced the earlier

---

[1] This author gives a good review of the literature of the subject.

terms "periplast" (Vejdovský), "attraction-sphere" (Van Beneden) and "centrosphere" (Strasburger).

This body varies greatly in structure in different kinds of cells and in different stages of development of the aster. In its most definite form (*e. g.*, as described by Boveri in *Ascaris*) it is a definite and homogeneous sphere from which the rays take their origin. In other cases, it is transversed by the astral rays, which may be traced into the centriole, as in *Thysanozoön* (Van der Stricht), *Unio* (Lillie) or *Nephelis* (Jörgensen). In such cases the centrosome seems to be merely the innermost zone of the aster, its boundary being formed as a rule by a circle of microsomes (Fig. 321); and this view of the centrosome is sustained by the fact that one or more additional concentric zones may sometimes be distinguished in the aster outside the inmost one.[1] In still other cases, illustrated by the segmenting eggs of *Thalassema* (Fig. 205), *Cerebratulus* (Fig. 322) or *Rhynchelmis* (Fig. 330) the centrosome or "centrosphere" is a larger and less sharply defined mass which is not traversed by the astral rays and shows a fine net-like or alveolar structure. Such centrosomes appear to arise by a breaking down of the inner region of the astral rays, a progressive process which in some cases leads to an enormous growth of the centrosome (Fig. 330). Such cases offer advantages for the study of the division of the centriole and the formation of the new amphiaster within it (p. 680).

4. Origin of the Amphiaster

In all cases the amphiaster is formed about the central bodies (centrioles) as foci; and in a large number of cases the latter undoubtedly arise by the division of a single original body. It is remarkable that division of the original centriole into two, which constitutes the initial step in mitosis, often takes place before completion of the preceding mitosis; the typical procedure, indeed, is its division *not later than the metaphase of the preceding mitosis* and sometimes much earlier.[2] In respect to the later stages we may distinguish two types as follows:

A. In one of these, well shown in the cleavage stages of *Ascaris* (Figs. 45, 48, 63), the formation of the new amphiaster is delayed until cell-division has been completed and the resting stage attained. In such cases the two centrioles, often surrounded by a centrosome or "attraction-sphere" and

---

[1] See p. 682.

[2] Striking examples of this are offered by the auxocytes of certain animals. In the primary spermatocytes of Lepidoptera and some other insects, for example, not only is the centriole double in the early prophases, but each half has already prepared for the second following mitosis by its double shape and structure. In prophases of the primary oöcytes of the snail *Arion* Lams ('10) found the centrioles already double and widely separated for the ensuing first polar mitosis, with each daughter-centriole also completely divided for the *second* polar mitosis.

sometimes by astral rays, continue to lie side by side during the vegetative phase of the daughter-cell.   The ensuing division is initiated by a progressive separation of the centrioles, accompanied by the development of a small aster about each and of a *primary spindle* between them (Figs. 48, 63).   As originally described by Van Beneden ('83, '87) and Boveri ('87, '07, etc.), this process takes place in the cytoplasm and the primary amphiaster is entirely extra-nuclear.   In such cases the whole structure, at least in its earlier

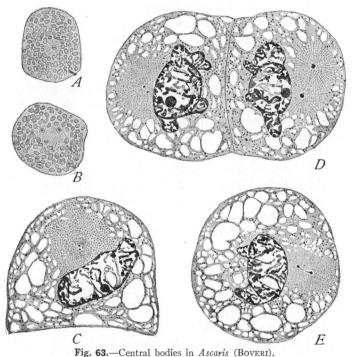

Fig. 63.—Central bodies in *Ascaris* (BOVERI).
A, B, early prophases of the spermatocytes; *C–E*, early prophases in 2-cell stage of cleavage.

stages, is undoubtedly of cytoplasmic origin.   The nature of the primary spindle is, however, a difficult question.   Heidenhain ('94) supposed it to arise from a specific substance surrounding the centrioles and forming between them a primary *centrodesmus*.   Others have supposed it to arise from the substance of the centrioles, or from hyaloplasm flowing centrifugally from the centers in the region between them (Bonnevie, '10).   Once formed the amphiaster rapidly enlarges by elongation of the spindle and extension of the astral rays; and at this time the crossing of the rays from the two astral systems in the equatorial plane outside the spindle is often conspicuously seen.

Where the outgrowing astral rays abut against the nuclear membrane the latter is often *pushed in or thrown into folds* (Fig. 239), a fact difficult to explain unless the rays are of considerable solidity and are actually growing. Sooner or later the wall of the nucleus liquefies and the astral rays grow actively into the interior, apparently by progressive differentiation out of the linin-network. The chromosomes are now quickly drawn upon the spindle, as if pulled into position by the action of the ingrowing astral rays with which they have come into attachment.

In this type of amphiaster-formation it seems clear: (1) that the fibers of the primary spindle may persist to form the continuous fibers of the definitive spindle; (2) that the chromosomal fibers, "traction-fibers," or half-spindle fibers likewise arise, in part at least, from astral rays that grow into the nucleus from outside; (3) that the primary spindle commonly persists as a *central spindle*, with the chromosomes lying in a ring about its equator, and with the half-spindle fibers, attached to the chromosomes, forming an investment of "mantle-fibers" on either side (p. 182).

In a second type the primary amphiaster arises at a much earlier period— already, indeed, during the anaphase or telophase of the preceding division. In such cases, common in the cleavage of the ovum (Figs. 47, 205, 322, 330), the centrioles separate and a new amphiaster forms at each pole of the spindle, inside the old centrosome and from its substance.[1] During this process the two centrioles usually move away from the original spindle-pole towards the periphery of the centrosome, now considerably enlarged, and may even pass outside it into the substance of the degenerating old aster. In the final telophase the two asters finally may pass to opposite poles of the reformed daughter-nucleus; and here the centrioles persist throughout the vegetative period of the cell. Meanwhile the primary spindle seems to disappear completely; though some observers have supposed that it may only have flattened out against the nuclear wall. The asters usually become much reduced or even disappear from view, but the centriole is usually surrounded by at least a portion of the centrosome, which forms the *sphere*.

During the ensuing prophases an aster redevelops about each centriole, the nuclear wall often being pushed in by the rays at each pole. At these two points the wall soon fades, and the ingrowing astral rays enter the nucleus, quickly invading the whole nuclear area and apparently growing at the expense of the linin-network. A new spindle is thus finally built up in

[1] *E. g.*, in *Salmo* (Henneguy, '91), *Thysanozoön* (Van der Stricht, '97), *Diaulula* (MacFarland, '97), *Thalassema* (Griffin '99), *Cerebratulus* (Coe, '99, Yatsu, '10), *Rhynchelmis* (Vejdovský and Mrazek, '03) or *Arion* (Lams, '10).

the nuclear area lying between the two centrioles, the chromosomes being from the first in intimate relation with it. In this case, accordingly, continuous fibers and half-spindle fibers are intermingled, and no central spindle can be distinguished as such. The two foregoing types, are connected by many intermediate gradations due to variations in the time of amphiaster-formation.

The inpushing of the nuclear membrane by the ingrowing astral rays, has been described in many different objects and by many observers who have found (*i. e.*, Van der Stricht, '95, Griffin, '99) that dissolution of the membrane begins at the points most deeply infolded. In certain cases the inpushing fibrillæ seem actually to compress the entire nucleus lying between the bases of the two astral cones and in such cases almost the entire spindle would seem to be of cytoplasmic origin (Vejdovský, '88, Vejdovský and Mrazek, '93). Other observers (Watase, '93) have concluded, on the other hand, that the nuclear wall is penetrated by the ingrowing rays, which then push the whole contents of the nucleus before them as they grow.

Among the many modifications of the foregoing types there are two of especial interest. The fact has earlier been mentioned (p. 29) that in certain cases the division-centers are intra-nuclear and at least the early stages of amphiaster-formation take place within the nucleus. Intra-nuclear centers are common among the Protozoa, though nearly all of these cases are of the anastral type (p. 204); in Metazoa they are of rare occurrence. In the spermatocytes of *Ascaris megalocephala univalens* the primary amphiaster is intra-nuclear, the central bodies only passing out into the protoplasm near the time of the metaphase (Fig. 323).[1] A somewhat similar case is described by Hegner ('08) in the oöcytes of the copepod, *Canthocamptus*. Again, in the oöcytes of the platode *Thysanzoön*, Schockært ('01) describes a remarkable intra-cellular division-center of elongate spindle-shape, which divides into two within the nucleus, the products passing to opposite poles of the germinal vesicle, shortening to a spheroidal form, and becoming the center of two conspicuous protoplasmic asters. These results, in general, are in agreement with earlier conclusions of Van der Stricht ('98) and are substantially confirmed by Kaltenbach ('15).[2] It is a surprising fact that an amphiaster may be formed synthetically by the secondary union or association of two asters or centers originally separate. Apparently no doubt concerning the fact can exist in the case of triasters or tetrasters in double-fertilized eggs (Fig. 79), where one or two of

---

[1] It is remarkable that in *A. megalocephala* var. *bivalens* the division-centers are extra-nuclear (Hertwig, Boveri, etc.).

[2] A number of others have reached more or less similar conclusions, *e. g.*, Julin ('93) in the spermatocytes of *Styleopsis*, Rückert ('94) in the eggs of *Cyclops*, Mathews ('05) in those of *Asterias;* but outside of the Protozoa none of these are as well substantiated as the foregoing.

the spindles, though indistinguishable from the others, must have had centers of different parental origin.

B. Anastral Types of Mitosis

As far as the history of the chromosomes is concerned the anastral types of mitosis (excepting for the moment those of Protozoa) do not differ in any important way from the amphiastral. The two types differ remarkably, however, in respect to both the structure and the mode of formation of the achromatic figure and often also in the mode of division of the protoplasmic cell-body; for the anastral spindle is not ordinarily formed between two definite focal points and is devoid of central bodies, and division of the cell-body typically does not take place by constriction but by the formation of a cell-plate (p. 159).

Anastral forms of mitosis are of common occurrence among Protista, including both unicellular plants and animals (p. 201). In Metazoa they seem to occur only in the maturation-divisions of the ovum (p. 508). In plants, on the other hand, they are of widespread occurrence and with few exceptions are characteristic of the vegetative divisions in the cormophytes from the bryophytes upwards.

In the seed-plants a number of the earlier observers, particularly Guignard ('91) believed that definite "centrosomes" could be demonstrated at the poles of the spindles and that the spindle-formation was initiated by their division. This result was, however, proved to be erroneous by the work particularly of Belajeff and his followers. It is, however, a very interesting fact that in *Ginkgo* and the cycads (*Cycas, Zamia,* etc.) and in some at least of the pteridophytes and bryophytes, the final or semi-final gamete-producing divisions of the male are characterized by the presence of conspicuous asters with central bodies known as *blepharoplasts,* because of their relation to the formation of cilia or flagella (p. 387).

Important questions concerning the nature and origin of anastral spindles have been raised by some of the latest studies in this field.[1] According to most of the current accounts the anastral spindles of higher plants and animals seem to be of two widely different types. The simpler of these occurs in the oöcytes of certain animals (Figs. 238, 243) *and arise wholly from the nucleus,* which is drawn out as a whole to form the spindle, without visible participation of the cytoplasm. The spindle-fibers here seem to arise by a direct transformation of the linin-network, and never to converge to definite foci at the poles as is the case in the amphiastral type.

By some of the earlier observers the absence of asters and centers in these cases was ascribed to defective fixation; but this seems to be excluded

[1] See especially Devisé, '21.

by the fact that the same preparations show conspicuous sperm-centers surrounded by sharply marked astral rays and central bodies.[2] During the cleavage of these forms asters and centers are always present; but here too the spindle seems to be largely of nuclear origin, as in the second

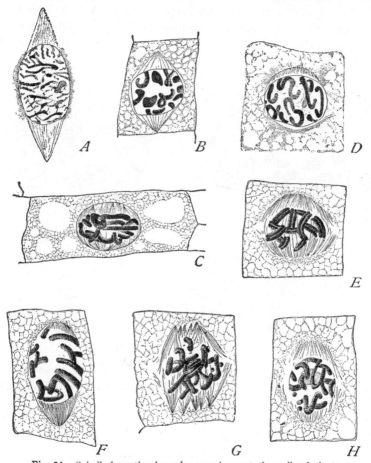

Fig. 64.—Spindle-formation by polar caps in vegetative cells of plants.
A, in *Psilotum* (ROSEN); B, *Ephydra*, C, *Vicia* (HOF); D, *Allium* (NEMEC); E–H, *Allium* (MC-COMB); C and G are multipolar diarch spindles.

or sea-urchin type, as above described (p. 146). When we consider that in lower forms generally (sponges, cœlenterates, platodes, annelids, mollusks or echinoderms) the maturation-spindles of the oöcytes are of typical amphiastral type, with conspicuous asters and centers, it seems probable

[2] *Cf.* Hill, '95, Conklin, '05a etc.

that the anastral spindles here in question have resulted from the disappearance of centers and asters that were present in the ancestral forms, the spindle-formation remaining in the main of similar type but simplified by loss of the central structures originally present at the poles.

The second, and more complicated type of anastral spindle is that found in the vegetative and spore-forming divisions of cormophytic plants. According to nearly all existing accounts these are in large part formed from

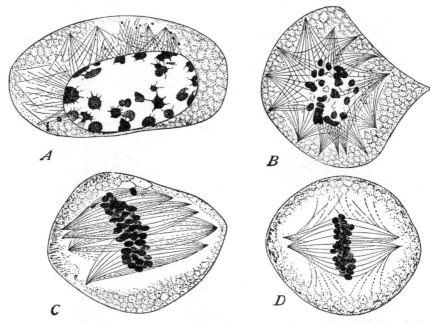

Fig. 65.—Division of spore-mother cells in *Equisetum*, showing anastral multipolar spindle-formation (OSTERHOUT).

A, early prophase, "kinoplasmic" fibrillæ in the cytoplasm; *B*, multipolar fibrillar figure invading the nuclear area, after disappearance of the nuclear membrane; *C*, multipolar spindle; *D*, quadripolar spindle which finally condenses into a bipolar one.

the cytoplasm immediately surrounding the nucleus by a process that seems to have little definite relation to that seen in the first or intra-nuclear type. In respect to their mode of origin they are of two principal types, namely, those that are always *bipolar* and those that are at a certain stage *multipolar*. The latter, in turn, were distinguished by Strasburger ('oo) as multipolar *diarchal* and multipolar *polyarchal*, the former showing more or less clearly a bipolar condition from the beginning, while the latter show at the start no trace of bipolarity (Figs. 65, 66). All these various conditions lead to the same final result, a spindle that is strictly bipolar but devoid of sharply marked polar foci and of definite asters such as are seen in the amphiastral type, though cytoplasmic strands often radiate irregularly from the poles. The simpler or bipolar type is characteristic in general of the vegetative divisions of the higher plants (Fig. 64), the multipolar of the spore-forming divisions.

In all these cases the spindle is said to arise from accumulations of fibrillar cytoplasm or *kinoplasm* near the nuclear wall. In the strictly bipolar forms characteristic of the vegetative mitoses these accumulations are first found at opposite poles of the nucleus, forming the so-called polar or kinoplasmic caps.[1] At first consisting of hyaline cytoplasm (kinoplasm), they later become fibrillar, forming two cones with their bases against the nuclear poles; and as the nuclear membrane disappears invade the nuclear cavity and come into relation with the chromosomes. The two polar caps thus finally give rise to an anastral spindle, often rather sharply pointed but sometimes truncated, in either case devoid of definite central bodies or asters. There is no evidence that the polar caps arise by the division of a single body; nevertheless it is not impossible that they arise from material which originally forms a single mass and later segregates into two polar masses, as is suggested by the facts in certain Protozoa (p. 208).

In the multipolar spindle-formation characteristic of the spore-forming divisions of higher plants [2] the process begins with the appearance of a perinuclear zone of "kinoplasm" which from an early period has a fibrillar structure, the fibrillæ being sometimes at first disposed more or less radially about the nucleus (Figs. 65, 66). Very soon they become contorted and closely aggregated to form a felt-like web closely surrounding the nucleus; and from this the fibrillæ are later drawn out into a variable number of irregular cone-like projections. In the diarchal forms these are from the first more or less polarized, in the polyarch quite irregular. Upon dissolution of the nuclear membrane the fibrillæ quickly invade the nuclear area and thus give rise to the "multipolar spindle." The cones now diminish in number, apparently by progressive fusion, until a bipolar spindle is formed of the same general type as that derived from polar caps.

From an early period considerable differences of opinion existed concerning the origin of the spindle-material. By a considerable group of observers, headed by Strasburger ('95, '00, '08) the spindle was supposed to be derived very largely, if not exclusively from the peri-nuclear cyto-

[1] These were first described by Rosen ('95), Nemec ('97), Juel ('98, '99), later by many others.

[2] This mode of spindle-formation was first carefully studied and figured in the pollen-mother-cells of *Larix* by Belajeff ('94), in *Lilium* by Farmer ('93, '95) and Strasburger ('95), in *Hemerocallis* by Juel ('97), in *Lilium*, by Sargent ('97), and Mottier ('97) and in *Equisetum* (Osterhout, '97); also in the vegetative cells of *Chara* (Debski, '98). The results have repeatedly been confirmed by later observers. Literature in Allen ('03), Davis ('04), Farmer and Digby ('10), Devisé ('12), Overton ('22) etc.

plasm; but others urged that the linin-network also contributes to its formation. For example, Lawson ('98, '00, '03) found in *Cobæa, Hedera, Gladiolus,* and other forms that the spindle is almost wholly of protoplasmic origin; while the observations of Williams ('99) on *Passiflora* indicated that it receives a large contribution from the linin-network. Still other observers found the spindle to be completely intra-nuclear in origin, *e. g.,* in the early cleavage of the ovum and in the division of the pollen-nuclei in gymnosperms. [1] Such divergences seemed hard to reconcile, but it should

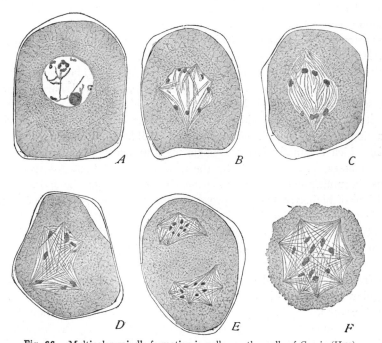

Fig. 66.—Multipolar spindle-formation in pollen-mother-cells of *Cassia* (Hus).

A, appearance of perinuclear zone of " kinoplasm" ;*B–D,* various conditions seen in prophase; *E,* multipolar diarch spindles, prophases of second division; *F,* multipolar polyarch spindle.

be recalled that in the amphiastral types, too, the spindle undoubtedly may be either intra-nuclear or extra-nuclear in origin, though the mechanism is here widely different (p. 148).

The whole question is placed in a new light by the recent work of Devisé ('21) from Grégoire's laboratory. These studies were made on the microsporocytes of the larch, *Larix,* the remarkable fine object on which Belajeff's conclusions were originally based, and by the use of the modern

[1] See Chamberlain, '97, Ikeno, '98, Murrill, '00, Ferguson, '01, Webber, '01, Coker, '03.

technique for demonstration of the chondriosomes. The results seem to show that the spindle is in reality strictly intra-nuclear in origin, the so-called multipolar spindle and the perinuclear feltwork and radial stage that precede it being artifacts produced by the destructive action of acetic acid in the reagents (Flemming's fluid) formerly employed. When properly fixed and stained (Benda's method) cells in the "resting" or vegetative stage are found to contain numerous scattered chondrioconts and in the early prophases these become radially disposed, later closely crowded and more or less contorted to form the perinuclear layer or "feltwork" (Fig. 67), which is visible as a granular zone in the living cell. In this

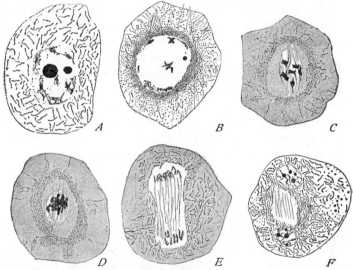

Fig. 67.—Mitosis in pollen mother-cells (primary sporocytes), of the larch, *Larix*, after Benda's fixation for chondriosomes (DEVISÉ).

A, beginning of the prophase, scattered chondrioconts; *B*, perinuclear felt-work of chondrioconts; *C*, disappearance of nuclear membrane, diarch spindle forming in central nuclear area; *D*, later stage of same; *E*, anaphase; *F*, late telophase (second division).

position the chondriocont-layer remains throughout all the succeeding stages of spindle-formation but taking no part in it. Collapse of the nucleus is followed by a concentration of the chromosomes towards the center of the nuclear area, the peripheral part of which forms a clear zone of linin limited externally by the chondriocont layer. Inside the latter, and quite separate from it, is formed the spindle, bipolar from the first, and closely associated with the chromosomes; and during the telophases the chondrioconts, or their products, become again dispersed through the cytosome. In the control material, fixed by Flemming's fluid, the chondrioconts fail to appear, but the multipolar spindles are shown as described by earlier observers. The observations of Nassonoff (p. 163) on chondriokinesis suggest a possibility that even the polar caps in the vegetative division of plants may represent the disorganized remains of chondriosomes at the poles of the nucleus.

These results must await confirmation by other observers before they can be unreservedly accepted. If well founded they go far towards reconciling the strange mode of mitosis seen in the so-called multipolar spindle-formation with the simpler type that appears in the anastral spindles of the animal ovum, as above described. For all the facts would fall into line under the assumption that in all the higher plants the spindle is intra-nuclear in origin and that the centers and asters, present in lower plants (p. 199), have disappeared, precisely as in case of certain animal ova. What has determined this is unknown. We are tempted to the conjecture that it may be correlated with the more extensive development of the cell-walls and a consequent general substitution of cell-plate formation (p. 159) for constriction in cleavage of the cell-body; but this suggestion is not supported by the anastral polar spindles of the animal egg, which seem to lead to division by constriction. That the anastral type in higher plants has been determined by some such condition is, however, supported by the presence of asters and central bodies (blepharoplasts) in the microgamete-producing mitoses. The central bodies seem here to have been retained because of the part which they play in forming the locomotor apparatus of the spermatozoids (p. 387); and this is supported by the fact that in the higher seed-plants (higher gymnosperms, angiosperms), where motile microgametes are absent, both blepharoplasts and asters are likewise absent. In their relation to the locomotor apparatus (flagella, etc.) the blepharoplasts of plants are obviously closely analogous to those of the sperm-forming cells in animals, and of the flagellated cells of sponges, both of which are known to be identical with centrioles; and the same is true, in many cases, of the blepharoplasts of the flagellated Protozoa which may very well represent the most primitive condition (cf. pp. 690, 696). It seems, accordingly, reasonable to assume that the presence of asters and blepharoplasts in the gamete-forming divisions represents the primitive amphiastral mode of mitosis that still exists in many thallophytes, and has persisted in the sperm-producing divisions because of a specific physiological motive. The possibility remains that although true asters seem to have disappeared in the higher plants central bodies may still be present, perhaps very small, so as to have been overlooked, or intra-nuclear in position as is the case in some Protista.

C. Cleavage. Division of the Cytosome

Superficially regarded the process of cytoplasmic division or cleavage of the cell-body offers a much simpler aspect than that of nuclear division; but this appearance may be deceptive. In the main it appears as a mass-division of the cytoplasmic substance; but it is important to bear in mind that the division is often unequal and that it is often accompanied or preceded by the separate division of individual structural elements, such as plastids, centrioles, flagella, and perhaps also of chrondriosomes and other structures. The fact remains that cytoplasmic cleavage is on the whole effected without any systematic general resolution of the cytosome into separately dividing elements comparable to the spireme-threads and chromosomes of the nucleus.

Cleavage is of two types or modes, entirely different in general aspect, namely: by *furrowing* or *constriction*, and by the formation of a *cell-plate*. The first is on the whole characteristic of the amphiastral type of mitosis, the second of the anastral; but there are some exceptions to this and there are also certain conditions intermediate between the two types. Broadly speaking, cleavage by constriction is characteristic of mitosis in higher animals, and cell-plate formation of higher plants. In both cases cleavage takes place in a plane approximately at right angles to the spindle-axis, and primarily across its equatorial plane.

1. Cleavage by Constriction or Furrowing

This mode of cleavage has given rise to many speculations concerning the possible function of the astral rays in mitosis. It is important, therefore, to bear in mind the fact that in some cases constriction occurs in division of the anastral type, as was first noted by Guignard ('97) in the pollen-forming divisions of various dicotyledonous plants; this process has recently been studied with care in the magnolia by Farr ('18).

Cleavage by constriction appears already in the one-celled organisms, both plant and animal, but is studied to greatest advantage in the cells of higher animals and particularly in the cleavage of the animal ovum. It is preceded by a progressive elongation known as the *karyokinetic elongation*, during which the cell, at first typically spheroidal, assumes the form of a prolate spheroid, the long axis of which coincides with (or is parallel to) that of the spindle. This constitutes the *karyokinetic axis;* and across it the cleavage-furrow typically cuts at right angles. The karyokinetic elongation first becomes clearly marked during the anaphases and reaches its climax in the telophase, just before the cell divides.[1] A furrow now makes its

[1] This is clearly shown in the photographs of the author's *Atlas of Fertilization and Karyokinesis* (Wilson, '95); see also '96.

appearance at the periphery, opposite the equator of the spindle and vertical to its long axis, and then progressively deepens until it cuts through the entire cell.

When the spindle-axis lies eccentrically the furrow always first appears on that side of the cell nearest the spindle, and progressively extends itself thence around the periphery to the opposite point (Fig. 47). An extreme case of this is seen in the ctenophore-egg (Fig. 83) where the constriction starts from one pole and travels thence downwards completely through the egg, without the appearance of any furrow at the opposite pole.

The process of constriction is preceded and accompanied by a change of surface-tension at the periphery of the egg that undoubtedly plays an important part in the process of division and may be its immediate cause. All the facts indicate that this change is a relative increase in the equatorial region and a corresponding decrease towards the poles. Evidence of this latter change is the fact that in many cases the polar region shows an outward bulging to form a more or less pronounced lobe, or even a group of lobes, which in some cases give this region an almost amœboid aspect (Figs. 68, 69).[1] To this point we shall return (p. 195). The region of the equatorial furrow is itself often marked out by an accumulation of the peripheral hyaloplasm, sometimes called the "cleavage-head" which in the ctenophore-egg persists during the whole process and travels steadily downward through the egg as the cleavage advances.[2] Even before the furrow actually appears the future cleavage-plane is often clearly foreshadowed by a peculiar structural modification of the protoplasm in the equatorial plane called the *diastem*, commonly a narrow, more lightly staining zone composed of larger alveoli (e. g., in *Crepidula*, Conklin, '02) or in some cases of vacuoles; examples of the latter case have been described especially in lower plants.[3] Cleavage is also preceded and accompanied by vortical streaming movements of the peripheral protoplasm (p. 194).

As the cleavage-furrow advances towards the center of the cell the spindle is usually constricted at its middle point and thus often assumes an hourglass shape (Fig. 62). When the furrow advances more rapidly from one side the center of the spindle is often bent more or less sharply at this point; but this result is clearly not due merely to the advance of the furrow but also to telokinetic movements of the asters (or spheres) and daughter-nuclei towards the surface (Fig. 62). These movements, which have been studied

---

[1] The polar bulging was described and figured by Van Beneden ('83) in the *Ascaris* egg; and later by several other observers. See Conklin, '02, '12, Vejdovský, '11–'12, Bowen, '20, etc. Conklin found that in certain cases the polar lobe may be seen even in the resting cell, foreshadowing the future spindle-axis.

[2] Ziegler, '98, Rhumbler, '99.

[3] See, for instance, Harper, '99, on *Synchytrium*, and other fungi, Swingle, '09, in *Phycomyces*. See also Rhumbler, '96, '03, Kostanecki, A. M. A. X.

with especial care by Conklin ('02), probably form part of the more general vortical movement of the protoplasm referred to above, and hence probably are traceable likewise to the equatorial increase of surface-tension at this time.

In or around the narrow neck formed by constriction of the spindle usually appear a series of granules, formed by thickening of the spindle-fibers in the equatorial plane and constituting the so-called *mid-body* (Fig. 50). In animals the mid-body is small and inconspicuous and offers the aspect of a vestigial structure which seems to play no active part in the division. In the end it usually becomes condensed into a single deeply staining body lying between the two cells after the cleavage-furrow has cut completely through. In many cases this body seems to disappear completely; in others it may persist for a considerable time at the boundary between the two cells, sometimes having the form of a very definite, deeply staining ring. The spindle itself usually disappears entirely; but in some cases it breaks down into a granular, often deeply staining mass, which persists for a considerable time and often forms a bridge between the daughter-cells. This body, known as the *spindle-remains* or *mitosome*, often persists to form a permanent protoplasmic connection between the daughter-cells. The best examples of this have been described in the germ-cells, *e. g.*, in the spermatogonia of Amphibia (Fig. 7), or in the nurse-cells of various insects, which thus remain in connection with the oöcyte (Fig. 155). In some of these cases the mid-body also persists for a considerable time in the form of a deeply staining ring lying between the sister-cells and traversed by the spindle-remains. A striking example of this is described by Mrázek in the spermatogonia of Lepidoptera.

Since the equatorial furrow or constriction always appears between two asters, whether in bipolar or in multipolar mitosis, and since the position of the asters (and hence of the furrows) may be artificially shifted by mechanical deformation of the cell (*e. g.*, by pressure), nearly all theories of mitosis have assumed that the astral rays play some definite rôle in the production of the furrow. It is therefore of interest that cleavage may take place by constriction in cells which divide without either asters or central bodies, (p. 157). It nevertheless remains probable that the astral rays, when present, may be concerned in causing an equatorial increase of surface-tension (p. 192).

2. Cleavage by Cell-Plate Formation. The Phragmoplast

This type of cleavage was first observed and carefully studied by Strasburger ('75, '80) in the cells of higher plants and since investigated by numerous observers. With few exceptions these cells (typically surrounded by firm cellulose walls) divide without the appearance of an equatorial furrow, by the formation of a protoplasmic partition-wall or *cell-plate*, which first appears in the equatorial plane of the spindle and extends itself thence completely across the cell at right angles to the spindle-axis. The cell-plate appears at first to be single, but sooner or later (often before it has reached the cell-periphery) splits into two parallel plates between which appears a new cell-wall which extends across the whole cell and thus cuts it in two.

The origin of the cell-plate is now generally agreed to be essentially as described by Strasburger ('88, '98), Timberlake ('oo), and Allen ('o1) by

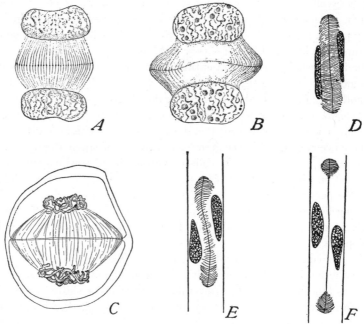

Fig. 67a.—Cell-plate formation. The phragmoplast. (*A, B,* from Strasburger; *C,* from Mottier; *D–F,* from Bailey.)

A, B, telophases of dividing endosperm-nuclei, *Fritillaria; C,* telophase of pollen-mother-cell; *Lilium,* splitting of cell-plate; *D–F,* later telophases in longitudinal division of cambium-cells, showing great elongation of cell-plate and disappearance of axial spindle-fibers.

whom the earlier literature is reviewed. The work of these and many other observers proves that at least the central region of the cell-plate is a product of the spindle-fibers and, to this extent at least, is comparable with the mid-body of the amphiastral types (p. 159). It first makes its appearance, as a rule, in the late telophase following reconstruction of the daughter-nuclei in the form of a series of thickenings in the connecting fibrillæ of the spindle in the equatorial plane (Fig. 67a). At this time the spindle becomes convex in the equatorial region so as to assume more or less of a barrel-shape in which condition it is often called the *phragmoplast.* In later stages the phragmoplast undergoes further lateral extension, apparently by the continual addition of new fibers outside the limits of the original spindle, until it extends completely across the cell in the equatorial plane. The equatorial thickenings of the fibers, at first separate and confined to the axial region of the spindle, extend progressively as the phragmoplast widens, and finally reach the periphery. At the same time they fuse to form a continuous cell-plate, a process which begins in the axial region, before the phragmoplast has reached the periphery, but finally extends across the whole cell. Meanwhile the spindle-fibers begin to disorganize and finally disappear; and this process, too, commonly begins in the axial region and often long before the cell-plate has reached the periphery, while the more peripheral fibers are still intact. This fact is remarkably shown in much elongated cells, as in the cambium, which divide lengthwise. Here the phragmoplast is seen as a continuous plate extending lengthwise for a long distance between the fully formed daughter-nuclei, and with a group of curved fibers at either end (Fig. 67a, D-F) by which the cell-plate is continually extended at its free margins until it finally cuts completely through the cell.[1]

Sooner or later the cell-plate splits into two layers between which a new cell-wall is laid down. It is an interesting fact, described already by the earlier observers (Treub, '78) that this process begins in some cases before the cell-plate has extended completely across the cell. It was believed by Strasburger that the separate spindle-thickenings might divide separately before fusing to form a continuous structure; but later observers have failed to confirm this (see Timberlake, '00).

The cell-wall first appears as a very delicate continuous layer between the two layers into which the cell-plate splits, and according to Allen ('01) is itself at first double. The wall thus formed becomes the middle lamella of the definitive wall, and is composed of pectose, while the two halves of the cell-plate itself form the plasma-membrane on each side.[2] Subsequently additional layers, consisting largely of cellulose, are laid down on each side of the middle lamella to form the secondary and tertiary thickenings of the wall (p. 56).

The process just described seems to have little in common with cleavage by constriction; but the gap seems to be partially bridged by conditions seen in some of the green algæ (*Spirogyra, Cladophora, Closterium*), where formation of the cell-wall proceeds centripetally in the form of a ring-like

[1] See especially Bailey, '19, '20; also Sharp '11.   [2] Treub ('78), Strasburger ('98), etc.

ingrowth from the lateral walls towards the center.   This involves a corresponding infolding of the plasma-membrane which may be considered
as a process of constriction and is possibly the cause rather than the result
of the ingrowth of the wall.

3. Meristic Division and Segregation in the Cytosome

As earlier indicated (p. 116), mitotic division of the nucleus is essentially
meristic, *i. e.*, is not merely a mass-division but one that affects every part
of its substance and is always equal, in both respects offering superficially
a striking contrast to cleavage of the cytosome, which has the general
aspect of a mass division, and one that may show all degrees of inequality.
Nevertheless the cytosome may contain differentiated smaller bodies,
such as the plastids, that multiply by division; and evidence has accumulated
to show that other formed elements are distributed in more or less definitely
ordered fashion to the daughter-cells, and may have similar powers of
division.   The clearest case of this is offered by the centrioles, as earlier
described (p. 120), and further possibilities are opened by the behavior
during division of the plastids, chondriosomes and Golgi-bodies.   It
thus becomes possible that the contrast between nucleus and cytosome in
respect to mode of division is not in fact as great as it superficially appears;
and that cytoplasmic division, too, may at bottom be a meristic process
(p. 720).

a. Plastids.   In higher plants generally, where the plastids are numerous,
the division of these bodies is not known to be accompanied by any definite
apparatus of distribution to the daughter-cells, though the distribution
appears to be on the whole approximately equal.   In this respect these
plastids might be compared with the more diffuse types of chondriosomes
and Golgi-bodies, considered in the following sections.   In lower plants,
on the other hand, where the plastids are few in number, a definite correlation often exists between their division and that of the cell as a whole.
This commonly occurs among the simple algæ, for example in *Coleochæte*,
in which each cell contains a single plastid (Allen, '05), or *Zygnema* in which
two are present (Kursanow, '11), and the same is true in some of the mosses
as shown by Davis ('99), Scherrer ('14) and Sapĕhin ('15).   These facts strikingly illustrate how the division and segregation of purely cytoplasmic
formed elements may be synchronized with that of the nucleus and cytoplasm as a whole; and they perhaps indicate that the loss of such coördination
in higher forms may represent a secondary condition.   Too little is known
of this subject, however, to warrant any very far-reaching conclusions.
In this direction broader aspects are opened by the chondriosomes (of which
plastids may be derivatives, p. 709) and the Golgi-bodies.

b. Chondriokinesis. Benda and his successors emphasized the fact that the chondriosomes are distributed to the daughter-cells with approximate equality, and raised the question whether this process may not be regarded as a final stage in their division. Opinion concerning this question is still divided; and the most careful studies seem to show that wide differences exist between different species in respect to the precision and orderliness of the distribution. In this regard numerous gradations exist, beginning with a condition in which the chondriosomes show no definite orientation in respect to the centers or the spindle-poles and seem to be segregated into two groups passively, without themselves undergoing division during mitosis. Examples of this are offered by the dividing germ-cells of vertebrates, [1] by the cleavage-stages of the ovum, and by many forms of tissue-cells in both plants and animals. In such cases (as often in the division of plastids) there is almost no evidence of definite relation between the division of chondriosomes and that of the nucleus and cytosome as a whole. A good example of this is seen in the spermatocyte-divisions of certain scorpions (*Opisthacanthus, Vejovis, Hadrurus*) in which the chondriosomes, at first small and numerous, finally condense into a definite number of separate spheroidal chondriosomes, which certainly do not divide but are merely segregated passively into two nearly equal groups. In *Opisthacanthus*, where the number of chrondriospheres is 24 (each secondary spermatocyte receiving 12 and each spermatid 6), the writer ('16) found exact equality of distribution in about 75% out of 200 cases, about 25% having one more or fewer than the expected number (6) (Fig. 168).

In the spermatocytes of *Ascaris*, as described by Hirschler ('13) the numerous slightly elongated chondriosomes show a distinct orientation towards the centrioles, but are not known to divide. In the vegetative divisions of seed-plants (*Vicia*) as described by Nassonov ('18) the chondriosomes (in the form of thick chondrioconts) become segregated, but without evidence of division, into two very definite groups at opposite poles of the nucleus already in the thick spireme-stage and apparently before the nuclear wall breaks down or the spindle is formed. This is an interesting case, since no central bodies or asters are present; but the spindle is said to arise from polar caps (p. 153) about which the chondriosomes aggregate. In none of the foregoing cases is there satisfactory evidence of actual division of the individual chondriosomes. On the other hand, Fauré-Fremiet ('10) produced evidence that in ciliates the numerous scattered mitochondria divide synchronously with the nucleus (Fig. 346[a]).

The transitional conditions from the foregoing type of process to those in which the chondriosomes are actually cut in two during mitosis are most

---

[1] *Cf.* Benda ('03), or Duesberg ('10) on mammals.

clearly shown in the dividing germ-cells, especially the spermatocytes, which in general show in this respect more highly specialized conditions than either the gonia or the somatic cells. In many of the insects the chondriosomes have the form of numerous elongate rods or threads (chondrioconts) which already in the prophases show a definite orientation with respect to the centers[1] and in the metaphase are placed parallel to the

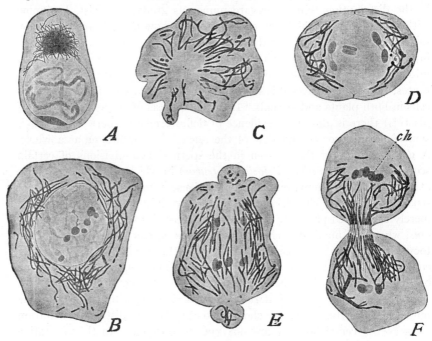

Fig. 68.—Chondriokinesis in the spermatocytes of Hemiptera (BOWEN).

A, early primary spermatocyte of *Euschistus*, with nuclear cap of chondriosomes; *B*, later stage with scattered chondrioconts; *C*, polar view of late prophase; *D*, lateral view of same stage; *E*, anaphase, showing polar lobes; *F*, telophase, separation of the chondriosomes nearly complete.

In all the figures the chondriosomes are black, the chromosomes pale; in the original preparations (Benda method) the former are deep blue, the latter yellowish.

spindle, which they closely surround like a mantle or "palisade"[2] (Fig. 68). There seems to be no doubt that during the ensuing cell-division many or some of these threads are cut across the equator. In many of these cases, nevertheless, it seems probable that at least some of the threads are passively drawn into one cell or the other without division. The process is

[1] On this point see Meves ('07) on the bee, Wilke ('13) on *Hydrometra*, Bowen ('20) on *Euschistus*.

[2] This type of chondriokinesis has been described by many observers, for example in *Coleoptera* by Benda ('03) and Duesberg ('10), Schaffer ('17), Voïnov ('16); in the *Hymenoptera* by Meves ('07); in *Hemiptera* by Fauré-Fremiet ('09), Montgomery ('11), Bowen ('20); and in *Orthoptera* by Gérard ('07), Duesberg ('09), Payne ('16) and (in the living object) by Lewis and Robertson ('16).

more definite in *Paludina* where the chondriosomes assume the form of four to six thick rod-like bodies which place themselves around the spindle and are cut across by the ensuing division.[1] The climax is reached in the scorpion *Centrurus* (Wilson) where all the chondriosome-material aggregates into a single ring-shaped body, which is placed tangentially to the spindle in the first spermatocyte and is cut across transversely by the division accurately into two half-rings. Each half-ring now breaks apart to form two parallel rods (Figs. 169, 170) which in the second mitosis are again cut across transversely into two shorter rods. The original ring thus is divided into eight equal parts, of which each resulting cell (spermatid) receives two, a process comparable in precision with the division of a heterotypic chromosome-ring, though very different in detail.[2]

It is certain from the foregoing that in some cases the chondriosomes are actually divided in the course of mitosis; but on the whole the present evidence points to the conclusion that the division is a passive and mechanical result of the cell-constriction. It must, however, be borne in mind that in many of these cases the larger chondriosomes seen during the actual divisions arise by the growth and aggregation of much smaller bodies; and we should keep clearly in view the possibility that the latter may be capable of division.

c. Dictyokinesis. Recent observations on the Golgi-bodies give substantial reason to extend the foregoing conclusions to them also, though the facts are even less completely known. An increasing number of observers have found that even when the Golgi-apparatus is of the localized or aggregate type, it returns in greater or less degree to a scattered or diffuse condition during mitosis, undergoing a process of *dictyokinesis* in the course of which it breaks up into smaller bodies or *dictyosomes*[3] ("batonettes, Golgi-bodies, etc.) which undergo a process of definite segregation to the daughter-cells.

This process has been most carefully examined in the spermatocytes of insects, mollusks and vertebrates, and shows considerable variation in different forms. In the simplest case, as offered by the scattered or diffuse type of Golgi-bodies, the dictyosomes do not aggregate at the equator of the spindle or near its poles, but are passively distributed, apparently at random,

---

[1] See Meves ('oo), Gatenby ('18).

[2] For further discussion of these cases, see p. 357.

[3] This term is due to Perroncito ('10). The main outlines of the process were clearly described and figured by Platner ('89) in the spermatocytes of *Helix* and by Murray ('98) in those of *Helix* and *Arion*, before the Golgi-apparatus was known as such. Platner derived the dictyosomes from a "Nebenkern," Murray from an "attraction-sphere" the true nature of which as a Golgi-apparatus was established in this case by Sjövall ('06), Weigl ('12), and later by Hirschler ('13, '17) and Gatenby ('17, '18). It was more carefully examined by Deineka ('12) and Cajal ('14) in tissue-cells, and later especially by Hirschler and Gatenby (as above), by Bowen ('20) in insects, and by Ludford and Gatenby ('21) in mollusks and mammals.

to the daughter-cells (Fig. 347). This has been described in only a few cases, excellent examples being offered by the segmenting ova of pulmonates.[1] More commonly the dictyosomes become definitely oriented with respect to the centers and segregate into two approximately equal groups near the spindle-poles.

There seem to be two somewhat different types of this process. In one, recently described by Ludford and Gatenby ('21), in the spermatocyte-

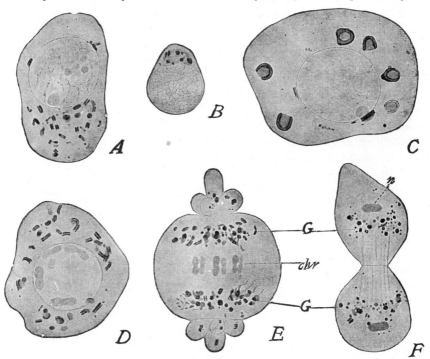

Fig. 69.—Dictyokinesis in the spermatocytes of Hemiptera (BOWEN).

(*A–D, Euschistus; E, F, Brochymena; chr., chromosomes; G, Golgi-bodies or dictyosomes.*)
B, late spermatogonium or early spermatocyte, Golgi-bodies aggregated about mitochondrial mass near nuclear pole; *A*, older spermatocyte, spreading of Golgi-bodies; *C*, later stage, growth of Golgi-bodies; *D*, late prophase, Golgi-bodies fragmenting into dictyosomes; *E*, first spermatocyte-metaphase with polar lobes, dictyokinesis completed; *F*, second spermatocyte-telophase with scattered dictyosomes.

divisions of mammals and mollusks, the whole localized apparatus ("archoplasmic mass," "centrosphere," etc.) divides into two parts which pass with the centrioles to opposite poles of the spindle and break up into separate Golgi-bodies or dictyosomes which scatter through the cell during the metaphase and again aggregate into a localized mass in the daughter-cells.

[1] See Hirschler ('13), Gatenby ('18).

In a second type, described by Deineka and Cajal in tissue-cells, and more in detail in the spermatocytes of insects by Bowen, the dictyosomes first scatter through the cell and subsequently aggregate in an equatorial belt surrounding the spindle, which separates into two groups that pass to opposite poles *in advance* of the chromosomes (Fig. 69), and later reaggregate to form a localized structure.   Bowen has also shown ('22) that in abnormal tripolar divisions (spermatocytes of *Chlorochroa*) the dictyosomes segregate into three groups towards the poles while the chromosomes are still in metaphase, and before the equatorial constriction has appeared.   This clearly indicates that the segregation of these bodies is not a simple mechanical result of cleavage but is oriented with respect to the centers.

In all of these cases the result is an approximately equal partition of the Golgi-elements between the daughter-cells; and this process, obviously, is in some manner closely correlated with the activity of the mitotic figure. Beyond this point little can be concluded with certainty.   Platner ('89), probably the first to observe dictyokinesis, believed the dictyosomes to undergo a regular process of longitudinal splitting during division; but this has failed of confirmation by later observers.   Bowen ('20) has clearly shown that the so-called longitudinal split of these bodies, though very conspicuous in the prophases, has apparently no connection with their division, and is an illusion produced by the presence of an axial non-staining substance (p. 361).

Fragmentation of the Golgi-bodies prior to division has been described by many observers beginning with Platner and Murray in case of the pulmonates.   Gatenby ('19), who describes it carefully in the oöcytes of *Lymnæa*, considers division of the batonettes to be accompanied by that of the clear "archoplasm" sphere by which each is accompanied.   Their actual number at the time of mitosis seems to vary widely.   In the primary spermatocytes of *Limax* Gatenby ('18) finds but eight, the number being halved at each mitosis, so that the spermatid receives but two.   In insects, as shown especially by Bowen ('20, etc.) the number is much greater (Fig. 69); but here too the evidence is that they do not split or otherwise divide during the actual mitosis but are passively sorted out into approximately equal groups.[1]

d. Review.   Too little is known of the foregoing phenomena to justify any very far-reaching conclusions; but they do not thus far greatly lessen the wide general contrast that has been drawn between nucleus and cytosome in respect to mode of division (p. 162).   In any case it must be admitted that neither chondriokinesis, dictyokinesis nor the phenomena of plastid-division can be compared with karyokinesis in respect to precision

---

[1] *Cf.* the analogous process demonstrated in the chondriokinesis of scorpions, p. 163.

of division and segregation; it is not certain that plastids always arise by the division of preëxisting bodies of the same kind; and it is much more uncertain whether the same is true of either chondriosomes or Golgi-bodies. Nevertheless the phenomena are significant as expressions of the care so often taken by nature (to use the words of old-fashioned teleology) to ensure the perpetuation and fairly precise segregation of specific formed elements in the daughter-cells. It is impossible to overlook the fact that in these phenomena we see a regrouping of preëxisting, specifically organized material that is preparatory to its definite segregation in the daughter-cells; and one which, if less precise than in case of the nuclear material, is a phenomenon of analogous type. Its broader significance appears in the possible relation of plastids to chondriosomes (p. 709), and that of the formed elements generally to the underlying organization of protoplasm (p. 717).

4. Monocentric Mitosis. The Monaster

It is a fact of much interest for the analysis of mitosis and for many problems connected with the chromosome-cycle that the cell may pass through a nearly complete cycle of mitosis, or even a series of successive cycles, without division of the central body or aster.[1] (Figs. 70–72). The figure thus formed, often spoken of as a *monaster*, shows all of the phenomena observed in a dicentric figure, including the normal formation and division of the chromosomes, with the following exceptions: (1) the daughter-chromosomes do not separate far but remain in a single group which gives rise to a single nucleus; (2) cleavage of the cytosome does not take place. Monocentric mitosis thus leads to a doubling of the chromosomes, without cell-division, the original chromosome-number being increased from the diploid to the tetraploid number or to a still larger number if the egg passes through subsequent monaster-cycles. As many as six such successive cycles have been observed in a single living egg.[2]

After passing through one or more monaster-cycles the cell may resume its normal mode of bipolar division, the increased number of chromosomes being retained. Boveri showed, in the case of sea-urchin-eggs, that monocentric mitoses artificially induced at the time of the first cleavage are often immediately followed by regular bipolar cleavage, and that this may lead to the production of young Pluteus larvæ having the tetraploid number of chromosomes, externally of normal appearance but having cells correspond-

---

[1] The monasters were first observed by Boveri in 1885–86 in the testis cells of the cray-fish, but not described by him until much later ('01, '05). They were in the meantime described by R. Hertwig ('96) in the eggs of sea urchins treated by strychnine ("half spindles," "fan-nuclei"), by Ziegler ('98) in sea-urchin eggs after mechanical injury (see p. 447), and by Morgan in strychninized eggs (1900). Their history was followed out in some detail by Wilson ('01, 1), M. Boveri ('03), and more recently by Painter ('16, '18).

[2] Wilson ('01a), Hinderer ('14), Herlant ('17).

ingly larger and fewer (p. 730) (Fig. 349).[1] These facts indicate one probable mode by which the normal number of chromosomes as seen in nature may change, whether from species to species, or in the appearance of tetraploid or polypoid chromosome-groups in certain of the tissue-cells (p. 870), or in the production of tetraploid mutants (often giants) (p. 885).

Although there is reason to believe that monocentric mitosis may occur spontaneously under natural conditions, it is no doubt a pathological phe-

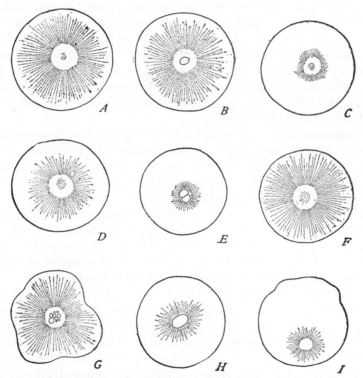

Fig. 70.—Successive monaster stages in living egg of *Toxopneustes* treated with hypertonic sea-water and returned to normal sea-water. *A*, 14m., first monaster; *B*, 17m., first resulting nucleus; *C*, 30m., second prophase, aster reduced; *D*, 37m., second monaster; *E*, 47m., second nucleus; *F*, 59m., third monaster; *G*, 69m., third monaster telophase; *H*, 75m., third nucleus (note increase in size); *I*, 157m., sixth monaster.

nomenon, and one that may be induced by various chemical, physical or mechanical agents.   Examples of these are strychnine, or chloral hydrate (Hertwig), CO_2 (Herbst), phenol urethane (Painter), hypertonic sea-water (Morgan, Wilson, Herlant), ether (Wilson) and mechanical agitation or

[1] This has been confirmed by various later observers. (See Herbst, '06, '09, '12, '14, etc.), Hinderer ('14).

injury (Boveri, Ziegler, Painter). The last method was employed by Boveri, who found that monocentric mitosis may be produced by shaking sea-urchin eggs a few minutes after fertilization; and it is of especial practical value, because of the comparative ease with which monasters may thus be obtained, and also because eggs thus treated have not been poisoned by drugs. Monasters are often formed in artificial parthenogenesis (p. 484), either in close association with the nucleus or lying quite apart from it in the cytoplasm, in which case they are variously called "accessory asters," "artificial asters," or more appropriately, *cytasters;* and these may ulti-mately divide, though no chromosomes are associated with them. These interesting structures will be considered elsewhere (p. 684). The monaster is typically symmetrical, with rays extending in all directions, but in some cases the rays are wanting in a considerable sector on the side opposite to the chromosomes (Fig. 228), thus giving the appearance of a "fan-nucleus," as first described by R. Hertwig ('96).

In its general history the monaster shows a remarkably close parallel to that of a normal amphiaster.[1] In the prophases the astral rays rapidly extend themselves through the cytosome, often giving a very striking ap-pearance; in the telophases they are rapidly reduced and may nearly or quite disappear during the interkinesis (Fig. 70). As the aster approaches its highest development it moves towards the cell-periphery, the centrosome (centrosphere) becomes flattened, elongating parallel to the nearest periph-ery of the egg and assuming, as seen in side-view, a more or less curved biscuit or lens-shape. This is followed, finally, by a reduction of the rays until they nearly or quite disappear while the nucleus re-forms.

The resemblance extends to other phenomena, both nuclear and cyto-plasmic. The chromosomes form in normal fashion, become longitudinally split and attach themselves to the astral rays, forming a group (Fig. 71), which typically lies in one side of the aster (as it likewise does in the am-phiaster). This stage, as M. Boveri shows, is of relatively long duration and corresponds to the stage of the equatorial plate in normal mitosis. The chromosomes now draw out along the astral rays and finally divide into two,[2] but the two halves do not move far apart, undergoing the typical tel-ophase-transformations *in situ* and becoming transformed into a common group of karyomeres or chromosonal vesicles, which finally fuse to form a single nucleus (Figs. 70–72).

Meanwhile the peripheral or ectoplasmic layer thickens, most *on the side furthest from the aster*, while in this region the contour of the egg becomes irregular or even amœboid, sometimes to such an extent that rounded pro-

---

[1] See especially Wilson, '01a, T. Boveri, '03, M. Boveri, '03, Painter, '16, '18, Herlant, '18, '19.
[2] See especially M. Boveri, '03.

toplasmic protuberances are cut off, and the whole egg may assume an irregular form.   These changes may lead to the complete destruction of the egg; and Painter's observations ('18) indicate that the severity of the action depends on the distance that the aster retreats from the center of the egg. If it is not too extreme the egg gradually recovers, resumes its spheroidal form as the nucleus re-forms and the aster dies down, and the egg passes into a "resting" condition.   As first pointed out by Boveri, the cortical dis-

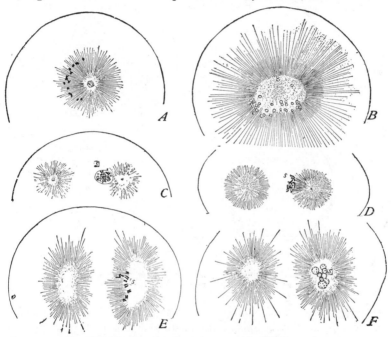

Fig. 71.—Monocentric mitosis in sea-urchins (M. BOVERI).

A, monaster-metaphase showing dividing chromosomes (*Paracentrotus*); *B*, telophase, karyo-meres; *C–F*, from enucleated fragments of *Echinus* fertilized by sperms of *Paracentrotus*, show-ing separation of the centers and unipolar chromosome-distribution; the figures show successive stages in the history of the sperm-nucleus (*s*).

turbance of the cytoplasm undoubtedly corresponds to the equatorial change of surface-tension and thickening of the ectoplasmic layer which in the normal cell leads to constriction and division.   The force of this com-parison is shown by Boveri's figure of an abnormally dividing egg that simulates two monaster eggs artificially associated (Fig. 72), which also shows the peripheral movement of the aster, the enlargement and change of shape of the centrosome, and the position of the chromosomes.

The failure (temporary or permanent) of the monaster to divide may be due either to a corresponding failure of the centrioles to divide or to separate after their division. The centrosome in these monasters is a rather large body within which, as Painter has shown, may in some cases be seen a minute pair of centrioles; and in the later phases of the cycle these may even go so far as to separate and to form a small spindle between them. Such monasters, no doubt, may be succeeded in the succeeding cycle by amphiasters and bipolar division may regularly follow. An interesting detail

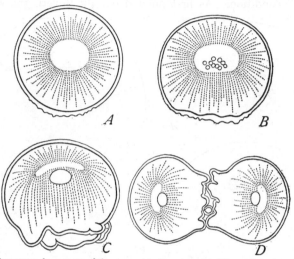

Fig. 72.—Monasters from eggs of the sea-urchin *Paracentrotus* (*Strongylocentrotus*) obtained by shaking (BOVERI).

A, middle period; *B*, early telophase karyomeres; *C*, later telophase with nucleus; *D*, abnormally dividing egg, like two monaster-eggs together.

of these figures noted by Painter is that the formation of the amphiaster is often accompanied by the appearance of spiral asters (p. 145).

5. Multipolar Mitosis

Multipolar or polycentric mitosis, like monocentric, is usually a pathological process and is characterized by the presence of more than two poles or centers. Such multipolar figures may have few or many poles and may be of either the astral or the anastral type, in the former case forming triasters, tetrasters, or polyasters, sometimes of great complexity (Figs. 79, 193). A noteworthy character of such mitoses is the fact that spindles are often formed between non-adjacent as well as adjacent centers. In tetrasters, for example, in addition to four spindles formed between the four centers in square formation, a fifth and even a sixth spindle may appear between diagonally opposite centers (Fig. 79). This fact is fundamentally important for the mechanics of mitosis (p. 186).

Multipolar mitosis may arise in various ways. As first observed by Fol and O. Hertwig in echinoderm-eggs, it is the usual result of pathological polyspermy; and it was shown by O. and R. Hertwig ('87) that this condition may readily be produced by the action of various toxic agents. In such cases the multipolar figure is usually formed synthetically by the union of amphiasters that are originally separate (since each sperm-nucleus is accompanied by a single amphiaster p. 440). Multipolar mitoses are also readily produced in tissue-cells dividing under the influence of poisons as

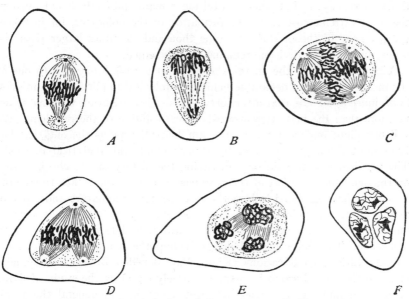

Fig. 73.—Pathological mitoses in human cancer-cells (GALEOTTI).

A, asymmetrical mitosis with unequal central bodies; *B*, later stage, showing unequal distribution of the chromosomes; *C*, quadripolar mitosis; *D*, tripolar mitosis; *E*, later stage; *F*, trinucleate cell resulting.

was long since observed by Galeotti ('93). They also have long been known in abnormal growths, such as tumors or cancers (Fig. 73), and were for a time supposed to be the active cause of such growths. It is now clear, however, that tumors, like normal tissues, grow primarily by typical mitosis, and that the multipolar figures are of secondary origin.

In mitoses of this type the chromosomes are found scattered at random on the spindles and hence undergo an irregular distribution to the poles (Figs. 79, 430). Boveri made effective use of this fact in his masterly analysis of the dispermic eggs of sea-urchin eggs with regard to the nuclear organization (p. 917).

IV. THE MECHANISM OF MITOSIS

We should distinguish clearly between the effect of mitosis and the nature of its mechanism. The effect of mitosis is obvious; it involves not a mere mass-division of the nucleus as a whole but one that is completely meristic and also exactly equal. In both respects the nuclear division shows a marked contrast to cleavage of the cytosome which gives the general appearance of a mass-division, though it can no longer be regarded as strictly non-meristic (p. 162). Division of the cytosome, is often unequal, sometimes extremely so, but nuclear division remains perfectly equal even in the most extreme cases. In the formation of the polocytes, for instance, (p. 493), one of the products may be thousands of times larger than the other, but nuclear division remains exactly equal.

A consideration of the energies at work in mitosis leads us into one of the most difficult and debatable fields of cytological inquiry; the admission must indeed be made that after forty years of investigation we have taken no more than the first steps towards a real solution of the problem. We will here limit our attention to the amphiastral type as the one that has been most thoroughly studied by experimental and analytical methods. The problem is a twofold one, involving the history of the chromosomes on the one hand and that of the amphiaster on the other. Most attempts to solve it have centered in hypotheses concerning the nature and mode of action of the amphiaster and may conveniently be classed as *fibrillar* and *dynamical* (Ziegler, '95), though logically the latter term is not very defensible. To the first group belongs the hypothesis of *fibrillar contractility* and its various modifications (Klein, Van Beneden Boveri, Heidenhain, etc.); to the second group hypotheses, largely based on the study of living protoplasm and on the view that protoplasm has in general the properties of a colloidal, viscid or semi-liquid substance commonly alveolar in structure. Some of these hypotheses have attempted to explain the phenomena as a result of radially disposed lines of diffusion-currents or of protoplasmic flow (Bütschli, Rhumbler), others as a result of electrical polarities in the protoplasmic field (Ziegler, Gallardo, Hartog, R. Lillie). A survey of these various hypotheses will drive us to the conclusion that none of them has yet afforded a satisfactory solution of the problem, though each has contributed interesting suggestions. We first offer a brief preliminary analysis based primarily upon the study of living cells.

1. General Analysis. Separability of the Factors

(1) Division of the nucleus without accompanying division of the cell-body is a common phenomenon in nature, where it leads to the formation of syncytia or plasmodia, as already indicated (p. 24). In some of these

cases the failure of cytoplasmic division is correlated with its overloading by inert matter, such as yolk; which leads to the suspicion that this phenomenon is in general due to a relative lack of energy in the general mass of protoplasm as compared with the nucleus and the cytoplasm within its immediate sphere of influence. [1] This view is sustained by the fact that the same result may be brought about experimentally by various agents which lower the protoplasmic activity, such as lack of oxygen (Demoor, Loeb, Schultze, Samassa, Godlewski), lowered temperature (O. and R. Hertwig), narcotics, such as chloral hydrate (Hertwig) or ether (Demoor, Wilson, Fig. 78), changes in the concentration of the surrounding medium (Hertwigs, Driesch, Loeb, and Norman) or mechanical shock (Boveri).[2] All of these agents cause a diminished development or even a complete suppression of the rays (O. and R. Hertwig, '87). Complete suppression of the rays is followed by complete suppression of division. Partial or complete recovery from the ether is followed by a partial or complete redevelopment of rays leading either to complete division or to the formation of more or less abortive cleavage-furrows, that approach to a complete cleavage in direct ratio to the development of the rays. In such cases, the cleavage-furrows always cut into the cell between the asters, and their depth is directly proportional to the development of the rays (Wilson, '01b, Teichmann, '03),—a result also established by study of the supernumerary asters or cytasters which often appear in the course of artificial parthenogenesis (p. 481).

The conclusion is irresistible that the central bodies are centers of cytoplasmic division, and that the astral rays are somehow concerned in the process, a result originally reached from a study of the normal phenomena by Van Beneden, Rabl, Boveri and their successors.

(2) The same experiments also demonstrate that the division of both the cell-body and of the nuclei as such may be suppressed while that of the chromosomes and the central bodies steadily proceeds. When the cytoplasmic activity is sufficiently reduced by the action of ether, etc., only slight separation of the daughter-chromosomes occurs, and they may give rise together to a single nucleus or to two closely approximated nuclei which finally fuse. By continuation of this process the number both of chromosomes and of centers continually increases, while the nucleus increases in size at each step. Thus arises a giant nucleus surrounded by many centers; and from it at each mitosis arises a polyaster having a large number of chromosomes scattered among the spindles.

(3) Progressive division of the chromosomes may take place without division of either the centers, the nuclei or the cell-body, as is seen in mono-

[1] *Cf.* Wilson, '83, p. 742. [2] Literature in Wilson, '01b.

centric mitosis (p. 168). This clearly indicates that both the separation of the daughter-chromosomes and the division of the cell-body are dependent upon the presence of a spindle.

(4) Of great interest is the fact, discovered by Boveri ('96) in sea-urchin eggs that *progressive multiplication of the centers, accompanied by the periodic formation of perfect amphiasters, may take place in the entire absence of nucleus or chromosomes.* Such enucleated masses of protoplasm containing a central body and aster are not uncommonly

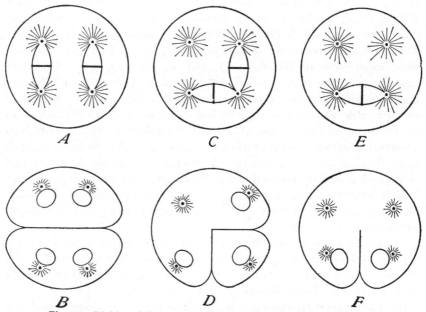

Fig. 74.—Division of dispermic eggs in sea-urchin eggs, schematic (BOVERI).

A, C, E, eggs before division, showing various connections of the asters; B, D, F, resulting division in the three respective cases, showing cleavage only between centers connected by a spindle.

formed by the passage of all the chromosomes to one pole of the spindle, so that each of the resulting cells contains an aster, but only one of them a nucleus.[1] Boveri, whose results have been confirmed by Ziegler, Wilson, Teichmann, Yatsu, McClendon and others, found that in later stages the central body and aster thus isolated continue to divide progressively and synchronously with the mitotic activity in the products of the nucleated blastomere. At each such division a perfect amphiaster is formed, later dividing into two separate asters which become much reduced in the

[1] This abnormality may be artificially induced by shaking of the eggs during their division (Boveri), by treatment with hypertonic solution or by etherization (Wilson), by sucking out the nucleus with a fine pipette (McClendon), and in other ways.

ensuing period of rest, quite as in the normal cleavage. Step by step the enucleated blastomere thus becomes filled with a constellation of asters.[1]

(5) These facts evidently constitute strong evidence in favor of the genetic continuity of the central bodies in successive mitoses. Another important fact is that the non-nucleated blastomere rarely divides at all, though the periodic formation of asters is followed by the appearance of cleavage-furrows between them. As a rule, such furrows soon disappear; or, if they cut completely through the cell, are subsequently obliterated.

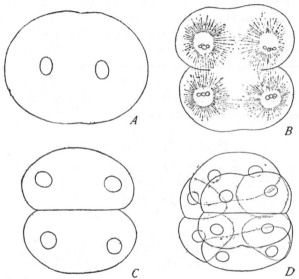

Fig. 75.—Mitosis in binucleate egg of the sea-urchin *Toxopneustes*, produced by obliteration of first cleavage as a result of shaking during first cleavage; from life.
A, rest-stage; *B*, next cleavage; *C*, product; *D*, 16-nucleus stage, 12 cells.

Boveri likewise found in the tetrasters of dispermic sea-urchin eggs, also in eggs in which the first cleavage-plane is suppressed by means of pressure, lowered temperature or shaking (Fig. 75), that complete and permanent cleavage only occurs across the chromosome-bearing spindles. Boveri concluded from this that the presence of chromosomes on the spindle is somehow necessary for complete and permanent division.

In respect to the last conclusion, later work has given somewhat contradictory results, that of Teichmann ('03) supporting Boveri's conclusions,

---

[1] M. Boveri ('03) has demonstrated that in such cases the two asters separate more rapidly and are cut apart sooner than in the chromosome-bearing amphiasters (the same is true of mitosis in which all of the chromosomes pass to one pole). The facts indicate that the centers (or asters) repel one another, but are held together by the spindle, and that the latter action is more effective in the case of nuclear spindles.

while that of the writer ('01b), of Yatsu ('09), and of McClendon ('08) showed that exceptions may occur (Figs. 75, 332–335). Nevertheless, there can be no doubt from all these observations that the chromosomes play some part, indirect though it be, in cleavage of the cell-body; and that we cannot, therefore, regard the spindle or the astral rays as the sole agents involved.

From the foregoing it would seem (as was urged especially by Boveri) that a fundamental dualism exists in the phenomena of mitosis, the origin and transformation of the achromatic figure being in large measure independent of those occurring in the chromatic elements. Mitosis consists, in fact, of two closely correlated but separable series of events.[1] This conclusion greatly facilitates an experimental analysis of the general problem.

(6) An important factor in cleavage is a change of surface-tension at the equator of the cell (*i. e.*, at those points furthest removed from the astral centers) as indicated by monocentric mitosis (p. 168), and by the formation of polar lobes in dicentric mitosis (p. 158).

2. Fibrillar Hypothesis of Mitosis

The earlier attempts to analyze the mechanism of mitosis were based largely on the study of fixed material and were accordingly dominated by fibrillar hypotheses of protoplasmic structure. In recent years these attempts have steadily lost ground, but they are of lasting interest since they enable us clearly to visualize the distribution of energies, whatever be their nature, in the karyokinetic field. The hypothesis of *fibrillar contractibility* suggested by Klein ('78), and elaborated by Van Beneden ('84, '87),[2] will here be indicated only in its most general outlines. Klein and Van Beneden considered the amphiaster as merely an image produced by the radial grouping of a preëxisting protoplasmic reticulum about two "centers of attraction," which Van Beneden compared to two magnetic poles.[3] Division of the center, originally a single body, leads to the grouping of the contractile fibrillæ about two centers and thus to the formation of a double radial muscular system in which the central bodies constitute focal organs of insertion. The two antagonizing groups (asters) of contractile fibrillæ thus established determine both the movements of the chromosomes and cleavage of the cytosome.[4] Van Beneden described the astral rays (in *Ascaris* and in tunicates) as differentiated into several groups (Fig. 76). One set, forming the "principal cone," extend from the central body at each

---

[1] *Cf.* Boveri, '88, '97.

[2] Especially by Boveri ('88, etc.), and Rabl ('85, '87); also by Flemming, Strasburger, O. Hertwig, Hermann, Drüner, Kostanecki and particularly by Heidenhain. Further references in text.

[3] '83–'84, p. 550.

[4] '87, p. 280.

pole to the chromosomes, and by their contractions pull the chromosome-halves apart towards the poles; this action is supplemented by an "antipo-dal cone" of astral rays oppo-site to the spindle-pole which draw the centers towards the periphery and thus cause them to move apart.[1]

Boveri's slightly later stud-ies on the *Ascaris* egg ('88, 2) led to essentially similar con-clusions. He demonstrated that during the fertilization of *Ascaris*, the astral rays become attached to the chromosomes of the pro-nuclei; that the longitudinal halves of each split chromo-some become attached to rays connecting with the cor-responding poles; that the chromosomes, at first irregu-larly scattered in the egg, are drawn into a position of equilibrium in the equator of the spindle by the shortening of these rays; and that *the rays thicken as they shorten.* He concluded that the initial separation of the chromo-some-halves in the early ana-phases is not due to the action of these rays but to a *divergence of the centers,* caused by contractions of the antipodal rays. This was based on the fact that when

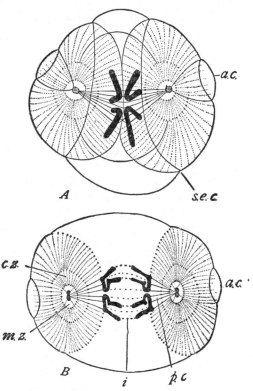

Fig. 76.—Slightly schematic figures of dividing eggs of *Ascaris*, illustrating Van Beneden's theory of mitosis (VAN BENEDEN and JULIN).

A, early anaphase; each chromosome has divided into two; *B*, later anaphase during divergence of the daughter-chromosomes; *a. c.*, antipodal cone of astral rays; *c. z.*, cortical zone of the "attraction-sphere"; *i.*, interzonal fibers stretching between the daughter-chromosomes; *m. z.*, medullary zone of the "attraction-sphere"; *p. c.*, principal cone, forming one-half of the contractile spindle (the action of these fibers is reinforced by that of the an-tipodal cone); *s. e. c.*, sub-equatorial circle, to which the astral rays are attached.

the daughter-chromosomes first separate in the earlier anaphases they do not come any nearer to the poles. The latter movement occurs only in

[1] Van Beneden describes a definite "polar circle" of microsomes marking the base of the antipodal cone, and also a "sub-equatorial circle" limiting the extension of the central rays towards the equator (Fig. 76); but this still lacks sufficient confirmation.

the later anaphases, a conclusion long afterwards substantiated by studies on monasters and on certain anomalies seen in merogonic fertilization (Fig. 71).

Boveri modified Van Beneden's conception by the assumption that the amphiaster is not a mere regrouping or image in a general reticulum but a new formation developed from a specific granular substance, *archiplasm* (originally written *archoplasm*) that collects about the central bodies and then differentiates into astral rays and spindle-fibers.[1] Rabl, on the other hand, extended Van Beneden's hypothesis by the assumption that the fibrillæ are persistent structures, permanently attached at one end to the original chromosome, at the other to the center. Division of the latter, therefore, leads to a corresponding division, first of the fibrilla and ultimately of the chromosome to which the latter is attached (Fig. 390). The hypothesis was further developed by Kostanecki in the hypothesis that the astral rays are likewise persistent structures that split lengthwise (*"omnis radius e radio"*); but this latter assumption was soon found to be untenable by numerous observations which proved that the old rays disappear after each mitosis to be replaced by new asters developed within the old (p. 680). On its physiological side the hypothesis was developed especially by Heidenhain ('94, '96), who devised ingenious models to simulate some of the phenomena of mitosis. In its simplest form the model consists of a ring to the periphery of which are attached at equal intervals a series of rubber bands (astral rays) the central ends of which are attached to a pair of small rings fastened together which play the part of central bodies. In the position of equilibrium, when the rays are stretched at equal tension, they form a symmetrical aster with the pair of rings at the center (Fig. 77). If the connection between the central rings be severed, they are immediately dragged apart to a new position of equilibrium with the rays grouped in two asters, as in the actual cell. If a round pasteboard box of suitable size (nucleus) be inserted between two of the rays, it assumes an eccentric position, the cell-axis being formed by a line passing through its center and that of the pair of small rings, and upon division of the aster it takes up a position between the two asters. In a second form of the model the peripheral ring is formed of two half-rings of flexible steel, joined by hinges; the divergence of the small rings is here accompanied by an elongation and partial constriction of the model in the equatorial plane; and if, finally, the hinge-connection be removed, each half of the ring closes to form a complete ring (Fig. 77). Heidenhain, like Rabl, assumed the astral rays to be permanent "organic radii," of equal length and tension, and permanently attached to the centers. In the resting cell they are commonly relaxed and

---

[1] For further account of this hypothesis, see p. 723.

lost to view, though sometimes permanently visible
(leucocytes, pigment-cells).
As mitosis begins, their
tension increases by a tonic
contraction, the astral rays
then straightening and
coming into view as such,
while the equilibrium of
the system is maintained
by turgor of the cell.
Upon separation of the
two centers they are me-
chanically drawn apart
while a spindle forms be-
tween them, and in the
end the continued tension
leads both to division of
the cell-body and the
continued divergence of
the daughter-centers. A
new condition of equilib-
rium is thus established
in each daughter-cell until
again disturbed by division
of the center.[1]

The fibrillar interpreta-
tion of the aster received
support through Schau-
dinn's ('96, 3) interesting
discovery that the "cen-
tral granule" of the
Heliozoa (*Acanthocystis*
and others, Figs. 85, 325),
plays the part of a central
body in mitosis. Further
supposed support was
found in the structure of

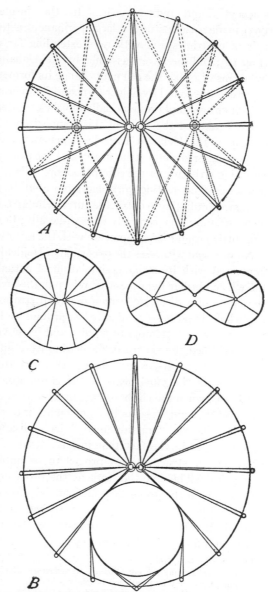

Fig. 77.—Heidenhain's model of mitosis (mainly from
HEIDENHAIN).

A, dotted lines show position of the rays upon severing
connection between the small rings; B, position upon insertion of "nucleus"; C D, models with flexible hinged hoops
showing division.

[1] In a modification of the apparatus devised by Rhumbler ('97)
the same effect is produced without the hinges.

leucocytes and pigment-cells. In the former, of which Heidenhain ('93) made a close study, a large permanent aster is present, centering in a pair of centrioles and with rays extending far out through the cytosome (Fig. 10); and these were assumed by Heidenhain to be contractile elements by means of which the cell may change its form and creep about. A similar structure was found by Solger ('91) and Zimmermann ('93b) in the pigment-cells or chromatophores especially of fishes. Later researches have, however, much weakened the force of this comparison. The axial filaments or axopodia of the Heliozoa have been generally regarded as non-contractile supporting or skeletal structures [1] and the same view has been taken of the radiating structure of the chromatophore-cells (Franz, '08, etc.). Ballowitz, in a series of interesting works has advocated the view that this structure is a system of radiating, contractile intra-cellular canals within which the pigment-granules flow centrally or peripherally; but such a structure seems to offer little ground for comparison with the mitotic aster.[2]

No one who witnesses the operation of Heidenhain's models can fail to be impressed with its striking simulation of actual cell-division; and even if the whole fibrillar hypothesis be rejected, the analogy is of value as showing the effect of a dicentric system of radial strains in the cell. Nevertheless the whole hypothesis gradually lost ground and is now almost abandoned despite various attempts to modify and improve it.[3] So far as the asters are concerned the theory of fibrillar contractility breaks down in the case of anastral mitosis, where these structures are absent. It offers no explanation of the movements of the chromosomes during the later phases of mitosis, when the chromosomes proceed to the extreme end of the spindle and even beyond it, so as to enter bodily into the substance of the centrosome, while the "traction-fibers" have disappeared.[4] Its most serious weakness lies in the fact that it was based primarily on a conception of protoplasmic structure that proved to be untenable as a general theory. It steadily fell behind, therefore, as the proof accumulated that protoplasm has in general the properties of a colloidal system, and in the end was overshadowed by attempts to analyze the phenomena from the new standpoint thus given. It was proved, for instance, that the astral rays are paths of centripetal flow of hyaloplasm towards the astral centers; that they quickly

[1] See Doflein, '16a, '16b.

[2] See Ballowitz, '14a, '14b, etc. For general review see Schmidt, '18.

[3] Among these may be mentioned Hermann's hypothesis ('91) of the central spindle as a non-contractile supporting organ; that of Drüner ('95) that the central spindle is an actively elongating structure by which the centers are pushed apart (indicated by the contorted course of its fibrillæ during the anaphases); and the hypotheses of Watasé ('93) and of Meves ('97c) that all the fibrillæ of both spindle and asters operate as pushing organs, a view suggested by the inpushing of the nuclear membrane in the early stages of mitosis (p. 148). For a more recent careful study of the amphiastral system and a critical review of the literature, see Yatsu ('09), Lams, ('10). Cf. p. 680.

[4] Wilson, '95, R. Hertwig, '98.

disappear under the action of such agents as cold, ether or chloroform, which diminish protoplasmic activity without destroying its structure, and redevelop upon restoration of the normal conditions; that the astral fibrillæ are not visible as such in the living object, but appear only as radiating tracts of hyaloplasm between the alveolar spheres; and that astral fibrillæ

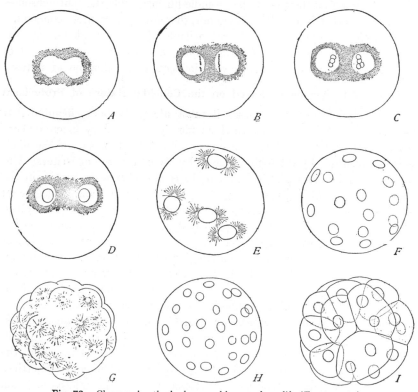

Fig. 78.—Cleavage in etherized sea-urchin eggs from life (*Toxopneustes*).

A, etherized in early anaphase, asters and spindle have disappeared; *B–D*, successive stag. ·or a slightly etherized egg; *E*, 4-nucleate egg, after slight etherization; *F*, 16-nucleate egg; *G*, the same in the ensuing abortive division; *H*, 32 nuclei; *I*, blastula, from the division of a 16-nucleate egg when replaced in water.

may be produced as artificial coagulation-products along radial lines of strain in a homogeneous colloidal solution. All this helped to turn investigation of the subject into new channels, the result of which appears in the so-called "dynamical theories" of mitosis now to be considered. The theory of fibrillar contractility was in fact a first naïve attempt; nevertheless it gave a powerful stimulus to further inquiry, and served to place the whole problem before us in clearly defined form. In spite of all this,

in the writer's view it still seems far from certain that the "fibrillæ" seen
in sections may not really preëxist approximately as such in the living cell—
a possibility strongly suggested by the relations of the axial filaments of
the Heliozoa (p. 680), by the active growth of the astral rays against the
nuclear wall which they push before them (p. 148), by the definite and
constant relations between the spindle-fibrillæ and the chromosomes
(p. 130) and other facts.   We should not, therefore, prematurely condemn a
theory which may yet prove to be reconcilable with the so-called dynamical
theories now to be considered and which, admittedly, have themselves
thus far offered no more than a very inadequate explanation of mitosis.

3. Dynamical Hypotheses Based on the Colloidal Nature of Protoplasm

In considering these hypotheses it must always be borne in mind that
the amphiaster cannot be regarded as merely a temporary image or configuration of the colloidal cell-substance (alveolar cytoplasm, or the like),
as it was regarded by Bütschli and even by some more recent writers. Undoubtedly it involves physical and perhaps also chemical changes in the
material itself which gives to the amphiaster a considerable degree of
coherence as a definite structure.   This is demonstrated in several ways.
The amphiaster may rotate or move bodily through the cytoplasm either
in the normal condition of the cell (e. g., in the polar mitoses, p. 493), or
as a result of displacement by centrifuging or otherwise.   This might indeed be due, as suggested by Lillie ('09), to a progressive regrouping of the
cytoplasmic material as the centers move (as in a moving electrical or
magnetic field in a suitable medium).   Many observers have, however, observed distortions of the spindle or asters in smear-preparations, and especially in fixed eggs after centrifuging.[1]   The spiral asters (p. 145) illustrate a similar phenomena; and Chambers ('17) has shown that the
sperm-aster, or the amphiaster in the eggs of sea-urchins and nemertines
may be pulled about, stretched or displaced with the micro-dissection
needle, meanwhile undergoing a variety of distortions that are more or
less persistent.   These facts clearly indicate that, however the amphiaster
may originally form, it finally becomes a coherent, and to a certain extent
a persistent, structure.

  a. Hypothesis of the Polarized Field of Force.   Every close observer of
the amphiaster must be impressed by its striking superficial resemblance
to the polarized magnetic or electrostatic field of force.   "The whole picture, which is of extreme clearness, vividly recalls the arrangement of
iron filings about the two poles of a magnet."[2]   This comparison was

---

[1] See Morgan, '08, '10; Lillie, '09; Spooner, '11; Conklin, '12, etc.

[2] Fol, '73.   In the same work first appears also the idea that the astral foci are *centers of attraction,*
a view afterwards advocated by Van Beneden, Boveri and other observers.   See also Giard ('76).

developed by Errera ('80), Ziegler ('95) and Rhumbler ('03), who imitated
some of the main phenomena by magnetic models, of which interesting
photographs were reproduced.   Hartog ('05) modeled the polarized magnetic field to a certain extent in three dimensions by suspending powdered

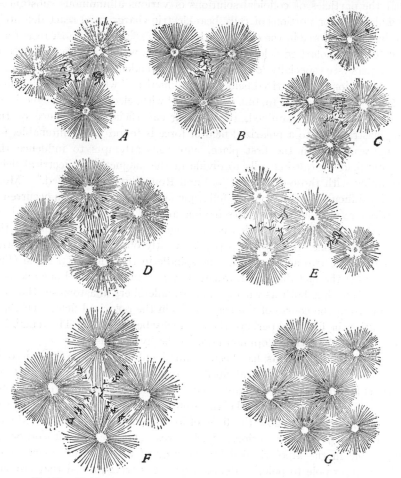

Fig. 79.—Multipolar mitoses in double-fertilized sea-urchin eggs (BALTZER).
A, B, triasters, the latter exactly symmetrical; *C–F*, various types of quadripolar figures; *D*,
with one diagonal spindle, *F* with two; *G*, multipolar figure, with three acromatic spindles.

magnetite in glycerin in a magnetic field. Gallardo ('96), modifying an
earlier experiment of Faraday's, produces a similar tridimensional model
in the electrostatic field, by introducing two electrical poles into a glass
trough containing finely powdered sulphate of quinine suspended in tur-

pentine. Gallardo at first advanced the view that the kinetic field is actually a bipolar electric field ('96) but greatly modified his interpretation ('06, '09, '12). Nevertheless, electrical hypotheses of mitosis continued to attract attention because of the fact, demonstrated by Hardy, R. Lillie and others, that the particles of colloidal solutions of various albuminous substances, and also cells or portions of cells, bear electric charges and react definitely to the lines of force in the electrostatic field (p. 189). The most recent advocate of the polarized field in mitosis is Hartog, who in a series of interesting papers (see especially '05, '09, '14) has contended that the amphiaster is the expression of a polarized field of "mitokinetism" which he considers as a "new force" analogous to, but not identical with, electricity or magnetism.[1]

When critically examined, the striking superficial resemblance of the amphiastral field to a polarized field of force is found to be untenable, for many reasons. In the first place, numerous attempts to influence the mitotic field by causing cells to divide in the magnetic or electrical field, beginning with those of Errera ('90) and Roux ('91), have failed.[2] More specific difficulties arise from the following facts: (1) the common occurrence of tripolar (pathological) figures having an odd number of poles, and (2) of quadripolar figures in which occur diagonal spindles in addition to the four primary ones (Fig. 79); (3) the frequently observed crossing of astral rays from the two asters outside the spindle in the equatorial plane (Fig. 189 B); (4) the fact that separate asters (*e. g.*, cytasters) repel one another; (5) the fact that both astral rays and spindle-fibers anastomose, thus departing from the course of the trajectories in the polarized field. Of these difficulties the fifth and perhaps the third may be obviated. The remaining three are in the writer's opinion fatal to the hypothesis.

The fifth difficulty, as has been pointed out by Hartog ('05), is only apparent; for the amphiastral fibrillæ are either coagulation products or represent "chains of force," produced by the segregation of viscid protoplasmic substances, which, like the iron-filings in a magnetic field, can only approximately follow the lines of force. The third difficulty (Meves, '96, Wilson, '96), is more serious. Such a crossing of the rays is theoretically impossible in the bipolarized field; the lines of force are necessarily continuous from pole to pole.[3] Reinke ('00), it is true, proved that crossing of the rays may experimentally be produced in the magnetic field by intermittent and non-synchronous action of two opposite poles; but clearly the conditions of such an experiment are fundamentally different from those observed in the mitotic field.

[1] Literature in Hartog, '13.
[2] See Conklin '12.
[3] Gallardo's ('01, '02) attempt to show that the crossing of the rays is but an optical illusion due to foreshortening is obviously futile.

The most serious difficulty is offered by tripolar figures, or such as have any odd number of poles, a condition physically impossible in the polarized field since it is the essence of such fields that spindle-figures (in which the lines of force pass continuously from pole to pole) can only be formed between poles of different sign, *i. e.*, plus or minus. This is not alone true of the magnetic or electrostatic field but also of those in which the lines

Fig. 80.—Diagrams of the polarized field (the curves only approximate).

A, bipolar field with unlike signs (spindle-figure); *B*, the same, like signs, anti-spindle figure; *C*, tripolar field; *D*, quadripolar field, with poles of alternating signs; *E*, quadripolar field arranged to give diagonal spindle (two anti-spindle figures); *F*, condition observed in the mitotic field.

of force or trajectories are represented by lines of liquid flow between a source and a sink; of heat-radiation between poles of higher and of lower temperatures (Maxwell, Kelvin), of oscillations in a liquid surrounding two bulbs that expand and contract in opposite rhythms (Bjerknes) or of diffusion-currents between centers of osmotic pressure and depression (Leduc, Damianowich).[1] Between two like poles, is formed an "anti-spindle" figure, in which the lines of force do not pass from pole to pole and have the opposite curvature to that of the spindle, *i. e.*, they are convex to the axis instead of concave (Fig. 80). In the mitotic field, however, multipolar figures (though commonly abnormal) are of common occurrence; and the evidence indicates that any two centers, if near enough together, may become connected by complete spindles. A pretty demonstration of this is offered in the *Ascaris* type of fertilization. When in such eggs the

[1] *Cf.* Hartog, '05, '14; Gallardo, '09, etc.; Leduc, '02, '04; Lamb ('08).

sperm-amphiaster approaches the second polar amphiaster (*e. g.*, in *Nereis*) the inner center of the latter may become connected by definite spindles with the sperm-centers (either or both) and thus produce striking triasters (Figs. 199, 470). Such figures afford crucial evidence against the whole hypothesis of polarized forces; for by the hypothesis two of the centers must be of the same sign.[1]

The difficulty presented by the diagonal spindles in quadripolar figures, as urged especially by Baltzer ('08) is of the same nature. A tetraster with consecutive spindles connecting the four poles is possible provided the centers be so placed that minus and plus poles alternate (Fig. 80). In such a figure diagonally opposite poles are of the same sign; nevertheless one or even two diagonal spindles connecting such poles are often seen (Fig. 79). This fact, as Baltzer shows, is readily demonstrated in dispermic eggs of sea-urchins, which (p. 917), typically develop four centers and divide at once into four. The double-fertilized egg sometimes gives rise to a triaster (owing to the failure of one sperm-aster to divide, and the same result may often be produced by shaking the eggs soon after fertilization.[2] In all these cases the facts clearly indicate that spindles readily form between any two adjacent asters, provided only that they are sufficiently near together during the prophases.

Lastly, separate asters do not attract but repel one another, an obvious indication that they are of like sign. M. Boveri ('03) proved that two separate asters (unconnected by a spindle) always move more widely apart than those which are connected by spindles; and Baltzer found a similar relation in case of the diagonal spindles of tetrasters. The spindle, therefore, seems to serve, at least in the earlier stages of mitosis, to hold the asters together in opposition to their reciprocal repulsion.

As a result of these difficulties Gallardo ('06) changed his original hypothesis, by the assumption that the centers are of like sign and the chromosomes of opposite sign; but again a fatal difficulty is offered by the existence of achromatinic spindles, wholly devoid of chromosomes (p. 176). Hartog's attempts to meet these difficulties ('05, '14) are ingenious, but hardly more convincing. The diagonal spindles of tetrasters may be imitated in the magnetic model, as he shows, by introducing a neutral pole of charcoal-iron into the center of the tetraphase figure, when chains of force detach themselves from the remainder of the system to anchor upon it, thus simulating the diagonal spindles. This seems, however, a very dubious analogy in view of the fact that the diagonal spindle is distinctly seen during

[1] See Rhumbler's excellent photographic figures ('03) illustrating these points. The difficulty offered by tripolar mitosis was first urged by Boveri ('88) and has been emphasized by many later writers. *Cf.* Ziegler ('95), Wilson ('00), Rhumbler ('03), Baltzer ('08), etc.

[2] Morgan, '95, Boveri, '02.

the anaphases of mitosis traversing the center of the field after the daughter-chromosomes have moved away from it (Fig. 430). Again, Hartog also shows that the triaster may be modeled in the bipolar magnetic field by introducing a neutral third pole (of soft iron), which then becomes connected by spindles with the two original poles. This effect is, of course, one of magnetic induction, the neutral pole becoming itself polarized. Since this pole is, however, necessarily weaker than the others, the two new spindles are correspondingly weaker, and such triasters are always asymmetrical, having the form of an obtuse-angled isosceles triangle. The triasters seen in cells may, however, be quite symmetrical;[1] and even were this not the case we should have to postulate the existence of three kinds of centers, plus, minus and neutral, practically a *reductio ad absurdum*.

For these various reasons the theory of the dual polarized field of force as applied to the mitotic figure seems to be untenable in any form thus far developed. We turn, therefore, to other attempts to arrive at a solution of the problem.

b. Other Hypotheses concerning the Rôle of Electrical Phenomena. A prominent place among attempts to advance our understanding of mitosis is occupied by the experiments of R. S. Lillie ('03–'11, etc.) which offer many important suggestions for further inquiry. Their point of departure was given by the demonstration (Lillie, '03) that a marked difference of electrical potential exists between the nuclear substance ("chromatin") and the cytoplasm, the former being on the whole electronegative, the latter electropositive. When suspended in a medium through which an electrical current is passed, free nuclei, or cells with a relatively large amount of nuclear substance (*e. g.*, sperm-heads, thymus-nuclei) move or tend to move towards the anode (positive pole) while cells with voluminous cytoplasm (large leucocytes, erythrocytes, smooth muscle-cells) show the reverse behavior. This result, extended to the chromosomes by the similar experiments of Pentimalli ('09) and McClendon ('10), is in harmony also with the fact (Hardy, '99, etc.) that the colloidal particles in a hydrosol are electrically charged, acid particles being negative and basic ones positive (p. 649). It was thus suggested that it may be such potential-differences which constitute the primary and determining conditions of mitosis (Lillie, '03, p. 275).

From this starting-point Lillie proceeded to an artificial imitation of many of the phenomena of mitosis by means of magnetic models.[2] The spiremethreads and chromosomes may be represented by magnetized needles, similarly oriented, each passed through a small cork float so as to stand vertically in the water and strung at short regular intervals along a silk thread to form a flexible filament (spireme-thread). Such a filament

[1] See Baltzer, '08, Figs. 3, 4.   [2] '05, 1, '05, 2.

straightens out by reciprocal repulsion of its similarly charged units; but if a large magnetic pole, of opposite sign to the upper needle-poles be brought vertically above the filament its attraction causes the filament to draw to-gether into a convoluted spireme-like form. Several such filaments in association offer a close semblance to a segmented spireme, the filaments crowding together but without touching one another (owing to mutual

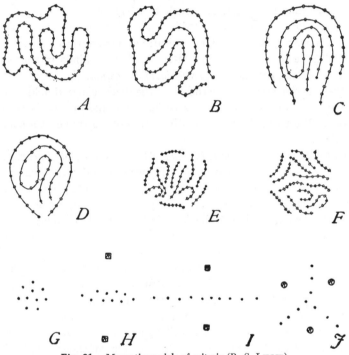

Fig. 81.—Magnetic models of mitosis (R. S. LILLIE).

A, *B*, spireme-configuration of floating magnetized needles strung on single silk-thread, drawn together by larger attractive pole; *C*, *D*, similar figures given by several separate threads (seg-mented spireme); *E*, *F*, figures with short flexible threads; *G*, group of single floating magnetized needles, drawn together by larger attractive pole; *H*, similar group between two repellent poles, *R*, *R*; I, similar group with repellent poles nearer equatorial plate; *J*, tripolar figure, with three re-pellent poles.

repulsion). If the needles be strung upon flexible wires bent into U-shapes, etc., to imitate chromosomes, the centripetal attraction of the large magnet causes them to assume groupings closely similar to those seen in the actual equatorial plate (Fig. 81). If a group of separate needles thus centripetally aggregated by a magnetic pole vertically above them be approached by two additional poles of like sign (and opposite to the overhead pole) the repulsion of the latter causes them to aggregate in a linear series transverse to the axis connecting the repellent poles.

All this, evidently, suggests that the spireme-threads tend to become straight, but are thrown into convolutions because of their confinement within the nuclear membrane. The elongate chromatin-threads of the spireme repel one another because of their similar (negative) electric charge, but are held together (action of the vertical magnet) by the nuclear membrane; hence the close convolution of the threads *without coming into contact*, as actually observed. When set free by dissolution of the nuclear membrane the chromosomes approach the equator of the spindle and spread out in a flat equatorial place because this is the position of equilibrium resulting from: (1) their repulsion by the two negatively charged poles; (2) their attraction by the positive mid-region of the spindle; (3) their reciprocal repulsion by one another. The initial separation of the daughter-chromosomes may likewise be due to such a repulsion; but this leaves unexplained the later movement to the poles, which indeed seems to contradict the assumption of a negative charge at the poles.

In spite of the latter difficulty it is possible that thus far the analogy drawn by Lillie may have a substantial basis. His attempts to explain the achromatic figure, are less convincing. Both spindle-fibers and astral rays are assumed to arise by the polarization of the colloidal particles lying between regions of relatively positive and negative charge, and the consequent serial alignment of these particles. The centers or spindle-poles are assumed to be electronegative, the equatorial region electropositive; hence the formation of continuous linear cytoplasmic tracts (spindle-fibers) between the former in spite of their similar charge. The astral rays are assumed to arise in like manner between the electronegative centers and the electropositive cell-periphery, the peripheral positive charge being ascribed to a depolarization of the plasma-membrane caused by changes of permeability, which operate as a stimulus to cell-division, and to which the whole series of phenomena may be traceable.

Unfortunately this part of the hypothesis encounters many difficulties and becomes quite unmanageable when the attempt is made to apply it, for instance, to the formation of great numbers of cytasters scattered through the cytosome (p. 482); but it nevertheless offers many suggestions to the cytologist. One of the most interesting of these is the possibility that the serially aligned polarized colloidal particles may fuse to form fibrils ('11, p. 728) by a process analogous to coagulation and once formed may long persist after the originating conditions have disappeared. This helps us

to understand how fibrillar formations may come and go in a structure
that primarily is alveolar and has the general properties of a colloid. We
see further how spindle-fibers or astral rays, once formed, may undergo
twisting (as in the spiral asters) or other deformations, such as have been
described by many observers; how they may differ in physical consistency
and staining-reaction from the general protoplasmic meshwork; and how
asters and spindles, once formed, may move through the protoplasmic
substance. It also may help us to understand how changes of protoplasmic
viscosity may play an important part in mitosis as demonstrated by the
recent work of Chambers and Heilbrun (p. 197).

On the whole, however, Lillie's analysis leaves us far short of any adequate
understanding of mitosis; and as he himself points out, the problem is no
doubt far too complex to be solved by so simple a series of assumptions.
This will be more evident after considering another series of facts and assumptions as follows:

c. *Diffusion-streams, Protoplasmic Currents* and *Surface-tension in Mitosis.* That the astral rays may represent lines of diffusion-currents or of protoplasmic flow was suggested by some of the earliest observers of mitosis.[1]
Auerbach regarded the rays as an "expression of the paths along which
fine currents of nuclear sap pass outward into the protoplasm." Bütschli
('76, '03) considered the aster as an expression of radial diffusion-currents;
and with various modifications this has been accepted by many later observers. Hertwig, Fol and Strasburger regarded the currents as a *centripetal*
flow of the hyaloplasm towards the astral centers, where a progressive
accumulation of this substance as the aster grows may readily be observed
in the living egg. This observation has been confirmed by many later
observations [2] and the fact may now be regarded as well established.

This flow may readily be observed in the living eggs of *Toxopneustes*
(Wilson, '01, 2), where, as the aster enlarges, the hyaloplasm accumulates
at the center while the alveolar spheres move away from it. At the height
of its development the center of the aster is occupied by a large *hyaloplasm-
sphere,* which shows no trace of alveolar structure, while around it the alveolar spheres are disposed in radiating rows between which lie the astral
rays. In the living object the latter appear simply as radiating tracts of
hyaloplasm between the alveoli and cannot be seen as fibrillæ; and Chambers
('17) has more recently shown that small protoplasmic granules, artificially
introduced into the astral ray in the living object by means of the micro-
dissection needle, are carried by the stream inward towards the center.

---

[1] Auerbach ('74), O. Hertwig ('75), Bütschli ('76), Fol ('79) and Strasburger ('80).
[2] Ziegler ('95), Rhumbler ('86, '99), Wilson ('01b), Giardina ('02), Teichmann ('03), Vejdovský
and Mrazek ('03), Chambers ('17).

Bütschli ('76) suggested that the movements of the chromosomes towards the poles might be due to protoplasmic currents in the spindle; also that the ultimate effect of diffusion-currents, set up in the astral rays as a result of specific chemical changes in the centers, must be a *change of surface-tension;* and this, he argued, will be greatest when the peripheral actions of the two asters coincide, *i. e.,* in the equatorial region. Assuming the change of surface-tension to be an increase, the effect will accordingly be greatest at the equator, least at the poles; and from this should result the karyokinetic elongation in the axis of the spindle (p. 157), and ultimately the equatorial constriction and cleavage. In an important later modification and development of this view ('92, 1900) he assumes an absorption of liquid and its chemical fixation in the central region so as to cause here a diminution of volume. The result of this must be a tractive force upon the surrounding region to which the aster owes its origin, and which may also play a direct part in cell-division. This was supported by the bubble-experiments (p. 66) which prove that both asters and spindle (*i. e.,* an amphiaster) may be closely simulated by the coagulation of hot melted gelatin-solution about two adjoining air-bubbles, the tractive force being here exerted by the contraction of the bubbles, as they cool.[1]

These conclusions are developed at length by Rhumbler ('96 '99) who combines Hertwig's and Fol's conclusion as to a centripetal flow of hyaloplasm with Bütschli's conception of an absorption of liquid at the centers. The latter process, evidently, must give rise to a progressive increase of viscosity along the astral rays from the center towards the periphery; and should create adhesion-stresses or tractive forces in the astral rays, having the same general configuration as the tensions postulated by Heidenhain, Van Beneden and Boveri. Rhumbler thus reaches a conception essentially in harmony with that of fibrillar contractility or tension, though under a widely different view of the structure of the amphiaster.[2] On the other hand, Giardina ('02) and Teichmann ('03) reject the assumption of traction in the astral rays; each in his own way explains cleavage as due to a change of surface-tension directly caused by the central movement of hyaloplasm.[3]

Rhumbler, like Bütschli, emphasizes the effect of surface action at the equator, but imagined this as a process of increased growth which finally produces an infolding of the superficial layer at this point; and the way for this is prepared by the formation of a modified protoplasmic region or "diastem" through the equatorial plane, likewise determined by the traction of the astral rays. Of similar type is the assumption of Ziegler ('98,

---

[1] See the remarkable photographs in Bütschli's work of 1898.   [2] See also Wilson, '01, 2.
[3] See also Gurwitsch, '04 and Bonnevie, '06.

'03) that the infolding is directly caused by the hyaline or ectoplasmic layer described beyond (pp. 261, 413), thus explaining the remarkable cleavage of the ctenophore egg in which the thickening or "cleavage-head" cuts downward from one pole through the whole egg (Fig. 83). This assumption seems, however, to break down in view of Herbst's discovery (p. 1046), that in calcium-free sea-water the ectoplasmic layer disintegrates completely or disappears, yet constriction and division proceeds as before though the reuniting cells do not hold together.

d. *Surface-Tension and Vortical Currents in Mitosis.* The assumption that changes of surface-tension may constitute the immediate agent of

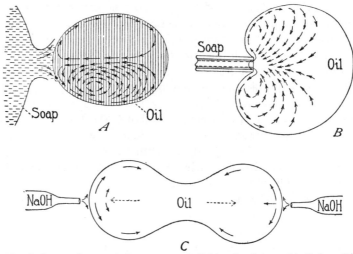

Fig. 82.—Surface-tension, cortical currents and division in oil-drops (*A, B,* from Bütschli; *C,* constructed from two figures by McClendon).

A, oil-drop suspended in water, in contact with soap-solution at left pole; *B,* similar drop, soap applied by means of pipette; *C,* drop of oil and chloroform suspended in water with simultaneous application of NaOH solution at opposite poles.

cleavage is made plausible by experiments on oil-drops which clearly bring out also the relation of such changes to currents in the cortical cytoplasm as recorded by many observers, especially in the later stages of mitosis. Bütschli's important studies on oil-drops ('92, '00) were based on investigations, especially by Quincke ('88, '89) [1] which proved that whenever the surface-tension of a drop of liquid (such as oil) be locally diminished (*e. g.,* by the local application of soap-solution) streaming movements are produced in the drop which flow away from the area of diminished tension, and thus give rise to vortical movements. This is shown in Fig. 82 in which the currents, indicated by the arrows, were made visible by mixing lamp-

[1] See also Berthold, '86, Lehmann, '88.

black with the oil. As shown in A, the superficial currents pass inwards as they approach the pole farthest from the soap to form an axial current within the drop passing forwards to the pole next the soap. Corresponding currents are likewise produced in the soap-solution; but these may here be left out of account. The same result may be produced by applying the soap-solution by means of a capillary pipette in which case the action is more gradual and the currents may continue for hours.

If we imagine two such areas of lowered surface-tension at opposite poles of a liquid drop, or (what amounts to the same thing) an increase of tension in the equatorial zone midway between the poles, two sets of vortical currents should be set up, having the disposition shown in C, superficial currents flowing from both poles towards the equator and thence into the interior. *Vortical currents of the same type occur in the dividing cell*, as was early observed by Bütschli's pupil, Erlanger ('97). This observer was able to see, in the living eggs of certain nematodes during division, definite streaming movements of the protoplasm which pass superficially from the regions opposite the spindle-poles towards the equator and thence along the cleavage-furrow into the interior of the egg (Fig. 83). In the mean time several observers had observed movements of pigment-granules towards the cleavage-furrow during or just previous to cleavage,[1] and Loeb was also led to the conclusion that vortical movements of the protoplasm may play an important part in protoplasmic cleavage. Conklin's studies ('99, '02) on the eggs of the gasteropod *Crepidula* showed that as the spindle elongates in the later stages of mitosis the yolk-spherules at the periphery of the cell move towards the equator, and thence in toward the middle of the cell in the plane of the future cell-wall.

More recently these conclusions have received a striking confirmation in the work of Spek ('18), who describes vortical currents in divisions of the living eggs of various forms, including nematodes, leeches, copepods and gasteropods. In the simplest of these cases division is symmetrical, the cleavage-furrow cutting in equally around the whole equator of the egg. In such cases, as is occasionally seen in the first cleavage of *Rhabditis dolichura*, the superficial currents conform exactly to the general theoretic scheme (Fig. 83), the flow being symmetrically from the poles to the equator. The movements are more complicated in the frequent case when the furrow is one-sided, first cutting into the egg from one pole and only later from the opposite pole. In such cases, a reversal of movement occurs, the currents at first flowing towards the first-formed furrow, but later

---

[1] In the embryonic cells of Amphibia by Nussbaum ('93) and Van Bambeke ('96), in segmenting eggs of accœlous Turbellaria by Gardiner ('95), and in the segmenting eggs of the fish *Ctenolabrus* by Loeb ('95).

in the opposite direction towards the delayed furrow. In all such cases the direction of flow is always towards that furrow which is actively cutting into the egg, while that on the opposite side has come to a standstill. We may therefore expect, as Spek points out, to find in the ctenophore egg (where, as above indicated, p. 194, the furrow is formed only on the upper side of the egg) that the vortical currents flow only towards one side; but

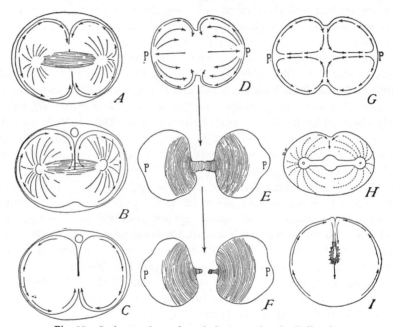

Fig. 83.—Surface-tension and vortical currents in mitosis (SPEK).

A, superficial vortical currents (indicated by arrows), in the living egg of the nematode *Rhabditis dolichura*, with symmetrical furrows; B, C, the same, with asymmetrical furrows; D, E, F, vortical currents, leading to division in an oil-drop to which a crystal of soda is applied at each pole (*p*); G, theoretic course of the currents in a drop with diminished surface-tension at the poles; H, Erlanger's figure of the currents in *Rhabditis*; I, cleavage of the ctenophore-egg, showing expectation concerning the currents.

this has not yet been observed. All these observations, obviously, bring support to Bütschli's hypothesis.

Evidence which seems to be conclusive is given by further ingenious experiments on oil-drops by McClendon and Spek, by which the actual division of the cytosome, may be imitated in the artificial model. McClendon ('10, '12, '13) employed drops of olive oil floating on the surface of water, or drops made heavier than water by the addition of chloroform to the oil. To opposite poles of these oil-drops is applied a solution of NaHO by means of two fine pipettes (Fig. 82), thus diminishing the surface-tension at these points, so that a relative increase is produced in the equatorial zone. The result is a constriction and then a complete division of the drop in the equatorial zone, midway between the pipettes; and McClendon also showed, by adding fine particles of lampblack to the oil, that vortical currents are produced in the drop which flow from the poles to the equator and thence into the interior, precisely in accordance with the theoretical postulates of Quincke and Bütschli and with the vortical currents actually observed in living cells, as described above. These results are fully confirmed by Spek, who improved the method by employing in place of the pipettes solid crystals of "soda." Drops thus treated show the vortical currents, as described by McClendon, followed by an equatorial constriction and often by complete division (Fig. 83). So striking is the analogy between these drops and the actual division of cells that the correctness of the conclusions of Bütschli and his followers can hardly be doubted. If they are finally substantiated important progress will have been made towards a comprehension of cleavage, at least in its more general aspects.[1]

e. Changes of Protoplasmic Viscosity in Relation to Mitosis. Changes in the physical consistency of the protoplasm during the mitotic activities were indicated by early observations on alterations of the refractive index of cells during division (Flemming, '82) and were later noted by many other observers, such as Driesch, Morgan, Albrecht and Yatsu, who were engaged in experiments on shaking or cutting eggs to pieces. More recently this phenomenon has been examined by Heilbrunn and Chambers [2] by more effective methods, the former observer by studying the rate and degree of displacement of the protoplasmic granules when the egg is centrifuged at different periods during artificial parthenogenesis and fertilization, while Chambers relied upon direct observation by means of the micro-dissection needle (p. 55). Both observers observed a marked increase of viscosity in the prophases, and Chambers found (in the eggs of sea-urchins and nemertines) that this continues throughout mitosis, reaching a maximum just before actual cleavage begins and later diminishing. Heilbrunn found (in the eggs of echinoderms, mollusks and annelids) two maxima, one in the prophase and a second just before cleavage, with a decided decrease in the intermediate period.[3] Chambers' observations proved that the increase in

---

[1] Roberston ('09, '11, '13) reached a contrary conclusion by applying to the oil-drops threads soaked in the NaHO solution, whereupon division took place in the plane of the thread; he therefore concluded in opposition to all others, that division takes place along a plane of *diminished* surface-tension. The explanation of this result is not yet entirely clear. Both McClendon and Spek have criticised it in detail. The weak point in Robertson's conclusions seems to be his failure to take into account the vortical movements, which afford so strong a confirmation of McClendon's conclusions.

[2] See especially Heilbrunn, '15, '17, '19, '21; Chambers, '17a, b, '19; Seifriz, '18, '20.

[3] Seifriz on the other hand, using the same method as Chambers, found a decided decrease in viscosity of the central region from the middle prophase up to the late anaphase. This result hardly seems tenable in view of the essential agreement between the other observers.

viscosity affects especially the asters, spreading out in all directions as they grow, and diminishing from the central region outwards; the firmness of the protoplasm is thus greatest near the central hyaloplasm-sphere and least towards the periphery. The aster as a whole thus becomes a "sphere of solidification," which extends itself as the aster grows until only a relatively small peripheral zone remains liquid. Since two such growing spheres are present the egg elongates (karyokinetic elongation) as a result of their reciprocal pressure and finally divides along the more liquid equatorial zone (Chambers, '19).

This work further shows that the solidification of the astral region affects only the alveolar protoplasm lying *between* the true astral rays. Like his predecessors Chambers found the rays themselves to be composed of liquid hyaloplasm flowing centripetally into the central hyaloplasm-sphere. On the other hand, F. Lillie ('09) and Conklin ('17) believe the rays to be of firm or even elastic consistency, though Conklin also accepts the fact of a centripetal flow along them. Chambers found further, that the return of the semi-solidified protoplasm to the more liquid state first begins in the equator of the egg, spreading thence towards the poles as the hyaloplasm collects at the astral centers and the cell divides.

These various observations constitute an important advance in our knowledge of the mechanism of mitosis, though they have not yet been brought into very definite relation with the changes of surface tension meanwhile in progress. An important point established by Heilbrunn's work is that the solidification-process is favored by abstraction of water from the egg; and he would thus interpret the effect of hypertonic solutions on dividing eggs or in artificial parthenogenesis (p. 473). Since Chambers has proved that the viscosity of the aster decreases from the center towards the periphery we can thus in a measure bring all these observations into harmony with the view of Bütschli and of Rhumbler (p. 193) that the aster as a whole is a radial system of tractive forces. An important modification of this conception is necessitated by Chambers' demonstration that it is not the astral rays themselves but the alveolar inter-radii in which the change takes place; but so far as cytokinesis is concerned the effect would be the same.

4. Division of the Chromosomes

Since division of the chromosomes is not dependent upon that of the central bodies or the formation of a spindle (see monocentric mitosis, p. 168) the conclusion is clearly indicated that the primary act of division is due to an autonomous activity on the part of the chromosomes, essentially like that seen in the division of the central body or a plastid in the cytosome. It is an interesting fact that the mitotic transformation of the nucleus very rarely if ever takes place without the appearance of at least one central body and aster. An exception seems to be offered, according to Kautzsch ('12) by abnormally large second polocytes occasionally found in *Ascaris*, in which the nuclear changes are said to take place in the entire absence of centers, asters, or spindle. The chromosomes here form and split lengthwise as usual but the daughter-chromosomes fail to separate (as in monocentric mitosis).[1]

The nature of the initial act of doubling in the spireme-thread (or earlier) is still unsettled.[2] Some recent writers have questioned the traditional conception that the doubling of the thread, or of smaller components from which it is built up, is fundamentally an act of fission. It has been conjectured[3] that each ultimate component of the threads (or of the nucleus from which they arise) may attract from the surrounding medium (cytoplasm?) its component materials and by a process of "autocatalysis" mould them into its own counterpart, in immediate juxtaposition to itself. Such a process would involve an accurate meristic duplication of the nucleus without involving any actual division. At present, however, this remains a pure speculation, and there is nothing in the facts thus far known to contradict the more usual view. The question here raised belongs, however, to the fundamental problem of growth and self-perpetuation in living things generally and has not yet found an adequate biophysical or biochemical answer.

V. MITOSIS IN LOWER ORGANISMS

1. In Lower Metazoa and Metaphyta

As earlier indicated (p. 152) the anastral mitoses of higher plants, and of the animal ovum in certain cases (p. 508), are undoubtedly of secondary origin and derived historically from the amphiastral type. In animals the latter type is found in all Metazoa including the cœlenterates, sponges and even such simple forms as the dicyemids.[4] Among multicellular plants amphiastral mitoses with both asters and central bodies are of common occurrence in the thallophytes, including both algæ and fungi. Typical

[1] A remarkable feature of the case is the fact that in spite of the absence of an achromatic figure these cells may divide by a constriction occurring after reconstruction of the nucleus and often dividing the latter irregularly. These facts are interpreted to mean that the central bodies are not primary or even necessary organs of division but are rather regulative or directive agents which bring about a more precise division than could otherwise take place. See also Boveri ('97) and Hogue ('10). It seems possible, however, that the process observed by Kautzsch is no more than a kind of fragmentation without special significance.

[2] Bonnevie ('08), has described the chromosome as traversed by a central axis which splits lengthwise as division begins, but this has not yet been confirmed.

[3] See Troland ('17), Muller ('22), Bridges ('22), Sands ('22). The prototype of these speculations is found in Haeckel's hypothesis of the plastidules and their "perigenesis" (1874).

[4] It was in these animals that Van Beneden first discovered the central bodies (1876).

examples of this are seen in the diatoms (Lauterborn, '96, Karsten, '00) in the algæ *Sphacellaria* and *Stypocaulon* (Swingle, '97) *Dictyota* (Mottier, '00), or in the fungus *Phyllactinia* (Harper, '05). In all these the central body is an extra-nuclear centriole lying in the protoplasm as in *Ascaris*, and the

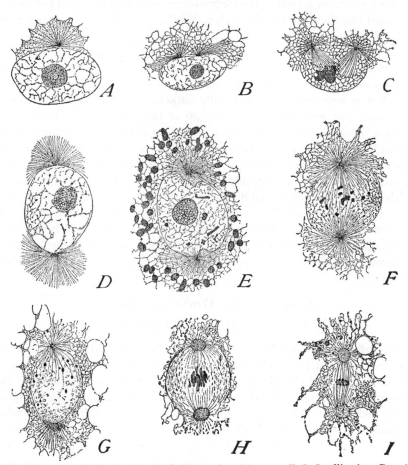

Fig. 84.—Central bodies in algæ (*A–G, Dictyota* from MOTTIER; *H, I, Corallina* from DAVIS). *A*, "resting"-nucleus of epidermal cell; *B, C*, prophases of second division of tetraspore mother-cell; *D*, prophase of first division of same; *E, F, G*, later stages of same; *H, I*, prophase and metaphase in *Corallina*, showing "centrospheres."

aster or its center appears to be a persistent structure that arises by division, quite as in *Ascaris* or in *Acanthocystis*. The mode of spindle-formation in these forms (Fig. 84), commonly approaches the second type as seen in animals. In some of these cases the nuclear membrane seems wholly to disappear during mitosis (*e. g.*, in *Dictyota*, or *Stypocaulon*) in others to persist throughout the whole process (*Erisiphe, Synchytrium*).

In some of the thallophytes the centers of the asters are said to be formed by "centrospheres" (*i. e.*, centrosomes) in which no centrioles have yet to be distinguished, and which seem not to arise by division but by forming separately and *de novo*.[1] Such conditions have been supposed to represent an early condition from which by disappearance of the rays might have been derived the polar caps of the cormophytic plants and ultimately the multipolar spindle-formation of the spore-forming divisions. Possible intermediate conditions are found in certain of the bryophytes and pteridophytes. In the moss *Polytrichum* Allen ('12) found each pole of the spindle occupied by a flat polar plate which behaves as a division-center though not surrounded by an aster. This body persists in the resting cell, divides in the prophases to form two polar plates from which protoplasmic fibrillæ grow towards the nucleus and finally form a spindle. In the later divisions the polar plate is represented by a group of granules or "kinetosomes" which divides into two similar groups during the prophase, as before. Comparable with this, possibly, is the division in *Isoëtes* as described by Marquette ('07). Here a large rounded "starch-body" containing starch-granules, lies at each pole of the spindle, persists as a single body in the resting cell and divides to form two similar bodies, which become flattened in the prophase while a spindle develops between them, very much as in *Polytrichum*. The resemblance of this body to a plastid lends some color to the attempt of Sapĕhin ('13) to identify Allen's polar plates, and central bodies generally, with plastids.

That this series represents any approach to the actual phylogenetic series is, however, very doubtful. It seems probable that more thorough studies will reveal the presence of centrioles within the "centrospheres" of the algæ. The true nature of the pole-plates of mosses and the starch-bodies of *Isoëtes* is still uncertain, while the work of Devisé, as earlier indicated, (p. 154) raises still further doubts concerning the nature of the polar caps and the multipolar spindles of the seed-plants. This part of the subject, therefore, does not yet seem ripe for critical discussion.

2. Mitosis in Protista

In turning to the mitosis of Protista we find ourselves on somewhat more secure ground, though here too we are confronted by many difficulties. The phenomena in these simplest plants and animals might be expected to throw light upon those seen in higher forms; and in fact these organisms

---

[1] *E. g.*, in *Fucus* (Farmer and Williams, '06, '98), *Corallina* (Davis, '98), shown in Fig. 84, *Erisiphe* (Harper, '97, '99), and *Pellia* (Farmer and Reeves, '94, etc.)

exhibit many interesting modifications and simplifications of the process.[1]

From the multitude of varied phenomena that have here been recorded two salient facts stand out. First, a few of the Protozoa, including representatives of both the rhizopods and the flagellates, exhibit a process of mitosis that appears to be in all essential respects of the same type as in higher animals. Secondly, this process appears to be connected by successively simpler types with modes of division hardly, if at all, distinguishable from direct or amitotic division. This series is most evident in case of the "achromatic" structures, although it is now certain that definite chromosomes are present in some Protista, and there is reason to suspect that an evolution of the chromosomes, as well as of the achromatic elements, may yet be traced among these organisms. Taken as a whole the phenomena unmistakably point to the general conclusion that the entire mitotic apparatus was originally of nuclear origin. Concerning the evolution of the more complicated types of mitosis in detail no general agreement has yet been reached. It is difficult, therefore, to give a brief connected account of the matter or to offer a simple grouping of the phenomena, as may be judged from the fact that while Chatton ('10) distinguishes three distinct types of nuclear division in the Protozoa, Alexeieff ('13) increases this number to five, or if the sub-types be reckoned in, to twelve, without counting various forms of multipolar division.

a. The "Achromatic" Structures. It must be borne in mind that the various modifications of the chromatic and the achromatic structures in Protista by no means run closely parallel.

(1) In a first group may be placed the comparatively rare cases in which both nucleus and cytoplasm contribute to the formation of the mitotic figure ("metamitosis" of Chatton) in a process that agrees in its essential features with that seen in the Metazoa generally. Examples of this are offered by certain of the flagellates, Sporozoa, diatoms, and by the heliozoan rhizopods *Acanthocystis* (Schaudinn, '96), *Wagnerella* (Zülzer, '09) and *Oxnerella* (Dobell, '17). All these are characterized by the presence of a persistent central body or division center, lying in the cytoplasm outside the nucleus, which elongates and finally divides to form the basis of a central spindle.

The best examples are offered by the Heliozoa above mentioned (Figs. 85, 325). The division-center is here a rather small, well-defined spheroidal body or *centroplast*, long known under the name of the "central granule." This body occupies in the vegetative cell the center of a very large per-

---

[1] The term Protista will here be employed to designate all unicellular organisms, whether plants or animals.

manent aster, the rays of which are definite fibrillæ extending out into the radiating pseudopodia, of which they constitute the axes (axopodia). So far as the achromatic figure is concerned the general history of the mitosis is here almost identical with that seen in higher forms, the centroplast dividing into two halves which pass to opposite poles of the nucleus and play the part of division-centers during the ensuing mitosis.[1] The centroplast is said to contain a sharply defined central granule or centriole (Key-

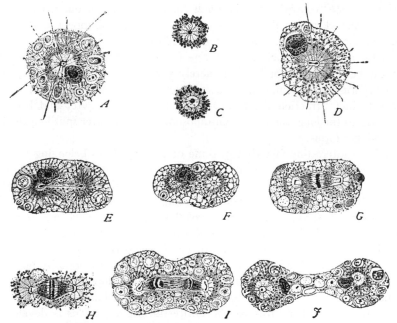

Fig. 85.—Mitosis in the heliozoön *Oxnerella* (DOBELL).

A, vegetative cell (pseudopodia mostly retracted by fixation), showing nucleus, central body (centroplast) and axopodia; *B, C*, enlarged views of centroplast in different phases; *D, E, F*, division and separation of centroplast; *G*, metaphase: *H, I*, anaphase; *J*, telophase.

sellitz, '08, Zülzer, '09, Dobell, '17) the division of which initiates the whole process of mitosis. It seems clear, therefore, that in these animals the centroplast and central granule play the parts respectively of centrosome and centriole; and the observations of Zülzer and Dobell indicate that here too the centriole is the only permanent central body while the centroplast is a temporary structure (p. 681).

Cases of this type also occur among the gregarines. An example is *Monocystis magna* (Doflein, '11), in which the extra-nuclear centers are

---

[1] Sassaki ('94) in *Gymnosphæra*, Schaudinn ('96) in *Acanthocystis* and several other forms. Zülzer ('09) in *Wagnerella*, Dobell ('17) in *Oxnerella*.

likewise surrounded by conspicuous asters by the rays of which the nuclear wall is pushed in very much as in the first maturation-mitosis of many animal eggs. In *Noctiluca* (Ishikawa, '94, Calkins, '98) the division-center is a large cytoplasmic "sphere" which by its division gives rise to daughter-spheres connected by a conspicuous fibrillated spindle; in the daughter-spheres, distinct centrioles are found at least at certain stages, but true astral rays seem to be wanting. In the diatoms (Lauterborn) the division-center ("centrosome") is much smaller and is surrounded by conspicuous astral rays in the resting-cell, but the latter disappear as the centrosome elongates to form the spindle. No centrioles are here seen. In both these cases the nuclear membrane for the most part persists and the spindle becomes more or less completely surrounded by the nucleus, and in *Noctiluca* the membrane fades away along the surface of contact where very distinct "traction-fibers" grow into the nuclear cavity and become attached to the long, thread-like chromosomes. The latter split lengthwise as in higher forms.

It is an interesting fact that in some of the flagellates belonging to this type the division-center or central body is identical with, or is very closely associated with, the basal body or "blepharoplast" that lies at the base of the flagellum; and the same is true of the flagellated swarm-spores of certain Myxomycetes (Jahn, '04). Examples of this are offered by various monads, in some of which the flagella persist during the whole mitosis. A well determined case of this kind is shown in *Trichomonas* (Fig. 86).[1] The blepharoplast here divides into two parts which migrate to opposite poles of the nucleus, within which a spindle is meanwhile developed. Asters appear to be wanting unless they be represented by the flagella.

(2) In many other Protozoa the entire mitotic apparatus is developed from the nucleus alone and the division-center, when such is present, lies inside the nucleus. A transition from the conditions seen in the first group occurs in *Acanthocystis*, where the center is said to have an extra-nuclear position only during the process of binary fission. In the budding process this center takes no part, a new center arising in the buds inside the nucleus (Fig. 325) from which it is finally extruded, taking up a cytoplasmic position that is retained through all subsequent processes of fission until budding again occurs. In *Centropyxis* the division-center is said to be permanently intra-nuclear (Fig. 90).

In many cases the intra-nuclear division-center is a large, nucleolus-like body, usually staining deeply with nuclear dyes, and variously known as the "endosome," "karyosome," or "nucleocentrosome"; and within this a number of observers have described a minute central body, or centriole.

---

[1] See Kuczynski ('14), Kofoid and Swezy ('15), Wenrich ('21).

By Nägler ('09) the mode of division thus characterized has been termed *promitotic* (promitosis); and this term will here be employed, though its significance has been considerably modified by later writers.[1] In nuclei of this type the chromatin may be wholly confined to the karyosome or may also be present as "peripheral chromatin" in the space surrounding the karyosome; and in mitosis the chromosomes or chromatic elements may apparently be derived from either or from both sources. An intra-nuclear

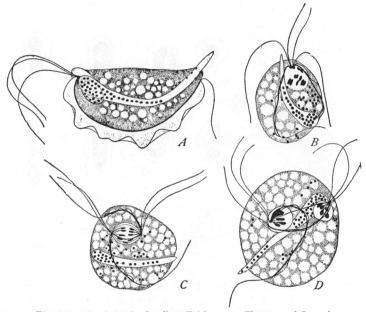

Fig. 86.—Mitosis in the flagellate *Trichomonas* (KOFOID and SWEZY). *A*, vegetative individual (trophozoite); *B*, same, blepharoplast (*b*) divided; *C*, early anaphase; *D*, telophase.

spindle is found by elongation and ultimate division of the karyosome, a process in which the way is led by division of the centriole when this is present. The poles of the spindle, in typical cases, are occupied by deeply staining "polar masses" or "polar caps" derived directly or indirectly by division of the karyosome. The spindle itself appears to be formed in some cases entirely from the karyosome (*e. g.*, in *Arcella*, Swarcewsky, '08), in other cases in part at least from the linin-substance of the peripheral nuclear zone surrounding the karyosomes (Fig. 87).[2] As a rule, neither karysome nor centriole is surrounded by astral rays; nevertheless it is evident that they correspond in a general way to the centrosome and cen-

---

[1] *Cf.* Alexeieff, '13.   [2] *Amœba tachypodia*, Gläser, '12.

triole of metazoan mitoses,[1] whence Keuten's term "nucleo-centrosome" ('95).

Interesting questions grow out of the various relations of the karyosome to the chromatic elements; for, as stated above, this structure not only acts as a division-center but may also give rise to chromosomes. Three cases are here to be distinguished. In *Euglena* and certain other euglenoid flagellates the karyosome, though intensely basophylic, seems to take no

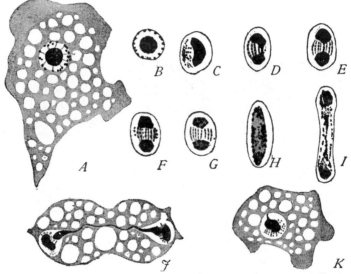

Fig. 87.—Promitosis in *Amœba tachypodia*, from fixed preparations (GLÄSER)

A, vegetative individual with "resting" nucleus showing large karyosome and peripheral chromatin; *B*, nucleus more extracted, to show structure of karyosome; *C–F*, elongation and division of karyosome to form "polar bodies"; *G*, a more extracted form like *F*; *H*, breaking up of polar bodies; *I, J*, telophases; *K*, daughter-cell, just after division.

part in the formation of the chromatic elements, these being derived wholly from the peripheral chromatin. In case of *Euglena* it is doubtful whether a centriole is present in the karyosome, though its presence has been maintained by some observers (Haase, '10). In the related form *Peranema* a distinct centriole is described by Hartmann and Chagas ('10), while in *Astasia* Bělař ('16) demonstrates its presence and division by means of photographs [2] (Fig. 88). Examples of the same type of karyosome in

---

[1] Intra-nuclear asters seem to be found in *Mastigella* (Goldschmidt), and *Centropyxis* (Schaudinn), while Gläser ('12) describes distinct cytoplasmic asters in *Amœba verrucosa*. Definite centrioles appear to be absent in the last case.

[2] The relations between karyosome, centrosome and centriole constitute an intricate question of which some discussion is given at another place (p. 690). Some protistologists (*e. g.*, Hartmann, Nägler, Chatton, Minchin, Bělař) regard the centriole as of wide if not universal occurrence; others (*e. g.*, Dangeard, Dobell, Gläser, Alexeieff) believe it to be exceptional.

the rhizopods are given by *Chlamydophrys* (Doflein, '09) and *Amœba crystalligera*. In both these, according to Schaudinn, the chromatic elements are formed entirely from the peripheral chromatin, while the karyosome produces only the spindle (as in *Euglena*); and the same is described by Keysselitz in *Oxyrrhis* (Fig. 89). In the former species well-defined chromosomes appear, in the latter they seem to be absent.

In a second series of forms, illustrated by certain Amœbas of the *limax* type, a part of the chromatic elements are derived from the peripheral

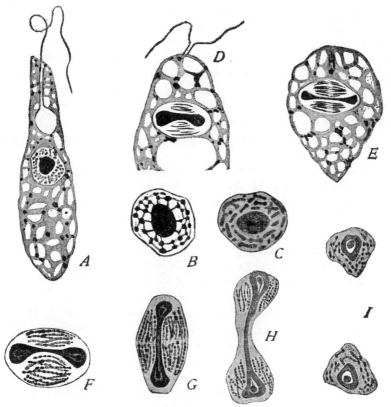

Fig. 88.—Mitosis in the euglenoid *Astasia* (BĕlAŘ).

A, vegetative individual; B, nucleus more enlarged; C, later stage, more extracted, showing dividing centriole and chromosome-formation, from peripheral chromatin; D–F, metaphase figures; G–I, later stages, apparently transverse division of chromosomes.

zone, a part from the karyosome. An example of this is given by *A. diplomitotica*, in which, according to Aragao ('09) definite rod-shaped chromosomes are formed, both from the peripheral chromatin and the karyosphere, the latter then dividing to form the polar masses while the chromosomes remain in the equatorial region. In this species two modes of mitosis are described. In one a definite equatorial plate occurs, dividing into two daughter-plates that pass as such to the poles; in the other no definite equatorial plate forms but the chromosomes scatter irregularly along the spindle, and pass some to one pole, some to the other, without visible process of division. Gläser ('12) has more recently given a careful description of *A. tachypodia*, producing clear evidence of a similar double origin of the chromosomes, and confirming Aragao's observation that the karyosome may by proper staining be differentiated so as to show a polar basis of "plastin" in which very definite chromatin-granules are imbedded (Fig. 87).

In a third type all the chromosomes arise from the karyosome. Examples are given by *Amœba lamellipodia* and *A. verrucosa* (Gläser, '12), *A. glebæ* and *A. fluvialis* (Dobell, '14), and *A. diplogena* (Bělař, '15). This author ascribes a distinct centriole which by its division leads the way in division of the karyosome; on the other hand, careful study (*e. g.*, by Gläser, Dobell and others) has failed to reveal the presence of such a structure in several other *Amœbæ*.

In the typical form of promitosis, as already mentioned, the karyosome divides bodily to form the deeply staining polar caps; and in such cases the spindle during the late anaphases and telophases often becomes compact and deeply staining, so that the chromosomes can for a time no longer be distinguished. A very characteristic appearance is thus given, for instance, in *Amœba tachypodia* (Fig. 87). There are, however, many modifications of this process. In *Arcella*, for example (Swarcewsky, '08) the polar caps are said not to be formed by direct division of the karyosphere, but by the breaking up of the latter into fine granules which then accumulate at the two poles, while the chromosomes appear in the equatorial region. In other cases (which Alexeieff, '12, places in an entirely distinct class) the karyosome breaks up but no polar caps are found, nor are centrioles present at the spindle-poles (*e. g.*, *Amœba glebæ*, *A. fluvialis*). Such cases are analogous to the anastral polar spindles of certain metazoan eggs later described (p. 508), while the phenomena in *Arcella* may give the key to the mode of division seen in Infusoria which are placed below in a fourth group.

(3) In a third group may be placed forms in which division is characterized by the presence of distinct centrioles, separate from the karyosome, which play the part of division-centers, and occupy the spindle-poles during mitosis. The karyosome no longer divides to form polar caps, but either gives rise to the chromosomes (like the karyosphere of metazoan nuclei) to a nucleolar-like body of reduced size, or even disappears altogether.

This is the *mesomitosis* of Chatton ('10), who has shown that it is connected with the preceding type by many intermediate steps. In these forms pointed spindles are found with centrioles at their apices, much as in Metazoa, but the whole spindle is still intra-nuclear. In certain cases (*Centropyxis*) towards the close of division the nuclear membrance disappears at the poles, and the result is the appearance of *cytoplasmic* asters about them (Fig. 90). In other cases the karyosome seems to disappear altogether, leaving only the centriole, or becomes much reduced. According to Chatton *Euglypha* is probably of this type, though the division of the center has not actually been seen (Fig. 91).

(4) In a fourth group may be placed certain forms, in which individualized division centers have not yet very definitely been recognized. Prominent among these are various ciliates, in which the whole nucleus transforms itself bodily into a spindle, at the poles of which appear rather definite polar plates; but it is doubtful whether the latter arise by the division of a single division center or by a process similar to that mentioned above in the case of *Arcella*. In *Paramœcium* Calkins and Cull ('07) conclude that the division of the "division-center" "is in reality only a flow of substance in opposite directions" to the poles of the spindle. Such a process would seem to approach in some respects the mitosis of higher plants in which individualized division-centers seem to be wholly absent (p. 152).

(5) We may lastly place in a distinct group the division of the chromidial nuclei by a process of constriction, without the formation of chromosomes or the participation of a division-center; and such a process, evidently, is strictly amitotic. Such a mode of division was long since described by Bütschli, Schewiakoff, and others in bacteria and related organisms, more recently by Schaudinn ('02), Dobell ('11) and others. Nothing like a "division-figure" is here found, the s c a t t e r e d granules merely separating into two groups as the cell divides; but in *Achromatium* Sche-

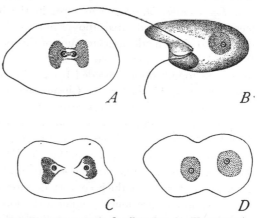

Fig. 89.—Mitosis in the flagellate *Oxyrrhis* (KEYSSELITZ). *B*, vegetative individual; *A, C, D,* successive stages of division.

wiakoff asserts that the individual chromatin-granules multiply by fission (Fig. 32). Such a mode of division graduates by intermediate stages, on the one hand, into the direct division of a more compact type of nucleus, as Dobell in particular has shown in the case of bacteria (Fig. 33). On the other hand, the chromidial mode of division seems to show possible transitions to the mitotic processes of higher forms. In the much debated case of the Cyanophyceæ, for instance, where the nuclei approach the chromidial type, different observers have been unable to agree as to whether division is mitotic or not even in case of the same species.[1]

A surer basis of comparision is given by certain of the flagellates. In *Tetramitus* as described by Calkins the nucleus during the vegetative phase is in the form of scattered chromidia, but a small, spheroidal "division center" is also present in the cell. At the time of division the chromidia are said to aggregate into a single mass about the center, the latter divides into two halves which separate, the chromidial mass likewise dividing into two and afterwards breaking up into granules scattered through the daughter-cells (Fig. 32). Such a mode of division leads into that seen in other flagellates, such as *Oxyrrhis* where the nucleus consists of a localized mass of granules (chromidia) not surrounded by a membrane and inclosing a karyosome which acts as a division-center (Fig. 89). Similar types of nuclei are seen in *Trachelomonas*, *Lagenella* and *Chilomonas*, and also in the euglenoid flagellates, though in the latter case the chromidial granules seem in some cases to be inclosed by a definite nuclear membrane. From such a mode of division it is easy to pass to the more complicated form of mitosis.

b. The Chromatin. Some features in the history of the chromatic elements have been indicated above, but as already indicated it is not yet possible to give an adequate account of this part of the subject in Protozoa. It seems beyond doubt that in some cases definite thread-like chromosomes are found, often preceded by a spireme-stage, and splitting lengthwise quite as in higher forms. Chromosomes of this type are seen in *Noctiluca* (Calkins, '98), in *Paramœcium* (Calkins and Cull, '08), *Actinophrys* (p. 597), and are said to occur also in *Euglypha* (Schewiakoff, '00), *Acanthocystis* (Schaudinn) and some other forms. In other cases, such as *Trichomonas* (Kofoid and Swezy, '15, Wenrich, '21) the chromosomes are much shorter and thicker, but still appear to split lengthwise in the prophases when in the form of a thick contorted spireme. In many cases, however, the chromosomes are much smaller and more numerous and the question of their division becomes correspondingly difficult.

There is considerable ground for the conclusion that among the Protozoa longer thread-like chromosomes, which split lengthwise (as in the forms just mentioned) arise by the linear aggregation of much smaller elements or

---

[1] This subject is reviewed in Sharp ('21). See also Acton ('14).

chromioles that are comparable to the chromidia of the scattered or chromidial nuclei, and may be capable of independent growth and division; but the data are as yet too uncertain to justify any very definite conclusions on this point. Of special interest is this connection is the type of mitosis called *haplomitosis* (Dangeard, '01), which is characteristic of the euglenoid flagellates and appears in some other Protozoa. In this type it was at first supposed that true chromosomes are not formed; and such is possibly the correct view, though it has recently been disputed. In *Oxyrrhis*,[1] for example (Fig. '89), nothing resembling chromosomes is seen, the nucleus consisting of a mass of fine granules and dividing as such bodily into two. But

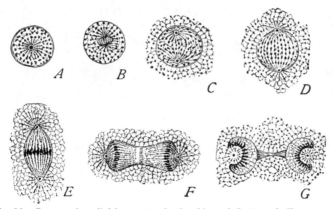

Fig. 90.—Intra-nuclear division-centers in the rhizopod *Centropyxis* (SCHAUDINN).

for the presence of the division-center this would doubtless be regarded as a process of amitosis. More or less similar to this is the process, according to Alexeieff ('11) in *Scytomonas* and some other flagellates, where the chromatin-granules, without forming spireme-threads, draw apart into two masses which pass to opposite poles of the elongating division-center to form "pseudo polar plates" (*crypto-haplomitosis* of Alexeieff). In *Euglena* and other forms, on the other hand, the nuclear granules give rise to spireme-like, moniliform threads or "chromospires" (Dangeard), but these seem not to split lengthwise, either drawing apart into two groups without division (hence Dangeard's term *haplomitosis*), or placing themselves parallel to the spindle and dividing transversely at the middle point. An example of the latter process is seen in the euglenoid *Astasia* (Fig. 88), as recently described by Bělǎr ('15); and a similar transverse division of "chromospires" or chromosomes has also been asserted to take place in various other Protozoa, of which conspicuous examples are offered by *Aulacantha* and *Ceratium*, as described by Borgert ('09, '10).

[1] See to the contrary, Hall, 1925. *Univ. Calif. Pub. Zoöl.*, 16.

At first sight this seems quite in opposition to what is known in higher forms; but a possible explanation is offered by the recent work of Tschenzoff ('16) on *Euglena*. This observer produces evidence that a longitudinal division takes place during the *anaphases* as the sister-chromosomes separate. The double chromosomes thus produced build up the daughter-nuclei, and the duality is assumed to be retained during the vegetative stage, the daughter-halves coming together again in the succeeding prophases, to be finally separated in the anaphases. The appearance of transverse division in the

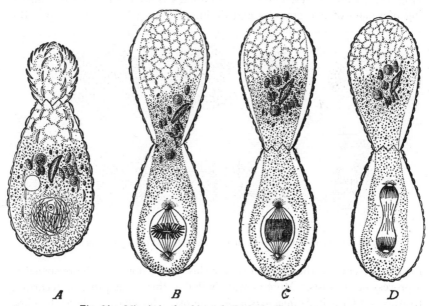

A   B   C   D

Fig. 91.—Mitosis in the rhizopod, *Euglypha* (SCHEWIAKOFF).

In this form the body is surrounded by a firm shell which prevents direct constriction of the cell-body. The latter therefore divides by a process of budding from the opening of the shell (the initial phase shown at A); the nucleus meanwhile divides, and one of the daughter-nuclei afterwards wanders out into the bud.

metaphase is considered by Tschenzoff to result from a terminal attachment of the chromosomes, quite as in higher forms. The general interpretation thus offered is in accord with that of various observers who have accepted the anaphasic splitting in higher forms generally (p. 138). In view, however, of the doubts hanging over this point the case of *Euglena* and similar ones call for further critical study.

Among the rhizopods the facts seem somewhat clearer. In some species of *Amœba* no equatorial plate is formed and the "chromosomes" or chromatic granules wander irregularly towards the poles (*Amœba lacertæ*, Dobell,

'15) the whole karyosome meanwhile drawing out into a spindle-shape and finally dividing. It is doubtful whether we can here speak of "chromosomes" or even of "mitosis"; but such a type of division, evidently, might well form the point of departure for the evolution of a true mitotic process. On the other hand, in *Amœba glebæ* numerous minute and granule-like "chromosomes" are formed from the karyosome, and become aligned in a single series to form a spireme which finally assumes the shape of a ring. This lies at the equator of a spindle developed by elongation of the karyosome, and splits lengthwise—a process which seems to be brought about by division of each constituent granule or "chromosome." [1]

Conclusion. The foregoing brief survey indicates five main conclusions:

(1) It seems beyond question that in some unicellular forms a true process of mitosis has been evolved, and one that in all essential features is of the same type as in the higher animals.

(2) From such a condition, most clearly evident in the heliozoan rhizopods (*Acanthocystis, Oxnerella,* etc.), progressively simpler conditions can be traced in almost unbroken series to anastral types of mitosis (ciliates, *Amœba,* etc.) and finally to conditions hardly to be distinguished from amitosis.

(3) This series leads to the conclusion that the most primitive forms of mitosis were of the anastral type; further, that the division-centers and spindle were primitively intra-nuclear (as in the existing forms of pro-mitosis); while the asters were a later acquisition, probably developed in the cytosome. The loss of the asters in various higher forms might thus in a sense be regarded as a return to a more primitive type; and the same view might be taken of the intra-nuclear origin of the anastral spindles in many cases (p. 156).

(4) We may therefore entertain the hypothesis that mitosis has arisen from a condition superficially similar to amitosis but in which the basic phenomenon is the growth and multiplication of small bodies, such as chromidia or chromioles, by the aggregation and alignment of which have arisen the spireme-threads and chromosomes of higher forms.

(5) The central bodies or division-centers have probably arisen by the localization of a substance ("plastin" or the like?) which once formed the general basis of the nucleus in which the chromioles were suspended. By the gradual separation from the latter of this substance arose a distinct division-center, which ultimately assumed an independent existence in the cytosome and became the center of the astral system. [2]

---

[1] This whole process is remarkably like that described by Stout ('12) in the sedge *Carex* and is also comparable to the pro-somatic divisions of *Ascaris megalocephala* (p. 323).

[2] *Cf.* p. 694.

VI. DIRECT DIVISION. FRAGMENTATION. AMITOSIS

1. General Outline

Amitosis differs from mitosis essentially in that neither spireme nor chromosomes are formed, the nucleus dividing bodily into two by a simple mass-division.   A classical example is given by the leucocytes, where the process was long ago continuously followed in the living object by Ranvier, Arnold and other observers.   Here the nucleus elongates, assumes an hour-glass shape and finally draws apart into two, sooner or later followed by a similar division of the cell-body (Fig. 92).   This type of division has been described more recently by Nowikoff ('09, '10) in the cells of various con-nective tissues (Fig. 93).   In a second type, of common occurrence, the

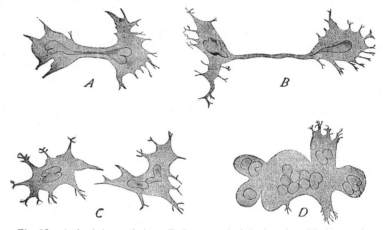

Fig. 92.—Amitosis in wandering cells (leucocytes) of the frog, from life (ARNOLD).

A–C, successive stages of division in the same individual, A at 11.00, B, 11.30, C, 11.50; D, multi-nuclear leucocyte, presumably arising by amitotic division of the nucleus.

nucleus divides by the formation of a transverse partition or "nuclear plate" by which the nucleus is cut in two.[1]   The two types may occur side by side in the same tissue (cf. Gross, '10), and are connected by various intermediate forms.   In either case division of the nucleus may be preceded by that of the nucleolus, as in Remak's original scheme (Fig. 44); but the nucleolus often seems to remain undivided, passing into one of the daughter-nuclei.

There are some cases in which a single central body or "sphere" is present and seems to play some rôle in the nuclear division.   For example, in the testis-cells of urodeles Meves ('91) found that the sphere lies in a nuclear constriction, and gives rise to a ring-like band encircling the nucleus which

[1] Wassielewski ('02) proposed to designate these respectively as *diaspasis* (in Latin form *distrac-tion*); and *diatmesis* (*dissection*); but these terms are not in common use.

seems by contraction to cut the latter in two. Again, in leucocytes, according to Heidenhain, the astral sphere always lies in a bay on the concave side of the nucleus and may be concerned in its division (Fig. 10). Such cases are, however, exceptional.

If the chromosomes possess a persistent individuality or are genetically connected from one cell-generation to another (p. 828) amitotic division should produce a halving or irregular reduction in the number of chromosomes. It is therefore a fundamental question whether amitosis accompanied by complete cell-division may intervene in the succession of mitotic division as part of the normal process of development. Apart from this question, however, an interesting problem is offered by the physiological significance of amitosis.

2. Physiological and Theoretical Aspects of Amitosis

a. Early Views. With the discovery of mitosis and the demonstration of its widespread occurrence, two views arose concerning its relation to amitosis. Already in 1876, in his classical work on the dicyemids, Van Beneden drew a sharp distinction between mitosis ("nuclear division") and amitosis ("fragmentation"), regarding the latter as a rare and special phenomenon of secondary origin. For a time it was supposed by some writers that amitosis represents a primitive type of division from which mitosis has been derived, and is perhaps a direct survivor of a simpler type occurring in the Protista.[1] This view soon gave way, however, to the reverse conclusion, developed especially by Ziegler, Flemming and vom Rath, that amitosis is a secondary and simplified type that is an accompaniment of extreme specialization, and is commonly a symptom of approaching degeneration and death; and this is the conclusion which on the whole still seems most probable, though it requires some qualification.

With the progress of the inquiry the following main facts gradually became evident. If we leave aside the Protista and certain other low forms, mitotic division is highly characteristic of vigorous and actively proliferating cells, as seen for example in the cleavage of the ovum; in the division of embryonic cells generally, both in normal development and in regenerative processes, and in the maturation of the germ-cells—in short, in cells of unspecialized character, unimpaired vitality and high reproductive capacity. Amitotic division, on the other hand, is of frequent occurrence in cells of the opposite type, *i. e.*, such as are of weakened vitality, highly specialized, or on the road to degeneration. Some of the most striking examples of this are as follows:

Amitosis is especially frequent in cells of transitory nature, such as those

<hr>

[1] Strassburger, '82, Waldeyer, '88.

of the vertebrate decidua, the embryonic envelopes, the periblast of mero-blastic ova, the accessory nutritive cells connected with the developing germ-cells, and the like. In many cases such cells may be seen side by side with those of embryonic or progressive type, the former dividing amitoti-cally, the latter mitotically. In the fish-egg, for example, all the earlier divisions are of strictly mitotic type; but the resulting cells later become differentiated into two groups, a central one belonging to the complete cells

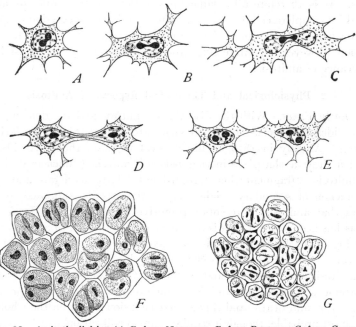

Fig. 93.—Amitotic division (*A–E*, from NOVIKOFF, *F*, from PREUSSE, *G*, from GROSS).

A–E, stages selected from fixed and stained preparations of sinew-cells in the mouse, arranged to show a series of apparent amitotic divisions; *F*, follicle-cells from the ovary of the bug *Nepa*; *G*, similar view from *Syromastes*, showing various stages of supposed amitosis.

of the embryo proper, and a peripheral group which lie free in the extra-embryonic region, are not surrounded by cell-boundaries, and constitute a merely transitory structure, the periblast, concerned in the absorption of the yolk. As shown by Ziegler ('87, '91, '96) and many later observers, the cells of these two groups show a remarkable contrast in respect to their later division. For a time both groups of nuclei divide by typical mitosis, but this only continues in case of the embryonic nuclei of the central group, while those of the periblast soon begin to show simplified forms of mitosis and finally numerous amitoses. In many other cases it was found that amitotic division of the nucleus is often not followed by cleavage of the cytosome, so that binucleate or multinucleate cells are formed (**Fig.** 93). A striking example is offered by the observations of Dogiel ('90) on the stratified epithelium from the bladder of the mouse. Here the nuclei of the more superficial layers regularly divide amitotically giving rise to large binucleate or multinucleate cells which finally degenerate and are cast off, while the new cells that take their place are always formed by mitotic division of cells of the deeper layers

These conclusions have been supported by many other observations on various animals, though some of the facts are still to some extent in dispute. In the case of insects and other arthropods many of the earlier observers (Mayer, Carnoy, Will, Brandt, Korschelt, Preusse) emphasized the frequency of amitosis in the embryonic envelopes, and in the nutritive cells and follicle-cells of the ovary. Vom Rath's studies on the testis of vertebrates, mollusks and arthropods ('93) led him to conclude that amitosis never occurs in the sperm-producing cells (spermatogonia, etc.), but only in the supporting cells (Randzellen, Stützzellen). The question here raised has been carefully studied in the ovaries of insects with results which on the whole sustain the conclusions of Ziegler, Flemming and vom Rath. The careful studies of de Bruyne ('99) and of Gross ('01) on the testes of Hemiptera and other insects, with which the observations of the writer are in agreement, show that the ovary grows largely by the multiplication of an apical group of cells near its tip, which always divide mitotically. From the products of these cells arise (a) the oögonia and ova, (b) in Hemiptera the nutritive cells of the end-chamber, by which the growing ova are nourished, and (c) the follicle-cells surrounding the ova, which likewise probably contribute for a time to the growth of the egg, and ultimately secrete the thick chorion or secondary egg-envelope. According to nearly all observers mitosis is confined to the actively dividing apical group, to the oögonia, and to the young follicle-cells, while amitosis is characteristic of the nutritive cells and of the older follicle-cells. In all these cases we are struck by the correlation between the mode of division and the functional character of the cells, and also by the failure of nuclear amitosis to be followed by cleavage of the cytosome. The same is true of various gland-cells, such as those of the mucous skin-glands of the Amphibia (Klein) or the salivary glands of isopods (*Anilocra*, vom Rath, '95). In all these, amitotic nuclear division seems clearly not to be a step in cell-division but, as held by Korschelt, Chun and Flemming, is rather a means of increasing the nuclear surface. In all, again, amitosis is characteristic of cells that are highly specialized or are entering upon a period of degeneration, soon to be terminated by death. Another striking example appears in the ciliates in which both *macro-nucleus* and *micro-nu-*

cleus divide at each cell-division (Fig. 301), the former by an amitotic process, the latter by one which though of simple type, is clearly mitotic in character. This difference is obviously correlated with profound functional differences between the two nuclei, the macro-nucleus being an active metabolic nucleus, especially concerned with trophic functions and periodically undergoing complete disorganization and death, the micro-nucleus a generative nucleus from which, or its products, the macro-nucleus is periodically rebuilt (p. 608).

On the basis of such facts Flemming ('91) concluded that so far as the higher plants and animals are concerned amitosis is "a process which does not lead to a new production and multiplication of cells, but wherever it occurs represents either a degeneration or an aberration, or perhaps in many cases (as in the formation of multi-nucleated cells by fragmentation) is tributary to metabolism through the increase of nuclear surface." In this direction Flemming sought an explanation of the fact that leucocytes may divide either mitotically or amitotically (Peremeschko, Löwit, Arnold, Flemming). In the normal lymph-glands, where new leucocytes are continually regenerated, mitosis is the prevalent mode. Elsewhere (wandering cells) both processes occur. "Like the cells of other tissues the leucocytes find their normal physiological origin in mitosis. Only those so produced have the power to live on and reproduce their kind through the same process. Those that divide amitotically are on the road to ruin." Amitosis in the higher forms was thus conceived as a purely secondary process, not a survival of a primitive process of direct division from the Protozoa, as earlier supposed.[1]

b. Later Views. The most recent and thorough studies in this field have left little doubt that the conclusions of Flemming and Ziegler were correct in principle, though they require some qualification. Those conclusions met, however, with energetic opposition; and the enunciation of the so-called "mitosis dogma"[2] was followed by a marked, though temporary, reaction of opinion. It was clearly proved by a number of observers that the occurrence of amitotic division of the nucleus by no means precludes a subsequent resumption of mitosis. Meves ('94) showed that in the salamander the nuclei of the spermatogonia may divide amitotically at certain seasons of the year, subsequently resuming the mitotic mode of division and (presumably) giving rise to normal sperms; and these results were subsequently confirmed in *Amphiuma* by McGregor ('99). A considerable number of later observers have reached similar conclusions, both in adult

---

[1] "When once a cell has undergone amitotic division it has received its death-warrant; it may indeed continue for a time to divide amitotically, but inevitably perishes in the end" (vom Rath, '91, p. 331).

[2] Wassielewsky, '02.

and in embryonic tissues. Examples of this are given by the work of Bardeen ('02) on regenerating planarians, and especially of Child ('04, '07) on various invertebrates and vertebrates, in particular in the spermatogonia of cestodes, in the developing hydranths of hydroids, in regenerating platodes, in the larvæ of *Amphioxus*, and in the cells of chick embryos. Patterson ('08) reports similar results from various stages of development in the pigeon's egg; Maximow ('08) in the embryonic tissues of animals; Nowikoff ('09, '10) in cells of the connective tissues; Wiemann ('10) for the early germ-cells of the beetle *Leptinotarsa;* Cilleuls ('14) in the regenerating uterine epithelium of mammals, and in other cases. C. W. Hargitt ('04–'06) even went so far as to assert that in hydroids the cleavage of the ovum, perhaps even the maturation-divisions, were accomplished by amitotic division. The farthest point in the reaction was reached by Child. Especially in the cestodes (*Moniezia*) this observer asserted the occurrence of numerous amitoses not only in various tissue-cells but also in the embryonic cells of the most rapidly growing regions, in the oögonia and spermatogonia, and even in the early cleavage of the ovum, mitosis being rarely seen after the first cleavage, while amitosis is of frequent occurrence. Even in higher forms he found in actively growing embryonic tissues very few mitoses, while amitoses frequently occur. From all this Child concluded that amitosis is to be regarded as "an important factor in growth in many organisms, and in some cases at least, either form of division may be changed into the other by altering the conditions " ('07, II, p. 211). The implications of this statement were towards the conclusion, that the occurrence of amitosis does not *per se* constitute any evidence of degenerative or senescent character of the cell; that such division may be an important means of progressive cell-multiplication; that it may alternate with mitosis; and that under certain conditions it may play an equally important rôle in development.

The foregoing conclusions, based on the observation of cell-division under normal conditions, seemed at first to be borne out by experimental studies. Pfeffer ('99) and Nathansohn ('oo) in a widely cited series of experiments, found that if the cells of *Spirogyra* be slightly etherized the nuclei seem to divide by amitosis, but upon restoring the normal conditions mitotic division is resumed, and normal growth proceeds; hence the conclusion (probably erroneous) that, in this case, at least, an organism which normally divides by mitotic division is capable under appropriate conditions of continued amitotic division, of producing cells that contain all of the embryonic potentialities unimpaired, and of resuming the normal mode of mitotic division. In like manner Wassielewski ('02, '04) found that under the action of solutions of chloral hydrate the nuclei of root-tips in higher plants showed many amitotic divisions which were succeeded by mitotic division upon restoration of the normal conditions.

More critical examination showed that these observations are open to a quite different and far more probable interpretation. Haecker ('00) showed that slight etherization of the segmenting eggs of copepods (*Cyclops*) caused the nuclei to divide by a process that gives a deceptive appearance of amitosis (Fig. 94), but actually is only a modified type of mitosis in which

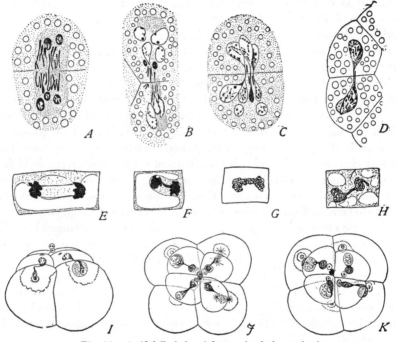

Fig. 94.—Artificially induced figures simulating amitosis.

A–D, early cleavage-figures of *Cyclops* slightly etherized (HAECKER); *E–H,* from root-tips of *Vicia* after slight chloralization (NEMEC); *I–K,* from early cleavage of *Crepidula* in dilute sea-water (CONKLIN). The final stages in all (*D, G, H, J, K*) simulate amitosis owing to the telophasic transformation of lagging chromosomes.

the chromosomes are formed and divide but fail to separate in normal fashion; and this was confirmed by Schiller ('09) and by the studies of Nemec ('04) on chloralized root-tips. These observers showed that the effect of the narcotic is to cause a degeneration or suppression of the spindle-fibers and often an incomplete separation of the daughter-chromosomes. Thus in the telophase may readily be formed two nuclei in close apposition or connected by a narrow bridge (Fig. 94); and many evidences were also found that two separate nuclei thus formed may subsequently fuse together.[1] It is obvious that such conditions of incomplete separation or of fusion subsequent to separation might readily be mistaken for amitosis. Results essentially similar to these were also reached by Conklin ('12, '17) in an important study of gasteropod eggs (*Crepidula*) after treatment by hypotonic solutions (Fig. 94).

In all these cases the constriction between two nuclei is shown to offer "no evidence of amitosis, but rather of the scattering of chromosomes along the spindle, at the previous division of these cells" (Conklin, 552). It is clear, therefore, that evidence of amitosis, unless based on direct study of the living cell, must be received with the greatest caution; and it is extremely probable that the results of Sachs and Nathansohn are susceptible of an interpretation similar to the foregoing one.

As was urged by Boveri, most of the observations on amitosis have failed to demonstrate (1) that the two nuclei of binucleate cells actually result

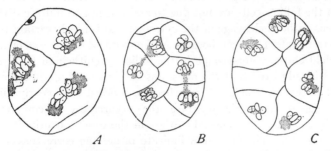

A   *B*   *C*

Fig. 95.—Polymorphic nuclei resulting from failure of the telophase-karyomeres to fuse. From the cleavage of the tardigrade *Macrobiotus* (WENCK).
A, from section of 7-cell stage; *B, C*, from 16-cell stage.

from division; (2) that division of the nucleus is actually followed by that of the cell-body; (3) that the cells thus produced subsequently divide mitotically with the normal number of chromosomes. In point of fact the so-called "amitotic cleavage" of the egg in hydroids was subsequently proved by Beckwith ('09) and G. T. Hargitt ('09) to be illusory, arising merely from the fact that the karyomerites or chromosomal vesicles formed in the telophase of each division do not completely fuse to form a single nucleus (Fig. 95). Again, although cytoplasmic cleavage following upon amitotic nuclear division has often been described and figured, nearly all such cases are based on the study of fixed material where decisive proof cannot be obtained. That cytoplasmic cleavage *may* follow upon amitotic nuclear division seems it is true to be clearly established by the observations of

[1] All this is in harmony with the phenomena earlier observed by the Hertwigs ('87) and the writer ('01, a, b) in etherized sea-urchin eggs (*cf.* p. 183).

Ranvier and Arnold on living lymphocytes (Fig. 92); but the existing evidence indicates that this is a rare and secondary occurrence.

In the case of cestodes the careful studies of Richards ('09, '11) have shown that mitosis is more frequent and amitosis less frequent than Child believed; that no evidence could be found of cytoplasmic cleavage following nuclear division; that the cleavage of the ovum is almost certainly mitotic throughout; and that the pre-oögonial and oögonial divisions are also probably mitotic. Similar contradictions exist in case of the insects. In Hemiptera Foot and Strobell ('11) concluded, in opposition to the earlier conclusions of Gross and others, that the oöcytes of *Protenor* are derived by amitotic division from cells of the nutritive end-chamber (p. 332). This, however, is contradicted by Payne ('12) who found in *Gelastocoris* that the oöcytes are derived directly from the apical group, passing thence downwards through the nutritive end-chamber but always distinct from them. Again, E. B. Harvey ('13) concluded that the binucleate cells so often observed in the follicle-cells are not due to amitosis but to mitotic division of the nucleus without cleavage of the cytosome. It is nearly certain that this is to a certain extent correct, because of the frequent occurrence of multiple or polyploid chromosome-groups in the follicular epithelium (p. 870).

It must be admitted that the questions here involved are in a somewhat unsettled state; nevertheless it has become evident that nearly all of the evidence supposed to demonstrate the occurrence of complete cell-division by amitosis as a normal process in the genetic continuity of cells is untrustworthy. The facts now indicate rather the correctness of Flemming's conclusion that amitosis means merely a fragmentation of the nucleus, often of temporary nature, which is only rarely followed by cleavage and probably plays some special part in the cell-metabolism by increase of the nuclear surface. The frequent occurrence of amitosis in embryonic cells, therefore, by no means proves that the multiplication of *cells* is thus effected. An important contribution to this question is made by the studies of Macklin ('16) carried out by means of continuous observations on living cultures of embryonic cells of various tissues from the chick. Binucleate cells are frequently observed in such cultures, and this condition certainly results in some cases from typical amitotic division of the nucleus, as was determined by continuous observation of the living cells (Fig. 96). *In no case, however, was amitotic division found to be followed by division of the cytosome.* The cytoplasmic cleavage of a binucleate cell seems only to take place after a subsequent mitotic nuclear division; and Macklin was able to observe in the prophases of such a mitosis in the living cell that *the two original nuclei fuse together and give rise to a single group of chromosomes associated with a single spindle.* The amitotic nuclear division here forms no part of cell-division but is only a temporary fragmentation of the nucleus into two karyomerites. Such a process, evidently, is in no way incompatible with the occurrence of perfectly normal mitosis following

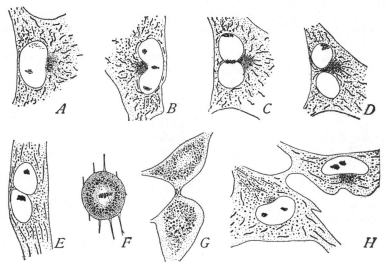

Fig. 96.—Nuclear amitosis in living cells (MACKLIN).

A–D, successive drawings of a living connective-tissue cell (cytosome only partly shown) in hanging-drop culture, from an embryo chick of five days, showing complete division of nucleus without division of cytosome; the dark bodies are chondriosomes, in some degree massed about the "centrosphere" at one side of the nucleus; *E–H,* successive stages of mitosis of a binucleate cell from life; the bipolar mitotic figure *F* was followed by complete division.

upon amitosis, and does not contradict the individuality or genetic continuity of the chromosomes.

In the light of the foregoing observations it may fairly be concluded that the general conclusions of Flemming and of Ziegler still remain unshaken and that they may probably be accepted as valid in principle. No doubt the subject will repay further critical study; and it would be rash to deny that amitosis may play a larger rôle in cell-division, particularly in cells of highly differentiated type, than now seems probable. That some sort of amitosis may play an important part in the multiplication of some unicellular organisms seems very probable; but it is also probable that in these cases the nucleus may be of far simpler composition than in higher forms and that its division may involve a correspondingly simpler mode of distribution. In higher forms, on the other hand, the whole force of the accumulating evidence, direct and indirect, tends to emphasize the fundamental importance of mitosis as a primary factor in every form of reproduction.

LITERATURE II

(See also V, VI, XI, XIII. For abbreviations see General Literature List.)

Boveri, Th. (IX, XI).

Bowen, R. H., '20. Studies on Insect Spermatogenesis, I: *B. B.*, XXXIX.

Chambers, R., '19. Changes in Protoplasmic Consistency and their Relation to Cell-Division: *J. G. P.*, II.

Conklin, E. G., '02. Karyokinesis and Cytokinesis in the Maturation, Fertilization and Cleavage of *Crepidula* and other Gasteropoda: *Jour. Acad. Nat. Sci. Philadelphia*, XII.

'12. Experimental Studies on Nuclear and Cell Division, etc.: *Philadelphia*, 12.

'17. Mitosis and Amitosis: *B. B.*, XXXIII.

Deineka, D., '12. Der Netzapparat von Golgi, etc.: *A. A.*, XLI.

Devisé, R., '21. La figure achromatique et la plaque cellulaire, etc.: *L. C.*, XXXII.

Fauré-Fremiet, E., '10 (IV).

Flemming, W., '79a, '80, '81. Beiträge sur Kenntniss der Zelle und ihre Lebenserscheinungen. I, II, III: *A. M. A.*, XVI, XIX, XX.

Gallardo, A., '09. La division de la cellule, etc.: *A. Entwm.*, XXVIII.

Grégoire and Wygaerts, '03. La reconstitution du noyau et la formation des chromosomes, etc.: *L. C.*, XXI.

Grégoire, V., '06. La structure de l'élément chromosomique au repos et en division, etc.: *L. C.*, XXIII.

Harper, R. A., '99. Cell-division in Sporangia and Asci: *A. Bot.*, XIII.

Hartog, M., '14. The true Mechanism of Mitosis: *A. Entwm.*, XL.

Heidenhain, M., '96. Ein neues Modell zum Spannungsgesetz der centrierten Systeme: *Verh. d. Anat. Ges.*

Hertwig, O. and R., '87. Ueber den Befruchtungs- und Theilungs-vorgang des thierischen Eies unt. d. Einfluss äusserer Agentien: *J. Z.*, XIII.

Klein, E., '78, '79. Observations on the Structure of Cells and Nuclei: *Q. J.*, XVIII, XIX.

Küster and Brue¹, '15. Zelle und Zellteilung: *Handwörterb. d. Naturwiss*, X., *Fischer, Jena*.

Lawson, A. A., '00. Origin of the Cones of the Multipolar Spindle in *Gladiolus; B. G.*, XXX.

'03. Studies in Spindle-Formation: *B. G.*, XXX.

Lewis and Robertson, '16. The Mitochondria and other Structures observed by the Tissue Culture Method, etc.: *B. B.*, XXX.

Lillie, R. S., '03. On the Differences in the Direction of the Electrical Currents of Certain free Cells and Nuclei: *A. J. P.*, VIII, 4.

'05. On the conditions determining the Disposition of the Chromatic Filaments and Chromosomes in Mitosis: *B. B.*, VIII, 3.

'05-'11. The Physiology of Cell-Division, I–VI, especially: I, *A. J. P.*, XV, 1. IV, *J. M.*, XXII, 3.

Ludford and Gatenby, '21. Dictyokinesis in Germ-Cells, etc.: *P. R. S.*, B. 92. No. B, 646.

Lundegårdh, H., '12. Chromosomen, Nucleoli, etc., bei der Karyokinese: *Beitr. Biol. Pflanz.*, XI.

Macklin, C. C., '16. Amitosis in Cells growing *in vitro;* Carnegie Inst. Pub.

Meves, Fr., '96, '98. Zelltheilung: *E. A. E.,* VI, VIII.

Mottier, D. M., '00. Nuclear and Cell-division in *Dictyota; A. Bot.,* XIV.

Müller, H. A., '11. Kernstudien an Pflanzen, I, II: *A. Zf.,* VIII.

Němec, B., '03. Ueber die Einwirkung des Chloralhydrats auf die Kern- und Zelltheilung: *J. W. B.,* XXXIX.

Osterhout, W. J. V., '97. Ueber Enstehlung der karyokinetischen Spindel bei *Equisetum; J. W. B.,* XXX.

Overton, J. B., '22. The Organization of the Nuclei in the Root-tips of *Podophyllum: Trans. Wis. Acad. Sci.,* XX.

Prenant, A., '10. Théories et interprétation physique de la mitose: *J. A. P.,* XLVI, 5.

Rabl, C., '89. Ueber Zelltheilung: *A. A.*

Rhumbler, L., '03. Mechanische Erklärung der Aehnlichkeit, etc.: *A. Entwm.,* XVI.

Richards, A., '09, '11. The Method of Cell-division . . . in *Tænia: B. B.,* XVII; and *Moniezia: Ibid.,* XX.

Roux, W., '83. Ueber die Bedeutung der Kerntheilungsfiguren: *Engelmann, Leipzig.*

Sharp, L. W. '13. Somatic Chromosomes in *Vicia: L. C.,* XXIX.
    '20. Somatic Chromosomes in *Tradescantia: A. J. B.,* VII.

Spek, J., '18a. Oberflächenspannungsdifferenzen als Ursache der Zellteilung: *A. Entwm.,* XLIV, 1.
    '18b. Die amöboiden Bewegungen, etc.: *Ibid.,* XLIV.

Strasburger, E., '80. (Int.)
    '88. Ueber Kern- und Zelltheilung im Pflanzenreich, nebst einem Anhang über Befruchtung: *Jena.*
    '95. Karyokinetische Probleme: *J. W. B.,* XXVIII, 1.
    '00. Ueber Reductionstheilung, Spindelbildung, etc.: *Histol. Beiträge,* VI.

Timberlake, H. G., '00. The Development and Function of the Cell-plate, etc.: *B. G.,* XXX.

Van Beneden, E., '83–'84, '87. (Int.)

Vejdovský and Mrazek, '03. Umbildung des Cytoplasma während der Befruchtung und Zelltheilung: *A. M. A.,* LXII.

CHAPTER III

REPRODUCTION AND THE LIFE CYCLE. INTRODUCTORY

" In both the rejuvenated infusorian and the fertilized egg-cell we see the onset of an energetic multiplication by cell-division which leads in the one case to the formation of a multicellular organism and in the other to a series of cell-generations. Morphologically, therefore, we must compare the sum of all the individuals of these generations to the multi-cellular higher organism that arises from the fertilized egg and itself in turn gives rise to eggs."

BÜTSCHLI.[1]

Growth and cell-division constitute the central phenomena in every process of reproduction; upon them, therefore, depend the genetic continuity of living organisms and the phenomena of heredity. The cyclical character so conspicuously shown in the life-histories of plants and animals generally prominently raises the question whether growth and cell-division are fundamentally rhythmic. We shall here briefly examine this subject from a general and elementary point of view in order to prepare the way for the cytological problems of reproduction to be considered in the four succeeding chapters.

It is obvious that the conditions on which the life-cycle depends are in part internal, in part external to the organism, but the relation between these has not yet become entirely clear.[2] We must also distinguish between the life-cycle of the individual and that of the species as shown in the succession of generations. In higher animals generally the individual life runs its allotted course in a certain sense automatically, in the absence of any corresponding cycle of external conditions. Given the normal conditions, and barring accident, every individual displays a succession of youth, maturity, old age and death as progressive phases of a process that goes forward without pause from the moment that the egg begins its development. In youth the constructive activities are in the ascendent, in age the destructive, while maturity is a period of relative physiological balance. To a certain extent the course of this process can be diverted by experimental modifications of external conditions; but sooner or later the end is inevitable.

In lower organisms many cases are known in which the life-cycle of the *species*, as shown by the alternation or succession of generations, is dependent upon changes of the external environment (for instance, in the

---

[1] *Studien über die ersten Entwicklungsvorgänge der Eizelle, die Zelltheilung und die Conjugation der Infusorien: Abh. d. Senckenberg. Naturforsch. Ges.* X, 3, 4, Frankfort, 1876, p. 420.
[2] For an interesting discussion of these relations see Jost, '07, '13.

rotifers, daphnids, or aphids, and in some of the Protista),[1] it is possible that such changes may play a leading perhaps even an exclusive part in the determination of the life-cycle.

In the highest animals (*e. g.*, in vertebrates) the life-cycle is a strictly sexual one which, so far as the race is concerned, may be said to begin and end with the egg (or sperm).[2] In many lower animals, and very generally in plants, the life-history is complicated by the occurrence of various forms of asexual reproduction, so that we may distinguish asexual cycles as well as sexual, often in regular alternation. At the opposite extreme, among the simplest forms of life, we find some cases such as the Bacteria and Cyanophyceæ in which no sexual cycle is yet certainly known. Some observers, it is true, have accepted the occurrence of a sexual process in certain of the bacteria in the form of a reunion of two incompletely separated daughter-cells; and an "autogamous" conjugation between sister-cells has been described in the yeasts and various other simple plants and animals examples of which are offered by the rhizopods *Actinophrys* or *Actinosphærium* (p. 581). In case of the bacteria, however, it seems probable that the phenomenon that has thus been interpreted is probably not to be regarded as a degenerate process of conjugation, but an abortive cell-division.[3]

We are not yet, therefore, in a position to maintain that sexuality is a fundamental property of all living matter; nevertheless the occurrence of a sexual process in some form is all but universal among living things; and among Protista a definite sexual cycle may often clearly be distinguished, sometimes in alternation with an asexual cycle or cyles, as is seen in many sporozoa and in certain rhizopods (*e. g.*, *Polystomella*, Fig. 284). In free-living Protista such alternation may be correlated with external conditions of the environment, such as seasonal changes; in parasitic forms (*e. g.*, in the Hæmosporidia) with a change of hosts. The relation of the Protistan sexual cycle to that of multicellular forms is considered beyond (p. 238).

The group of problems that center in the sexual reproduction of higher organisms may be approached by a brief review of

I. THE REPRODUCTIVE PROCESSES IN GENERAL

Morphologically the reproductive processes of multicellular organisms may conveniently be distinguished as *somatogenic* and *cytogenic*,[4] the former in-

---

[1] A valuable discussion of this question is given by Morgan ('07).

[2] "The egg is the mid-passage or transition stage between parents and offspring, between those who are, or were, and those who are about to be." Harvey, *De Generatione*, 1651, Trans., p. 271.

[3] Dobell, '09, where further references to the literature are given.

[4] These terms are due to Hartman ('04) and Waldeyer ('06).

cluding asexual multiplication by fission or budding in which the body itself divides to produce offspring that are essentially multicellular fragments of itself. Cytogenic reproduction (cytogony) on the other hand, is effected by means of unicellular *germ-cells* which by growth and division may build up a new multicellular body. In the Protista this distinction does not properly exist, since the whole body is itself unicellular; here also, nevertheless, it is convenient to speak of reproduction as cytogenic.

Somatogenic reproduction is always asexual (*monogony*) while cytogenic may be either asexual or sexual (*amphigony*),[1] the latter characterized by a preliminary process of *syngamy* (*fertilization* or its equivalent, *conjugation*) in which two germ-cells or gametes unite and most commonly fuse to form a zygote. Asexual germ-cells or *agametes* are in general incapable of fertilization or activation by the sperm, and develop without a preliminary union of germ-cells, as is typically illustrated by the spores of higher plants.[2] Sexual germ-cells, on the other hand, have in general the power of union in syngamy, the product of their union being the *zygote*, with which a new life-cycle begins. In many higher organisms the gametes are incapable of development unless activated by process of syngamy. In other cases the gametes of the female (ova) may be activated without syngamy, and develop by the asexual process of *parthenogenesis*, which is analogous, broadly speaking, to the development of a spore. This phenomenon occurs naturally in many plants and animals, including especially the rotifers, lower crustaceans (daphnids, ostracodes), and insects (aphids, gall-flies, bees, etc.) and in some cases can be artificially induced by physico-chemical means in the sexual eggs of animals that do not naturally undergo parthenogenesis (p. 472). In many cases the ovum has completely lost the capacity for fertilization and has become a true agamete, developing only by parthenogenesis. Such ova occur in rotifers, daphnids, ostracodes, aphids and phylloxerans, and differ markedly from the sexual ova in mode of maturation and other characters. There is, however, reason to conclude that they have been derived from true sexual ova capable of fertilization (p. 794).

The relations between sexual reproduction and parthenogenesis as they occur in nature are widely varied. In some species parthenogenesis is a rare process which seems to be interpolated irregularly in the succession of sexual generations. This is often spoken of as *facultative* parthenogenesis. In others it becomes a constant feature of the life-cycle occurring only at certain periods, sometimes in regular alternation with the sexual process. In

[1] These terms are Haeckel's.

[2] The term spore is of broad and vague meaning, and some kinds of "spores" (*e. g.*, *auxospores* of diatoms) are zygotes that result from a process of conjugation. Spores in the strict sense of the word do not occur in higher animals though found in many Protista.

this case the sexual generations are often morphologically different to such a degree as to have received different generic names (gall-flies); and thus arises a true alternation of generations. By further encroachment upon the sexual process parthenogenesis may come to constitute the major part of the life-cycle, the sexual forms only appearing at intervals following a certain number of asexual generations, as is the rule among rotifers, aphids, phylloxerans, daphnids and ostracodes.

In nearly all such cases the parthenogenetic eggs are incapable of fertilization and differ characteristically from the sexual eggs in mode of maturation (p. 467). This type of parthenogenesis is often called *obligatory;* but experiment has proved that the sexual process may in some cases be induced by changes in the environment [1] and has also shown that under suitable conditions the succession of parthenogenetic cycles may be greatly prolonged, perhaps indefinitely. The classical example of this is offered by the rose aphid, the normal life-history of which includes a series of parthenogenetic cycles during the summer months later terminated by a sexual process. If, however, the insects are cultivated in the greenhouse, the sexual cycle may be wholly suppressed, reproduction now continuing solely by parthenogenesis even through a series of years.[2] The process of senescence, it is true, still continues in each generation; for the life of the individual is limited as before; but the race is continued by a process in which syngamy plays no immediate part.

In rotifers the researches of Maupas ('90, '91) showed that the appearance of the sexual forms may readily be induced by changes of temperature (later shown to produce this result by affecting the microörganisms on which the rotifers feed). The work thus initiated has more recently been developed with marked success by Whitney and by Shull [3] with results slightly different in detail but similar in principle. When *Hydatina senta* is consecutively cultivated in old culture-fluid (infusion of horse-manure in spring-water) parthenogenesis may long go forwards without the appearance of sexual forms, but the latter quickly appear if the animals be transferred to fresh culture-fluid. Since this effect is produced even after filtration of the culture-fluid (the rotifers normally feed on flagellates) it is ascribed by Shull to dissolved substances that progressively accumulate in long-continued cultures. The same result follows from a suitable change of food. In *Hydatina* fed upon a uniform diet of the colorless flagellate *Polytoma* Whitney obtained 289 successive parthenogenetic generations, extending through nearly two years without the appearance of sexual

---

[1] This must not be confused with the determination of sex itself. *Cf.* p. 815.
[2] Kyber, '15, see Morgan, '07.
[3] Whitney, '07, '10. '14, '16; Shull, '10, '10a, '11.

forms; but the sexual process could at any time be induced within a few hours by changing the diet from the colorless *Polytoma* to the chlorophyll-bearing *Chlamydomonas*. Results similar in principle were obtained in other rotifers (*Brachionus, Diaschiza, Diglena, Pedalion*).[1]

In the foregoing cases the sexual process still forms a regular part of the life-cycle under the natural conditions of life, though parthenogenesis seems to play the main rôle. A step beyond this are cases in which parthenogenesis has assumed still greater importance, males being extremely rare or even entirely unknown, *e. g.*, among the free-living nematodes (Maupas) and in various insects, including certain species of walking-sticks (*Phasmidæ*), saw-flies (*Tenthredinidæ*), gall-flies (*Cynips, Rhodites*), scale-insects (*Coccidæ*) and Lepidoptera (*Psychidæ*). Similar differences in respect to sexuality and parthenogenesis between related species occur in various genera of plants. In *Alchemilla* (*Eualchemilla*) only a few species are sexual while many are exclusively parthenogenetic [2] and a somewhat similar condition seems to exist in *Rosa*.[3] Both sexual and parthenogenetic species occur also in *Wikstrœmia, Antennaria, Hieracium* and other genera.[4]

The evidence makes it highly probable that in all these cases the original mode of reproduction was sexual and that it has in greater or less degree been supplanted by parthenogenesis. This change seems to have taken place very readily, for even within the limits of a single genus some species may reproduce only by the sexual process, others by parthenogenesis only, still others by both. Remarkable examples of the plasticity of the reproductive phenomena in respect to these relations are offered among the free-living nematodes [5] in which even closely related species, *e. g.*, of *Rhabditis* or *Diplogaster*, may show very striking differences. Many of the species are ordinary diœcious and strictly sexual forms, with the sexes in approximately equal numbers. Other forms are hermaphrodites having the morphological aspect of females (and formerly often described as such), but also producing sperm and being self-fertilizing; but these same species may have in addition true males, and sometimes also true females (*e. g.*, in *Rhabditis*). In most of the hermaphroditic forms true females are absent and the males, when present, are extremely rare, often only a small fraction of 1%. Beyond all this, some species are parthenogenetic, wholly or in

---

[1] It is a remarkable fact, determined by Maupas and confirmed by both Whitney and Shull, that the result of changed diet is not manifested in the individuals first affected but in their daughters, the effect being to induce the parthenogenetic production of daughters which produce sexual eggs, capable of fertilization. If unfertilized, these eggs produce males, if fertilized females, so that the definitive somatic effect first appears in the grandchildren of the forms originally treated.

[2] Murbeck, '01, Strasburger, '04.

[3] Täckholm, '20.

[4] See Winkler, '08a, b, Strasburger, '09, Tischler, '15, Ernst, '18.

[5] Sharp ,'95, Maupas, '00, Potts, '10.

part; and some show an alternation of generations between hermaphroditic and diœcious phases (p. 809). The evidence indicates that in all these various cases the primitive condition was diœcious, with equality of the sexes; and that hermaphroditism, parthenogenesis, etc., are derivative forms of reproduction accompanied, at least in some cases, by underlying cytological changes.

Varied relations between sexual reproduction and parthenogenesis have also been observed in insects of various orders. In the gall-fly *Rhodites rosæ*, for example, males are very rare, while they have not thus far been found at all in *Cynips Kollari*, a species which seems to reproduce solely by parthenogenesis.[1]

Here too, such differences sometimes appear between nearly related species, *e. g.*, in moths of the genus *Solenobia* (Seiler, '23) in which occur both modes of reproduction. In *S. pineti* the sexual forms predominate in northern Germany, with the sexes in nearly equal numbers, while towards the south the males become less numerous and in the neighborhood of Munich are of extreme rarity, parthenogenesis being the predominant type. In *S. triquetrella* these conditions are reversed, the sexual forms being very rare while only parthenogenetic forms are found over a large area in Germany, Austria, and Switzerland, (p. 805). The evidence clearly indicates in this case that the sexual and the parthenogenetic forms are distinct races that differ genetically and are not determined by external conditions.

The same fact appears with still greater clearness in cases where different strains or races *of the same species* differ in mode of reproduction, and are found to differ correspondingly in the underlying cytological conditions. A classical case of this is offered by the phyllopod *Artemia salina*, a cosmopolitan species which in general morphological type appears to represent a single species, but differs in the number of chromosomes. As shown by Artom ('11, '12, '21) this species includes two distinct races, one of which is strictly parthenogenetic, the other strictly sexual. The former, from Capodistria (near Trieste) and various other localities, produces only parthenogenetic eggs which give off only one polocyte and develop by diploid parthenogenesis, with 84 chromosomes. The second race, from Cagliari (Sardinia) and other localities, produces only sexual eggs, which give off two polocytes, undergo complete reduction (to 21 chromosomes) and upon fertilization develop with 42 chromosomes. Here, too, it is evident that the two races differ genetically, though their only constant morphological differences, apart from the chromosome-number, consist in the larger size of the nuclei and cells of the parthenogenetic race ("bivalens") and also the larger size of the body.

[1] For an account of the cytology of these forms see p. 803. See Hogben ('20a).

A close parallel to this is offered in plants by the long known case of *Chara crinita*.[1] This widespread species likewise occurs in two forms, one strictly parthenogenetic and diploid, and the other sexual and haploid. The diploid race, like a parthenogenetic aphid, undergoes no process of reduction and develops with the diploid number of chromosomes, 24. The sexual haploid race produces gametes having 12 chromosomes, which by their union must produce zygotes with 24 chromosomes. The resulting plants nevertheless have but 12 chromosomes, *i. e.*, the haploid number; hence it is practically certain that reduction here is zygotic, *i. e.*, occurs during the first two divisions of the zygote, as in *Spirogyra* or *Zygnema* (p. 491). Intermediate forms between the two races do not occur, and it is clear that they are genotypically distinct.

In both the foregoing cases there is strong reason to conclude that the parthenogenetic race has been secondarily derived from the sexual; and the same conclusion probably applies to many other cases of strictly or mainly parthenogenetic forms.

The relation of parthenogenesis to sex in these various cases will be considered later (p. 789). We here only refer to the remarkable variations which they sometimes show. In the homopterous insect *Trialeurodes vaporariorum*, for example, as shown by Williams ('17) and Schrader ('19), unfertilized eggs of the English form produce females, of the American form only males. A parallel to this is offered by the hymenopteran parasite *Trichogramma pretiosa*, the unfertilized eggs of which are said to produce males alone in the U. S. and in Europe either both sexes or females only (Howard and Fiske, '11). The explanation of these cases is still imperfectly known, but is no doubt to be looked for in underlying cytological conditions in the germ-cells.

Taken as a whole, the phenomena clearly prove that sexual reproduction may readily become much restricted or wholly dispensed with, even in relatively high organisms, and hence cannot be regarded as a fundamental necessity of continued life. A singular fact, which bears on this question, is that in the Hymenoptera generally the males appear always to arise from parthenogenetic eggs, the females from fertilized ones (p. 795).

II. SEXUAL REPRODUCTION. SYNGAMY AND ITS EFFECTS

The essential nature of the sexual process and the part which it plays in the life-cycle constitute one of the oldest riddles of biology, yet its final solution still eludes us. As far as we can see there is no *a priori* reason why, barring accident, one cell-division should not succeed another in endless succession. Such may actually be the case in some of the lowest forms of

---

[1] See especially Ernst, '18.

life, such as the Bacteria and Cyanophyceæ; but in vastly the greater number of living forms the succession of cell-divisions is periodically interrupted by a sexual process of which the essential act is syngamy or fusion of two cells (gametes) into one. This process is not in itself an act of reproduction (p. 580). It can at most be regarded as only an antecedent condition of reproduction, obligatory in the highest forms of life but in lower organisms often held in abeyance for long periods of time or even in some cases, it would seem, dispensed with altogether.

Why the sexual process should be necessary in any case is unknown; but we are able to perceive some of its morphological and physiological effects. Morphologically the most important effect of syngamy (together with the accompanying processes of maturation) is to bring about a periodic reorganization of the nucleus; but in parthenogenesis or endomixis (p. 244) an essentially similar reorganization is accomplished by other means. Physiologically we may recognize four distinct effects of syngamy. In higher animals the most conspicuous of these is the *activation or initiation of development* in the egg, thus inaugurating a new cycle of activity. It has long been held that an analogous effect is produced by the conjugation of unicellular organisms, and this view is strongly supported in certain cases by some of the most recent researches (Calkins, '19); but the fact has repeatedly been disputed. A second obvious physiological effect of syngamy is temporarily to bring into close association two previously separate lines of heredity; *i. e.*, *biparental heredity* by means of *amphimixis* (Weismann).

A third effect, less obvious than the foregoing, is an *increase of external diversity* in the offspring, conspicuously seen in the extremely variable offspring of the seed-progeny of many cultivated races of plants as compared with their relatively uniform offspring produced by asexual cuttings, grafts, tubers or bulbs. This is undoubtedly a recombination-effect resulting from the heterozygous nature of these races. A fourth effect, also most obvious in heterozygous forms of hybrids between different strains or races, is an *increase of vigor* in the offspring. This effect, superficially similar to the first of those enumerated above, is of interest in its bearing on the general theory of senescence and rejuvenescence. We cannot here consider *in extenso* the intricate physiological problems involved in these various effects of syngamy; but a brief survey of them is desirable as an introduction to the cytological phenomena to be considered in the following chapters.

1. Senescence, Syngamy, and Rejuvenescence

By an important group of investigators syngamy has been regarded as a direct cause of rejuvenescence, operating as the corrective to a progressive process of senescence which otherwise would sooner or later culminate in natural death.   Certainly when we consider only the higher plants and animals we must admit that the assumption contains at least a measure of truth; for in most cases the germ-cells die if they are not fertilized.   Here, as Loeb has said, fertilization is a "life-saving act" which initiates a new cycle of assimilation, growth, and cell-division.   It does not, however, follow that senescence and natural death are fundamental phenomena inherent in all living protoplasm, still less that syngamy is their only remedy.   In some animals parthenogenesis may replace fertilization for long periods of time; in others it is the only known method of reproduction; in still others parthenogenesis may experimentally be substituted for fertilization, at least for a time, as in case of the rose-aphid (p. 229).

Further doubts are raised by experiments on normal somatic cells cultivated outside the body *in vitro* [1] and on tumor-cells transplated from individual to individual.   Fibroblasts obtained from the heart of a chick-embryo in 1912 were thus cultivated *in vitro* by Carrel and Ebeling for more than ten years and were still growing (1922) with undiminished vitality and without change of type.   More than 30,000 cultures have thus been obtained from an original small fragment, the cells having passed through about 1900 generations; and had it been possible to preserve all the cells thus produced their combined volume to-day would be far larger than the sun. [2]   Even more remarkable examples of this are offered by tumors (sarcoma) of rats and mice.   One of these, discovered by Jensen in 1903, has been cultivated for many years in unbroken descent by inoculation from one animal to another, and has thus been spread to a large number of experimental laboratories throughout the world.   This tumor is still growing with undiminished vigor though many generations of mice have meanwhile come and gone.[3]   The descendants of such a tumor—a sarcoma or connective-tissue tumor of the rat, discovered in 1908, also by Jensen,—are still actively growing in the Crocker Research Laboratory of Columbia University after more than twelve years of continuous transplantation from rat to rat.[4] Accurate studies on this tumor during the past seven years have shown that, if we assume an unlimited supply of rats and the ability to make the transfer of all of every tumor at intervals of 23.7 days

---

[1] That embryonic cells isolated from their fellows may continue to multiply and differentiate was shown by the early work of Chabry, Driesch, Wilson and others (p. 1048).   The continued cultures of such cells *in vitro* was successfully accomplished by Leo Loeb ('97, '07, etc.) and especially by Harrison ('07, '10, etc.) and later much extended by the work of Carrel and Burrows ('11), M. and W. Lewis ('11), Ebeling ('19) and others.

[2] Ebeling, '22.

[3] See Leo Loeb ('01, '02, '08, '15, '17, etc.).

[4] I am indebted for the calculations based on these data to the statistician of the laboratory, Miss Mary R. Curtis.

the entire mass of tumor produced in 21 months would be 1.7 times the space occupied by the solar system as far as the orbit of Neptune. The mass at the end of three years can only be stated in units represented by the distance of the sun to the polestar. Such a statement impresses us with the limitless power of increase of living matter by growth and division, and with the fact that even in the cells of mammals this power seems under proper conditions to undergo no perceptible decrease in the complete absence of any process of syngamy.

The same fact is brought home to us by the history of certain cultivated plants which have systematically been propagated for very long periods of time by tubers, cuttings, grafts,[1] or other strictly somatogenic processes without impairment of vigor. A climax is reached in those species which have become sexually completely sterile and reproduce exclusively by parthenogenesis, apogamy or other asexual processes, a condition rare among animals but not uncommon in higher plants (p. 230). Such facts support Weismann's contention that senescence of the somatic cells, though real, does not result from an inherent property of living protoplasm as such, but is due to secondary conditions. The one-celled organisms, in Weismann's view,[2] undergo no process of senescence and death; these organisms he believed to be endowed potentially with unending life; but here apparently his conclusion was pushed too far, as we shall presently see (p. 246).

The causes of senescence in higher organisms have long been a subject of inquiry. Herbert Spencer early suggested that it arises from a progressive increase of protoplasmic stability, i. e., "an approach towards molecular equilibrium,"[3] in which condition energy is less readily liberated by chemical action. Syngamy operates to overcome this condition by the mixture of two slightly different protoplasms, thus rendering the protoplasm more labile, "reëstablishing active molecular change in the germ" by which energy is set free, and also leading to increased variability. It may be doubted whether any later writer has offered a more satisfactory interpretation of senescence, though many have endeavored to render it more specific. Weismann [4] ascribed senescence to progressive *differentiation* by which the cell gradually loses its plasticity, and reproductive power; and this view has been widely adopted by later writers.[5] Minot, and later R. Hertwig [6] sought for a quantitative explanation of the phenomena, as-

---

[1] In some cases for centuries, e. g., in the willow, poplar, sugar-cane or the cultivated banana (see Jost, '07).

[2] Weismann, '81, '83, '84, '13.

[3] *Principles of Biology*, 1866, Am. Ed., p. 234. It is interesting to recall that in connection with this Spencer emphasized the colloidal nature of protoplasm.

[4] *Life and Death*, 1883.

[5] See Kassowitz ('99), Enriques ('07, '09), Child ('11, '14, '15), Conklin ('12, '13), Schleip ('15), etc

[6] See Minot ('90, '95 '08), R. Hertwig ('89, '99, '02, '03, '05, '08.

cribing senescence to a disturbance in the normal karyoplasmic ratio, *i. e.*, in the equilibrium between nuclear and cytoplasmic mass. Minot as-sumed this to result from a progressive increase of the cytoplasm, accom-panied by differentiation or *cytomorphosis* with the products of which the cytosome gradually becomes overloaded.[1] This condition, in his view, is counteracted by the cleavage of the ovum, in which he believed the nu-clear material to be rapidly increased while the cytoplasm remains nearly stationary.

Hertwig's assumption was in one principal respect the opposite of Mi-not's, senescence being ascribed to a progressive increase in the nuclear volume as compared to the cytoplasmic, a result counteracted either by an extrusion of chromidia from the nucleus (in Protozoa) or by the nuclear reorganization that takes place in the course of maturation and syngamy. In the case of multicellular forms Hertwig regarded both sperm and egg as senescent or in a state of depression, owing to their relatively abnormally large nuclei and an accompanying accumulation of differentiated com-ponents in the cytosome. This condition is overcome, in part by the libera-tion of a large amount of nuclear substance during maturation (a well-known fact) [2] in part by syngamy and cleavage. The first of these three processes reduces the size of the egg-nucleus (p. 259) far below the normal, while the second and third gradually restore it to the normal. Hertwig, like Minot, thus assumed that cleavage involves a large increase of nu-clear material.[3]

It cannot be said that either of the above two hypotheses has had much result, except in so far as both recognize the importance of differentiation as a cause of senescence. So far as the karyoplasmic relation is concerned, facts may be cited in favor of each. The great increase in size of the cy-tosome as compared with the nucleus in many tissue-cells of both plants and animals has long been recognized. Eycleshymer, for instance ('04), found that in the striated muscle-cells of *Necturus* the increase of plasma-volume was about ten times that of the nuclear in the growth of larvæ from 8 mm. long to the adult condition, and an even greater increase has often been noted in the growth of plant-cells. On the other hand, the rel-atively large nuclei of both egg and sperm in higher forms and in the stages of depression in various Protozoa (*e. g.*, in *Actinosphærium*) are also ob-served facts. Later studies have, however, shown that some of the assump-tions of Minot and Hertwig cannot be sustained.

It has been shown that the karyoplasmic ratio is in some cases subject to wide variations even at the same period of the life-history (p. 731), and

[1] '08, pp. 161 ff.   [2] *Cf.* pp. 328, 356.
[3] For an interesting development of Hertwig's views see Popoff ('08).

that in these cases the adult tissue-cells show no marked increase of cytoplasm over nucleus as compared with the blastomeres.[1] Concerning the increase of nuclear volume during cleavage assumed by Minot, Hertwig and other writers the existing data are contradictory. Godlewsky ('08) found in sea-urchins that the nuclear volume almost doubles at each cleavage up to the 64-cell stage, but thereafter the increase is very slight up to the 256-cell stage. Godlewsky assumes, however, that the nuclei grow richer in "chromatin" during this period. Erdmann ('08) found in *Paracentrotus* (*Strongylocentrotus*) that in the pluteus stage the ratio of chromatin to plasma is about seven times greater than at the beginning of development. On the other hand, Conklin found in *Crepidula* that the average nuclear growth in *Crepidula* up to the 32-cell stage is not more than 5 to 9% for each division and is greatly decreased subsequently. This is perhaps in part explained by the fact, determined by Erdmann ('08) and by Baltzer ('08), that both the nuclei and the chromosomes grow progressively smaller as cleavage advances. In sea-urchins Erdmann found that the chromosomes in the pluteus had only about ¼ the volume of those of the first division; and Conklin observed a similar decrease of size in the chromosomes of *Crepidula*.[2]

These various facts show on how precarious a basis rest theories of senescence and rejuvenescence which refer these processes to changes in the karyoplasmic ratio. On the other hand, nearly all modern observers have emphasized the importance of those underlying processes of metabolism that are expressed in the phenomena of differentiation and the resulting accumulation in the cytosome of relatively inactive products. Child refers senescence to a decrease in the rate of metabolism (which may result from any cause) while conversely rejuvenescence results from an increase in the rate, due to "the removal in one way or another of the structural obstacles to metabolism" ('11, '15). This conclusion, in substance closely akin to that of Spencer, Weismann and other early writers, is probably well founded; but unfortunately none of these conclusions seems to touch the bottom of the problem. The long-continued cultivation of tissue-cells *in vitro*, or of tumor-cells by successive transplantations, shows that even differentiated cells may live far beyond the normal span of life under suitable conditions. There is much force, therefore, in the contention of Pearl ('22) that the senescence of higher organisms is a consequence of the complex balance between the mutually dependent cells of which they are built up, a balance readily upset by pathological changes that may take place in any particular part and which may be beyond repair by the normal regulatory powers of the organism.

[1] See Conklin, '12.   [2] Marcus ('06), Erdmann ('08), Baltzer ('08), Conklin ('12).

Physiological Effects of Conjugation in Protista. While "rejuvenescence" as a consequence of fertilization is an obvious fact in the higher plants and animals, such is far from the case in Protista; here, indeed, the physiological effect of conjugation constitutes one of the most ardently debated problems of general biology.[1] It was suggested already by Dujardin (1841) that simple cell-division in Protozoa cannot go forward indefinitely, and a similar notion was entertained by Balbiani ('60) and by Claparède and Lachmann ('60). H. Spencer raised the same question, but the problem first appeared in clearly defined form with the classical works of Bütschli ('76) and Engelmann ('76). These observers produced experimental evidence, drawn from the study of ciliates, to show that after a certain number of divisions there begins a gradual process of degeneration which ultimately leads to death unless counteracted by a remedial process of reorganization and rejuvenescence (*Verjüngung*) that is brought about by conjugation. Enlarging this conception, Bütschli pointed out the close analogy of the individual metazoön and the protozoan sexual cycle. In both cases, he urged, syngamy inaugurates a new cycle of growth and division. In the protozoön the resulting cells separate to lead independent lives, in the metazoön, they remain in close association to form a multicellular individual;[2] but in each case the cells of the cycle undergo progressive senescence, which culminates in death if not counteracted by conjugation or fertilization. Syngamy was thus regarded by Bütschli as a *conditio sine qua non* of continued life, a conclusion also supported by Engelmann ('76) and Balbiani ('82). It was challenged in Weismann's suggestive essay on life and death (1881), which offered a formidable argument against natural or inherent senescence in the Protista. Under suitable conditions, urged Weismann, the unicellular organisms are capable of indefinitely continued growth and division. Senescence and natural death in multicellular organisms were regarded by Weismann as secondary phenomena resulting from a diminution or loss of growth and reproductive power on the part of the somatic cells; and this loss he ascribed to their specialization and differentiation for other functions.

The celebrated researches of Maupas ('88, '89) on the ciliate Infusoria seemed at first to bring conclusive experimental confirmation of Bütschli's and Engelmann's conclusions; and similar results were reached by R. Hertwig and by many other observers;[3] but later studies revealed many complicating factors which raised fresh doubts concerning their validity. Mau-

---

[1] A critical review of this subject down to 1914, is given by Dobell ('14). See also Calkins ('19, '20), Jennings ('21), Pearl ('22).

[2] *Cf.* pp. 103, 1031.

[3] R. Hertwig, '89, '00, '04, etc.; Joukowsky, '98; Simpson, '01; Calkins, '02, '04, '06, '07, '13; Calkins and Cull, '07; Calkins and Gregory, '13; Gregory, '09; Woodruff, '05; Moody, '12, etc.

pas found that in pure cultures of various ciliates (*Stylonychia, Oxytricha, Leucophrys,* and others) the animals passed through a definite cycle of changes comprising, first, an "agamic period" of adolescence and vigor during which conjugation does not take place; then one of "puberty" and sexual maturity or "eugamic" condition, during which conjugation readily occurs; finally, a period of age or "senescence," when the animals become sickly, degenerate and finally die of old age. The effects of senescence

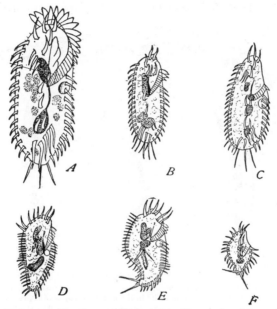

Fig. 97.—Progressive degeneration in *Stylonychia pustulata* (MAUPAS).

A, first stage, disappearance of micronuclei, slight reduction of size; *B, C*, second stage, fragmentation of macronucleus, disappearance of frontal membranellæ; these animals no longer feed; *D, E*, individuals in second stage shortly after division; *F*, last stage, shortly before death.

appear in structural changes in the protoplasm, reduction of size, and degeneration of the nuclear apparatus, commonly involving the disappearance of the micronucleus and the fragmentation of the macronucleus. This is followed by reduction or disappearance of the anterior appendages, such as the membranellæ and mouth-parts of the heterotrichous forms, by external deformities, inability to take food, rapid decrease in size and finally by death (Figs. 97, 98). Maupas believed that in its earlier stages senescence may be counteracted by conjugation but later is irremediable. The length of the cycle as measured by number of divisions was found to vary with the species; in *Stylonychia pustulata* the number was 316, in *S. mytilus* 319, in *Oxytricha* and *Onychodromus* 320–330, in *Leucophrys patula*, 660.

The length in time varied materially with conditions of food and temperature, as was to be expected. In a culture of *Stylonychia pustulata* the agamic youthful period extended to about the 130th division (when the first conjugations appeared), the eugamic or mature period to the 170th, the aged or senescent period to the 316th, when the race died out. The effect of conjugation was tested in another culture by isolating an individual in the mature state, and allowing it to conjugate with a wild individual from another stock. The offspring of the ex-conjugants continued to divide for

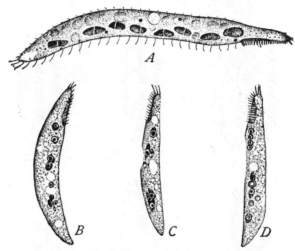

Fig. 98.—*Uroleptus mobilis* (CALKINS).

A, Normal individual, with eight macronuclei and four micronuclei; *B*, *C*, *D*, dwarfed and degenerate individuals (drawn to the same scale) in the last stages of senescence; *B*, from " *F* series," 315th generation; *C*, from the "C-series" 316th generation, a sister-cell of the last individual of the cycle, showing degeneration of macro- and micronuclei.

more than 300 generations before death supervened; while the control animals, prevented from conjugation, lived for only 89 generations.

Results similar in all essentials to the foregoing were obtained in *Paramœcium* and various other Infusoria by R. Hertwig, Calkins, Doflein, Popoff, Joukowsky, Simpson and many others who found that under standardized conditions of food, temperature and other external conditions the life of these Protozoa runs in cycles, periods of activity being followed by periods of *depression* (Calkins) followed by death, if conjugation does not take place. The length of such cycles was found to vary widely in different species and even in the same species under different conditions. In Calkins' original cultures of *Paramœcium* the periods of depression occurred at intervals of about six months, the number of divisions being approximately 200, or in some cases considerably lower (Fig. 99).

Maupas and his successors showed that the animals reach sexual maturity long before marked depression sets in; in the final period of the cycle, indeed, they are often incapable of conjugation. Even at the period of maturity conjugation does not necessarily take place. The animals have only attained a condition in which conjugation may readily be induced by a change of physiological conditions, most readily by a sudden decline in nutritive conditions that have previously been favorable—a fact that seems to be parallel to the incitement of sexual reproduction in plants by checking the food supply. In like manner the classical researches of Klebs [1] have shown that conjugation in various simple algæ, such as *Chlamydomonas, Spirogyra* or *Œdogonium* may be incited by a reduction in the quantity of in-

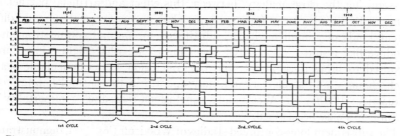

Fig. 99.—Curve of complete history of a culture of *Paramœcium caudatum*, extending over 23 months; steps in the curve are 10-day mean division-rate, ordinates daily division-rate; abscissas indicate time by 10-day periods; limits of cycles (when change of diet occurred) indicated by heavy dotted lines. The lines of the curve carried to the base indicate dying out of the control culture when not stimulated by change of diet. Four cycles are shown, each of 5–6 months, and 200 divisions (CALKINS).

organic salts accompanied by the action of bright light, or in some cases by the addition of sugar solution.

Continued research soon revealed the existence of unsuspected factors. The duration and character of the life-cycle were found to be markedly affected by external factors, such as food, accumulated waste products, and the like (Calkins, Enriques and others). It was found that the larger life-cycle (as limited by conjugation) is complicated by the existence of minor asexual cycles or "rhythms," analogous to the parthenogenetic cycles of higher animals (rotifers, aphids, daphnids, etc.), in some cases apparently independent of external conditions (Woodruff, Erdmann, R. Hertwig) in others apparently determined by them (Woodruff, Jollos). It was found, finally, that in respect to the duration and character of the life-cycle wide differences may exist even between different races or strains of the same species (Jennings, Calkins); and here was found a partial explanation of the conflicting data of earlier observers.

[1] Klebs, '96, etc., reviewed in Klebs, '04, '13.

These researches can here be reviewed in only the briefest manner. Calkins ('02, '03–'04) discovered that in cultures of *Paramœcium* cultivated in hay-infusion the periods of depression might for a time be overcome without conjugation by a change of culture-medium (*e. g.*. from hay-infusion to beef-extract),[1] or by temporary treatment with simple salt-solutions such as potassium phosphate or chloride. Control animals, not thus treated, died out at the end of about six months (200 generations); while those placed under the new conditions entered upon a new cycle. This was repeated for three succeeding cycles of six months, the depression in each case being overcome by similar treatment. The race was thus kept alive for 23 months, when in spite of every effort it died out at the 742d generation. Recognizing the close analogy between this effect and artificial parthenogenesis of the animal egg (pp. 472, 476) Calkins suggested that many different kinds of stimuli might be substituted for normal conjugation and produce like results—"It is often surprising to see what slight stimuli are required to bring these about; and the conclusion seems undeniable that such changes, and similar stimuli, may operate in the natural habitats of Infusoria. If they do, Weismann's conclusions regarding "immortality" of Infusoria may be justified." [2]

The subsequent long-continued studies of Woodruff ('05–'21), demonstrate that when *Paramœcia* are cultivated in infusions of various organic materials taken at random from natural ponds they may be kept in a flourishing condition, without fatal periods of depression and *without conjugation* for very long periods. Woodruff's main culture of *Paramœcium aurelia* was thus maintained without conjugation, for a period of more than thirteen years in the course of which more than 8,000 generations were passed. This result is not due, as first suspected, to an inability of this particular race to conjugate, for conjugation was induced in it after six years (4102d generation) and again six and a half years later. So far as this particular race is concerned, therefore, syngamy evidently is not an indispensable condition of continued life.[3]

Meanwhile it was demonstrated by several observers,[4] that periods of depression like those described by the earlier observers, may be due to the prolonged action of bacterial toxins, excretion-products, or similar unsuitable conditions. The suspicion thus arose that the cyclical aspect of infusorial life in artificial cultures may be due to this cause rather than to an intrinsic tendency towards senescence and death.

Further complications arose from conflicting results concerning the

---

[1] These ciliates feed on the bacteria that develop in such infusions.
[2] '02, p. 138.
[3] See also Enriques ('16) on *Glaucoma* and Hartman ('17, '21) on *Eudorina*.
[4] Enriques, '03–'10; Popoff, '09; Woodruff, '11; Baitsell, '12, and others.

effect of conjugation on the division-rate, which by many investigators had been taken as an index of vitality. Maupas himself denied the original conclusion of Bütschli and Balbiani that conjugation increases the division-rate ('89, p. 504); R. Hertwig ('89) even found the rate in some cases diminished. Hertwig later pointed out that the relation between syngamy and the division-rate differs in different organisms; in some Protozoa it is increased by conjugation, in others unaffected or somewhat retarded, in still others conjugation is followed by complete cessation of division for a considerable period (flagellates, rhizopoda), and the same is true of many lower plants (*Spirogyra*, desmids, *Mucor*, etc.). Some later observers found distinct evidences of increased division-rate following conjugation, in particular Calkins; but this in turn was contradicted by Jennings ('13, '21) whose extended researches on *Paramœcium* not only produced no evidence of an increased division-rate after conjugation but actually showed in many cases an increase of mortality among the ex-conjugants. This led him to a sweeping denial that conjugation restores the declining rate of division during periods of depression and to a decided scepticism concerning the whole theory of senescence and rejuvenation in the Protozoa. Jennings, indeed, considered the evidence overwhelming that the degeneration observed in laboratory cultures is "simply a result of bad conditions." His work led also to the interesting discovery that in the same species exist distinct races or strains differing characteristically in respect to the conditions of conjugation. Some of these races conjugate very rarely (as in Woodruff's culture), others frequently and with great readiness. This shows with how much caution we must regard all results based on material of which the genetic nature is not fully known.[1]

With the publication of these results the reaction from the conclusions of Bütschli, Maupas and Hertwig reached its climax; but the pendulum of opinion now began to swing in the opposite direction. This movement began with the important discovery of *endomixis* or natural parthenogenesis in ciliates, a process correlated with the minor asexual cycles or reproductive rhythms referred to above. The time-duration of such rhythms differs considerably in different races but in each race is nearly constant even under considerable variation of external conditions, but the number of divisions seems to be more modifiable by such means (Woodruff, '17). In *Paramœcium aurelia*, rhythmic periods of depression occur at intervals of about four weeks or forty generations (Fig. 100), while the major cycle of earlier observers extended through three to six months, or from 200 to 600 generations (Woodruff, '05–'07).

---

[1] Similar differences in respect to the tendency to conjugate were observed by Calkins and Gregory ('13) among the offspring of single ex-conjugants, reared under identical conditions.

Cytological study proved [1] that recovery from the periods of depression between successive rhythms is *accompanied by a process of reconstruction of the nuclear apparatus*, to which was given the name of endomixis in contradistinction to the *amphimixis* effected by syngamy. In both processes the old macronucleus breaks down, disappears and is replaced by one derived from the micronucleus; but in endomixis no process of karyogamy is concerned. In these respects, as will later be shown, amphimixis and endomixis show a close analogy, respectively, to fertilization and parthenogenesis in the multicellular organisms.[2] Woodruff ('17) has shown that after cessation

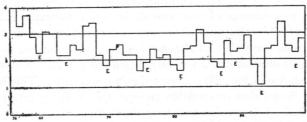

Fig. 100.—Curve showing endomictic periods in *Paramœcium aurelia* in varied culture-medium, laid out in 5-day periods. Ordinates show number of divisions daily, abscissas, number of 5-day periods. Time of endomixis indicated by *E, E,* etc. Total length of time 222 days. The endomictic periods are from 20 to 30 days in length, and average about fifty divisions each. (WOODRUFF.)

of the endomictic process (such as finally occurred in some of his cultures) the culture soon dies out. It is probable, therefore, that endomixis is necessary for the continued life of the race; and that endomixis and conjugation play essentially the same physiological rôle.[3]

This discovery placed the whole problem in a new light. *Paramœcium* and its allies, evidently, is an unfavorable form for experimental analysis, owing to the complication of the sexual cycle by periodic parthenogenesis (endomixis) and by its susceptibility to variations in the environment. A more favorable object is offered by the hypotrichous ciliate *Uroleptus mobilis*, a form in which, as in some other hypotrichs, endomixis takes place only during encystment, conjugation only during the free swimming condition. Here, therefore, the two processes are kept separate by nature. The results of an extended experimental study of this form by Calkins ('20) show conclusively that conjugation here operates as an activator of cell-division and a renewer of vitality. As is now customary in such experiments the many pure lines studied were of known pedigree, all alike being descendants of a *single individual*, isolated immediately after conjugation

[1] Woodruff and Erdmann, '14.

[2] The cytological phenomena of endomixis and conjugation are considered more in detail in Chapter VII (p. 613).

[3] Woodruff and Erdmann, '14, pp. 490–492. See also Calkins, '02, and R. Hertwig, '00–'04, '14

and carried on in isolated cultures under identical conditions of food, temperature, and other conditions. All therefore consisted of the same protoplasm subjected to the same external conditions. Descendants of this individual were separated into many separate pure lines each starting with an ex-conjugant. In spite of complete uniformity in the external conditions, such lines were found to vary markedly in vitality as measured by the rate of growth and division. All alike, however, show a gradual slackening of the rate as time goes on; and if conjugation does not occur finally die out.

(1) In round numbers, the length of life in the stronger lines lay between 200 and 300 days, comprising from 250 to 350 divisions. Calkins distinguishes somewhat arbitrarily, between an earlier period of "youth," in which the mean division rate is more than ten for a period of ten days, and a period of "age," in which the rate is lower than ten. The period of youth and maturity (the mean of sixteen pure lines) was 139 days or 214 divisions; that of age 94 days or 65 divisions. Conjugation tests showed that in all the lines sexual maturity (i. e., capacity for conjugation) is not ordinarily attained before the fiftieth day, appears in full vigor from about the sixtieth day, and persists until near the end of the cycle.

(2) In lines prevented from conjugation the division-rate begins to slacken in the second 60-day period, drops somewhat further in the third 60-day period, and very markedly in the fourth and fifth. The animals now become weakened, degenerate and dwarfed, the micronuclei disappear and the macronuclei show degenerative changes; but no evidence of cytoplasmic degeneration appears (Fig. 98). The power of division is finally lost and death invariably follows, although such degenerate individuals may live for a month.

(3) If at any time during the period of sexual maturity (i. e., after the first 60 days) conjugation takes place (between members of the same series) the division-rate is nearly or quite restored to the original maximum and a new cycle is originated which runs the same course as before. This effect is the more striking the later the period at which conjugation is induced, as will be seen from the curves in Fig. 101 which shows a primary cycle (A) and two of its offshoots, H and J, taken at different periods. In every case the ex-conjugant soon returns approximately to the normal ex-conjugant rate (15–22 divisions per 10-day period), and the period of death is delayed, in H for about 120 days, in J for more than 100 additional days. By taking off successive lines in this manner, each initiated by an act of conjugation, the life of the culture, the product of a single original individual, has thus been extended from the normal limit of 200–300 days to more than five years.

If, therefore, endomixis is here really excluded by the conditions of the experiment, there seems to be no escape from the conclusion (1) that in the absence of either conjugation or endomixis the protoplasm of this species, placed under standardized and constant external conditions, undergoes a progressive change, involving successively a period of immaturity, sexual maturity, decline, degeneration and finally death; and that (2) conjugation

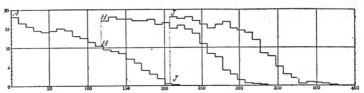

Fig. 101.—Curves showing "rejuvenescence" following conjugation in *Uroleptus* (adapted from CALKINS).

The ordinates show the mean division-rate per ten days, the abscissas the time in days. Each curve begins with an individual isolated immediately after conjugation; its meeting with the baseline shows the death of the line.

A, the original line (220 days); *H*, second line taken from the original one and permitted to conjugate after 116 days, with life prolonged to 335 days; *J*, third line taken from *A* near the end of its life (205 days), with extension of life to 428 days.

initiates a new cycle of activity by a restoration of the waning metabolic activities involved as expressed in growth and division.

There are still points to be cleared up in these results. Calkins's data show that under the conditions of these experiments there has been a slight falling off in the mean rate of division; in other words, conjugation has not in the long run been able to maintain the original rate unimpaired. Although these cultures have now been carried on for more than five years under the artificial conditions of the experiment it still remains to be seen whether they can be indefinitely prolonged. Further, until more adequate demonstration is produced that endomixis is excluded by the conditions of the experiment a certain reserve on this point seems justified. Nevertheless the outstanding fact seems to be inescapable that, in this particular case at least, *conjugation does in fact renew the failing metabolic activities of the cell*, and initiates a new cycle of growth and division. How this effect is produced is not certainly known; but since it seems also to result from endomixis or parthenogenesis there is considerable ground for the conclusion that it is connected with a reorganization of the nucleus that takes place during the processes of maturation. Such an explanation, however, would be inadequate in the case of higher organisms; for in most of them the maturation-process does not in nature lead to activation unless followed by syngamy.

We should be cautious in any attempt to extend these results to other ciliates or to Protista generally. In certain species of ciliates races or strains have been discovered that are devoid of micronuclei and hence are unable to go through with the normal process of conjugation. Such a race was found by Dawson ('19) in the hypotrich *Oxytricha hymenostoma* and carried on for more than two years without the occurrence of true syngamy (though plastogamy frequently occurred). More convincing are the experiments of Hartmann ('21) on the phytoflagellate *Eudorina elegans*, a form in which the gametes are markedly heterogamous, and hence readily recognizable. This form was cultivated under carefully controlled conditions for 1300 generations, covering a period of five years, without the occurrence of syngamy or discoverable endomixis, and without undergoing periods of depression and regulation so long as the normal conditions were maintained. The climax appears in such organisms as the bacteria and the Cyanophyceæ in which no process of syngamy is yet known.

From all this emerges the large fact that the original theory of a universal, fundamental and innate tendency to senescence and death on the part of living protoplasm can no longer be maintained. The opposite conclusion would seem nearer the truth, namely, that barring accident or secondary limiting conditions, many forms of protoplasm are capable of indefinitely continuing life. In the vast majority of living organisms, however, such limiting conditions undoubtedly occur. In higher organisms generally it is only the germ-cells, as Weismann urged, that are endowed with an apparatus of periodical release, which may counteract such conditions; and the facts clearly indicate that a leading part in this process is played by a nuclear reorganization effected by maturation, by syngamy or by both combined. And such results as those observed in *Uroleptus* indicate that the same is true in some of the Protista even if not in all.

2. Increase of Vigor by Heterosis (Heterozygosis) [1]

The increase of size or vigor or both in crosses between different races, varieties or species long since attracted the attention of horticulturists, breeders of domesticated animals and students of heredity. Darwin's admirable researches on the beneficial effects of cross-fertilization in higher plants directed general attention to the subject. More recently it has been carefully reëxamined from the standpoint of the Mendelian analysis by East, Shull, Emerson, Jones, and others who have strikingly demonstrated the remarkably favorable effects produced by crossing different strains of maize and other plants; and Whitney ('12) has produced evidence in the same direction in the case of rotifers. The earlier results in this field gave rise to a rather widespread belief that crossing is *per se* a cause of increased vigor and that inbreeding is in the same sense a cause of decreased vigor or degeneracy. Darwin seems on the whole to have held to this view

[1] For recent general discussions of this subject, see Shull ('10), East and Hayes ('12), Jones ('17).

of inbreeding, though he was well aware of the difficulties offered by plants, such as Leguminosæ, that are habitually self-fertilizing. On the other hand, he showed that it is not the mere crossing of any two individuals which is beneficial to the offspring; for it does not appear, or is very slight, in plants of the same stock intercrossed during several generations.[1]

From this and much other evidence of the same type Darwin concluded that the benefit results from some "difference of constitution between the sexual elements," or, in more modern terms, a difference of transmissible factors in the gametes; and this is fully borne out by the recent Mendelian analysis of the problem. The precise nature of these factors is still a subject of discussion.[2] The increased vigor of hybrids has been cited by some writers in support of the theory of rejuvenescence; but the argument undoubtedly loses much of its weight in view of the facts that have been outlined, and it is wholly rejected by East and Hayes.[3] It may be added that since the factors which determine increase of vigor in heterozygosis are transmissible they are probably borne by the chromosomes; but the evidence is conclusive that the initiation of development is not in general due to the nuclei or their union, but to other factors (p. 395). Hybrid vigor may therefore be a phenomenon wholly different from the stimulus to development given to the egg by the sperm, or effected by conjugation in the Protista. Nevertheless the suspicion cannot be avoided that a key to rejuvenescence (if we may so designate the activation of the egg by the sperm and its consequences in higher organisms) may yet be found in the study of heterosis.

3. Syngamy, Heredity and Variation

In diœcious organisms syngamy obviously brings together two originally separated lines of heredity and thus effects *amphimixis* (Weismann). It is less obvious, but probably equally true, that new combinations of hereditary traits may also result from autogamy or self-fertilization and the associated processes of maturation, as will later appear (p. 950). As above indicated (p. 233) sexual reproduction often yields a more varied progeny than asexual; and out of this fact grew the conclusion that syngamy is a source of variation—a view long since suggested by Treviranus and later developed by Darwin, Spencer, Brooks ('83), Weismann ('91) and many later writers, including some of the most recent experimenters. In case of Protista, Jennings ('11-'13) has made an elaborate experimental study of the phenomena in *Paramœcium* the results of which, as already indicated, are quite in harmony with the conclusions of Weismann. "Conjugation

---

[1] *Effects of Cross-and Self-Fertilization*, p. 269.   [2] *Cf.* Jones ('17).
[3] *Op. cit.*, p. 38.   See also Shull.

produces within a pure race heritable differentiations; so that as a result races diverse in their heritable characters arise from a simple race with uniform heritable characters. . . . What conjugation does is to bring about

Union of the Haploid Groups. Fertilization.

Egg · Sperm · Zygote

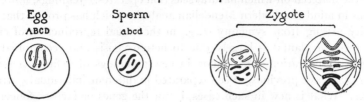

Division of the Diploid Group. Mitosis.

Reduction of the Diploid Groups to Haploid. Meiosis.

Synapsis · Disjunction · Haploid Groups. Gametes.

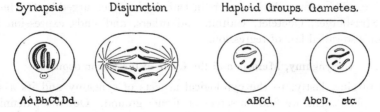

Aa,Bb,Cc,Dd. · aBCd, AbcD, etc.

Recombinations in Fertilization.

etc.

Fig. 102.—General diagram of the chromosome-cycle in animals, the haploid groups assumed to contain four chromosomes of different sizes. Paternal and maternal chromosomes in white and black respectively. Complete gonomery of the diploid groups in the initial stages, later lost. Only two of the 16 possible chromosome-combinations in the gametes shown (cf. Fig. 105), and only seven zygote-combinations out of 256 possible ones.

new combinations of germ-plasm, just as is done in the sexual reproduction of higher animals. One result of this is to produce biparental inheritance; another is to give origin to many variations, in the sense of inherited differentiations between different strains. Some of the new combinations are better adapted to the existing conditions than others; these survive while the others die out" ('13, p. 378). On its face this seems to be essentially the same conclusion as that of Weismann that amphimixis produces variations—or rather assures their "mingling and persistent renewal "—thus giving the material on which natural selection operates. Jennings, however, here has in mind the modern Mendelian analysis, which has proved that the diversity arising from syngamy (e. g., in the sexual reproduction of cultivated races of plants) is largely due to heterozygosis and recombination, i. e., to the separation and reunion in new groupings of definite heredity factors that have previously been separated in different individuals, strains or races. What is new in such cases, is not the genes or factors concerned but only their particular modes of combination. It is, therefore, a debatable question whether syngamy can produce new variations in the sense that this word was employed by Weismann and the earlier writers; and the origin of really new elements or factors out of which new characters may be built up constitutes one of the main problems now before students of genetics.

Lastly it may be added that a number of writers, even including some of those who have recognized syngamy as a source of variations, have held that syngamy also serves to maintain the stability of species through intercrossing. This view, which appears in Darwin, has been urged by O. Herting, Strasburger, Quetelet, Galton, and others, and finds expression in Galton's so-called law of regression.

4. Syngamy, Meiosis and the Cycle of the Chromosomes

In turning, lastly, to the cytological aspects of syngamy and its associated phenomena we find ourselves on firmer ground. Our most definite knowledge in this field relates to the history of the nuclei and the cycle of the chromosomes, which alone will be considered at this point. Syngamy, it is true, often involves a union of gamete-protoplasms (*plastogamy*) as well as of nuclei (*karyogamy*); but this aspect of the phenomena is still too little known to be profitably taken up here.

Concerning the history of the chromosomes, we are now able to state three principal conclusions, each of fundamental importance for the problems of heredity. Two of these are in principle well established for many higher plants and animals, while the third is hardly less certain. They are essentially as follows:

a. Karyogamy and Establishment of the Diploid Chromosome-Groups. In the course of syngamy the two gamete-nuclei unite or become closely associated (*karyogamy*) each giving rise meanwhile to a single or haploid group of chromosomes the number of which is half the typical somatic number of the species ("Van Beneden's Law"). The two groups thus associated in the zygote, respectively of maternal and paternal origin, are nearly alike in respect to both the number and the size-relations of the chromosomes (Figs. 103, 104) and are in other respects nearly equivalent. The double or *diploid* group thus produced is perpetuated throughout the life of the resulting individual, being handed on by progressive division to all the nuclei of the body without change in its essential character. Certain

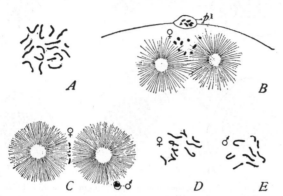

Fig. 103.—Diploid and haploid chromosome-groups in the sea-urchin *Echinus microtuberculatus* (BOVERI).

A, diploid group, 18 chromosomes, polar view of first cleavage of the fertilized egg; *B*, prophase of second polar spindle, haploid group, 9 chromosomes; *C*, partial fertilization, sperm-nucleus at ♂; *D*, polar view of same, 9 chromosomes; *E*, polar view of metaphase-group from sperm-amphiaster in merogony (first cleavage), 9 chromosomes.

deviations from the typical phenomena as just outlined will later be described (pp. 75, 841).

b. Meiosis. Reduction of the Diploid Groups to Haploid. At a certain period during the life-cycle the number of chromosomes is again reduced to one-half; *i. e.*, the double or diploid chromosome-groups are reduced to single or haploid ones (Fig. 102). These numbers and other characteristics of the chromosome-groups are thus held constant from generation to generation. This process, known as *reduction* or *meiosis*, belongs among the general phenomena of *maturation*, which will form the subject of Chapter VI. At this point we indicate only certain of its most general features.

The period at which meiosis takes place varies widely in different cases (p. 488). In animals generally it constitutes one of the steps in the formation of the gametes themselves. In the male it takes place in the testis during the formation of the sperms. In the female it is delayed until after the egg has attained its growth often until after it has left the ovary, or even until after the sperm has entered, meiosis then being intimately associated with fertilization (p. 398). In most plants, on the other hand, meiosis has no immediate relation either to fertilization or to gamete-formation, but takes place long before, during the process of spore-formation. In a third and much rarer case meiosis takes place in the zygote immediately after karyogamy, so that the developing zygote and all of its products are of haploid constitution. This is known only in certain algæ and a few other

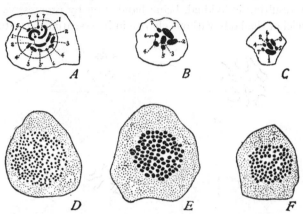

Fig. 104.—Diploid and haploid chromosome-groups, *A–C* in the aphid *Aphis rosæ* (STEVENS), *D–F* in the crayfish *Cambarus virilis* (FASTEN).

A, diploid group, 14-chromosomes, metaphase of second cleavage of a parthenogenetic egg showing size-differences and chromosome-pairs; *B*, pseudo-haploid group from metaphase of first spermatocyte-division, 7 bivalent chromosomes; *C*, true haploid group, second spermatocyte-division, 7 single or univalent chromosomes.

D–F, corresponding series in a species having numerous chromosomes with only slight size differences. *D*, diploid group, 200 chromosomes, from spermatogonial division; *E*, pseudo-haploid group, metaphase of first spermatocyte 100 bivalents; *F*, true haploid group, second spermatocyte, 100 univalent chromosomes.

simple forms. In all of these cases the final result is the same; the gamete-nuclei receive a single or haploid group of chromosomes.

    c. Segregation, Regrouping and Random Assortment of the Chromosomes. Reduction is brought about by a modified form of mitosis in which the chromosomes undergo a regrouping or segregation, the diploid group separating into two haploid groups without undergoing division in the usual sense. In the course of this process, as will later be shown (Chap. XII), is also effected a regrouping of the original paternal and maternal chromosomes (*i. e.*, of their individual descendants), such that all possible recombinations of them are delivered to the resulting gametes, in so far as this does not alter the integrity of the group as such. This will be made clear from the diagram (Fig. 105). If, for example, the number of chromosomes be assumed to be four, the original maternal haploid group may be designated as *A B C D*, and the paternal group as *a b c d*, and the zygote receives the diploid group *ABDC abcd*. In maturation every gamete receives a group of four chromosomes, corresponding to the original groups, but any particular member of the group may be of either maternal or paternal origin. If this distribution follows the law of chance, 16 such combinations should result,

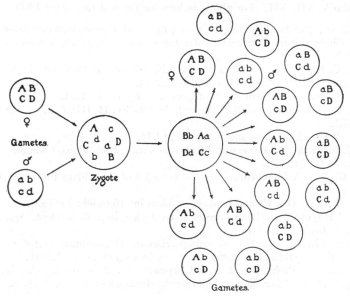

Recombinations with Independent Assortment.

Fig. 105.—Diagram applicable either to chromosomes or to hereditary factors, to show Mendelian segregation and independent assortment. (Linkage phenomena are here left out of account.) Maternal components (chromosomes or factors) in capitals, paternal in small letters. The haploid number assumed to be four (*cf.* Fig. 102).

in equal numbers, of which only two (*ABCD* and *abcd*) are identical with the original ones. The same rule holds with larger numbers.

d. Chromosomes and Mendelian Heredity. In these facts, as will be set forth in Chapter XII, lies the explanation of the Mendelian segregation of the factors of heredity. The history of the chromosomes in the life-cycle runs exactly parallel to that of these factors. Like the chromosomes, the factors or Mendelian units are single or haploid in the gametes, double or diploid in the zygote, and its products; their redistribution and recombination in the gametes follow precisely the same course as that of the chromosomes.[1] The critical study of these facts and a multitude of others has removed all doubt that the chromosomes play an essential rôle in heredity.

We now proceed to a more detailed examination of the phenomena by an examination of the structure and origin of the germ-cells (Chap. IV), their

---

[1] The phenomena of linkage are here left out of account.

union in fertilization (Chap. V), and their history in maturation and reduction (Chap VI).

LITERATURE III

(See also V, VII, XII. For abbreviations see General Literature List).

Bütschili, O., '76. Studien über die ersten Entwicklungsvorgänge der Eizelle, die Zellteilung und die Conjugation der Infusorien: *Abh. Senck. Nat. Ges. Frankfort*, X.

Calkins, G. N., '02–'04. Studies on the Life History of Protozoa: I–IV: I, *A. Entwm.*, XV; III, *B. B.*, III, 1; IV, *J. E. Z.*, I.

'16. General Biology of the Protozoan Life-Cycle: *A. N.*, L.

'19, '20. Uroleptus mobilis. A Study in Vitality, II, III: *J. E. Z.*, XXVIII, XXXI.

'23. What did Maupas mean?: *A. N.*, LVII.

Child, C. M., '15a. Senescence and Rejuvenescence: *Univ. Press, Chicago*.

Conklin, E. G., '12 (I).

Dobell, C., '14. A Commentary on the Genetics of the Ciliate Protozoa: *J. G.*, IV, 2.

Doflein, F., '13. Das Unsterblichkeitsproblem im Tierreich: *Freiburg*.

East and **Hayes,** '12. Heterozygosis in Evolution, etc.: U. S. Dept. Ag., *Plant Indust. Bull.*, CCXLIII.

Hartmann, M., '04. Die Fortpflanzungsweisen der Organismen, etc.: *B. C.*

'21. Die dauernd agame Zucht von *Eudorina elegans: A. P.*, XLIII.

Hartog, M., '13. Problems of Life and Reproduction: *John Murray, London*.

Hertwig, R., '89. Ueber die Conjugation der Infusorien: *Abh. Kgl. Bayr. Akad. Wiss.*

'08. Ueber neue Probleme der Zellenlehre: *A. Zf.*, I.

'14. Ueber Parthenogenesis der Infusorien: *B. C.*, XXXIV.

Jennings, H. S., '12. Age, Death, and Conjugation in the Light of Work on Lower Organisms. Harvey Lectures 1911–1912: *Pop. Sci. Mo.*, 80.

'13. The Effect of Conjugation in *Paramœcium; J. E. Z.*, XIV.

'20. Life and Death, Heredity and Evolution in Unicellular Organisms: *Badger, Boston*.

Jollos, W., '16. Die Fortpflanzung der Infusorien und die potentielle Unsterblichkeit der Einzelligen: *B. Z.*, XXXVI.

Jost, L., '13. (See I.)

Klebs, G., '96. Die Bedingungen der Fortpflanzung bei einiger Algen und Pilzen: *Fischer, Jena*.

'12. Fortpflanzung der Gewächse: *Physiologie. Handw. d. Naturw., Jena*.

'17. Ueber das Verhältnis von Wachstum und Ruhe bei den Pflanzen: *B. C.*, XXXVII.

Kofoid, C. A., '23. The Life Cycle of the Protozoa: *Sci.*, LVII.

Maupas, M., '88. Recherches expérimentales sur la multiplication des Infusoires ciliés: *A. Z. E.*, 2me série, VI.

'89. Le rejeunissement karyogamique chez les Ciliés: *A. Z. E.*, 2me série, VII.

'91. Sur le determinisme de la sexualité chez *l'Hydatina senta; C. R., Paris*.

Minot, C. S., '08. The Problem of Age, Growth and Death: *Putnams, New York*.

'13. Moderne Probleme der Biologie: *Fischer, Jena*.

Morgan, T. H., '07. Experimental Zoölogy: *Macmillan, New York.* Especially Chapters XIX–XXIII.

Osterhout, W. J. V., '22. Injury, Recovery and Death, etc.: *Lippincott, Philadelphia.*

Pearl, R. R., '22. The Biology of Death: *Lippincott, Philadelphia and London.*

Schleip, W., '15. Lebenslauf, Alter und Tod des Individuums: *Kultur der Gegenwart,* III, Th., IV, Abth. Bd. I.

Shull, A. F., '10, '11. Studies in the Life Cycle of *Hydatina; J. E. Z.,* VIII, X.

Strasburger, E., '09 (V).

Tischler, G., '15 (XI).

Weismann, A., The Duration of Life ('81); Life and Death ('83). In Essays on Heredity (Trans.), *Oxford,* '89.

'13. Vorträge über Deszendenz Theorie, 3d Auflage: *Fischer, Jena.*

Whitney, D. D., '14. The Influence of Food in controlling Sex in *Hydatina; J. E. Z.,* XVII.

Winkler, H., '08. (See also V.) Parthenogenesis und Apogamie im Pflanzenreiche: *P. R. B.,* II, 3.

Woodruff, L. L., '05. An Experimental Study of the Life History of Hypotrichous Infusoria: *J. E. Z.,* II.

'08. The Life Cycle of *Paramœcium* when subjected to a Varied Environment: *A. N.,* XLII.

'12. A five years' Pedigree Race of *Paramœcium: P. S. B. M.,* IX.

'14. On so-called conjugating and non-conjugating Races of *Paramœcium: J. E. Z.,* XVI.

'21. The present Status of the long-continued Pedigree Culture of *Paramœcium,* etc.: *P. N. A.,* VII, 1.

Woodruff and Baitsell,' 11. Rhythms in the reproductive Activity of Infusoria: *J. E. Z.,* XI.

Woodruff and Erdmann, '14. A normal periodic Reorganization Process without Cell-fusion in *Paramœcium: J. E. Z.,* XVII.

CHAPTER IV

THE GAMETES

"Not all the progeny of the primary impregnated germ-cells are required for the formation of the body in all animals; certain of the derivative germ-cells may remain unchanged and become included in that body which has been composed of their metamorphosed and diversely combined or confluent brethren; so included, any derivative germ-cell may commence and repeat the same processes of growth by imbibition and of propagation by spontaneous fission as those to which itself owed its origin; followed by metamorphoses and combinations of the germ-masses so produced, which concur to the development of another individual."   RICHARD OWEN. [1]

"The fertilized egg, accordingly, divides into cells that constitute the individual and cells for maintenance of the species."   M. NUSSBAUM.[2]

The structure and mode of origin of the gametes offer to the student of development and heredity a series of problems of such fundamental interest as to have made them the object of innumerable researches on the part of both botanists and zoölogists. The difficulties of observation which they offer have only in part been overcome; nevertheless we now possess a fairly adequate acquaintance with the main features of the subject.

It is probable that in their most primitive condition the gametes of both sexes were motile and structurally alike (isogamous), as is still the case in many of the lower existing forms. Deferring to a later point (Chap. VII) an account of these more primitive types, we here consider only the higher heterogamous forms in which the gametes differ widely in form and function, the macrogamete or ovum being a very large, quiescent cell, while the microgamete or sperm is a very minute and usually motile cell, typically provided with one or more flagella or cilia. This difference is clearly the result of a physiological division of labor between the gametes of the two sexes. The ovum has to supply most of the material for the body of the embryo, and often also to provide for its protection and maintenance during development. For this service it prepares by extensive growth, accumulating a large amount of protoplasm, commonly laden with reserve food-matter (*yolk* or *deutoplasm*), and in many cases becoming surrounded by membranes or other protective envelopes. During its

---

[1] Parthenogenesis, p. 3, 1849.   [2] *Arch. mik. Anat.*, XVIII, p. 112, 1880.

early history, therefore, the ovum is characterized by predominance of the constructive or anabolic processes of metabolism.

The microgamete or sperm, on the other hand, makes but an insignificant contribution to the mass of the embryo, and is relieved from the task of providing food and protection for the embryo. Physiologically the microgamete shows a most striking contrast to the ovum in its active movements and in its type of metabolism, which is characterized by the predominance of the destructive or katabolic processes by which the energy necessary for these movements is set free.[1] When finally matured, accordingly, the gametes of the two sexes have diverged almost to opposite extremes of cell-differentiation; and it is not surprising that while Schwann recognized, somewhat doubtfully, the fact that the egg is a cell, it was not until many years afterward that his successors proved the sperm to be of the same nature.

I. THE GAMETES OF ANIMALS

A. THE ANIMAL OVUM [2]

1. General Structure

The animal egg (Figs. 106, 107) is a cell of giant size, almost always laden with reserve food-materials in the form of suspended drops, semi-solid spheroids, granules, and other metaplasmic bodies which collectively constitute the yolk or *deutoplasm*. To this fact the egg owes, in part, its enormous size as compared with the sperm; and the question has even been raised whether the egg really contains a greater quantity of "living" (*i. e., active*) protoplasm than the sperm.[3] In some cases, however, no yolk can be distinguished other than the alveolar spheres of the protoplasm; such, for instance, are the eggs of certain sea-urchins and starfish, which offer classical examples of the alveolar structure as described by Bütschli. It seems evident, therefore, that the egg does in fact contain a much greater quantity of active protoplasm than the sperm. Like other cells the ovum tends towards a spheroidal form, and this form is commonly realized more or less nearly; in its earlier stages, however, the oöcyte is often irregular in shape, and sometimes actually amoeboid. The full-grown egg is often

---

[1] The metabolic contrast between the germ-cells has been discussed in a suggestive manner by Geddes and Thomson in their work on the *Evolution of Sex*. These authors regard this contrast as but a particular manifestation of a metabolic contrast characteristic of the sexes in general.

[2] The term *ovum*, or egg, is commonly applied to the female germ-cell, whether it has undergone the changes of "maturation" (*i. e.*, has formed its polar bodies) or not; but strictly speaking the unmatured egg, so long as the germinal vesicle remains intact, is still an oöcyte (p. 314). This distinction may here be disregarded, and the following account will apply primarily to the full grown egg before maturation has been completed.

[3] *Cf.* Waldeyer, '06.

more or less flattened at the poles, and sometimes elongated to a ellipsoid or almost cylindrical form (Fig. 112). In some groups, notably in the insects, the eggs of different species are of definite and characteristic shapes, which display a remarkable diversity. The most interesting of these are forms in which the bilateral symmetry and antero-posterior differentiation

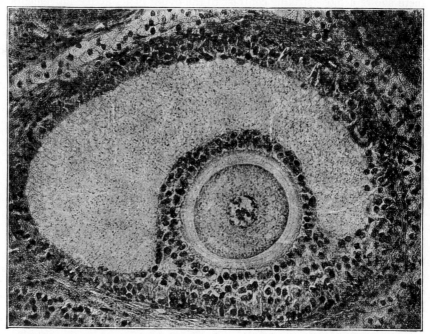

Fig. 106.—Ovum of the cat, within the ovary, from a photograph of a preparation by DAHLGREN. (Enlarged 235 diameters.) The ovum lies in the Graafian follicle within the *discus proligerus*, the latter forming the immediate follicular investment (*corona radiata*) of the egg. Within the *corona* is the clear *zona pellucida* or egg-membrane.

of the future embryo are clearly discernible in the shape of the egg before it has been fertilized, or even before it has left the ovary (p. 275).

The eggs of some animals have been described as naked; but it is certain that in all cases the egg is bounded by a plasma-membrane (p. 55), and in many if not all cases also surrounded by a delicate *vitelline membrane* or *fertilization-membrane* closely applied to the periphery (p. 272). This membrane is often succeeded by other envelopes, and these show a great variety of structure. In many species the egg-envelope is perforated by a minute opening or *micropyle* (or a group of such openings), through which the sperm may enter the egg during fertilization (Figs. 113, 114); but in many cases no micropyle can be distinguished; and others such as the nemertine or the sea-urchin, in which the sperm makes little use of the micropyle, being able to perforate the envelope at any point (p. 408).

Before maturation has taken place the nucleus of the egg is ordinarily of great size and is commonly called by its old name of *germinal vesicle* (Purkinje, 1825). During maturation the germinal vesicle breaks down in preparation for the formation of the polocytes (p. 398), and after completion of the process the nucleus is reformed as a much smaller body, a large part of its substance having been cast out into the cytosome. In this form the nucleus is commonly called the *female pronucleus* (Van Beneden), or more simply, the *egg-nucleus*. The germinal vesicle commonly occupies an eccentric position, lying nearer the upper or animal pole; but its position is sometimes nearly central, especially in the earlier stages of the oöcyte. As the growth of the egg proceeds, the eccentricity usually increases, and in the extreme types of telolecithal ova (such as those of elasmobranchs, birds, or reptiles) it ultimately lies close to the periphery, sometimes actually in contact with the membrane.[1] Its form is typically that of a spherical sac, surrounded by a very distinct membrane; but during the growth of the egg it may become irregular or even amœboid (Fig. 153), sometimes sending forth conspicuous pseudopodia towards the source of food (Bambeke, Korschelt).

The relative size of the germinal vesicle varies widely in different species or groups; and this is to a certain considerable extent correlated with the mode of nutrition of the ovum, as Jörgenssen ('13) in particular has pointed out. In eggs that are accompanied by nutritive nurse-cells, follicle-cells or the like, which play an important part in elaborating food for the egg, the germinal vesicle is often relatively small— a condition conspicuously shown in many insects. When such accessory nutritive structures are wanting the germinal vesicle is commonly very large, as might be expected in view of the importance of the nucleus in nutrition. Many departures from this rule are, however, known.

In its earliest stages the oöcyte contains a pair of central bodies lying beside the nucleus in the oöplasm, and surrounded by a rounded body commonly called the *sphere* or *idiozome*, about which in turn are grouped Golgi-bodies and chondriosomes, which later, in some cases at least, scatter through the oöplasm (p. 342). The central bodies are most commonly lost to view in later stages, though there are a few cases in which they are said to be present at every period (*e. g.*, in the leech *Pisciola* (Jörgenssen, '13) and at least one case (*Thysanozoön*), in which the central body lies within the nucleus from an early stage of the oöcyte (p. 97). It is possible, therefore,

[1] *Cf.* Harper, '04, Loyez '06,

that the central bodies are always present, though often hidden among the cytoplasmic granules or in the nucleus.

2. The Oöplasm

The oöplasm (cytoplasm) of the full-grown egg always shows, more or less clearly, an alveolar or pseudoalveolar structure owing to the presence of closely crowded alveolar spheres or yolk-spheres suspended in the continuous hyaloplasm in which lie also numerous smaller granules of various kinds. As has earlier been indicated (p. 73) we can draw no precise line of demarcation between the larger disperse components (alveolar spheres) of an alveolar protoplasmic structure and the passive metaplasmic or paraplastic formed elements ("inclusions"), collectively designated as yolk or deutoplasm. In practice we are accustomed to restrict the latter terms to bodies distinguished from alveolar spheres by their larger size and which also differ in physical character and often in staining-reactions.[1] When such differences do not appear, as in many echinoderms (*Asterias*, *Toxopneustes*, *Parechinus*), the egg is commonly spoken of as *alecithal* or

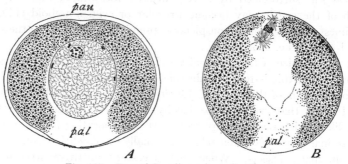

Fig. 107.—Eggs of *Dentalium* prior to Fertilization.

A, in vertical section shortly after discharge, showing intact germinal vesicle, nucleolus, and scattered chromosomes, polarization, with upper (*p. a. u.*) and lower (*p. a. l.*) clear areas, yolk black; *B*, egg after disappearance of germinal vesicle and formation of first polar spindle. (See also Fig. 509.)

homolecithal. Such eggs offer classical examples of a true alveolar structure as described by B ütschli.

The yolk is commonly more or less definitely localized, sometimes being more concentrated in the central region (*centrolecithal* type) more frequently in the vegetative hemisphere (*telolecithal* type), sometimes in other regions (*Dentalium*, Fig. 107). In such cases both types of structure appear in the same egg, the "pseudalveolar" in the yolk-bearing regions,

---

[1] *Cf.* p. 74. See Wilson, '99.

the "true" alveolar in the remaining; and in the latter the egg-nucleus most commonly lies.

As a rule the egg develops a more or less definite peripheral *cortical layer* ("ectoplasm," "peri-vitelline" layer) bounded externally by the plasma-membrane, often also by the vitelline membrane.[1] Cytological observation and physiological experiment alike demonstrate the extreme importance of this layer for many of the processes of development. It is for the most part free from yolk in the ordinary sense, but often contains specific granules of various kinds,[2] and sometimes differs in staining reaction from the entoplasmic material. It is this layer which first reacts to the contact of the sperm (p. 409); and during the processes of maturation, fertilization and early development it is often the seat of streaming movements towards particular regions of the egg by means of which some of the most important localizing activities of the egg are manifested (p. 415). It is from the cortical layer that the blastoderm is in large measure formed in eggs of the extreme centrolecithal (insects) or telolecithal (birds, reptiles) types; and from local thickenings of the same layer arise such structures as the polar rings (Fig. 192) of leeches (Whitman, '78, etc.) and oligochætes (Vejdovský, '87), or the "polar lobe" of certain annelids and mollusks which plays so important a part in the development (p. 1063). In some cases, the peripheral region of the cortical layer is radially striated and forms a "zona radiata" which in some cases seems undoubtedly to constitute a vitelline membrane (*e. g.*. in the eggs of fishes, Mark, '90). In the case of *Nereis* (Lillie, '11) proved that the *zona radiata* represents a radially disposed alveolar layer of protoplasm, the alveolar contents of which are discharged, after insemination, to form a thick jelly-envelope investing the egg.

a. The Deutoplasm or Yolk. Owing to the presence of yolk-spheres, chondriosomes, Golgi-bodies, fat-drops, pigment granules, and various other formed components, the oöplasm forms a complex system which varies widely in different species, and offers a difficult problem both chemically and cytologically. It is not easy to define precisely what is meant by the terms "yolk" or "deutoplasm"; and since the various components of the oöplasm can only be imperfectly separated for chemical analysis, statements concerning the composition of the "yolk" apply for the most part to a heterogeneous mixture of substances. The chemical nature of some of the formed elements may, however, in a measure be indicated by their cytological characters, *e. g.*, in the case of fat-drops, glycogen, or chrondriosomes.

With the grouping of the yolk in the egg we are here only indirectly con-

---

[1] This layer is not to be confused with the so-called hyaline or ectoplasmic layer which first appears after fertilization. See p. 413.
[2] For review of this subject see Lillie, '06.

cerned. It is a very important fact that this grouping, as seen at the time cleavage begins, must be regarded as a secondary character of the egg resulting from processes of segregation that take place earlier or later during the growth-period, though often completed only at the time of maturation and fertilization (p. 1096). Apart from the general distribution of the yolk more specialized groupings are often seen, some of them of much interest to the student of development. An example of these is offered by the stratification or layered condition found in birds, elasmobranchs and reptiles, where two kinds of yolk (in the hen's egg known as the white and the yellow) occur in alternating and approximately concentric layers. Riddle ('11) has produced evidence that in the hen's egg this is an expression of the daily growth of the egg, one pair of layers being produced each day, including a white one laid down during the poorer nutritive conditions prevailing during the later hours of the night, and a yellow one during the remaining part of the day.

When analyzed chemically *en masse* the yolk of the hen's egg is found to consist of water and solid matter in nearly equal parts [1] and contains various inorganic salts of sodium, potassium, calcium, magnesium, iron, phosphorus and silica. Of the solids about 23% are fat, 11% lecithin and other phospholipins, 16% protein and 1.5% cholesterol, while the inorganic salts form about 3% (less according to some authorities). The protein consists largely of ovo-vitellin, a compound phospho-protein resembling the nucleo-proteins, but differing from them in that the acid component is stated to be not true nucleic acid,[2] though like the latter it is an organic acid rich in phosphorus. Carbohydrates seem to be nearly absent from the hen's yolk, but in some eggs are present in considerable quantity in the form of glycogen (insects). The yolk of the hen's egg contains, in addition to the foregoing, a small quantity of "hæmatogen," an iron-containing compound resembling "nuclein," and supposed to be the mother-substance of hæmoglobin.

The yolk is thus seen to contain the principal foodstuffs required by the developing embryo.[3] To a certain limited extent these are sometimes morphologically recognizable. Many eggs, for example, contain fat-drops easily recognizable as such (Fig. 470), and in such cases, owing to their lightness, they may determine the position of the egg with respect to gravity (p. 1016). Glycogen occurs in many eggs (*Ascaris*, insects) in the form of granules or irregular bodies recognizable by their staining reactions (Kemnitz, '12, Brammertz, '13). The ordinary yolk-spheres are probably largely

---

[1] For a general account of the chemistry of the yolk see Mathews ('15).

[2] Since it yields no purine bases; *cf.* p. 643.

[3] Riddle ('14–'17) has made an interesting attempt to show that in mammals and birds the male-producing and female-producing eggs show recognizable chemical differences. *Cf.* p. 807.

proteid in nature but undoubtedly contain in many cases lipoids and other substances that may not be recognizable as such by the eye; they are typically spheroidal but in some cases they are oval, ellipsoidal bodies (Amphibia) or even flattened and plate-like (elasmobranchs). The meaning of these variations is little understood, as are also their variations in physical characters and staining-reactions. In physical consistency they vary from viscous liquid drops to almost solid bodies; and they likewise vary widely in permeability to light, in specific gravity (p. 262) and in staining reactions. They are often intensely basophilic but may be oxyphilic in various degrees. In general, however, it may be stated that by the ensemble of their staining reactions they may as a rule be readily distinguished from the mitochondria and Golgi-bodies (with which they are often intermingled) and also from the fat-drops.[1] It is an interesting fact that in *Patella*, according to Gatenby, many of the Golgi-bodies (in the form of crescentic rodlets) are attached to yolk-spheres.

b. Pigment. Many ova are more or less colored, sometimes in definite patterns—a fact of much practical importance for studies on the early stages of development (pp. 1016, 1094). In some cases the pigment appears to be diffuse, and perhaps has its seat in the hyaloplasm (*e. g.*, in *Myzostoma*, p. 1096). More commonly it is borne by formed elements, sometimes by the yolk-spheres or alveolar spheres but most often by smaller granules, as in the eggs of frogs, ascidians, ophiuroids or sea-urchins. A striking case is offered in the eggs of *Ophiura*, in which the yolk-spheres vary from reddish brown to olivaceous, while the "microsomes" scattered between them are clear lemon-yellow, offering a striking picture (Wilson, '99). In the ascidian *Styela* (*Cynthia*) Duesberg ('15) has proved that the yellow pigment-granules show the characteristic staining-reactions of mitochondria and probably arise by transformation of the latter.

The distribution of pigment in the egg often follows a definite pattern correlated with the promorphological characters of the egg, and thus offers a valuable means of embryological observation (Figs. 512, 524). It is usually most abundant in the cortical layer of the egg, and sometimes confined to it (*Styela*, *Paracentrotus*), but may also be scattered through the oöplasm (*Arbacia*). The pigment pattern sometimes appears early in the ovarian life of the egg. In other cases the pigment takes on a definite pattern by a sudden localizing activity at the time of maturation or fertilization. Striking examples of this are offered by the eggs of the sea-urchin *Paracentrotus lividus* or the ascidian *Styela partita* (p. 1094). It is an interesting fact, of unknown meaning, that in some cases the pigment-granules show a marked tendency to collect about the nuclei of the segmenting egg.

[1] A comparative review of these reactions is given by Gatenby ('20).

c. Chondriosomes and other Formed Elements. Besides the larger formed components the oöplasm always contains numerous small granules described as "microsomes," which graduate in size down to the limits of microscopical vision; [1] often also fibrillæ or rod-shaped elements lying between the yolk-spheres. Most of these bodies are basophilic in various degrees and by some authors have actually been described as "cytoplasmic chromatin" (p. 724) but much confusion still exists concerning their real nature. By a considerable number of observers (Goldschmidt, Popoff, etc.) these granules, or many of them, were believed to be chromidia emitted from the nucleus, as such or in the form of larger bodies that subsequently fragment. Meves, Duesberg, Fauré-Fremiet and a large group of other observers have however shown clearly that both the rod-like or fibrillar formations [2] and many of the granules (especially those of larger size) are chondriosomes. On the other hand, Schaxel has endeavored, in a series of careful studies, to show that both views are correct, both chromidia and chondriosomes being present in the oöplasm (p. 703). How dubious is the evidence based on the staining-reactions is strikingly shown by studies on *Chætopterus* by F. R. Lillie ('06),[3] who himself seems to favor the view that microsomes are in large measure "chromatin particles." Lillie found that although the cytomicrosomes are strongly basophilic those of nuclear origin are purely oxyphilic until their liberation from the germinal vesicle (at the time of maturation) when they generally become basophilic. In some cases certain of the oöplasmic granules have recently been identified as scattered Golgi-bodies which at an earlier period of the oöcyte are aggregated about the central bodies of the idiozome (p. 345).[4]

In addition to the foregoing the ovum often contains other components of doubtful character, whose relation to those already enumerated is not very clearly determined. Among these may be mentioned the so-called "archiplasm," in the form of irregular clumps of finely granular material, which may be differentiated from the remainder of the cytoplasm by certain staining-reactions (p. 723). Of similarly vague meaning is the term "ergastoplasm," originally applied by Garnier and Bouin to the basophilic fibrillar formations in certain types of cells, especially in the gland-cells, and subsequently much extended in meaning by Prenant and other writers so as to designate collectively many differentiated cytoplasmic substances of basophilic staining capacity, including the chondriosomes (p. 724). This

---

[1] See Wilson, '99.

[2] This does not apply to the general reticulum described in the eggs of echinoderms and other forms by Retzius who considers this structure to be typical of protoplasm generally. Reasons for doubting this are given at p. 70.

[3] This work contains a valuable study of the various types of granules in the egg.

[4] See especially Hirschler, '18; Gatenby, '20, etc.

term has recently been resuscitated by Jörgenssen ('13), Buchner ('15), Gajewska ('20), and some others, as a non-committal term applied to strongly basophilic cytoplasmic material, in the form of irregular flocculent masses, resistant to peptic digestion, and not clearly to be identified, or of a perinuclear ring.[1] It is now clear, as will later appear, that the latter is equivalent to the "pallial" or "vitellogeneous" substance, known to consist largely of chondriosomes, but also containing Golgi-bodies, and in some cases perhaps extruded nucleolar fragments (p. 340). The term ergastoplasm thus seems to be of very questionable utility.

Two other formed elements of doubtful character, known only in the insects, may here be mentioned. One of these includes the so-called accessory or *secondary* nuclei, found in the oöcytes of several orders of insects, especially the Hymenoptera (p. 347). A second and even more remarkable component of the oöplasm, likewise known only in certain insects, are rod-like or rounded bodies, sometimes present in great numbers, and variously known as "bacterioids," or "intracellular symbionts." In the ova of certain Hymenoptera (ants), Orthoptera (cockroaches) and Lepidoptera, and in some aphids, they are rod-like in form and divide by fission. In those of aphids, coccids, and some other insects they are more or less rounded and yeast-like, and like yeasts multiply by a process of budding. Blochmann ('84, '87), who first observed the bacterioid form (in *Camponotus, Formica, Blatta* and *Periplaneta*)[2] found that in their earlier stages the oöcytes are free from these bodies but are later infected with them from the surrounding cells. He therefore concluded that they are bacteria-like organisms that live symbiotically in the oöcyte and in many of the somatic cells derived from it, and this has been confirmed by many later observers who have also found the same to be true of the yeast-like symbionts of other insects. Both the bacteroid and the yeast-like forms are said to have been successfully cultivated in artificial cultures outside the body of the host,[3] and many different genera and species of them have been described.

It seems probable that in some species the presence of these intracellular fungi is due to accidental infection; but in many cases, they are invariably present as a characteristic feature of the species, the association between host and symbiont having apparently become permanent if not obligatory. A remarkable feature of such cases is that in some of them the egg is provided with special structural features which seem expressly designed to provide for its infection by symbionts from the surrounding tissue-cells.

[1] See Jörgenssen, '13.
[2] A full historical treatment of the subject is given in Buchner's interesting paper on the intracellular symbionts of Hemiptera ('12).
[3] Krassilstschik ('89), Mercier ('06, '07), Pierantoni ('10), Sulc ('10).

In the aphids this structure, which has long been known, is developed from a group of infected follicle-cells, always at the posterior pole of the oöcyte. These cells (mycetocytes) constitute the "mycetoma," long ago described by Huxley (1858) as the *pseudo-vitellus*, and they appear to be the sole means by which the egg is infected. Concerning the physiological relations between symbionts and host, nothing definite is yet known.

3. The Egg-nucleus or Germinal Vesicle

Owing to the great size of the germinal vesicle the nuclear phenomena here appear on a large scale and in spectacular fashion, but they are com-

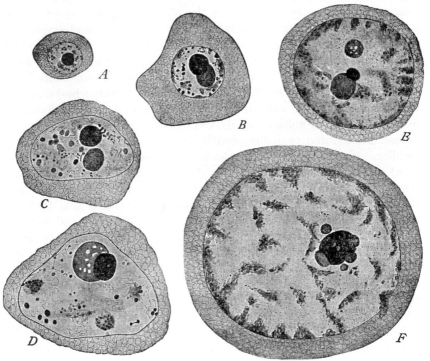

Fig. 108.—Germinal vesicles of growing ovarian eggs of the pelecypod, *Unio* (*A–D*), and the spider, *Epeira* (*E–F*) (Obst).

A, youngest stage with single (principal) nucleolus; *B*, older egg, showing accessory nucleolus attached to the principal; *C*, the two nucleoli separated; *D*, much older stage, showing the two nucleoli united; *E*, germinal vesicle of *Epeira*, showing one accessory nucleolus attached to the principal, and one free; *F*, later stage; several accessory nucleoli attached to the principal.

plicated by the fact that we are dealing with a nucleus during a period not alone of intense constructive activity and growth but also of meiosis or the reduction of the chromosomes. In this respect the nucleus of the animal ovum offers a much more intricate problem than that of plants, where in general the meiotic phenomena take place at another period of the life-history (p. 489). The structure of the germinal vesicle in the full-grown egg can therefore only be understood in the light of its earlier history. At this point we limit our consideration, so far as practicable, to the germinal vesicle at or near the time of its full maturity.

The germinal vesicle offers many of the same features seen on a smaller scale in the nuclei of the tissue-cells in their "resting" or vegetative condition; but in most cases shows also certain characters of a prophase-nucleus. Its structural details in the full-grown egg vary widely; we may usually distinguish, as in the somatic nuclei, a *nuclear framework* in the form of a fine network or alveolar structure, a well-defined nuclear wall or membrane, and one or more conspicuous nucleoli (the "germinal spots" of early observers); but in many ova, as they approach maturity, the nucleoli are already in course of disappearance.

3. The Chromosomes and the Nuclear Framework. The general framework of the germinal vesicle is commonly but slightly basophilic and may even be purely oxyphilic; but in this respect wide differences exist between different species. In all cases, the full-grown germinal vesicle when ready for the final stages of maturation contains the formed chromosomes (bivalents or tetrads) now more or less strongly basophilic and preparing to pass through the final prophases of the meiotic divisions (p. 546). In many cases, particularly in the case of relatively small eggs, they are scattered irregularly through the germinal vesicle or around its periphery, sharply marked off from both the framework in which they are suspended and from the nucleolus or nucleoli. This condition, widely prevalent among invertebrates, is exemplified in the annelids (Fig. 199), mollusks (Figs. 107, 239) or teleosts (Fig. 162).

In other cases, as the germinal vesicle approaches its full term, the chromosomes show a tendency to aggregate in a definite group, suspended in the framework, and often lying near the center of the nucleus. This condition is commonly seen in the large eggs of vertebrates, such as the birds, reptiles, and in lesser degree the amphibians and fishes. In some cases they tend to aggregate in the immediate vicinity of the nucleolus, with which they may come into such intimate relation as to seem actually to arise from it. An example of this is seen in the echinoderms,[1] where a number of observers have described a nucleolar origin of the chromosomes, wholly or in part, while others have found only a close association between the two (Buchner, '11). It seems, however, to be well established

[1] *E. g.*, R. Hertwig ('96), Wilson ('01), Hartmann ('02), Günther ('03), Jordan ('07). See also Conklin ('02), Lillie ('06).

that in some cases the central aggregation of the chromosomes may go so far as to give rise to a more or less compact and nucleolus-like body which in its more extreme forms may fairly be called a karyosphere (p. 93). This condition seems almost to be reached in some of the vertebrates (Loyez, '06), where many gradations exist in the concentration of the chromosome-groups, the process reaching a maximum in certain of the birds and reptiles (Fig. 110).[1] In such cases the chromosomes, though much reduced in size and closely crowded together, do not differ very markedly from those of the elasmobranch or reptilian egg just before the polar mitoses, when

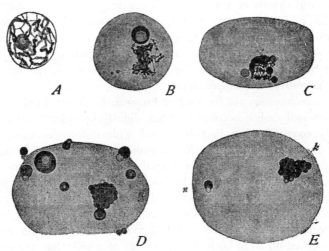

Fig. 109.—Formation of karyosphere in germinal vesicle of the leech, *Nephelis* (Jörgenssen).

A, early post-synaptic spireme; *B*, beginning of concentration; *C, D*, later stages, showing amphinuclei; *E*, fully formed karyosphere (*k*) and one amphinucleolus (*n*).

they are likewise very small and closely crowded, though not actually forming a karyosphere (Fig. 110).[2] On the other hand, in a few of the invertebrates the chromosomes become so closely aggregated as to form a true karyosphere (Fig. 109) hardly to be distinguished from those that are sometimes found in the spermatocytes of insects and myriapods (Fig. 37).

Lastly it may be noted that the extent of the general nuclear framework as compared with that of the chromosomes also varies very widely. In some cases (*e. g.*, in certain platodes) [3] the chromosomes constitute the main bulk of the nuclear substance with only a relatively sparse amount

---

[1] By some writers this has been characterized as a second contraction-figure (synizesis or "synapsis." See Vejdovský '11, '12).

[2] *E. g.*, in the dragon-fly (McGill, '06), in the pelecypod *Cumingea* (Jordan, '10) and the leech *Nephelis* (Jörgenssen, '08).

[3] *Cf.* Gelei ('21 '22).

of framework.   More commonly the framework constitutes the major part of the nucleus, the chromosomes being reduced to relatively small bodies suspended in it, while in extreme cases, represented by the large ova of elasmobranchs, amphibians, birds or reptiles, the chromosomes at the end of the growth-period constitute but a minute fraction of the nuclear substance.   These different conditions are a consequence of the varying degrees in which the germinal vesicle returns towards the condition of a resting or vegetative nucleus.   In the course of this process the chromosomes assume a more or less net-like condition and in extreme cases may even temporarily disappear from view altogether, as in an ordinary tissue-cell.   In all cases, however, the germinal vesicle always retains a spireme-like character during a considerable part of the growth-period and sometimes throughout the whole of it; and even when this character seems to be wholly lost, the ensuing changes demonstrate that the germinal vesicle has undergone a far-reaching change in the earlier stages that stamps it with a type of organization widely different from that of a tissue-cell owing to the synaptic conjugation of the chromosomes.   This was long since recognized by Rückert,[1] and all subsequent studies have shown that his conclusion was fundamentally correct in substance if not precisely in form.

c. *The Nucleoli.*   The diversity of conditions shown by the nucleoli is as striking as that of the nuclear framework and the chromosomes.   In the very young oöcytes the nucleolus is almost always single; and this condition may persist during the whole growth-period of the egg.   In many cases, however, additional nucleoli appear, being sometimes numbered by hundreds (Fig. 111).   As was long since recognized by Haecker ('95, '99, etc.) the nucleolus commonly remains single in relatively small eggs while it is usually multiple in large eggs heavily laden with yolk.   The former condition ("echinoderm type" of Haecker) is of rather wide occurrence among invertebrates (various cœlenterates, echinoderms, platodes, annelids, mollusks, etc.) and appears also in many insects (Fig. 111) and in some of the chordates (tunicates, *Amphioxus, Bdellostoma,* mammals).   Multiple nucleoli ("vertebrate type" of Haecker) occur with few exceptions in the large yolk-laden eggs of elasmobranchs and other fishes, amphibians, birds and reptiles; also in some arthropods.   Conspicuous exceptions to Haecker's rule are, however, known, and nearly related forms sometimes differ markedly in this respect, but the meaning of these variations is not yet clear.[2]

Like the nucleoli of tissue-cells, those of the germinal vesicle may be

---

[1] "The germinal vesicle is to be regarded as a daughter-spireme of the oögonium grown to enormous dimensions, with its chromosomes double and arranged in pairs " ('92, 2, p. 51).

[2] See Jörgenssen, '13.

either basophilic, oxyphilic or of intermediate character; and in many cases both extremes coexist in the same germinal vesicle, often being united to form amphinucleoli (p. 94). Most commonly the nucleoli are strongly basophilic, and are often markedly resistant to hydrochloric-peptic digestion (Zacharias, Jörgenssen). In these respects they show a remarkable contrast to the general oxyphilic framework and often also to the chromosomes, during the middle growth-period of the egg (p. 351), a contrast

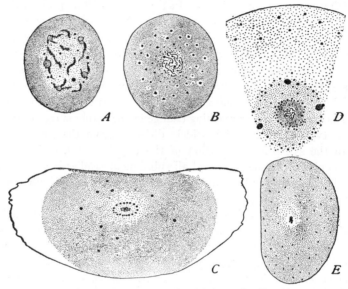

Fig. 110.—The germinal vesicle in reptiles (LOYEZ).

(A–C, *Anguis*, D, E, *Lacerta*). A and B, successive stages in the centripetal movement of the chromosomes; C, shortly before maturation, chromosomes very small, crowded at center and surrounded by nucleoli; D, portions of full grown germinal vesicle, with chromosomes massed at center, surrounded by nucleolar fragments; E, entire germinal vesicle, less magnified, showing massed chromosomes.

heightened by the fact that these nucleoli are typically spheroidal in form and sharply marked off from the framework in which they are suspended. These nucleoli often appear perfectly homogeneous; frequently, however, especially in the later stages of the uninucleolar type, they become more or less vacuolated, showing a large central vacuole or numerous smaller ones scattered through their substance. At the same time they often become less strongly basophilic and less resistant to hydrochloric-peptic digestion (Jörgenssen). In the eggs of many invertebrates, after double-staining with basic and acidic dyes, two nucleolar substances are often differentiated, one strongly basophilic and resistant to pepsin-hydrochloric digestion, the other slightly basophilic or even oxyphilic and readily digestible. These substances have the same general character as those which in other species appear in the form of separate oxyphilic and basophilic nucleoli, or of two such nucleoli closely apposed to form an amphinucleolus

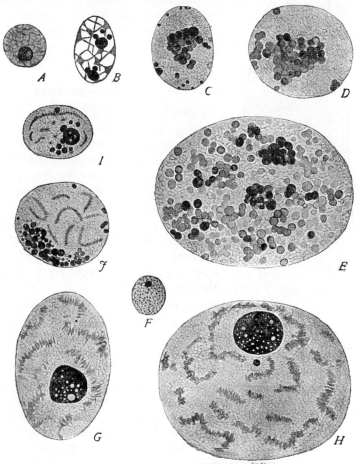

Fig. 111.—The germinal vesicle during the growth-period of tracheates (Jörgenssen).

A–E, progressive stages of the myriapod *Scolopendra*, showing multiplication of basichromatic nucleoli, chromosomes invisible as such; *F–H*, the cockroach *Blatta*, with single basichromatic nucleolus and oxychromatic chromosomes; *I, J*, the mole-cricket *Gryllotalpa*, oxychromatic chromosomes, basichromatic nucleoli.

(p. 270). The latter condition is common in annelids, mollusks, arthropods and other invertebrates (Fig. 108). Such amphinucleoli are commonly single, but in a few cases (*Patella cœrulea*), many are present in the same nucleus (Jörgenssen, '13b). In cases of this type both substances are often

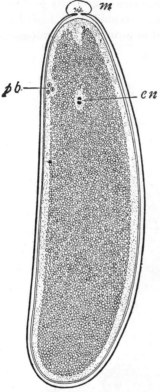

Fig. 112.—Schematic figure of a median longitudinal section of the egg of a fly (*Musca*), showing axes of the bilateral egg, and the membranes (from Korschelt and Heider, after Henking and Blochmann).

e. n., The pronuclei uniting; *m.,* micropyle; *p. b.,* the polar bodies. The flat side of the egg is the dorsal, the convex side the ventral, and the micropyle is at the anterior end. The deutoplasm (small circles) lies in the center surrounded by a peripheral or peri-vitelline layer of protoplasm. The outer heavy line is the chorion, the inner lighter line the vitelline membrane, both being perforated by the micropyle, from which exudes a mass of jelly-like substance.

united in a nucleolus that is externally single but shows internally an oxyphilic basis in which are imbedded a number of sharply differentiated, rounded, elongate or cap-like basophilic bodies. The changes of staining reaction, and remarkable structural transformations of the nucleoli during the growth of the oöcyte will be later considered (p. 353).

4. The Egg-envelopes

Following Ludwig ('74) it is convenient to class the egg-envelopes as *primary*, formed by the egg itself, *secondary*, formed by the follicle-cells immediately surrounding the egg, and *tertiary*, formed by the oviduct or other maternal structures not immediately connected with the egg.

(1) The primary or "vitelline" envelopes include at least three types of structures, namely: (1), the *fertilization-membrane*, or *vitelline membrane* (p. 258), commonly structureless and very delicate; (2) a thicker and more conspicuous envelope, sometimes showing a pronounced radial striation and in such cases called the *zona radiata*; (3) a much thicker, structureless jelly surrounding the egg. Of these the fertilization-membrane is the most constant and is probably always present though often difficult to see before fertilization (p. 411). At the instant of fertilization this membrane suddenly separates from the egg, often to a considerable distance, thus affording a ready means of determining when the egg is fertilized. This membrane was formerly supposed to be formed only at the moment of fertilization; but it is now certain that in many cases it is present before the sperm touches the egg.

The *zona radiata* of the vertebrate ovum, conspicuously shown in the fishes, is a thick and often double membrane traversed by fine radial canals through which in many cases fine protoplasmic bridges are said to pass from the follicle-cells into the cortical protoplasm of the egg (Fig. 156). By some observers this has been supposed to be a product of the surrounding *granulosa* or follicle-cells, but the evidence seems decisive that in certain cases, at least, the *zona radiata* is formed by the egg itself.[1]

In many cases this layer has been called a "chorion"; but it is doubtful whether this term can properly be applied to it. In the egg of the annelid *Nereis* the recent studies of F. R. Lillie demonstrate that the so-called *zona radiata* is formed by the closely crowded, palisade-like cortical alveoli; and that upon fertilization the clear contents of these are discharged to the exterior through the vitelline membrane and swell up in the water to form a thick layer of jelly by which the egg is surrounded.

(2) The secondary envelope is a product of the follicle-cells surrounding the ovum and hence is a purely maternal product. This membrane, typically seen in the insect-egg (Fig. 112), is the *chorion*. Owing to its mode of formation it is comparable to a cuticular membrane, and like the latter is often composed of a hard substance related to chitin, which forms a solid and almost impervious outer protection to the egg (insects). It is often marked by a more or less complicated pattern, determined by the activities of the surrounding follicle-cells, which commonly appears in the form of polygonal areas, often complicated by the formation of spines and other characteristic forms of sculpturing.[2]

Both the primary and the secondary envelopes are in some groups perforated by a *micropyle*, or a group of them, most commonly at or near one pole of the egg. In echinoderms, insects, cephalopods and fishes the micropyle is near the upper pole (Figs. 113, 512) while in other mollusks and nemertines it is near the lower pole. When single the micropyle sometimes is in a deep infolding of the membrane or *micropylar canal* (Fig. 114). When several micropyles are present they are usually grouped at the anterior end, sometimes at some distance from the original pole of the egg, sometimes

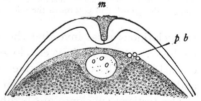

Fig. 113.—Upper pole of the egg of *Argonauta* (Ussow).

The egg is surrounded by a very thick membrane, perforated at *m* by the funnel-shaped micropyle; below the latter lies the egg-nucleus in the peri-vitelline layer of protoplasm; *p. b.*, the polar bodies.

in a circle surrounding a pit-like micropyle-field. In other cases, a ring of micropyles seems to surround the egg some distance below the anterior end. A good example of this is seen in *Metapodius* (Fig. 485), though the nature of the 40–50 "micropyles" is here not certain. It is possible that the pres-

[1] See especially Eigenmann ('90), Mark ('90).
[2] For a fuller account see Korschelt and Heider ('02) and literature there cited.

ence of several or many micropyles in the insect egg may be correlated with the fact that in these animals several sperms normally enter the egg, though only one of them actually fertilizes it. In some cases, perhaps always, the position of the micropyle marks the point at which the oöcyte is attached to the ovarian wall during the period of its growth (p. 1023).

(3) The tertiary envelopes include a great variety of protective and nutritive structures. Some are formed as secretions of the walls of the oviduct or uterus, or of special glands connected with them. Examples of these are the albumin, shell-membrane, and shell of birds and reptiles; the egg-capsules of the selachians, chimæroids, mollusks and platodes; or

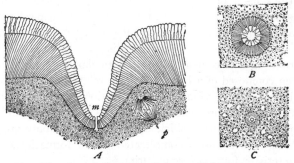

Fig. 114.—The micropyle in the egg of the ganoid *Lepidosteus* (MARK).

A, radial section through micropyle (*m*) at bottom of the micropylar funnel, traversing the outer villous layer and inner zona radiata of envelope; both these layers are believed to be products of the egg itself, hence "vitelline "membranes; at *p* is the anastral polar spindle; *B*, transverse section through the funnel, and *C* through the micropylar canal.

the gelatinous mass investing the ova of various fishes, amphibians, and mollusks. Other tertiary envelopes are secreted by the external surface of the body, such as the protective capsules and nutritive fluids of the leeches and earthworms and a variety of other structures.

The tertiary envelopes are highly characteristic of different groups and species, and sometimes assume a definite form that may in some degree foreshadow that of the future embryo. A remarkable example of this is offered by the fish *Chimæra*[1] which produces an egg-capsule (Fig. 115) of elongate form, showing a perfect bilateral symmetry, dorso-ventral differentiation and antero-posterior differentiation that accurately correspond to those of the future embryo. This is of much interest because the general shape of the capsule does not correspond to that of the egg (which is elongate ovoid), but to that of the developed embryo, having an enlarged anterior region in which the head and body came to lie and a long posterior portion for the reception of the tail. The capsule is, there-

[1] See Dean, '03, '04, '06.

fore, moulded neither on the egg nor on the embryo to be developed from it, but is an apparently independent product of the wall of the oviduct. This capsule, like the insect egg (p. 1020) is definitely oriented in the oviduct, lying with its larger (anterior) end turned backwards; and at this end the capsule is provided with a valvular opening through which the embryo makes its escape. How this striking adjustment between embryo and capsule has come into existence forms an interesting puzzle of adaptation.

5. Promorphological Features of the Ovum [1]

The animal egg always shows in greater or less degree certain features that foreshadow general characters of the future embryo and adult and for

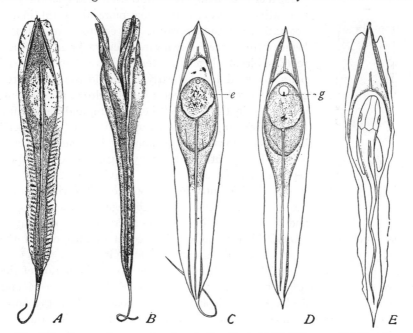

Fig. 115.—Egg-capsule, egg and embryo in the chimæroid fish *Chimæra collici* (DEAN).

A, egg-capsule in dorsal view; *B*, the same in lateral view, with open valve after escape of the young fish; *C, D, E*, successive stages in dorsal view, after removal of portion of capsule-wall to show the egg and embryo; *C, e*, the egg, "late blastula"; *E*, young *Chimæra* nearly ready to hatch.

this reason are spoken of as *promorphological*. The most important of them are as follows:

a. Polarity, probably of universal occurrence in the ova of animals, though not always clearly evident to the eye before the egg begins its development. Its fundamental nature is unknown; but it is made evident

---

[1] A further account of this subject is given at p. 1014.

in many ways. One of its most constant manifestations is the formation of the polar bodies or polocytes at the so-called upper pole, and the correlated fact that before these bodies have been formed the egg-nucleus or germinal vesicle often lies excentrically towards this pole. In correlation with the axis thus marked out the egg very often shows a polarized or stratified disposition of its cytoplasmic components, such as the granules, yolk, and pigment. In many cases these components show differences of specific gravity; and when they are symmetrically grouped with respect to the egg-axis, as often happens, the egg floats in a constant position with the axis vertical and one or the other pole turned upward. In the telo-

Fig. 116.—Schematic cross-section of egg of cockroach, showing bilateral shape and distribution of yolk (BLOCHMANN).

lethical eggs of many vertebrates, for example, the yolk is relatively heavy, and being more abundant in the vegetative hemisphere causes the egg to float with this hemisphere turned downwards (elasmobranchs, frogs, reptiles, birds)—hence the terms "lower" and "upper" poles, as used by the early embryologists, and often still employed. In other cases fat-drops are present, commonly in the "lower" hemisphere, and thus cause this hemisphere to be turned upwards and the "upper" hemisphere downwards (commonly in pelagic annelid-eggs, fish-eggs, etc.). In many eggs, however, no perceptible difference of specific gravity exists, the egg floating indifferently in any position. Polarity is often shown also by the form of the egg and its envelopes, and by the position of the micropyle or micropyles (when such are present) which are often situated at or near one of the poles, or sometimes symmetrically grouped around it.

The polarity of the egg shows a definite relation to the formation of the future body, the outer germ-layer or ectoblast being formed in a general way from the so-called upper hemisphere, at the pole of which the polar bodies are formed, while the inner germ-layer or entoblast is formed in the lower hemisphere (p. 1014).

b. Bilaterality. In the eggs of some bilateral animals the egg is bilaterally symmetrical in form, and sometimes also in the grouping of its cytoplasmic components, thus foreshadowing the form of the future embryo. Remarkable examples of this are offered by the eggs of insects and of cephalopods (Figs. 116, 484) in which all the future axes of the body are often clearly distinguishable in the egg before it has been fertilized and even before it has been laid (insects). It was suggested by Van Beneden that the eggs of all bilateral animals may also be bilateral; but there is little evidence to support this. Both polarity and bilaterality were assumed by Driesch and Boveri to be referable to the properties of minute particles of which the oöplasm were assumed to consist (p. 110); but this is quite hypothetical.

c. Sexual Dimorphism. From the genetic evidence on birds and Lepidoptera we are led to infer the existence in these groups of a sexual dimorphism of the eggs in respect to their nuclear constitution analogous to that known to exist in the sperms (p. 748). Such a dimorphism has, in fact, been demonstrated in certain of the Lepidoptera by Seiler, who shows in several species that maturation causes the production of two kinds of eggs, one of which receives one chromosome more than

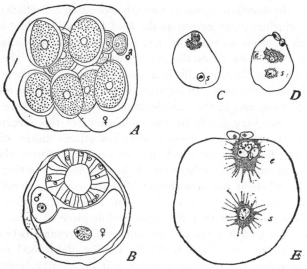

Fig. 117.—Sexual dimegaly of the eggs in *Dinophilus apatris*; (*A*, from Korschelt; *B–E* from Nachtsheim.)

A, egg-capsule, containing large (female-producing) and small (male-producing) eggs; *B*, cross-section of female individual, showing the two kinds of eggs in the ovary, *C, D*, small male-producing eggs, two stages of fertilization; *E*, similar stage of the female-producing egg.

e, egg nucleus; *s* (sperm-nucleus).

the other, and gives rise to males (p. 784). Externally these two types of eggs show no visible structural differences, so far as known, and hence can hardly be considered as examples of promorphology in the egg. Not to be confused with these cases is a visible sexual dimorphism or *dimegaly* in certain animals, the eggs being of two sizes, the larger ones producing females, the smaller males; and this is a case of true promorphology, since it foreshadows a corresponding size-difference between the adult sexes. This condition is known with certainty in only a few cases (rotifers, phylloxerans, *Dinophilus* (Fig. 117; see also p. 806).

B. The Animal Sperm

Introductory

The sperms of different species of animals exhibit remarkable differences of size, form and structure, nearly related species often differing characteristically in this respect. Many of these variations seem to be of little or no physiological significance; and beneath the structural diversity of the sperms exists a fundamental common plan of organization.

Most commonly the animal sperm is a motile, flagellate cell, though non-flagellate forms occur in several groups of invertebrates. In its more typical form the flagellate sperm is a greatly elongated cell which commonly shows two principal parts known as the *head* and the *flagellum* or *tail*, between which is often seen a third region called the *middle-piece* or *connecting-piece*. In most cases the sperm swims actively by the whip-like lashings of the flagellum, usually in a more or less spiral course and with the head directed forwards. In some animals the tail bears a longitudinal fin-like membrane, and in the urodele amphibia the sperm, here relatively very large, moves very slowly by the undulations of this structure. The middle-piece is extremely variable, being sometimes hardly distinguishable from the flagellum (of which it then obviously forms the anterior part), as in mammals; in other cases it is apparently wanting (insects), while in still others it appears sharply distinct from the flagellum, both in structure and in mode of origin (salamanders, echinoderms, fishes, etc.). It is now evident that the name middle-piece or connecting-piece has been applied to a number of quite different structures between which no exact homology exists; but if this be clearly understood no harm is done by employing the word as a convenient descriptive term. As will be seen, the middle-piece often forms a considerable part of the flagellum (mammals, birds, reptiles) or even its major part (urodeles, some gasteropods).

Sperms of this general type are found in all the main groups of animals from the sponges and cœlenterates up to man, showing many modifications, of which the most complicated, perhaps, occur among the amphibians, birds and mammals. Atypical forms of flagellate sperms occur in certain Turbellaria (rhabdocœles), Bryozoa, myriapods and some Crustacea, notably the barnacles, copepods, ostracodes, isopods and schizopods and in a few insects. In a few of the rhabdocœles (*e. g., Procerodes*, Fig. 127) two separate flagella are present, attached at an acute angle near one extremity of the elongate head, so as strongly to recall the sperm-cells of lower plants. Biflagellate sperms are, however, of great rarity among animals save as abnormalities. Sperms of the flagellate type are closely paralleled in both form and structure by the vegetative forms of certain flagellates, in particular by species of *Leptomonas* (*Herpetomonas*) (Fig. 286) and related forms.

Non-flagellate sperms occur only in the nematodes, the chilognathous myriapods, the Crustacea (Cladocera, Decapoda), and a few arachnids (mites). In some of these cases the sperms appear to be non-motile; but as a rule they perform slow movements, either by amœboid changes or by the operation of spine-like processes (decapods). Some of these sperms are of strange forms and complicated structure (Figs. 128, 129), but the study of their development shows (as Koltzoff has demonstrated) that they are constructed upon the same fundamental plan as the flagellate forms. It is almost certain, therefore, that non-flagellate sperms have arisen secondarily from those of flagellate type, a conclusion borne out by the fact that the latter alone are found in the lowest Metazoa (sponges, cœlenterates), while flagellated microgametes are common in the Protista and in lower metaphytes.

1. Structure of the Flagellate Sperm

General Outline

In considering the structure of the mature sperm we encounter many difficulties of terminology; for it displays so great a diversity of form and structure in different species and groups that its morphology can only be understood through a study of its development. An account of the formation of the sperm in detail will be given later (p. 356); but our account of the mature sperm will be facilitated by mention of the following main facts. The sperms arise by differentiation of cells known as *spermatids* (Figs. 166–171, etc.), which have a well-developed cytoplasmic cell-body containing a nucleus, one or two centrioles, mitochondrial formations, and Golgi-bodies. The centrioles at first lie close together near the periphery of the cell, with one nearer the nucleus, the other nearer the periphery (Fig. 167); the former is then designated as the inner or *proximal*, the other as the *distal*. All these structures take part in the formation of the sperm, but a considerable amount of "residual protoplasm" is ultimately cast off. The centrioles take an important part in the formation of the flagellum, the distal one playing the part of a blepharoplast from which the axial filament of the tail grows forth.

The conventional grouping of the sperm-structures into head, middle-piece and tail, as shown at the left, below, is based on merely superficial characters. A more careful study, which takes into account the development of the sperm, shows that in many cases each of these parts typically consists of two regions, as in the middle column.

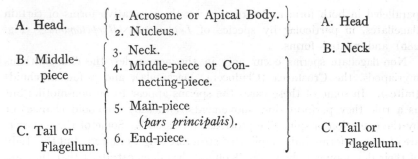

A. Head.	{ 1. Acrosome or Apical Body. \ 2. Nucleus.	}	A. Head
B. Middle-piece	{ 3. Neck. \ 4. Middle-piece or Con- \ necting-piece.		B. Neck
C. Tail or Flagellum.	{ 5. Main-piece \ (*pars principalis*). \ 6. End-piece.	}	C. Tail or Flagellum.

Some writers (*e. g.*, Waldeyer, Retzius) prefer to group these regions somewhat differently, as in the right column. In the following account we shall adhere on the whole to the old-fashioned grouping shown at the left (Fig. 118) reckoning, however, the neck as a separate region (as at the right) whenever it is convenient to do so. All the regions posterior to the head are recognized here in a *merely topographical sense,* for no satisfactory basis for a consistent morphological classification has yet been found.

a. *The Head,* considered as a whole, displays a great diversity of form in different species and groups. It may be spheroidal (common among invertebrates, teleosts), conical (*Cyprina, Flustra*), or lance-shaped (salamanders), rod-shaped or filiform (insects), spirally twisted (passerine birds), flattened or spoon-shaped (man, guinea-pig, and many other mammals), hood-shaped (opossum), hook-shaped (mouse, rat, etc.), as may be seen from the accompanying figures. So great is the diversity in this respect that it is hardly an exaggeration to say that most species of animals might be identified from the sperm alone. The functional significance of these various forms is practically unknown.

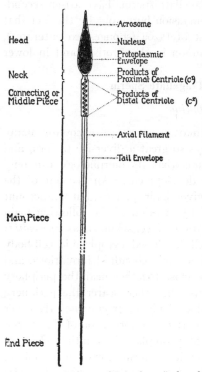

Fig. 118.—Diagram of animal sperm, based on the conditions found in mammals. A long section of the flagellum, indicated by dotted lines, is omitted. In some cases the mitochondrial sheath extends far beyond the middle-piece.

The main bulk of the head is constituted by:

(1) The *Nucleus,* which occupies all but the anterior tip of the head. It often seems to consist of a solid and homogeneous mass of basichromatin that stains with great intensity in all nuclear dyes, but in some cases shows a more deeply staining cortical layer and a lighter central region. In a few forms the nucleus is represented by a group of separate chromosomes, visible even in the living object, so that they may readily be counted (some nematodes, Fig. 357). In a few cases, as shown by Retzius and Koltzoff, the nucleus is traversed by a fine cytoplasmic axial rod or filament that extends from the base of the flagellum through the nucleus to its anterior extremity. Examples of this are offered by the annelid *Nereis* (Fig. 119, I, J) and the spider *Opilio* (Fig. 119A). These cases have an important bearing on certain theories of fertilization; for, although the origin of the cephalic axial filament is not known, it may possibly be a derivative of the centriole, like that of the middle-piece and flagellum. This filament is not to be confused with a longitudinal extra-nuclear filament (Fig. 119B) described in various forms (*Aurelia, Formica*) and in certain cases known to be an acrosome (p. 282).

The foremost part of the head is typically occupied by:

(2) The *Apical body* or *Acrosome,* often known also as the *perforatorium* (Waldeyer) in allusion to its formerly supposed function as a means of boring into the egg. This structure is usually much smaller than the nucleus; in a few cases, however (passerine birds), it is the larger of the two (Fig. 125). It exhibits a great diversity of form, varying from a small granule or knob to a large conical or spine-like process, which in extreme cases (urodeles) is provided with a prominent barb like that of a fish-hook (Fig. 123). By a further development of this type, the acrosome may be drawn out into a long filiform process that almost simulates an anterior flagellum (some Lepidoptera). By a different type of modification it spreads out to form a large, crescent-shaped body molded upon the anterior part of the nucleus (Fig. 126) of which it was formerly supposed to be a part (a condition commonly seen in mammals). In this case, the most peripheral layer of the acrosome (or by some writers the whole acrosome) is called the " head-cap," which often extends backwards over a considerable part of the nucleus. In such sperms the head is often flattened, the acrosome forming a thin, knife-like edge, which has been supposed to faciliate the entrance of the sperm into the egg (Waldeyer); but its function is still problematical (p. 716). [1] In some animals the acrosome lies more or less on the side of the nucleus, and is sometimes drawn out along almost the

---

[1] For this type of acrosome see especially the work of Papanicolau and Stockard ('18) on the guinea-pig.

entire length of the nucleus (in certain Coleoptera, Bowen, '22, '23). In Lepidoptera, Bowen found the acrosome, the basal portion of which lies beside the nucleus, to be drawn out anteriorly far beyond the nucleus to form a very long attenuated filament.[1]

The development of the sperm shows that both nucleus and acrosome are covered by a very thin cytoplasmic covering, perhaps a cell-membrane;

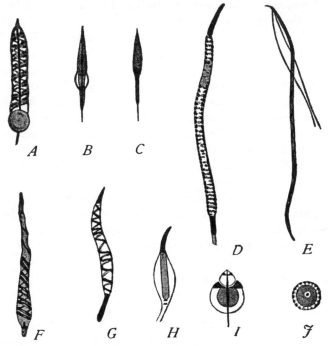

Fig. 119.—Details of sperms of various animals after staining with methyl-green-acid-fuchsin (Biondi mixture) dark portions red (oxyphilic) in the preparations, light portions mostly green (basophilic) (KOLTSOFF).

A, head and middle-piece of the spider *Opilio*, showing axial filament of head and spiral cytoplasmic fibrillæ; *B, C*, from the medusa *Aurelia*, to show *superficial* longitudinal filament of head; *D, Lumbricus* with spiral cytoplasmic fibrilla; *E*, biflagellate sperm of the turbellarian *Monotus*, spiral cytoplasmic filament; *F*, head of sperm in the gasteropod *Paludina*, double cytoplasmic spiral filament; *G*, from the domestic fowl, *Gallus*, single spiral; *H*, from the snake *Coluber* (plasmolyzed) showing oxyphily of acrosome and neck-knobs (as in *D*); *I*, from the annelid *Nereis* showing *axial* oxyphilic filament of head; *J*, the same in optical cross-section.

but in the mature sperm it is of such tenuity and so closely applied to the underlying structures as to be invisible under ordinary conditions. Its presence, as shown by Koltzoff ('09), is often readily revealed by plasmolysis, which causes it to separate from the nucleus. After such treatment

---

[1] For the even more extraordinary condition of the acrosome in *Lepisma*, see p. 296.

accompanied by suitable staining, the heads of many kinds of sperms have been found to contain cytoplasmic fibrillæ which stain intensely in various plasma-dyes, and have various arrangements which are characteristic of different forms (Koltzoff, Retzius). Most often these fibrillæ lie in the cytoplasmic investment of the nucleus, winding spirally about the latter (Fig. 119); thus recalling the spiral fibrillæ of the tail-envelope. This gives some reason to suspect that these fibrillæ may likewise be of mitochondrial origin, but of this nothing is certainly known. Koltzoff regards them as skeletal or supporting structures.

b. The Neck. This region, often not externally distinguishable, owes its name to the fact that in a few cases (among mammals) it is narrower than the regions between which it lies, and thus forms, as it were, a stalk by which the flagellum is attached to the head (Fig. 126). Internally it is distinguished by the presence of one or more centrioles, or their derivatives, in the form of basal granules, basal rods, "end-knobs," or the like. In some cases these are lost to view in the mature sperm, either by passing into the base of the nucleus or being converted into larger bodies or plate-like structures (urodeles). The relations of the centriolar apparatus to the neck-region are of great interest because of the evidence that *from this region of the sperm, or in its neighborhood arises the sperm-center during the fertilization of the egg* (p. 440). This region often appears not to be surrounded by a mitochondrial sheath such as is so characteristic of the succeeding regions.

In the urodeles (Fig. 123) the neck is a clearly marked, short cylindrical region (the "middle-piece" of earlier writers), which constitutes a basal body that arises by enlargement of the anterior centriole (Meves). The short and often indistinguishable "middle-piece" of insects and of most anurans is also a neck region, in which lie two basal bodies (centrioles). In some forms (*e. g.*, in *Paludina*, Fig. 167), the basal body is pushed up into the basal region of the nucleus, in which case no neck region can be distinguished as such; but it seems probable that the basal body here represents only a part of the proximal centriole (p. 380).

The neck region marks the beginning of the *axial filament*, originally a very delicate fibrilla which in the mature sperm is often considerably thickened and by maceration may be split up into still finer parallel fibrillæ (Jenson, Ballowitz). This, among other reasons, has led to the conclusion that the axial filament is a contractile structure, analogous to a muscle-fiber, by which the whip-like movements of the tail are performed. The axial filament is surrounded by a thin envelope or sheath, the anterior portion of which is composed largely of chondriosome-substance derived from the chondrioma of the sperm-producing cells. This sheath typically begins just behind the neck region, and extends to the end of the main piece.

c. *The Middle-piece or Connecting-piece.* By Waldeyer and Meves, the term "middle-piece" or "connecting-piece" is restricted to the region of

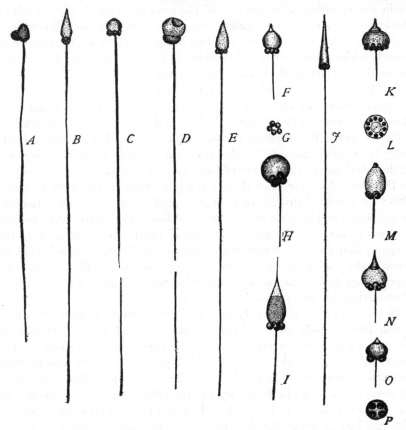

Fig. 120.—Sperms with primitive type of middle-piece (Retzius).

A, of the cœlenterate *Tealia*, with lateral middle-piece; *B*, the sea-urchin *Arbacia*; *D*, the starfish *Asterias*; *E*, the sea-urchin *Sphærechinus*; *F*, the nemertine *Carinella*; and *G*, axial view of same; *H*, the annelid *Glycera*; *I*, the mollusk *Chiton*; *J*, the pelecypod *Cyprina*; *K*, the pelecypod *Modiola*; *L*, the same in axial view; *M*, the limpet *Patella*; *N*, the pelecypod *Mytilus*; *O*, the protochordate *Ptychodera*; *P*, the same in axial view.

the distal centriole, since this body commonly divides into two parts which move apart, the proximal one marking the anterior limit of the middle-piece and the distal one the posterior. This definition, though perfectly valid in case of the mammals, and probably also in birds, reptiles, elasmo-branchs, and some invertebrates, breaks down in other cases, *e. g.,* in urodeles, where the posterior half of the distal centriole moves out nearly to the tip of the flagellum.

The middle-piece is traversed through its center by the axial filament; but in some forms, which have a short and rounded middle-piece, it lies eccentrically (*Nereis, Fundulus*), apparently at the side of the axial filament or even of the nucleus (Fig. 121). Its main bulk is constituted by a mitochondrial sheath surrounding the axial filament, and in its turn probably surrounded by a very delicate cytoplasmic covering. The mitochondrial sheath often shows a distinct spiral structure, being differentiated into one or more delicate fibrillæ which wind spirally about the axial filament, often in very fine and closely coiled turns. The backward extension of the mitochondrial sheath seems to vary widely in different species. In many cases it seems to cease at the posterior limit of the middle-piece, a condition characteristic of most of the mammals, in which the thin sheath of the main piece is believed by some observers to have a different origin.[1] Like all other parts of the sperm, this region displays a remarkable diversity; sometimes it is short and rounded (as in the "nebenkernorgan," later referred to), in other cases, cylindrical and more or less elongated, so as often to appear as a part of the flagellum (mammals, some birds). Its posterior limit is often marked by a disc-shaped or ring-shaped body, a derivative of the distal centriole, and its anterior limit by the basal bodies of the neck-region. These limits are often clearly marked externally (as in the sperm of man, Fig. 126), but in other cases can only be clearly seen during the early development.

d. The Flagellum. The middle-piece is followed by the flagellum proper, which consists of two regions. The first and more extensive is:

(1) The *Main-piece* or *pars principalis*, which comprises the greater part of the flagellum. Like the middle-piece, this region is traversed by the axial filament, often considerably thickened, which is surrounded by a very delicate sheath, the origin of which has been much discussed. In the case of the mammalian sperm, some of the most competent observers believe that the mitochondrial formations do not extend into the main-piece,[2] and that the sheath of the axial filament in this region may be a differentiation of the thickened axial filament itself. On the other hand, as above noted, the spiral chondriosome-formations have been described as extending far out into the flagellum in the bats (Ballowitz, Retzius, Fig. 126); and the same is true of the sperm of some birds (Fig. 125), gastropods and scorpions (Fig. 170). In the urodeles, the cytoplasmic sheath (probably in large measure mitochondrial in origin) extends throughout the whole of the main-

[1] See Meves, '99, Korff, '02, Benda, '97, '06, Jordan, '11, Duesberg, '08, '20, etc.
[2] *E. g.*, in the guinea-pig (Meves, '99) and the rat (Duesberg, '09).

piece to the beginning of the end-piece, at which point lies the distal half of the centriole (p. 378). We are thus confronted with the paradox that if the middle-piece be characterized as the region of the distal centriole (Waldeyer) and the main-piece as that lying beyond the region of the mitochondrial sheath (Meves, Duesberg), the entire flagellum consists of middle-piece and end-piece.

The axial filament is sometimes supplemented by longitudinal accessory filaments, and the flagellum may be further complicated by the presence of an undulating membrane that strongly suggests that seen in the trypanosomes. In the urodeles this membrane is an outgrowth of the axial filament (McGregor, '99), and is thickened along its free edge to form a contractile marginal filament that runs along its free edge and by the movements of which those of the membrane seem to be produced, while the axial filament itself shows no sign of contraction.

The main-piece is succeeded, finally, by:

(2) The *End-piece*, which has no envelope, being formed by the naked axial filament after it has issued from the envelopes to form the extreme tip of the flagellum. This seems to be one of the most constant and well-defined features of the flagellum, and it is an interesting fact that in some of the flagellate Protozoa the flagellum likewise consists of a protoplasmic sheath traversed by an axial filament which forms a naked end-piece near the tip;[1] and here, too, the evidence indicates that the axial filament is the contractile element.

The foregoing structures will be further considered in connection with the processes of spermiogenesis, or histological differentiation of the sperm (p. 368). In fertilization the entire sperm usually enters the egg. Only the nucleus is yet known with certainty to play an essential part in the process; but there is strong evidence that the centriole or its products is likewise of importance. These two bodies accordingly have often been spoken of as the "essential structures" of the sperm; but more recent researches have shown that the acrosome and the mitochondrial elements are also carried by the sperm into the egg and may likewise be of functional importance (p. 434).

Comparative Details. Flagellate sperms conforming more or less nearly to the type just described are widely distributed throughout the animal kingdom. The brief sketch here offered is based largely on the extended work of Ballowitz and of Retzius, whose indefatigable labors have made known the sperms of a great number of animals from the cœlenterates up to the mammals.[2]

The sperms of sponges, cœlenterates and echinoderms are for the most

---

[1] See Doflein, '09, p. 36.　　[2] Retzius, *Biologische Untersuchungen*, 1902–1914.

part of typical flagellate type and usually have relatively short heads and a distinct, short middle-piece. In the cœlenterates first occurs an interesting simple type of sperm in which the middle-piece is formed by a ring of large spheroidal bodies at the base of the nucleus, the axial filament of the

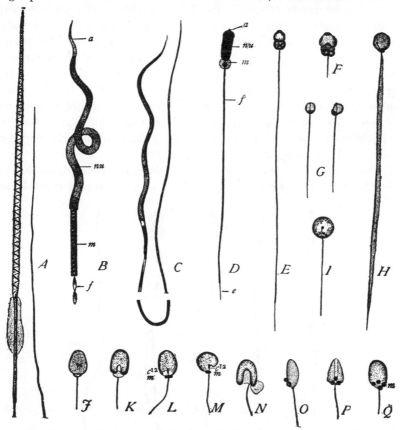

Fig. 121.—Sperms of fishes and protochordates (*A, C, F–I,* from RETZIUS; *B, C, J–N,* from BALLOWITZ; *O–Q* from DUESBERG).

A, sperm of the elasmobranch *Scyllium,* stained to show spiral cytoplasmic head-filament; *B, Raja,* spiral envelope of middle-piece; *C, Chimæra; D,* the sturgeon, *Acipenser; E, F, Amphioxus; G,* the tunicate *Oikopleura; H, I,* the pike *Esox; J, K,* the trout *Salmo,* living *L, M,* the same stained to show middle-piece and both centrioles; *N,* the herring *Clupea,* living; *O–Q,* the salt water minnow *Fundulus,* stained to show middle-piece (nebenkern-organ).

flagellum passing through the center of the group up to the base of the nucleus, or even into it (Fig. 120). This structure, called by Retzius the "nebenkern-organ," is found in various Hydromedusæ, Scyphomedusæ, and Anthozoa and also in several of the higher groups. This simple type of sperm resembles an embryonic type of sperm which in many higher animals only appears as a transitory stage in the formation of a more highly elaborated type (p. 371). With slight modifications it appears also in nemertines, archiannelids (*Polygordius*), some polychætes and gephy-reans, Amphineura (*Chiton*), many pelecypods (*Mytilus*, *Arca*), some of the lower gastropods (*Haliotis*, *Patella*), and also in the protochordate *Ptychodera*, though in some of these cases the ring of spheroidal bodies is less regular or obscured by close crowding or partial fusion of its spheroi-dal components. It seems probable, therefore, that many of the forms of sperms having a short and rounded middle-piece may arise from such a ring or group of nebenkern-spheroids; and according to Retzius traces at least of such a structure may be seen in the middle-piece of echinoderms (Fig. 120), *Amphioxus* and even in the teleost fishes (Fig. 121). It is not known in such cases to what extent (if any) the mitochondria may con-tribute to the tail-formation.

The sperms of platodes and of bryozoa, though flagellated, are for the most part of unusual type (p. 295). Those of annelids and mollusks are

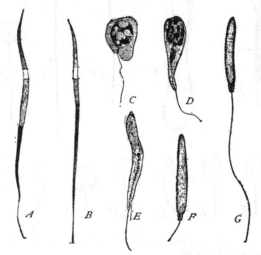

Fig. 122.—Sperms and spermiogenesis in frogs (BROMAN).

A, Mature sperm of *R. fusca* (osmic vapor); *B*, same after staining with gentian violet, cen-trioles; *C–E*, spermatids of same; *F*, head of sperm, *R. mugiens*; *G*, sperm of *R. esculenta*.

most commonly more typical, often with elongate head and middle-piece. In the mollusks, the sperm is often characterized by a much elongated head, often also by a very long middle-piece which in some cases seems to constitute the greater part of the flagellum (*e.*, *g.*, in the nudibranchs), a condition that seems to be parallel to that seen in the urodele Amphibia. In some of these forms the flagellum conspicuously shows two or more fibrillæ twisted into a close spiral and in some cases even the head region is also spirally twisted (as in the passerine birds).

The sperms of arthropods display a great diversity; some are of simple flagellate type (insects), others non-flagellate and often of extremely complex structure (decapod Crustacea). In insects generally the sperms commonly possess rod-shaped heads, sometimes even filiform and hardly distinguishable from the flagellum until after suitable staining. The middle-piece is inconspicuous or invisible externally and of limited extent, showing no sharp external line of demarcation with either the head or the flagellum. Flagellate sperms of the ordinary type are the rule among the arachnids (spiders, scorpions), but non-flagellate sperms also occur in this group (mites). In the Crustacea the diversity of the sperm reaches its maximum. Flagelliform sperms occur in ostracodes, barnacles, schizopods, amphipods and isopods, but are always of modified type. In most of the higher Crustacea the sperms are non-flagellated and not actively motile (p. 297).

In the vertebrates the sperms, always of the flagellate type, show a multitude of special modifications. The simplest forms occur in the teleosts where (as also in *Amphioxus*) the head is usually spheroidal with a very short middle-piece, probably comparable to the nebenkern-organ of lower types. In some cases (*Esox*, *Perca*) the flagellum bears an undulating membrane of simple type. The axial filament terminates anteriorly (sometimes inside the nucleus) in one or two centrioles or basal bodies. The elasmobranch sperm is of more complicated aspect, the head being much elongated and more or less spirally twisted (*Raja*) and showing both an axial filament and spiral peripheral apparatus continuous in front with the acrosome. A fairly short cylindrical middle-piece is present, with a spiral envelope. The flagellum is constituted by two or three filaments connected by a membrane and spirally twisted around each other (Fig. 121).

The sperms of Amphibia are of two main types of which the simpler appears with many variations, in the Anura. In most of these forms the head is much elongated, [1] and a distinct middle-piece often does not appear, though present in some forms (*Hyla*, *Rana*). In the toads (*Bufo*, *Alytes*, etc.) the middle-piece is very short and hardly distinguishable externally. In *Alytes* (Fig. 123) two definite basal bodies are present, a proximal and a distal; and the same is true in *Bombinator*, where Bromann ('oo) has traced them directly to the spermatid-centrioles (Fig. 124). In *Rana esculenta* no definite middle-piece is externally visible, but at the base

---

[1] A remarkable example of this is offered by the anuran *Discoglossus* (Ballowitz, '03) in which the head is quite filiform and constitutes fully half the length of the sperm. In linear dimensions these sperms are among the largest known in animals, measuring upwards of 2 mm. in length; but this is far surpassed by those of the hemipter *Notonecta*, said by Pantel and Sinéty ('06) to measure more than 12 mm. in length.

of the nucleus (neck-region) are two deeply staining basal bodies. In *R. temporaria* Bromann finds a distinct middle-piece, containing a distal and a proximal centriole, and in *R. mugiens* this has a spiral envelope

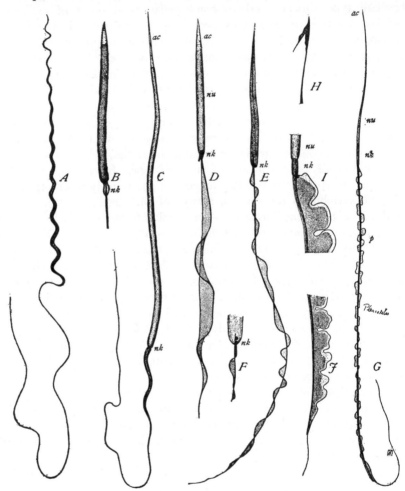

Fig. 123.—Sperms of Amphibia (Retzius).

A, of the toad *Pelobates; B*, head and middle-piece of the tree-toad *Hyla; C*, the frog *Rana esculenta: D*, the toad *Bufo; E*, the obstetrical toad *Alytes; F*, neck-region of same; *G*, the salamander *Pleurodeles; H*, acrosome of similar sperm of the salamander *Molge; I*, neck-region of same; *J*, terminal part of flagellum.

(Fig. 122). Retzius, on the other hand ('06), finds in *R. esculenta* two basal bodies lying side by side. In the tree-toad, *Hyla arborea*, a short middle-piece is present, showing at its proximal end a group of about four granules, and at its distal two distinct pairs of such granules. These no doubt represent the centriole-apparatus, but their genesis is not yet known.

In the toads generally the flagellum contains two longitudinal filaments between which stretches an undulatory fin-membrane which in some cases closely simulates that of the salamanders, as described below (*Alytes*, Fig. 123). A singular modification of this type of sperm occurs in the toad *Bombinator* which in its general aspect recalls a *Trypanosome* flagellate, and also somewhat resembles the sperms of certain Turbellaria (*Macrorhynchus*, Fig. 124).[1] The flagellum is here inserted at one side of the elongated head, near the anterior end, running thence along the head and attached to it along one side, terminating in a free end-piece. The flagellum possesses a thick axial filament (non-motile) and a conspicuous undulating membrane along the free edge of which runs a contractile marginal filament (as in salamanders), which is continued to form the end-piece. These filaments terminate in the centriole-pair, and no middle-piece is present. Since Bromann has traced these granules to the spermatid-centrioles we find here some reason to think that in some other Anura (as in the insects) both centrioles remain in the neck-region of the sperm and that no true middle-piece is present.

The urodeles offer a type of sperm superficially similar to that of some of

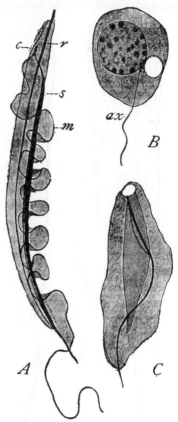

Fig. 124.—Sperm of the toad *Bombinator igneus* (BROMAN).

A, mature sperm, showing two persistent centrioles (*c*), the axial rod (*r*), the supporting fiber (*s*), and the undulating membrane and marginal filament (*m*); B, younger and C, older spermatid.

the Anura (*e. g., Alytes*) owing to the presence of a conspicuous undulating membrane, but apparently very different in its underlying morphology. In these sperms the head is typically of elongate lance-shape and terminates in a long, sharp perforatorium, barbed at the tip. Behind the nucleus lies a distinct, short, so-called "middle-piece," followed by the flagellum with its undulating membrane and terminal end-piece (Fig. 123). The develop-

[1] Bromann, '00.

ment of the sperm, as earlier indicated (p. 283), proves that the middle-piece is a large basal body derived from the proximal centriole alone (hence the true "neck" of the sperm), while the true middle-piece or connecting

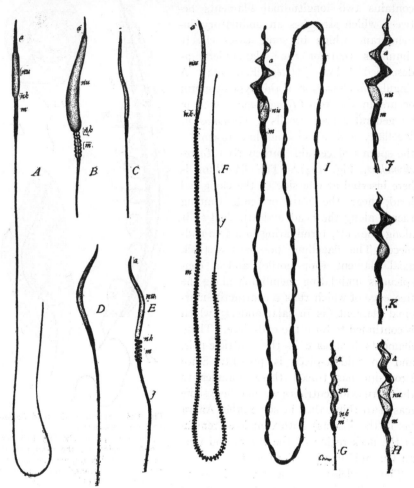

Fig. 125.—Sperms of reptiles and birds (Retzius).

a, acrosome; f, flagellum; m, middle-piece; nk, neck; nu, nucleus.

A, of *Chameleon;* B, *of Testudo;* D, E, of the fowl *Gallus;* F, of the pigeon *Columba* with enormously long middle-piece; G, anterior part, *Corvus;* H, *Passer;* I, nearly complete sperm of *Chloris;* J, *Chrysomitris;* K, *Fringilla.*

piece (region of the distal centriole) is so enormously elongated as to con-stitute almost the whole of the flagellum except the short "end-piece" (*cf.* p. 379).

The sperms of Sauropsida are of two general types (Ballowitz), of which one, of simpler aspect, is common to reptiles and most birds (*e. g.*, *Gallus*), and is designated by Ballowitz and Retzius the "sauropsid" type, while the other and more complex type is characteristic of the passerine birds. In the former type generally the sperm is straight and clearly shows three typical regions of the ordinary type. The middle-piece in this type is sometimes greatly elongated so as to constitute a large part of the flagellum (*e. g.*, in the snake *Coluber*, or in the pigeon *Columba*, Fig. 125). It appears always to possess a spirally twisted envelope, no doubt developed from the mitochondria, as in mammals. The second, and more complex type appears in most of the passerine birds and is characterized by the pronounced spiral character of the head-region and the enormous development of the acrosome, which in some cases may be three or four times the length of the nucleus (*Fringilla*, Fig. 125) and by earlier writers (Ballowitz, etc.) was described as belonging to the latter. The nucleus is sometimes cylindrical and more or less spirally twisted, sometimes almost spheroidal. The acrosome shows a pronounced spiral twist, and bears a conspicuous spiral membrane traversed near its free edge by a marginal filament which in some cases may be traced into connection with a spiral filament surrounding the nucleus (*Pica, Turdus*) and is said even to extend into the tail-region. The head is followed by a short cylindrical or conical and deeply staining middle-piece the true nature of which is still uncertain. The tail or flagellum shows one or two conspicuous spiral filaments twisted about the axial filament but ceasing some distance from the tip so as to leave a long end-piece.

The mammals as a group possess fairly typical sperms, with a well-developed cylindrical middle-piece and a simple flagellum and end-piece; the envelopes of the former show a spiral structure as in so many other forms. The middle-piece follows a short neck-region which contains two or more basal bodies (Figs. 126, 173) derived in part from the proximal centriole. The middle-piece is limited proximally by the basal bodies of the neck-region, distally by a disc or ring derived from the distal centriole (*cf.* p. 377).

The diversity of the mammalian sperm is due mainly to modifications of the head-region, and they are to a certain extent characteristic of different groups. It is interesting to find that the sperms of the monotremes (*Echidna*) are quite of the sauropsid type (Fig. 126) which, so far as known, does not occur elsewhere among the mammals. In mammals generally the acrosome is commonly spread out laterally to form a cap-like structure moulded on the anterior part of the head and called by the earlier observers the "head-cap." In the mice, rats and some other Rodentia, the acrosome is drawn out to form a remarkable perforatorium curved like a nook

(Fig. 126). In the marsupials generally the head is greatly flattened and is attached to the middle-piece by a very narrow neck in which two or more distinct basal bodies are distinguishable. In the opossum, *Didelphys* (Fig. 132), it is hood-shaped, surrounding the proxial part of the flagellum;

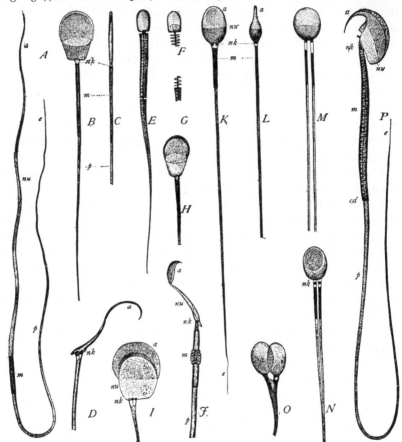

Fig. 126.—Sperms of mammals (RETZIUS).

a, acrosome; *c*, *d*, distal centriole or its products; *c. p.*, proximal centriole or its products; *e*, end-piece of flagellum; *m*, middle-piece or connecting-piece; *nu*, nucleus; *nk*, neck; *p*, main piece of flagellum.

A, sperm of *Echidna*; *B*, *C*, of the deer, *Cervus* (*C* in side-view); *D*, of the squirrel *Sciurus* in side-view; *E*, of the bat *Vesperugo*; *F*, *G*, details of same, after slight maceration; *H*, of the wolf; *I*, head and neck, sperm of guinea-pig; *J*, same in side-view; *K*, *L*, human sperm, *K*, in face view, *L* in side-view; *M*, *N*, *O*, abnormal, partially double sperms; *P*, sperm of the field-mouse, *Mus agrarius*.

and these sperms (p. 305) are typically coupled by their heads, two by two (Fig. 132). In the insectivores (*Talpa*, *Erinaceus*, *Bradypus*) appears a type of sperm that is widely distributed among mammals, including man and other primates [1] characterized by a head of rounded, ovate, or obovate outline, and more or less flattened, in extreme cases becoming spoon-shaped and reduced to a thin plate. The extreme forms of this type occur among rodents (squirrel, guinea-pig), where the front margin is drawn out into a conspicuous hook-like perforatorium (rat, mouse, Fig. 126). In the guinea-pig the head is extremely flat and rounded in front, but sharply flexed at the margin. In many of these forms the basal bodies or centriole-products are seen with great clearness. In all these forms the flagellum is of simple type and shows no fin-membrane. The middle-piece commonly shows a conspicuous spiral mitochondrial envelope, which ordinarily cannot be traced beyond its distal limit.

We cannot here further consider the special modifications of the sperm which have been studied with so much zeal and patience by Ballowitz, Retzius and their fellow spermatologists. A not infrequent anomaly may here be mentioned, namely, the presence of two flagella attached to the head side by side (Fig. 126), and either separate or united posteriorly, branching in front like a Y, and in such cases two heads are commonly present (p. 303).

2. Atypical Flagellate Sperms

The most interesting of the atypical forms of flagellate sperms occur in the lower Turbellaria (Fig. 127) where they show a resemblance in some cases to trypanosome flagellates, in others to the spermatozoids of lower plants. The first type is represented by a number of forms among the rhabdocœles and accœles (*Plagiostoma, Aphanostoma, Darwinia*) and in certain polyclades (*Leptoplana*). In these cases the distinction between head and tail is often scarcely apparent until after careful study, the sperm being pointed at both ends and bearing two undulating membranes along nearly its whole length. In *Macrorhynchus* the sperm is similar, but possesses only one undulating membrane.

These interesting forms of sperms come into relation with those of the more ordinary type through those seen in some of the Crustacea. In the barnacles (*Lepas, Balanus*, Fig. 127) occur very long and apparently head-less sperms that were until recently supposed to be devoid of nuclei or "apyrenous." Koltzoff demonstrated, however, that as in *Macrorhynchus* the nucleus is present in the form of a long filament of chromatin from one end of which a still longer cytoplasmic filament runs along the side of the nucleus and attached to it, finally extending beyond it to form the terminal part of the flagellum. These sperms, like those of *Bombinator* (p. 291), give the impression of being sharply flexed at the neck-region, so that the

---

[1] Retzius has shown that the sperms of the anthropoid apes are closely similar to those of man, and that the resemblance is closer in case of the chimpanzee than in that of the orang.

head is directed backwards; and this is still more striking in certain of the schizopods (*Paradopsis, Protosiriella*) in which the head seems to be turned straight backwards from the point where the flagellum is attached (Fig. 127). Recent studies in certain atypical insect sperms indicate, however, that the true explanation of these cases is a different one. In the tiger beetle *Cicin-*

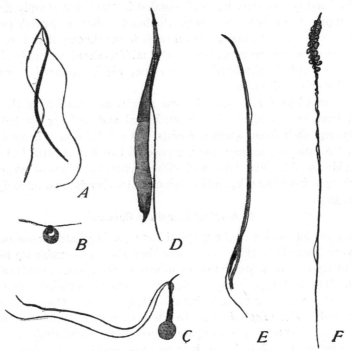

Fig. 127.—Aberrant types of flagellate sperms (KOLTZOFF).

A biflagellate sperm of the platode *Procerodes; B, C,* earlier and later spermatids of same; *D,* sperm of the schizopod *Protosiriella; E,* of the barnacle *Balanus* (slightly macerated); *F,* of the platode *Macrorhynchus* with undulating membrane and marginal filament.

dela the centriole was found by Goldsmith ('19) to pass to the *anterior* end of the nucleus; and this has been confirmed by Bowen ('23), who has traced every step in the backward growth from it of the axial filament alongside the nucleus and into the flagellum. The sperm, therefore, is not flexed on itself, but the flagellum reverses the usual rule by being attached to the *anterior* instead of the posterior end of the nucleus! A similar explanation probably applies to the barnacles and other exceptional cases referred to above. Even more remarkable are the conditions described in *Lepisma.* Here too,[1] as in *Cicindela*, the centriole passes to the anterior tip

[1] Bowen, *op. cit.,* also Charlton, '21

of the nucleus and the axial filament grows backward from it; but the acrosome remains in the neck-region, sending backwards a long filamentary outgrowth alongside the axial filament into the flagellum. Here, accordingly, the usual positions of acrosome and neck-region are reversed (!)

3. Non-flagellate Sperms

Non-flagellate sperms occur in the nematodes and arthropods (certain myriapods, arachnids, and crustaceans). In all cases, probably, these have

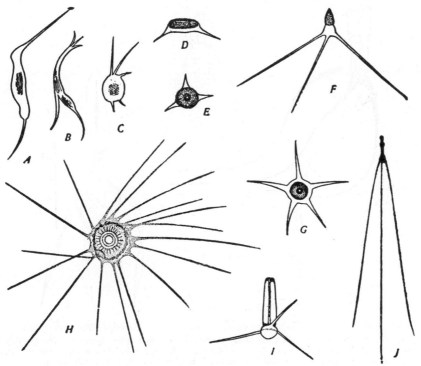

Fig. 128.—Non-flagellate sperms of Crustacea, A, B, C, living amœboid sperms of *Polyphemus* (ZACHARIAS); D, E, sperms of crab, *Dromia*, F of *Ethusa*; G, of *Maja*; H, of *Inachus* (GROBBEN); I, sperm of lobster, *Homarus* (HERRICK); J, sperm of crab, *porcellana* (GROBBEN).

been derived from flagellate forms, for the lowest Metozoa have flagellate sperms (p. 286). In the Crustacea all the higher types have non-flagellate sperms (decapods) while in many of the lower forms they are of the flagellate type (schizopods, amphipods, isopods, cirripeds, ostracodes). The tracheates generally (including *Peripatus*) have flagellate sperms, but in the myriapods only the chilopods have flagellate sperms, the chilognaths non-flagellate. Again, among the arachnids the typical forms, such as the scorpions and spiders, have flagellate sperms, the aberrant mites non-flagellate. An interesting transitional form between the two is seen in some chilognaths of the *Julus* group (Œttinger, '09).

So far as can be judged from the rather scanty data non-flagellate sperms agree with the typical forms in the presence of nucleus, mitochondrial formations, and centrioles or their products. In their simplest form, seen in some of the nematodes, they are spheroidal in shape with the power of slow amœboid movement. In some of the daphnids the sperms are more actively

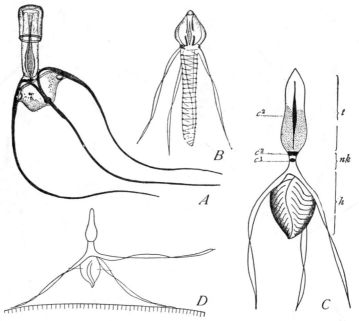

Fig. 129.—Sperms of decapod Crustacea (*A* from Retzius, the others from Koltzoff).

A, Nephrops (Macrura); B, Eupagurus (Anomura), showing spiral formation (presumably mitochondrial) in tail-region; *C, D, Galathea (Anomura),* in *D* attached to the egg-periphery; c^1, c^2, products of the proximal and distal centrioles; *h*, head-region; *nk*, neck; *t*, tail-region.

amœboid and may undergo extensive changes of shape (Fig. 128). In these cases there is no approach to the flagelliform type of sperm. In others, such as those of *Ascaris*, the sperm may be regarded as a much shortened and thickened flagelliform cell with a relatively large amount of cytoplasm and a very short and non-vibratile tail. In this case, the sperm contains numerous spheroidal chondriosomes of peculiar type which, as Meves ('11) has proved, are carried into the egg in the process of fertilization (p. 436).

The most remarkable types of non-flagellate sperms occur in the decapod Crustacea, where they have been studied by many cytologists. These sperms are in general characterized by a rounded, conical or cylindrical body from which radiate a number of rather stiff but movable processes by means of which the sperm may slowly move and by means of which it attaches itself to the egg. The morphology of these sperms, long an un-solved puzzle, has been cleared up by the valuable researches of Koltzoff ('06) who has demonstrated that they are in every detail reducible to the ordinary type and like the latter often show spiral envelopes of mitochondrial origin. These studies have proved that the radiating processes (which contain derivatives of the mitochondria) are developed from the neck region of the sperm; that the rounded portion in which the nucleus lies corresponds to the head; while the conical or cylindrical part, formerly regarded as the head-region, is the homologue of the tail of the flagelliform types. The proximal centriole passes into the neck region, the distal divides into two, of which one remains in the neck while the other elongates to form a kind of axial filament that traverses the posterior extension of the sperm. (Fig. 129) A complete homology thus seems to exist between the several parts of these sperms and those of the flagellate type.

A singular peculiarity of these sperms is the presence in the central-posterior region of a chitinous capsule, containing a rod-like or tube-like "central-body" which was shown by Koltzoff ('06) to be a derivative of the distal centriole. After attachment of the sperm to the egg by its an-terior tip the capsule suddenly "explodes," evaginating to the exterior and carrying with it the central body; and both structures may be thrown off entirely. Koltzoff considers that the force of the explosion drives the sperm upon, or even into, the egg.[1]

4. Dimorphism and Polymorphism of the Sperms

In many animals the sperms are of different classes, in some cases visibly distinguishable in size, structure or both, so that we may speak of the sperm as dimorphic, or in some cases even as polymorphic. Dimorphism is of two main types, which may be characterized respectively as *sexual* and *pathological;* the latter again comprising several different forms. The latter result from pathological processes in the testis, through which are pro-duced in addition to the normal or *eupyrene* sperms, certain definite struc-tural aberrations (*oligopyrene* and *apyrene* sperms) and also giant sperms, normally formed, but of twice or four times the normal size.

Besides the preceding types of dimorphism we have to recognize a poly-morphism or *polymegaly* characteristic of certain insects in which two or several sizes of sperms are produced by different lobes of the same testis.

a. Sexual Dimorphism of the Sperm. This subject, treated more fully

[1] See Koltzoff, '06, Binford, '13, Fasten, '21.

in Chapter X, is here only touched on in passing. In many animals two kinds of sperms are produced, equal in number, which are respectively male-producing and female-producing, and differ in respect to the composition of their nuclei. These classes can rarely be distinguished by the eye in the mature sperm. Two such cases are offered by the nematodes *Ancyracanthus* (Mülsow) and *Filaria* (Meves), in which the nuclei of the sperms consist of separate chromosomes, readily visible in preparations, and in *Ancyracanthus* even in life. In both these cases the two classes are at once recognizable by the number of chromosomes, which is respectively 5 and 6 (Figs. 357, 358). In most cases the two classes do not seem to differ visibly; but exact measurements have shown that in certain cases (*e. g.*, among nematodes, insects, and mammals) the sperms fall into two groups with respect to their heads (or nuclei), which are measurably larger in one group than in the other. Conclusive demonstration of the existence of the two classes is afforded by the history of the sperms during the spermatogenesis (p. 751).

b. Degenerative Dimorphism. Oligopyrene and Apyrene Sperms. Dimorphism of this type, much more marked than the foregoing, is displayed in the presence of so-called *oligopyrene* or *apyrene* sperms which differ markedly in structure from the normal or *eupyrene* forms. During the development of these sperms in the testis the oligopyrenes retain only a part of the original chromosomes of the spermatocytes, while in the apyrenes all of the chromosomes degenerate and the mature forms are non-nucleated. It is now nearly certain that neither of these forms of sperms is functional, the eupyrene sperms alone being capable of fertilizing the egg.[1]

The oligopyrene type (Fig. 130) was first described by von Siebold (1837) in *Paludina*, under the name of the "worm-shaped" sperm, in contradistinction to the "hair-shaped" normal (eupyrene) form, and have since been described in various other protobranch gastropods by many observers. In *Paludina* they are of elongate cylindrical form, and consist of three main regions, namely, (1) a short head, containing a small cap-shaped nucleus, (2), a very long cylindrical middle-piece which constitutes the main body of the sperm, (3) at the distal end a tuft of long cilia, each attached at its base to a basal body, or blepharoplast, which is morphologically a centriole. The middle-piece is traversed by a thick axial rod, through which run 12 axial filaments, each terminating distally in one of the blepharoplasts, while in front they end in a cap-like plate surrounded by the cap-like nucleus, and composed of centriolar substance. The genesis of this strange sperm was first determined by Meves ('00, '02), who found

---

[1] Literature of the subject in Meves ('03), Kuschakewitsch ('13) and Gatenby ('17).

thaᵼ during one or both spermatocyte-divisions a varying number of the chromosomes are lost, first lagging on the spindle and then becoming separately converted into karyomeres which finally degenerate in the cytoplasm (Fig. 130). Only a few of the chromosomes undergo regular division and distribution to the poles, their number in the first division varying from one to four. In the second division only a single chromosome

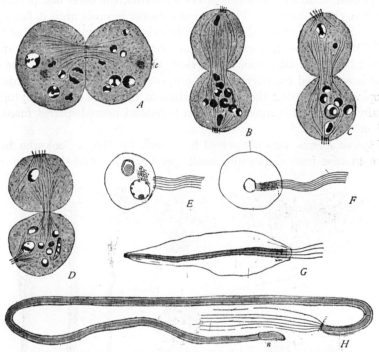

Fig. 130.—Formation of the oligopyrene sperms in *Paludina* (MEVES).
  A, telophase of first spermatocyte-division, with scattered chromosomes (karyomerites) and multiple centrioles (*c*); *B*, telophase of second division, one chromosome to each pole; *C*, *D*, similar stages, slightly later; *E*, *F*, early spermatids; *G*, middle spermatid; *H*, fully formed sperm, showing multiple centrioles (*c*) and flagella; nucleus at *n*.

undergoes regular division, all the others (now in the form of karyomeres) entering one of the daughter-cells where they degenerate. The nucleus of the sperm is formed from the single normal chromosome in each cell (hence the term *oligopyrene*).

In the meantime each of the original centrioles has undergone a remarkable process of multiplication so that two groups of centrioles are produced, ultimately lying at the poles of the first mitosis. In the interkinesis these centrioles scatter through the cell and lie near its periphery; and here they often form the foci of fibrillæ which radiate through the cytoplasm—a fact of much interest for its bearing on the mechanism of anastral mitosis. In the second mitosis they are again gathered together in two groups which lie at the spindle-poles (Fig. 130). Each spermatid thus receives one such group, lying close to the periphery; and each of them repeats the history of the centriole (blepharoplast) in the normal spermatogenesis. Each becomes double, an axial filament grows forth from the outer one (which remains at the periphery). The inner one moves inwards until it lies upon the nuclear membrane, while a delicate axial filament stretches between each inner and the corresponding outer centriole. The mature sperm is formed by simple elongation. It is clear, therefore, that so far as the nucleus is concerned the oligopyrene sperm is defective, while as regards the cytoplasmic structures the reverse statement might be made. Cytoplasmically this sperm is somewhat like a bundle of normal sperms fused together.

Apyrene sperms were discovered in *Pygæra*, by Meves ('oo) who found them to arise from abnormally small spermatocytes; and they have since

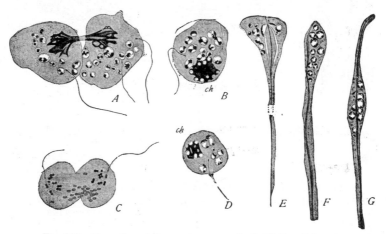

Fig. 131.—Formation of the apyreme sperms in *Lepidoptera* (MEVES).

A, telophase of first spermatocyte-division; scattering of the chromosomes, division of chondriosome-mass, axial filaments present; *B*, second spermatocyte, with karyomeres and chondriosome-mass; *C*, second spermatocyte-anaphase; mitochondria below; *D*, young spermatid, with nebenkern at *ch;* *E–G*, elongation of the spermatids.

been described in various other Lepidoptera and in certain gasteropods by Kuschakewitsch, Reinke, Gatenby and others. In *Pygæra* these sperms are similar in appearance to the normal, but a study of the spermatogenesis shows that they are *entirely devoid of a nucleus*. The chromosomes divide normally in the first division (Fig. 131) but the karyomeres to which they give rise fail to unite into a single nucleus. In the second division they give rise separately to chromosomes which are irregularly distributed to the poles and after being again converted into karyomeres wander out along the outgrowing tails, undergo chromatolysis and degenerate, probably being sloughed off finally with the residual protoplasm of the primitive tail-sheath. In *Pieris* Gatenby ('17) found a somewhat different process, the spermatid-nucleus being re-formed in the normal manner but subsequently moving backward into the tail region and finally degenerating; and the same was found also by Bowen ('23) in *Callosamia* and other saturnid moths. The final result is the same as in *Pygæra*. The anterior tip of these sperms is occupied by the blepharoplast or centriole, from which the axial filament extends backwards. The outgrowth of the axial filament, formation of the nebenkern, and general history of the tail are similar to those of the eupyrene sperm. The acrosome, as is more recently shown by Gatenby ('17) follows the chromatin down along the outgrowing tail. This author finds that in the Lepidoptera (species of *Smerinthus*, *Pygæra*, *Spilosoma*) various degrees of nuclear degeneration occur, some of the sperms being completely devoid of a nucleus, others oligopyrene in various degrees; he therefore concludes that apyrene, oligopyrene and eupyrene sperms are all variants of a single type. In *Strombus* (Reinke, '12, '14) the apyrene sperms, of enormous size and peculiar type, are said to arise directly form the primary spermatocytes without dividing or elimination of protoplasm, hence their great size.

The functional significance of these peculiar sperms is a long-standing subject of controversy, now apparently terminated by the conclusion that they are abnormalities or degeneration products, which degenerate without ever reaching the sperm-receptacle.[1]

c. *Dimegaly and Polymegaly of the Sperms.* The occasional presence of sperms that are nearly or quite normally formed but of unusually large size has been observed in many groups of animals, notably in insects, nemertines, annelids, amphibians, and birds. Such sperms are formed in two wholly different ways, one of which is a pathological process, the other apparently normal. Both these types occur in the insects where their history is now fully known.

(1) *Pathological Dimegaly.* This form of dimegaly, first made known in Hemiptera by Henking ('91) and more fully worked out by Paulmier ('99) results from incomplete division of the spermatocytes, both nucleus and cytosome remaining undivided (or reuniting after division) while division of the centrioles and the outgrowth of the axial filaments proceed (p. 363).

---

[1] See R. Hertwig ('03), Popoff ('02), Lams ('10), Kuschakewitsch ('12), Reinke ('14), Goldschmidt ('15), Gatenby ('19).

Paulmier showed in *Anasa* that the giant sperms arise from giant spermatids which are either twice or four times the size of the normal. The internal structure of these spermatids shows that they are likewise either double or quadruple in respect to the blepharoplast (centriole) and axial filament, those of double size having two, and those of quadruple size four, of these structures.[1] It is practically certain, therefore, that the double forms are due to a suppression of the second spermatocyte-division, the quadruple ones to suppression of both divisions, in respect to all the sperm-forming elements excepting the centriole and the chondriosome-apparatus. The latter have completed their allotted number of divisions and subsequent differentiations. A remarkable demonstration is here given of the genetic continuity of these structures. A result similar to this in all of its essentials has been reached in case of the insects by several later observers, including Zweiger ('06) and Buchner ('09); also by G. Smith ('12) in the case of hybrid pigeons, where the giant sperms are said to arise directly from the secondary spermatocytes. Whether such sperms may fertilize the egg is unknown.

(2) *Physiological Dimegaly or Polymegaly.* In some insects all the sperms formed in certain follicles of the testis are much larger than those from other follicles, a fact discovered by Montgomery ('98, '10) in *Euschistus*. In this insect the testis consists of six parallel tubular lobes disposed side by side in a nearly flat plate; these may be designated by numbers 1–6. In all alike the spermatogonia and the very young spermatocytes are of the same size; but as the growth-period advances the spermatocytes and their products become constantly much larger in lobes 4 and 6 than in the others while in 5 they are somewhat smaller than in 1, 2 and 3. These lobes give rise to sperms of three correspondingly different sizes, all of the same structural type and normally formed. The observations of Bowen ('22) show that conditions more or less similar are found in nearly twenty additional species and genera of Heteroptera (Pentatomidæ), some species showing only two sizes (dimegaly) of spermatocytes or sperms, others three sizes (polymegaly). In each case the size of these cells is constant for particular lobes.

Montgomery found that during the spermatocyte-divisions the chromosomes of the two sizes of spermatocytes are of nearly or quite the same size, the greater size of the sperm-nuclei in follicles 4 and 6 being due to a subsequent compensatory growth of the spermatid-nucleus. This has been confirmed in the polymegalous forms by Bowen who also found that the cytoplasmic components, including the centrioles, chondriosomes, acroblast

---

[1] Analogous double spermatids have been observed in the cycads (Ikeno, '03) and mosses (M. Wilson, '11); and in the latter case both the limosphere (acroblast) and blepharoplast (central body) were likewise found to be double.

and chromatoid body, vary with the size of the cytosome (*Cf.* p. 732). What determines the various sizes is unknown, nor is it known whether all three forms of sperms are functional. Montgomery believed the size-difference to result merely from differences of nutrition in the respective follicles traceable to corresponding differences in the accessory nurse-cells; how the latter differences arise was, however, not determined, nor are we yet better informed.

5. Conjugate Sperms

A remarkable phenomenon is the regular occurrence in certain animals of "twin sperms," or "double sperms," consisting of two sperms closely united by their heads, leaving the tails more or less free (Fig. 132).[1] The meaning of this singular condition is still unknown; but Selenka and Ballowitz found the union to be secondary, the sperms being at first single and

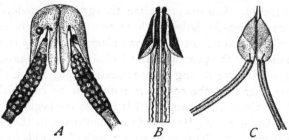

Fig. 132.—Conjugate sperms.

A, in the opossum (RETZIUS); *B* in the beetle *Dytiscus* (BALLOWITZ); *C* in the gasteropod *Turritella* (RETZIUS).

free in the duct of the testis, and only later uniting two by two. In this condition they may actively swim together in the *vas deferens*, but later separate so that single sperms are again found in the freshly discharged sperm and (in *Dytiscus*) in the *receptaculum seminis* of the female. During the period of their association (as Selenka pointed out in *Didelphys*), the two sperms are of different but corresponding shape, being mirror figures of each other, or "right" and "left" handed. This, however, seems to be a result of their mode of attachment and not of a preëxisting morphological difference. These facts still constitute an unsolved puzzle.

II. THE GAMETES OF PLANTS

The maternal and paternal gametes of plants show differences that are broadly parallel to those of animals; but non-motile sperms, so rare among Metazoa, are not uncommon among plants, being found in all the seed-

[1] In the opossum (*Didelphys*) (Selenka, '86), in the beetle (*Dytiscus*) (Ballowitz, '95), and in the gasteropod *Turritella* (Retzius, '06).

plants except the cycads and Ginkgoales, and with rare exceptions (*Monoblepharis*) in the fungi and red algæ. The microgametes of plants seem to be almost as diverse in structure as those of animals. The macrogametes, on the other hand, are in certain respects less varied owing to the greater uniformity of the conditions under which development of the zygote takes place. We shall attempt no more than a brief mention of a subject hardly less complicated than in the case of animals, though as yet less completely known. Some additional details concerning the gametes of lower plants will be found in Chap. VII.

1. The Ovum

In the higher plants the ovum rarely attains the dimensions or complexity of structure shown in animal ova, in part because it remains attached to and imbedded in the maternal tissues by which it is nourished and protected (Figs. 211, 214, etc.). As a rule, therefore, the egg is not provided with complex envelopes or heavily laden with reserve food-matters such as the deutoplasm of animal ova. In the second place, the history of the nucleus is not complicated by the phenomena of meiosis, since this process is completed in the sporophyte during spore-formation, long before the ovum is formed. Here, therefore, the egg-nucleus differs in no essential way from the nuclei of the tissue-cells except that it is from the beginning of haploid constitution. An interesting feature of the plant ovum in the archegoniate plants is the frequent (perhaps general) presence of plastids in the form of small colorless leucoplasts which according to the researches of Schimper, Meyer and their successors multiply by division and thus form the source of the plastids of the embryonic cells and ultimately of the tissue-cells of the mature plant. This is a point of much theoretical interest in relation to the view that the plastids are persistent morphological bodies traceable in direct genetic continuity from one generation to another through the germ-cells. In the lower plants (algæ) plastids may occur in the gametes of both sexes; in the higher forms they seem to occur in the egg alone, and in such cases the plastids of the embryonic body appear to be of purely maternal origin. In plants, as in animals, however, it is probable that both gametes contain mitochondria and as already stated (p. 47) it is possible that these may be fundamentally identical with plastids and give rise to them.[1]

The plant ovum attains its greatest size in the gymnosperms (Figs. 213–215). In the conifers the protoplasm contains many fibrous bodies, the origin of which has been much disputed (Ferguson, '01), Miyaki, '03, Coker, '03, etc.). These bodies are more numerous in the lower half of the

[1] See Meves, '16, '17.

egg, while near the upper pole the protoplasm is clearer and in some cases contains a vacuole which has been described as marking a kind of receptive spot, since it is at this point that the pollen tube discharges the generative nuclei into the eggs (Ferguson, Murrill, etc.). The egg is likewise very large in cycads, but seems to lack the protein vacuoles and fibrillar formations seen in the conifers. In the angiosperms the egg has at first no definite external boundary, being represented by an egg-nucleus lying in the syncytial protoplasm of the embryo-sac and accompanied by two synergid-nuclei which probably represent the vestige of an archegonium. In later stages the egg, like the synergids, acquires a definite boundary by gathering a clearly defined, spheroidal protoplasmic cytosome about it (Figs. 216–217).

2. The Sperm

The microgametes or sperms of plants have received many names, the motile forms being commonly designated as *antherozoids* or *spermatozoids*. The latter, like the sperms of animals, move by means of flagella or cilia, and a study of their development shows many analogies to animal sperms in other respects. Uniflagellate sperms seem, however, not to occur in plants, at least two flagella being present and in many cases numerous flagella or cilia.

In the lower archegoniates (bryophytes) the sperm is biflagellate (Fig. 134) with an elongate and somewhat spiral body near the anterior end of which are attached two long flagella directed backwards.[1] The body is occupied mainly by an elongate nucleus with a delicate cytoplasmic investment, and leaving a small purely cytoplasmic region at the anterior end and a larger one at the posterior. The development of these sperms shows that the flagella grow forth from a basal body or blepharoplast

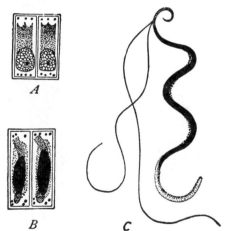

Fig. 133.—Sperms of *Chara* (BELAJEFF).

A, mother-cells with reticular nuclei; *B*, later stage, with sperms forming; *C*, mature sperms (the elongate nucleus black).

that passes into the anterior cytoplasmic region; also that this region receives a body that is comparable to the acrosome or acroblast of the

[1] *Cf.* the closely similar sperms of certain platodes, p. 295.

animal sperm (p. 391). Sperms of this type are found also in the Charales (Fig. 133).

The sperms of most pteridophytes are similar in general type to those of bryophytes but differ in the more pronounced spiral form of the cytosome and in the presence of numerous cilia arranged in a series along a considerable region of the spiral cytosome. An elongated, spiral nucleus occupies

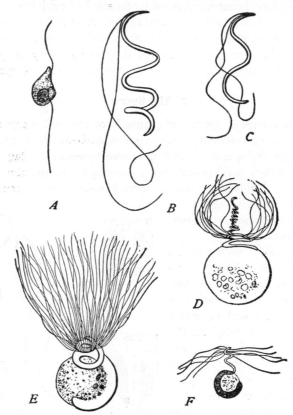

Fig. 134.—Sperms of plants. (*A, B, C, E*, after Guignard; *D, F*, after Strasburger).
A, of an alga (*Fucus*); a red chromatophore at the right of the nucleus; *B*, liverwort (*Pellia*); *C*, moss (*Sphagnum*); *D, Marsilia; E*, fern (*Angiopteris*); *F*, fern, *Phegopteris* (the nucleus dark).

the lower turns of the spiral, while the cilia are confined to the upper or middle turns (Figs. 134, 180), borne upon an elongated, spirally twisted blepharoplast of which they are outgrowths (p. 387). The cytosome bears a large "cytoplasmic vesicle" attached to the lower turns of the spiral which is cast off after the sperm is set free and before it enters the ovum. This structure seems to correspond exactly to the "residual protoplasm" that is cast off from the developing animal sperm (p. 367). Sperms of this general type occur in all the pteridophytes save a few forms (*Lycopodium*, *Selaginella*, *Phylloglossum*) in which occurs a simple biflagellate sperm somewhat like that of bryophytes.

The pteridophyte type of sperm is connected by interesting intermediate forms with the non-motile sperm-cells of the higher gymnosperms and angiosperms. Sperms of this type but somewhat simplified are still present in the cycads and Ginkgoales, but reduced in number and of great relative size. In *Microcycas* their number is 16–20, in *Ceratozamia* exceptionally 4 but usually 2, in other cycads and in *Ginkgo* always 2; and in all of these cases they are carried within the tip of the pollen-tube, never being discharged to lead a free-swimming life in the water.[1] These sperms are obtusely conical in shape, with a large rounded nucleus, and a band-shaped blepharoplast which forms several spiral turns around the upper region and bears a close series of short cilia by which the sperm slowly swims (Fig. 182). These are probably the largest sperm-cells known in either plants or animals, reaching in *Zamia* a diameter of more than 300μ and readily visible to the naked eye (Webber). In the higher gymnosperms the cilia and associated structures have been lost, but in most cases the sperm, temporarily at least, is a complete cell (Figs. 214, 215) with a definitely bounded cytosome, closely similar to the young sperms of cycads (*Thuja*, *Sequoia*, *Taxus*, etc.); but no trace of blepharoplasts has yet been found in them. These cells are typically two in number, and usually equal; but in some cases (*Taxus*, *Torreya*) are unequal, only the larger being functional. In *Pinus* the cytosome finally breaks down, only the nucleus retaining its individuality. In the seed-plants, finally, these are but two sperms represented by two "generative nuclei" borne within the growing pollen-tube near its tip and by most observers described as not surrounded by definite cytosomes. In a few cases, however, the sperm-cytosome is said to be definitely marked off and even to enter the egg during fertilization; but little is known concerning its structure.[2] It has been supposed that at the time of fertilization these gametes (or nuclei) though not ciliated, may have some power of movement within the egg; but this is conjectural (p. 452).

[1] *Cycas* (Ikeno, '96, '98, '04), *Ginkgo* (Hirase, '06, '98), Webber, '97, '01), *Stangeria* (Lang, '00), *Dioön* (Chamberlain, '09), *Microcycas* (Caldwell, '07), *Ceratozamia* (Chamberlain, '07).

[2] See Welsford, '14 (*Lilium*), Wylie, '22 (*Vallisneria*). For further details concerning the gametes of plants, see Chaps. V and VII.

III. ORIGIN, GROWTH AND DIFFERENTIATION OF THE GERM-CELLS

A. GENERAL OUTLINE

1. Introductory, Terminology

The origin of the germ-cells during ontogeny, and their processes of growth and differentiation, have long occupied a central position of interest for obvious reasons. Attention was concentrated upon their mode of origin, particularly because of Nussbaum's contention ('80) that the germ-cells are not, strictly speaking, produced by the parental body (as was explicitly or tacitly assumed by earlier writers), but only have a common origin with it from a preceding germ-cell.[1] As extended and developed by Weismann, this conception made the multicellular individual appear to us as a kind of dual organism [2] in which germ-cells and somatic cells lead quasi-independent lives. The far-reaching influence of this conception on the modern study of heredity is evident (p. 12).

As Weismann himself recognized, no hard and fast line can in many cases be drawn between germ-cells and somatic cells: hence his theory of a continuity of germ-*plasm* rather than of germ-*cells*, which has so long been a subject of controversy. The distinction between germ-cells and somatic cells, like that between "germ-plasm" and "somatoplasm," was however too sharply drawn by Weismann and his followers, and led to an opposition to his views in which the fundamental truth which they expressed often seemed to be lost sight of. A large body of evidence has accumulated in favor of the view that fundamentally any cell may be tototipotent (*i. e.*, contain the heritage of the species) and that the limitations of potency that it may display are due to secondary inhibitory conditions (p. 1078). Nevertheless the fact is patent that heredity is effected by germ-cells which transmit a specifically organized protoplasmic system (*i. e.*, "germ-plasm") from generation to generation, and the general principle of genetic continuity as applied to both germ-cells and germ-plasm is so obviously true as to have survived all criticism.

In most higher animals the germ-cells seem to arise in the "germinal epithelium," which occupies a localized region of the peritoneal or cœlomic epithelium.[3] By Waldeyer ('70) and many later observers down to the

---

[1] A review of the history of this conception, with an account of the earlier views of Owen, Galton and Jäger is given in Weismann's book on the *Germ-plasm* (1892).

[2] *Cf.* Waldeyer, '06.

[3] This fact is in harmony with the so-called gonocoele theory, according to which the cœlome of the higher forms represents the enlarged gonad-cavity of the platodes or related ancestral types. See especially Lang ('04).

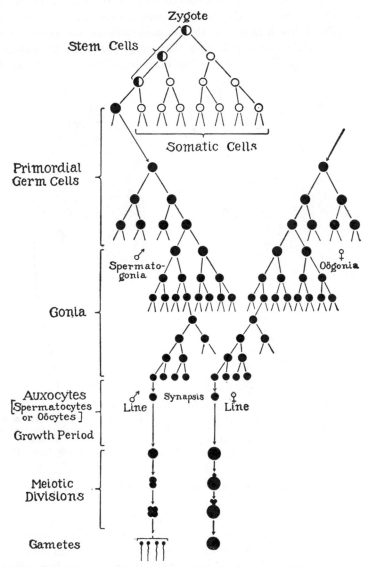

Fig. 135.—General diagram of the germ-line in animals, showing parallelism between the male line (left) and the female (right). The number of divisions (except in meiosis) is actually much larger than here shown.

present time the germ-cells were believed to arise from the germinal epithelium itself.[1]   This may indeed correspond to the facts in some cases
(p. 318); nevertheless it is certain that in some animals the germ-cells are
set aside from the somatic cells at a very early period in the ontogeny,
so that we can actually trace their line of ontogenic descent or *germ-line*

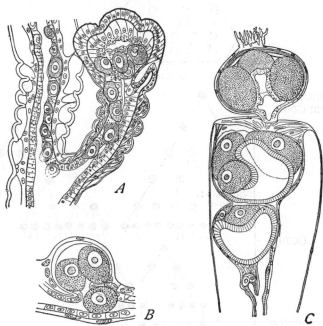

Fig. 136.—Early history of the germ-cells in *Gonothyræa Loveni* (WEISMANN).

A, female blastostyle at an early period, showing eggs passing into it from the main stem of the
hydroid at the left; *B*, early stage in gonophore budding from the blastostyle with three eggs
passing into it; *C*, terminal portion of blastostyle surrounded by the gonotheca with 3 young
female gonophores, each with eggs, and a terminal mature gonophore (sessile medusoid) with
ripe eggs.

backwards to early stages of development, sometimes even to the initial
cleavages of the egg.   In such cases the primordial germ-cells seem to
lead an independent life within the soma, almost as if they were parasitic
or symbiotic organisms.   This fact should not be unduly emphasized.
Germ-cells, like somatic cells, result from a process of histogenetic differentiation, and the somatic line of ontogenetic descent is not less real than
the germ-line.[2]   Nevertheless, the germ-line has an especial interest of
its own, since it represents the actual as distinguished from the theoretically
possible line of heredity from one generation to another.

[1] For a general review see Waldeyer ('03) and Gutherz ('18). *Cf.* Allen ('23).
[2] See Eigenmann ('97); O. Hertwig ('16).

Terminology. The germ-cells of animals are originally derived from *stem-cells* (Fig. 135), which give rise by division to both germ-cells and somatic cells, and in certain striking cases may be clearly distinguished as early as the 2-cell stage of development (*Ascaris, Cyclops*, pp. 315, 323). From the stem-cells arise the *primordial germ-cells*, which after a certain

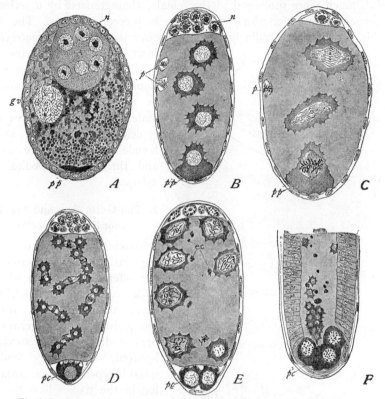

Fig. 137.—Primordial germ-cells and diminution in the fly *Miastor* (KAHLE).

A, unfertilized egg, enclosed in its follicle with group of nurse-cells (*n*) and *polar plasm* (*p. p.*); *B*, 4 nucleus stage, with nutritive cells (*n*), polocyte-nuclei (*p*) and polar plasm (*p. p.*); *C*, third cleavage, diminution in progress in upper two spindles; *D*, 15-cell stage, germ-cell below, second diminution completed in somatic nuclei; *E*, later stage, with eliminated chromatin (*e. c.*); *F*, inwandering of primordial germ-cells at posterior pole.

number of divisions enter upon a quiescent period of considerable duration. They are then converted into the *gonia*, which most frequently aggregate to form localized *gonads* or "germ-glands." These cells show the same general characters in both sexes, but are sooner or later distinguishable by the eye as primary *oögonia* or *spermatogonia*. Resuming the process of active division, they give rise to secondary oögonia or spermatogonia and also, in many cases, to accessory cells such as nurse-cells in the ovary or Sertoli-cells in the testis. These cells lose the power of further development and are devoted to nutritive or supporting functions tributary to the growth and differentiation of the functional germ-cells. At the end of a certain period division of the gonia ceases and they enter upon a *growth-period*, much more prolonged in the female, characterized by a series of phenomena that differ widely from those in preceding stages. The cells of this period are accordingly called *auxocytes* (*oöcytes* or *spermatocytes*), from which the gametes are finally produced by two divisions known as the *maturation* or *meiotic* divisions. In the male these divisions give rise typically to four sperms, in the female to the mature ovum and three "polar bodies" or *polocytes*.

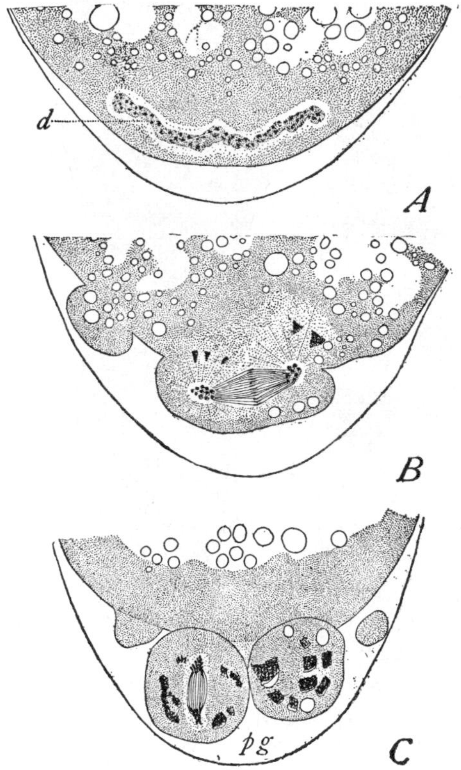

2. The Germ-line and the Primordial Germ-cells

Striking examples of early segregation of the germ-cells are offered by certain of the hydomedusæ in which Kleinenberg, Weismann and others found the primordial germ-cells present already in the "asexual" hydroid, where they lead a quasi-independent life, wandering in the tissues like *Amœbæ*, and in some cases creeping through the mesoglœa from one layer to another. In some species, usually characterized by a great reduction of the gonophore or sexual generation (as in *Eudendrium*), the germ-cells are according to Weismann distinguishable several bud-generations before the appearance of the gonophore, passing successively from hydranth to hydranth as new buds form, then into the blastostyle, and at last into the gonophore where they finally aggregate to form localized gonads

Fig. 138.—Formation of the primordial germ-cells in the fly *Chironomus* (HASPER).

A, posterior region of the egg, showing polar disc or "germ-cell determinant"; *B*, first mitosis in this region; *C*, two resulting primordial germ-cells.

(Fig. 136).[1] No case so striking as this is elsewhere known; but in a considerable number of the higher invertebrates the primordial germ-cells, or the stem-cells from which they arise, can be identified with certainty in the early cleavage and can be traced thence onwards by means of cytological peculiarities of the nucleus, of the cytoplasm, or of both. The most certainly determined of these cases occur in insects, crustaceans, nematodes and chætognaths, where they have been the objects of numerous studies. [2]

Of these cases we can here consider only a few examples. The first of them to be described were found in the Diptera (*Miastor, Chironomus, Musca*) where the primordial germ-cells are budded forth from the posterior pole of the egg at a very early period, and hence were called by Weismann ('63) the *pole*-cells.   By Metschnikoff ('55, '66) and Leuckart ('65) these were identified as germ-cells and Metschnikoff actually traced them into the gonads of the larva, a result confirmed by many later observers who have described primordial germ-cells in the early stages especially of the Diptera, Coleoptera and Hymenoptera. [3] In some of these cases all the primordial germ-cells are traceable to a single pole-cell, formed at the posterior pole of the ovum in one of the early cleavages (Fig. 137). In other cases, two or more pole-cells seem to be extruded from the egg, simultaneously or successively (Fig. 138),so that no single complete pole-cell can be taken as ancestral to all the others. In *Calliphora* Noack ('01) found several pole-cells to be separately extruded from the egg: and the same has been found to be the case in beetles by Hegner ('14a) and in *Drosophila* by Huettner ('21).

Striking examples of the early differentiation of primordial germ-cells have been described in the Entomostraca; where the facts were early observed by Grobben ('79) in *Moina* and latter by other observers in a number of daphnids and copepods,[4] in some of which the stem-cells are distinguishable as such from the first cleavage onwards (Fig. 139). Even more remarkable are the similar cases found among nematodes, as first made known by Boveri ('87) in *Ascaris megalocephala*, and later studied by him in a masterly manner, both by observation and experiment. In the hermaphroditic form *Sagitta*, R. Hertwig ('80) discovered four primordial germ-cells,

---

[1] See Weismann's remarkable memoir of 1887, in which many variants of this process are described. Many of his more detailed results are disputed in the later works of Götte ('07) and G. T. Hargitt ('13–'18). These observers nevertheless confirm Weismann and his predecessors on the main point, namely, the production of the germ-cells in some cases by the "asexual" hydroid long before the appearance of the sexual zooids or gonophores.

[2] See especially Hegner 14a, 14b.

[3] See especially Balbiani ('82), Heymons ('91), Ritter ('90), Noack ('01), Hasper ('11), Silvestri ('06, '08, '09, 14), Kahle ('08), Hegner (08, '09, '12, '14, '15), Gatenby ('19, '20), Martin ('14), etc.

[4] Weismann and Ishikawa ('89), Haecker ('97), Amma ('11), Kühn ('11, '13) and others.

distinguishable already in the early gastrula and (as later determined by Elpatiewsky, '09) derived from a single original cell. Of these four, two are said to give rise to the testes and two to the ovaries, so that the seg-

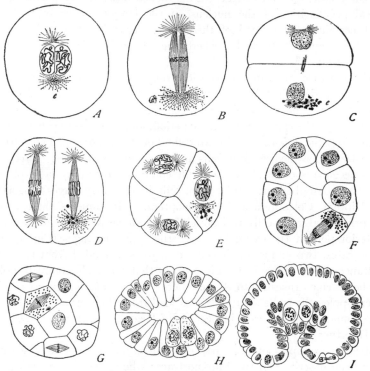

Fig. 139.—The germ-line and "germ-cell determinants" in the copepod *Cyclops* (Amma).

e, the ectosomes or "germ-cell determinants"; *g*, primordial germ-cells; *s*, stem-cells.

A, conjugation of gamete-nuclei; *B–D*, first and second cleavages; *E*, from 12-cell stage, gonomery seen above; 15-cell stage, in optical section; *G*, sixth cleavage in progress, division of stem-cell; *H*, *I*, earlier and later gastrulas, primordial germ-cells.

regation of male and female germ-cells would here seem to be accomplished by a single cell-division (Fig. 143).

In the vertebrates the case is still uncertain. Views on this subject were long dominated by the conclusion of Waldeyer, put forward in his classical work *Eierstock und Ei* (1870), that the germ-cells arise relatively late in the ontogeny by direct transformation of epithelial cells in the "germinal epithelium" of the young embryo; but a considerable group of later observers found that the primordial germ-cells arise at a much earlier period widely scattered in other regions of the germ to wander thence through the embryonic tissues to their final destination in the germinal epithelium. [1] In most of these cases the primordial germ-cells, so called, are scattered either in the entoblast, in the splanchnic mesoblast, or between these layers (Fig. 140) and appear to pass from this position, as development advances, towards the axial region, and finally into the germinal epithelium of the genital ridge; but in some instances they are distinguishable still earlier and still further away from their final destination. In the tortoise, Allen found them in the entoblast near the junction of the

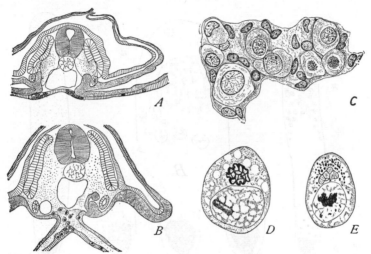

Fig. 140.—Primordial germ-cells in vertebrates (*A–C*, from ALLEN; *D, E*, from BEHRENBERG-GOSSLER).

A, cross-section of early embryo turtle (*Chrysemys*) germ-cells in the entoblast; *B*, later stage, germ-cells migrating into mesentery; *C*, group of young oöcytes from cortex of ovary; still in the peritoneal epithelium; *D*, primordial germ-cell of duck-embryo (110 hrs.), showing Golgi-apparatus; *E*, the same from chick of 60–72 hrs.; Golgi-apparatus and chondriosomes.

pellucid and the vascular areas, lateral to the embryo; while in the birds, Swift found them already in the stage of the primitive streak, lying in the entoblast where it joins the germinal wall, and quite outside the embryonic area.

More recently doubts have arisen in regard to the subject. Some observers have found that many of these cells may, as it were, lose their way and remain outside the ovary; [2] or that they may enter the blood-vessels

[1] Among the earlier advocates of this conclusion may be named especially Jungerson ('87) and Eigenmann ('92, '97) in the case of teleosts; Hofmann ('93) and Nussbaum ('01) in birds; Beard ('00–'04) and Woods ('03) in elasmobranchs. Prominent among later works are those of Rubaschkin ('07), Berenberg-Gossler ('12–'14), and Swift ('13) on birds; Allen ('06, '09) on reptiles and fishes; Jarvis ('08) on reptiles; Dodds ('10) on teleosts, and Rubaschkin ('07, '10) and Fuss ('11) on mammals, including man. Literature in the papers especially of Berenberg-Gossler, Allen, Dodds, Swift, and Hegner. *Cf.* Allen, '23.

[2] See Jarvis, '08, Firket, '14, Berenberg-Gossler, '14–'15.

and thus be carried to all parts of the embryo and vascular area, later passing out of the vessels into the tissues, degenerating, or giving rise to ordinary mesoblast-cells.[1] Winiwarter and Saintmont, in a careful study of the histogenesis of the ovary of the cat ('09), found that the large, rounded cells seen in early stages of the ovary do not in fact give rise to ova but degenerate; and the same is true of a second group of similar cells formed by proliferation from the germinal epithelium. The definitive germ-cells

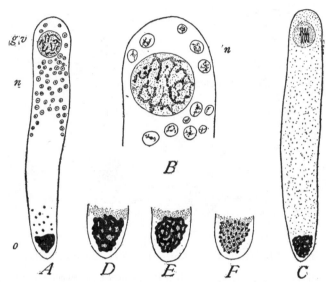

Fig. 141.—Oöcyte of the hymenopter *Apanteles glomeratus* showing secondary nuclei and "germ-cell determinant" or oösome (HEGNER).

A, entire oöcyte with germinal vesicle (*g. v.*), secondary nuclei (*n.*), and oösome (*o*) at lower pole; *B*, upper portion of same, enlarged; *C*, oöcyte with first polar spindle forming; *D–F*, successive stages of oösome.

are formed by a third proliferation in the kitten of 3–4 months; but the authors leave it undecided whether they arise from primordial germ-cells left over from the earlier generations (failing to degenerate) or from indifferent cells of the epithelium. These results are confirmed in their essentials, though with some variations of detail, by several later observers.[2]

A remarkable fact observed by Winiwarter and Saintmont is that before degeneration the primordial cells undergo some of the nuclear changes characteristic of auxocytes, passing through characteristic leptotene, pachytene and diplotene stages.[3] The same fact was described by Firket in the

---

[1] Dantschakoff, '08, Berengberg-Gossler, Swift (*op. cit.*).

[2] Rubaschkin ('12), Firket ('14), Kingery ('14, '17, '18), Kirkham ('16), Swingle ('21).

[3] *Cf.* the similar changes undergone by the nurse-cells of insect-eggs (p. 336).

chick, and by several observers in mammals. Kingery found in the mouse that the primordial germ-cells might even proceed to the formation of a polocyte and second polar spindle before their degeneration. More recently Swingle ('21) found in the male bull-frog that a first generation of germ-cells of the young tadpole pass though a partial maturation-cycle, showing characteristic tetrad-formation, up to the anaphase of the first division

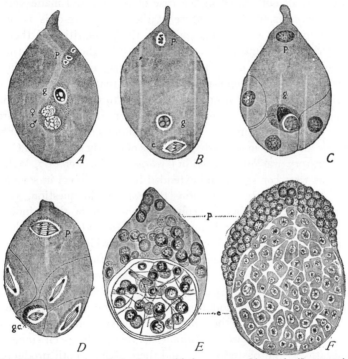

Fig. 142.—Early germ-cells in the parasitic hymenopter *Litomastix* (SYLVESTRI).

A, gamete-nuclei in conjugation, polar-nuclei above, "oösome" or " germ-cell determinant" at *g*; *B*, first cleavage-figure below, polar nuclei fusing; *C*, 4-cell stage, germ-cell at *g*, polar fusion-nucleus above; *D*, third cleavage in progress, polar fusion-nucleus dividing above; *E*, *F*, later stages, with embryonic mass below (*e*) and polar mass above.

but then degenerate, the definitive germ-cells arising from a second genera-tion of uncertain origin.[1]

These curious facts seem to afford strong evidence that the "primordial germ-cells" of the vertebrates really are such. Why they should degenerate to be replaced by cells of later origin is an interesting puzzle: but we find in these facts further ground for the conclusion that the differentiation between primordial germ-cells and somatic cells is not a fixed or fundamental

[1] *Cf.* p. 310.

one, and that it varies greatly in respect to the time at which it appears
and in the extent of the morphological changes that it involves (contrast
Ascaris with the bird or mammal).

3. Differentiation of the Primordial Germ-cells

(a) *Cytoplasmic Characteristics.* *"Germ-cell Determinants."* It has been
experimentally demonstrated in the case of *Ascaris* and made very probable in other cases, that the nature of the early germ-cells is primarily
determined by their cytoplasm, and that the pecularities of their nuclei
(when such are distinguishable) are called forth by the region of the egg in
which they lie (p. 1091). At this point we may examine certain visible
characteristics of the cytoplasm of these cells that have by some writers
been supposed, though on insufficient grounds, to determine their nature.[1]
A number of the early observers (Weismann, Metschnikoff, Grobben,
Ishikawa) observed the presence of deeply staining granules or other specific
cytoplasmic inclusions in the early germ-cells of certain insects and Crustacea
and their history was later traced in *Cyclops* by Haecker ('97, '03), whose
observations were confirmed and extended by Amma ('11) in several other
genera of copepods. In these forms the granules in question, known as
ectosomes ("Aussenkörnchen"), collect at one pole of the spindle in the
first cleavage of the ovum, and continue to be segregated in a single cell until the end of the fourth division; and the cells which then receive them,
can later be identified (by their lagging mitosis) as the primordial germ-cells
(Fig. 139). In insects the existence of such granules (as distinguished from
yolk) was observed by Ritter ('90) in the egg of *Chironomus* before the pole-
cells are formed. This account was confirmed by many later observers
in several orders of insects, though the details vary more or less in different
species. Hasper ('11) showed in *Chironomus* that at the 4-cell stage one nucleus migrates to the posterior pole and there divides, both products being
extruded as pole-cells into which the granules pass (Fig. 138). In *Miastor*
(Kahle, '08) the origin of the pole-cells is slightly different, since the fourth
nucleus divides at the posterior pole to produce one pole-cell and one somatic
cell (Fig. 137). The specific granules have not been described as such;
but a definite mass of "polar plasm" enters the pole-cells, which are further
distinguished by nuclear characters, as explained beyond. On the other
hand, distinct polar granules in the polar plasm are described by Noack
('01) in *Calliphora*, and more recently by Huettner ('21) in *Drosophila*.

Analogous phenomena in Coleoptera and Hymenoptera have been carefully studied in an interesting series of papers by Hegner ('08, '14), Sylvestri

---

[1] A valuable historical and critical review of this subject is given by Hegner ('14). See also the
review in Amma ('11).

('06, '08, '15) and Gatenby ('19 '20,). In the chrysomelid beetles (*Callig-rapha*, *Lepintotarsa*) Hegner found a polar disc at the posterior pole of the unsegmented egg, composed of deeply staining granules, the so-called "germ-cell determinants," which pass into the primary pole-cells formed at the posterior pole. Hegner succeeded in killing with a hot needle the pos-

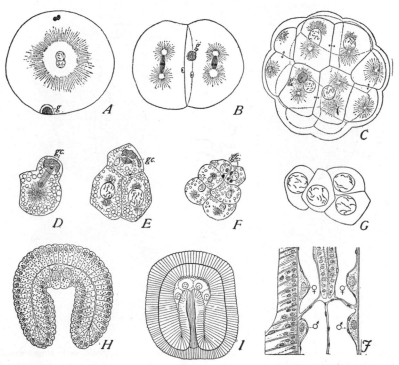

Fig. 143.—Primordial germ-cells in *Sagitta* (*A–G*, from ELPATIEWSKY, *H–J* from R. HERTWIG).

A, fertilized egg with "germ-cell determinant" at *g*; *B*, 2-cell stage; *C*, 16-cell stage; *D*, division of stem-cell during fifth cleavage to form primordial germ-cell *g. c.* in *E*; *F*, first division of *g. c.*; *G*, result of second division of *g. c.*; *H*, gastrula with two primordial germ-cells; *I*, later stage with four germ-cells; *J*, portion of much later embryo showing the two anterior germ-cells (primary oögonia) in front of transverse septum (*s*) and two posterior ones (primary spermatogonia) behind it.

terior region of the egg, containing the polar disc, before the pole-cells had been formed. Such eggs produced a normal blastoderm up to a certain stage, *but no trace of germ-cells was found*. Analogous phenomena occur in the Hymenoptera. In *Copidosoma* (*Litomastix*), a cytoplasmic spheroidal body, the "oösome" (Fig. 142), is present in the unsegmented egg, passes to the posterior end, and enters the posterior cell of the 4-cell stage (this form undergoes a total cleavage) where it breaks up into granules which were assumed by Sylvestri to pass into the germ-cells.[1]   In *Tricho-gramma* and *Apanteles* densely aggregated polar granules are present, more like those of the Coleoptera.[2]

The nature and origin of the cytoplasmic "germ-cell determinants" is still problematical.   They have been supposed to come originally from the

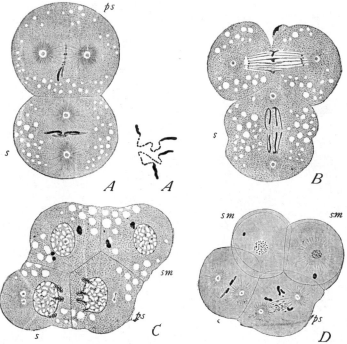

Fig. 144.—Stem-cells and primordial germ-cells in *Ascaris megalocephala*, early stages showing diminution (BOVERI).

p. s., primordial somatic cell; *s*, stem-cell.

A, second cleavage in progress; *A*[1], polar view of chromosomes of the upper cell (*p. s.*) to show diminution in progress; *B*, later stage, elimination-chromatin at equator of upper spindle (T-stage); *C*, 4-cell stage, showing eliminated chromatin in upper two cells; *D*, third cleavage in progress, second diminution at *p. s.* (later stages in Fig. 145).

nucleus (Haecker, Sylvestri, in their earlier work) or from chondriosomes (Hegner).   In *Sagitta* (Fig. 143) a special cytoplasmic body is handed on from the unsegmented egg to a particular cell of the 32-cell stage, which is then recognizable as the first primordial germ-cell.   Elpatiewsky ('09), to whom these observations are due, considered this body to be of nucleolar origin; Buchner ('10), on the other hand, regards it as a mass of chromidia

---

[1] A closely similar body was found in *Paracopidosomopsis* by Patterson ('21) who, however, was unable to find any direct evidence that it enters the germ-cells.

[2] Hegner ('15), Gatenby ('19, '20).

derived from an accessory cell that fuses with the egg. In the case of the daphnid *Polyphemus* the work of Kühn ('11, '13) seems to show that it arises from one or more accessory "nurse-cells" that migrate into the egg. The most recent studies on these bodies have produced no definite reason for identifying them with any of the other known types of formed elements.[1] Whether they can properly be called germ-cell "determinants" is equally problematical. So far as the facts at present show they may be no more than accompaniments or by-products of the true determining factors in the cytoplasm; and on the whole this seems more probable (pp. 1067, 1090).

(*b*)   *Nuclear Characteristics of the early Germ-cells and the Process of Chromatin-diminution.*   Foremost in interest among the cases here concerned is that of the nematode *Ascaris megalocephala*, the object of a masterly series of studies by Boveri ('87, '92, '99) which threw a clear light upon the lineage of the germ-cells in general, and opened a new field of cytological inquiry.   Related phenomena have since been observed in the beetle *Dytiscus* (Giardina, '01), the fly *Miastor* (Kahle, '08, Hegner '12) and a few other cases.

In *Ascaris megalocephala* (Figs. 144, 145) the germ-line may be followed without a break back to a stem-cell that is distinguishable as such already in the 2-cell stage of the embryo, and in each succeeding cleavage. This cell differs from the somatic cells at every stage in the fact that it alone retains the sum-total of the nuclear substance, while every somatic nucleus has cast out a portion of its chromatin, having undergone the process of so-called *chromatin-diminution*. The somatic nuclei are in consequence both smaller and paler than those of the stem-cells and thus from the first readily distinguishable by the eye. More in detail, the process is as follows: In the first cleavage two long chromosomes are present, dividing in the usual manner. In the prophases of the second cleavage the two chromosomes reappear in each cell but differ in their behavior. In the stem-cell they undergo simple division, as before. In the sister-cell, destined to produce only somatic cells, the thickened ends of the chromosomes are cast off into the cytoplasm, where they ultimately degenerate, while the central portion segments into a large number of small chromosomes,[2] which split lengthwise and are distributed to the daughter-cells. In the ensuing division each of the diminished nuclei divides with numerous small chromosomes, and the same is true of all their descendants (which give rise only to somatic cells). The undiminished nuclei of the two stem-cells, on the other hand, repeat the process seen in the 2-cell stage, one of them undergoing diminu-

---

[1] Gatenby, '20, Huettner, '21.
[2] The observations of Geinitz ('15) indicate that the number is in the female 30, in the male either 22 or 30 (see p. 773).

tion and giving rise to somatic cells with numerous small chromosomes, the other dividing into two without diminution. This process takes place in each of the three succeeding cleavages (*i. e.*, four times in all, according to

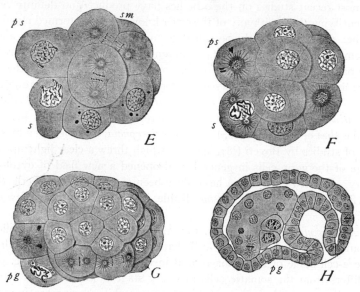

Fig. 145.—(continuing Fig. 144).

E, 10-cell stage, showing mitosis of somatic cells with diminished nuclei; *F*, 12-cell stage, third diminution in progress at *p. s.; G*, about 32 cells, fourth diminution in progress, leaving primordial germ-cell (in prophase) at *p. g.; H*, gastrula completed with two primordial germ-cells.

Boveri) after which the segregation of the somatic and the germ-cells is complete.

At the 16-cell stage two cells are left with undiminished nuclei one of which becomes the ancestor of all the germ-cells, undergoing no further diminution and giving rise to no further somatic cells. This cell, accordingly, is the first primordial germ-cell. It soon divides into two cells (32-cell stage) which later sink into the interior and multiply to form the primary cells of the gonads. It thus comes to pass that *only the germ-cells receive the sum-total of the chromatin present in the fertilized egg, while all of the somatic cells have lost a portion of their heritage.* "The original nuclear constitution of the fertilized egg is transmitted, as if by a law of primogeniture, only to one daughter-cell, and by this again to one, and so on; while in the other daughter-cell the chromatin in part degenerates, in part is transformed, so that all of the descendants of these side-branches receive small, reduced nuclei." [1] By an ingenious study of centrifuged and double-fertilized eggs

[1] Boveri, '91, p. 437.

Boveri was able to establish the fact that the process of diminution is not an autonomous act on the part of the chromosomes but is induced by their

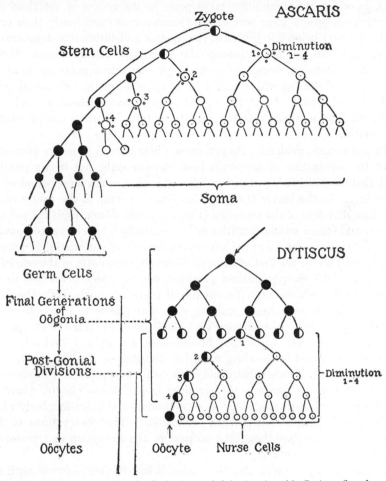

Fig. 146.—Diagram comparing the diminution-periods in *Ascaris* and in *Dytiscus* (based on the observations of BOVERI and GIARDINA).

In *Ascaris* it occurs during four cleavages, from the second to the fifth inclusive; in *Dytiscus* during the last four cleavages of the oögonia.

cytoplasmic surroundings in the egg, a conclusion of fundamental importance for our general conceptions of development.[1]

A somewhat analogous process of diminution was found by Meyer ('95) in three other species of *Ascaris*, and this is confirmed by Bonnevie ('01) in *A. lumbricoides;* but in these species the diminution is not accompanied by

[1] See p. 1091 for further account.

any increase in the number of separate chromosomes. Another well-determined case seems to be that of the fly *Miastor* (Kahle, '08; Hegner '12, '14), in which the diminution takes place in the course of the third and fourth cleavages, a large part of the chromosomes (apparently their ends, as in *Ascaris*) being left behind at the equator and ultimately degenerating (Fig. 137). In the third cleavage the fourth (posterior) nucleus divides without diminution, one of its products passing into a polar plasm at the lower pole of the egg with which it is cut off to form the primordial germ-cell or "pole-cell." From the 15-cell stage onwards, therefore, only the primordial germ-cell and its descendants contain the whole complement of chromatin.

In these cases, evidently, the process of diminution is somehow connected with the segregation of germ-cells from somatic cells; but it is a puzzling fact that diminution is sometimes deferred until a much later period of the ontogeny. In the beetle *Dytiscus* (Giardina) it occurs in the course of the last four divisions of the germ-line (Fig. 146) from which result the primary oöcyte and fifteen smaller nutritive or nurse-cells by which it is accompanied, the oöcyte alone retaining the whole complement of chromatin, as follows: In preparation for the first of these divisions the chromatin of the oögonium segregates into sharply distinct portions, one of which gives rise to the chromosomes, which enter the equatorial plate as usual, while the other forms a conspicuous deeply staining ring that passes to one pole of the spindle (Fig. 147). The ensuing division is unequal, and the ring passes into the larger cell, while the chromosomes are equally divided. This process is repeated in the three following divisions of the larger cell, while the smaller cells divide equally and with no further process of diminution, the ring finally passing into the germinal vesicle of the oöcyte, where for a time it is still distinguishable [1] as a voluminous nucleolus-like body which ultimately fragments into smaller "nucleoli." The observations of Debaisieux indicate that these take no part in the formation or transformation of the chromosomes.

In certain Lepidoptera, the diminution is still further deferred until the formation of the first polocyte during the maturation of the egg. This is well shown in *Phragmatobia*, *Orgyia* and *Limantria* (Seiler, '14), where a very considerable amount of basichromatin is cast off from the chromosomes during the metaphase. In *Orgyia* and *Limantria* this chromatin is seen during the anaphases as a double, plate-like structure which at first closely resembles a metaphase equatorial chromosome-plate (Fig. 148), and later

---

[1] All the essential features of Giardina's account are confirmed by Debaisieux ('09). A somewhat similar process is also described by Buchner ('00), in *Gryllus* and by Günthert ('10) in the beetle *Colymbetes*.

gives rise to a rounded mass in some cases closely resembling a nucleus, which ultimately disappears.

Taken together, the foregoing facts make it more than doubtful whether the process of diminution can be regarded as a primary cause of the dif-

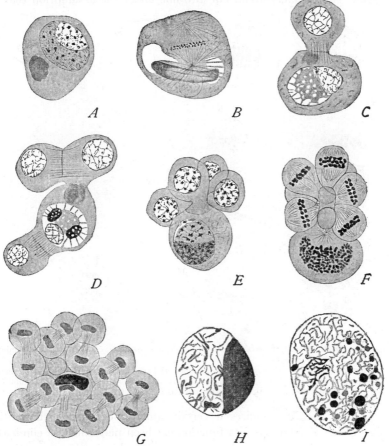

Fig. 147.—Egg-formation and diminution in Coleoptera. (*A–E, Dytiscus*, from GIARDINA; *H, I, Dytiscus* from DEBAISIEUX; *F, G, Colymbetes*, from GÜNTHERT.)

A, oögonium, differentiation of the chromatin; *B,* first differential division; *C,* result of last; *D,* second differential division; *E,* result of third division (only five of the 8 cells shown); *F,* the fourth differential division (2 cells not shown); *G,* telophase of same, oöcyte near center: *H,* nucleus of the final oöcyte, diminution-chromatin at right; *I,* later stage, diminution-chromatin fragmented to form nucleolus-like bodies.

ferentiation of the germ-line from the somatic line. It would seem rather that the eliminated material may have played some definite part in the earlier history of the germ-cells and has become superfluous. Such a conclusion would be akin to Weismann's early conception of an "öogenetic" plasma that is cast out of the egg in one of the polocytes (p. 498); and also to those dualistic conceptions of the nuclear substance which postulate the existence of a nutritive *trophochromatin* and a generative *idiochromatin* (p. 725). All the facts would fall into line under the assumption that the

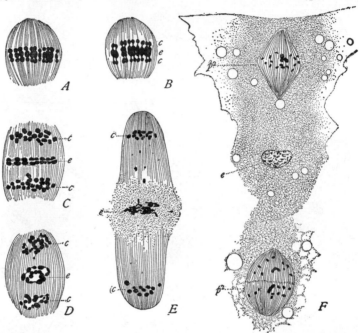

Fig. 148.—Diminution in the polar mitoses of *Lepidoptera* (SEILER); *e*, in each case the eliminated chromatin; *c*, the chromosomes.

A, B, first polar spindle of *Limantria*, showing equatorial accumulation of elimination-chromatin; *C, D*, anaphase and telophase, *Orgyeia; E*, late anaphase of *Phragmatobia; F*, same, outer and inner second polar spindles (p², p²) with elimination-nucleus between them.

evolution of the egg requires a certain amount of "trophochromatin" which, sooner or later after its function has been performed, is eliminated by the diminution-process. In harmony with this is the suggestion of Bonnevie ('05) that the process of elimination may be comparable to the extensive casting out of residual substance from the germinal vesicle during the prophases of the maturation of the egg as recorded by many observers (p. 355), and which is itself only a more conspicuous form of that which takes place in the somatic divisions generally. A broad field of inquiry is here offered, relating on the one hand to the general relations between nucleus and protoplasm, on the other to dualistic conceptions of the cell substance in general (p. 725).

B. THE AUXOCYTES

The starting point for the final differentiation of the gametes is given by the auxocytes (oöcytes or spermatocytes) which in their earliest stages are closely similar in the two sexes and contain the same components. The marked differences which they later display are due in part to the prodigious growth of the oöcyte as compared with the spermatocyte, in part to a different type of transformation in both cytosome and nucleus.[1] The auxocytes are of especial interest because in them take place the preliminary operations of meiosis or maturation that result in the reduction of the chromosomes; and also because in them preëxist the specific formed cytoplasmic materials for the building of the gametes.

In the very young auxocytes of both sexes the nucleus is a relatively very large vesicular body which has at first a reticulated structure ("resting stage"), and later assumes a more or less spireme-like structure (leptotene, pachytene, etc.). These changes are for the most part undergone while the auxocytes are still small and before they have entered upon the more active processes of growth. At this time the nucleus is probably always more or less eccentric, the investing layer of cytoplasm being therefore thicker on one side. In this thickened region, and usually close to the nucleus, lies a rounded cytoplasmic body within which are one or two centrioles (Fig. 149), and which is sometimes surrounded by cytoplasmic radiations to form an aster-like body. This body is now generally known as the *idiozome*.[2] This body is composed of a clear substance which we shall speak of as *sphere-substance*.

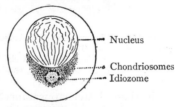

Fig. 149.—Diagram of early auxocyte.

In some cases (spermatocytes of mammals) it contains a considerable number of distinct "pro-acrosomic granules," which are believed to persist and by their aggregation to produce the acrosome of the sperm; but as a rule the specific acrosome-forming material is first seen at a later period (p. 361).

---

[1] In some cases the spermatocytes are of two or more sizes (p. 304) and they are sometimes so large as to take on more or less the aspect of oöcytes. This is characteristic of all or most of the spermatocytes in some animals, *e. g.*, in the myriapods (Blackman, '05, '07), and the hemipteran forms *Galgulus* (Payne, '08) and *Notonecta* (Pantel and Sinéty '06, Browne, '13). In other cases such large spermatocytes appear only as occasional variations (as in scorpions, p. 820), or as temporary stages in the development of a "pro-testis" destined to degenerate and disappear (frogs) or to form a special "Bidder's organ" (toads). By a considerable group of observers these cells have been regarded as actual oöcytes and the gonad, accordingly, as primitively hermaphroditic; but this view involves many difficulties (p. 820).

[2] See especially Meves ('99) who emphasized the fact, that the idiozome does not persist as such but sooner or later breaks up (Fig. 48), thus setting free the centrioles. The term *centrotheca*, was later proposed Meves ('02) as a substitute. Regaud ('10) proposed the form *idiosome* (early employed in a different sense, see Glossary) as the equivalent of idiozome. It seems preferable, however, to use Meves's earlier and equally non-committal term.

The idiozome is typically surrounded by Golgi-bodies ("batonettes," "platelets," etc.), sometimes so closely aggregated as to give the appearance of a network, or even of a continuous shell (Fig. 150) but

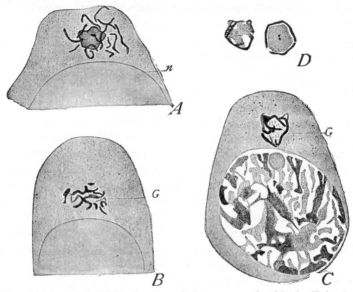

Fig. 150.—Idiozome and Golgi-bodies ("pseudochromosomes, chondriomites") in the spermatocytes of *Proteus* (HEIDENHAIN).
Both structures shown in *A*, the Golgi-bodies alone in *B* and *C; D*, two views of the "central capsule" formed by the Golgi-bodies, enclosing the idiozome and two central bodies.

both these latter appearances may be, wholly or in part, due to the technique.[1]

Lastly, the auxocytes always contain numerous chondriosomes in the form either of small mitochondria, rods, chondrioconts or chondriospheres. In earlier stages these are often more or less massed around the idiozome outside the Golgi-bodies and sometimes almost wholly confined to this region. They thus tend to form a cap on the nuclear wall (Figs. 157, 158) and may even extend completely around the nucleus to form a perinuclear zone, a condition especially common in the oöcyte.

[1] By earlier observers the Golgi-bodies associated with the idiozome were variously called " archoplasmic loops" (Hermann '91, '97) " pseudo-chromosomes" and "central capsule" (Heidenhain '00), or "peri-idiosomatic" bodies (Terni '12). Kuschekewitsch ('13) proposed to call the whole structure thus formed the *statosphere*, the Golgi-bodies or "spherosomes" forming a "sphærotheca" (central capsule) enclosing the idiozome and centrioles. The identification of the Golgi-apparatus in the auxocytes was first clearly indicated by Sjöval ('06) and has been confirmed by many later observers. Their subsequent dispersal through the cytosome is shown with especial clearness by the work of Weigl ('12) on insects, of Gatenby ('17–'18) on insects and pulmonates, of Hirschler ('19) on ascidians, and of Bowen ('20, '21) on insects.

C. Oögenesis. Growth and Differentiation of the Oöcyte

The phenomena of oögenesis offer numerous interesting problems, of which the most important are as follows:

(1) The morphological and physiological relations of the growing oöcyte to the accessory cells usually associated with it.

(2) The growth and transformation of the oöplasm, including the history of the central bodies, mitochondrial formations and Golgi-elements and the formation of yolk, pigment and other secondary structures.

(3) The history of the nucleus or germinal vesicle, in relation to the intense constructive processes of the oöplasm.

(4) The history of the chromosomes with reference to synapsis and meiosis.

(5) The localizing processes which result in the appearance of polarity, bilaterality and other promorphological features of the ovum.

We are at this point concerned primarily with only the first three of these, deferring the fourth to Chapter VI, and the fifth to Chapters XIII and XIV.

1. The Egg and Its Accessory Cells

During its period of growth the oöcyte very commonly becomes intimately associated with accessory cells that play an important part in its nutrition, though they may be absent. The two cases are distinguished respectively by Korschelt and Heider [1] as *alimentary* and *solitary* types of growth, the alimentary type being further characterized as either *follicular*, in which case the accessory cells form a continuous layer (follicle) surrounding the egg, or *nutrimentary*, in which the egg is accompanied by one or more nutritive *nurse-cells*, locally attached to it in various ways. These relations show many variations of which a few examples must here suffice. In the solitary type (*e. g.*, in pelecypods, or some echinoderms) the oöcyte, as it begins to enlarge, projects from the epithelial wall of the ovary and is finally set free, either into the cavity of the ovary or into the general cœlome or the genital duct. In some cases of this type it is set free at a very early stage and undergoes the greater part of its growth while floating in the cœlomic fluid (annelids); but in these cases the egg is often accompanied by nurse-cells (Fig. 151). More commonly the egg remains attached until nearly or full grown, often assuming a pear-shape, the narrow end forming a pedicel of attachment; and it has been shown in several such cases that the pedicel is situated at one pole of the egg and that the micropyle corresponds to the point at which it is finally withdrawn (p. 1023). The pedicel may be very long, *e. g.*, in the mollusk *Scrobicularia* (Fig. 488),

[1] '02, in which an extended review of the subject is given.

and still more so in the hemipteran insects, where it extends from the terminal nutritive end-chamber through a considerable part of the ovary to the growing egg (Fig. 152). It seems to have been proved in some of these cases that granular protoplasmic material (mitochondria?) actually flows from the other nutritive ovarian cells through the pedicel into the egg.[1]

In the follicular type, which is the most frequent, the egg is completely surrounded by a conspicuous follicle that often persists up to a late stage in its growth, or even until after its discharge. A good example of the latter case is offered by the ascidian egg. In many cases, however, the follicle

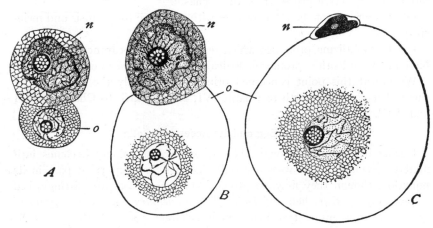

Fig. 151.—Oöcyte and nurse-cell in the annelid, *Ophryotrocha* (KORSCHELT).
A, young stage, the nurse-cell (*n*) larger than the oöcyte (*o*); *B*, growth of the oöcyte; *C*, late stage, the nurse-cell degenerating.

finally disappears, often after having secreted about the egg a resistant secondary envelope or chorion, as is typically seen in the insects. In other cases the follicle is ruptured and thrown off at the time the egg escapes from the ovary (mammals). The follicle-cells show wide differences of structure in different cases varying from an inconspicuous flattened epithelium up to high columnar forms, sometimes of remarkable type (ascidians) or to thick stratified epithelia (mammals). Their structural connections with the egg are referred to beyond (p. 335).

The follicular type of growth is connected by various intermediate conditions with the "nutrimentary," in which the egg is accompanied by a certain number of nurse-cells, which, however, do not completely surround

---

[1] This was suspected by some of the earlier observers, and seems to have been clearly established by more recent workers. See Jhering ('74), Stauffacher ('94), Wieman ('10), Dederer ('15), Nusbaum-Hilarowicz ('17).

it. In the simplest case there is but a single nurse-cell attached to the side of the oöcyte (*Sacculina, Ophryotrocha*). In the annelid *Ophryotrocha* (Korschelt, '93) the oöcyte and nurse-cell float in the cœlomic fluid, the nurse-cell being at first much larger than the oöcyte and containing a nucleus of wholly different type, being large, irregular and rich in basichromatin (Fig. 151). As the oöcyte grows the nurse-cell diminishes, being finally reduced to a mere rudiment, but without fusing with the egg. In *Myzostoma* (Wheeler, '97) the oöcyte is accompanied by two nurse-cells at opposite sides which fuse with the oöcyte at an early period, though their nuclei long persist at opposite poles. Owing to this fact Wheeler was able to show that the axis thus marked out persists as that of the mature egg, one nucleus lying in the region of the vacuolated cytoplasm at the animal pole, the other in that of the granular cytoplasm of the vegetative pole. In the annelid *Diopatra* Andrews ('91) found that the very young oöcyte lies between two long strings of nurse-cells attached to it on opposite sides; and here, too, there appears to be a constant relation between the nurse-cells and the egg (though a different one from that seen in *Myzostoma*).

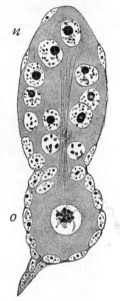

Fig. 152.—Ovary of parthenogenetic female of *Aphis rosæ*, showing mass of nurse-cells above and oöcyte below, connected with the former by nutritive root (DE BAEHR).

In a more frequent and rather widely distributed type the nurse-cells are aggregated in a coherent group at one side of the egg. In the annelid *Tomopteris elegans* (Chun) the germ-cells (oögonia) are set free from the ovary in groups of eight, one of which becomes the oöcyte, growing at the expense of the other seven which remain attached until a late stage at one side of the egg. The conditions are similar, but more extreme in the leech (*Pisciola* Jörgenssen, '10). Here the oögonia are set free from the solid portion of the ovary into the lumen in groups of four or five, which increase by division to the number of about fifty. Of these only one, as a rule, becomes an oöcyte, while all the others remain small and finally degenerate; two or even three of the cells may produce ova; and it is an interesting fact that *all of them, nurse-cells and oöcytes alike, may pass through the synaptic stages* (bouquet, etc., p. 543). There seems, therefore, to be no doubt in this case that the *nurse-cells are abortive eggs* which, by a physiological division of labor, sacrifice their own future to that of the functional egg (p. 336). This is confirmed by the conditions seen in various arthropods, particularly in the insects, which have been the object of numerous important investigations, prominent among them those of Korschelt ('86, '89), from which many of the following facts have been drawn.

In these animals the eggs and nurse-cells lie serially in the ovarian tubules and the eggs are usually surrounded by a follicle. In the grasshoppers the eggs typically lie in a single series, surrounded and separated by follicle-cells, but without other nutritive cells. In many other insects the eggs lie in a series, alternating with nutritive chambers in which lie one or more nurse-cells. In *Forficula* each nutritive chamber is occupied by a single

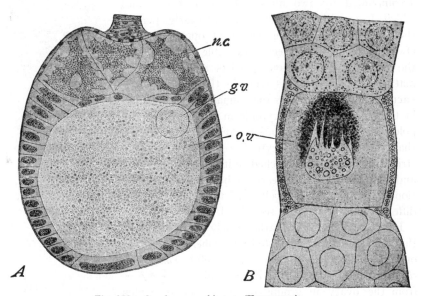

Fig. 153.—Ovarian eggs of insects (KORSCHELT).

A, egg of the butterfly, *Vanessa*, surrounded by its follicle; above, three nurse-cells (*n. c.*) with branching nuclei; *g. v.*, germinal vesicle; *B*, egg of water-beetle, *Dytiscus*, living; the egg (*o. v.*) lies between two groups of nutritive cells; the germinal vesicle sends amœboid processes into the dark mass of food-granules (chondriosomes?).

nurse-cell of great size and having in its fully developed state a very large branching nucleus (Fig. 320). In the coleopteran type the nutritive chamber contains a considerable number of closely packed nurse-cells (Figs. 153, 155), which in *Dytiscus* are 15 in number. The lepidopteran type is in some respects intermediate between the coleopteran type and that seen in *Forficula*, the nurse-cells lying (in *Vanessa*, Fig. 153) in a single layer so as to appear like enlarged follicle cells with very large branching nuclei.

In some cases an actual fusion takes place between the egg and the accompanying nutritive cells. In the tunicates, for example, follicle-cells migrate into the egg in considerable numbers to form the "test-cells," long a morphological puzzle.[1]   Nearly related with this are the phenomena in various cœlenterates (*Hydra*) and mollusks (*Helix*) where the egg fuses with or engulfs certain of the neighboring nutritive cells or follicle-cells (Fig. 154)[2] and the same occurs in certain cœlenterates (*Hydra*) and

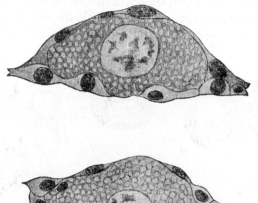

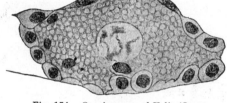

Fig. 154.—Ovarian eggs of *Helix* (Obst).

A, earlier stage, surrounded by follicle; *B*, later stage, showing inward migration and absorption of follicle-cells.

mollusks (*Helix*). In other cases the perinuclear zone of the oöcyte is connected directly with the nurse-cells by conspicuous protoplasmic bridges, through which the mitochondrial contents of the nurse-cells are said finally to pass inwards to the egg (Fig. 155).   A similar function, perhaps, is performed by the more numerous and delicate protoplasmic cell-bridges between the oöcyte and its surrounding follicle-cells, which have been described by many observers from an early period. They have recently been carefully studied by Retzius ('12) who has given a valuable review of the litterature and has published many remarkable figures showing how in all the main groups of vertebrates the follicle cells give off from their bases conspicuous protoplasmic processes or filaments which penetrate the so-called *zona radiata* (egg-envelope) and enter the cortical layer of the oöcyte (Fig. 156). Similar cell-bridges have also been demonstrated connecting the eggs of plants with the surrounding cells.[3]   It is not known whether

[1] See Floderus, '96, Bancroft '99, etc.   [2] See Doflein ('97), Floderus ('95), Obst ('99), etc.
[3] See Goroschankin, '83, Ikeno, '98, A. Meyer, '96, etc.

these bridges are lines of actual protoplasmic flow, but it can hardly be doubted in view of all the facts, that they are paths through which nutrient substances are in some form passed into the egg.

The morphological relationship of the nutritive or accessory cells to the oöcyte has long been a subject of controversy. In cases where a single nurse-cell or group of such cells is associated with the egg, it is beyond doubt that these cells have a common origin with the oöcyte and should be regarded as abortive or rudimentary eggs that have been specialized for

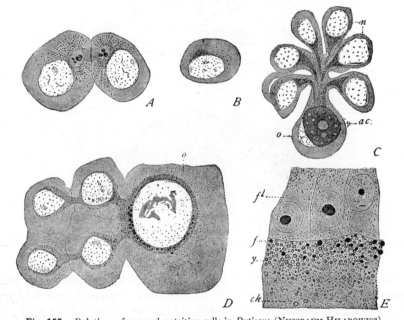

Fig. 155.—Relations of egg and nutritive cells in *Dytiscus* (Nussbaum-Hilarowicz).

A, B, oögonia, in division and in repose; *C,* oöcyte (*o*) showing six of the 15 nurse-cells (*n*) and the accessory body, *ac,* Giardina's ring; *D,* later stage, showing streams of mitochondria; *E,* peripheral region of much older oöcyte; *ch,* chondriosomes; *f,* fat-drops; *fl,* follicle-cells; *y,* developing yolk-spheres. (*Cf.* Fig. 147.)

the elaboration of food-materials at the expense of which the functional ovum grows. This is demonstrated, for instance, by Giardina's observations on *Dytiscus* (p. 326), or those of Jörgenssen ('13*b*) on *Pisciola*; and it is very probably true of many other cases of this type (*Orphryotrocha, Myzostoma, Diopatra,* etc.). A confirmation of this is given by the above mentioned remarkable fact (p. 333) that *the nuclei of the nurse-cells may form tetrads* closely similar to those seen in the oöcyte-nucleus,[1] and even may

[1] Woltereck ('98) in the ostracodes, Giardina ('02) in *Dytiscus,* Grünberg ('03) in *Pieris,* Marshall ('07*b*) in *Platyplax,* and others.

pass through characteristic leptotene, synizesis and pachytene-diplotene stages (p. 537), in the course of which they undergo pseudo-reduction.[1] In some of these cases, according to the observations of Dederer and of

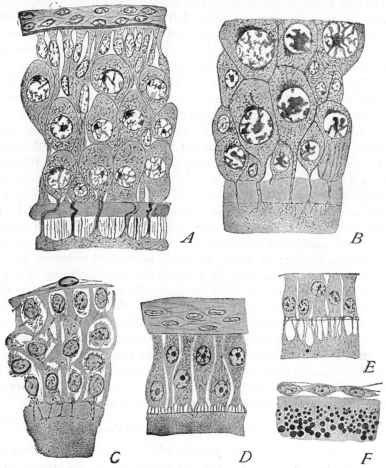

Fig. 156.—Connections between oöcyte and follicle-cells in vertebrates (RETZIUS).

A, in *Chimæra; B, Raja; C*, the rabbit; *D*, the pigeon; *E*, the domestic fowl. The foregoing from earlier stages of the oöcyte; *F*, late stage in *Lacerta*.

Hogben, these changes are passed through by all the cells before the nurse-cells can be distinguished from the functional oöcytes, all starting out along the same pathway, but many of them being arrested to form nurse-

[1] Doncaster ('12) in *Pieris*, Dederer ('15) in *Phyllosamia*, Hogben ('20a) in *Rhodites*. See also Paulcke ('00), McGill ('06).

cells before completing their development. Undoubtedly, therefore, the nurse-cells should in such cases be regarded as abortive ova (oöcytes) that are sacrificed for the benefit of their more fortunate brethren.

The case is by no means so clear in respect to the follicle-cells. In the insects the important investigations of Heymons ('95) and others seemed to demonstrate that the follicle-cells and terminal filament of the ovary were derived from mesoblastic cells not arising from primordial germ-cells and only secondarily associated with the latter. On the other hand, Marshall ('07) found in Hymenoptera and in the phryganids that both kinds of cells had a common origin; and a similar result has been reached by Vejdovský ('11, '12) in the orthopter *Diastrammena*; by Dederer ('17) in Lepidoptera, and by Hogben ('20a) in Hymenoptera. In the vertebrates a strong case has been made out for the common origin of ova and follicle-cells. Winiwarter and Saintmont, as above stated, leave this question in doubt. Bühler ('94) long since described the origin of germ-cells (presumably oögonia) by tangential division of columnar epithelial cells in the germinal epithelium of the mammals; and this is confirmed by the recent studies of Gutherz ('18) who also described the origin of oögonia by a direct metamorphosis of the epithelial cells without division. For the present, however, it seems necessary to suspend judgment on this difficult question. It is, after all, a question of detail, relating as it does only to the relative time at which the germ-cells are finally set apart from the somatic cells, in respect to which we know that very wide variations occur (p. 312). We should not permit such variations to obscure our view of the large fact, emphasized by Nussbaum, that sooner or later in the ontogeny the descendants of the original egg become differentiated into two groups, germinal and somatic; and the significance of this is not lessened by the fact (if, as the writer believes, it is a fact) that in theory any cell of the body many contain the potentiality of the whole.

2. General History of the Oöplasmic Components

The enormous increase in the cytoplasmic or oöplasmic substance during the growth of the oöcyte leads to the production of the largest known forms of cells (p. 98). In large and heavily yolk-laden eggs this enlargement is mainly due to the loading of the cytosome with passive reserve-materials (yolk or deutoplasm); but apart from this it seems clear that the ovum also contains an exceptionally large amount of active protoplasm. The growing oöcyte therefore forms a very advantageous object for study of the cytological changes; while, more broadly viewed, it offers problems of fundamental interest for the analysis of the problems of localization and differentiation. These considerations have naturally attracted the attention of cytologists to this subject from an early period, and have made it the center of an evergrowing mass of literature. Unfortunately, it offers difficulties that have not yet been overcome; and it must be admitted that in many respects we are still far from an adequate understanding of the phenomena.

In the young oöcyte, the cytoplasm is at first both very small in amount and simple in structure, often seeming to consist almost wholly of optically homogeneous hyaloplasm, which in the living object shows only a few scattered granules. As growth proceeds the structure becomes more complicated by the appearance of an alveolar or pseudo-alveolar structure, due to the formation of true alveolar spheres or of yolk-spherules (p. 73).[1] Since nothing is known of the manner in which the hyaloplasm increases, our study of cytoplasmic growth and differentiation thus reduces itself largely to the development of the yolk and other formed elements.

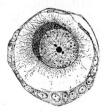

Fig. 157.—Young human oöcyte, surrounded by its follicle, showing the crescentic vitellogenous layer applied to the nucleus (VAN DER STRICHT).

In spite of numerous researches on the yolk-formation, extending over a period of more than fifty years, the subject still remains in so confused a state that all statements in regard to it must be made with considerable reserve. Even in the recent literature we find the origin of the yolk-spherules ascribed to chondriosomes, to Golgi-bodies, to chromidia, extruded nucleoli or nucleolar fragments; while some observers consider that the yolk arises *de novo* in the cytoplasmic substance without discoverable relation to other formed elements. We must, therefore, conclude either that there is no general uniformity in the mode of yolk-formation, or that many of the existing accounts of the subject are erroneous.

  a.   The Yolk-nucleus or Vitelline Body. (Dotterkern, corps vitellin). By these terms is designated a cytoplasmic body, first observed in the oöcytes of spiders by Wittich ('45) and called the "yolk-nucleus" by Carus ('50), and undoubtedly concerned in some manner with the yolk-formation.[2] The nature of this body has been a subject of long continued controversy.[3] In the greater number of cases it is a single body lying near the nucleus; but the same name has been applied to several or many cytoplasmic bodies scattered through the cytosome or in its peripheral layer. These latter in-

---

[1] *Cf.* Wilson, '99.

[2] The extended literature on this subject is reviewed in the works of Jordan ('93), Mertens ('93), Henneguy ('93, '96), Van Bambeke ('98), Crampton ('99), Korschelt-Heider ('02), Waldeyer ('06), Fauré-Fremiet ('10), Munson ('12), and others.

[3] The early view of Will ('11), Henneguy ('93), Balbiani ('83, '93) and a few others that the yolk-nucleus arises from the germinal vesicle, either by a process of budding or by the extrusion of nucleolar elements, has not been sustained by more recent studies.

clude amorphous masses of material that have been described by some observers as "archoplasm," "ergastoplasm," etc., and seem to be of varied nature. All these will here be left out of account except in so far as they may represent material arising by the fragmentation of one original yolk-nucleus or of material associated with it.

Wittich found the yolk-nucleus as a rounded body lying near the germinal vesicle, later enlarging markedly and acquiring a concentric fibrillated or laminated structure; and as a spheroidal body it was later described by a number of the earlier observers (Fig. 158).[1] Others found it as an elongated body, composed of finely granular material, either spread out like a crescentic cap at one side of the nucleus or extending completely around it to form a *perinuclear zone* closely applied to the nuclear wall (Fig. 157).[2]

Within the latter, in many cases, lies a well-defined, rounded body that corresponds to Wittich's yolk-nucleus, as was shown to be the case in Wittich's own object, the spider (*Tegenaria*) by Van der Stricht ('98) and later by Fauré-Fremiet ('10). As a matter of historical priority, therefore, it seems clear that the term "yolk-nucleus" should be restricted to the smaller spheroidal body within the crescent or ring. The latter has received various names.[3] We here make use of Bambeke's convenient and non-committal term *pallial layer* or pallial substance, employing the term *yolk-nucleus-complex* to the double structure formed by the yolk-nucleus together with the pallial substance.

(1) In many cases the yolk-nucleus has been found to contain one or two central granules closely similar to centrioles, thus suggesting its identity with the idiozome of the early spermatocytes.[4] It is in some cases surrounded by conspicuous astral rays but this seems exceptional.[5] A number of observers have failed to find any definite body surrounding the centriole; others have failed to observe either yolk-nucleus or central granules, but in all such cases it is doubtful whether the technical treatment has revealed the complete, normal structure. The identity of the yolk-nucleus with the idiozome of the early oöcyte or spermatocytes, accepted by most observers of the French and Belgian schools, receives strong support from the relation of the yolk-nucleus to the Golgi-bodies and the chondriosomes.

---

[1] *E. g.*, by Balbiani ('93) and Henneguy ('93).

[2] *E. g.*, by Holl ('90) in the hen, O. Schultze ('87) in the frog, Nemec ('97) in the myriapods, or Bambeke ('98) in *Pholcus*.

[3] *E. g.*, the *pallial layer* or *mantle-layer* (Van Bambeke); *vitellogenous layer* or *vitellogenous mass* (Van der Stricht); *yolk-matrix* (Crampton); *Dotterkernlager* of German writers.

[4] Balbiani ('93) first definitely urged this comparison, maintaining that the yolk-nucleus is equivalent to an "attraction-sphere plus a centrosome"; and the same conclusion was adopted by Van der Stricht ('98), Munson ('08, '04, '12), Lams ('07), Fauré-Fremiet ('10), Loyez ('11), Sonnenbrodt ('08) and many others. Meves ('98) adopted a similar view, recognizing the yolk-nucleus as an idiozome in the same sense as the "sphere" and central bodies of the spermatocytes.

[5] See Balbiani (*op. cit.*), Munson ('98, '04, '12), Lams ('07).

(2) The nature of the pallial layer is still but partially cleared up. It seems to include both chondriosomes and Golgi-bodies and according to some observers also extruded nucleolar material. That the pallial substance consists largely of chondriosomes has been maintained by many observers.[1] Nussbaum-Hilarowicz ('17) considers that in *Dytiscus* it is in large part derived from the nurse-cells associated with the oöcyte (Fig. 155). The Golgi-bodies of the pallial layer were recognized and figured by Holmgren ('oo) and by Sjövall ('o6) in the oöcytes of mammals and have recently been studied more carefully by Hirschler ('18) in the öocytes of ascidians and mollusks and by Gatenby ('19) in those of mollusks. In the latter case (*Paludina*) they show the typical relations, being aggregated about the idiozome with the mitochondria outside them. In the ascidian they are considerably modified, as will presently be indicated.

Although the data are still rather scanty, the conclusion seems on the whole justified that the yolk-nucleus-complex shows a close analogy to the idiozome-complex of the spermatocytes and that the two may be regarded as homologous formations. Some observers have, however, found a central body and aster lying quite outside the pallial mass or "yolk-nucleus," *e. g.*, in the myriapod *Polyzonium*, according to Nemec ('97). In other cases the mitochondria show but little tendency to aggregate about the yolk-nucleus, while the Golgi-bodies may be quite separate from it, *e. g.*, in the ascidian (Hirschler, '19) which also differs from the usual type in the fact that two yolk-nuclei are often present, in neither of which could central bodies be detected (Fig. 348). It seems probable, therefore, that the association between yolk-nucleus (idiozome) and the mitochondrial and Golgi-elements, though a very common one, is not essential.

Lastly, there is some reason to conclude that the pallial substance may also contain nucleoli or nucleolar fragments extruded from the germinal vesicle; but no general agreement has yet been reached concerning this point, which involves great difficulties of observation (p. 345); and the same may be said, with added emphasis, concerning the supposed extrusion of chromidia from the nuclear network described by Schaxel, Buchner, Hargitt and other observers (p. 700).

b. Formation of the Yolk. The pallial layer is found only in the earlier stages of the oöcytes and does not long persist as such. Sooner or later it separates from the germinal vesicle, moves outward toward the periphery, breaking up meanwhile into smaller and smaller fragments that are finally dispersed in a finely divided state through the cytosome; and this is followed by a rapid formation of yolk-spherules while the oöcyte enters upon an

---

[1] Van der Stricht ('o5, 'o9, etc.), Lams and Doorme ('o7), in mammals; Loyez ('o9), in ascidians; Fauré-Fremiet ('1o) in myriapods and arachnids, etc.

active process of growth. At the same time the yolk-nucleus commonly disappears from view and in most cases the central bodies cannot be distinguished until the period of maturation approaches.[1]

The details of these various processes vary widely in different species. In some cases, of which a remarkable example is offered by the spider

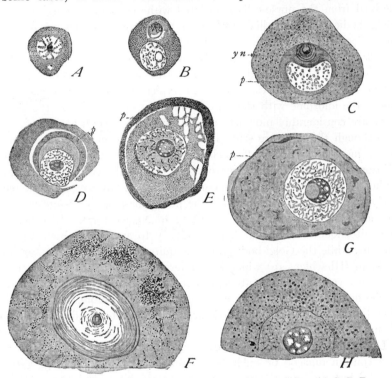

Fig. 158.—Yolk-nucleus, pallial substance and yolk-formation in spiders. (*A–C, F, Tegenaria,* from Van der Stricht; *D, E, G, H, Pholcus,* from Van Bambeke).

A, B, C, early stages, showing idiozome (yolk-nucleus) and pallial or vitellogeneous layer; in *B* the Golgi-bodies (pseudochromosomes) are shown; in *C* the pallial layer (*p*) completely surrounds the nucleus and yolk-nucleus; in *D* the pallial substance is separating from the nucleus in the form of a crescent; in *E* in the form of a ring; in *G* it is breaking up; *F*, yolk-nucleus and mitochondrial granules; in *H* the pallial substance is broken up and the deutoplasm is appearing; yolk-spherules pale, fat-drops black.

Pholcus (Van Bamkeke, '98) the pallial layer separates from the germinal vesicle, usually in the form of a very definite horse-shoe shaped cap which may nearly encircle the nucleus, or of a ring which moves outward nearly to the cell-periphery where it fragments at first into irregular masses

---

[1] In the spiders the yolk-nucleus persists throughout a large part of the growth-period; and in some species, as long since shown by Wittich, it remains nearly unchanged in the embryo throughout nearly the whole of its development.

(Fig. 158) and finally into very minute granules dispersed through the whole egg. A similar ring, having a similar history is described in the myriapod *Julus* by Fauré-Fremiet ('10) (Fig. 159). The process of disintegration and dispersal may take place while the pallial mass is still in contact with the germinal vesicle, for instance in the earthworm or the tunicate (Fig. 346). The process in the latter case was carefully examined by differential staining in *Molgula* by Crampton ('99), and later in *Ascidia* by Hirschler ('18) who employed modern methods for the differentiation of the mitochondria and Golgi-bodies. By the aid of these staining-reactions it is easy to follow the progressive breaking up of the pallial mass, its dissemination through the cytoplasm and the ensuing appearance of yolk-spherules.

The general type of transformation described above is of widespread occurrence, but shows many variations of detail. An interesting example of the latter appears in the amphibian oöcyte, which has been carefully examined by Lams ('07) in *Rana* and by Gajewska ('17, '19) in *Triton*. In both these cases the pallial substance forms in the early stages the usual cap-like mass within which Lams demonstrates the yolk-nucleus (idiozome) with one or two central bodies. In both a perinuclear ring or pallial layer may be formed, but this appears to be a regular process in *Triton* and only an occasional one in *Rana*. In both, the pallial substance spreads out through the oöplasm in a deeply staining and more or less net-like condition; and in *Triton* tends to accumulate near the periphery to form an "exoplasmic layer." Ultimately, as in other cases, this substance becomes finely disseminated through the oöplasm.

During or subsequent to the foregoing changes the deutoplasm begins to appear in the form of yolk-spherules, fat-drops or both, at first scattered and very minute but later rapidly enlarging and commonly becoming crowded so as to produce a "pseudo-alveolar" structure. The precise origin of these bodies is a question which the researches and controversies of fifty years have left still unsettled. Modern studies have indeed made it nearly certain that they are somehow connected with the pallial substance (hence the term "vitellogenous substance" or "vitellogeneous layer") but beyond this point the existing accounts are still widely divergent.

Concerning the relation of the original formed elements to the definitive yolk-bodies two divergent views have been held from an early period down to the present time. It has been held, on the one hand, that the original formed elements (dispersed fragments of the pallial substance or its derivatives) are directly transformed into yolk-spherules or fatty bodies; on the other, that most of the original formed elements are completely absorbed by the protoplasm and disappear while the deutoplasmic elements are formed *de novo*. Perhaps both views are correct, for the term yolk or deutoplasm designates a variety of storage materials in the egg, and these may differ in mode of origin, so far at least as the visible phenomena go. This possibility was clearly placed in evidence by the notable work on the spider's egg of Van Bambeke ('98), who concluded that there are two principal types of deutoplasm, namely, fatty granules which blacken greatly in osmic acid and are readily soluble in xylol, and ordinary yolk-spherules which show the opposite qualities and are presumably albuminous in nature. The former Van Bambeke believed to be directly derived

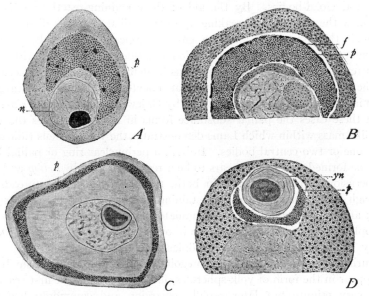

Fig. 159.—Yolk-nucleus, pallial substance and yolk in the oöcytes of myriapods and spiders (FAURÉ-FREMIET).

A–C, Julus; D, Tegenaria.

A, earlier stage pallial substance (*p*) separating from nucleus; *B*, later stage; in both these cases fatty deutoplasmic elements (black) developing in the pallial substance; *C*, the pallial substance has separated in the form of a ring. In *D*, the yolk-nucleus, *yn* (idiozome) is partly surrounded by the pallial layer and by fibrillar differentiations (chondrioconts?).

from finely divided pallial substance, the latter to be formed *de novo* in the cytoplasm; and this is substantially confirmed by the important later work of Fauré-Fremiet ('10) who brings forward evidence in the case especially of myriapods (*Julus, Lithobius*) and of the ascidian *Ciona*, that the fatty bodies are in some cases actually formed within the pallial layer (Fig. 159). It is, however, still doubtful in what measure this distinction holds for the yolk-formation generally. The close connection between chondriosomes and the yolk-formation has been urged especially by Van der Stricht and his followers. Van der Stricht himself ('05, '09) was inclined to the view that the mitochondria and chondrioconts (in mammals) are not actually converted into yolk but become clumped to form mitochondrial aggregates which give rise on the one hand to yolk-bodies, on the other to the scattered chondriosomes of the oöplasm. The results of Lams and Doorme ('07) on mammals likewise demonstrated a very close connection between the mitochondria and the yolk. Loyez ('09) found in some species of ascidians (*Ciona, Molgula, Ascidia*) a direct transformation of mitochondria into yolk-bodies; and Hirschler ('16) has recently confirmed this account in *Ascidia*. In an earlier work ('13) the latter author follows out very circumstantially the direct transformation of mitochondria into yolk-spherules by enlargement accompanied by differentiation of a central clearer substance, which no longer takes the crystal violet stain by Benda's method, and a peripheral one that at every stage is intensely stained by that dye. This seems to be the best evidence thus far produced of a direct origin of yolk-spherules from mitochondria. A similar possibility is indicated by the works of Gatenby ('20a, '20b) on the pulmonates and some others, though this observer seems inclined to a somewhat negative attitude concerning such a mode of yolk-formation.

The most recent addition to the list of supposed yolk-forming bodies is given by the Golgi-bodies. Hirschler believes that in the ascidian egg the Golgi-elements as they enlarge and spread through the oöplasm unite secondarily with enlarged mitochondria to produce the yolk-spherules, which are accordingly said to have a double origin; in *Ascaris*, on the other hand, Hirschler found no connection between the yolk and the Golgi-bodies; Gatenby ('20, etc.) also produces evidence that the Golgi-bodies may take part in the yolk-formation in the pulmonate mollusks and in *Patella*. In the sponge *Grantia*, however ('20c), he believes the yolk-spherules to form independently of other preëxisting formed elements in the cytoplasm.

The origin of yolk from extruded nucleoli or their fragments has been advocated by some of the latest as well as a number of the early observers, but has also met with contradiction in many cases. [1] The best evidence seems to be offered in Hogben's remarkable accounts of the yolk-formation in insects ('20a, in Hymenoptera and especially 20b in the cockroach). Here the yolk is said to arise from granules ("deutosomes") that are formed in vacuoles inside the nucleoli *while still inclosed in the nucleus*, and are later cast out into the cytoplasm, when they migrate towards the periphery

[1] An extrusion of nucleoli or nucleolar fragments into the cytoplasm has been maintained (among others) by Will ('84), Henneguy ('93), Kohlbrügge ('01), Loyez ('06) and Gajewska ('17, '20) in the case of vertebrates; by Will, Woltereck ('98), Vejdovský ('11–'12), Gatenby ('20), and Hogben (20a '20b) in arthropods; by Montgomery ('98) and Jörgenssen ('13) in leeches; Hempelmann ('06) and Buchner ('14) in chætopods; Gelei ('13) in platodes, G. T. Hargitt ('13) in hydomedusæ, and by Denby ('14–'15) and Gatenby ('20) in sponges; but some of these, *e. g.*, Gatenby and Gajewska, have been unable to find any connection between the nucleoli and the yolk.

and there enlarge to form the yolk-spherules. Interesting possibilities are raised by these various observations which, broadly speaking, are in line with those of earlier observers who believed the zymogen-granules of the pancreatic and other glandular cells to be likewise derived from extruded nucleolar fragments; [1] and also with the more recent work of Schreiner on the origin of fat and mucin (p. 705).

Nevertheless, in view of the contradictions even in the most recent literature of the subject the time has hardly yet arrived for a judgment upon the matter.

Summary. Existing accounts of the formation of the yolk and growth of the egg still show many apparent contradictions of detail, but nevertheless are practically unanimous in regard to two outstanding facts. First, an important part in the yolk-formation, and perhaps also in the general growth of the oöplasm, is played by cytoplasmic formed elements (chondriosomes, perhaps also Golgi-bodies) that are known to be handed on from one cell-generation to another by mitosis and possibly may have the power of multiplication by growth and division. Not less striking, secondly, is a close association of these formed elements with the egg-nucleus prior to the growth of the cytosome and the production of yolk. The meaning of this is unknown, but we may conjecture that it is an indication of a nuclear activity that plays a part in the later history of the oöcyte. One might imagine, for instance, that during this association the formed elements receive from the nucleus certain substances (enzymes or other chemical messengers) of which they become the carriers, transporting them to regions of the cytosome where they play their specific part. It is important to bear in mind the rapid increase in the number of the chondriosomes (and of Golgi-bodies?) that takes place during the growth of the egg. Only a part of them are used up in the production of other formed elements. The greater number persist, possibly to play some rôle in the fertilization of the egg (p. 434), in any case to be handed on to the embryonic cells by cleavage. Perhaps we catch here glimpses of a mechanism concerned not merely with the yolk-formation but with the general processes of determination, localization and heredity. To the same mechanism may perhaps belong also the extrusion of formed elements from the nucleus; but the occurrence of such a process does not yet seem sufficiently demonstrated.

The Secondary or Accessory Nuclei. We have lastly to consider the so-called secondary or accessory nuclei that appear in the oöcytes of Hymenoptera and other insects during the middle or later growth-period, and have

---

[1] See for instance Ogata ('83), Platner ('89), Melissinos and Nicolaides ('90), Galeotti ('95), Laguesse ('99, '00), *Cf.* Saguchi ('20).

exactly the appearance of small nuclei, but *which do not arise by division of the egg-nucleus*. They may be aggregated about the germinal vesicle, or may be quite separate from the latter, either scattered through the cytosome or more or less aggregated in a peripheral zone (Figs. 141, 160).[1] Buchner has found that the secondary nuclei of different species show characteristic differences similar in type to those existing between the main nuclei or germinal vesicles. Buchner has described some conditions in these nuclei which he considers as stages in budding or amitotic division, but the evidence is inconclusive. They have never been observed to divide by mitosis and finally disappear entirely before the period of maturation.

The history of these bodies prominently raises the question of the origin of nuclei *de novo* and has therefore been the subject of investigation by many observers. Blochmann considered them to arise from the germinal vesicle by a process of budding; and this has been supported by Marshall ('07) and a few others; Korschelt believed them to be derived from the surrounding follicle-cells, as is the case with the "test-cells" of ascidians (p. 334). Many observers, on the other hand, have produced evidence that they arise from minute granules extruded from the germinal vesicle (perhaps in some cases, according to Büchner, from the nuclei of the surrounding follicle-cells) which gradually grow into smaller nuclei. This view, advanced by Loyez ('08), has received support from the work especially of Hegner ('15), Buchner ('18), Gatenby ('20) and Hogben ('20a), all of whom have studied the phenomena especially in Hymenoptera of various genera, including ants, bees, and gall-flies. The process may take place close to the germinal vesicle, in which case (as in *Camponotus* or *Rhyssa*, Fig. 141) the germinal vesicle becomes surrounded by a nest of smaller nuclei. In other forms the secondary nuclei never show as such any discoverable relation to the germinal vesicle, first appearing scattered through the cytosome, or around the periphery of the egg (*Apanteles*, Fig. 141). In such cases it is assumed that the chromatin-granules from which they arise are extruded from the germinal vesicle at an earlier period and spread through the oöplasm before giving rise to secondary nuclei.

All recent researches seem to show that these bodies finally disappear completely. Their significance is unknown. Gatenby ('20) makes the plausible suggestion that they may be concerned with certain vegetative functions in the growing oöcyte, the egg-nucleus having become partly decentralized by the separation and migration of a kind of "trophochromatin" (p. 725) specialized for this purpose. If the foregoing results be well founded these structures would seem to be nuclei that are not built

[1] For a history of observations on this subject see especially Hegner ('15), Buchner ('18).

up from chromosomes—a condition unparalleled among Metazoa—and to this may perhaps be due their incapacity for division. We know, especially from Boveri's observations (p. 729), that perfect nuclei, capable of mitotic division, may be built up of a group of chromosomes far less numerous than the normal haploid group; that even single chromosomes that go astray

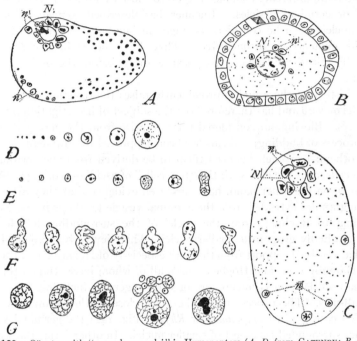

Fig. 160.—Oöcytes with "secondary nuclei" in Hymenoptera (A, D, from GATENBY; B, C, from HOGBEN; E–G, from BUCHNER).

A, oöcyte of *Myrmicina* with principal nucleus (N) and secondary ones (n); B, C, oöcytes of *Formica*, letters as before; D, series of stages in *Apanteles* between minute solid chromatoid granules and secondary nuclei; E–G, series of growth-stages of the secondary nuclei in *Solenius*.

on the spindle may give rise to small but perfect nuclei (Fig. 391). Meves has shown that a sperm-nucleus may be formed from a single chromosome in the oligopyrene sperms of Lepidoptera (p. 301). We see vesicular nuclei, in the form of karyomeres, regularly formed from single chromosomes in many cases of typical mitosis (p. 133); in the spermatogonia, and sometimes in the second spermatocytes of Orthoptera (Fig. 360) the X-chromosome regularly forms a small separate nucleus of its own (p. 764). There is no obvious reason why even smaller masses of "chromatin" should not likewise form nuclei or even why such nuclei should not divide by a kind of mitosis. We may, however, feel reasonably sure that such nuclei are strictly limited in potency; that they are not equivalent to those of the tissue-cells.

3. The History of the Nucleus

During the growth-period both the chromosomes and the nucleoli undergo a series of transformations analogous in a measure to those which may be observed in the tissue-cells, but in magnified form, so as to offer unusual opportunities for their study in detail. These phenomena show wide differences in different forms—sometimes even within the limits of

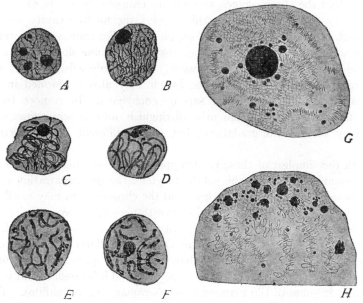

Fig. 161.—The germinal vesicle of the elasmobranch egg in the early and middle growth-period (Marechal).

(*A–F, Pristiurus, G, H, Scyllium.*)

A, presynaptic reticulum; B, leptotene; C, synapsis; D, polarized pachytene; E, later pachytene, non-polarized; F, diplotene; G, much later stage, loosening-up of the chromosomes; H, still later, "lamp-brush" chromosomes.

a single genus—and the conditions by which they are determined are still imperfectly understood.

a. The Chromosomes and the Nuclear Framework. In its earlier stages, the egg-nucleus is probably always netlike in character (*protobroch* stage of Winiwarter), and in many cases is nearly or quite oxyphilic while the single nucleolus is strongly basophilic. This is followed by the reappearance of the chromosomes in the form of fine, basophilic spireme-threads (*leptonema*) which pass through the synaptic stages and later become shorter, thicker, strongly basophilic (*pachynema*) and longitudinally double (*diplo-nema*). These are the bivalent chromosomes (later tetrads), which are haploid in number and are destined to divide in the polar or meiotic divisions that take place at the end of the growth-period. These changes will be considered in Chapter VI.

In the following stages, while the egg is rapidly growing, the chromosomes always become in some degree looser in texture, less regular in contour and less strongly basophilic, while the nucleus recedes in various degrees towards the "resting" or reticular condition, in some cases to such a degree that the chromosomes as such are temporarily lost to view, as in an ordinary tissue-cell. During this process the nuclear cavity becomes filled with a lightly staining, often oxyphilic, netlike framework or reticulum in which the chromosomes are suspended. Some doubt still exists concerning the origin of this framework. It certainly arises in part from fine branches of the chromosomes; but it may also be formed in part by coagulation of the nuclear sap or enchylema. In respect to the later stages we may conveniently distinguish four general types, connected by various intergradations, but widely different in their extreme forms.

(1) In the simplest of these (which approaches most nearly to the conditions commonly seen in the spermatocytes), the deconcentration of the chromosomes is but slightly marked, and the chromosomes may readily be traced individually throughout the growth-period, always retaining in some degree their basic staining-capacity. Typical examples of this are seen in certain of the copopods (*Cyclops*) and Turbellaria [1] which represent a condition roughly analogous to that seen in the spermatocytes, for instance of Amphibia or the Orthoptera (p. 552), and it is possible that it may occur also in some of the mammals (see Newman, '12, armadillo). These nuclei usually have a single large basophilic nucleolus.

(2) In a second type the growth and deconcentration of chromosomes proceeds much further, and at the same time the longitudinal halves of the diplotene separate more or less widely, so that the chromosomes seem to be grouped in pairs, the members of which are often twisted about each other. In the elasmobranchs, where the deconcentration process can be studied to great advantage, the chromosomes become loose in texture and in outline and finally give off numerous lateral thread-like radiating branches or loops that lose themselves in the general network. Thus arise the very loose so-called "lamp-brush" chromosomes (Figs. 161, 162), characteristic of the middle growth-period in large, yolk-bearing eggs, such as those of vertebrates (fishes, amphibians, sauropsida), and also of various insects,

[1] See especially Schleip ('07), Gelei ('13, '21, '22).

crustacea, or *Sagitta* (Fig. III). These chromosomes sooner or later become nearly or completely oxyphilic like the general framework in which they lie, so as to be distinguishable from the latter with difficulty; and at the same time they lose their resistance to peptic digestion,[1] which in their earlier basophilic state is very marked. In spite of these remarkable changes it appears to be certain that in some of these cases the chromosomes do not at any time disappear from view but persist without loss of their identity throughout the whole growth-period. One of the best determined of these cases is offered by the elasmobranch *Pristiurus* in which Rückert ('92, '95) was able to follow the chromosomes through the whole growth-period up to the late prophases, when they rapidly decrease in size, reconcentrate in structure, regain their basophilic character and pass upon the first polar spindle; and the same appears to be true in *Scyllium*. This conclusion was confirmed by the extended and accurate studies of Maréchal ('06) on these forms and on the teleost *Trigla;* and a similar result has been reached by several observers in other forms.[2] These facts afford conclusive proof that *the individuality and genetic continuity of chromosomes does not depend upon a persistence of "chromatin" in the older sense (i. e., basichromatin).* It is the expression of a morphological organization that is not destroyed by those chemical and physical transformations that lead to a netlike structure and a change from the basophilic to the oxyphilic condition (p. 652).

A third class includes those still more extreme cases in which the chromosomes are finally completely lost to view in the nuclear network (*dictyotic* stage of Winiwarter) and the whole structure becomes nearly or quite oxyphylic. The classical case of this is offered by the Amphibia, which have long been a center of controversy in this respect. Most observers are now in agreement that both in urodeles and anurans the deconcentration of the chromosomes finally reaches a point at which many or all of them become indistinguishable.[3] A similar conclusion has been reached in a number of other cases, belonging to various groups; but it is probable that a more accurate study will demonstrate the persistence of the chromosomes in some of these. In cases of this type the germinal vesicle shows only a fine, oxyphilic meshwork and one or more nucleoli in which the entire basophilic content of the nucleus is contained (Fig. 163, F). In the final stages the chromosomes reappear as localized areas in this meshwork, at first

---

[1] See Jörgenssen ('13) with references to the earlier literature. See also Lubosch ('13) whose results were somewhat different.

[2] See the critical reviews in the works of Loyez ('06), Lubosch ('13), Jörgenssen, ('13), and Stieve ('20).

[3] See, for instance, on Anura, Oscar Schultze ('87), Carnoy and Lebrun ('99), King ('08); and on Urodela, Born ('94), Carnoy and Lebrun ('98, '99), Schmidt ('05), Jörgenssen ('13) and Stieve ('20).

loose in texture, vague and irregular in outline, and oxyphilic or but slightly basophilic, as in class 2.

These facts at one time led a considerable number of observers to conclude that when the chromosomes disappear from view they go out of existence, to be re-formed from the nucleoli or otherwise at a later period; but there is very strong ground to doubt this. It is important to note that they

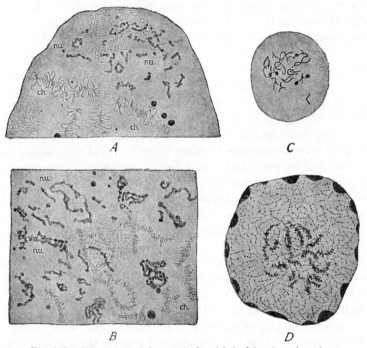

Fig. 162.—Later stages of the germinal vesicle in fishes (MARÉCHAL).

A–C, Scyllium; D, the teleost *Trigla.*

A, B, maximum stage of deconcentration of the lamp-brush chromosomes, spireme-like transformation of the nucleoli; C, the chromosomes near the end of the growth period, at the same enlargement; D, rather late growth-period, centripetal movement of the chromosomes.

do not disappear by breaking up into a structureless "magma" or mass of fine granules, as some observers have concluded; there is reason to believe that this account rests on faulty technique. As was early described by Rückert, in the elasmobranchs, the production of "lamp-brush" chromosomes takes place by the formation of lateral thread-like branches, radiating from a central axis which itself finally seems to disappear, leaving a thread-like framework in which the individual chromosomes *seem* to have been lost. Soon afterwards, however, they reappear by a condensation and convergence of the threads along an axial region, showing the same type of structure as before, and likewise grouped in twisted pairs. All this plainly indicates that *the chromosomes have not lost their identity during the period when they are temporarily lost to sight and hence are not subsequently formed de novo.* The view that they are re-formed from the nucleoli, is now completely exploded (p. 354).

(4) In a fourth group may be placed those rather exceptional cases in which all the chromosomes are condensed into a karyosphere from which they escape in the prophases of the polar mitoses (p. 93). This condition, too, has been assumed by some writers to involve a total destruction of the original chromosomes and their formation *de novo* from the karyosphere [1] and thus to offer a fatal difficulty for the hypothesis of the individuality of genetic continuity of the chromosomes; but here again the facts now point to a different conclusion. Karyosphere-formation, as earlier indicated (Fig. 109), is foreshadowed in many forms by a tendency to aggregate towards the center of the germinal vesicle, and both Vejdovský (in the case of *Diastrammena* and *Gordius*) and Jörgenssen (in *Nephelis*) have followed the process of their aggregation to form the karyosphere. Vejdovský shows also that the chromosomes, though much condensed and closely aggregated in the karyosphere, do not actually disappear; and the same observation has been made by Browne ('13) in the karyosphere of the spermatocytes of *Notonecta*. The formation of a karyosphere therefore offers no contradiction to the general theory of the genetic continuity of the chromosomes, even though its physiological meaning remains obscure.

b. The Nucleoli. The transformations of the chromosomes described above are accompanied by more or less parallel changes in the nucleoli, of which the most striking is the intensely basophilic character commonly assumed by the nucleoli during the greater part of the growth-period and retained by them even in cases where the chromosomes and general nuclear framework have become completely oxyphilic. This is in general true whether one or many nucleoli be present. In the latter case the multiplication of the nucleoli seems to be effected either by a progressive fragmentation of the original principal nucleolus or by new formation (as appears to be the case in fishes, reptiles and birds). These intensely basophilic nucleoli are sometimes so closely crowded as almost to conceal the oxyphilic network in which they lie (*Scolopendra*, Fig. 111). More commonly they migrate towards the periphery, sometimes lying against the nuclear membrane outside the chromosomes, which at this time have usually become diffuse, irregular, or have assumed the "lamp-brush" condition, may even have disappeared from view, or have more or less completely

[1] See for example Lubosch ('13), p. 296.

lost the basophilic character. This condition is characteristic of the ova of most fishes, amphibians, birds and reptiles and occurs also in the yolk-laden eggs of some invertebrates, though in some cases the nucleoli may be scattered irregularly through the germinal vesicle.

A remarkable feature of these nucleoli is that in many cases during or subsequent to their period of multiplication, they become drawn out into more or less convoluted thread-like bodies (Figs. 162, 163) which, because of their basophilic staining-reactions may closely simulate spireme-threads or chromosomes. For such (in case of the oöcytes of amphibians, elasmobranchs, and other fishes), they were actually mistaken by Carnoy and Lebrun ('97–'99), whose conclusions were supposed to constitute a strong argument against the individuality of the chromosomes. All this, however, was rendered untenable by later observations, in particular those of Maréchal, Loyez and Jörgenssen, which revealed the persistence of the chromosomes as such during the very stages in which the nucleoli are unraveling, and demonstrated the complete morphological independence of the nucleoli.[1]

The meaning of these curious modifications is almost wholly unknown; but it now seems probable that the nucleoli are not merely accumulations of waste products but contain materials that play some definite part in the metabolism of the growing egg. The deconcentration and partial or complete loss of basophily by the chromosomes during the growth-period may probably be regarded as an exaggeration of the process seen in the nuclei of tissue-cells during their vegetative state, and as connected in some way with the constructive processes in the cytosome. The facts suggest that this involves a splitting off of the nucleic acid component of the basichromatin and its storage wholly or in part in the nucleoli. This conjecture is, however, somewhat hazardous because of the physical effects due to changes of density and the like in both nucleoli and chromosomes; and to this cause may probably be traced many recorded inconsistencies in the results of both staining and digestion-tests as applied to these bodies (see p. 644.).[2]

In the latter part of the growth-period the nucleoli commonly again assume a condensed and spheroidal form and fragment into smaller bodies. As above stated, a considerable group of observers have maintained that many of the nuclear fragments are extruded as such through the wall of the germinal vesicle into the oöplasm, and some believe that such fragments may contribute directly to the formation of the yolk. There is, however, no general agreement on this point. It is certain that in some cases the nucleolus persists until after the germinal vesicle breaks down

---

[1] See Maréchal ('05,–'07), Loyez ('06), Jörgenssen ('13), Stieve ('20), etc.
[2] See the above cited works; also Floderus ('96), Popoff ('07), Stauffacher ('11).

and the polar spindle forms, when it is cast off in the cytoplasm as a "metanucleolus" which finally disappears.[1] Nevertheless the extrusion of nucleolar fragments in earlier stages of the oöcyte has been described so

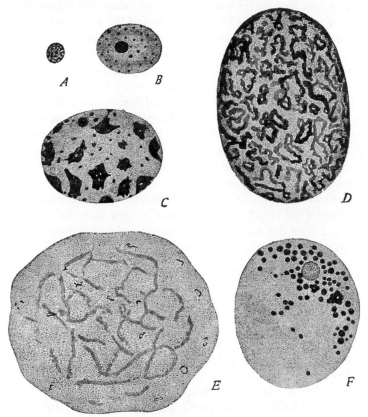

Fig. 163.—The germinal vesicle during the growth-period (JÖRGENSSEN).

(*A–E*, the teleost *Melamphaës*, *F*, the orthopter, *Gryllotalpa.*)

A, early stage, single basichromatic nucleolus; *B*, appearance of small marginal nucleoli; *C*, growth and transformation of the nucleoli; *D*, nucleoli converted into spireme-like threads; *E* (from a different species), much later stage, with deeply staining nucleoli, much reduced, and pale "lamp-brush" chromosomes; *F*, middle growth-period of the mole-cricket, after disappearance of the chromosomes, one oxychromatic nucleolus and many basichromatic.

circumstantially and by so many observers that the question must at least be held open (p. 345).

c. The Residual Substance. During the final stages of the germinal vesicle the chromosomes rapidly condense and decrease in size, until in the

---

[1] Long since observed by Haecker ('92) in the eggs of medusæ and in other cases by later observers.

final stages they constitute only a small fraction, sometimes a very minute fraction, of the total nuclear substance. At this time their grouping varies widely; in some cases they are scattered irregularly through the germinal vesicle; in others lie near the periphery; in still others are massed in a more or less compact group (Fig. 110). As the wall of the germinal vesicle breaks down and the chromosomes pass upon the spindle there is therefore left behind a large amount of "residual substance," comprising the remains of the nuclear framework and of the nucleoli, that mingles with the general cytoplasm of the egg (Fig. 199).[1] Both absolutely and relatively the amount of this substance varies widely in different cases, these variations corresponding, in some measure at least, to the varying degrees in which the chromatin of the germinal vesicle returns towards the net-like condition characteristic of the "resting" or vegetative state. Lillie ('06) has shown that in *Chætopterus* this material contains very numerous oxyphilic microsomes which, after their extrusion into the cytoplasm, quickly become basophilic like those of the cytoplasm generally, but seem not to lose their morphological identity. As will later be seen there are many reasons for the belief that this material is not merely waste but may play an important part in the phenomena of development (pp. 405, 1096).

Origin and Differentiation of the Sperm

The relation of the various components of the sperm to the cells from which it arises is of especial interest because we may here look for a basis of interpretation of the part played by the sperm in fertilization and heredity. The pioneer observations of Kölliker, Schweigger-Seidel and La Valette St. George early established the fact that the sperm is a cell, but it required a long series of subsequent researches by many observers to make known the whole course of the spermiogenesis. To La Valette is due the general terminology now universally adopted; it is indicated in the following main outlines, which hold true for animals generally.

The primary spermatocyte first divides to form two secondary *spermatocytes* or sperm-mother-cells, and each of these again divides—often without pausing and without the reconstruction of the daughter-nuclei—to form two *spermatids*. Each of the latter is then transformed into a single sperm, its nucleus becoming very small and compact, while from its cytoplasmic components arise the acrosome, middle-piece and flagellum. The basis

---

[1] This fact, emphasized by Rückert ('92), Van der Stricht ('95, '98), Gardiner ('98), Griffin ('99), and others has been described by many later observers and gave the first basis for various theories of nuclear dualism (*trophochromatin* and *idiochromatin*, etc.) (p. 725). In the platode *Polychœrus* Gardiner calculated that the amount of residual substance thus cast out is not less than 500 times that of the basichromatin that forms the chromosomes; and Conklin ('12) reports a similar condition in ascidians, gasteropods and other forms. The importance of this material in development is elsewhere discussed (pp. 405, 1096).

of the two latter is formed by the *axial filament* which grows forth from one of the spermatid-centrioles which plays the part of a *blepharoplast*. The envelope or sheath of this filament is in part formed from the chondriosomes of the spermatid, while the acrosome is a product of the Golgi-apparatus. All these structures thus arise from corresponding formed bodies in the spermatocytes which seem not to lose their identity during the divisions.

1. Source of the Sperm-forming Materials.   The Spermatocyte-divisions

a. The Central Bodies. Early in the growth-period as above described, the idiozome-complex breaks up more or less completely and its components ultimately scatter through the cytoplasm. During this process the centrioles are often lost to view; but it seems probable that they persist throughout the growth-period, hidden among the cytoplasmic granules or perhaps in some cases within the nucleus. In any case they reappear in the prophases of the first division,[1] and show the typical behavior. Their persistence during both divisions has been demonstrated by numerous observations which leave no doubt that the central bodies of the resulting four cells (spermatids or oötids) are direct descendants of those already present in the auxocytes.

The most striking demonstration of this is afforded by certain cases in which the axial filaments of the future sperms begin to grow forth from the centrioles of the spermatocytes *before the maturation-divisions have taken place*, persisting thenceforward through every stage up to the formation of the mature sperm, a phenomenon discovered by Meves ('97) and Henneguy ('98) in the Lepidoptera (*Bombyx, Pygæra*). In *Pygæra* the two original spermatocyte-centrioles lie near the cell-periphery and are V-shaped, with an axial filament extending outwards from the extremities of both V's, *i. e.,* four in all (Fig. 165). They divide at each pole in the first anaphase by breaking in two at the apex of the V, and the two rod-shaped products, each bearing a single flagellum, pass to the poles of the second division. A single rod-shaped centriole, bearing its flagellum, is thus delivered to each spermatid where it lies close against the nuclear membrane. Similar conditions have since been described in the Coleoptera, by Schäfer ('07) and Voïnov ('03), in birds and beetles by Korff ('01) and in Lepidoptera by Gatenby ('17a), and may no doubt be expected in other forms.[2] In *Bombyx* Henneguy found the centrioles as spherical granules rather than rods; and this is confirmed by Gatenby in *Smerinthus*

---

[1] An exception is offered by the anastral polar spindles of the oöcyte-divisions in many arthropods and vertebrates (p. 508). It is an interesting fact that in the sperm-producing divisions of many plants (*i. e.,* those having flagellated or ciliated sperms) central bodies (blepharoplasts) appear even in forms which are devoid of such bodies in the ordinary somatic divisions (p. 387).

[2] V-shaped centrioles are also described by Mottier ('98) in *Dictyota*.

and some other Lepidoptera. In most of these cases it would seem that
the spermatid-centriole is at first single, though Gatenby figures it as double
soon after the second division.

 b. The Chondriosomes. The chondriosomes of the oöcyte seem for
the most part to take little or no part in the polar divisions, remaining passively in the ovum. Those of the spermatocyte, on the contrary, undergo a conspicuous process of segregation or chondriokinesis,
an account of which has earlier been given (p. 163). The general ef-

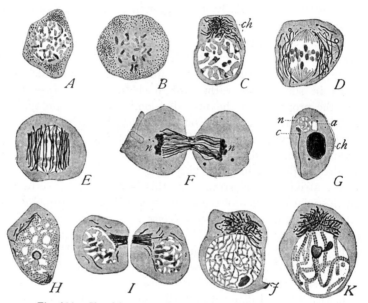

Fig. 164.—Chondriosomes and sperm-formation in insects (DUESBERG).

A–G in the beetle *Blaps;* *H–K* in the cockroach *Blatta.*

a, acrosome (acroblast); *c,* centriole; *ch,* chondriosomes; *n,* nucleus.

A, B, spermatogonia with granular mitochondria; *C,* early spermatocyte; *D,* first spermatocyte-
metaphase; *E,* anaphase of same; *F,* teleophase; *G,* early spermatid, chondriosomes massed to form
nebenkern or chondriosphere; *H, I,* spermatogonia; *J,* early growth-period; *K,* diplotene.

fect of this process is to distribute the spermatocyte-chondriosomes
with almost exact equality to the four spermatids. It is interesting to
compare the many variants of the process. In all cases the chondriosomes
of the early spermatocytes are small, numerous, and commonly aggregated
more or less definitely about the central bodies and idiozome (p. 329). In
later stages they most commonly spread through the cytosome in the form
of scattered mitochondria, spheres, rods or threads. In this condition they
often remain during the divisions, being segregated, apparently passively,
into four equal groups by the two divisions. In other cases they

enlarge, or in some cases become closely aggregated, perhaps even fuse, to form larger bodies.

In the middle and late growth-period the larger chondriosomes are of two principal types, being either more or less elongated threads or rounded chondriospheres. The former condition is seen in Orthoptera

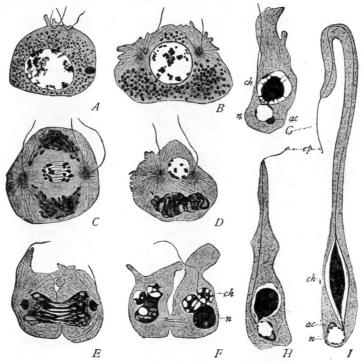

Fig. 165.—Spermatogenesis in the butterfly *Pygæra* (MEVES).

ac, acroblast; *c*, centriole; *ch*, chondriosomes, chondriosome-body, nebenkern; *ep*, end-piece; *n*, nucleus.

A, B, primary spermatocytes, V-shaped centrioles, axial filaments; *C*, first-division; *D*, inter-kinesis; *E, F*, telophases of second division; *G, H, I*, spermatids.

(Fig. 164), Coleoptera (Fig. 167), Hemiptera (Fig. 68), Hymenoptera and some gasteropods (*Paludina*), the latter in Lepidoptera and some of the scorpions. In the Lepidoptera, as shown by Meves ('oo) and Gatenby, the chondriosomes enlarge to form numerous spheroidal chondriospheres which appear like vesicles owing to the differentiation of a lightly-staining or chromophobic central or medullary region. Enlarging still more, perhaps in part by fusion, these crowd about the first spermatocyte spindle and often form a kind of mantle that completely surrounds the latter. This draws out (Fig. 165) and divides into two in both divisions, the individual chondriospheres apparently undergoing further fusion and often being drawn out almost into a thread-like form (Gatenby). Appearances indicate that these are to some extent cut across by the division, but considerable uncertainty exists on this point. The products fuse, or become closely aggregated in each spermatid to form a single condensed but more or less vacuolated body, the nebenkern or chondriosome-body. The chondriospheres of the scorpions have earlier been described, as have also those of the more frequent chondriocont type (p. 164).

The significant fact in all the foregoing cases is a distribution of the chondriosome-content by the spermatocyte-divisions with approximate equality

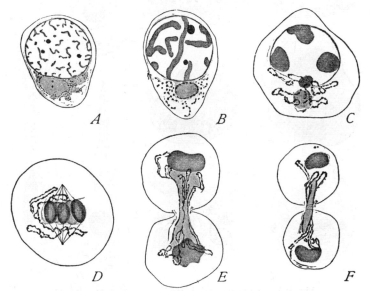

Fig. 166.—Spermatocytes of the snail *Paludina* (MEVES).

A, early growth-period, idiozome, central bodies and scattered mitochondria; *B*, *C*, later stages, formation of chondriomites and rings; *D*, first spermatocyte-metaphase; *E*, telophase; *F*, second telophase (*cf*. Fig. 167).

among the four resulting spermatids and its application to the formation of the tail-envelopes. The accuracy of this distribution varies considerably in different cases. In *Centrurus* (Figs. 169, 170), it takes place with a precision comparable with that seen in the distribution of the chromosomes; in other scorpions it is demonstrably less exact, and we may perhaps infer that a similar lack of precision exists in many other cases. In this fact we find good reason to doubt whether the chondriosomes, even though they be regarded as agents in heredity, can play as definite a part as the chromosomes or one that can be directly concerned in the Mendelian phenomena.

During the foregoing changes the material of the chondriosomes undergoes a differentiation into a cortical intensely chromophilic substance, and a central chromophobic one, the latter being left nearly or quite unstained by crystal violet (Benda method), hæmatoxylin and some other dyes by which the cortical layer is deeply colored. This is shown with great clearness in the chondriospheres of Lepidoptera and scorpions and has been described also for the smaller mitochondrial granules and even for the rods or chondrioconts.[1] These two substances can still be distinguished in the larger bodies, such as the chondriospheres or the nebenkern, formed by aggregation of the smaller chondriosomes. In the spermatids they undergo a complicated series of transformations, which have recently been investigated in part by Gatenby and more completely by Bowen. These transformations, as will be seen, involve the appearance in the original chromophilic substance of a third "medullary substance" that is of quite different nature from either of the original ones and plays an important part in the formation of the tail-envelopes (p. 371).

The Golgi-apparatus and Sphere-substance. The Golgi-bodies or dictyosomes undergo a process of distribution to the spermatids (dictyokinesis) somewhat similar to that of the chondriosomes. In the early auxocytes, as before stated, the Golgi-bodies are often more or less closely aggregated about the clear central sphere of the idiozome within which, in certain cases, are contained the pro-acrosomic granules (p. 329).[2] Sooner or later in the growth-period the idiozome breaks up and the Golgi-bodies scatter through the cytosome. The details seem to vary rather widely. In some cases (mammals) the disaggregation of the Golgi-bodies seems not to take place until after the first spindle has been formed, the idiozome-complex having meanwhile divided into two. In others (insects) it occurs much earlier, the Golgi-bodies fragmenting into much smaller elements before the division. In either case a temporary reaggregation may occur during the interkinesis, followed by a second dispersal before the second division; but this is not invariable (insects). In certain of the Hemiptera, as described by Bowen ('20) the Golgi-bodies enlarge, and apparently become reduced in number after their dispersal in the spermatocytes (Fig. 69).

There is considerable reason to suspect that during the disaggregation each Golgi-body or dictyosome may carry with it a small mass of sphere-substance; and this is almost certainly the case in the developing oöcytes of mollusks (Fig. 347); but this point is uncertain.[3] In any case it seems

---

[1] See Meves ('00, '07), Wilson ('16), Gatenby ('17, '18), Bowen ('21, '22c.).

[2] By Moore ('94) these bodies were called "archosomes," by Kuschekewitsch ('13) "sphærosomes," by Stockard and Papanicolaou "idiogranulomes." They are in some way connected with, perhaps products of, the Golgi-bodies.

[3] See especially Gatenby and Woodger ('21), and Bowen ('22).

probable that the proacrosomic granules of the idiozome (when such are present) *do not lose their identity but are scattered through the cytosome and passed on intact during the divisions into the spermatids.*[1]

Each spermatid thus receives a group of Golgi-bodies, more or less scattered, or in some cases temporarily grouped about the nebenkern (*Brochy-*

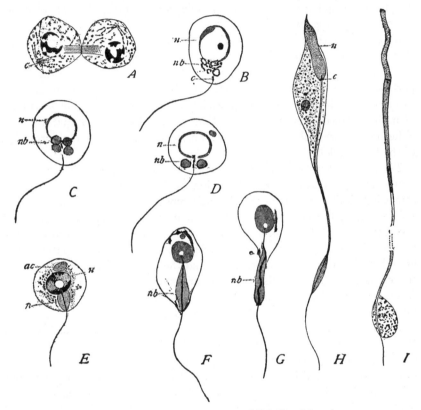

Fig. 167.—Sperm-formation in the snail *Paludina* (MEVES).

c, centrioles; *n*, nucleus; *nb*, nebenkern.

A, telophase of last division; *B*, early spermatid, with centrioles (*c*) and nebenkern forming; *C*, the quadripartite nebenkern in oblique view, and *D* from the side; *E, F, G*, later stages, elongation of distal centriole to form a rod, surrounded by the elongating nebenkern; *F, G*, later stages, to show centriolar apparatus in neck-region; *I*, terminal part of flagellum with residual cytoplasm.

mena, Fig. 172); and also in some cases (mammals) a considerable number of proacrosomic granules. In nearly all known cases this is quickly followed by a reaggregation to form a single, much larger rounded *acroblast* (Figs.

---

[1] Niessing ('02), Stockard and Papanicolaou ('18), Gatenby and Woodger ('21).

172, 176, etc.), from which, by a complicated transformation is formed the acrosome of the mature sperm (p. 381).

2. Composition and General History of the Spermatid

The four spermatids resulting from the spermatocyte-divisions are rather large, rounded cells of the ordinary type, and with certain exceptions,[1] of equal size (Figs. 167, 172, 174, etc.). They consist of the following principal components.[2]

(1) The *cytosome*, consisting of undifferentiated cytoplasm in which are contained the following formed elements:

(2) The *nucleus*, at first relatively large, vesicular and lightly staining. This is built up from a haploid group of single chromosomes received from the second spermatocyte-division.

(3) The *central apparatus*, in the form of a pair of centrioles (or one which soon divides into two). These typically lie close to the periphery of the cell

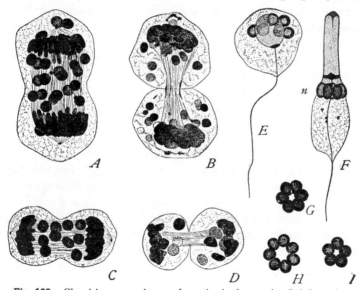

Fig. 168.—Chondriosomes and sperm-formation in the scorpion *Opisthacanthus*.

A, B, first spermatocyte-division, 24 scattered chondriospheres; *C, D,* second division, 12 chondriospheres; *E,* spermatid, sexpartite nebenkern; *F, G,* typical nebenkern; *H, I,* variations.

and are commonly surrounded by no special envelope, though a few observers have described them as inclosed in a "sphere" or "idiozome" supposed to be derived from a corresponding structure in the spermatocyte.

---

[1] In the spermatogenesis of bees, aphids, phylloxerans, and probably in rotifers and some other parthenogenetic animals (See pp. 797-799).

[2] For a detailed review of these phenomena as seen in insects, see Bowen, '22c.

The more peripheral or distal centriole plays the part of a *blepharoplast* or basal body from which grows forth the axial filament of the flagellum, while the proximal one, often also a portion of the distal, passes into the neck-region and in a few cases is pushed up into the base of the head (p. 380).

(4) The *chondrioma* or *chondriosome-apparatus*, which assumes many different forms in different animals. Among vertebrates it most commonly remains in a diffuse condition, consisting of small, scattered mitochondria or chondrioconts (Figs. 176, 175). On the other hand, in some of the invertebrates (characteristically in insects) the scattered chondriosomes sooner or later aggregate to form a single larger speroidal body, or in some cases several such (Figs. 171, 167, 172). When single (as in insects) this is called the *chondriosome-body* or *nebenkern*.[1] When two or more such bodies are formed (as in scorpions or some gasteropods) they may be called chondriosome-spheres or chondriosome-bodies, or collectively as the "nebenkern organ" (Retzius). These various forms are connected by many transitional conditions, and all have a similar origin in the small and often scattered chondriosomes of the early spermatocytes. In a single instance, the louse, the nebenkern is said to be present already in the spermatocytes (Doncaster and Cannon, '20).[2]

(5) The *acroblast*, typically a single rounded body (Figs. 176, 172, etc.), at first more or less lobulated, ultimately of rounded form. In structure it somewhat resembles the early idiozome of the spermatocytes, consisting of a clear sphere-substance, sometimes (mammals) containing the pro-acrosomic granules (p. 329), and bounded by an intensely chromophilic envelope composed of or derived from the Golgi-bodies.[3] For this reason it has been called by the same names (idiozome, idiosome, archoplasm-sphere, centrosphere, sphere, etc.). Morphologically, however, it is a new formation that has been rebuilt from the scattered remains of the original idiozome-complex, and it rarely if ever surrounds the centrioles. It seems preferable, therefore, when speaking of the spermatid, to employ the term acroblast [4] in place of "idiozome."

[1] The English equivalent of "nebenkern" should be *paranucleus*, but this form of the term has not come into general use.

[2] Platner ('89) described the nebenkern (in Lepidoptera) under the name "large mitosome," believing it to be derived from the spindle-fibers. Gatenby has recently revived the term in the form *macromitosome*. This seems inadmissible, both as a matter of priority and in reference to the structure of the nebenkern (p. 372).

[3] After fixation with reagents containing acetic acid this envelope may be wholly dissolved, so that only a pale sphere remains, as described by most observers until rather recently. With proper treatment the envelope may appear in the form of separate rodlets, of a net-like structure, or even of a continuous membrane.

[4] This word, due to King ('07) has been brought into more general use by Gatenby ('17) and Bowen ('20, '22a, '22b, etc.)·

In rare cases (certain Lepidoptera and Orthoptera) the Golgi-bodies fail to aggregate completely, so that several or many acroblasts are formed. Even in this case, however, the end-result is a single acrosome, which seems to be of the same general nature as in the first case. These cases lend support to the conclusion that in the single or massive type of acroblast the sphere substance is formed by the progressive fusion of the clear spheres of idiozome-substance by which each Golgi-body is accompanied. The difference between the two types is thus owing merely to the fact that in the one the coalescence of the clear sphere-substance is accompanied by a close

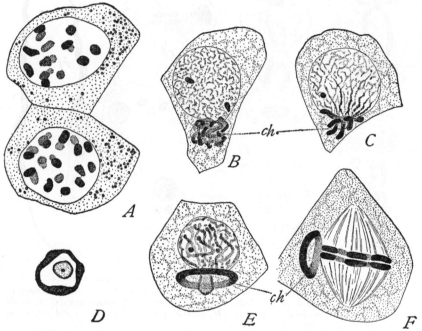

Fig. 169.—Chondriosomes in spermatocytes of the scorpion *Centrurus.*

A, spermatogonia with scattered mitochondria; *B*, *C*, early spermatocytes, with larger chondriosomes aggregated at nuclear pole (*ch*); *D*, *E*, chondriosomes fused to form a ring surrounding the idiozome; *F*, metaphase of first spermatocyte.

aggregation of the chromophilic Golgi-bodies or batonettes, while in the other these bodies always remain scattered (Bowen, *op. cit.*).

(6) The *chromatoid body*, a rather small, deeply-staining and highly refractive corpuscle (sometimes several such) of unknown significance. This structure (Fig. 178) is known in many cases to enter only certain of the spermatids and hence is probably a by-product which plays no direct part in the formation of the sperm (p. 382).

(7) The foregoing components are of widespread if not universal occurrence in the spermatids of animals. In addition to them other formed elements of more or less doubtful nature may be present. One of these is the *spindle-remnant*, sometimes called the "mitosome," a fibrillar or finely granular body, commonly lying near the periphery and derived from the spindle-fibers of the preceding mitosis. This body was believed by some earlier observers to play an important part in the sperm-formation, and was

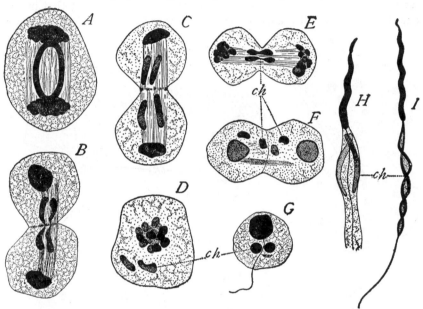

Fig. 170.—Chondriokinesis and sperm-formation in the scorpion *Centrurus*.

A–C, successive stages of first spermatocyte-division, division of the chondriosome ring; *D*, interkinesis; *E, F*, second division, completing division of original ring into eight parts; *G*, spermatid with double chondriosome-body (nebenkern); *H, I*, later spermatids, elongation and twisting of chondriosomes to form spiral tail-envelope.

confused with the nebenkern or with the acroblast; but later studies seem to show that it disappears without taking any definite part in the sperm-formation. Other obscure formations include deeply-staining granules of various kinds (not to be confused with mitochondria) and variously described as "seminal granules," "fat-droplets," "von Ebner's granules," or as products of the fragmentation of the chromatoid bodies. Little is known of their nature, and they are not known to play any definite part in the sperm-formation.

The later history of the spermatid may briefly be summarized as follows: The typical flagellate sperm assumes a filiform shape by an extensive elongation in an axis marked by the nucleus and the centrioles, the latter always lying at or near the posterior pole of the nucleus on the side of the cytosome from which the tail afterwards grows out. The tail-formation is initiated by outgrowth of the axial filament from the distal or outer centriole (blepharoplast), at this time close to the periphery, the filament projecting freely outside the cytosome to form a naked flagellum (Figs. 176, 171, 167, 174, etc.). Meanwhile, both centrioles move inward towards the posterior pole of the nucleus, in some cases carried inwards by a deep in-folding of the cell-periphery (urodeles), in others apparently by a movement of the centrioles themselves, thus lengthening the intra-cellular portion of the axial filament; and this is followed by a progressive drawing out of the whole posterior region of the spermatid to form the flagellum. The axial filament, which elongates *pari passu* with the surrounding cytoplasm, is thus provided with a cytoplasmic envelope, while its naked terminal or extra-cellular part forms the end-piece (Figs. 167, 175, etc.). During this process the chondriosome-formations are most commonly drawn out into the cytoplasmic envelope, of which ultimately they form a considerable and sometimes the principal part (p. 370), and often assuming a spiral structure (Fig. 175). The nucleus also often elongates, thus giving to the sperm-head the lance-shaped, cylindrical, rod-shaped or even filiform shapes found in many groups of animals.

Meanwhile the acrosome takes up its position typically at or near the anterior tip of the sperm-head, while the centrioles undergo various transformations and migrations which differ widely in different groups of animals. A remarkable feature of the spermiogenesis is the fact that only a portion of the spermatid is used in the formation of the sperm, a considerable mass of *residual protoplasm* being sloughed off late in the spermiogenesis and degenerating without taking any further part in the sperm-formation (Figs. 167, 175, 177). In this mass are included both the unused general cytoplasm, and certain remnants of the formed elements, including the chromatoid bodies, a remnant of the Golgi-apparatus or its products, and various other granules of uncertain nature.[1] A delicate investing peripheral layer of cytoplasm, by some observers regarded as the cell-wall, still surrounds the other structures. This certainly persists in the head-region and probably in all other parts of the sperm; and in or just below it are formed the peripheral spiral fibrillæ and other structures found in the head-region of many sperms (p. 283).

The casting off of the residual protoplasm takes place throughout a large series of both animals and plants and appears to be of general occurrence.

[1] It has been found in some insects that the remains of the residual protoplasm are ingested by the cells that form the walls of the cysts (Bowen, '22c).

In this respect the sperm-formation differs conspicuously from that of the egg which, with rare and doubtful exceptions retains the whole substance of the mother-cell. The sperm is nevertheless as truly a cell as the egg, the residual protoplasm doubtless representing only a portion of the cell-substance that has played its part in the nutrition and growth of the sperm and is then eliminated as needless ballast.

3. Further History of the Sperm-formation. Spermioteleosis.

A brief further account of the phenomena summarized in the preceding section is important for an understanding of the mature sperm.

a. The Telokinetic Movements. The second spermatocyte-division is followed by a series of telokinetic movements by which the polarized group-

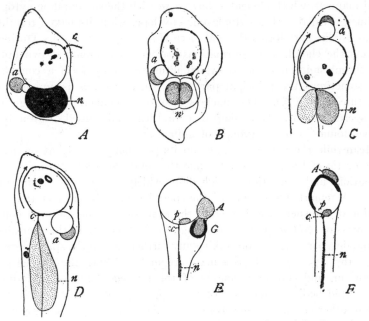

Fig. 171.—Movements of the spermatid-components in Hemiptera (after Bowen).

E, from *Euschistus* the others from *Murgantia; a*, acroblast; *A*, acrosome; *c*, centrioles; *G*, Golgi-remnant; *n*, nebenkern; *p*, pseudoblepharoplast.

A, early stage, soon after formation of acroblast and nebenkern; *B*, backward migration of the centrioles, division of the nebenkern; *C*, forward migration of acroblast; *D*, completion of migration of acroblast; *E*, backward flow of cytoplasm, separation of acrosome, from Golgi-remnant; final forward migration of acrosome, Golgi-remnant has passed out into the tail; *F*, acrosome in final position.

ing of the spermatid-components is early effected.[1] These include (1) a

---

[1] See Meves, '97, '99 (vertebrates); Henking, '91, Meves, '00, Montgomery, '11, and especially Bowen, '22a (insects).

rotation of the daughter-chromosome-plates towards (usually) one side of the spindle so as to lie nearly parallel to the latter; (2) a movement of the centrioles (which may temporarily disappear from view) finally to the posterior or distal pole of the spermatid-nucleus; (3) a corresponding movement of the nebenkern (when present) to the same pole; (4), a movement of the acroblast towards the anterior pole of the nucleus (Fig. 171). In the Hemiptera, as shown especially by Bowen, the acroblast undergoes a further migration, passing almost completely around the nucleus on the side opposite to its original position so as to lie near the nebenkern and centrioles. Upon separation of the acrosome from the Golgi-remnant the former again passes to the apical pole, the latter backwards into the tail-region where it degenerates (Figs. 174, 172).

b. The Nucleus. With two exceptions the transformation of the spermatid nucleus, so far as known, offers comparatively little of interest as compared with the other structures. One of these, which seems to be widely distributed, includes the differentiation of the nuclear substance into two substances prior to its final condensation to form the dense and intensely basophilic sperm-nucleus, the other an elimination of nuclear substance into the surrounding cytoplasm that takes place at a certain period.[1] Both these processes have been most carefully examined in the sperms of insects, but nothing is yet known concerning their physiological meaning. In many animals the breaking up of the telophase-chromosomes is followed by a progressive accumulation of the basichromatin to form a rather thin peripheral layer, while the central region is occupied by a nearly homogeneous and lightly staining substance (oxychromatin, Figs. 167, 172). A little later, before the nucleus elongates, the peripheral layer thins away and apparently dissolves on the side towards the flagellum; and this is followed by the extrusion into the cytoplasm of a drop-like mass of oxyphilic medullary substance (Montgomery, '11, Bowen, '22a). The nucleus then closes, elongates and undergoes a resegregation of its substance, the peripheral basophilic layer becomes thickened, vacuolated, and finally collapses towards the center of the nucleus where it ultimately forms a deeply staining axial core surrounded by a clear oxyphilic substance.[2] The relative positions of the basophilic and oxyphilic substances have thus been completely reversed. Ultimately the cortical layer disappears from view and the head appears as a solid mass (in this case a rod) of basichromatin.

c. The Chondriosome-apparatus. Wide differences are shown by the spermatids of different species in respect to the conditions of the chondriosomes in the earlier spermatids and their later behavior.

---

[1] See for instance Meves, '03 (*Paludina*), Montgomery, '11 (*Euschistus*), Duesberg ('18) fishes.
[2] See Bowen ('20).

In the simplest case (vertebrates generally, and in some invertebrates), the scattered mitochondria gradually concentrate around the axial filament in the elongating flagellum and finally aggregate to form one or more long threads which in many cases become spirally coiled around the axial filament (Figs. 175, etc). This process was first clearly followed out in mammals by Benda ('97, '06) and has been confirmed by many subsequent observers. This condition represents one extreme in a series of transitional forms leading to a condition in which all the chondriosomes, before drawing out to form

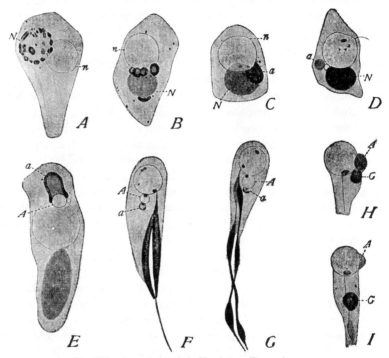

Fig. 172.—Spermiogenesis in Hemiptera (BOWEN).

a, acroblast; *A*, acrosome; *G*, Golgi-remnant = acroblast-remnant; *n*, nucleus; *N*, chondriosome-body or nebenkern.

A, *Brochymena*, aggregation of Golgi-bodies around the nebenkern to form the acroblast; *B*, *C*, fusion of the Golgi-bodies; *D*, *Euschistus*, differentiation of the acroblast; *E*, *Murgantia*, later stage, acroblast and acrosome at anterior pole; *F*, *G*, *H*, later stages of same; *H*, same, separation of the acroblast into the acrosome (*A*) and the Golgi-remnant (*G*); *I*, *Brochymena*, Golgi-remnant passing into the tail-region.

the tail-sheath, become concentrated into a single, large massive *nebenkern* or *chondriosome-body*.

A first step is seen in the pulmonates where the mitochondria, rather large and numerous and of two sizes, become concentrated in the posterior region of the cytosome and surround the axial filament, but without aggregating closely to form larger bodies.[1]

In the scorpions appear several further steps which culminate in *Centrurus*. In certain species, as previously mentioned (p. 364) the spermatids receive a rather small number of large separate chondriospheres (5–7 in *Opisthacanthus* or *Hadrurus*, 4–6 in *Vejovis*) which place themselves in a ring surrounding the axial filament and are then drawn out to form its sheath but in this case without twisting (Fig. 168, Wilson, '16).   These spermatids show a remarkable similarity to mature sperms of the first type, as seen in various nemertines, annelids, mollusks and other animals (pp. 287, 373) the ring of chondriospheres forming a "nebenkern-organ" that is here only a transient stage in the histogenesis.   In the snail *Paludina* there are four symmetrical chondriospheres which surround the axial filament, and draw out to form the tail envelopes, without twisting (Fig. 167).   A step beyond this is the scorpion *Centrurus* in which there are from the first but two chondriosome-bodies, received as such from the last division.   Later these draw out to form the tail-envelopes, but in this case twist to form a close double spiral, ultimately of such fineness as to be invisible as such (Fig. 170, Wilson , '16).

We are thus brought finally to cases in which at the close of the second spermatocyte-division the chondriosomes at once aggregate to form a single *nebenkern* or chondriosome-body, as is typical in the insects where the nebenkern was first discovered.[2]   Meves ('00) showed that it does not arise from spindle-fibers, as supposed by some earlier observers, but from numerous, crowded large mitochondria or small chondriospheres which form a dense sheath to the spindle.   At the close of the division this slips off and quickly aggregates to form an irregularly spheroidal, more or less vacuolated body, which typically divides into two symmetrical and closely applied halves, between or beside which runs the axial filament, and which ultimately draw out along the latter to form the sheath of the flagellum.[3]

In the course of the foregoing changes the chondriosomes sooner or later differentiate into a central or medullary lightly staining "chromophobic" substance, and a peripheral "chromophilic" one that is deeply stained by the usual chondriosome dyes (crystal violet, hæmatoxylin) (p. 47).

[1] See Gatenby, '17, '18. In these spermatids the Golgi-bodies closely surround a large spheroidal body which doubtless represents the acroblast (or the sphere-remnant) of other forms.   By earlier observers, as Gatenby points out, this body was called the "nebenkern"; but obviously this was a misnomer.

[2] By La Valette St. George ('67) who called it the "Nebenkörper"; the name "nebenkern" is due to Bütschli ('71). This has been called by many other names, and the term nebenkern has often been misapplied to other structures, such as the acroblast of the pulmonates (Fauré-Fremiet, '09, Weigl, '12, Gatenby, '18, '19), the secondary nuclei of the oöcytes (p. 346), the massed fibrillas of the pancreas-cell (Fig. 13), etc. The confusion in its use was first cleared up by Meves, ('00).

[3] See Benda, '98, Duesberg, '09.

When the smaller chondriosomes unite to form a single nebenkern, this body shows a multiple or mulberry-like appearance, the original chromophobic substance forming vacuole-like areas separated by partitions of chromophilic substance. Later the partitions partially break down, then offering the appearance of a framework which, as seen in sections has often been compared to the layers of a bisected onion.[1] In many cases this structure offers a spireme-like appearance, as if consisting of a convoluted thread; and as such it has been described (in Lepidoptera)[2] by Gatenby ('17a, '18); hence his proposed name *macromitosome* (p. 364). Bowen ('22b, '22d), however, has produced demonstrative evidence that in both Hemiptera and Lepidoptera the spireme-like appearance is given by optical section of a plate-work, forming the partition-walls between enlarged cavities closely pressed together. In later stages the chromophilic substance continually diminishes and finally disappears from view about the time the chondriosome-body divides into two. The chromophilic plate-work or thread-work is thus lost, while the chromophobic substance has come to occupy the main bulk of the nebenkern, now double and elongating to form the tail-envelope.

Meanwhile a third and new substance makes its appearance in the form of beaded cords running lengthwise in each half of the nebenkern.[3]

Their fate is still problematical. By some observers (Holmgren, Vejdovský) they were supposed to disappear entirely, leaving no trace of mitochondrial substance, at least in the flagellum. Bowen has, however, shown that the halves of the nebenkern (including both the cortical and the medullary substances) become drawn out into very thin threads which show at intervals conspicuous swellings or blebs (Fig. 172) which still later disappear. The same observer demonstrates very clearly that in some of the insects the axial filament is not actually surrounded by the two halves of the nebenkern but lies on one side of them in one of the bays or indentations where they meet.[4]

d. *Central Apparatus and Blepharoplast.* During the telokinetic movements of the centrioles (p. 368) or earlier the axial filament grows out from the *distal centriole* or *blepharoplast* to form the first foundation of the flagel-

[1] La Valette St. George ('86a, '87), Platner ('89), Henking ('91), Henneguy ('96), Wilke ('07), Stevens ('05), Gross ('07), Wassilieff ('07), Boring ('07), Doncaster and Cannon('20), Shaffer ('17), Bowen ('23), etc.

[2] See also the earlier figures of Giglio-Tos and Granata ('08), Baumgartner ('02).

[3] These structures were seen by several of the earlier observers, such as Paulmier ('99), Holmgren ('02), Boring ('07), Vejdovský ('12), but by most of them were erroneously considered as a product of the chromophilic substance. Their genesis was first fully worked out by Bowen ('22b) in the Hemiptera.

[4] In the case of *Peripatus* Montgomery ('12) held that the entire chondriosome-content of the spermatid is cast out with the residual protoplasm, making no direct contribution to the sperm-formation. This case, thus far unique, should be reëxamined.

lum. That the blepharoplast is identical with a centriole has been questioned in case of the plant-sperm (p. 388); and even in animals the blepharoplast has actually been traced to the spindle-pole of the preceding mitosis
only in a few cases, for in many forms there is a brief period in the telophase when it is usually lost sight of. The identity of the blepharoplast with
a centriole is, however, placed beyond doubt by the fact earlier described
(p. 357) that in some cases the axial filament is present already in the spermatocytes and may be traced through both divisions in direct connection
with the centrioles at the spindle-poles. The later history of the centriole
shows a diversity so great that only a single feature can be regarded as of
constant occurrence, namely, *that the anterior or proximal one, or its products,
passes into the neck region of the sperm.* Beyond this point any attempt to
give a summary treatment of the phenomena must at present be hampered
by the deficiencies of our knowledge on the comparative side of the subject,
nevertheless it seems necessary to offer some sort of provisional grouping of
the facts.   For this purpose we may distinguish at least five principal types
(Fig. 173), here designated by numbers in order to avoid terms that involve
doubtful questions of fact.

(1) In a first group may be placed those interesting forms of sperms,
perhaps representing the most primitive type, in which the mitochondrial
formations do not draw out to form an elongated sheath of the axial filament
but remain near the base of the head to form a very short "middle-piece" or
"nebenkern-organ" (p. 285). Though these sperms are insufficiently known,
the evidence indicates that both centrioles may here remain near the base of
the nucleus, *i. e.,* in the neck-region of the sperm, as in Fig. 173. The
recent observations of Ballowitz ('15, '17) on teleost fishes seem clearly to
show that such is the case in the trout *Salmo* (Fig. 121), and indicate that
the same may be true also in several other fishes. In invertebrate sperms
of this type the facts are less definitely known but point to the same conclusion. Boveri ('95, '01) describes two centrioles in the middle-piece of
Echinus both before and after entrance of the sperm into the egg, and Yatsu
('09) likewise shows with great clearness a basal body (possibly double) in
the middle-piece. (Fig. 207.)

(2) In a second group, may be placed such sperms as those of certain
insects, and probably also those of some anuran Amphibia. Here, too,
with an important exception presently to be noted, both centrioles remain
near the base of the nucleus, in the region of the neck, but the mitochondrial
formations (chondriospheres or mitochondria) are drawn out to form a more
or less elongated tail-sheath. These forms commonly do not show externally any distinct middle-piece, though a definite neck-region containing derivatives of the centrioles may be revealed by staining (Figs. 173, 165, 122).

Most of the earlier observers of the insect sperm believed the entire centriolar apparatus to remain permanently in the neck-region, either as a single body [1] or dividing into two or more bodies that remain in the neck-region; [2] and this has been confirmed by some of the most recent work. In

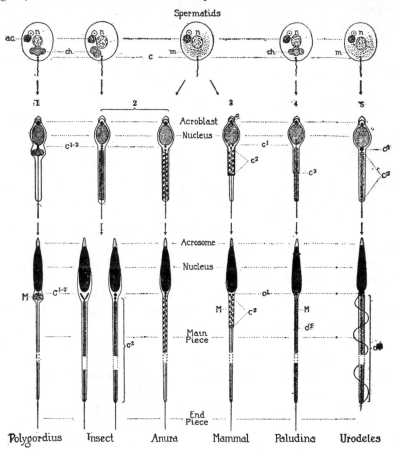

Fig. 173.—Diagram of various types of sperm-formation; c^1, the proximal centriole or its products, c^2, the distal.

Pygæra, as described by Meves ('00), in the Lepidoptera, the centriole seems clearly to be single as it enters the spermatid (Fig. 165) and Meves found no evidence of its division in the spermatid, though it elongates to form a short rod anterior to the chondriosphere, as is clearly seen in the apyrene

[1] E. g., Paulmier ('99) in *Anasa*, Pantel and Sinéty ('06) in *Notonecta*, Montgomery ('11) in *Euschistus*, Meves ('00) in *Pygæra*.

[2] E. g., in *Caloptenus* (Henneguy, '04), *Forficula* (Zweiger, '07), (Davis, '08), *Hydrometra* (Wilke, '07).

sperm (Fig. 131). In the grasshopper *Chorthippus* Lewis and Robertson ('16) in living cultures *in vitro* observed a pair of centrioles which were seen to pass into the neck-region and there to give rise, without separating, to the neck or "middle-piece," while the chondriosphere elongated. More recently a very careful study of the facts in Hemiptera (*Murgantia, Arvelius,* etc.) has been made by Bowen ('20, '22a), who clearly demonstrates that both centrioles, after outgrowth of the axial filament, assume the form of

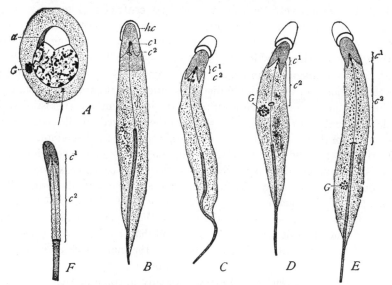

Fig. 174.—Sperm-formation in *Phalangista* (KORFF).

a, acrosome; c^1, c^2, proximal and distal centrioles; G, Golgi-remnant; h, c, head-cap.

A, early spermatid; B, later stage; C, division of proximal centriole; D, backward migration of ring; E, ring at final position, posterior limit of middle-piece; F. later stage after casting off of head-cap and residual protoplasm.

rods which lie side by side in the neck-region (at certain stages in *Murgantia*, approximating somewhat posteriorly so as to give a V-shaped figure), only one of them being connected with the axial filament (Fig. 173). These sperms accordingly are asymmetrical in respect to these structures.[1]

A curious feature in the history of the centrioles in some insects (Hemiptera, Orthoptera) is a temporary concentration of the chromatin on the inside of the nuclear membrane close to the centrioles (Figs. 171, 172) so as to give the appearance of a much larger single body or "pseudo-blepharoplast."[2] At a later period, however, according to Bowen, the chromatin-component

[1] In *Pediculus*, as described by Doncaster and Cannon ('20) both centrioles likewise persist in the neck-region, and each is said to give rise to an axial filament which traverses the tail-region.

[2] Bowen. '22a.

of this body disintegrates, when the rod-shaped centrioles again come into view and in this form pass into the mature sperm.

In the *Anura* the most satisfactory observations are those of Broman on *Bombinator* ('oo), *Pelobates* ('o1) and especially on *Rana* ('oo, 'o7). In all these, even in the highly modified sperms of *Bombinator*, the mature sperm shows two very distinct basal bodies in the neck-region close to the nucleus; and both in *Bombinator* and *Rana* (*fusca*) Broman shows that these are derivatives, respectively, of the two original centrioles (Figs. 122, 124). Meanwhile the mitochondrial granules are drawn out to form a sheath which assumes a spiral structure, and from this is formed a rather long and fairly distinct "middle-piece," which, in *Rana*, tapers gradually into the flagellum. In *R. esculenta, mugiens* and *arvalis* the two granules are likewise found in the neck-region, but the "middle-piece" is much shorter and more rounded. If this account is correct the anuran sperm is evidently rather similar in mode of formation to that of the insect and the so-called middle-piece seems to be no more than a thickening of the basal region of the flagellum.

(3) In this type and the following ones the history of the centriolar apparatus is complicated by a movement of the distal centriole, or one of its products distally for a certain distance along the axial filament. The point at which it remains marks the posterior limit of the true "middle-piece" or "connecting-piece" as defined by Waldeyer (e. g., in mammals, birds or reptiles); but it must be borne in mind that in a few forms (urodeles) this point lies nearly at the junction between the main-piece and the end-piece, so that Waldeyer's terms lose their meaning (p. 378).

This backward movement is initiated already in some of the Anura and insects. In *Hyla*, for instance, Retzius found that the two centrioles separate somewhat, so as to mark off a short middle-piece; and a somewhat similar process seems to take place also in the myriapod *Lithobius* according to Tönniges (Korschelt-Heider, 'o2). In some of the insects the movement is more extensive, a derivative of the distal centriole passing out nearly to the tip of the tail. The earlier observers believed this migration to be performed by the whole distal centriole (which is here somewhat smaller than the proximal) [1] but such a peripheral movement of the whole distal centriole is to say the least anomalous. In point of fact observations on the sperm-formation in the orthopter *Œcanthus* made in my laboratory place the facts in a different light. Preparations by C. R. Driver and H. H. Johnson (Johnson, '22) clearly show that the distal centriole divides into two parts, *one of which remains in the neck-region with the proximal centriole, while the distal*

[1] See Prowazek ('o1 on the beetle *Orycytes*) whose results seemed to be confirmed by those of Holmgren ('o2) on *Silpha*, Buchner on *Pyrrhocoris* and *Syromastes* ('o6), and *Œdipoda* ('15), and by those of Otte ('o7) on *Locusta*. Something similar is indicated by the observations of Vejdovský ('11) on *Locusta* and of Gatenby ('17) on Lepidoptera.

part alone performs the outward migration (Fig. 173). This case thus becomes quite comparable with those of the mammal, bird or urodele, and for the first time we are able to connect the latter types of sperms with the simpler insect-type of Class 2.

(4) A fourth type is exemplified by the mammals, and is probably characteristic also of birds, reptiles and perhaps of other groups. The sperm-

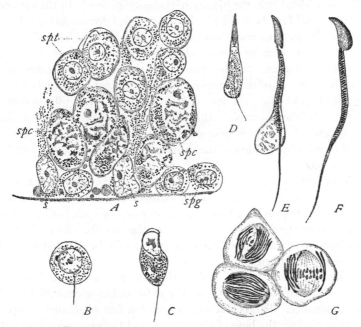

Fig. 175.—Mitochondria in sperm-formation (BENDA).

A, wall of testis-tubule in the mouse; *s*, Sertoli-cells; *spc.*, spermatocytes; *spg.*, spermatogonia; *spt*, spermatids, all with scattered mitochondria; *B–F*, stages of spermiogenesis, drawing out of mitochondria to form the spiral sheath; *G*, spermatocyte-divisions in the beetle *Blaps*, chondriosomes.

formation of mammals has been examined by many observers [1] but only a limited number of cases have been thoroughly studied. These (man, rat, guinea-pig and a few others) show a fair degree of uniformity on the main points. Apparently in all cases the distal centriole, after giving off the axial filament, assumes a disc-like shape and then separates into a small central body, to which the axial filament is attached, and a peripheral ring (Figs. 174, 177). The former constitutes a basal body (with which the axial filament maintains its attachment) while the ring, surrounding the axial filament,

[1] Especially (to mention only a few) Niessing ('96), Lenhossék ('98), Meves ('98, '99), Benda ('97, '06, etc.), Korff ('02), Duesberg ('08, '20), Jordan ('11), Oliver ('13), Stockard and Papanicolaou ('18). Gatenby and Woodger ('21), etc.

migrates backward to a position *at the junction between the middle-piece and the flagellum.* The basal body meanwhile moves forwards or remains near the proximal centriole at the base of the nucleus and there forms a part of the centriolar apparatus of the neck. The middle-piece thus becomes definitely marked off, extending from the original basal body, which remains in the neck-region, to the ring. In respect to the details the sperms of different species differ considerably in the history of these structures.[1] In the rat according to Meves and Duesberg the proximal centriole becomes flattened against the base of the nucleus and there remains, while the basal body or end-knob divides to form two centriole-like bodies. In man Meves finds the facts to be similar. In the guinea-pig they are complicated by the fact that both the proximal centriole and the original basal body break up into smaller basal bodies, the former into three, the latter into two or more (Fig. 177). In the marsupials the facts appear to be somewhat simpler (Fig. 174), there being three granules in the neck-region[2] of which two are supposed to arise by division of the proximal centriole, while the third is the distal basal body.

In spite of certain contradictions in the literature the broad fact now seems well established that in all cases the proximal centriole remains at or near the base of the nucleus as a basal body, or group of such bodies, while the principal part of the distal one passes as a ring to the distal limit of the middle-piece. Such a type of sperm might readily be derived from either of the first two described above.

Attention may here be directed to the *caudal sheath* ("Schwanzmanchette"), a structure characteristic of the mammalian spermatid but of unknown significance. This is a delicate tubular or funnel-shaped cytoplasmic structure encircling the base of the nucleus and the centrioles and extending a short distance backward in the rather early spermatid (Fig. 176, E).[3] This structure, originally formed from cytoplasmic fibrillæ (Meves), seems to disappear completely without contributing directly to the formed components of the sperm, though it has been supposed to form the peripheral part of the middle-piece (Oliver, '13).

(5) In a fifth group we may place the sperms of the urodele amphibia, which may be thought of as an extreme development of the preceding type, with which it seems to be connected by certain intermediate conditions; in the sperms of the pigeon, for example, according to Retzius, the middle-piece is greatly elongated, so as to occupy a large region of the flagellum (Fig. 125). In the urodele this region is still further extended. The proxi-

[1] A critical review is given by Meves ('00). See also Duesberg ('08, '20), Oliver ('13).
[2] Korff, '02, in *Phalamgista*, Duesberg, '20, in *Didelphys*.
[3] See Meves ('99), Duesberg ('08, '20).

mal centriole, as usual, passes to the base of the nucleus, remains undivided, and undergoes great enlargement to form a conspicuous rounded, ovoidal or, in some species, rod-shaped body. This is the so-called "middle-piece" (properly the *neck*) which is closely applied to the base of the nucleus, and

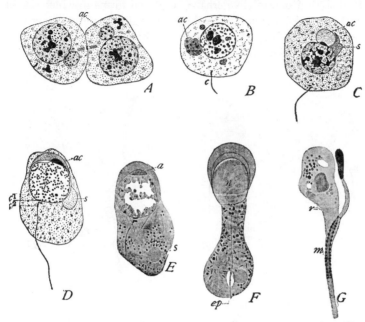

Fig. 176.—Earlier stages of sperm-formation in the guinea-pig. History of acroblast (*A–D*, from MEVES, *E–G*, from DUESBERG).
   ac, acroblast, acrosome; c^1, c^2, centrioles; *ep*, end-piece; *n*, nucleus; *r*, residual cytoplasm; *s*, "sphere" (= Golgi-remnant).
   A, young sister-spermatids, *B*, slightly later stage; both showing acroblast with proacrosomic granules; *C*, *D*, middle stages; *E–G*, later stages, *G*, in side-view.

by some observers is described as actually lying inside it. (Meves, Mc-Gregor).[1]
   After giving off the axial filament, the distal centriole, as in the mammals, is converted into a ring which elongates, assumes a pessary-shape, and finally draws out along the axial filament, until it extends through the whole length of the main-piece. Its proximal or anterior moiety gives rise (in *Salamandra*) to a deeply-staining plate-like body just behind

[1] Meves ('97). McGregor ('99) believed the "middle-piece" (in *Amphiuma*) to arise from the remains of the "sphere" (idiozome), while the proximal centriole lies inside it as a much smaller body; but this seems to have been an error. Bowen ('22) has shown that the smaller body in question (in *Plethodon*) is formed by division of the proximal centriole into two parts, one of which enlarges to form the "middle-piece" while the second may be a blepharoplast from which grows forth the marginal filament of the fin-membrane.

the neck-region while its distal half finally passes to the limit of the main-piece of the flagellum at the beginning of the short end-piece, while the elongate narrow middle part becomes closely applied to the axial filament (Fig. 173).

(6) In a sixth group might perhaps be placed forms in which one or the other of the centrioles is stated to elongate bodily to form a long filament extending out to the base of the end-piece. In *Paludina*, for example, it is the distal centriole which thus elongates (Figs. 166, 167), while the proximal one is pushed up into the nucleus, having close behind it a ring-shaped

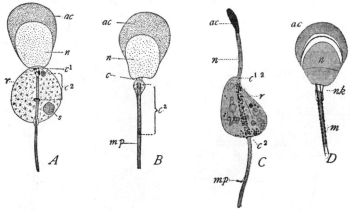

Fig. 177.—Later stages of sperm-formation in the guinea-pig. (*A*, *B*, from MEVES, *C*, *D*, from DUESBERG.)

ac, acrosome; *c¹*, *c²*, proximal and distal centriole-derivatives; *m*, middle-piece; *mp*, main piece of flagellum; *n*, nucleus; *nk*, neck; *r*, residual cytoplasm; *s*, "sphere" (= Golgi-remnant).

A, centrioles, early acrosome, Golgi-remnant; *B*, later stage; *C*, side-view, residual cytoplasm; *D*, nearly mature sperm.

centriole-derivative of unknown origin (Meves, '03). On the other hand, in the elasmobranch (Suzuki, '98) and in *Helix* (Korff, '99) it is the proximal centriole which thus elongates and the ring, here said to be derived from the distal centriole, is carried out to the junction of the main-piece and the end-piece.

Conclusion. It is impracticable to enter here into other modifications of the central apparatus of the sperm, most of which are still imperfectly known. The fact that at least one of the centrioles passes into the neck-region seems to be common to nearly all forms of sperms, and is unmistakably correlated with the appearance of the sperm-center during fertilization from, or in close association with, this region of the sperm in the egg (p. 441). A second point of general interest is the complete demonstration offered by the sperm-formation of animals that the centriole may play the part not only of a division-center but also of a blepharoplast. In this fact, possibly, we may find a clue to the remarkable diversity of behavior on the part of the distal centriole during spermiogenesis. It seems possible that the all but invariable separation of this centriole into two parts means that it is a dual structure, being differentiated into two components, one concerned with division, the other with the flagellum-formation, as is known to be the case with the basal bodies of certain flagellates (p. 696). The backward movement of the ring or its representative in so many sperms may therefore represent the removal of the blepharoplast-component while the basal body represents the division-center. If this conjecture has any value, we might consider that the proximal centriole alone represents the persistent active center of the sperm, and that the puzzling variations of behavior on the part of the distal one have no particular physiological significance.

e. *Acroblast and Acrosome.* The most conspicuous feature in the history of the acroblast is its ultimate separation into two parts one of which moves to the anterior pole and there gives rise to the definitive acrosome, while the other and often larger portion constitutes the *acroblast-remnant* (idiozome-remnant) *containing the original Golgi-bodies* surrounding the sphere. This body passes backwards commonly into the tail region, disintegrates, and most of its substance appears to be finally eliminated with the residual protoplasm (Figs. 176, 172, 177).[1] By Gatenby and Woodger ('21) a portion of this body is believed to contribute to the formation of the middle-piece (in the guinea-pig).

The definitive acrosome seems always to be formed from or within a clear vacuole-like space that appears within that part of the acroblast that passes to the anterior nuclear pole. Within this space appears a small deeply staining spheroidal body which by some of the earlier observers was mistaken for a centriole;[2] and by its enlargement and differentiation (Figs. 172, 176) gives rise to the central or principal portion of the acroblast, undergoing a great variety of changes in different species. The most divergent extremes of these are on the one hand the greatly elongated and filiform acrosome of the Lepidoptera (Bowen, '22), and on

---

[1] This has been observed more or less fully by many investigators, including Henking ('91), Niessing ('97), Lenhossék ('98), Meves ('99), Voïnov ('03), Sjövall ('06) and more recently by Montgomery ('11), Schitz ('16), Schaffer ('17), Gatenby ('19), Bowen ('20) and Duesberg ('20). This process, or indications of it, has been seen in insects, arachnids, mollusks, and vertebrates and is undoubtedly of widespread occurrence.

[2] This granule was designated by Lenhossék ('97) as the "acrosome" the term being expanded by later writers so as to apply to the completed structure. By Stockard and Papanicolaou ('16) the clear vesicle is called the *idiosphærotheca*, the central granule (acrosome of Lenhossék) the *idiosphærosome*, the inner zone derived from the latter the *idiocryptosome*, the outer zone the *idiocalyposome*, the head-cap the *spermiocalyptrotheca*, and the idiozome-remnant the *idiophthartosome*. This terminology, though etymologically excellent, seems too cumbersome. For other synonyms see Gatenby and Woodger ('21).

the other, the cap-like one of many mammals (guinea-pig, Fig. 177) which spreads out over the anterior part of the nucleus, while the clear substance gives rise to a thin outer zone. Both zones are surrounded by the so-called *head-cap* which is derived from the peripheral layer of the clear vesicle or outer zone.[1]

In the mammals the concordant results of many observers, beginning with Moore ('94) make it nearly certain that the acrosome-granule in question is formed by the fusion or aggregation of the proacrosomic granules (p. 329) already present within the spermatocyte-idiozome. These granules are set free in the cytosome when the idiozome breaks up, persist during the first division, reaggregate in the interior of the idiozome of the second spermatocytes, are again dispersed in the second division, and once more aggregate within the substance of the acroblast where they are surrounded by small vacuoles (Fig. 176, A, B, D). A progressive process of fusion now sets in[2] the vacuoles running together until they produce the usual large clear vesicle, while the granules progressively fuse until they form a single much larger body (Fig. 176, C, D). In many other cases, however (insects), no proacrosomic granules have been observed, the acrosome first appearing as a single intensely chromophilic granule within the acroblast-vesicle. It seems probable that the foregoing two modes of acrosome-formation differ only in degree, *i. e.*, in the earlier or later appearance of the granule-material. The fact that both vacuoles and granules are in the one case multiple, in the other single, clearly points to the conclusion that in the former case they are produced separately by elements that are themselves still separate, in the latter case as the single common product of these same elements intimately united or fused. In any case it seems certain that the Golgi-bodies are somehow concerned in the production of the acrosome. It seems incredible that so elaborate a process should be necessary for the formation of a structure whose only function lies in the attachment of the sperm to and penetration into the egg; and the process seems still more remarkable in view of the fact that the Golgi-apparatus, though it gives rise to the acroblast, seems for the most part to be itself cast out of the sperm. Interesting questions for further research are here raised (p. 716).

f. Chromatoid Bodies. Nearly all observers are thus far agreed that the bodies thus called do not directly give rise to any of the formed elements of the sperm. They first make their appearance in the protoplasm of the primary spermatocytes, usually lying near to the nucleus but not in contact

---

[1] In the marsupial *Phalangista* the head-cap is said by Korff ('02), to be cast off (Fig. 174).

[2] This was carefully described by Meves ('99) in the guinea pig, and more recently by Stockard and Papanicolaou ('16) and by Gatenby and Woodger ('21).

with it (Fig. 178). As a rule but one such body appears; but two or several may be present. The most diverse accounts have been given of its origin and later history, and it is far from certain whether all the bodies which go under this name are of the same nature.[1]

In insects [2] the chromatoid body is usually single, and stains intensely in hæmatoxylin, safranin and other dyes. With the Benda alizarin-violet

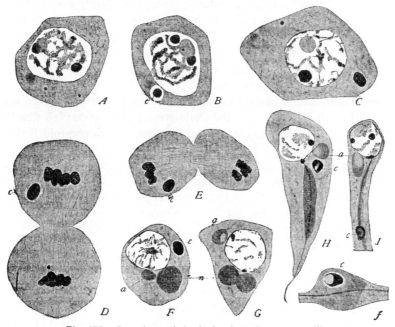

Fig. 178.—Spermiogenesis in the hemipter *Pentatoma senilis*.

A, early spermatocyte, chromatoid granules in cytoplasm; B, later stage, single chromatoid body, (c), plasmosome, two chromosome-nucleoli (X and Y); C, later, confused period; D, first spermatocyte division; E, second division; F, early spermatid, with chromatoid body, acroblast (a) and chondriosphere (n); G, later spermatid, with double chondriosphere, blepharophast, no chromatoid body; H, I, later spermatids, outwandering of chromatoid body; J, portion of tail-region with chromatoid body, shortly before casting off of residual protoplasm.

method it is stained bright purple; with Auerbach's rubin-methyl-green mixture it is red while the nuclei are green; with Altmann's mitochondrial stain bright red (Plough). It might be supposed from these reactions that this body is of mitochondrial origin; but Plough has shown that this

---

[1] This body, figured by some of the earlier observers in the mammals (Brunn, '76, Brown, '85), was more carefully studied by Benda ('91) who called it the "chromatoider Nebenkörper" or " chromatoider Körper"; subsequently by Niessing ('96), Lenhossék ('98), Meves ('99), Schoenfeld ('oo)-Korff ('o2), Van Molle ('o6), Duesberg ('o8) and other spermatologists. It was later observed in the fishes (*Myxine*, Schreiner, '05), in insects (Schaefer, '07, Wilson, '13), Crustacea (Fasten, '14, '18) and other invertebrates, and is probably of wide occurrence in animals generally.

[2] Wilson ('13), Lewis and Robertson ('16), Plough ('17).

body is not stained *intra vitam* by Janus green but is stained by neutral red. Its history in the hemipter *Pentatoma senilis*, where it is of large size, is as follows: [1]

It is first seen in the early spermatocytes in the form of several small, deeply staining granules, lying in the *cytoplasm*. Slightly later it typically becomes single and much larger. It persists during both spermatocyte-divisions, but fails to divide in either, passing over bodily first into one of the second spermatocytes and then into one of the spermatids (Fig. 178). It thus comes to pass that *this body enters only one spermatid out of four*—a result fully confirmed by counts of the spermatids. In the spermatid it is finally carried out into the outgrowing flagellum and sloughed off with the residual protoplasm in this region.

The facts are similar in almost every detail in various other Hemiptera and also (as Plough has shown) in the Orthoptera.[2] In the crayfish *Cambarus* (Fasten, '14) the facts are similar, except that two chromatoid bodies of equal size are present. These likewise persist without division during the spermatocyte-divisions and most commonly pass together to one pole, more rarely to opposite poles. In the foregoing cases there can be no possibility of regarding the chromatoid body as an extruded nucleolus (as assumed by some earlier observers), for during the whole period of its formation and growth both the spermatocyte-nucleoli (plasmosome and chromosome-nucleolus) remain intact within the nucleus. Its physiological meaning remains completely in the dark, but the facts suggest that if it have any function it must be performed not later than the spermatocyte-divisions. It may, however, be no more than a by-product of other activities, and in this sense a functionless excretion-product.

In respect to the vertebrates, the existing accounts are still conflicting and confused in respect to almost every point in the history of the chromatoid. Most of the earlier writers, relying mainly on the staining-reactions, regarded it as probably of nuclear origin,[3] and several of them accepted the probability that it is an extruded nucleolus or is formed from a nucleolus (Lenhossék, Meves and particularly the Schreiners, who have made an extended study of the phenomena in *Myxine*). These observations, however, stand alone, all other observers having failed to observe the origin of the chromatoid body, or having relied wholly on indirect evidence. By Benda, Moore, Niessing, Lenhossék, and more recently Regaud ('10), it was observed already in the growth-period of the primary spermatocytes; on the other hand Ebner, ('99), and especially Duesberg ('08) were not able

---

[1] Wilson, '13.

[2] The passing of the chromatoid body into the tail is also described in *Dytiscus*, by Schäfer ('07).

[3] Benda ('91), Moore ('93), Lenhossék ('98), Meves ('99.)

to find it until the second spermatocyte-division, and Meves ('99) first describes it in the telophase of that division. Lenhossék asserted (in case of
the rat and guinea-pig) the persistence of the chromatoid body (or bodies)
during both divisions though it may temporarily break up into a number of
granules; and he also asserts its presence, "one in every spermatid.[1]
In later stages it fragments and disappears, as was also observed by
Niessing. Duesberg ('08) concluded that in the rat the chromatoid body
(first seen in the second spermatocytes) divides into two, so that every
spermatid receives one. Regaud ('10), on the other hand, found in the same
object that during the first division this body (already present in the first
spermatocyte) disappears, or perhaps fragments into small granules, but is
reconstituted in the second spermatocyte to form a single body which
passes undivided to one pole. This account implies that but half the spermatids receive such a body. In *Myxine*, the Schreiners found that a single
chromatoid body is present in every spermatid and in later stages *passes into
the nucleus* to form an integral part of the sperm (!) In respect to this point
the Schreiners' account differs from those of all other observers.

Conclusion. In surveying the complicated phenomena of sperm-formation we are impressed alike by their astonishing diversity in detail and by an
underlying uniformity in respect to the most fundamental features of the
process. In both respects the sperm-cell is comparable with the flagellated
Protista, with which it shows so far-reaching an analogy. The fundamental uniformities of the sperm-formation have been sufficiently emphasized,
particularly in respect to the nucleus, chondriosomes, central bodies, Golgi-
bodies and the acrosome. Its diversities and their physiological meaning
may serve to remind us of our ignorance of an immense field of inquiry in the
exploitation of which cytology has made a mere beginning.

In a broad view of the phenomena, what most arrests our attention is
the large measure in which the sperm-forming materials are already preformed in the spermatocytes to be distributed to the spermatids by the
spermatocyte-divisions with at least approximate equality. This applies
alike to the chromosomes, central bodies, chondriosomes and Golgi-bodies.
When we consider how recent is our acquaintance with these facts, we cannot help suspecting that there may be still other elements of equal importance, as yet unseen, that may be similarly distributed. The possible larger
significance of this will become apparent in the course of the discussion of
cell-organization in general offered in Chapter IX.

[1] '98, 272.

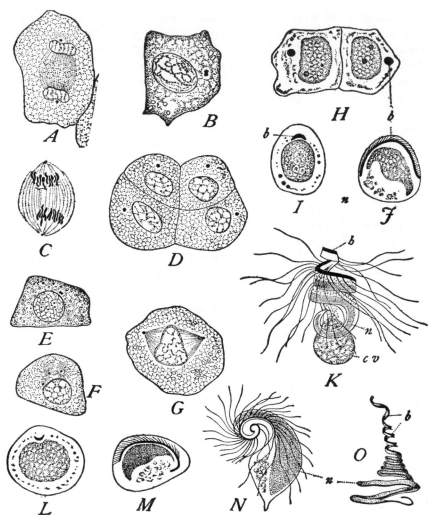

Fig. 179.—Formation of the sperms in the pteridophytes *Marsilia* (*A, D, E, G,* BELAJEFF; *B, C,*
O, SHAW), *Gymnogramme* (*H, K,* BELAJEFF) and *Equisetum* (*L, N,* BELAJEFF).

  A, primary spermatogonium (two generations before the primary "spermatocytes") in division,
showing centrioles; *B,* primary spermatocyte with pair of "blepharoplastoids" (centrioles); *C,*
spindle of primary spermatocyte (first maturation-division); *D,* four of the eight secondary "spermatocytes" with blepharoplast; *E–G,* prophase of second division; *H,* pair of spermatids (*Gymnogramme*) with blepharoplasts; *I–J,* formation of the ciliated band from the blepharoplast; *K,* nearly
ripe sperm, showing ciliated band (*b*), nucleus, and "cytoplasmic vesicle" (the latter is ultimately
cast off); *L, M,* spermatids of *Equisetum; N,* ripe spermatozoid from above, showing spiral ciliated
band; *O,* ripe sperm of *Marsilia* with very long spiral ciliated band.

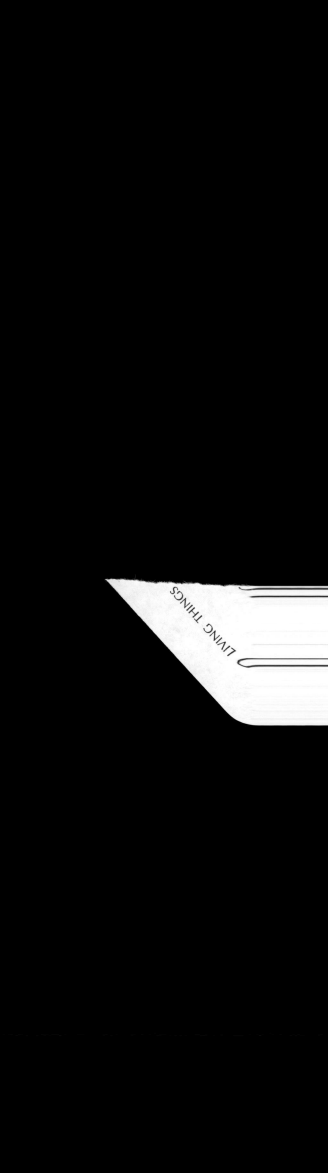

to find it until the second spermatocyte-division, and Meves ('99) first describes it in the telophase of that division. Lenhossék asserted (in case of the rat and guinea-pig) the persistence of the chromatoid body (or bodies) during both divisions though it may temporarily break up into a number of granules; and he also asserts its presence, "one in every spermatid.[1] In later stages it fragments and disappears, as was also observed by Niessing. Duesberg ('08) concluded that in the rat the chromatoid body (first seen in the second spermatocytes) divides into two, so that every spermatid receives one. Regaud ('10), on the other hand, found in the same object that during the first division this body (already present in the first spermatocyte) disappears, or perhaps fragments into small granules, but is reconstituted in the second spermatocyte to form a single body which passes undivided to one pole. This account implies that but half the spermatids receive such a body. In *Myxine*, the Schreiners found that a single chromatoid body is present in every spermatid and in later stages *passes into the nucleus* to form an integral part of the sperm (!) In respect to this point the Schreiners' account differs from those of all other observers.

Conclusion. In surveying the complicated phenomena of sperm-formation we are impressed alike by their astonishing diversity in detail and by an underlying uniformity in respect to the most fundamental features of the process. In both respects the sperm-cell is comparable with the flagellated Protista, with which it shows so far-reaching an analogy. The fundamental uniformities of the sperm-formation have been sufficiently emphasized, particularly in respect to the nucleus, chondriosomes, central bodies, Golgi-bodies and the acrosome. Its diversities and their physiological meaning may serve to remind us of our ignorance of an immense field of inquiry in the exploitation of which cytology has made a mere beginning.

In a broad view of the phenomena, what most arrests our attention is the large measure in which the sperm-forming materials are already preformed in the spermatocytes to be distributed to the spermatids by the spermatocyte-divisions with at least approximate equality. This applies alike to the chromosomes, central bodies, chondriosomes and Golgi-bodies. When we consider how recent is our acquaintance with these facts, we cannot help suspecting that there may be still other elements of equal importance, as yet unseen, that may be similarly distributed. The possible larger significance of this will become apparent in the course of the discussion of cell-organization in general offered in Chapter IX.

[1] '98, 272.

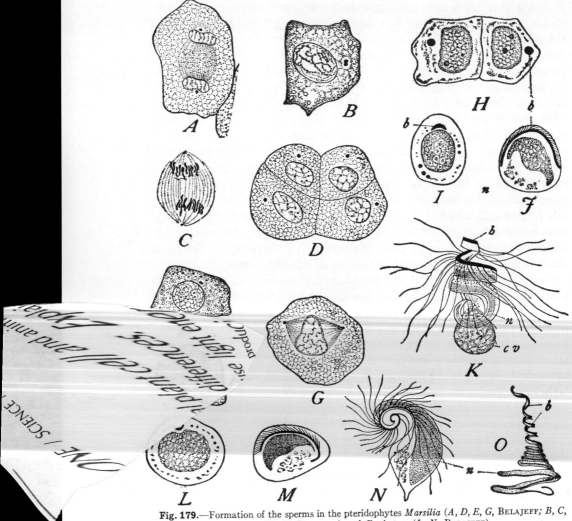

Fig. 179.—Formation of the sperms in the pteridophytes *Marsilia* (*A, D, E, G*, BELAJEFF; *B, C, O*, SHAW), *Gymnogramme* (*H, K*, BELAJEFF) and *Equisetum* (*L, N*, BELAJEFF).

A, primary spermatogonium (two generations before the primary "spermatocytes") in division, showing centrioles; *B*, primary spermatocyte with pair of "blepharoplastoids" (centrioles); *C*, spindle of primary spermatocyte (first maturation-division); *D*, four of the eight secondary "spermatocytes" with blepharoplast; *E–G*, prophase of second division; *H*, pair of spermatids (*Gymnogramme*) with blepharoplasts; *I–J*, formation of the ciliated band from the blepharoplast; *K*, nearly ripe sperm, showing ciliated band (*b*), nucleus, and "cytoplasmic vesicle" (the latter is ultimately cast off); *L, M*, spermatids of *Equisetum; N*, ripe spermatozoid from above, showing spiral ciliated band; *O*, ripe sperm of *Marsilia* with very long spiral ciliated band.

IV. THE GAMETE FORMATION IN PLANTS

As earlier indicated, the gamete-formation of higher plants offers a some-what simpler problem than that of animals, because it is uncomplicated by the phenomena of meiosis which here take place at a different period of the life-history. Apart from this the process shows a fundamental agreement with that of animals, though the analysis of its details thus far remains much less complete. The phenomena can here be examined in only a cursory manner, especially with reference to the motile type of sperm-cells in higher forms.

As in animals the final generation of spermatogenous cells may be called spermatids, but spermatocytes, in the sense in which this term is employed

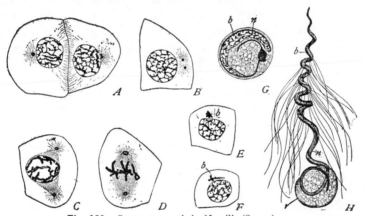

Fig. 180.—Spermatogenesis in *Marsilia* (Sharp).

A, products of third spermatogenous mitosis; *B, C, D*, stages of fourth and last spermatogenous mitosis; *E, F*, spermatids; *H*, mature sperm-cell, partly uncoiled, showing nucleus (*n*), much elongated blepharoplast (*b*), and residual protoplasm (*r*).

in animal spermatogenesis, do not occur in plants, being represented rather by the *sporocytes* which precede the formation of the microspores (p. 496).[1] In all the sperm-producing divisions, accordingly, the mitoses are of the ordinary somatic type so far as the chromosomes are concerned. It is an interesting fact that *in these mitoses the acromatic figure often shows at the spindle-poles distinct central bodies, sometimes surrounded by conspicuous asters, which ultimately play the part of blepharoplasts from which the flagella or cilia grow forth* (Figs. 179, 180, 182). Recent studies have further demonstrated, in a few cases, that in addition to the central bodies the spermatids and sperms of plants receive also chondriosomes and probably an

[1] By Allen '12, ('17) the spermatids as above defined are called *androcytes*.

acroblast closely analogous to that of the animal spermatid, though the Golgi-bodies have not yet actually been identified.

The relation of the blepharoplasts to the central bodies in plants, first indicated by the work of Belajeff, Shaw, Webber, and others, was clearly established by subsequent observations.[1] The blepharoplasts of the spermatids have been traced beyond a doubt to a position at or near the spindle-poles of the last division by many observers beginning with Shaw, Belajeff and Webber. Many botanists, including those just mentioned, have hesitated to recognize their homology with the central bodies in the animal spermatid, for the following reasons. In all the forms here in question the ordinary somatic mitoses, and often also the earlier spermatogenous, are of anastral type and devoid of central bodies (p. 150). The latter, as seen in the spermatid-producing division, must therefore be new formations to which the law of strict genetic continuity seems not to apply. In the cycads, as shown especially by Webber, they seem to play no actual part in the division, but merely lie opposite the spindle-poles without direct connection with them. In the cycads and some of the ferns, they seem to arise separately, either in the spermatids or in the preceding cell-generation, not by the division of a single body as is typically the case with true central bodies.

The force of these objections is much weakened by the discovery that in many cases the blepharoplasts are in fact produced by the division of a single body which behaves in all respects as a central body; further, that such bodies are sometimes present in earlier generations of the spermatogenous cells. Shaw ('98) found central bodies at the spindle-poles in the last two divisions of *Marsilia*, and followed their division in the telophases of the penultimate division to form the centers of the last division while Belajeff ('99) and Sharp ('14) found such bodies, surrounded by astral rays, at the spindle-poles in all of the four spermatogenous divisions excepting the first. Belajeff also believed that these centers divided after each mitosis to form the centers for the ensuing mitosis. Sharp ('12) demonstrated the division of the center in the prophase of the last spermatogenous mitosis in *Marsilia* and its behavior as a typical central body in that mitosis (Fig. 180); and the same was also shown by Allen ('12) in the moss *Polytrichum*. Ikeno ('03) found (in *Marchantia*) central bodies at the spindle-poles in each spermatogenous division, dividing into two at the close of each mitosis and after

---

[1] The initial work on this subject was done by Guignard ('89) on certain mosses, ferns and algæ, extended by that of Belajeff ('92, '94, '97, '99) on *Chara* and the pteridophytes *Gymnogramma, Equisetum* and *Marsilia*. To the same period belongs the important work of Shaw ('97, '98) on *Marsilia* and the ferns; of Webber ('97, '01) and Ikeno ('98) on cycads, and of Hirase ('94, '98) and Fujii ('98, '99, 'oo) on *Ginkgo*. See also Ikeno ('03, '04, '06, *Marchantia, Cycas*), Miyake ('06, *Ginkgo*), Escoyez ('07, *Marchantia*), Caldwell ('07, *Microcycas*), Yamanouchi ('08, *Nephrodium*), Chamberlain ('09, *Dioön*), Allen ('12, '17, *Polytrichum*), Sharp ('12, '14, '20, *Equisetum, Marsilia, Blasia*).

For literature see Wilson ('00), Prenant ('09), Allen ('12), Sharp ('12, '14, '21), Meves ('18).

the last one persisting to form the blepharoplasts. In view of these facts
and the later history of these bodies it is impossible to doubt the correctness
of the view, early urged especially by Belajeff and Ikeno, that the blepharoplasts of higher plants are of the same nature, morphologically and physiologically, as those of animal sperms. The only doubts that can arise relate

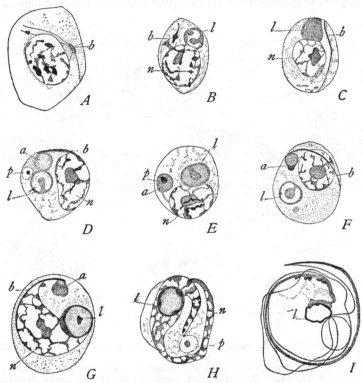

Fig. 181.—Spermiogenesis in the moss *Polytrichum* (ALLEN).

a, the apical body; b, blepharoplast; l, limosphere (probably the Golgi-apparatus or Golgi-
remnant); n, nucleus; p, probably the percnosome, which may be equivalent to the acrosome-
granule.

A, androcyte (spermatid) with nucleus and blepharoplast; B, appearance of the limosphere,
elongation of blepharoplast; C, further elongation of blepharoplast; D, the apical body (a) has
separated from the limosphere; E, F, slightly later; G, nucleus beginning to elongate; H, later stage
(blepharoplast not shown); I, sperm fully formed but still coiled within its enclosing vesicle of
residual cytoplasm, l, probably the limosphere.

to the nature of the central body itself and its proper definition in the light
of these facts (p. 672).

In the early spermatid the blepharoplast is in most cases, as in animals,
a small spheroidal granule; but in the cycads it is a much larger spheroidal
body which has a complicated structure and metamorphosis, and is sur-

rounded by conspicuous astral rays (Fig. 182). In all the higher forms, the
blepharoplast, or the group of granules produced by its fragmentation,
grows out into an elongate flattened band or ribbon, at first coiled within the
cell, from which grow forth the cilia or flagella (Figs. 179, 182).   In later
stages it uncoils more or less, but seems always to retain its spiral course in
some degree, in general following the spiral coiling of the cytosome so con-

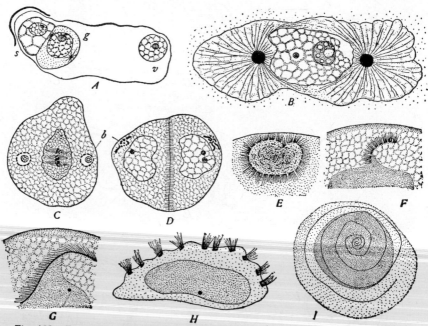

Fig. 182.—Formation of the sperms in the cycads and Ginkgoales (*A, Ginkgo; B–D, Zamia,*
WEBBER; *E–I, Cycas,* IKENO).

A, developing pollen-tube, showing stalk-cell (*s*), vegetative cell (*v*) and generative cell (*g*), the
latter with two blepharoplasts; *B,* generative cell, somewhat later, with blepharoplasts and asters;
C, the same in the prophases of division, showing breaking up of blepharoplasts; *D,* the two spermatids formed by division of the generative cell; blepharoplasts fragmented; from these fragments
arises the cilia-bearing band; *E,* blepharoplast of *Cycas,* at a stage somewhat later than Fig. C;
cilia developing; *F,* later stage; ciliated band (derived from the last stage) attached to a prolonga-
tion from the nucleus; *G,* cilia-bearing band continuous; *H,* nearly ripe sperm with nucleus in the
center; ciliated band, shown in section, forming a spiral; *I.* slightly later stage, viewed from above,
showing the spiral course of the band (cilia omitted).

spicuous in the pteridophytes. In the cycads the blepharoplast forms a
closely coiled band in the upper part of the conical sperm-cell and remains
in this condition until after the sperm has entered the egg (Fig. 213).

In some cases the blepharoplast, before or during its elongation, fragments
into smaller bodies which seem to play the part of basal bodies from each of
which a cilium or flagellum grows forth, *e. g.,* in *Equisetum* according to Sharp

('12) and in the cycads according to Webber, Ikeno and other observers. In the bryophytes and certain pteridophytes, but two flagella are thus produced, though the blepharoplast is much elongated. In *Chara*, which has a similar type of sperm, each flagellum is attached basally to a short, rod-shaped body (Meves '20). In most pteridophytes and in cycads numerous and usually closely crowded cilia grow forth along the course of an elongated spiral blepharoplast (Figs. 179–182), which in many cases seems, at least in its later stages, to be quite homogeneous.

The remaining components of the sperm-cells have been very incompletely traced. Neither chondriosomes nor Golgi-bodies as such have been identified during the spermiogenesis, but, as earlier stated, Meves ('20) has found chondriosomes in the mature sperms of *Fucus* (p. 594); and in the gymnosperms the microgametes probably contain plastids which may be derivatives of chondriosomes (p. 455). In the spermiogenesis of mosses appears a body that seems almost certainly to be the acroblast, though the Golgi-bodies are not in evidence, probably because of inadequate technique. This is a rather large, spheroidal body, of uncertain origin, described by M. Wilson ('11) as the *limosphere* and more carefully examined by Allen ('12, '17). It lies near the anterior end of the elongate blepharoplast (Fig. 181), and divides into two unequal parts, of which the smaller gives rise to an "apical body" while the latter persists until a rather late stage when it disappears from view. It seems very probable that the two portions into which the limosphere divides represent the acroblast and the acrosome and acroblast-remnant respectively; but this cannot be positively asserted without further examination. Wilson described also a smaller cytoplasmic *percnosome*, which may be a chromatoid body; but this, too, is uncertain.[1]

LITERATURE IV

(See also V, VI, XI, XIII, XIV. For abbreviations see General Literature List.

Allen, C. E., '17. The Spermatogenesis of *Polytrichum: A. Bot.,* XXXI.
Allen, Edgar, '23. Ovogenesis during sexual maturity: *A. J. A.,* XXI.
Amma, K., '11. Ueber die Differenzierung der Keimbahnzellen bei den Copepoden: *A. Zf.,* VI.
Ballowitz, K., '13. Sperma, Spermien, Spermatozoen, Spermiogenese: *H. Nw.,* IX, *Fischer, Jena.*
Beckwith, C. J., '14. The Genesis of Plasma Structures in the Egg of *Hydractinia: J. M.,* XXV.
Belajeff, W., '94. Ueber Bau und Entwicklung der Spermatozoiden der Pflanzen: *Flora,* LIV.
Benda, C., '98. Ueber die Spermatogenese der Vertebraten und höherer Evertebraten. 2. Die Histogenese der Spermien: *Verh. d. Phys. Gesell., Berlin.*

[1] Allen compares the limosphere to the "chromatoider Nebenkörper" (chromatoid body?) found by Ikeno ('03) in *Marchantia.*

v. Berenberg-Gossler, H., '14. Ueber Herkunft und Wesen der sogenannten primären Urgeschlechtszellen der Amnioten: *A. A.*, XLVII.

Boveri, Th., '99. Die Entwicklung von *Ascaris megalocephala* mit besonderer Rücksicht auf die Kernverhältnisse: *Festschr. f. C. von Kupffer.* '10a (XIII).

Bowen, R. H. Studies on Insect Spermatogenesis, I, '20. History of the cytoplasmic Components: *B. B.*, XXIX; II, '22a, Components of the Spermatid: *J. M.*, XXXVII; III, '22b. Nebenkern: *B. B.*, XLII; IV, '22c. Polymegaly: *Proc. Am. Ac. Arts. Sci.*, LVII; V, '22d. Lepidoptera: *Q. J.*, LXVI; '24. The Flagellate Sperm (in press).

Buchner, P., '10. Die Schicksal des Keimplasmas der *Sagitta; Festschr. R. Hertwig, I, Jena.*
'18. Die akzessorischen Kerne des Hymenoptereneies: *A. M. A.*, XCI.

Champy, C., '13. Recherches sur la spermatogénèse des Batrachiens et les éléments accessoires du testicle: *A. Z. E.*, LII.

Dodds, G. S., '10. Segregation of the Germ-cells of the Teleost, *Lophius: J. M.*, XX, XXI.

Duesberg, J., '10. Nouvelles recherches sur l'appareil mitochondrial des cellules séminales: *A. Zf.*, VI.
'20. Cytoplasmic Structures in the seminal Epithelium of the Opossum: *Carn. Inst. Washington, Contrib. to Emb.*, 28.

Fauré-Fremiet, E., '10. Étude sur les mitochondries, etc.: *A. A. M.*, XI.

Gatenby, J. B. The Cytoplasmic Inclusions of the Germ-cells. I ('17a), Lepidoptera: *Q. J.*, LXII; II (17b), *Helix aspersa: Ibid.;* III ('18), other Pulmonates: *Ibid.;* LXIII; IV ('19a), *Paludina* and *Testacella: Ibid.;* V ('19b), *Lymnæa: Ibid.;* VI ('20a), *Apanteles: Ibid.;* VII ('20b), Technique: *Ibid.;* LXIV; VIII ('20c); *Journ. Linn. Soc.;* IX ('21, with Woodger), *Cavia: Q. J.*, LXV; X ('22), *Saccocirrus: Ibid.;* LXVI.

Gatenby and **Woodger,** '20. On the Relationship between the Formation of the Yolk and the Mitochondria and Golgi-Apparatus, etc.: *J. R. M. S.*, 2.

Giardina, A., '01. Origine dell 'Oöciti e delle Cellule nutrici nel Dytiscus: *Monatschr. Anat. und Phys.*, XVIII.

Goette, A., '07. Vergleichende Entwicklungsgeschichte der Hydropolypen, etc., *Z. W. Z.*, LXXXVII.

Haecker, V., '93. Das Keimbläschen, seine Elemente und Lageveränderungen: *A. M. A.*, XLI.

Hargitt, G. T., '13–'18. Germ Cells of Cœlenterates, I–VI: *J. M.*, XXIV, XXVII, XXVIII, XXXI, XXXIII.

Hasper, M., '11., Zur Entwicklung der Geschlechtsorgane von *Chironomus: Z. J.*, *Anat. Abt.*, 31.

Hegner, R. W., '14. The Germ-Cell Cycle in Animals: (Earlier papers cited), *New York.*
'15. Studies on Germ-Cells, IV; Protoplasmic Differentiation in the Oöcytes of certain Hymenoptera: *J. M.*, XXVI.

Hirschler, J., '18. Ueber die Plasmakomponenten der weiblichen Geschlechtszellen: *A. M. A.*, LXXXIX.

v. Jhering, H., '77. Zur Kenntniss der Eibildung bei der Muscheln: *Z. W. Z.*, XXIX.

Jörgenssen, M., '13*a*. Morphologische Studien zum Problem des Eiwachstums: *A. Zf.*, X.

'13*b*, Die Ei- und Nährzellen von *Pisciola: Ibid.*, X.

Koltzoff, N. K., '06, '09. Studien über die Gestalt der Zelle: I, *A. M. A.*, LXVII; II, *A. Zf.*, II.

v. Korff, K., '02. Zur Histogenese der Spermien von *Phalangista: A. M. A.*, LX.

Korschelt and **Heider,** '03 (V).

'13. Ei- und Eibildung: H. Nw., III. *Fischer, Jena.*

Loyez, M., '06. Recherches sur le développement ovarien des œufs méroblastiques, etc., : *A. A. M.*, VIII.

Maréchal, J., '06. Sur l'Ovogénèse des Selaciens et le quelques autres Chordates: *L. C.*, XXIV.

Meves, F., '99. Ueber Struktur und Histogenese der Samenfäden des Meershweinchens: *A. M. A.*, LIV.

'00. Ueber den von La Valette St. George entdeckten Nebenkern, etc.: *A. M. A.*, LVI.

'01. Struktur und Histogenese der Spermien: *Erg. Anat. u. Phys.*, XI.

'03. Ueber oligopyrene und apyrene Spermien, etc.: *A. M. A.*, LXI.

Mottier, D., '04 (V).

Perroncito, A., '10. Contribution a l'étude de la biologie cellulaire: *A. I. B.*, LIV.

Regaud, C., '10. Études sur la structure des tubes séminifères, etc.: *A. A. M.*, XI.

Retzius, G. Biologische Untersuchungen, Stockholm: *Jena.* Especially for the comparative morphology of the sperms: X (Man, Mammals, Selachians) '02; XI (Invertebrata) '04; XII (Invertebrates, Fishes) '05; XIII (Invertebrates, Vertebrates, etc.), '06; XIV (Invertebrates, Vertebrates), '09; XV (various) '10; XVI (Vertebrates, also ova), '11; XVII (Gastropods, Birds, Primates), '12; XVIII (*Ascaris*, vertebrates, also ova).

Rubaschkin, W., '12. Zur Lehre von der Keimbahn bei Säugetieren: *An. Hf.*, XLVI.

Sharp, L., '12, '14, '20. Spermatogenesis in *Equisetum: B. G.*, LIV; in *Marsilia, Ibid.*, LVIII; in *Blasia; Ibid.*, LIX.

Sjövall, E., '06. Ein Versuch das Binnennetz von Golgi-Kopsch bei der Spermato- und Ovo-genese zu homologisieren: *A. A.*, XXVIII.

Stieve, H. '20, '20a. Die Entwicklung der Keimzellen des Grottenolmes (*Proteus*): I, Spermatogenese: *A. M. A.*, XCIII; II, Die Wachstumsperiode der Oözyte: *Ibid.*, XCV.

Strasburger, E., '92. Schwarmsporen, Gameten, pflänzliche Spermatozoiden und das Wesen der Befruchtung: *Histol. Beitr.*, 4.

Swift, C. H., '14. Origin and Early History of the Primordial Germ-cells in the Chick: *A. J. A.*, XV.

Swingle, W. W., '20. Neoteny and the sexual Problem: *A. N.*

Waldeyer, W., '70. Eirstock und Ei: *Leipzig.*

'06. Die Geschlechtszellen: *In Handbuch vergl. u. exp. Ent. d. Wirbeltiere.* O. Hertwig, I, 1.

CHAPTER V

FERTILIZATION AND PARTHENOGENESIS

"Fertilization is not alone a physico-chemical process, as physiologists so often assume, but also a morphological phenomenon." O. HERTWIG.[1]

"It is conceivable, and indeed probable, that every part of the adult contains molecules derived from the male and from the female parent; and that, regarded as a mass of molecules, the entire organism may be compared to a web of which the warp is derived from the female and the woof from the male." HUXLEY. [2]

Fertilization comprises two closely associated but experimentally separable events. One of these, primarily of interest from a physiological point of view, is the *activation of the egg by the sperm.* The second, of especial importance for the study of cytology and genetics, is *a union or association of corresponding maternal and paternal elements*, which results in biparental heredity.[3] Both these results are brought about by a union and fusion of two germ-cells or *gametes* to form a single cell, the *zygote*—a process which finds its prototype in the conjugation of unicellular organisms.

It was the first of these effects alone that was commonly designated as "fertilization" or "fecundation" ("Befruchtung," "fécondation") by early embryologists who had not the least notion of the real nature of the process. The word has often been employed in the same sense by modern writers; and this usage is often convenient. Some writers, however, have sometimes almost seemed to forget that fertilization comprises a second and not less important series of events of which the most conspicuous is *karyogamy,* i. e., the union of the gamete-nuclei or pronuclei to form the cleavage-nucleus or primary nucleus of the embryo. The fact of central interest here is the *union and close association of two corresponding groups of chromosomes* derived from the two respective pronuclei and hence respectively of maternal and paternal origin. Fertilization commonly involves also a process of plastogamy or union of gamete-cytoplasms; but in higher forms generally the amount of paternal cytoplasm introduced into the egg is both absolutely and relatively very small, and we still know little of its history in the zygote.

By O. Hertwig ('75) and some other early writers the activation of the

---

[1] *Jenaische Zeitschrift*, XVIII, p. 291.

[2] *Evolution*, in *Science and Culture*, p. 296, from Enc. Britt., 1878.

[3] "Fertilization is the incitement of the egg to development together with the conveyance of paternal qualities to the egg." (Roux, '12, p. 48). See also Giard ('01), Fick ('05), O. Hertwig ('05), Boveri ('07).

egg in fertilization was ascribed to karyogamy, or union of the gamete-nuclei, but this was disputed by Boveri ('87, '91) on cytological grounds and is evidently inconsistent with the phenomena of parthenogenesis, of partial fertilization (p. 458), merogony (p. 465) and gynogenesis (p. 460) in none of which does activation involve a process of karyogamy.

For the rest, the problems of fertilization are intimately bound up with those of cell-division. Superficially regarded, the two processes seem to be opposites; for fertilization involves the fusion of two cells into one, while mitosis results in the division of one cell into two. Fundamentally, however, the same cytological elements are involved in both, and the same end-result sooner or later follows, namely, the formation of a mitotic figure and the resulting process of cleavage. This is still clearer when we regard parthenogenesis or the activation of the egg by some agency other than the sperm, a process which, as will later be shown, is connected with true fertilization by intermediate gradations (p. 458). The analogy of fertilization to cell-division is thus made perfectly clear. Fertilization and parthenogenesis possess, however, a far-reaching interest of their own, for they set in motion the mechanism not alone of cell-division, but also of development; and here cytology merges with embryology and genetics.

In their essentials the phenomena of fertilization are closely similar in animals and plants, but show many minor differences which often involve a wide divergence of external aspect. For purposes of description, therefore, it is convenient to separate the two groups.

I. FERTILIZATION OF THE ANIMAL EGG

A. GENERAL SKETCH

In outlining the main features of fertilization in animals we may take as a basis of reference the phenomena as seen in the eggs of sea-urchins and of *Ascaris megalocephala* (the parasitic threadworm of the horse) the study of which between 1873 and 1890, laid the main basis of our knowledge both of fertilization and maturation and in large measure also of mitosis. Both objects, made classical by these pioneer researches, have repeatedly been investigated by more recent observers and experimenters. They differ materially in respect to certain details of the process and hence offer a broader view when considered together.

In animals generally, the entire sperm enters the egg (Fig. 183); but in the sea-urchin and the starfish several observers have found that at least a part of the tail is left outside the egg. The sperm thus carries into the egg all of the components that have entered into its formation, in particular a nucleus, a central body or its derivatives, a certain quantity of chondriosome-material, an acrosome (a product of the Golgi-bodies) and a small amount of general cytoplasm. The fate of these components is completely known only in case of the nucleus, though interesting facts have been made known concerning the central bodies and the chondriosomes.

Almost immediately after its entrance the sperm-head rotates through an angle of 180°, so that the middle-piece or basal region of the nucleus is directed inwards; and at the same time, or a little later, a single *sperm-*

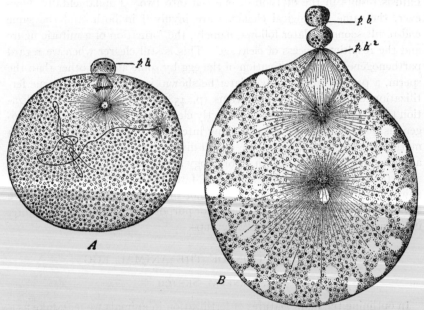

Fig. 183.—Fertilization of the egg of the snail *Physa* (KOSTANECKI and WIERZEJSKI).

A, the entire sperm lies in the egg, the first polocyte has been formed, the second is forming; *B*, the enlarged sperm-nucleus and sperm-aster lie near the center; second polar body forming and the first dividing. The egg-centers and asters afterwards disappear, their place being taken by the sperm-centers.

aster appears in the region of the middle-piece or actually centering in it (Figs. 184, 207). The sperm-nucleus now slowly enlarges, approaches the egg-nucleus and sooner or later unites with it (Figs. 185, 186). In the sea-urchin the two pronuclei completely fuse to form a *fusion-nucleus* or *cleav-age-nucleus* in which all traces of the original maternal and paternal constituents are temporarily lost to view. In *Ascaris* (Fig. 187), the two nuclei place themselves side by side in close contact but do not actually fuse. In either case the synkaryon thus formed sooner or later undergoes a typical mitotic division, thus producing duplicates of itself in the nuclei of the first

two cells of the embryo.   During this process the daughter-nuclei receive
maternal and paternal chromosomes, usually in equal number; and from
them, by continued division arise all the nuclei of the resulting organism.   In

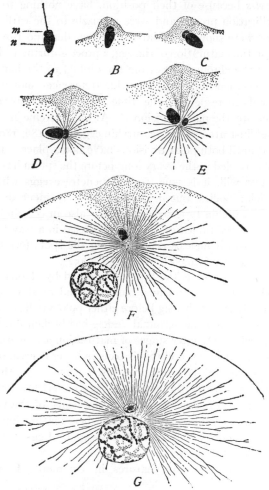

Fig. 184.—Entrance and rotation of the sperm-head and formation of the sperm-aster in the
sea-urchin *Toxopneustes* (*A–E*, × 1600; *F, G*, × 800).

these phenomena we see the physical counterpart of biparental heredity,
an effect that may appear in any portion of the offspring.

Relations between Fertilization and Maturation of the Egg.   It is necessary
to consider at this point certain relations between fertilization and the
"ripening" or maturation of the egg.   The latter process is accomplished

in the animal ovum by means of two successive "polar divisions," in the course of which the egg buds forth two small and often extremely minute cells at or near its upper pole (Figs. 183, 233). These cells, called *polar bodies* or *polocytes* because of their position, have nothing to do with the process of fertilization proper and were a puzzle to the earlier observers.[1] Ultimately they were shown by Mark, Van Beneden and Boveri to belong to the final act in the maturation of the egg, a process during which is effected the reduction of the chromosomes from the diploid to the haploid number. We are here concerned only with the wide differences shown by different species of animals in respect to the time at which the sperm enters the egg with respect to the polar divisions.[2] At one extreme is the comparatively rare case illustrated by the sea-urchin egg (Figs. 186, 189) which cannot be fertilized until both polar divisions have taken place. The polocytes are in this case extruded in the ovary long before the sperm has access to the egg. The sperms will, it is true, readily penetrate eggs which have not formed their polar bodies; but in this cases development does not ensue (p. 405). The sea-urchin type seems to occur also in certain cœlenterates, possibly in some of the tunicates[3] and is paralleled in a way by the eggs of higher plants in which meiosis occurs during the spore-forming divisions, so that no polocytes are formed by the egg (p. 452).

At the opposite extreme is the type represented by *Ascaris* and various other nematodes, platodes, annelids, mollusks, and crustaceans,[4] in which the sperm normally enters the egg before either polocyte has been extruded, and in some cases before the germinal vesicle has broken down (Figs. 187, 197). Here, therefore, the later stages of maturation are overlapped by the earlier stages of fertilization; and this is true, in lesser degree, of many cases intermediate between the two extremes just outlined. In this fact lies a source of great diversity in the general aspect of fertilization in different animals; and to it also is due the greater complexity of the phenomena in animals generally, as compared with plants, where maturation and fertilization are most commonly widely separated (p. 491). Eggs of the two types are shown together in Fig. 188.

All these cases have certain features in common. In all cases the

---

[1] The polocytes were first observed by Carus (1824) in the gasteropods. The most diverse views concerning their origin and nature were held by other early observers. They were supposed to arise by the extrusion of the nucleolus or even of the germinal vesicle, wholly or in part (Van Beneden, Bütschli, etc.), but were regarded by O. Hertwig ('76), and Giard ('77) as products of two successive unequal divisions of the egg—a conclusion fully confirmed by all later observers.

[2] For further details see Korschelt-Heider, '03, p. 630 ff.

[3] See Boveri, '90 (*Tiara*), Morgenstern, '01, Wulfert, '02 (*Cordylophora*), Hill, '96 (tunicates); see, however, Conklin, '05.

[4] See, for instance, Boveri,'87 (*Ascaris*), Wheeler, '95 (*Myzostoma*), Rückert, '95 (*Cyclops*), Haecker, '95 (copepods), Van Name, '99 (*Turbellaria*) Griffin, '99 (*Thalassema*), Kostanecki, '02 (*Mactra*), Lillie, '01 (Unio), and '12 (*Nereis*), Goldschmidt, '02 (*Polystomum*). etc.

sperm-nucleus is unable to conjugate with the egg-nucleus until after the polar divisions have been accomplished. In all cases the polar divisions are initiated by the breaking down of the germinal vesicle (as in ordinary

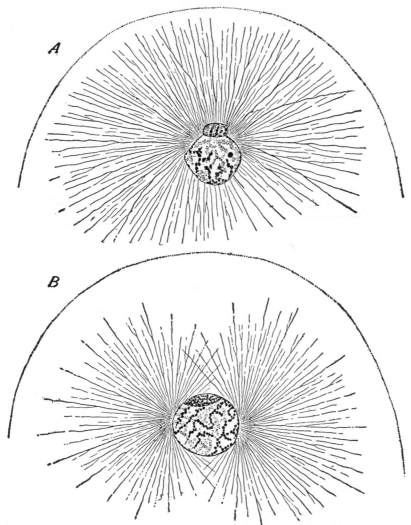

Fig. 185.—Conjugation of the gamete-nuclei and division of the sperm-aster in the sea-urchin *Toxopneustes*, × 1000. (For later stages see Fig. 58.)

mitosis), and the formation of chromosomes and of an achromatic figure. In all cases the re-formed egg-nucleus, after the completion of both divisions, is much smaller than the original germinal vesicle; and in almost all cases the sperm-nucleus, as it advances within the egg, is typically preceded by a *sperm-aster* which sooner or later divides to form an *amphiaster* that is the forerunner of the *cleavage-amphiaster*.   In other respects the two extreme types display the following conspicuous differences:

(1) In the sea-urchin type the pronuclei conjugate immediately after entrance of the sperm and apparently fuse completely to form a *fusion-nucleus* (Figs. 185, 186). Owing to the short time elapsing between entrance of the sperm and nuclear union the pronuclei are as a rule, still

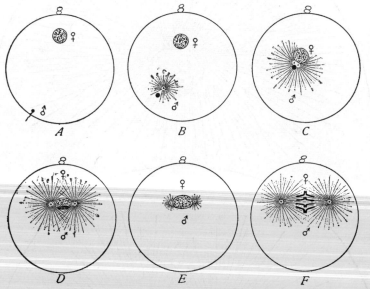

Fig. 186.—Diagram of sea-urchin type of fertilization.

A, matured egg, entrance of sperm; *B, C*, approach of pronuclei, division of sperm-center; *D*, sperm-aster divided, fusion of pronuclei; *E*, fusion-nucleus in the "pause," reduction of asters; *F*, first cleavage figure.

very unequal at the time of union, while the sperm-aster does not ordinarily divide until after the nuclei have united, though the central body is already double (Boveri, 95) from an earlier period (Fig. 186, A–C). Fusion of the pronuclei in most of these cases appears to the eye to be complete, so that the maternal and paternal elements cannot be distinguished as such either in the fusion-nucleus or in the resulting division-figure. This type of fertilization, rather infrequent in animals, is (so far as the nuclei are concerned) common in plants (*Œdogonium, Fucus*, bryophytes, pteridophytes, and many seed-plants (p. 453).

(2) In the second or *Ascaris* type (Fig. 187, D–F) the sperm-nucleus pauses within the egg until the polar divisions have been accomplished, with

the three following consequences: (1) During the pause the sperm-nucleus enlarges, assumes a vesicular structure, and finally may become as large as the egg-nucleus, and indistinguishable from it, except by its position, the pronuclei being exactly alike at the time of union (Figs. 197, 198, 200). (2) In many cases each pronuclus at the time of union has already given rise to a group of chromosomes for the ensuing division; hence no true fusion-nucleus is formed and the maternal and paternal nuclear elements remain in distinct groups that lie side by side throughout the whole process.

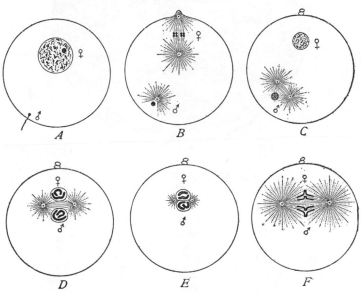

Fig. 187.—Diagram of *Ascaris* type of fertilization.

A, unmatured egg, entrance of sperm; *B*, sperm-aster and first polar spindle; *C*, sperm-amphiaster, polar divisions completed; *D*, union of the pronuclei; *E*, ensuing "pause," reduction of asters; *F*, first cleavage-figure.

Ascaris megalocephala, first worked out by Van Beneden in 1883–84, offers the classical example of this; but many other similar cases have since been described by other observers. (3) The sperm-aster typically divides to form an amphiaster before karyogamy has taken place (Figs. 187, 200, etc.).

The difference between the two foregoing types is determined mainly by the time-element, *i. e.*, the length of the interval between entrance of the sperm and conjugation of the pronuclei; for it has been shown experimentally (Wilson, '01b) that by artificially prolonging this pause by slight etherization of eggs of the first type (*Toxopneustes*) the phenomena of fertilization take on more or less completely the character of the second type

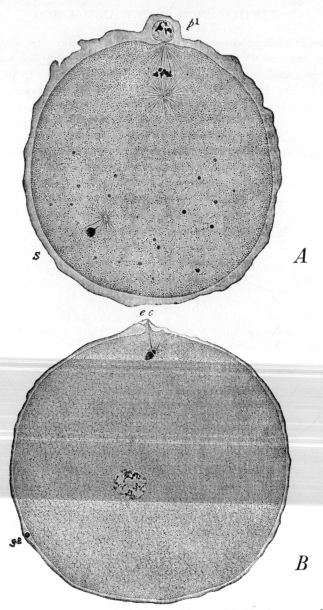

Fig. 188.—The *Ascaris* type and the sea-urchin type of fertilization compared.

A, egg of the worm *Thalassema* (*Ascaris* type) soon after insemination, surrounded by the fertilization-membrane; at p^1 the first polocyte and the second polar spindle. Near *s* the sperm-nucleus and sperm-aster, already completely rotated. Pseudoalveolar structure of the cytoplasm.

B, egg of the sea-urchin *Toxopneustes* about two minutes after insemination surrounded by the fertilization-membrane. Both polocytes have earlier been extruded and cast off. Below, the vesicular egg-nucleus; above the entrance-cone (*ec*) and below it the sperm-head and middle-piece beginning their rotation, with the first indications of the sperm-aster. At s^2 a second sperm that has not entered the egg.

(Fig. 209). It is, therefore, not surprising to find the two extremes connected in nature by a graded series of intermediate forms, due to the varying relation between the time of polocyte-formation and entrance of the sperm.[1] In certain extreme cases of this type the sperm appears to enter the egg at a much earlier period, even in the immature ovarian egg (oöcyte), there to remain in a quiescent state until the latter has completed its growth.[2]

Among the series of intermediate stages between the two extremes there are many forms in which the first polar spindle is fully formed and advances as far as the metaphase and then pauses until the sperm enters the egg, whereupon the polar divisions immediately proceed. This condition seems to be of rather widespread occurrence among invertebrates, typical examples being offered by the nemertine, *Cerebratulus*, the annelid *Chætopterus*, the mollusk *Dentalium* (Wilson) and various insects (Fig. 189).[3] In the annelid *Ophryotrocha* the first polar spindle may advance into the anaphase before entrance. In the next stage entrance of the sperm normally does not take place until after the first polocyte has been extruded from the egg. This condition has been found in some invertebrates and is widespread among the chordates.[4] In many of these cases (frog, mouse) the second spindle forms and proceeds to the metaphase before the sperm enters. In others this spindle may advance to the anaphase, as in *Siredon* (Fig. 189) or in the bat [5] but goes no further unless the sperm enters. One step more brings us to Type A, in which both polocytes must be extruded before fertilization, as in the sea-urchins, and in a number of cœlenterates (Boveri, Wulfert, Morgenstern). These various intermediate stages show at the time of karyogamy varying conditions of the gamete-nuclei and astral systems which in a general way run parallel to the relations between maturation and fertilization, though the correlation is not very exact.

That the eggs of different animals should display these various time-adjustments is an unexplained and curious fact; but they involve no essential differences in the main phenomena.[6]

---

[1] For review of these and other cases, see Korschelt-Heider, '03, pp. 630 ff.

[2] Examples of this have been described in certain platodes (*Otomesostoma*, v. Hofsten, '09, *Brachycœlium*, Kemmitz, '13) and in the annelid *Saccocirrus*, Buchner, '14. Further study of these cases seems desirable.

[3] See Henking, '90, '91 (insects), Mead, '98, Lillie, '99 (*Unio*.), '06 (*Chætopterus*), Coe, '99, Wilson, '04, Yatsu, '09 (*Cerebratulus*), Wilson, '03 (*Dentalium*), etc.

[4] See Maas, '99 (sponges), Bigelow, '02 (barnacles), Sobotta, '95 (*Amphioxus*), Fick, '93 (Axolotl), O. Schultze, '87 (frog, salamander), Sobotta, '97 (mouse), etc.

[5] Schultze, '87 (Siredon), Van der Stricht, '02 (bat).

[6] As might be expected these various intermediate conditions seem in certain cases to vary somewhat in the same species. See Schultze ('87), Korschelt ('95), Bigelow ('07), In *Asterias*, O. Hertwig ('78) long ago found that when the sperm enters prior to the formation of the first polar spindle the fertilization approximates to Type B, the pronuclei being of equal size at the time of union, but if entrance be deferred until after the polar bodies are formed the pronuclei are very unequal, as in the first type. This is evidently in harmony with the results of etherization.

The physiological and cytological aspects of fertilization offer a series of problems of which the most important are: (1) the general conditions of fertilization; (2) the union of the gametes and the fertilization-reaction; (3) the history of the gamete-nuclei, and the origin of the chromosomes;

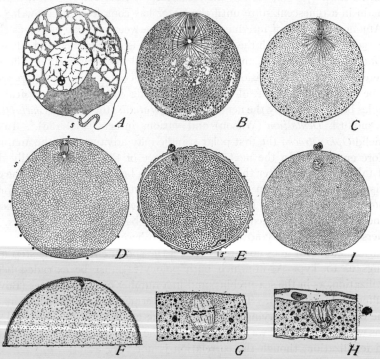

Fig. 189.—Different conditions of the egg when ready for fertilization.

A, the annelid *Myzostoma*, germinal vesicle intact, the sperm just entering egg (WHEELER); *B*, the annelid *Chætopterus*, first polar spindle in metaphase (LILLIE); *C*, the nemertine *Cerebratulus* (COE); *D*, the annelid *Ophryotrocha* (KORSCHELT); *E, Amphioxus* (SOBOTTA); *F*, the urodele *Siredon;* *G, H*, second polar spindles of same, enlarged, to show variations (O. SCHULTZE); *I*, the sea-urchin *Toxopneustes* (WILSON).

(4) the origin and history of the sperm-center, cleavage-centers and the associated cytoplasmic structures, and (5) history of the mitochondrial formations.

B. UNION OF THE GAMETES

1. General Conditions of Fertilization

Fertile union of the gametes only takes place when both have attained a certain physiological state of "maturity," (not to be confused with the result of "maturation" or meiosis). If insemination occurs at a period earlier than the normal the sperm either does not enter the egg or fails to initiate development. In the latter case many sperms may enter (*e. g.*, in the sea-urchin), but the nuclei do not penetrate far below the surface, do not enlarge, and sperm-asters do not make their appearance (O. and R. Hertwig, '87). Experiments especially on the eggs of echinoderms and nemertines have clearly proved that a condition of "cytoplasmic maturity" is necessary for the normal transformation of the sperm within the egg, and they indicate that this condition results from the setting free of certain substances from the nucleus. This conclusion was established by Delage ('99, '01) by cutting the individual eggs of sea-urchins and starfishes in two with the scalpel and fertilizing the fragments. When this operation is performed after breaking down of the germinal vesicle, both fragments of the egg, the nucleated and the non-nucleated, may be fertilized and undergo development. When the operation is performed before dissolution of the germinal vesicle the non-nucleated fragment cannot be fertilized. Similar results were subsequently obtained in the nemertine *Cerebratulus* (Wilson, '03). When the egg is cut in two before breaking down of the germinal vesicle and then fertilized, only the nucleated fragment develops (having first formed the polocytes); when the egg is cut after disappearance of the germinal vesicle both fragments develop, the cytoplasmic substance having become fertile.

This is in harmony with the results both of normal fertilization and of artificial parthenogenesis. Previous to maturation the sea-urchin egg is not only incapable of normal fertilization, but, as was shown by Morgan ('96, '99), it is also incapable of forming asters when chemically treated, a result which explains the failure of later observers to cause the immature eggs to undergo artificial parthenogenesis. This was experimentally tested in *Cerebratulus*, by Yatsu ('04, '05) who found that cytaster-formation is readily induced in enucleated fragments by treatment with $CaCl_2$ solution *if the egg be cut after fading of the germinal vesicle*, but in no case at an earlier period. There is reason to believe that this change affects especially the cortical layer of the egg; for egg-fragments or extra-ovates which lack this layer are incapable of fertilization.[1]

2. Approach of Egg and Sperm

We need not here consider the innumerable modes by which the germ-cells are brought together, further than to recall the fact that their union may take place inside the body of the mother or outside, and that in the latter case both eggs and sperm are as a rule discharged into the water, where fertilization and development take place. Both egg and sperm may

[1] Chambers, '19, '21; Just, '23.

live for a long time before discharge and for a considerable time afterwards without losing their capacity for fertilization; but this differs widely in different species.   As a rule the sperms are motionless while within the testis and only begin to swim when acted upon by secretions of the ducts or their accessory glands, or when set free into the water.   Their movement is ordinarily produced by whip-like lashings of the flagellum which drive the sperm onwards, head foremost, and usually in a spiral course.   To this latter circumstance, probably, as shown by Ballowitz ('90) and by Buller ('02) is due the fact that when the sperm comes in contact with a solid surface it remains in contact with it, rotating rapidly in a constant direction.[1] It is noteworthy that *Nereis*, the insects and the sea-urchins should agree in the fact that the direction of rotation is anti-clockwise.

What brings the sperm and egg together is still imperfectly known.   In plants it seems certain, both in case of the motile sperms of bryophytes and pteridophytes and the growing pollen-tubes of the gymnosperms and angiosperms, that the approach of the germ-cells is conditioned by chemical stimuli.   Pfeffer's classical studies ('84) demonstrated that the free-swimming sperms (antherozoids) of ferns and mosses react positively to weak solutions of certain chemical substances, crowding about and entering the ends of capillary glass tubes containing such solutions as they do about the opening of the archegonia in nature; and this has been fully confirmed by later observers.   In the case of ferns Pfeffer, followed by Buller ('00), found the most active substances to be the salts of malic acid (*e. g.*, sodium malate), but a number of other salts, both organic and inorganic, produce the same effect, though none are as active as the malates.   Most of these substances (tartrates, oxalates, phosphates, nitrates, chlorides, etc.) are of common occurrence in the cell-sap of plants.   Shibata ('05) reached similar results with the sperms of *Isoëtes*.   On the other hand, the sperms of mosses were shown by Pfeffer to be indifferent to the compounds of malic acid, but react positively to solutions of cane-sugar.   In *Fucus*, Strasburger believed he had evidence of chemotactic attraction; but this is not sustained by the more recent work of Bordet ('94) and Robbins ('16).   In the seed-plants there is a considerable body of evidence to show that the direction of growth of the pollen-tube is a chemotropic phenomena, determined by substances set free by various tissues of the pistil and ovules.[2]

The facts thus briefly reviewed have been generally taken as proof of a positive chemotaxis between the egg and sperm; but the question remains whether this may not be interpreted as a form of "trap-action."   In the

---

[1] This phenomenon was discovered by Dewitz ('86) and since studied by Ballowitz, Buller, Lillie ('13) and others.

[2] Molisch, '89, '93, Miyoshi, '94, Lidforss, '95, Buller, 'oo, '02.

case of animal sperms, the evidence is conflicting. Most of the experiments on the question have seemed to give a negative result. Neither von Dungern ('01, '02) nor Buller ('00, '03), after careful studies, were able to find any satisfactory evidence of a directive reaction between egg and sperm, though von Dungern proved that the movements of the sperm may be accelerated or depressed by various substances. Yatsu ('09) found in *Cerebratulus* that the sperm, after completely traversing the thick membrane, may sometimes be distinctly seen in the large peri-vitelline space, again entering the membrane from the inside instead of passing into the egg. Additional evidence was produced by Morgan ('04, '10), in his studies on cross-and self-fertilization in ascidians; and the conclusions of all these observers are in harmony with the earlier ones of Dewitz ('86) and Massart ('88, '89) which showed that the sperms of insects and frogs come into contact with the egg-envelope by accident, but having once done so remain in contact with it.

These results indicate that the sperm and egg are not brought together by an actual "attraction" between them as was once assumed. More recently the question has been reëxamined by De Meyer and F. R. Lillie. De Meyer found that the sperms of sea-urchins actively enter capillary tubes filled with egg-extract, while few or none enter similar tubes containing only sea-water. The extended experiments of Lillie ('13, '14, '15), were carried out by an adaptation of the method of Jennings in his well-known studies of chemotaxis among Protozoa. Drops of the substance to be tested were introduced by means of a capillary pipette into water containing numerous sperms in suspension. Drops of egg-extract, under these conditions, become surrounded by a multitude of sperms which penetrate the drop and form a double ring just within its margin, while such aggregation fails to occur in a drop of ordinary sea-water. A similar though less vigorous effect is produced by drops of weak solutions of CO_2 and of various acids (acetic, nitric, hydrochloric, sulphuric), while the sperms are indifferent to alkalis (KOH, NaOH) which have the same agglutinative effects upon them as have egg-extracts.

The facts in these experiments are perfectly clear; but they seem to offer nothing that is not explicable as a result of "trap-action," *i. e.*, that the sperms which accidentally enter the drop are unable to leave it. It seems probable, therefore, that the approach of egg and sperm is accidental and that no "attraction" between them exists. Sperms that enter the egg-envelopes or come into contact with the egg-periphery remain there; and as a rule no reaction between egg and sperm seems to take place save upon actual contact.[1] An exception to this is, however, offered by the starfish

[1] This subject is closely connected with the block to self-fertilization in hermaphrodites and to the entrance of additional sperm after fertilization has taken place (p. 421).

(*Asterias*), as was long ago described by Fol ('79) and recently confirmed by Chambers ('23). Here the sperm first attaches itself to the outer surface of the thick gelatinous envelope of the egg, and passes thence slowly inward. Fol figured the cone, some time before contact with the sperm, drawing out into an almost filamentous form to meet the latter. Chambers finds the cone present when the sperm is still at the periphery of the jelly-layer, the two already connected by a long protoplasmic thread that appears to be spun out from the cone to meet the sperm, and later drags the latter inwards to the egg-periphery. Further observation will be necessary to determine the origin of the thread and the nature of its activities.

In many cases (*e. g.*, insects, fishes, cephalopods) the sperm reaches the egg through a definite micropyle, the point of entrance being thus predetermined or limited. When no micropyle is present, the sperm passes bodily through the substance of the membrane, and it is a singular fact that even in the presence of a micropyle the sperm may enter by traversing the membrane at some other point. This fact has been clearly established in the sea-urchin by Boveri ('01), where the gelatinous envelope of the egg is perforated by a very definite funnel-shaped micropyle at the upper pole (Fig. 512), yet the sperm may enter at any other point. Another striking example is the egg of the nemertine *Cerebratulus*, which is surrounded by a thick membrane drawn out at the lower pole into a hollow projection, in some cases at least open at the tip. The sperm does not, however, enter through the opening, but penetrates the membrane at any point (Coe, '99, C. B. Wilson, '99, E. B. Wilson, '03, Yatsu, '09). This fact is less anomalous than at first appears, for the micropyle-lobe of *Cerebratulus*, is merely the remains of a stalk of attachment in the ovary, as is also the case with the micropyle in the sea-urchin and in pelecypods and other mollusks; and such micropyles may never have played more than an accidental part in fertilization. The perforation of the egg-membrane by the sperm is a widespread phenomenon and probably represents a more primitive condition.

How the sperm penetrates the membrane is not clearly known. It was formerly supposed that the sperm, once attached, bores its way actively through the envelope; and Dewitz has suggested, in case of the insect egg, that the rotary movements of the sperm on the surface may enable the egg to find its way to the micropyle by which it enters. It is probable, however, that another, and more important factor lies in some physical action that causes the sperm to be drawn passively into and through the membrane, somewhat as is the case with the entrance of the sperm into the egg, as described beyond. Bataillon ('19) has observed that naked frogs' eggs, whether from the body-cavity or after dissolution of the jelly-envelope by the action of potassium cyanide, are incapable of fertilization by the sperm, though they may readily be activated to parthenogenetic development by the puncture-inoculation method (p. 474). Somehow, therefore, the envelope of the egg is in this case necessary for entrance of the sperm.[1]

The point at which the sperm enters varies widely in different cases. When entrance is effected through a micropyle the point is to that extent predetermined, but it must be borne in mind that several micropyles may be present. When single the micropyle is most commonly at or near one pole of the egg, e. g., at the upper pole in the cephalopod (Fig. 113), in various fishes (Fig. 114), and in most insects (Fig. 112), at the lower pole in the pelecypods (Fig. 488). When the micropyle is absent or is not used for entrance the point of entrance may be indeterminate (e. g., in sea-urchins), but more commonly is more or less definitely localized. In telolecithal eggs with a large amount of yolk (e. g., birds, reptiles, elasmobranchs) entrance commonly takes place in the region of the upper pole; in smaller ova, such as those of platodes, mollusks, tunicates, or *Amphioxus*, the sperm more commonly enters in the lower hemisphere and often near the lower pole.[2] The relation is, however, too variable to be brought under any general rule.

It is not wholly certain whether the point of entrance (when constant) is predetermined by special structures in the cortical layer. A specially modified "receptive spot" in the neighborhood of the micropyle, or at the upper pole of the egg, has been described in many forms, e. g., in insects (Henking, '91), and in *Petromyzon* (Herford, '96); and various receptive structures have been described as preëxisting at this point, such as the "attraction cone" of *Asterias* or the funnel-shaped depression described by Metschnikoff ('86) in *Mitrocoma*. Many of these cases need reëxamination, for it is now certainly extremely doubtful whether the entrance-cone is ever formed before attachment of the sperm to the egg or its envelope.

3. Reaction of the Egg. Entrance of the Sperm [3]

Contact of the sperm calls forth a powerful and almost instantaneous reaction by the egg that is responsible not only for entrance of the sperm, but also for many other changes in the oöplasm. This reaction first appears in the peripheral or cortical layer of the egg, which thus plays an essential

---

[1] *Cf.* p. 421.

[2] See Wheeler ('97), Conklin ('05), Sobotta ('97).

[3] For modern reviews of the literature of this subject see especially Loeb ('13), Lillie ('19), Hyman ('23), Just ('12–'23).

part in fertilization; and in its absence the egg is unfertilizable.[1] The most obvious features of the reaction are: (1) the sudden throwing off of a *fertilization-membrane or activation-membrane*, which entirely surrounds the egg and separates from it to a considerable distance; and (2) by the sudden formation at the point of contact of a protoplasmic prominence, the *entrance cone* or *fertilization-cone* (Fig. 190), by which the sperm is swallowed up. These two events are so closely connected that they can hardly be separated in the description. They are often accompanied or followed by changes in the viscosity of the oöplasm and by active movements of its substance (p. 415).

a. The Cortical Changes. Loeb ('04, '13, etc.) has brought forward a large body of evidence to show that the cortical change is primarily a cytolytic or destructive process which is regarded by him as the first essential step in the activation of the egg, whether by the sperm or in artificial par-

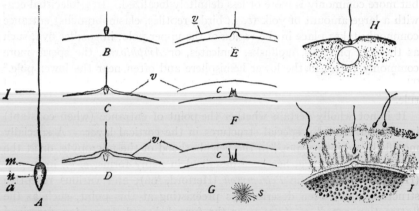

Fig. 190.—Entrance of the sperm into the egg. *A–G*, in the sea-urchin *Toxopneustes;* *H*, in the medusa *Mitrocoma* (METSCHNIKOFF); *I*, in the star-fish *Asterias* (FOL).

A, sperm of *Toxopneustes*, × 2000; *a*, the acrosome; *n*, nucleus; *m*, middle-piece; *f*, flagellum; *B*, contact with the egg-periphery; *C*, *D*, entrance of the head, formation of the entrance-cone and of the fertilization membrane; *E*, *F*, later stages; *G*, appearance of the sperm-aster (*s*) about 3–5 minutes after contact; entrance-cone breaking up; *H*, entrance of the sperm into a preformed depression; *I*, approach of the sperm, showing a supposedly preformed entrance-cone.

thenogenesis, through its effect upon the oxidative-processes of the egg (p. 475). This particular conception of the cortical change has, however, met with considerable opposition on the part of some observers.[2] R. S. Lillie ('09, '15, etc.) has especially championed the view that its most im-

[1] See Chambers ('21a, 21b), Just ('23). By tearing the egg-cortex the endoplasm may flow out to form an extravate which may contain the nucleus and assume a spheroidal form. Such fragments are often devoid of a cortical layer, and are then unfertilizable. If, however, cortical material be present such a fragment may be fertilized and undergo cleavage.

[2] See especially F. R. Lillie ('19), Just ('20).

portant physiological effect is an increase in the permeability of the egg, thus altering the electrical equilibrium within the egg and initiating the process of mitosis (p. 191). That such a change of permeability occurs at the time of fertilization has been experimentally demonstrated by many observers, but we are here concerned more particularly with the cytological changes.

Whether the fertilization-membrane preëxists as such before fertilization is a long debated question concerning which the evidence now seems to weigh in favor of the affirmative. O. and R. Hertwig ('87) denied its preexistence, for the reason that if ripe eggs be shaken to pieces and sperm be added the egg-fragments, like entire eggs, throw off membranes on fertilization by sperm. More recently the same conclusion was reached by Harvey ('10, '14) and by Loeb, who on the basis of a series of studies (summed up in '13) believed the membrane to be formed immediately before it is thrown off as a result of a cytolysis of the cortical layer. On the other hand, Fol ('79) considered the membrane to preëxist in the form of a delicate "couche enveloppante"; and the same result was reached by Theel ('92) and by Herbst ('93) who found that by crushing the sea-urchin egg the contents might be pressed out, leaving a delicate membrane-like surface film behind. More recently Kite ('12, '13) found that the fertilization-membrane preëxists in the unfertilized egg as a surface-film of firm consistency forming a vitelline membrane which may be dissected off from the egg by the micro-dissection needle. A similar conclusion was reached on various grounds by F. R. Lillie ('11, '14), Glaser ('13), Heilbrunn ('15) and Chambers ('21).[1]

Though the foregoing observations show considerable differences of detail, it is now generally agreed that the fertilization-membrane is not a wholly new formation produced at the moment of fertilization, but probably is derived from a preëxisting vitelline membrane which itself arises by a direct transformation of the plasma-membrane or modified surface-layer of the oöplasm. It is usually thrown off very suddenly, and there is now a general agreement that its separation from the egg is due to a sudden accumulation of liquid between them (Fol '79). Some observers have ascribed the result to a sudden contraction of the egg by which liquid is extruded from it.[2] Were this the only explanation, however, the diameter of

---

[1] Some observers have believed the fertilization-membrane to consist of two layers. Fol believed that in the sea-urchin only the peripheral layer is thrown off while the inner one remains to form the ectoplasmic layer (p. 413). A somewhat similar account is given by Brachet ('14). In the immature egg of *Amphioxus*, Sobotta ('97) described a delicate preëxisting vitelline membrane beneath which, upon discharge into the water, is formed a second and thicker membrane by direct transformation of the cortical oöplasm. If the egg remains unfertilized both membranes remain close to the egg; but immediately upon fertilization they spring out from the egg, fusing together to form a double "fertilization-membrane."

[2] See especially Bataillon, '00, '12, '14.

the unfertilized egg should be equal to that of the fertilized egg plus the perivitelline space; but as was long ago determined by Fol, Theel, Herbst and more recently by many others, such is not the case, the diameter of the sphere bounded by the fertilization-membrane being always greater and sometimes much greater than that of the unfertilized egg.[1] Clearly, therefore, the egg does not merely shrink away from the membrane but actually "throws it off." Fol considered this to result from a sudden imbibition of sea-water by a colloidal substance formed by the egg below the membrane; and such is also the conclusion of Loeb ('08, '13), who has demonstrated its correctness by interesting experiments.[2] Somewhat different from this is the process made known by F. R. Lillie ('11) in a careful study of the cortical changes in *Nereis*. Here, too, the unfertilized egg is surrounded by a delicate vitelline membrane, and within this is a "zona radiata," formed as a cortical alveolar layer with large, radially disposed alveoli. Immediately after attachment of the sperm the liquid contents of the cortical alveoli are discharged to the exterior, passing through the vitelline membrane, and swelling up outside it to form a thick layer of homogeneous jelly surrounding the egg. The zona radiata thus almost disappears as such, its remains, filled with liquid, now constituting a perivitelline space bounded peripherally by a delicate plasma-membrane lying just within the vitelline membrane (Fig. 191).

Considerable discussion has arisen, as to the behavior of the membrane as it separates from the egg. Fol ('77, '79) maintained that it rises from the surface of the egg in wave-like progress from the point of contact progressively around the egg (Fig. 190), and a similar account is given by many later observers.[3] Other observers, however, have failed to observe this and believe that the membrane rises simultaneously at all points, or at a number of separate points, around the periphery.[4] It is possible that both accounts are correct, or that the wave-like progress of elevation may, in some cases be too rapid to be readily observed. Loeb (*op. cit.*) has produced convincing evidence in favor of the second view by cooling the eggs (of sea-urchins) by which the process may be greatly slowed down for observation. It may then readily be seen that the membrane separates from the egg at

[1] In *Sphærechinus granulosus* Herbst found the diameter of the egg itself, whether fertilized or unfertilized, to be 0.88–0.96 mm., while that of the fertilized egg, membrane included, is 1.20–1.28.

[2] Whether the egg undergoes a change of volume upon fertilization is still a disputed question. That the egg shrinks after fertilization has been maintained by Bataillon as above, by Glaser ('13) in *Arbacia* and *Paracentrotus*, and by some others, especially by Okkelberg ('14) whose measurements on the lamprey seem convincing. Many observers, however, have found little or no evidence of such shrinkage, *e. g.*, Calberla ('77), Loeb ('08), McClendon ('10) and Chambers ('21). Perhaps different species differ in this respect.

[3] See Calberla ('78), Theel ('92), Herbst ('93), Wilson ('96); and more recently Ries ('09). Okkelberg ('14), Just ('19), etc.

[4] Harvey ('10), Heilbrunn ('15), Loeb ('08, '13).

many points, thus forming vesicles or blister-like projections from the egg around its whole periphery. By fusion of these vesicles the egg becomes surrounded by a continuous perivitelline space, filled with liquid and bounded externally by the continuous and evenly rounded fertilization-membrane. This space is often very extensive, yet the egg does not (at least in the early stages of development) move freely within it. It is probable, therefore, as was long since concluded by Fol ('79), that the liquid within it is of jelly-like consistency and does not consist merely of water.

The throwing off of the membrane is followed, sometimes after a considerable interval, by the appearance of the hyaline or ectoplasmic layer immediately around the periphery of the egg (p. 261). Most later observers have considered it as a separate product of the cortical oöplasm, formed either as a jelly-like secretion or by a direct transformation of the peripheral oöplasm which first becomes free of granules and then more sharply marked off from the egg.[1] The part played by this layer in cell-division indicates that in any case it should be regarded as a peripheral zone of active cytoplasm rather than a true membrane.

b. The Entrance-cone. The formation of the entrance-cone, long since described by Fol ('79) in starfish and sea-urchins, has often been studied by later observers. In the sea-urchins it is formed very rapidly by a sudden rush of the peripheral protoplasm towards the point of contact, generally forming a conical prominence into which the head of the sperm almost instantly passes (Fig. 190). After the sperm has entered, the cone persists for a short time, then assumes a ragged flame-shape and finally breaks up. In the sea-urchins the entrance-cone certainly is not formed until the sperm touches the egg; but in *Asterias*, as above indicated (p. 408), the evidence seems to show that it is formed while the sperm is still outside the jelly-envelope at a considerable distance from the egg-periphery.

In *Nereis* (Lillie, '11), which offers peculiar advantages for the study of the process, the conspicuous entrance-cone is formed essentially in the same manner as in the sea-urchin and extends outwards through the cortical "zona radiata" until it comes in contact with the membrane at the point where the sperm is attached (Fig. 191). Within a few minutes the entrance cone is retracted, drawing the membrane down to form a depression in which the sperm-head lies. When the cortical zone narrows by discharge of the jelly-forming substance (p. 412) the entrance-cone is again prominent externally and so remains for 10-15 minutes, when it rather suddenly disappears into the egg.

c. Entrance of the Sperm. The sperm was formerly supposed to bore its way actively into the egg by lashing movements of the flagellum; but this

---

[1] See especially Goldschmidt and Popoff ('08), Loeb ('08, '13), Painter ('18).

explanation, obviously inadmissible in the case of non-flagellated sperms, was undoubtedly erroneous.   It is now generally agreed that movements of the flagellum quickly cease after attachment of the sperm to the egg, and that the egg plays an active part in the process of entrance by its instan- taneous formation of the entrance-cone into which the head is as it were engulfed,[1] drawing the middle-piece and flagellum after it.   An unrivaled

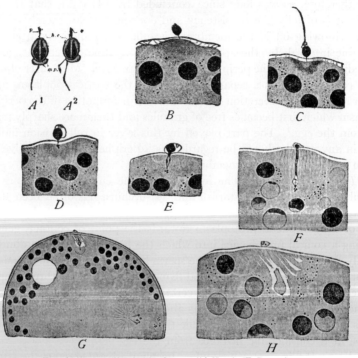

Fig. 191.—Fertilization in the annelid *Nereis* (F. LILLIE).

A¹, A², sperm-heads, the latter from the side to show asymmetrical attachment of flagellum (*h*, *c*, "head-cap," *m*, *p*, middle-piece, *p*, acrosome); B, sperm-head attached to egg-periphery; C–H, successive stages of entrance of the head, leaving the middle-piece and flagellum outside.   The elapsed time between B and H is from 40 to 50 minutes.

opportunity for study of this process is offered by the egg of *Nereis* where the sperm-head is not completely taken into the egg until forty or fifty minutes after its attachment.   Lillie's important studies (*op. cit.*) showed that the sperm is fixed to the egg-periphery by the tip of the long and spike- like acrosome, which penetrates the plasma-membrane and in about fifteen minutes has entered the cortical layer of the egg, leaving the nucleus out- side (Fig. 191, *B–D*), to enter the egg later.   Throughout these and the

[1] Kupfer and Benecke on the lamprey ('78). Fol on echinoderms ('79), etc.

later stages the sperm remains motionless and passively anchored to the entrance-cone. The head is now drawn into the egg in the form of a thick thread which perforates the vitelline membrane, and after its entrance enlarges to form a vesicle within the egg (Fig. 191), while *both the middle-piece and the flagellum are left outside.* In this respect *Nereis* at present remains a solitary exception. Certainly in most cases both middle-piece and flagellum are drawn into the egg after the head; for the entire sperm may often be seen after its entrance lying within the egg (Fig. 183). Another exception has been described in the sea-urchins, in which the earlier observers believed the flagellum, or its distal portion, to be left outside or to disintegrate in the remains of the entrance-cone; [1] it has more recently been asserted, however, that the flagellum enters the egg (Ries, '09). The case of *Nereis* conclusively demonstrates, however, that the flagellum is not necessary for the fertilization of the egg. More remarkable is the case described in the crab *Menippe* by Binford ('13), who could find no direct evidence that the nucleus enters the egg. He suggests, however, that the chromatin may go into solution, pass into the cytoplasmic capsule, and thus be carried into the egg. F. R. Lillie made the remarkable discovery that the sperm is still capable of fertilizing the egg after not only the tail and middle-piece but a portion of the head has been removed by centrifuging the eggs before the head has completely entered (p. 445). Still more remarkable is the result of Just ('22) who found that the egg may actually be fertilized by sperm that has been boiled [2] in oxalated sea-water (!) but the explanation of this is not yet apparent.

d. *Movements and other Changes of the Oöplasm.* The reaction of the egg to the sperm is shown in many other ways. The egg sometimes undergoes wave-like changes of form and the physical consistency of the oöplasm often alters. Active streaming movements of the oöplasm often take place, particularly in the cortical layer, and the relative distribution of protoplasm and yolk may undergo marked changes. For example, in pelagic fish-eggs a rush of the cortical oöplasm takes place towards the point where the sperm has entered, near the upper pole, and this gives rise to the germinal disc in which the blastoderm is formed (Agassiz and Whitman, '84). In the tunicate *Styela* (Fig. 524) the sperm, entering near the lower pole, calls forth a sudden down-flow of the cortical substance toward the entrance-point, and later a movement of this substance towards the posterior side of the egg (Conklin, '05). An interesting phenomenon is the formation of *polar rings*, described by Whitman ('78) in the eggs of leeches (*Clepsine*), by Vejdovský ('87) and by Foot ('96) in the naids (*Rhynchelmis*) and earth-

---

[1] Fol, '79, Wilson, '95, etc.
[2] *Cf.* artificial parthenogenesis by puncture of the egg with a glass stylet (p. 474); also the phenomena of gynogenesis (p. 460).

worms (*Allolobophora*). In the first two of these cases the polar rings are formed as thickenings of the cortical layer in the polar regions which con-

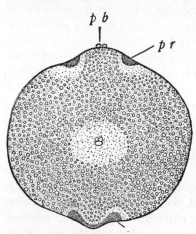

Fig. 192.—Egg of the leech *Clepsine*, during fertilization (WHITMAN).

p, b, polar bodies; *p, r,* polar rings; cleavage-nucleus near the center.

tract about the poles as they thicken, the polocytes being formed at the center of the upper ring (Fig. 192). Vejdovský's work has shown that the material of these rings has a definite prospective value in the development, giving rise in part to the teloblasts from which arises the main basis of the germ-bands (p. 1005). In *Allolobophora* the polar rings are believed by Foot to arise from a specific "archoplasm," originally scattered through the oöplasm. These movements of the oöplasm play a definite and essential part in the morphogenic process and are comparable to, perhaps are not separable from, those which take place as a consequence of maturation (p. 1005). From this point of view they are of the first importance in relation to the fundamental problems of prelocalization in the egg (p. 1062).

4. Monospermy, Dispermy, Polyspermy

Normal fertilization seems always to be accomplished by a single sperm, though more than one sperm may enter the egg. In this respect two well-marked types of eggs are to be distinguished. In the more frequent case fertilization is monospermic, the egg being normally adjusted for the entrance of a single sperm (echinoderms, nematodes, platodes, mollusks or mammals). The entrance of more than one sperm is in this case abnormal (*pathological polyspermy*) and nearly always leads to pathological or monstrous development. In a second type, mainly confined to eggs heavily laden with yolk (insects, elasmobranchs, amphibians, reptiles, birds), the egg is normally entered by several sperms (*physiological polyspermy*) [1] of which, however, only one is concerned in the further operations of syngamy.

Remarkable differences between these two types exist in respect to both the earlier and the later stages of development. In physiological polyspermy but one sperm-nucleus conjugates with the egg-nucleus (Figs. 194, 195) the

[1] For review of the earlier literature see Rückert, '99. See Kupffer, '70 (urodeles, anura), Kupffer, and Benecke, '78 (*Petromyzon*), Fick, '92 (axolotl), Braus, '05 (*Triton*), Oppel '91–'92 (reptiles), Blochmann, '87, '89, Henking, '92 (insects), Rückert, '90, '91. Beard, '96, Sobotta, '96 (elasmobranchs), Harper, '04 (birds).

others sooner or later degenerating without conjugating either with the egg-nucleus or with one another. In some cases, the degeneration takes place very early (urodeles, insects). In others, as was first demonstrated by Rückert ('90, '92, '99) in the elasmobranchs, the supernumerary sperm-nuclei may enlarge, assume a vesicular form and divide repeatedly by mito-sis, thus giving rise to numerous small nuclei (*merocytes*) that lie around the

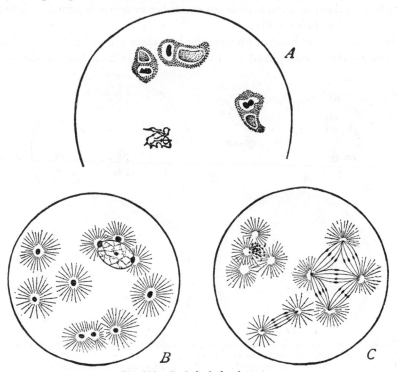

Fig. 193.—Pathological polyspermy.

    A, polyspermy in the egg of *Ascaris;* below, the egg-nucleus; above, three entire spermatozoa within the egg (SALA).
    B, polyspermy in sea-urchin egg treated with 0.005% nicotine-solution; ten sperm-nuclei shown, three of which have conjugated with the egg-nucleus; *C*, later stage of an egg similarly treated, showing polyasters formed by union of the sperm amphiasters (O. and R. HERTWIG).

periphery of the early blastoderm and may there even imitate a kind of ac-cessory cleavage, *e. g.*, in the pigeon's egg (Harper). In both these cases these nuclei divide with the reduced or haploid number of chromosomes, and seem ultimately to degenerate, without making any direct contribution to the embryo. Very different is the result of polyspermy in the normally mon-ospermic egg. In these cases dispermy or polyspermy is sometimes merely accidental, owing to the fact that two or more sperms strike the egg at the same instant, a conclusion justified by the fact that dispermy and poly-spermy is often readily produced experimentally merely by adding a very large excess of sperms to the eggs (sea-urchins, frogs). The same effect may, however, be produced as O. and R. Hertwig ('87) long ago showed in sea-urchin eggs, by subjecting them to the action of small quantities of nicotine, strychnine or morphine, to abnormally high temperature (31° C.), by allowing them to stand long in sea-water before sperm is added, or other-wise weakening their vitality.

In respect to the internal phenomena two cases are to be distinguished. In one of these, exemplified by the ascidian (Conklin, 'oo) or the frog

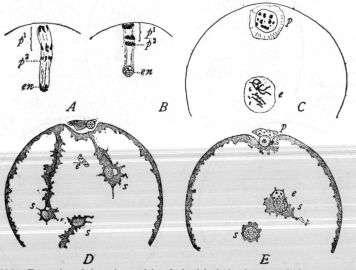

Fig. 194.—Formation of the polar nuclei and physiological polyspermy in insects; *A–C*, in the gall-fly *Rhodites*; *D, E*, in the bug *Pyrrchoris* (HENKING).

A, the second polar division in progress, in the egg; *B*, reconstruction of the egg-nucleus (*e, n*), three polar nuclei at p^1, p^2; *C*, polar fusion-nucleus (*p*) and egg-nucleus below; *D*, three sperms (*s*) in the egg, each lying in a granular sperm-track; egg-nucleus at *e*; *E*, conjugation of one sperm-nucleus with the egg-nucleus.

(Brachet, '10, Herlant, '11) but one sperm-nucleus conjugates with the egg-nucleus; in the second case two or more as in the sea-urchin (Fol, Hertwig, Boveri). In both cases development is abnormal for different reasons. In the ascidian dispermic or polyspermic eggs do not develop at all (Conk-lin, '05a). In the frog, as shown by Brachet and Herlant, a progressive cleavage may take place, each nucleus (including the fusion-nucleus) with ts attendant astral system giving rise to a separate bipolar mitotic figure in a manner that will be made clear from Fig. 195. The cleavage thus produced is more or less irregular, according to the number of sperms that have entered the egg, and many of the resulting blastomeres are binucleate. Owing, however, to the fact that the mitotic figures remain separate, each nucleus divides regularly and symmetrically with a bipolar spindle. A normal distribution of the chromosomes is effected at each mitosis; hence the resulting embryos contain nuclei of two kinds, diploid ones descended from the original fusion-nucleus, and haploid ones derived from the supernumerary sperm-nuclei. In this condition, no doubt, lies the explanation of the fact that the resulting embryos or larvæ are abnormal in various degrees and incapable of complete normal development. Herlant nevertheless determined the surprising fact that dispermic and even trispermic eggs may exhibit a development which up to a certain point is outwardly nearly normal. The dispermic egg develops its normal plane of symmetry, gastrulates and gives rise to a tadpole, one of which lived for three months; but all such larvæ, without exception, perish before reaching maturity.

In a third type of pathological polyspermy, exemplified by the sea-urchin egg, two or more sperm-nuclei conjugate with the egg-nucleus to form a triploid or polyploid fusion-nucleus, while other sperm-nuclei may remain separate in the protoplasm (as in the frog, the sperm-nuclei do not conjugate with one another). Such eggs undergo a multipolar cleavage, the nature of which is best studied in dispermic eggs, where both sperm-nuclei conjugate with the egg-nucleus. Such eggs usually produce a quadripolar or tripolar spindle (Fig. 430) and divide at once into four or three cells. When a large number of sperms enter the egg the resulting spindles do not remain separate (as in the frog) but unite to form all kinds of multipolar spindles (Fig. 193). In all these cases the chromosomes are distributed at random, and almost always irregularly, to the three, four or more poles. The resulting nuclei, therefore, receive varying numbers or combinations of chromosomes. After the initial tripolar or quadripolar division, the dispermic eggs continue to segment by bipolar mitosis, and often produce free-swimming larvæ; but in the great majority of cases development sooner or later becomes abnormal or monstrous and death ensues. Boveri has demonstrated by a brilliant experimental analysis ('02, '07) that the pathological effect is here due not to the abnormal chromosome-numbers but to their *false combinations*. Decisive proof is thus given of the qualitative differences of the chromosomes (p. 916).

It is an interesting question how the entrance of supernumerary spermatozoa is prevented in normal monospermic fertilization. In the case of echinoderm eggs, Fol suggested that it is accomplished mechanically by means of the vitelline membrane formed instantly after the first spermatozoön touches the egg. Immature eggs, before the formation of the polar bodies, have no power to form a vitelline membrane, and the spermatozoa always enter them in considerable numbers. O. and R. Hertwig found that in polyspermy induced by poisons the vitelline membrane is only slowly formed, so that several spermatozoa have time to enter. The fertilization-membrane seems in fact to be impermeable to the sperms; but it is now certain that this is not the only block to penetration of the sperm. It was long since shown by Driesch that the fertilization-membranes may be removed by shaking the fertilized eggs before cleavage; and such eggs cannot again be fertilized, i. e., cannot be rendered dispermic or polyspermic. The writer found ('03) that if the egg of *Cerebratulus* be cut in two

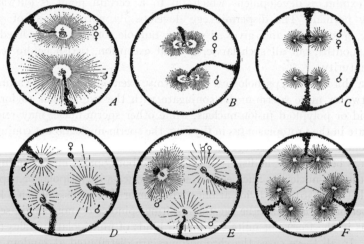

Fig. 195.—Dispermic and trispermic frog's eggs, from reconstruction of sections. The lines of black granules show the paths of the sperms in the egg (HERLANT).

A, B, C, dispermic eggs, in *A* and *B* one sperm-nucleus conjugating with the egg-nucleus above; *D, E, F* trispermic eggs; in *D* egg-nucleus at ♀; *E, F*, in each case one sperm-nucleus only conjugates with the egg-nucleus.

shortly after the entrance of the sperm and additional sperm be added, only one fragment develops (presumably that which contains the sperm-nucleus) while the other extrudes the polocytes but is unable to develop. If the same experiment be performed prior to fertilization both fragments, as earlier stated, develop in case the germinal vesicle has previously broken down, while only one develops if the germinal vesicle be still intact (p. 405). In all these cases alike the fragment lacks the protection of a fertilization-membrane (since in the first case the fragments have fresh-cut surfaces). Hence the failure of the fertilized fragment to development is not due to such protection but to some change in the oöplasm due to fertilization. To restate the facts in this case: the egg passes through two critical periods, the first

marked by the breakdown of the germinal vesicle and the consequent liberation of some substance into the oöplasm, the second by the entrance of the
sperm. The first of these events renders the oöplasm fertilizable, the second
establishes some kind of block that renders it once more infertilizable.[1]

An interesting further demonstration of this is offered by Just ('19) who
found in *Echinarachnius* that as soon as the sperm-head begins to enter the
egg the oöplasm becomes impermeable to other sperms even at points where
the raising of the membrane has not yet taken place, a "wave of negativity"
sweeping around the egg-periphery from the point of entrance towards the
opposite pole in advance of the membrane-formation. A similar, though
less simple result is obtained by causing the egg to throw off an activation-
membrane by treatment with butyric acid or similar agents (p. 475), then
rupturing or removing the membranes by shaking the eggs, and finally adding sperm. Such eggs, as shown especially by Moore ('16) and Just ('20),
if the butyric activation has been of a certain optimum degree, have wholly
lost the capacity for fertilization by the sperms. The latter may indeed enter the egg-periphery, but remain inert, "like foreign bodies" (Moore).
On the other hand, eggs either underexposed or overexposed to the membrane-producing agent are still capable of fertilization by sperm and of subsequent development, though often abnormal, particularly in the case of
overexposure.[2] The reaction thus shows a quantitative relation, its optimum being represented by normal fertilization, which causes total immunity of the oöplasm to action of the sperm.[3]

F. R. Lillie [4] has devoted an interesting series of works to establish the
conclusion that the fertilizable condition is due to the presence of a soluble
colloidal substance, *fertilizin*, which in some sense forms a chemical link
between the egg and sperm. This substance is characterized by its aggluti-
nating effect upon the sperm, and may thus readily be detected in the sea-
water. By means of experimental tests thus made possible it has been
shown that fertilizin is first produced at the time the germinal vesicle breaks
down; that its formation proceeds actively for some time after maturation;
and that it wholly ceases with fertilization or parthenogenetic activation.[5]

---

[1] Wilson, '03, p. 419.

[2] Thus, apparently, are explained the earlier results of Herbst ('06, '12) and of Loeb ('13) who
found that complete development might take place in eggs treated as above. The work of Moore
makes it probable that in these cases the eggs did not receive the optimum exposure.

[3] An interesting nearly related question is why in many hermaphroditic organisms the egg cannot
be fertilized by sperm from the same individual, though perfectly fertilizable by sperms from other
individuals. Morgan ('23) has recently shown that in ascidians the block to self-fertilization is
removed if the egg be freed from its membranes; apparently, therefore, it must lie in the membrane or structures associated with it (follicle-cells, test-cells, or their products). *Cf.* p. 586.

[4] Lillie, '13, '14, '15, '19, etc. See also in support of these conclusions Just, '15, '19, etc.

[5] Lillie found also that in *Nereis* the egg-exudate poured forth upon contact of the first sperm par-
alyzes the movements of the sperm and thus prevents their approach to the egg.

The substances set free into the oöplasm at the first critical period may therefore include fertilizin or its chemical antecedents. Since fertilizin may be extracted by sea-water an explanation is here offered of the fact noted by many observers that the fertilizing capacity of the egg, commonly diminishes progressively, and sometimes very rapidly, if the eggs lie un-fertilized in the water.[1] The total disappearance of fertilizin at the second critical period (upon activation) results, as plausibly assumed by Lillie, from a neutralization or binding of the fertilizin by some other substance brought in or activated by the sperm. These conclusions should, perhaps, not be taken too literally; but they have the great merit of opening the way to exact experimental studies of the problem on its physiological side.[2]

History of the Pronuclei

1. General

From the standpoint of heredity the central fact of syngamy is the *equivalence* of the gamete-nuclei. This does not mean that these nuclei are absolutely identical; both cytology and genetics have proved that such is often not the case. It means only that they, or their products, play approximately *corresponding* parts in development, as appears from the fact that in the main the offspring inherit equally from both parents. Morphologically, this equivalence is made visible to us in the fact that during the process of fertilization the gamete-nuclei undergo parallel changes, which in the end renders them nearly or quite indistinguishable. As a final result of these changes they give rise to corresponding, and in most cases almost identical, groups of chromosomes, the number of each being haploid or half that of the diploid (somatic) number characteristic of the tissue-cells. This remarkable fact (p. 426) has been designated as Van Beneden's Law (O. Hertwig). The only known exceptions to it (except in hybrids) are given by the sex-chromosomes and supernumerary chromosomes, and these are of such a nature as only to give additional weight to the conclusion.

2. Movements and Paths of the Pronuclei

Since the time of Van Beneden's early work on fertilization in the rabbit (1875) the sperm-nucleus and egg-nucleus within the fertilized egg have commonly been designated as "male" and "female" "pronuclei" respectively,[3] though by many authors they have been called *germ-nuclei* (O. Hertwig), or simply sperm-nucleus and egg-nucleus.

[1] See Lillie, '19, Just, '15, with further references.
[2] For more critical discussions see Loeb ('13) and especially Lillie ('19) with literature-lists.
[3] These nuclei are not "male" and "female" but paternal and maternal; and they differ from the somatic nuclei only in the haploid number of chromosomes.

After extrusion of the second polocyte a haploid group of chromosomes is left in the egg from which the egg-nucleus is built up. This commonly takes place by the formation of a group of chromosomal vesicles or karyomeres, as was long since observed by Bütschli ('70) in the eggs of gasteropods and nematodes and has since been described in a great variety of animals. In nearly all cases these fuse progressively to form a single vesicular nucleus with which the sperm-nucleus conjugates; but in a few cases (*e. g.*, in certain trematodes) karyogamy occurs before these vesicles have completely fused. The history of the sperm-nucleus in the egg differs from that of the egg-nucleus in that its s′arting-point is a greatly condensed and almost homogeneous solid mass; buṫ in many cases this, too, gives rise to a vesicular nucleus of the ordinary type before union. As already indicated (p. 401) in the *Ascaris* type of fertilization this nucleus finally becomes precisely similar in appearance to the egg-nucleus, and is indistinguishable from it except by its position.

The rotation of the sperm-head, already referred to (p. 396), is a very widespread if not universal phenomenon. It begins almost immediately after entrance of the sperm and is quickly completed as the sperm advances —in *Toxopneustes* the whole process is completed within two or three minutes from the time of insemination. Nothing is known as to the causes or physiological significance of this process. Its effect is to reverse the original position of the sperm-head and the middle-piece, the nucleus thus coming to lie with its base turned inward with the middle-piece lying in front of it. As a result of this the sperm-aster, which is sooner or later developed in the neighborhood of the middle-piece (sometimes already during the rotation) also typically lies in front of the sperm-nucleus and leads the way in the march towards the egg-nucleus (Figs. 184, 207).[1]

Both pronuclei now move through the protoplasm to their meeting-point, the direction and the extent of the movements varying widely in different species and within certain limits even in the same species. In general, the movement of the egg-nucleus is less extensive than that of the sperm-nucleus; but the paths of both pronuclei vary both with the point of entrance of the sperm and the position of the egg-nucleus at the time of insemination. The egg-nucleus, it is true, often lies eccentrically towards, and sometimes very near to, the upper pole; but Boveri's studies ('02) on *Paracentrotus* prove that in this sea-urchin at least the egg-nucleus, after formation of the polocytes, may wander to almost any point in the egg.

The first accurate study of the paths of the pronuclei was made by Roux ('87, '85) in case of the frog, where the course of the sperm is marked

[1] The rotation of the sperm-head seems first to have been definitely described by Flemming ('81) and has since been studied by many observers.

by a trail of pigment-granules carried in from the periphery as the sperm advances (Fig. 195). This study, which in its essential results has been confirmed by many subsequent studies on other animals, showed that the track of the sperm-nucleus is typically curved, and may be resolved into

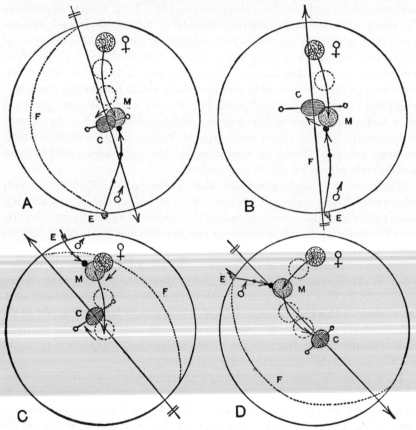

Fig. 196.—Diagrams showing the paths of the pronuclei in four different eggs of the sea-urchin *Toxopneustes*. From camera drawings of the transparent living eggs.

In all the figures the original position of the egg-nucleus (reticulated) is shown at ♀; the point where the sperm enters at *E* (entrance-cone). Arrows indicate the paths traversed by the nuclei. At the meeting-point (*M*) the egg-nucleus is dotted. The cleavage-nucleus in its final position is ruled in parallel lines, and through it is drawn the axis of the resulting cleavage-figure. The axis of the egg is indicated by an arrow, the point of which is turned towards the upper pole. Plane of first cleavage, passing near the entrance-point, shown by the curved dotted line.

two components, a *penetration-path*, nearly vertical to the surface, and a *copulation-path* along which the sperm-nucleus moves towards the point of union with the egg-nucleus. These two paths often form a considerable angle. To these may be added a third, the *cleavage-path*, along which the united nuclei move together to the definitive position of the first cleavage-nucleus. These facts are well illustrated in the sea-urchin egg (Fig. 196), where the egg-nucleus at first occupies an eccentric position near the point at which the polar bodies are formed but later (before fertilization) may wander to any position. Entering the egg at any point, the sperm-nucleus first moves rapidly inward along an entrance-path that shows no constant relation to the position of the egg-nucleus and is approximately but never exactly radial, i. e., toward a point near the center of the egg. After penetrating a certain distance its direction changes slightly to that of the copulation-path, which, again, is directed not precisely toward the egg-nucleus, but toward a meeting-point where it comes in contact with the egg-nucleus. The latter does not begin to move until the entrance-path of the sperm-nucleus changes to the copulation-path. It then begins to move slowly in a somewhat curved path toward the meeting-point, often showing slight amœboid changes of form as it advances through the cytoplasm. From the meeting-point the apposed nuclei move slowly along the cleavage-path to their final position, which is always in the egg-axis and slightly eccentric towards the animal pole. In this respect the sea-urchin is typical of a large number of animals, though the eccentricity is often much greater than in the sea-urchin.

In the tunicate *Styela*, where Conklin ('05) has carefully studied the phenomena, the egg-nucleus typically lies at first near the upper pole and the sperm enters near the lower pole. After its penetration the sperm-nucleus moves along nearly parallel to the surface towards the posterior side of the egg, while the egg-nucleus moves towards the same region. Their union takes place in the posterior region of the egg, not far from the equator, after which the two move in conjunction to the usual position in the egg-axis, not far from the upper pole (Fig. 524).

The causes that determine the movements of the pronuclei during fertilization of the egg are unknown. It was assumed by some of the earlier observers that approach and union of the nuclei were determined by some kind of attraction between them; [1] but this assumption is very insecurely based and the same may be said of the assumption that they are passively drawn together by the rays of the sperm-aster or by protoplasmic currents in the oöplasm (Conklin, '94, '99). Lillie has suggested that "as both sperm-nucleus and egg-nucleus are in physiological relation to the same mass of cytoplasm which is preparing to divide, they must reach the same position of equilibrium within the cell, and hence of necessity meet." [2] This, however, is contrary to the observed facts in the sea-urchin egg[3] where it is easy to see that the meeting-point of the pronuclei rarely if ever coincides with the

---

[1] See Wilson, '00, p. 204.   [2] '19, p. 65.   [3] See Wilson, in Wilson and Mathews, '95.

ultimate position of the fusion-nucleus and the cleavage-amphiaster and is sometimes far from it. It is readily seen, also, that the paths show no fixed predetermination but vary with the relation between the entrance-point and the position of the egg-nucleus. It seems clear also that the penetration-path is not affected by the position of the egg-nucleus, but is due to some relation between the sperm and the oöplasm—a conclusion further supported by the fact that in merogony (p. 465) the sperm penetrates an enucleated egg or egg-fragment.

The copulation-path, on the other hand, is clearly influenced by some relation between the pronuclei (Fig. 196 D). This is indicated by the fact that in cases of dispermy in sea-urchin eggs if one of the sperm-nuclei is the first to meet the egg-nucleus the movement of the second is immediately retarded;[1] and of similar significance is the fact that in cases of physiological polyspermy but one sperm-nucleus, as a rule, conjugates with the egg-nucleus. The nature of that relation is unknown; and nothing seems to be gained by the assumption of an actual attraction between the pronuclei. On the other hand, the movement of the fusion-nucleus to its final position (cleavage-path) evidently accomplishes somehow an equilibrium in the cell-system; but the nature of this, too, is unknown. The fact that the cleavage-nucleus takes up a definite position with respect to the egg-axis and the poles of the egg proves that the movements of this nucleus are accurately correlated with the organization of the egg as a whole; for the polarity of the egg, as Boveri clearly proved, is predetermined before fertilization and cleavage (p. 1067).

3. Conjugation of the Pronuclei. General History of the Chromosomes.

a. Karyogamy and the Chromosomes. Van Beneden's Law. As early as 1881, Mark clearly showed that in the slug *Limax*, the two pronuclei merely come into contact without actual fusing. Van Beneden in his epoch-making work on *Ascaris* ('83–'84) demonstrated that the pronuclei not only fail to fuse but give rise to two separate groups of chromosomes which enter the equatorial plate and there independently divide, their products passing separately into the daughter-nuclei (Fig. 197). Van Beneden thus first established the fact that the number of chromosomes contributed by each pronucleus is the haploid number—in this particular case two (*Ascaris megalocephla bivalens*) or one (*A. megalocephla univalens*).[2] This result was soon after extended by Carnoy ('87) to other nematodes, and the subject was more broadly studied in a striking paper by Boveri ('90) who showed

---

[1] Wilson, '96.
[2] This case is atypical in that these chromosomes are compound bodies which later break up into a larger number of small chromosomes. *Cf.* p. 323.

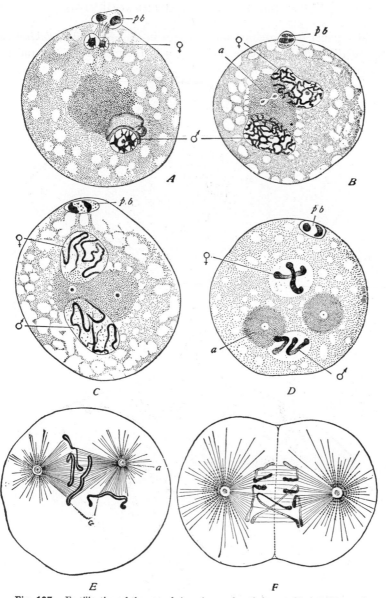

Fig. 197.—Fertilization of the egg of *Ascaris megalocephala*, var. *bivalens* (BOVERI).

A, the sperm has entered the egg, its nucleus is shown at ♂; above are the closing phases in the formation of the second polocyte (two chromosomes in each nucleus); *B*, the two pronuclei (♀, ♂) in the reticular stage; the sphere (*a*) contains the dividing central body; *C*, chromosomes forming in the pronuclei; the central body divided; *D*, each pronucleus resolved into two chromosomes; sphere (*a*) double; *E*, mitotic figure forming for the first cleavage; the chromosomes (*c*) already split; *F*, first cleavage in progress, showing divergence of the daughter-chromosomes toward the spindle-poles (only three chromosomes shown).

that the number from each pronucleus is 9 in the sea-urchin, *Echinus*, the
worm *Sagitta* and the tunicate *Ascidia;* 14 in the medusa *Tiara;* and 16 in

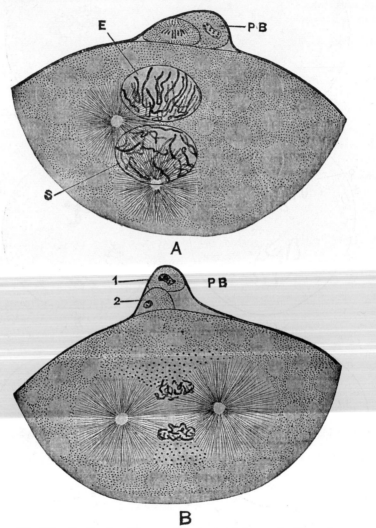

Fig. 198.—Fertilization of the egg of the gastropod *Pterotrachea* (BOVERI).

A, the egg-nucleus *E*, and sperm-nucleus *S*, approaching after formation of the polocytes; the
latter shown above (*P, B*); each pronucleus contains sixteen chromosomes; the sperm-amphiaster
fully developed; *B*, later prophase of the first cleavage.

the gastropods *Pterotrachea* (Fig. 198), *Carinaria* and *Phyllirhoë*. Similar
results have since been found in a large number of animals and plants.

Even when the pronuclei seem to fuse into a single cleavage-nucleus before formation of the chromosomes the validity of Van Beneden's law is established by numerous experimental and other data. Before reviewing this evidence we may briefly recall the various conditions observed in the gamete-nuclei at the time of their approach and union.

In the *Ascaris* type, as already described (p. 401) the pronuclei are at this time large, vesicular nuclei of the ordinary type, indistinguishable from each other save by their position. This condition, described by many of the early students of the subject, was first fully analyzed in detail in *Ascaris* by Van Beneden ('84, '87), whose epoch-making discoveries were confirmed and further extended by Boveri's early work on the same object ('88). It is now known to be of very wide occurrence. In some of these cases the pronuclei fuse while still in the reticular condition to form a single synkaryon (fusion-nucleus or cleavage-nucleus); and this may occur exceptionally even in *Ascaris*. On the other hand, such fusion is the typical process in many animals. This condition graduates almost insensibly into one in which no actual fusion takes place. In some forms the nuclei come together when in the spireme stage (*Triton, Pristiurus*); in others the chromosomes are still in the form of rather long threads (*Pterotrachea, Sagitta*); in still others they have nearly assumed their final form (*Ascaris, Ciona*). In some of the trematodes (*Polystomum*) the germ-nuclei at or shortly before the time of union are in the form of separate chromosomal vesicles or *karyomerites*.[1] Here the karyomerites formed after expulsion of the second polocytes, persist as such, while the sperm-nucleus is transformed into a corresponding group. As already indicated (p. 423), this is a common mode of formation of the egg-nucleus, and a more or less similar transformation of the sperm-nucleus has been observed in a number of cases;[2] but in most cases this condition is followed by the vesicular one.

That Van Beneden's law holds for all these various cases is demonstrated by a large body of evidence drawn from many sources, some of which may briefly be summarized as follows:

(1) The chromosome-number that appears in the first cleavage of the zygote is always the sum of the haploid numbers received by the gamete-nuclei in meiosis.

(2) In hybrids between forms having different chromosome-numbers the zygotic number is always (with certain exceptions that emphasize the rule) equal to the sum of the two parental haploid numbers (p. 841).

(3) An egg deprived of its nucleus, or an enucleated egg-fragment fer-

[1] See Goldschmidt, '02.
[2] E. g., in *Physa* (Kostanecki and Wierzejski, '96), *Prosthecereus* (Klinckowström, '97), *Thysanozoön* (Van der Stricht, '98), *Allolobophora* (Foot and Strobell, '00).

tilized by a sperm (*merogony*), segments with the haploid number of chromosomes (p. 465).

(4) Conversely, an egg activated by some other agent than the sperm develops with the haploid number of chromosomes (haploid parthenogenesis) unless the number be increased by a compensatory process (p. 477).

(5) A dispermic egg (in sperms normally monospermic) begins its development with the triploid number of chromosomes (p. 920).

(6) If the pronuclei be prevented from union by any cause, as in "partial fertilization" (p. 458), after etherization (p. 447) or in physiological polyspermy (p. 417), each produces the haploid number of chromosomes.

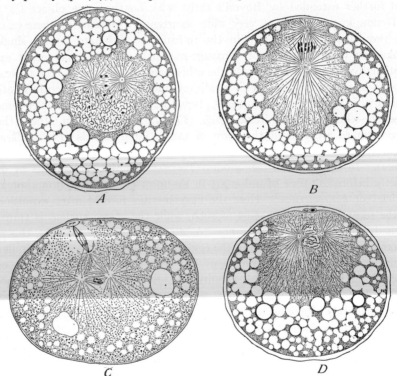

Fig. 199.—Fertilization in *Nereis* (*C* from Lillie).

A, egg shortly after entrance of sperm, in early prophase of the first polar mitosis; *B*, metaphase of first polar mitosis; *C*, anaphase of second polar mitosis; below, sperm-nucleus and amphiaster, the latter connected with inner polar center; *D*, karyogamy.

(7) If one of the pronuclei be destroyed or rendered impotent, the remaining one gives rise to the haploid number of chromosomes, and development may proceed with that number, as in gynogenesis (p. 460) or androgenesis (p. 464).

The foregoing cumulative evidence affords a complete demonstration of Van Beneden's law and likewise contributes to the proof that the chromosomes behave as if they were independent individuals which do not lose their identity from generation to generation but conform to the general law of genetic continuity by division. To this important subject we shall return in Chapter XI.

b. Cleavage and the Chromosomes. The Theory of Gonomery. Since the chromosomes of the fertilized egg are derived equally from the two gamete-

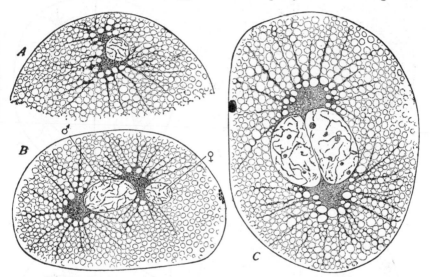

Fig. 200.—Fertilization of the egg in the copepod *Cyclops strenuus* (Rückert).

A, sperm-nucleus soon after entrance, the sperm-aster dividing; *B*, the gamete-nuclei approaching; ♂, the enlarged sperm-nucleus with a large aster at each pole; ♀, the egg-nucleus reformed after formation of the second polar body, shown at the right; *C*, the apposed reticular pronuclei, now of equal size; the spindle is immediately afterwards developed between the two enormous sperm-asters; polar body at the left.

nuclei, they are traceable equally to the two parents; and since each of these chromosomes (as in any other mitosis) splits into identical halves that are transported to opposite poles of the spindle during the first cleavage,[1] it follows that the primary diploid nucleus of the fertilized egg is exactly duplicated in the two daughter-nuclei. The latter therefore are built up from two haploid chromosome-groups that are respectively of maternal and paternal origin.

From the genetic standpoint, evidently, this fact constitutes the central

[1] That the chromosomes are already longitudinally split in the pronuclei at the time of their union, was first demonstrated in *Ascaris*, by Van Beneden ('83–'84), whose results were confirmed by Boveri and later observers.

phenomenon in fertilization.   Since the result of every normal mitosis is an exact duplication of the diploid mother-nucleus in the daughter-nuclei, it comes to pass that every nucleus of the embryo and finally of the adult is a dual structure to which the two gamete-nuclei have made equal contributions; [1] and here, evidently, is offered the basis for a physical explanation of

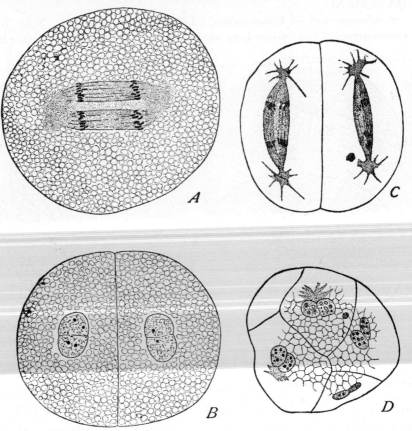

Fig. 201.—Independence of paternal and maternal chromatin in the segmenting eggs of *Cyclops* (*A–C*, from RÜCKERT; *D*, from HÄCKER).

A, first cleavage-figure in *C. strenuus;* complete independence of paternal and maternal chromosomes; *B*, resulting two-cell stage with double nuclei; *C*, second cleavage; chromosomes still in double groups; *D*, blastomeres with double nuclei from the eight-cell stage of *C. brevicornis*.

the fact that no detail in any part of the offspring is too small to be beyond the influence of both original germ-cells.

Van Beneden's demonstration of the independence of these two groups during the whole of the first cleavage in *Ascaris* soon led to attempts to

---

[1] Here again a reservation must be made in respect to the sex-chromosomes (p. 751).

trace them as such into later stages. It was shown by Haecker ('92b) and by Rückert ('95c,) that in certain copepods of the genus *Cyclops* the two groups not only remain distinct during the first cleavage, but give rise to *double nuclei* consisting of two distinct though closely united components. These observers also found that from these double or bilobed nuclei arise in each cell double spiremes and double chromosome-groups which again divide separately and give rise to double nuclei in the 4-cell and 8-cell stages; double nuclei were often observed in later cleavage stages even up to the time when the germ-layers were being formed (Fig. 201).

Out of these observations grew the conception of *gonomery*, *i. e.*, that the maternal and paternal chromosomes might remain in separate groups throughout life, even though inclosed in a common nuclear membrane. Haecker and Rückert believed that distinct evidences of such a duality could be discerned even in the germinal vesicle of the young ovum, indicating that the original gonomery had been maintained throughout the whole cycle of individual life, from egg to egg. Some evidence in favor of this conception has in fact been obtained. Conklin ('01, '04) found in the early development of the gasteropod *Crepidula* conditions closely analogous to those described in the copepods. The double character of the nuclei is here most clearly seen in the telophases and is usually partially lost in the resting-stage, though still indicated by a groove on one side of the nucleus in which the central spindle for the following mitosis appears. It is also indicated by the presence of two nucleoli in the "resting-nuclei," while each gamete-nucleus has but one (Fig. 202). By these indications Conklin traced the double character of the nuclei in all the cleavages up to the 29-cell stage, and in some cases to the 60-cell stage. Beard ('02) likewise found double nuclei in the embryonic stages of *Raja batis;* and more recently Bertram Smith ('19) has found in *Cryptobranchus* that all the nuclei are distinctly double from the 2-cell stage throughout the cleavage, and are still recognizable as late as the gastrula.

It has been conclusively demonstrated that the theory of gonomery is at best of limited application, double nuclei appearing only in certain cases, and only in the earlier stages of development. When the chromosomes show conspicuous and constant differences of size (a common condition in both plants and animals), they do not, in vastly the greater number of cases, show any trace of gonomeric grouping, nor are the nuclei externally double (see, for instance, Figs. 394, 395, 396). Conclusive proof of this is offered by hybrids in which the parental types of chromosomes can be distinguished by the eye. In *Menidia-Fundulus* hybrids (Fig. 400) Moenkhaus clearly showed that the two parental *groups* remain distinct as such only during the first two or three cleavages, the two kinds of chromosomes being thereafter intermingled indiscriminately. Substantially the same result is given by the later work of Morris ('14) on the fish-hybrids *Fundulus* × *Ctenolabrus*, and that of Harrison and Doncaster ('14) on moth-hybrids (Fig. 405). Again, in the Diptera the work of Stevens ('08), Metz ('14–'22), and others has conclusively established the fact that from an early stage in the ontogeny all or most of the chromosomes are arranged in pairs, each one of which consists recognizably of a maternal and a paternal descendant (Fig. 396). This, obviously, is quite incompatible with gonomery; and the chromosomes show traces of such a paired arrangement in a number of other animals and plants (p. 837).

It appears, therefore, that gonomery, though occasionally to some extent recognizable, represents no more than a tendency on the part of the chromo-

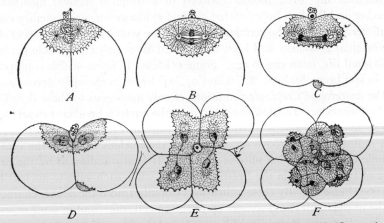

Fig. 202.—Gonomery in the early cleavage of the gastropod *Crepidula* (CONKLIN).

A, conjugation of the gamete-nuclei; *B*, spindle, with separate maternal and paternal chromosome-groups *C–F*, later stages, showing at each stage double nature of the nuclei.

somes to remain in separate maternal and paternal groups during a part of the earlier development; but this seems to be of somewhat exceptional occurrence, and is in any case soon lost, chromosomes of maternal and paternal ancestry becoming intermingled as development proceeds.[1] This only throws into stronger relief the fact that the maternal and paternal *chromosomes*, individually considered, do not lose their identity, but conform to the principle of genetic continuity throughout the ontogeny.

D. THE CYTOPLASMIC STRUCTURES

The history of the cytoplasmic structures in fertilization offers many problems that are still urgently in need of further investigation. The most

[1] See the figures of cleavage-nuclei and chromosomes in Hemiptera by Morrill ('10) and Hoy ('16), and in Diptera by Metz (*op. cit.*).

obvious of these relate to the central bodies, the chondriosomes and the Golgi-bodies or their products (acrosome); but it is probable that other cytoplasmic elements may be concerned in fertilization. After entrance of the sperm into the egg the acrosome, middle-piece and flagellum sooner or later disappear as individualized bodies, though some of their products may in some cases persist during the earlier stages of cleavage. In the bat, for example, Van der Stricht ('09) found that the sperm-tail (including the middle-piece) may still clearly be seen in one of the first two blastomeres.[1] In the sea-urchin Meves has shown [2] that the middle-piece may be traced with little change, at least up to the end of the fifth cleavage, being clearly distinguishable in one blastomere of the 32-cell stage. It seems clear, therefore, that neither middle-piece nor flagellum as such plays any direct part in the operations of fertilization. Nevertheless, the possibility remains that one or both these regions may bring into the egg certain structural elements that play such a part. From the region of the neck and middle-piece the egg receives two important structural elements, one of which, at least, is in fact believed to play an important part in fertilization. These are the chondriosomes and the central bodies, the history of which has raised many interesting questions.

1. The Acrosome

The acrosome has long been treated with rather scanty respect, often being regarded as no more than an organ of attachment to, or penetration into, the egg. Since, however, it seems always to be a product of the Golgi-bodies (p. 381) and since it enters the egg, we may suspect that it plays a more important rôle, though nothing is yet certainly known of this (p. 716). Lillie ('12) has made a careful study of its history in *Nereis*, showing that after entering the egg with the nucleus it passes inwards with the remains of the entrance-cone (Fig. 191) and breaks up into a small group of deeply staining granules which persist near the apex of the sperm-head until after the latter has completed its rotation and assumed a vesicular form, and after the sperm-aster has appeared. Finally, still connected with the remains of the entrance-cone, it separates from the sperm-nucleus and disappears from view. Bowen ('23), urging the analogy between the formation of the acrosome and that of the secretory granules (p. 716) has suggested the interesting possibility that it may be the bearer of some substance (?enzyme) that plays a part in the activation of the egg; but this is wholly hypothetical.

2. The Chondriosomes

Benda predicted that mitochondria would be found to be brought into the egg by the sperm and might play a definite rôle in fertilization.[3] The

---

[1] See also Lams ('10) and Levi ('15).   [2] '11, '12a, '12b, '14.   [3] '03, p. 781.

first part of this prediction has been realized, especially through a series of studies by Meves, which conclusively demonstrate that mitochondria are actually brought into the egg by the middle-piece, and perhaps also by the flagellum.[1] This was first observed in *Ascaris* (Meves, '11, Held, '12, '17), where the sperm-mitochondria are at first much larger and much less numerous than those of the egg (Fig. 204); and are thus distinguishable for some time after their escape from the disintegrating sperm-cytosome. As they

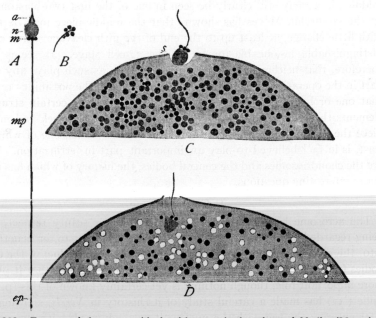

Fig. 203.—Entrance of the sperm, with chondriosomes, in the pelecypod *Mytilus* (MEVES).
A, mature sperm; *B*, middle-piece, to show chondriospheres; *C, D*, entrance of sperm into the egg. The black bodies are chondriosomes, the paler ones yolk-spheres.
a, acrosome; *ep*, end-piece; *m*, middle-piece; *n*, nucleus; *s*, sperm-head.

scatter through the egg they fragment into smaller bodies indistinguishable in size from the egg-mitochondria with which they are now mingled. The mitochondria are now distributed by cleavage with approximate equality to the resulting blastomeres. Meves assumed on theoretical grounds that sooner or later a conjugation must take place between the maternal and the paternal mitochondria (as also surmised by Benda); but no satisfactory support of this has been found.[2] Held endeavored to show that the paternal

---

[1] This fact, as Meves has pointed out, had earlier been briefly noted in the case of *Ascaris* by the brothers Zoja ('91), the mitochondria being described as "plastidules."

[2] See Retzius ('11), Vejdovský ('11-'12), Held (*op. cit.*), Kemnitz ('12), Romeis ('13). For a rejoinder to these criticisms see especially Meves ('13 and '18).

and maternal mitochondria remain quite distinct and may be distinguished from one another at every stage by certain characteristic differences of staining-reaction, even after the sperm-mitochondria have become as small as those of the egg. Like Meves, he found that mitochondria from both sources are passed on bodily to the cells of the early embryo.

In subsequent papers Meves extended his conclusions to other forms, showing that mitochondria are brought by the sperm into the egg in the sea-

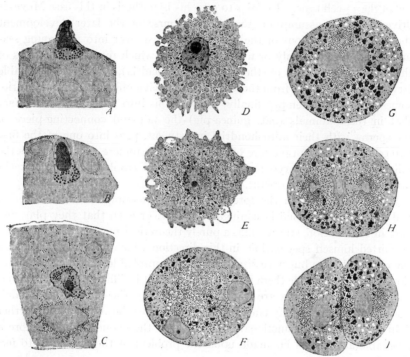

Fig. 204.—Mitochondria in the fertilization of *Ascaris megalocephala* (*D, E,* from HELD, the others from MEVES.

A–C, entrance of the sperm containing mitochondria, much larger than those of the egg; *D, E,* the sperm-cytosome disintegrating, setting free the sperm-mitochondria, which mingle with those of the egg; *F, G,* the sperm- and egg-mitochondria, now intermingled and indistinguishable in size; *H, I,* first cleavage, distribution of the mitochondria to the daughter-cells. The larger black bodies in Figs. *F–I* are yolk.

urchin ('12, '14) in the tunicate *Phallusia* ('13) in the nematode *Filaria* ('15) and in the mollusk *Mytilus* (Fig. 203, '15b). In *Filaria* the phenomena are similar to those in *Ascaris*, a number of larger chondriosomes being set free from the sperm soon after its entrance and fragmenting into smaller mitochondria indistinguishable from those of the egg before the first cleavage. In later stages of cleavage the numerous minute mitochondria originally present have been replaced by a much smaller number of thick, short chon- driomites which Meves assumed to arise by the linear alignment of both maternal and paternal mitochondria, which thus unite to form a common product. In *Echinus*, *Phallusia* and *Mytilus* the sperm-chondriosomes are less numerous and form a more or less compact mass of granules or short rods. In *Phallusia* and *Mytilus* their fate could not be traced; but in *Echinus*, as already stated, they could be followed in the cleavage as far as one cell of the 32-cell type. In order to save his hypothesis in this case Meves is driven into the assumption that in the course of the later development the permanent portions of the larva, which pass over into the young sea- urchins, are derived only or mainly from cells which receive derivatives of the middle-piece (*i. e.*, of the sperm-mitochondria), while the perishable larval structures arise from those cells that receive only maternal chondrio- somes(!) Meves attempts, finally, to bring this into relation with the fact that in the mammals (bat, guinea pig) the tail and connecting-piece of the sperm, with their mitochondrial investment, pass into one of the first two cells, the assumption here being that the blastomere which receives the tail produces the embryo proper, the other the trophoblast of Hubrecht (an accessory nutritive organ).[1]

It will be seen from the foregoing that the assumption that maternal and paternal mitochondria conjugate or fuse, or even that they play any part in fertilization, still remains a purely theoretical postulate. Meves has permitted himself speculations in this direction which not only far outrun the observed facts but necessitate the most improbable subsidiary assump- tions in order to make them fit. Nevertheless, it is difficult to believe that the sperm-mitochondria are wholly functionless in the egg or that Benda's surmise was an absolutely empty guess. We must, however, await further light on the general functional significance of the chondriosomes before a profitable attack can be made upon the problem of their relation to fer- tilization.

3. The Central Bodies and the Cleavage-Amphiaster [2]

The source of the cleavage-centers of the fertilized egg has been a subject of prolonged study, at first largely dominated by the general belief in the persistence of the division-center ("centrosome") as a permanent organ of the cell. Van Beneden somewhat doubtfully suggested that the cleav- age-centers are derived from the egg alone; and a similar conclusion was afterwards adopted by Wheeler ('97) in the case of *Myzostoma*, and more

---

[1] For further development of these conclusions, see Meves, '18.

[2] For fuller reviews of the literature, see especially Korschelt and Heider ('03), Kostanecki ('96 '02, '04, '06), Boveri, ('07), Nekrassoff, ('09).

recently by a few other observers (p. 442). Rabl ('89) urged, on the other hand, that if the doctrine of the persistence of the central body be well founded, we should expect fertilization to involve a conjugation not alone of nuclei but of central bodies; and in fact Fol soon afterwards published a

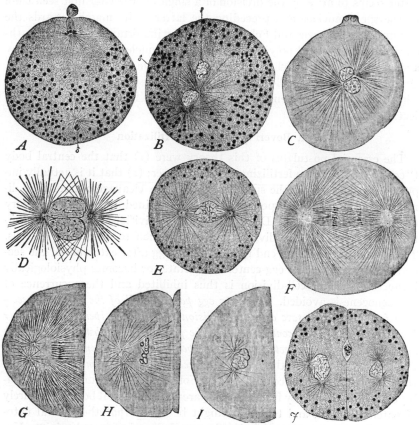

Fig. 205.—Fertilization in an annelid (armed Gephyrean) *Thalassema* (GRIFFIN).

A, second polocyte forming; sperm-nucleus and centrioles below; *B*, approach of the egg-nucleus and sperm-nucleus, the latter accompanied by the sperm-amphiaster; *C*, union of the pronuclei; *D*, later stage of last; *E*, prophase of cleavage-spindle; *F*, anaphase of the same, centriole divided; *G*, *H*, *I*, successive stages in the nuclear reconstitution and formation of the daughter-amphiasters for the second cleavage; *J*, two-cell stage.

remarkable paper entitled the "Quadrille of the Centers" ('91), in which he described precisely such a phenomenon in the sea-urchin egg. This result seemed at first to be confirmed by certain observations, but was later overthrown and, considered as a general theory of fertilization, is now regarded as obsolete.

From the first it stood in opposition to very specific earlier observations by a number of excellent observers,[1] which showed that after extrusion of the polocytes the aster remaining in the egg, together with its central body, disappears without discoverable relation to the cleavage-amphiaster. The latter seems to arise by the division of a single sperm-aster first seen close to the sperm-nucleus and preceding the latter in its march towards the egg-nucleus. Hertwig and Fol established the important fact that in pathological dispermy and polyspermy each sperm-nucleus is accompanied by a single sperm-aster which in each case may divide to form an amphiaster. On these facts primarily Boveri based his celebrated theory of fertilization,[2] which may form a convenient point of departure for a survey of the subject.

4. Boveri's Theory of Fertilization

The essential postulates of this theory were (1) that the central body ("centrosome") is the fertilizing element proper; (2) that it is actually imported into the egg by the sperm; (3) that the cleavage-centers arise directly by division of this sperm-center.[3] As outlined by Boveri the theory took the following form: During the somatic divisions the center is continuously handed on by division from generation to generation of cells. This process comes to an end in the mature egg after extrusion of the second polocyte, when the egg-center degenerates or becomes physiologically ineffective; further cell-division is thus inhibited and the occurrence of parthenogenesis avoided. *The ripe egg possesses all of the elements necessary for development save an active division-center. The sperm, on the other hand, possesses such a center but lacks the protoplasmic substratum in which to operate. In this respect the egg and sperm are complementary structures;* their union in syngamy thus *restores to each the missing element necessary to further development.*[4] Accepting this it follows that the nuclei of the embryo are derived equally from the two parents; the central bodies are purely of paternal origin; and to this it might be added that the general cytoplasm of the embryo seems to be almost wholly of maternal origin. Unfortunately this simple and clear conception can no longer be accepted in its original form, as Boveri ('14) himself finally admitted. Nevertheless, in the author's opinion, to reject it *in toto* would leave unexplained many striking facts.

When Boveri's theory was first put forwards nothing was definitely known concerning the history of the central body in the formation of the

---

[1] Fol ('79), O. Hertwig ('84), Vejdovský ('87, '89), Boveri, (87a, 88b, etc.).

[2] Boveri, '87b, '88a, '92, '95, '02a, '05, '07, '14.

[3] A nearly similar conclusion was independently reached by Vejdovský ('88).

[4] '87b, p. 155.

sperm. Observations by Platner ('89) and others seemed to show that this body passes into the apical region. Later observations demonstrated that the central body, or a derivative from it, all but invariably lies behind the nucleus in the region of the neck or middle-piece (p. 283). In harmony with the theory, therefore, was the fact, determined by numerous later observers, that the sperm-aster in the egg is typically focused at a point near the base of the nucleus, often very near to, or actually within the middle-piece—a relation now known to exist in most of the principal groups of animals.[1] A strong case is thus established in favor of the conclusion that a direct genetic relation of some sort exists between the central bodies of the spermatid, and those of the sperm-aster and cleavage-amphiaster in the egg.

In addition to the conditions observed in dispermic and polyspermic eggs (p. 416), Boveri's theory further fits with the following well-determined facts: In merogony (p. 465) non-nucleated egg-fragments are readily penetrated by the spermatozoa, and may segment and give rise to perfect larvæ. In "partial fertilization" as shown by Boveri ('88) the sperm-center and aster may separate from the sperm-nucleus, travel through the cytoplasm to the egg-nucleus and cause cleavage, the sperm-nucleus afterward fusing with one of the nuclei of a later stage (p. 458). Still more remarkable was the discovery of Boveri, earlier cited (p. 176), that during the first cleavage one of the resulting cells may receive only the division-center without a nucleus, and that this center may continue for a considerable period to multiply at the same rate as in the nucleated cell, though the nucleus is absent. Clearly therefore, (1) something is introduced into the egg by the middle-piece of the sperm that either is a central body or has the power to incite the formation of one; (2) this body is structurally independent of both nuclei and may divide independently of them; (3) independently of the division of the nucleus or cell-body some kind of specific genetic relation exists between the central bodies of successive generations. In harmony with Boveri's theory, also, are those numerous cases (nematodes, arthropods, chordates) in which the central bodies seem not to take any part in the polar mitoses (p. 508). This fact is particularly striking in cases, such as the ascidians (Hill, '95, Conklin, '12) in which the sperm-asters and the polar spindles may be seen lying side by side in the same section, the former with conspicuous asters and central bodies, the latter without trace of such structures. In this particular case Conklin (always

---

[1] E. g., in echinoderms (Flemming, '81, O. and R. Hertwig, '86, Wilson and Mathews, '95, Boveri, '95, etc.), nematodes (Meyer, '95), insects (Henking, '91), annelids (Korschelt, '95, Foot, '97), gastropods (Kostanecki and Wierzejski, '96, Linville, '00), platodes (Van der Stricht, '98, Francotte, '98), tunicates (Hill, '95, Golski, '99, Conklin, '05), amphibians (Fick, '93), elasmobranchs (Rückert, '99), etc.

skeptical concerning the universality of Boveri's theory) long since admitted that "there could not possibly be a clearer case of the origin of the cleavage centrosomes from the middle-piece of the spermatozoön." [1]

On the other hand, Boveri's theory was weakened by accumulating evidence that the central bodies seem in some cases to arise *de novo* (p. 684). It lost further ground with the final demonstration, that no central bodies are concerned in the fertilization of higher seed-plants, and that the cleavage-spindles are here devoid both of such bodies and of asters (p. 150). Even in the fertilization of those plants (*e. g.*, the cycads) where the whole sperm, including the blepharoplast (a derivative of a central body) enters the egg, no one has yet shown that this latter body plays any direct part in fertilization. Strasburger ('97) suggested that the essential fact in fertilization is the importation into the egg of a certain quantity of "kinoplasm," whether in the form of a definite central body (animals, generally) or in more diffused state (higher plants); but this still remains quite hypothetical. A third difficulty is offered by artificial parthenogenesis in such forms as sea-urchins, where the egg at the time of activation has long since extruded the polyctes, and all traces of central apparatus have disappeared from view. These eggs, evidently, must either form a new center or rejuvenate a preëxisting one.

A more specific difficulty appears in the fact that in a few cases no sperm-center or aster is found at any time associated with the sperm-nucleus. An early described case of this was that of *Myzostoma* (Wheeler, '95, '97), and more recently the same condition is described by Nekrassoff ('09) in the pteropod *Cymbulia;* in a number of the trematodes; [2] in the spider *Theridium* (Montgomery, '07); and in the mouse (Lams and Doorme, '07). Some of these cases are no doubt owing to a delayed development of the sperm-aster; and Kostanecki ('06) has proved such to be the case in *Myzostoma*, demonstrating that if union of the germ-nuclei be delayed by treating the eggs with hypertonic sea-water a sperm-aster and amphiaster develop as usual in close association with the sperm-nucleus. Nekrassoff found in *Cymbulia* a conspicuous egg-aster and center at every stage up to the period of karyogamy, though it finally disappears. Gille, on the other hand ('14), believes the egg-center to persist and give rise to the cleavage-centers (in trematodes). Again, in case of the honey-bee Nachtsheim ('13) believes the cleavage-centers to be derived from the egg, supporting this by the observation that in the mitosis of supernumerary sperms in the egg the spindles are of the anastral type, like those of the polar mitoses, while conspicuous

---

[1] '05, p. 23, '12, p. 545. For a full review of the earlier literature see Kostanecki, '04 (on *Mactra*) and '06 (on *Myzostoma*).

[2] Goldschmidt ('05), Katheriner ('04), Henneguy ('06), Schellenberg ('11), Gille ('14).

centers appear in the cleavage. This conclusion though accepted by Boveri ('14), does not seem very strongly grounded.

Still another, and apparently better founded, conclusion is reached by Conklin [1] in the case of the gastropod *Crepidula*, in which appears a division-center in connection with each pronucleus and persists up to the time of union or karyogamy (Fig. 206). These centers seem to disappear before cleavage; nevertheless the facts indicate that the two cleavage-centers

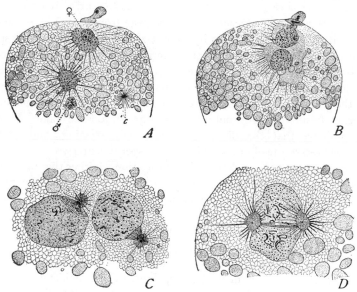

Fig. 206.—Fertilization in the gastropod *Crepidula* (CONKLIN).

A, approach of sperm-nucleus (♂) and aster to those of the egg (♀); at *c*, a cytaster or accessory aster; *B*, pronuclei nearly in contact; *C*, enlarged view of pronuclei somewhat later, a central body, aster and half-spindle in connection with each; *D*, late prophase.

which subsequently appear are still associated, one with each pronucleus, as before.

Even in the typical case (*e. g.*, in the sea-urchin, tunicate, or nematode) two difficult questions still remain, namely, whether the cleavage-centers are actually derived from the sperm-center, and whether the latter is actually brought into the egg by the sperm. (1) Doubts concerning the first of these questions arise from the fact that conjugation of the gamete-nuclei is always followed by a "pause" during which the sperm-asters, in some cases also the centers, become more or less reduced and may even wholly disappear from view. Examples of this occur in nearly all groups,[2] showing many degrees in the reduction of the asters at this time. These more extreme

[1] '03, '04, '12.   [2] On this point, see especially Coe, '98.

cases led to the opinion expressed by several writers [1] that the cleavage-centers are not directly connected with those of the sperm-amphiaster but are formed *de novo*. To establish such a conclusion is evidently difficult; for the centrioles are bodies of such extreme minuteness that if not surrounded by astral rays they might readily be lost to view among the protoplasmic granules of the egg or they may even become reduced to ultramicroscopical dimensions. Full weight must also be given to the fact, urged by several good observers, that the cleavage-centers arise at or very near the points at which the sperm-asters disappear from view.[2] A remarkable demonstration of this was found by Lillie ('12) in *Nereis*, where the sperm-amphiaster is from the beginning heteropolar, both aster and center being larger at one pole than the other and thus foreshadowing the unequal cleavage (Fig. 475). During the pause following union of the germ-nuclei the larger aster and center are always present while the smaller one disappears from view, but only to reappear at a later stage. It is here highly probable that the disappearance is only seeming, and that the cleavage centers are really identical with the sperm-centers.

Of the same type as the foregoing is the question whether the sperm-center is actually brought into the egg as a preformed structure in the neck or middle-piece of the sperm near which it so often lies (p. 396). The earlier opinion that the entire middle-piece is converted into the sperm-center was long since proved erroneous, by the observation that this structure is left behind near the egg-periphery and degenerates.[3] It is, however, a matter of great difficulty actually to trace the centriole of the sperm-aster to the neck or middle-piece of the sperm in the egg, though direct evidence of such an origin has been produced by several observers.[4] In the nemertines a minute, intensely staining granule (probably an "end knob") is readily seen within the globular middle-piece before entrance of the sperm. Within the egg the aster forms about the middle-piece but the outer portion of the latter is soon cast off, leaving the central granule as the sperm-center, which early divides into two to form the amphiaster (Fig. 207). This is probably the nearest approach yet made to a demonstration of the actual derivation of the sperm-center from a preformed structural element within the middle-piece.

An interesting argument against such a derivation has been based by F. R. Lillie ('11, '12) on the fact in *Nereis*, that the middle-piece, like the

[1] Lillie,' 97, Foot, '97, Child, '97, etc.

[2] See especially Kostanecki and Wierzejsky ('96) on *Physa*, Coe ('98), Kostanecki ('02), and Yatsu ('09) on *Cerebratulus*.

[3] Field, '05, Wilson. '97, Meves, '12, '14, etc.

[4] See Hill, '05, Kostanecki and Wierjeski, '96 (*Physa*), Boveri, '00 (sea-urchins), Conklin, '05 (tunicates) and especially Yatsu '07, '09 (nemertines).

tail, is left outside the egg (p. 415), and that a sperm-aster containing a central body appears *when only a fragment of the nucleus enters the egg*. This observation is made possible by the fact, already mentioned (p. 415), that as the sperm-nucleus enters the egg it is drawn out into an elongate rod-like form, so that at this time the portion left outside the egg may readily be removed by centrifuging the eggs. Here there cannot be the least doubt that

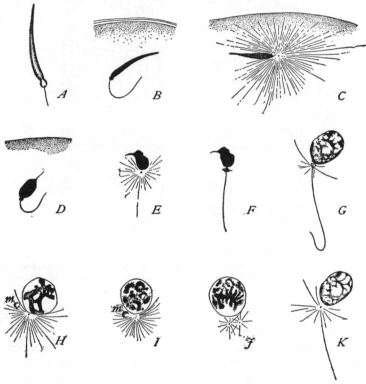

Fig. 207.—Early history of the central bodies in the fertilization of the nemertine *Cerebratulus* (YATSU).
A, the sperm-head and middle-piece before entrance; B, the sperm in the egg, rotation of the head; C, precocious development of sperm-aster; D, E, F, rotation completed, rounding of head; G, nucleus vesicular; H–K, later stages, showing cast-off middle-piece at m.

both the middle-piece and the basal region of the nucleus are left outside the egg. Nevertheless, the partial sperm-nucleus (which may be larger or smaller) rotates as usual after its entrance and *a sperm-aster of correspondingly diminished size is developed in relation to its most basal point* (Fig. 208). Such asters divide to form amphiasters and possibly may lead to cleavage, though this could not be determined with certainty.

Lillie considered that these results gave crucial evidence against the existence of any genetic relation between the sperm-center within the egg and that of the sperm or spermatid, and concluded that "the centrosome and aster owe their existence to an interaction between nucleus and cytoplasm, and not to any third element"; further, that the position in which they arise is "a function of polarity of the sperm-nucleus." The theory that a

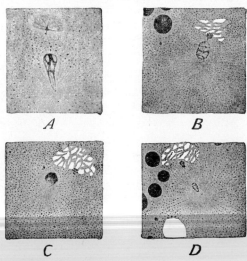

Fig. 208.—Fractional fertilization in *Nereis* (Lillie).

A, entire sperm-nucleus after entrance and rotation, with aster below and entrance-cone and acrosome above; *B, C, D*, three nuclear fragments, progressively smaller in size, with accompanying asters.

centrosome introduced by the sperm is necessary for such formation is therefore shown to be incorrect." [1]

This conclusion, however, is not justified by the facts, for Koltzoff ('09) has shown that the sperm-head of *Nereis* (Fig. 119) is traversed by a cytoplasmic axial rod extending throughout its whole length from middle-piece to acrosome, as is also the case in sperms of certain other animals (p. 281), and in some of these cases the rod is known to arise as a forward growth from the proximal centriole [2] seen in the middle-piece of *Helix*, or in the basal part of the nucleus in *Paludina* (p. 380). If such be the case in *Nereis* all the phenomena are simply explained by assuming the sperm-aster to be developed about the exposed end of this body; and the case falls into line with what is shown in other forms.

[1] '12, pp. 437–8, 445.
[2] In *Murex* (Stepan, '03), *Aporrhais* (Schitz, '20), *Fasciolaria* (Hyman, '23, with lit.).

Boveri's theory, evidently, must not be taken in too narrow or mechanical a sense; but there are facts still to be considered that tend to support it, in principle if not exactly in form. In the artificial parthenogenesis of sea-urchins, an egg that is normally adjusted to fertilization, and in which the whole mitotic apparatus seems to have disappeared, is still able, upon purely physico-chemical activation, to give rise to a normal cleavage-amphiaster. Further studies have shown that this egg is likewise able to produce (or rejuvenate) an active division-center as a result even when activated *by the sperm*. This was long since shown by O. and R. Hertwig ('87) by treating the eggs just after fertilization with solution of chloral hydrate or sulphate of quinine, or by subjecting them to abnormal temperatures. By these agents the union of the gamete-nuclei is often prevented, yet both nuclei may separately undergo the mitotic transformation accompanied by the development of a central body and aster. Ziegler ('98) attained the same result by constricting the egg with a fiber of cotton in such a way as to keep the gamete-nuclei apart. The writer ('01b) found the same phenomenon in eggs slightly etherized so as to retard or prevent the union of the gamete-nuclei; and Conklin ('04) reached a similar result in *Crepidula* by treating the eggs with hypertonic solutions.

In all these cases an aster or division-center arises in the neighborhood of each nucleus; but it is a significant fact that in the sea-urchin the sperm-center and aster typically divide to form an amphiaster, while the egg center, typically *gives rise to a monaster*, which rarely if ever divides to form an amphiaster (Fig. 209). This is exactly comparable to the production of a monaster in cases of incomplete activation in artificial parthenogenesis (p. 484).[1] These facts and those observed in etherized or chloralized eggs (as above) demonstrate that "*in these eggs the egg-center and sperm-center, under the same conditions, differ in potency, or in susceptibility to the activating agent;* and this supports Boveri's contention that in normal fertilization the spermatozoön imports into the egg an active central body which replaces one that has disappeared or become relatively ineffective."[2] "In normal fertilization the egg receives through the entrance of the sperm a strongly localized stimulus which affects the entire egg (as shown by the cortical reaction, etc.) and at the same time induces a local activity about the middle-piece which is transferred to the cleavage-nucleus by copulation of the germ-nuclei. This activity takes the place—or perhaps, to speak more accurately, becomes a

[1] On this point the observations of the Hertwigs, of Ziegler and the writer are in agreement, except that the Hertwigs also observed abnormal "pseudo-tetrasters." In Ziegler's case (a single egg only) the egg-nucleus passed through three successive mitotic cycles without division (p. 168). In the writer's material one case was observed in which the egg-nucleus produced a tetraster at the second cleavage. See also Painter ('18).

[2] Wilson, '01, p. 364.

part—of an activity on the part of the egg-nucleus *that would have ensued even had the germ-nuclei not united.*" [1]

From the point of view thus gained it is not difficult to interpret the observed departures from the more usual case formulated in Boveri's theory. In *Crepidula*, where both egg-center and sperm-center are present during fertilization (p. 443), Conklin ('04) observed that in eggs fertilized

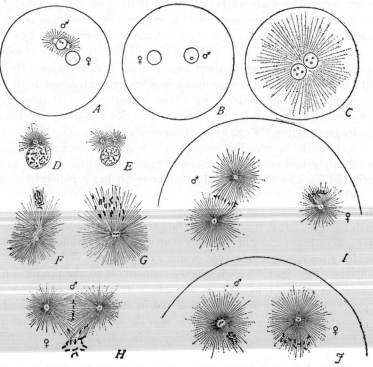

Fig. 209.—Fertilization of etherized eggs in *Toxopneustes*.

A–C, from living eggs, showing various observed conditions; *D–J*, from sections; *D–F*, sperm-nucleus and aster, showing division of latter; *G*, sperm-monaster; *H*, metaphase, sperm-amphiaster and chromosomes above, egg-chromosomes below; *I*, at the left, sperm-amphiaster in metaphase, at the right egg-nucleus with monaster; *J*, both sperm-nucleus and egg-nucleus have given rise to monasters.

in hypertonic sea-water the gamete-nuclei often fail to unite, in which case a division-center appears near each of them and both centers may divide to form amphiasters (Fig. 210). In this case, therefore, the egg-center and sperm-center seem to be nearly equally balanced and if kept separate go through the same changes. In the normal fertilization the two become

[1] Wilson, '01a, p. 582.

associated to form a single amphiaster, the division of both being thus for the time inhibited (p. 443). In the bee, on the other hand (assuming the correctness of Nachtsheim's observations), we might assume the egg-center to be readily capable of complete activation, while that of the sperm has become relatively, or perhaps completely, inactive. Such an interpretation is hardly more than a restatement of the facts as actually observed; but it

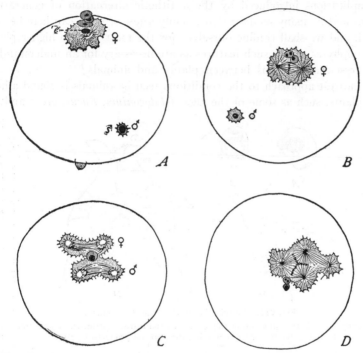

Fig. 210.—Fertilization of *Crepidula* eggs in slightly hypertonic sea-water (CONKLIN).

A, sperm-nucleus, below (♂), egg-nucleus (e) above, with small amphiaster; B, later stage, with well-developed egg-amphiaster; C, complete but separate egg-amphiaster and sperm-amphiaster lying side by side; D, the two amphiasters connected to form a quadripolar figure.

takes into account an essential element of truth in Boveri's theory which should not be ignored.

II. FERTILIZATION IN PLANTS [1]

So far as its broader features are concerned the problem of fertilization in plants, both in its morphological and its physiological aspects, is identical with that offered in animals, though its details are different. Neither in

[1] In the brief sketch here offered free use has been made of the valuable reviews of Mottier ('04) B. M. Davis ('05), Campbell ('05), of the works of Coulter and Chamberlain on the *Morphology of Angiosperms* ('03), and the *Morphology of Gymnosperms* ('17) and of Sharp's *Cytology* ('21).

higher nor in lower plants are individualized central bodies yet known to play any definite part in the process, which in this respect wears a somewhat simpler aspect than in animals; and in no plants above the thallophtyes is there an overlapping of the process of fertilization with that of meiosis such as is so commonly seen in animals (p. 398). Externally, on the other hand, the phenomena in plants seem more varied and intricate because of complications introduced by the antithetic alternation of generations (p. 496) and its many modifications. Only a few of these can here be considered, and we shall confine ourselves for the most part to higher plants or cormophytes and to such features as are necessary for an understanding of the essential relations between plants and animals.[1]

The nearest approach to the conditions seen in animals is found among lower plants, such as some of the algæ (*Œdogonium*, *Fucus*, etc.), and the

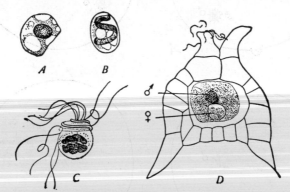

Fig. 211.—Fertilization in *Pilularia* (CAMPBELL).

A, B, early stages in the formation of the sperm; *C,* the mature sperm; *D,* archegonium during fertilization. In the center the ovum containing the apposed pronuclei (♂, ♀).

bryophytes and pteridophytes generally, in which a large quiescent egg-cell is fertilized by a minute free-swimming sperm-cell. In the seed-plants, ciliated sperms have been retained only in certain of the gymnosperms, and here lead no free-swimming life, being inclosed in the pollen-tube and discharged thence directly into the ovum.[2] In the lower archegoniates the en-

---

[1] A few of the lower forms are considered in Chapter VII.

[2] The formation of the pollen-tube, and its growth down through the tissue of the pistil to the ovule, was observed by Amici ('23), Brongniart (26), and Robert Brown ('31); and in 1833–34 Corda asserted the entrance of its tip into the ovule. The botanists of the eighteenth century engaged in the same fantastic controversy regarding the origin of the embryo as that of the zoölogists of the time. Moreland (1703), followed by Étienne François Geoffrey, Needham, and others, placed himself on the side of Leeuwenhoek and the spermatists, maintaining that the pollen supplied the embryo which entered the ovule through the micropyle (the latter had been described by Grew in 1672)· and even Schleiden adopted a similar view. On the other hand, Adanson (1763) and others maintained that the ovule contained the germ which was excited to development by an aura or vapor

tire sperm enters the egg, as in animals generally; and in the pteridophytes, the entire sperm seems even to enter the egg-nucleus (*Nephrodium*, Fig. 212).[1] In these forms more than one sperm may enter, but only one of them unites with the egg-nucleus (Mottier). As in many animals, entrance of the sperm is followed by the formation of a fertilization-membrane.

In the cycads the sperms are discharged from the tip of the pollen-tube into the archegonial chamber and there swim in a liquid discharged from

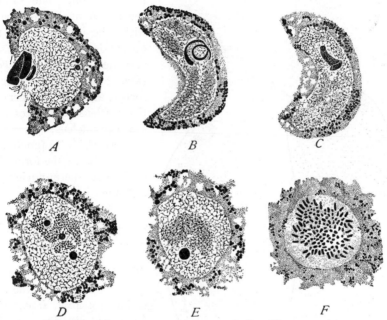

Fig. 212.—Fertilization in the fern *Nephrodium* (YAMANOUCHI).

A, sperm entering the egg-nucleus; B, C, the sperm lying within the egg-nucleus (two successive sections); D, E, disintegration of the sperm inside the egg-nucleus; F, metaphase-group of the first cleavage of the zygote, 128 chromosomes.

the pollen-tube. Several sperms may thus reach the same egg, but only one normally enters it, passing in with its spiral apex in advance. All observers have found that the entire sperm enters; but, as was first shown by Webber in *Zamia* and Ikeno in *Cycas*, both the spiral blepharoplast, with its cilia, and the protoplasmic body of the sperm, are left behind near the periphery (Fig. 213), while the nucleus "slips out of its cytoplasmic sheath and passes on alone from this point to the egg-nucleus " (Webber).

emanating from the pollen and entering through the tracheæ of the pistil. For a further account of the history of this subject see Coulter and Chamberlain ('03, Chap. VII).

[1] Yamanouchi, '08.

In all higher gymnosperms, and in angiosperms, the tip of the pollen-tube actually penetrates the upper pole of the embryo-sac and discharges into it both generative nuclei (*cf.* p. 309) and also, in higher gymnosperms one or two sterile or vegetative nuclei (the "tube-nucleus" and "stalk-cell-nucleus"). In the gymnosperms only one of the generative nuclei conjugates with the egg-nucleus, the other degenerating, as do also the two vegetative cells (Fig. 214). In the angiosperms also, but one generative nucleus conjugates with the egg-nucleus; but here the second is also functional, taking part in the formation of the endosperm-nucleus, as explained beyond.

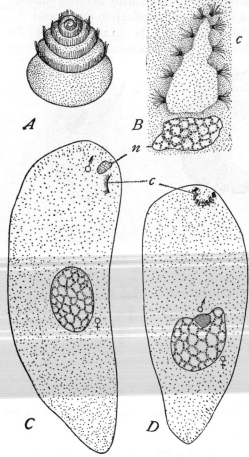

Since in all these cases the egg does not form polocytes or their homologues, we should expect to find fertilization similar in general type to that seen in the sea-urchin (p. 400), *i. e.*, with pronuclei differing in size and structure at the time of their union; and such is, in fact, often the case (Figs. 211, 213, 218), sometimes to an extreme degree, as in the fern (Fig. 212).

Fig. 213.—Fertilization in a cycad, *Zamia* (WEBBER).

A, sperm; *B*, the same after entrance into the egg, showing nucleus (*n*) and cilia-bearing band (*c*); *C*, the ovum shortly after entrance of the sperm; *D*, union of the pronuclei, cilia-bearing band near periphery (*c*).

In angiosperms the sperm-nucleus is in many cases elongated and vermiform, and often has a sigmoid or spiral form. This fact, first noted in the lily by Mottier ('97), and more carefully studied by Nawaschin ('09) in several other angiosperms (*Fritillaria, Juglans, Helianthus*) led the last-named observer to conclude that the sperm-nucleus is motile, and makes its way through the embryo-sac to the egg-nucleus by its own worm-like activity. The same conclusion is reached in a more recent work on the lily by Blackman and Welsford ('13), but no evidence of this has been found in some cases [1] and probably a decisive result can only be reached by observations on living material.

In *Lilium*, according to the authors last named, both germ-nuclei at the time of their union are in a spireme-like condition (Fig. 218), but during

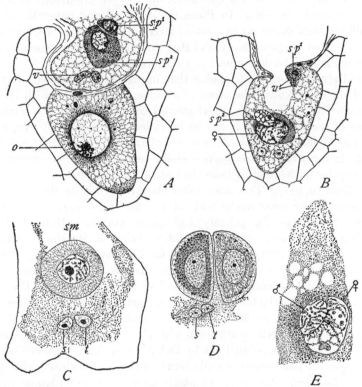

Fig. 214.—Fertilization in conifers (*A*, *B*, from COULTER and LAND; *C–E*, from COKER).

A, *Torreya*, the ovum (*o*) below, with the tip of the pollen-tube above, containing two unequal generative cells or sperm-cells (*sp*) and two vegetative cells (*v*); *B*, tip-contents discharged into the egg, conjugation of pronuclei below, second sperm-cell and vegetative cells above; *C*, *Taxodium*, tip of pollen-tube, sperm-mother-cell (*sm*) and vegetative nuclei (*s*, stalk-nucleus; *t*, tube-nucleus); *D*, two equal sperm-cells, one showing that dense sheath of starch-granules and "plastin-granules" surrounding the nucleus; *E*, conjugation of pronuclei, starch-bearing zone (from the sperm) extending around the nucleus.

the process of fusion (as earlier shown by Mottier) the sperm-nucleus gradually enlarges so as to become indistinguishable from the egg-nucleus (Fig. 217), and most observers have found that the paternal and maternal

[1] *e. g.*, in *Vallisneria*, Wylie ('22).

spiremes soon become indistinguishable. Recently, however, it has been found by Nothnagel ('18) that in *Lilium martagon* and in *Trillium* the paternal and maternal spiremes remain separate and give rise to separate groups of chromosomes; and similar results were obtained by Weniger ('18). In gymnosperms there is a more marked tendency for the pronuclei to remain distinct, and in a few cases each gives rise to its own spireme before fusion;[1] such cases approximate to the condition seen in *Ascaris* or the copepods (p. 426). In *Pinus* the maternal and paternal spiremes are still distinguishable up to a rather later stage of the spindle-formation (Fig. 215); and Ferguson has found that the number of chromosomes from each nucleus may be determined as 12 before their union.

It will appear from the foregoing that in plants, as in animals, fertilization of the egg involves the union of a single sperm-nucleus with the egg-nucleus. The angiosperms are characterized by a remarkable secondary process of fertilization (if it can so be called), discovered by Nawaschin ('99) and Guignard ('99) in *Lilium*, *Fritillaria*, and *Endymion*, and other forms. It consists in a conjugation of the second generative nucleus with the two polar nuclei derived from the vegetative structures of the maternal prothallium (p. 621). This union takes place either before, during or after the fusion of the polar nuclei with each other (Figs. 217, 218); and the product constitutes the primary endosperm nucleus. Here, therefore, there is a "double fertilization" the embryo being (in Strasburger's terms) the product of a primary or "generative fertilization" of the egg; while the endosperm formerly reckoned as a purely maternal structure results from a secondary or "vegetative fertilization" of the polar nuclei. The physiological motive for the latter is unknown, though Strasburger conjectured that it might effect an activation of the endosperm, analogous to that received by the egg-cell by its union with the first generative nucleus. It is highly probable, as pointed out by DeVries ('99, '00), Webber ('00) and others, that the phenomena of xenia here find their cytological explanation.

The Cytoplasmic Structures. In plants none of the cytoplasmic components of the sperm are yet known to play any definite part in fertilization, in spite of the fact that in many of the higher forms, as in the lower ones, a considerable quantity of cytoplasm enters the ovum. This is clearly seen in cycads and Ginkgoales, where the whole sperm enters; and the same is true of those higher gymnosperms in which the sperm-nuclei are surrounded by definite cytosomes, as is shown with great clearness, for example, in *Taxodium* (Coker, '02) or *Torreya* (Robertson, '04, Coulter and Land, '05). In both these cases the generative nuclei are surrounded by well-defined

---

[1] See especially Ferguson ('04) on *Pinus;* Noren ('07) and Nicholson ('10) on *Juniperus*, Miyake ('10) on *Cunninghamia*.

cytosomes, composed of finely granular protoplasm (Fig. 214). The whole contents of the terminal part of the pollen-tube are here forcibly discharged into the egg, including both generative cells, the tube-nucleus and stalk-cell-nucleus, and no doubt also part of the general protoplasm of the pollen-tube. The protoplasm of the generative cell is clearly visible after its entrance accompanies the nucleus in its advance towards the egg-nucleus, and spreads out to form an investing layer around both nuclei as they con-jugate (Fig. 214, B, E); and according to Coulter and Land may still be distinguished in the 4-cell stage of the embryo. Coker shows in *Taxodium* that this material contains numerous minute starch-grains and "plastin-granules," the latter staining intensely with safranin. The question is here prominently raised whether the pollen-tube may not introduce into the

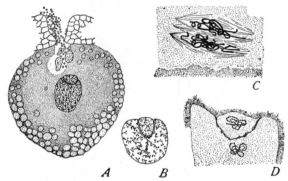

Fig. 215.—Fertilization in *Pinus* (FERGUSON).

A, the large ovum below, conjugation of the pronuclei near its center; the three small nuclei above are the second sperm-nucleus and two vegetative nuclei; *B*, more enlarged view of con-jugating pronuclei; *C*, later stage of union, each pronucleus has formed its own spireme; *D*, first cleavage-spindle, maternal and paternal spiremes still distinct.

egg plastids or chondriosomes, or both; thus offering another analogy to fertilization in animals (p. 435). A similar discharge of protoplasm into the egg takes place in *Pinus* (Ferguson) and probably in other gymnosperms, where the generative nucleus has no definite cytosome. In the case of angiosperms it still remains doubtful whether cytoplasm always accom-panies the generative nuclei as they enter the egg, but it seems probable that such is the case. In *Vallisneria*, as recently described by Wylie ('22) both sperms are said to enter the egg in the form of complete cells, the cytosome of one of them being still present at the time the gamete-nuclei unite.

That the sperm-protoplasm as well as nucleus enters the ovum, in many higher plants, is thus well established; but little or nothing is known as to its functional significance. By analogy with fertilization in animals we

are led to suspect that in plants likewise the egg is not activated by karyogamy but by some other factor; and many attempts were made by the earlier
observers to trace this action to centrosomes or corresponding structures.[1]
Later observations, in particular those of Mottier, Strasburger, and their
followers, gradually established the conclusion that in the seed plants no
centers or true asters are present in the mitotic figure at any stage of fertilization.[2]   Strasburger assumed the ovum to be predominantly tropho-
plasmic, its main function being to manufacture and store formative material,
while the sperm-cytosome is largely kinoplasmic.   The relative deficiency of
kinoplasm in the egg is responsible for the more or less complete inhibition of

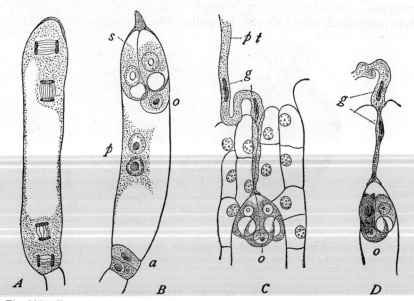

Fig. 216.—Formation of the ovum and penetration of the pollen-tube in angiosperms (STRAS-
BURGER).
    A, embryo-sac of *Monotropa*, showing the division that follows the two meiotic divisions and
produces the upper and lower "tetrads"; B, the same, ready for fertilization, showing ovum (o),
synergidæ (s), upper and lower polar cells (p), and antipodal cells (a); C, penetration of the pollen-
tube (p, t) in *Orchis;* o, ovum, with synergidæ at either side, g, generative nuclei in the pollen-
tube; D, slightly later stage with generative nuclei entering the micropyle.

its capacity for division.   The sperm overcomes this deficiency by bringing
a fresh supply of kinoplasm into the egg, either in the form of individualized
centers or of less definitely circumscribed kinoplasmic substance.[3]   Stras-

---

[1] See, for instance, Guignard ('91), who described in the lily a conjugation of paternal "centrosomes" with maternal closely agreeing with the "quadrille of centers" as depicted by Fol (p. 439).
[2] *Cf.* p. 150.
[3] '97, p. 420; see also '00, '01, etc.

burger thus sought to reconcile the apparent discrepancy between the higher plants and those forms in which definite central bodies are present (animals generally and various thallophytes such as *Fucus* or *Dictyota*). Strasburger

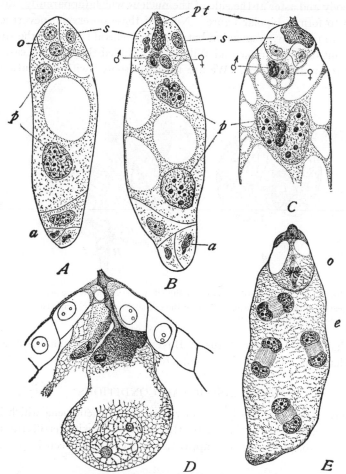

Fig. 217.—Fertilization in the lily (*D* from Mottier, the others from Guignard).

A, embryo-sac, ready for fertilization; *B*, both generative nuclei have entered the embryo-sac; one is approaching the egg-nucleus, the other uniting with the upper polar nucleus; *C*, union of the pronuclei; below, union of the second generative nucleus and the two polar nuclei; *D*, the fertilized egg, showing fusion of the gamete-nuclei; *E*, the fertilized egg dividing; below, division of the endosperm-nuclei; *a*, antipodal-cells; *o*, the oösphere or ovum; *p*, polar nuclei; *p*, *t*, pollen-tube.

and later Farmer and Williams ('98) showed that the fertilized egg of *Fucus* divides with well-developed asters and central bodies, and the same was found in *Dictyota* by Williams ('04) and in the bryophyte *Preissia* by Graham ('18). Williams found, further, that in *Dictyota* the parthenogenetic egg divides without asters or centers, the spindle being primarily multi-polar and intra-nuclear, while the fertilized egg develops a single well-marked central body and aster at the side of the nucleus which (apparently) divides into two to form a bipolar figure. None of these observers, nevertheless, were able to trace any connection between this central body and the sperm; and in point of fact Farmer and Williams concluded that in both cases the centers are formed *de novo*. We are thus confronted with a situation not

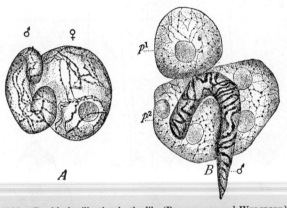

Fig. 218.—Double fertilization in the lily (BLACKMANN and WELSFORD).

A, conjugation of one sperm-nucleus (♂) with the egg-nucleus; *B*, conjugation of second sperm-nucleus (♂) with the two polar nuclei (p^1, p^2).

unlike that offered by the status of Boveri's theory in animals, save that the evidence in plants is less complete.

III. TRANSITIONAL CONDITIONS

We may here conveniently consider a group of phenomena which in respect to the activation of the egg by the sperm agree with fertilization, but in certain cytological respects approach the condition seen in partheno-gensis.

1. Partial Fertilization

In normal fertilization, as earlier indicated (p. 396), the sperm-aster (or amphiaster) always leads the way in the march of the sperm-nucleus towards the egg-nucleus, sometimes far in advance. Boveri ('88a) discovered in sea-urchin eggs (*Echinus*) that occasionally the sperm-nucleus may be left entirely behind, the aster alone uniting with the egg-nucleus. In such cases the aster and the egg-nucleus divide normally, and the first cleavage of the egg takes place without participation of the sperm-nucleus.

Karyogamy first takes place, as a rule, in the 2-cell stage, when the sperm-nucleus conjugates with the nucleus of one cell, and such eggs may continue their development at least as far as the blastula-stage. To this phenomenon (of course pathological in character) Boveri gave the name of *partial fertilization*, and saw in it fresh proof that fertilization of the eggs is not dependent on karyogamy, but on the sperm-center as the immediate agent of cleavage. Boveri found that in some cases karyogamy may be

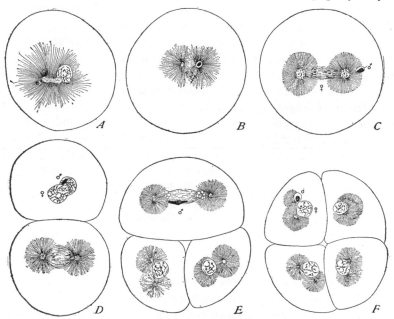

Fig. 219.—Partial fertilization in the sea-urchin *Echinus* after exposure of the sperms to weak KOH solution (TEICHMANN).

A, approach of pronuclei, sperm-aster dividing; B, egg-chromosomes below, sperm-nucleus and amphiaster above; C, anaphase, sperm-nucleus near one pole; D, 2-cell stage, conjugation of sperm-nucleus with cleavage-nucleus; E, late second cleavage, sperm-nucleus lagging on the upper side; F, 4-cell stage, with sperm-nucleus still separate, three cells with maternal nuclei only.

delayed until the 4-cell or 8-cell stage; and this is confirmed by Teichmann ('03), who has made a more extended study of the phenomenon (Fig. 219).

Since some of the nuclei in such embryos are purely maternal and others of biparental origin, we should expect to find the former of smaller size and dividing with the haploid number of chromosomes (9 in *Echinus*), the latter with the diploid or possibly a higher number; and such appears to be the case, though exact data are still lacking, in the pure-bred larvæ. In hybrids between *Sphærechinus* and *Paracentrotus* Herbst has observed a closely analogous case in which the nuclei are of two sizes and in some cases show small (maternal) nuclei on one side of the larva, and large (hybrid) nuclei on the other. This case, as will later be shown (p. 968), affords important evidence concerning the determinative action of the chromosomes in heredity.

2. Gynogenesis

In partial fertilization *sensu stricto* karyogamy still takes place, and the paternal nucleus takes part in development, though in more or less restricted degree. In a nearly related phenomenon, which may be called *gynogenesis*, the sperm penetrates (and in some cases activates) the egg but otherwise takes no part in the processes of development. Most such cases are pathological, but two remarkable cases have been made known in nematodes in which the phenomenon appears to be normal. In *Rhabditis aberrans* (Krüger, '13) the eggs are produced by individuals having the aspect of females, but producing sperms as well as eggs, and self-fertilizing; true males also exist, but are of extreme rarity. The eggs here seem to be set, as it were, for the diploid type of parthenogenesis, producing but one polar body without reduction of the chromosome-number (18). These eggs are *regularly penetrated by the sperm* which, however, takes no part in the development, degenerating *in situ* without any fusion with the egg-nucleus. In this case it is uncertain whether entrance of the sperm is necessary for activation of the egg, since in some cases no sperm-nucleus could be found.

In the closely similar case of *Rhabditis pellio*, on the other hand, *the eggs fail to develop unless penetrated by the sperm*. This species is normally diœcious, with males and females in nearly equal numbers. In a culture of this species P. Hertwig ('20) found a mutant that produced only females which, together with their offspring, showed the same cytological behavior as *R. aberrans* (Fig. 220), forming but one polocyte without reduction and developing with the diploid number (14). Here, however, development fails without entrance of the sperm. Both these cases are analogous to the parthenogenetic aphid or rotifer except that in one of them at least the eggs require activation by the sperm. The two cases thus offer, in the words of Brachet ('17) "a veritable bridge set up by nature between fertilization and natural parthenogenesis."

All other known cases of gynogenesis are pathological, occurring either in heterogeneous or incompatible crosses, or in cases where the sperm has been experimentally incapacitated to a certain extent by the application of external agents. An example of this is the activation of toads' eggs (*Pelodytes, Bufo*) with the sperms of a urodele (*Triton*) observed by Bataillon ('06, '09) in which the sperm traverses the envelopes and penetrates the egg-periphery but takes no other visible part in the development, and in *Pelodytes* remains near the surface without completely entering the egg. In neither case does the sperm-nucleus unite with the egg-nucleus, nor can a sperm-aster at any time be seen. Nevertheless, as a result of the action of the sperm the egg expels the second polocyte, the egg-nucleus re-forms, moves toward the center and there gives rise to the first cleavage-figure. Cleavage, in this particular case, is slow and irregular and soon

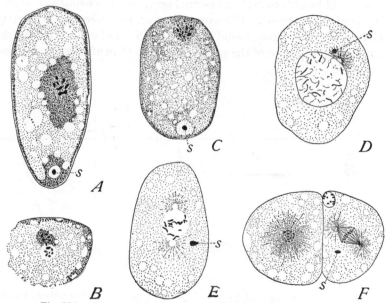

Fig. 220.—Gynogenesis in the nematode *Rhabditis pellio* (P. HERTWIG).

A, normal sexual egg showing above the 1st polar metaphase with 7 bivalents (the haploid number), sperm-nucleus at *s; B,* anaphase of first polar mitosis; *C,* corresponding stage of gynogenetic diploid egg, showing above the 1st polar metaphase with 14 univalents; *D, E,* prophases of the first cleavage of such an egg; *F,* 2-cell stage of same, with sperm-nucleus at *s.*

comes to an end; but in others, presently to be described, may lead to the production of nearly or quite normal tadpoles.[1]

Gynogenesis in various modifications has been observed in many other heterogeneous crosses (p. 970). Among such crosses have been found many transitions between gynogenesis and partial fertilization, the sperm-nucleus in some cases remaining wholly passive, in others conjugating with the egg-nucleus followed by a partial or complete elimination of the sperm-

[1] Bataillon considered this phenomenon as a true process of parthenogenesis, and the same term is applied by P. and R. Hertwig to the analogous radium gynogenesis described below. If, however, we adhere to our definition of fertilization as the activation of the egg by the sperm (p. 394) it is evident that the term parthenogenesis cannot properly be applied to such cases.

chromatin at a later period of development. Such cases have afforded important genetic data bearing on the relations between heredity and the chromosomes (p. 965). Bataillon's initial observations on Amphibia have been much extended by the studies of the Hertwigs [1] on the so-called "radium parthenogenesis" in amphibians and echinoderms, and on hybrids in fishes and amphibians. O. Hertwig showed that when the sperms of frogs and toads have been exposed to radium emanations in a certain degree they may still be able to activate normal eggs, but development is more or less delayed or abnormal. The same observer, confirmed by G. Hertwig in the case of echinoderms, found the abnormality to be much less marked after prolonged exposure of the sperm to radium than after a much shorter

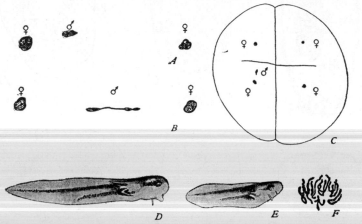

Fig. 221.—Gynogenesis in eggs of Amphibia fertilized by sperm exposed to radium (A–C, from P. HERTWIG; D–F, O. HERTWIG).

A, B, first cleavage telophases of frog, lagging sperm-chromatin at ♂; C, 4-cell telophase, sperm-chromatin at ♂; D, normal tadpole of *Triton*, 17 days; E, gynogenetic tadpole of same age; F, haploid chromosome-group from tail epidermis of such a larva (from a photograph).

exposure. This paradoxical result was explained by the assumption that after shorter exposures the sperm-nucleus, though injured by the radium emanations, is still able to conjugate with the egg-nucleus and to take part in cleavage and development; but abnormalities result because of the pathological influence of the affected sperm-chromatin. Longer exposures, on the other hand, kill the sperm-nucleus or render it incapable of taking part in the development. The egg, therefore, while still activated by the sperm, develops with only the normal maternal chromosomes. This explanation was borne out by cytological studies. In the sea-urchin G. Hertwig found that after prolonged treatment of the sperm the sperm-nucleus often fails

[1] O. Hertwig, '10, '11, '13; G. Hertwig, '11, '12, '13, '18; P. Hertwig, '13, '16, '17, '20.

to unite with the egg-nucleus, remaining passively in the protoplasm, sometimes near the equator, sometimes near one pole. In either case the egg-nucleus divides normally, with the haploid number of chromosomes. The sperm-nucleus often degenerates (gynogenesis in the strict sense), but there is evidence that in some cases it may later fuse with one of the cleavage-nuclei (partial fertilization). Many cases were also found in which the sperm-nucleus completely fuses with the egg-nucleus; but in such cases cleavage is of a very abnormal character.

In Amphibia the phenomena are of the same type. O. Hertwig ('13) showed that after intensive radiation of the sperms of *Triton* the fertilized eggs might give rise to nearly or quite normal tadpoles, in which, at the age of 24 days, the dividing epidermis-cells clearly showed the haploid number of chromosomes, 12 (Fig. 221). In the frog, similarly treated, P. Hertwig ('13) found that during the first cleavage only the egg-nucleus divides (presumably with the haploid number of chromosomes) while the sperm-nucleus is left behind near the equator and may be seen as a clump of chromatin in the 2- and 4-cell stages. No fusion with the egg-nucleus at any stage could be detected. "The entrance of the sperm here operates in the same manner as puncture by a fine needle in Bataillon's experiments." [1]

Further studies on hybrid amphibians and fishes,[2] in some cases preceded by radium treatment of the sperms, have yielded many other interesting results that can here be only briefly reported. Some of these crosses, such as *Rana arvalis* ♀ × *fusca* ♂, *Bufo communis* ♀ × *viridis* ♂, and *Triton tæniatus* ♀ × *cristatus* ♂, produce true hybrids as proved by the characters of the offspring; and G. Hertwig has shown in the first of these hybrids that the nuclei are as large as those of normal (pure-bred) larvæ and hence presumably diploid. In other crosses the nuclei are for the most part only approximately half the normal size and hence presumably haploid; examples of such crosses are *Bufo viridis* ♀ × *Hyla arborea* ♂ (with or without preceding radium treatment of the sperm) and *Bufo communis* ♀ × *Pelabates fusca* ♂. The larvæ thus produced are noteworthy both for their small nuclei and slow and often abnormal and dwarfed development. Others however—and this is the striking fact—are of normal size and development and have nuclei of normal size (hence presumably diploid). In some of these crosses the same result appears after intensive radiation of the sperm, a treatment which as shown by O. and P. Hertwig, the sperm-nucleus is killed. The conclusion seems probable, therefore, that even in such (presumably) diploid larvæ development is gynogenetic, the diploid number

[1] P. Hertwig, p. 178.
[2] See especially O. Hertwig, '10, '11, '13; G. Hertwig, '13, '18; P. Hertwig, '11, '12, '13, '18; P Hertwig, '13, '16, '17, '20; G. and P. Hertwig, '14; Oppermann, '13.

having been restored by a doubling of the maternal haploid group. G. Hertwig's studies, especially of the cross *Rana esculenta* ♀ × *Bufo viridis* ♂ show that such diploid larvæ arise from eggs in which the first cleavage stages are notably delayed as compared with the haploid ones; this author finds reason herein for the conjecture that the diploid number may be restored by a monocentric mitosis (p. 168) occurring before cleavage begins.

The slow and often dwarfed development of the haploid larvæ is ascribed by G. and P. Hertwig to the disproportion between the nuclear and the cytoplasmic volume of their cells, raising the question whether such larvæ are capable of complete development unless the diploid number be restored by a compensatory doubling.[1] To this question we shall later return.

3. Androgenesis

By this term we may designate the activation of the egg by the sperm followed by development without the participation of the egg-nucleus.

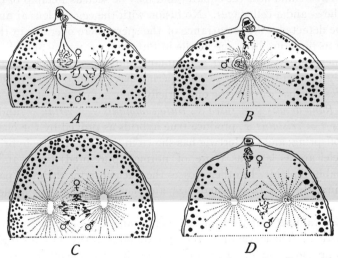

Fig. 222.—Androgenesis in *Chætopterus* after treatment of the eggs by radium and fertilization by normal sperm (PACKARD).

A, abnormal karyogamy in progress; *B*, defective formation of the egg-nucleus (♀) after second polar mitosis; *C*, maternal chromosomes (♀) lagging and degenerating on the spindle; *D*, maternal chromosomes wholly eliminated.

G. Hertwig ('11, '13) first demonstrated this phenomenon in the eggs of frogs or toads that were first treated by radium and then fertilized by normal frog-sperm. The result is closely similar to that of the converse experiment in which the normal egg is fertilized by the radiated sperm. As in the latter

---

[1] See especially P. Hertwig, '20, Nachtsheim, '21.

case, development is more or less disturbed or abnormal, more so after shorter or less intensive treatment of the egg than after longer or more intensive; and in the latter case the nuclei of the resulting larvæ are markedly smaller than in the former. Hertwig therefore concluded, though without further cytological evidence, that in this case the egg-nucleus is incapacitated, and that the nuclei of the embryo are solely of paternal origin, i. e., descendants of the sperm-nucleus alone. This process is designated as "androgenetic" or "merogonic" development ('13, p. 119); but as will presently be shown such a use of the word "merogonic" is hardly justifiable.

Analogous results were reached by Packard ('18) on radiated eggs of the annelid, *Chætopterus*, fertilized by normal sperm. Sections of these eggs show that already during the formation of the polocytes marked abnormalities occur in the history of the egg-chromatin and that the resulting egg-nucleus sooner or later degenerates without taking part in cleavage, while the sperm-nucleus and sperm-asters go through their normal transformations and form the first cleavage-figure and its successors (Fig. 222). The nuclei of the embryo, accordingly, are of purely paternal origin, and of haploid constitution, showing at each division 9 chromosomes instead of the diploid number, 18.[1] As in the foregoing case it is unknown whether such larvæ may develop into the adult stage.

4. Merogony

The climax is reached in the phenomena of *merogony* (Delage, '01) or the development of an egg-fragment *devoid of a nucleus* fertilized by a normal sperm.[2] This was discovered by O. and R. Hertwig ('87), who found that the eggs of sea-urchins may readily be shaken to pieces which quickly round up to a spheroidal form and may be fertilized by the sperm as if they were whole eggs. Some of the fragments are nucleated, others non-nucleated; but both kinds alike may be penetrated by the sperm, throw off fertilization membranes and undergo development. Boveri ('89, '95, etc.) and later observers demonstrated that such embryos may even develop into perfectly formed dwarf larvæ, in some cases not more than one-fourth the normal volume (Fig. 459). Boveri showed that non-nucleated egg-fragments of one species might be fertilized by the sperm of a different species, an experiment of remarkable interest to students of heredity. A possible source of error in some of these experiments, as shown in a posthumous paper by Boveri ('14) is the fact that in the operation of shaking

---

[1] A nearly similar process was described by Goldschmidt ('12) in normal eggs of the evening primrose, *Œnothera biennis* when fertilized by pollen of *Œ. muricata;* but in a later work ('16) this conclusion is withdrawn.

[2] This name would seem to apply etymologically equally well to the fertilization of a nucleated egg-fragment, but the term has not been generally employed in this sense.

the eggs to pieces the egg-nucleus may collapse so as to become invisible in the living material, though sections show that it may still give rise to a group of chromosomes. Such an error is excluded if the eggs be cut singly with a knife into two halves and both fertilized. In nemertines, where this experiment may readily be performed, both the nucleated and the enucleated fragment may upon fertilization undergo development; and the same is true in *Dentalium* (pp. 405, 1065).[1] Merogony was demonstrated in the alga *Cytosira* by Winkler ('01); and more recently Spemann ('14) and Baltzer ('21) found it to be possible even in vertebrates (*Triton*).

Merogonic embryos or larvæ are remarkable for the fact that their cytoplasm is of maternal origin, their nuclei (and possibly also their central bodies) of paternal, in this respect agreeing with the androgenetic larvæ described in the preceding section. As in the latter case, we should expect them to develop with the haploid number of chromosomes and with much smaller nuclei than in case of normal larvæ; and in sea-urchins such is the fact, as shown especially by the work of Boveri ('95, '05), Morgan ('96) and other observers. Boveri showed that dwarf larvæ derived from nucleated fragments have at first nuclei as large as those from whole eggs, thus contrasting in a striking way with the merogonic larvæ from non-nucleated fragments. Later, however, this difference is equalized in the process of cleavage, by which the normal karyoplasmic relation is restored (p. 728).

In the newt (*Triton*) Spemann ('14, '19) ingeniously obtained merogonic larvæ by cutting the fertilized egg in two by means of a noose formed by a fine hair. This egg is normally polyspermic (p. 416), one sperm-nucleus conjugating with the egg-nucleus while the others remain apart and sooner or later degenerate. It thus becomes possible to cut in two the fertilized but still unsegmented egg in such a manner that one half contains the fusion-nucleus, the other a single sperm-nucleus.[2] Both fragments may develop into tadpole larvæ; and Baltzer ('22) was able to rear one such haploid merogonic larva to a period (100 days) when the metamorphosis was already beginning. The nuclei of this larva, as was to be expected, were found to be only half the size of corresponding diploid larvæ from nucleated fragments.

5. Summary

The various cases reviewed above clearly demonstrate that fertilization, *i. e.*, activation of the egg by the sperm, does not depend upon karyogamy or a union of gamete-nuclei but is a reaction between egg and sperm that

[1] Wilson, '03, Yatsu, '04, '10, Zeleny, '04.

[2] The approximate position of the egg-nucleus in these eggs is indicated by the polar body, while the entrance points of the sperms are seen as dark spots on the surface of the egg. The plane of section can thus be determined during the operation.

may take place in the presence of only a single haploid nucleus. Genetically the facts have an important bearing on the chromosome theory of heredity, for they offer the probable explanation of "false hybrids" (Millardet) which show the characters of one parent only. As such, for example, G. Hertwig designates the gynogenetic larvæ from the cross *Rana esculenta* ♀ × *Bufo viridis* ♂, which show only the color of the mother.

In the same category belong those cases of hybrids in which some or many of the sperm-chromosomes degenerate without taking part in the latter development (*e. g.*, in sea-urchins, p. 843), and which in consequence show a more or less pronounced matriclinous heredity. Such cases should not be confused with those of simple Mendelian dominance; for the eliminated chromosomes represent lost characters which presumably cannot reappear in the offspring of such hybrids.[1]

IV. PARTHENOGENESIS

True parthenogenesis differs from all the foregoing cases in that activation of the egg is effected by some agent other than the sperm. It may conveniently (though not very logically) be divided into *natural parthenogenesis*, which forms a normal part of the life-history as it occurs in nature, and *artificial* or *experimental parthenogenesis* in which the egg is artificially activated by laboratory methods.

1. Natural Parthenogenesis

Natural parthenogenesis is of two clearly marked types, which differ in respect to the number of the chromosomes and may be designated respectively as *diploid* and *haploid*. Of these the diploid type is most frequent, being characteristic of aphids, phylloxerans, daphnids, ostracodes and some other animals, and occurring occasionally in many others, such as the phyllopods, orthopterans, lepidopterans, trematodes, echinoderms and nematodes. Haploid parthenogenesis is characteristic of many Hymenoptera (bees, ants, wasps) and is also found in some Hemiptera and arachnids; while both types occur in the rotifers and the gall-flies. The two types are connected by certain transitional cases in which development begins with the haploid number of chromosomes but later becomes diploid. The best known of these cases occur in the Lepidoptera and Hymenoptera (p. 803) and are paralleled by the conditions found in certain cases of artificial parthenogenesis (p. 476).

The haploid parthenogenetic egg is a sexual egg which undergoes complete reduction and is capable of fertilization, but may develop without any process of syngamy. Such eggs most commonly develop with the haploid

[1] *Cf.* p. 965. See also Sutton ('03).

number of chromosomes, and in this case so far as known always produce males, which are themselves of haploid constitution (as in case of the drone bee, p. 794). In diploid parthenogenesis the egg typically undergoes no general reduction and hence develops with the diploid number of chromosomes (Fig. 223). These eggs, exemplified by the parthenogenetic broods of aphids, rotifers or daphnids, are in a certain sense asexual, and so far as known are incapable of fertilization; and even if fertilization took place the product would be a triploid and hence abnormal zygote.[1] The cytological evidence indicates that eggs of the diploid type were originally sexual eggs, capable of fertilization and of undergoing a process of complete reduction

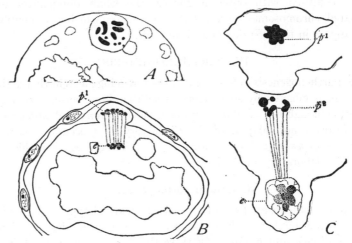

Fig. 223.—Maturation of the egg in the rose-aphid, *Aphis rosæ* (STEVENS).

A, diploid metaphase-group of polar spindle of parthenogetic egg, in polar view; *B*, the same in early telophase, side-view; *C*, second polar division of sexual egg, showing the first polocyte (*p¹*), the haploid group of chromosomes of the second polocyte (*p²*), and the haploid egg-nucleus (*e*) already reformed.

(p. 793); but the two types as they now exist have become widely different in nature and belong to different phases of the life-history. In the rotifers and gall-flies, the two types of eggs are produced by different generations of females, which in the gall-flies often differ in constitution, external structure and habits, so that a true alternation of generations exists. In the aphids and phylloxerans, likewise, the sexual forms often differ markedly from the preceding parthenogenetic females, but the sexual egg, so far as known, is here incapable of parthenogenesis.

In animals the two types are generally distinguishable externally by the number of polocytes formed during maturation; eggs of the diploid type

---

[1] See, however, the exceptional case of *Rhabditis*, p. 460.

typically produce but one polocyte, those of the haploid type, two. This difference was known long before the underlying internal differences were determined.[1] That no reduction in the number of chromosomes occurs where but one polocyte is formed was determined in the ostracodes by Woltereck ('98) and Schleip ('09), in the rotifers by Lenssen ('98) and especially by Whitney ('09), and in aphids, Stschelkanocew ('04), and Stevens ('05).[2] In all these cases the egg segments with the diploid number of chromosomes like a fertilized egg. In one or two somewhat doubtful cases diploid parthenogenesis is said to follow upon a suppression of both meiotic divisions, e. g., in the gall-fly *Neuroterus* (Doncaster, '10, '11).

In higher plants parthenogenesis is not uncommon, but without careful study is often difficult to distinguish from the widespread process of vegetative apogamy.[3]

In all the seed-plants thus far accurately studied true parthenogenesis is of the diploid type; and as in animal diploid parthenogenesis no reduction-division occurs, one or both of the spore-forming divisions of the primary macrosporocyte being suppressed. The female gametophyte (embryo-sac), including the egg-nucleus, is therefore diploid and produces a diploid embryo, quite as in the case of animals.[4] Recent studies on this subject have shown that in some plants reproducing only by apogamy (presumably vegetative) the meiotic divisions of the primary sporocytes in both sexes are subject to many interesting irregularities that are closely similar to those of hybrids (p. 845). This question is thus prominently raised whether

---

[1] The fact that parthenogenetic eggs of the diploid type form but one polocyte was observed by Balbiani ('69–'72) in aphids, by Weismann ('86) in the daphnids (*Polyphemus*), later by Weismann and Ishikawa ('88) in ostracodes and rotifers. At the same time Blochmann ('88, '89) determined the fact that in the aphids the parthenogenetic eggs forms but one polocyte, the sexual (fertilized) eggs two, while in the bee (*Apis*) the parthenogenetic egg forms both polocytes and is indistinguishable from the sexual egg. This observation was subsequently confirmed by Paulcke, Weismann, Petrunkewitsch ('01), Phillips ('03), Hewitt ('06), Schleip ('09), Nachtsheim ('13), and others. A similar type of parthenogenesis was also described in Lepidoptera by Platner ('89) and Henking ('92), later in rotifers by Erlanger and Lauterborn ('97), Mrazek ('97), and Whitney ('09).

[2] Also in the pædogenetic fly *Miastor* (Kahle, '08); in the phyllopod *Artemia* (Brauer, '94), Petrunkewitsch, '02, Fries, '10, Artom, '12); in daphnids (Kuhn, '08, Chambers, '12); in trematodes (Cary, '08) and in nematodes (Krüger, '13, P. Hertwig, '19).

[3] Considerable difference of opinion still exists among botanists concerning the use of the terms parthenogenesis and apogamy. (See Winkler, '08, '20, Ernst, '18, Strasburger, '09, etc., Vines, '11, Sharp, '21.) The term parthenogenesis is here applied, as in the case of animals, to the development of an egg or oösphere without fertilization (oöapogamy). Strasburger considered that this term should be restricted to the haploid type; but this position seems untenable in view of the fact that the word was first applied to diploid parthenogenesis (in arthropods). Some botanists, on the other hand, would restrict the term "apogamy" to the so-called vegetative type of this process (e. g., to the development of a sporophyte, whether haploid or diploid, from the vegetative tissues of the gametophyte.

[4] This was first made known in *Antennaria* by Juel ('00) and subsequently in many other forms, e. g., in *Thalictrum* (Overton, '02). In *Taraxacum* (Murbeck, '04), *Hieracium* (Rosenberg, '06), *Burmannia* (Ernst, '09, '18) in some of the ferns (Farmer, '07) and *Marsilia* (Strasburger, '07).

apogamous species may not have arisen as hybrids.[1] True haploid parthenogenesis possibly may take place in certain lower plants, *e. g.*, in the
case of the parthenospores of the Zygnemaceæ. There seems to be no
a priori reason why it should not occur in higher plants; for haploid sporo-

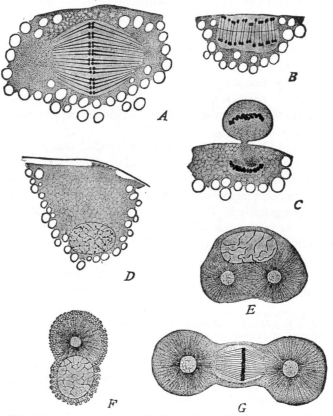

Fig. 224.—First type of maturation in the parthenogetic egg of *Artemia* (BRAUER).

A, the first polar spindle; the equatorial plate contains 84 tetrads; *B*, *C*, formation of the first
polocyte; 84 dyads remain in the egg, and these give rise to the egg-nucleus, shown in *D; F*, appearance of the egg-centrosome and aster; *E*, *G*, division of the aster and formation of the cleavage-
figure; the equatorial plate consists of 84 supposedly bivalent chromosomes.

phytes have been described in several cases of vegetative apogamy in ferns; [2]
and Blakeslee and Belling have recently found haploid mutant sporophytes
in the seed-plant *Datura* which were reared to full maturity (p. 572).

Certain exceptions to the foregoing general statements (some of them to
be considered at a later point) are important both for the theory of ferti-

[1] See Winge, '17, Rosenberg, '17, Ernst, '18, Holmgren, '19, Täckholm, '22.
[2] In *Lastræa* (Farmer and Digby, '07), and *Nephrodium* (Yamanouchi, '08), (Steil, '19).

lization and because they demonstrate the possibility of diploid parthenogenesis even in the sexual egg after the completion of reduction. One of
these is a reunion of the second polocyte (or polar nucleus) with the egg
nucleus subsequent to maturation, a process first described by O. Hertwig
('90) in the natural parthenogenesis of the starfish, *Astropecten*,[1] and more

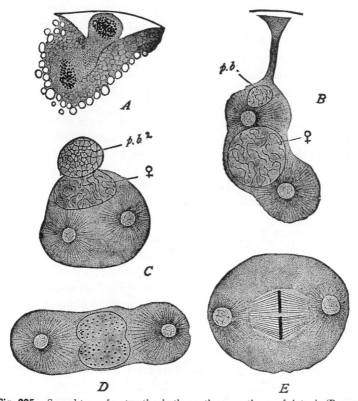

Fig. 225.—Second type of maturation in the parthenogenetic egg of *Artemia* (BRAUER).

A, formation of second polocyte; *B*, return of the second polar nucleus (*p. b.²*) into the egg; development of the egg-amphiaster; *C*, union of the egg-nucleus (♀) with the second polar nucleus
{*p. b.²*}; *D*, cleavage-nucleus and amphiaster; *E*, first cleavage-figure with equatorial plate containing 168 chromosomes in two groups of 84 each.

fully by Brauer ('94) in the phyllopod, *Artemia salina*. In the latter case
two modes of parthenogenesis were discovered, the egg in one case undergoing but one polar division (Fig. 224), in the other, two. In the second
case the second division produces a polar nucleus which subsequently re-
unites with the egg-nucleus to form the cleavage-nucleus (Fig. 225), quite

[1] A similar process was later observed in the artificial parthenogenesis of echinoderms, annelids,
and mollusks (p ͡⁻⁻)

as in *Astropecten*. In view of this fact we should expect these eggs to develop with double the haploid number of chromosomes, and such Brauer
found to be actually the case. Later observations, especially those of
Artom ('21, etc.) have led to the suggestion that Brauer's results were based
on pathological conditions; [1] but judging by the conditions found by Seiler
in Lepidoptera (p. 805) it seems possible that Brauer's material was from
a distinct race, tetraploid as compared with that of the other forms (p. 870).
There seems to be no doubt that a doubling of the haploid number due to
such a fusion between egg-nucleus and second polar nucleus actually occurs
in some forms of parthenogenesis (p. 477). Possible modes of doubling
by monocentric mitoses or by the occurrence of a second equation-division,
are considered at another place.[2]

Concerning the history of the cytoplasmic structures in natural parthenogenesis little is positively known. It has been assumed that after the formation of the polocytes the egg-center may persist and give rise directly to
the cleavage-centers; but this seems never to have been actually demonstrated. The problem here involved is essentially the same as that presented by artificial parthenogenesis which likewise still remains somewhat
unsettled (p. 481).

2. Artificial Parthenogenesis [3]

The fact that mitotic activities may be incited in the unfertilized egg by
artificial means was observed by a number of observers prior to the actual
discovery of artificial parthenogenesis. R. Hertwig ('96) observed that the
unfertilized egg of the sea-urchin, treated by weak solutions of strychnine,
might give rise in a bipolar mitotic figure, and even divide irregularly.
Morgan ('96, '99, '00) found that under the action of salt-solutions such
eggs may segment more or less regularly, and previous to division often
develop numerous small asters or "artificial astrospheres" (cytasters)
containing central bodies. Mead ('98) found that in the normal development of the annelid *Chætopterus* the discharge of the egg into the sea-
water leads to the appearance of numerous minute asters, two of which
persist to form the first polar amphiaster while the others disappear.
The mitotic figure thus formed normally pauses at the metaphase until
entrance of the sperm, when the polar divisions proceed. If, however, the
egg, without being fertilized, is placed in sea-water to which a small quantity of KCl has been added, it at once proceeds to form the polocytes

---

[1] Petrunkewitsch ('01) and Fries ('10) found in this species only ordinary diploid parthenogenesis
with a single polocyte and 84 chromosomes; and the same result was reached by Artom (p. 231).

[2] Further details concerning the chromosomes of parthenogenetic eggs will be found in Chapter
X, p. 787.

[3] For recent general reviews of the subject see Bataillon ('12), Loeb ('13, '19), Delage and Goldsmith ('13), Brachet ('17), Herlant ('17, '18, '19), F. R. Lillie ('19), Just ('19, '22).

and undergoes the concomitant changes of form characteristic of the fertilized egg.

These observations prepared the way for the brilliant discovery by Loeb, in 1899, that after appropriate treatment of the egg of the sea-urchin the initial mitotic activities may be followed by complete parthenogenetic development and the production of normal larvæ, a discovery soon confirmed and extended by the work of Delage, the writer, Bataillon and many others, and by a long series of investigations by Loeb himself. By these works it was shown that artificial parthenogenesis may be incited in the eggs of various animals among which may be mentioned especially the sea-urchins, starfish, annelids, mollusks and frogs. Delage ('04 '08, '12, etc.) succeeded in rearing a few artificially parthenogenetic larvæ both of sea-urchins and of starfish through the metamorphosis; and this was accomplished on a somewhat larger scale by Shearer and Lloyd ('13) in the case of *Echinus*.

Loeb later succeeded in rearing up to the period of metamorphosis more than eighty tadpoles from parthenogenetic eggs treated by the puncture-method (p. 474) and of these more than twenty passed successfully through the metamorphosis into the adult stage.[1] Only in case of the frog has it thus far been possible to rear larvæ from artificially parthenogenetic eggs up to sexual maturity (p. 806).

Artificial parthenogenesis in plants has been accomplished in only a few cases. An example of this is offered by *Fucus*, in which Overton ('13) induced development by the use of hypertonic sea-water; and under the same head, perhaps, may be classed the artificially induced production of parthenospores in a number of green algæ by Klebs ('96, etc.) and more recently by Faber ('12) in *Spirogyra* and by Ernst ('17) in *Chara*.

It is beyond the scope of this work to enter far into the methods for producing artificial parthenogenesis and the complicated physiological problems that it involves. These have been fully set forth in the general works of Loeb, R. S. Lillie, F. R. Lillie, Bataillon, Brachet, Herlant, Just, and many others. Nevertheless a brief outline of this side of the subject is necessary for an account of the cytological phenomena involved. Loeb's original method for sea-urchins consisted in exposure of the eggs to hypertonic sea-water; but later ('05, etc.) this procedure was greatly improved by development of the so-called double method, presently to be described. In the meantime, and subsequently, many other agents were found to be effective, including chemical, physical or even merely mechanical ones.[2] The chemical agents include such substances as neutral salts (KCl, etc.),

---

[1] Loeb, '18, '21; Parmenter, '20.

[2] Since most of these experiments have been made on marine animals ordinary sea-water may be taken as the normal medium unless otherwise stated.

CO_2, and weak acids or bases added to the water in small quantities without noticeably raising its concentration. The physical agents include increase of osmotic pressure, either by adding to the sea-water neutral salts, sugar, urea and the like, or by simple evaporation of the sea-water (Hunter, Kostanecki); thermal changes (Delage, Greely, R. Lillie), or electrical stimulus (Delage, Bataillon, Schücking, McClendon). The mechanical agents include agitation of the eggs by shaking, or (in frogs) puncture of the egg-periphery with a fine needle (Guyer, Bataillon, Loeb), thus producing "traumatic parthenogenesis."

The eggs of different species display a marked specificity in their reaction to these various activators, those highly effective for a particular species being often useless for other species. For instance, the eggs of starfish (Delage) or of the annelid *Thalassema* (Lefevre) are readily activated by simple treatment with CO_2, but this agent is ineffective with sea-urchin eggs. Again, the eggs of the American leopard frog (*Rana palustris*) may be completely activated by simple puncture (Loeb), whereas in *R. fusca* and other European frogs Bataillon ('10, '12, etc.) obtained complete activation only when the puncture is accompanied with or followed by an inoculation of blood or lymph into the egg.[1]

Treatment of the eggs by agents unsuited to their physiological idiosyncrasy often leads to a variety of interesting pathological phenomena including irregular and multipolar cleavages, fusion of blastomeres, and especially irregular division of the nuclei without protoplasmic cleavage, often followed by more or less extensive fusion of the nuclei. The fact of greatest interest is that this process may give rise to syncytial embryos, unsegmented but containing a variable number of nuclei, of different sizes, or not infrequently a single giant nucleus. Such embryos, as F. R. Lillie ('02, '06) discovered in *Chæopterus*, may develop into ciliated, actively free-swimming larvæ (Fig. 521), which may show a considerable degree of resemblance to normal larvæ, not only in external form but also in the distribution of internal materials. These larvæ, though obviously pathological, are of great interest for the general problem of development, and will later be more carefully described.[2]

Loeb and other earlier observers found that sea-urchin eggs activated by hypertonic sea-water alone are in general characterized by

---

[1] The discovery that the unfertilized frog's egg may be activated by puncturing with a fine-pointed capillary tube filled with blood or lymph is due to Guyer ('07) and this has been confirmed by a number of later observers, including besides Bataillon: Dehorne ('10), Henneguy ('11), Brachet ('11), and McClendon ('11).

[2] See p. 1083. This phenomenon has been observed also by Treadwell ('02), in *Podarke*, Fischer ('02, '03) in *Amphitrite* and *Nereis*, Scott ('06) in *Amphitrite*, Allyn ('13) in *Chaetopterus*, by Lefevre ('07) in the eggs of *Thalassema* activated by weak acids, and (for the early stages) by Kostanecki ('02, '04), in *Mactra*.

defective formation of the fertilization-membrane and by the frequent occurrence of multipolar cleavage leading to abnormal or pathological larvæ. On the other hand, there are certain agents which cause the mature but unfertilized sea-urchis egg to throw off a fertilization-membrane indistinguishable from that produced by the fertilized egg but ordinarily without inducing a subsequent cleavage or development.[1] If, however, the membrane-producing agent be followed by an appropriate second agent normal cleavage and development follow in a large percentage of cases. Loeb's improved or double method (especially applicable to sea-urchins) consists accordingly in treatment of the eggs first with a fatty acid such as butyric and then by sea-water made rather strongly hypertonic by the addition of NaCl or $MgCl_2$,—a procedure often followed by a percentage of normal development nearly or quite as high as when the eggs are fertilized.

From these results Loeb concluded that complete parthenogenetic activation of the egg involves two phases or series of activities (which need not follow each other in the same order). One is a destructive or cytolytic process, affecting the cortex, which leads to a sudden and very marked increase in the oxidative processes of the egg [2] (a process proved by experiment to take place in both artificial parthenogenesis and normal fertilization).[3] The primary effect is in itself, however, inadequate to produce complete development and actually leads to destruction of the egg by the excess of oxidative processes if its life is not saved by a corrective action (in this case hypertonic sea-water) in the course of which the chemical equilibrium of the egg is restored. Loeb ('13) even extended this conception to normal fertilization, suggesting that the sperm may bring to the egg a lysin which initiates the cortical change, and a second substance which plays a part in the regulation of oxidation similar to that of the hypertonic solution.

There are many reasons for doubting the validity of this ingenious hypothesis. Loeb himself showed that in sea-urchins the usual order of treatment might be reversed, i. e., that perfect activation may be effected by employing the hypertonic sea-water first and the cytolytic agent afterwards, which obviously necessitates considerable modification of the interpreta-

---

[1] O. and R. Hertwig ('87) observed this phenomenon in unfertilized eggs exposed to chloroform; Herbst ('93) found that the same effect may be produced by benzol, xylol, creosote and certain other substances. Many other such agents were subsequently made known, many of which, as Loeb especially has emphasized, have a destructive or cytolytic action on protoplasm. Without further treatment such eggs soon die and disintegrate, while control eggs, under normal conditions, live much longer. Cf. p. 484.

[2] Warburg ('08) showed that after fertilization the egg of *Arbacia* consumes six to seven times as much oxygen as before. See also Loeb and Wasteneys ('08).

[3] R. S. Lillie ('09, '11, '12) has suggestively urged the view that the cortical change involves an increase of ionic permeability in the plasma-membrane (or peripheral cortical region) and a consequent electrical disturbance by which the mitotic phenomena are set in motion in the egg. Cf. p. 191.

tion.   More serious, secondly, is the fact, recently demonstrated by Just ('22) that perfect activation of the sea-urchin egg may be effected by hypertonic sea-water alone without use of the cytolytic agent, *provided the solution be of the proper concentration.*   Thirdly, in very many other cases, also, a single agent is completely effective, such as CO_2, weak acids, mechanical agitation, heat or (in the case of the American frogs, cited above), simple puncture by a needle.   All these facts point to the conclusion that the necessity of two agents in certain cases is due to the fact that one of them alone produces incomplete activation, and that the second agent merely supplements the first.   As will later be shown, this conclusion is borne out in a striking manner by the cytological facts (p. 484).   Valuable as Loeb's method is in practice, and for purposes of experimental analysis in particular cases, it may be doubted whether it can be taken as the basis of a general interpretation of fertilization or even of artificial parthenogenesis.[1]

a. History of the Nucleus.   Artificial parthenogenesis, like natural, may be of either the haploid or the diploid type, or exceptionally may take place with higher chromosome-numbers, these differences being primarily dependent on the condition of the egg with respect to maturation at the time when the activation of the egg takes place.   When (as in the sea-urchin), the egg is treated subsequently to the extrusion of both polocytes the egg undoubtedly begins its development with the haploid number of chromosomes (Fig. 228);[2] and this number (18 in *Toxopneustes* and *Strongylocentrotus*) is known to be retained at least through the metamorphosis (Shearer and Lloyd, '13).   Whether the haploid number persists through the entire development is not known.   Delage ('01) found what he believed to be the diploid number (18) in parthenogenetic larvæ of *Paracentrotus* (*Strongylocentrotus*) *lividus*, but did not sufficiently examine normal controls.   As pointed out by Boveri, however ('02, '04), the diploid number is 36 in this species, which is therefore in conformity with the others cited.

A more complicated problem is offered by such eggs as those of starfish, nemertines, mollusks, annelids and frogs, in which the egg may be activated prior to the completion of maturation.   In such cases, as a number of observers have found,[3] the maturation of the egg is subject to wide variations, one or both maturation-divisions often being suppressed or variously modified.   The cytological phenomena in these cases are not yet sufficiently known and are complicated by frequent abnormalities of development.   It is certain, however, that the number of chromosomes varies, being some-

---

[1] For an interesting special argument against Loeb's theory as applied to normal fertilization, see Conklin ('17) on the giant polocytes of *Crepidula* (p. 494).

[2] Wilson, '01, Hindle, '10.

[3] *E. g.*, in the starfish (Delage, '02), in *Mactra* (Kostanecki, '04, '11), *Podarke* (Treadwell, '02) *Amphitrite* (Scott, '06), *Thalassema* (Lefevre, '07) etc., *Chætopterus* (Lillie, '06), Allyn, '13.

times haploid, sometimes diploid, and in some cases variable. These variations are undoubtedly traceable in part to corresponding variations in the maturation-process; but perhaps, also, in part to irregularities in cleavage.

In the simplest case both polocytes are extruded and the egg is said to develop with the haploid number of chromosomes. This is described by Lefevre ('07) in the annelid *Thalassema*, where the cleavage is of quite normal type and the haploid number (12) could be identified at least as late as the gastrula stage. Such embryos developed into normal trochophore larvæ. In the mollusk *Cumingia*, also, eggs that extrude both polocytes segment with the haploid number 18; but such eggs seem not to divide more than once or twice (Morris, '17). Eggs that have undergone complete meiosis may nevertheless restore the diploid number in at least three ways. In the mollusk *Mactra* it was found by Kostanecki ('04, '11) that the completion of maturation is commonly followed by a third mitosis of more or less suppressed type, in which the chromosomes divide and separate to form two nuclei (each receiving the haploid number of chromosomes, 12) which then fuse together to form a single cleavage-nucleus containing the diploid number. Such eggs, however, do not develop normally. A second possible mode by which the original haploid number may be doubled (as indicated by Boveri, '00) is by monocentric mitosis (p. 168) in the course of which each chromosome splits into two followed by the reconstruction of a single nucleus. This case, obviously, is nearly related to that described in *Mactra;* but, as Boveri showed experimentally, such eggs are capable (in the case of fertilized eggs) up to a certain point of normal development (p. 729).

A third case is seen when one or both polocytes fail to be extruded from the egg. When neither polocyte is formed the first polar spindle forms as usual and the chromosomes may have the usual tetrad structure (Lefevre, '07), but the spindle fails to take up its normal position, remaining "submerged" within the egg; and the same may be true of the second spindle after normal extrusion of the first polocyte. Lefevre believed that in either of these cases (in *Thalassema*) the submerged polar spindle may directly become the first cleavage-spindle, though satisfactory proof of this is lacking. More commonly either the first or the second "submerged" polar spindle produces two nuclei within the egg which then fuse together to form the cleavage-nucleus (Fig. 229), as also described in the natural parthenogenesis of *Astropecten* or *Artemia* (p. 471).[1] This process, like that described by Kostanecki for the first cleavage-spindle in *Mactra*, must obviously

---

[1] This is described for the second polar spindle by Lefevre ('07) in the annelid *Thalassema*, by Buchner ('11) in *Asterias*, by Allyn ('13) in the annelid *Chætopterus*, and by Morris ('17) in the mollusk *Cumingia*. A similar fusion following the *first* polar mitosis is also described by Lefevre and by Morris.

double the number of chromosomes; but we cannot precisely state the expected result in either case, since the original chromosomes are quadruple chromosomes or tetrads, and it is not known whether the reduction-division takes place in these cases or not. In *Thalassema* Lefevre found clearly more than 12 (the haploid number) in the cleavage-spindle of eggs without polocytes, or with only one polocyte. In *Asterias*, after the second division, Buchner found the haploid number (18) in each nucleus, and the diploid number (36) in the division of the fusion-nucleus. On the other hand, in the eggs of *Cumingia* devoid of polocytes, Morris found in the cleavage 50 or

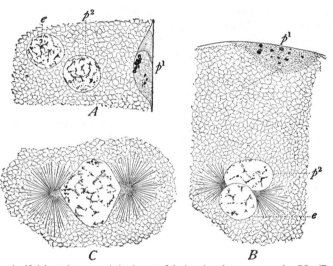

Fig. 226.—Artificial parthenogenesis in the star-fish *Asterias* after treatment by CO_2 (BUCHNER).

A, first polocyte (p^1), second polar nucleus (p^2) and egg-nucleus (e) after completion of the two polar divisions; *B*, union of the two nuclei to produce *C*, the cleavage-nucleus.

60 small chromosomes instead of the normal diploid number (36) of large ones. The explanation of this fact is not yet evident.

An especial interest attaches to the case of the frog; for the parthenogenetic larvæ (puncture method) have in this case been successfully reared through the metamorphosis and up to sexually mature frogs more than a year old.[1] According to Bataillon ('10) the mature eggs at the time of activation by puncture have extruded the first polocyte and contain the second polar spindle in metaphase (as is the case prior to fertilization). Following puncture (in *R. fusca*) this division is completed and the second polocyte is thrown out. We should, therefore, expect the egg to begin its development with the haploid number; and Bataillon actually found this number (12)

---

[1] Loeb, '16, '18.

during cleavage, up to the "morula" stage. On the other hand, Parmenter's work ('20) on Loeb's parthenogenetic sexually mature frogs (*R. palustris*) leaves no doubt that some of them, at least, were diploid (24–26 chromosomes), in agreement with earlier observations by Goldschmidt ('20, also in Loeb, '18), Henneguy ('11) and Brachet ('11). Additional more detailed studies will be necessary to reveal the explanation of this result, and the same may be said of the more recent ones of Hovasse ('22). This observer has found widely varying numbers in parthenogenetic tadpoles obtained by Bataillon's method, and has thus been led to reject the whole theory of the specific constancy of chromosome-numbers and of genetic continuity of the chromosomes. It is to be regretted that a conclusion so sweeping should be based upon data so inadequate. Hovasse records, however, two important observations which there seems to be no reason to doubt. First, the observed numbers, in spite of their great variability, show two principal mean values, one of which (8–14) is about half the other (22–27), presumably near the haploid and diploid numbers respectively. Secondly, the frequency of the haploid numbers is greatest in the early stages (7–24 hrs.) and in later stages decreases until in the oldest larvæ (18, 50, 64, and 84 days) only the diploid number is found. Hovasse insists that this is not due to differential mortality; but the data on which this is based do not seem convincing. A satisfactory explanation of these results must await the result of more definite information concerning the behavior of the egg-nucleus and the polar spindle, of the rôle of the cytasters during cleavage, and many other questions.

Résumé. It appears from the foregoing that the artificially parthenogenetic egg may develop up to a certain point with either the haploid or the diploid number of chromosomes. After extrusion of both polocytes the egg seems most commonly to develop with the haploid number of chromosomes and this number may be retained at least as late as the larval stages (sea-urchins). Whether such larvæ may develop into haploid adults is not yet certain. Since the size of the nucleus (*i. e.*, the number of chromosomes) is known to have an important effect on the rate and extent of growth (p. 654), we should expect haploid embryos and larvæ to be less vigorous in this respect than the normal diploid ones. In point of fact, as is the case of gynogenesis (p. 460) and merogony (p. 465), many observers have noted in the case of both sea-urchins and frogs, the slower rate of growth, greater number of abnormalities and higher mortality in artificially parthenogenetic larvæ as compared with the normal; and this becomes especially noteworthy as the time of metamorphosis approaches, so that comparatively few such larvæ have actually been reared to the adult condition. This difference is well shown by Fig. 227. It is perhaps due to

the disproportion between protoplasmic mass and the number of chromosomes (nuclear mass). Herlant ('13) found that in parthenogenetic frogs'
eggs, believed to be haploid, the cleavage-spindles are markedly smaller
than in normally fertilized diploid eggs so as to be relatively ineffective in
cleavage (*cf.* 484). It is possible, therefore, that in species not normally
parthenogenetic the artificially parthenogenetic egg may often be unable

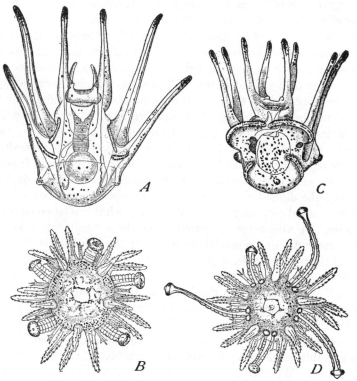

Fig. 227.—Comparison of young sea-urchins, *Echinus esculentus*, from artificially parthenogenetic
eggs and fertilized eggs (SHEARER and LLOYD).

A, parthenogenetic pluteus, 25 days (Loeb's method); B, young sea-urchin of same origin; C, pluteus from fertilized egg, 22 days; D, young sea-urchin from fertilized egg.

to undergo complete development unless the number of chromosomes be
doubled, as is assumed to be the case in androgenesis or gynogenesis by
G. and P. Hertwig (p. 464). This process might take place by monocentric
mitosis, by reunion of the second polar nucleus with the egg-nucleus, or
in some other way; and it is also possible that when the egg has completed
but one polar mitosis at the time of activation (as is the case with the frog)
the oöcyte-nucleus may be directly converted into the cleavage-nucleus.

the dyads separating into univalent chromosomes before cleavage takes place. All these possibilities demand further examination.[1] It must not be forgotten, however, that natural haploid parthenogenesis may lead to complete development (p. 794) and that the same, beyond a doubt, is true of haploid mutants of *Datura* (p. 572) and of the haploid sporophytes observed in certain ferns.[2] There seems to be no *a priori* reason, therefore,

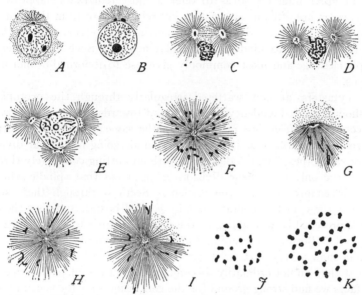

Fig. 228.—Artificial parthenogenesis (activation by hypertonic seawater) in the sea-urchin *Toxopneustes*.

A, B, egg-nucleus with aster and central bodies; *C, D*, prophases of first cleavage; *E*, early tripolar figure; *F*, monaster with about 36 chromosomes, probably from the second cycle; *G*, "fan-nucleus"; *H, I*, two sections through the same monaster from the first cycle, 18 chromosomes; *J*, haploid chromosome-group from early cleavage-stage; *K*, diploid group from fertilized egg.

why haploid larvæ may not in some cases be capable of complete development.

b. Central Bodies and Asters. The history of the asters and cleavage spindle in artificial parthenogenesis offers many interesting phenomena of which the most striking is the fact that under certain conditions the egg not only gives rise to a bipolar cleavage-amphiaster but often also to accessory or supernumerary asters or *cytasters* scattered through the cyto-

---

[1] In *Toxopneustes* (Wilson, '01) there appear to be two types of nuclear prophases in one of which the chromosomes arise from the general nuclear network, in the other from a massive karyosphere. The former process seems to occur after treatment by weaker solutions (of MgCl₂), the latter after stronger ones. This observation still remains without confirmation, but I have no reason to doubt its correctness.

[2] *Lastræa* (Farmer and Digby, '07), *Nephrodium* (Yamanouchi, '08, Steil, '19).

some, sometimes in great numbers, and often having no connection with the actual cleavage-figure (Figs. 331–333).[1] After the best methods of activation few or no cytasters make their appearance; the cleavage-figure is bipolar and cleavage proceeds nearly or quite normally. With less suitable methods—for instance in sea-urchin eggs treated by the earlier simple hypertonic solutions (Wilson, '01)—cytasters almost always appear, sometimes in great numbers so as to offer a most remarkable appearance.[2] The cytasters are often at every stage entirely separate from the cleavage-asters; but one or more of them may come into connection with the latter so as to form various kinds of multipolar figures. Such eggs undergo a multiple cleavage and most commonly give rise to abnormal or monstrous embryos.

The cytasters, at first scattered irregularly through the protoplasm, later show a marked tendency to migrate out towards the egg-periphery and here commonly *divide into two*, while at the same time cleavage-furrows are formed about them, as if the egg were undergoing multipolar division. In most cases, these furrows disappear without cutting completely through the egg, the only permanent division being across that spindle which is formed in connection with the nucleus. Sections through these stages show that the cytasters contain definite central bodies, and that their division is preceded by a doubling of the centers and the formation of a central spindle. Both in structure and in relation to cytoplasmic cleavage the cytasters show a very close analogy to normal cleavage-asters despite the fact that they do not ordinarily become centers of complete cleavage. In these facts we find strong ground for the conclusion that the central bodies of these asters are true division-centers, and that they are formed *de novo* (p. 684).

It is not yet known (and perhaps cannot directly be determined) whether the egg always contains a preformed central body (p. 259).

---

[1] "Accessory asters," closely resembling those seen in artificial parthenogenesis, were described by Carnoy in the normal maturation-divisions in the egg of *Ascaris*. "Rien de plus curieux ou plus élégant tout á la fois que des œufs constellés. Quel travail que cela de la cinèse!" ('85, p. 47.) Accessary asters in normal development were also described by Reinke ('94), Watase ('95), Mottier ('97), Lillie ('97), Conklin ('98), Mead ('98), Griffin ('99), Smallwood ('01) and other observers.

[2] The cytasters are more numerous after longer exposure to hypertonic sea-water than after shorter, and also in higher concentrations (Wilson, '01, Chambers, '21, Just, '22). Herlant has shown that the number of cytasters formed after Loeb's double method (activation by butyric acid followed by hypertonic sea-water) is affected by the length of treatment by the first agent, though the cytaster-formation first takes place after transference of the eggs to the hypertonic solution. Thus, in a particular experiment the number of cytasters steadily increased after butyric treatment up to 30 minutes, diminished to nearly zero after 45–50 m., and again increased after longer exposures—a result which fits well with Moore's results ('15) on the rhythmical susceptibility of the eggs to hypertonic sea-water. Just ('22) has shown that at a certain optimum time or concentration of the sea-water no cytasters are formed and development proceeds normally. Under-exposure causes only the formation of a monaster. over-exposure the appearance of cytasters.

Most investigators have found that a single aster is first formed centering in a central body that lies upon or near the nuclear membrane and subsequently divides into two to initiate the formation of an amphiaster (Fig. 228), but the point is a difficult one to determine with certainty.[1] Those who accepted this view considered the cytaster-formation as a non-essential epiphenomenon,[2] due, as it were, to an outburst of the mitotic activities which may assume a pathological character or even prevent altogether the normal development of the egg. As will presently appear, however,

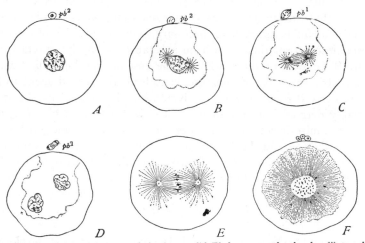

Fig. 229.—Artificial parthenogenesis in the annelid *Thalassema*, activation by dilute acid (LE-FEVRE).

A, egg after extension of the second polocyte; *B*, "simultaneous appearance" of the cleavage-centers, on opposite sides of the nucleus; *C*, "submerged" second polar spindle; *D* products of preceding mitosis; *E*, cleavage-spindle, probably identical with first polar spindle; *F*, monaster, after maturation.

later studies have raised the question whether the cytaster-formation may not play a definitive and perhaps essential part in development.

The physiological distinction between the primary activation of the egg and the actual achievement of cleavage (in the double process of activation), is in a measure paralleled by the cytological phenomena. By the first agent—*e. g.*, butyric acid in Loeb's method for sea-urchins, simple puncture or electric shock in Bataillon's method for frogs—is initiated the cortical change and the throwing off of an activation-membrane; also, in case of the frog's egg, the completion of the second polar mitosis, expulsion of the second polocyte, and the internal redistribution of material

[1] Wilson ('01a), Kostanecki ('04), Hindle ('10) Chambers ('21). In *Asterias* Tennant and Hogue ('06) first find two centers close together which later pass to opposite poles of the nucleus. In *Thalassema* Lefevre ('07) found the two centers appearing independently at opposite poles of the nucleus.

[2] Wilson, *op. cit.*

that results in the rotation of the egg into its final position of orientation and the appearance of the gray crescent (p. 1069). In these cases the mitotic activities of the egg are set on foot, but do not ordinarily lead to cleavage and apparently never to complete development. Both in the sea-urchin and in the frog, *the egg thus activated ordinarily goes no further than the formation of a monaster* (p. 475), which is only rarely able to give rise to a bipolar figure and thus to cause cleavage.[1] The latter occurs only when the first agent is followed by a second (hypertonic sea-water in sea-urchins, inoculation in Bataillon's frogs). The most probable explanation of this fact is that the monaster-formation is due simply to incomplete activation, and that further stimulus is necessary to induce division of the center and amphiaster-formation. Such, in substance, is the interpretation offered by Bataillon ('12, etc.), who, in the case of frogs' eggs first activated by electric shock or by puncture, considered the second agent to be a catalyzer derived from the blood or lymph cells introduced by the stylet, presumably derived from the foreign nuclei. Its effect, in his view, is to heighten the mitotic activity of the egg-center to a point where it becomes capable of division and the production of an amphiaster, thus rendering the egg capable of cleavage. The complete development produced by puncture alone in Loeb's *Rana palustris*, or by single agents such as CO_2 in the case of other eggs, might, therefore, be explained merely as a result of a greater susceptibility of these eggs to the stimulus of one agent.

This conclusion harmonizes with those of Just ('22) on Loeb's double method (p. 476). On the other hand, Herlant ('14, '17) has developed a more complicated interpretation, which ascribes an essential rôle to the cytasters. Bataillon had found that inoculation of the frog's egg with blood or lymph causes the formation of a cluster of cytasters in the neighborhood of the puncture. According to Herlant, activation of the egg by simple puncture causes the egg nucleus to become surrounded by a monocentric radiation, constituting the "female energid," which then gives rise to a small dicentric figure or amphiaster, but protoplasmic cleavage fails in this case because of the insufficient size of the amphiaster. Cleavage is made possible by the cytasters in two ways, namely (1) by repelling the "female energid" so as to cause its approach to the surface, where it becomes more effective and (2) by placing themselves on either side of the future cleavage-plane and establishing between them a "diastem" or plane of least resistance along which the first cleavage-plane cuts through the egg. Complete cleavage

---

[1] This fact, observed by a number of earlier workers, was first clearly placed in evidence in the case of sea-urchin eggs by Herbst ('07, '09), Hindle ('10) and Herlant ('17); and by Bataillon in the case of frogs' eggs activated by simple puncture. Herbst found in one culture of *Sphærechinus* that out of 800 eggs treated with valerianic acid 791 produced monasters and not one an amphiaster ('21, p. 2).

is thus made possible, despite the abnormally small size of the amphiaster. One cannot consider this interpretation without considerable scepticism; and serious objections to it have been pointed out by Bataillon ('19).

This scepticism grows in view of Herlant's interpretation of the phenomena in sea-urchin eggs activated by Loeb's double method, which ascribes a totally different rôle to the cytasters. Like his predecessors Herlant found that the monaster incited by the first agent (butyric acid) only rarely gives rise to a bipolar figure. In this respect these eggs show an evident analogy to fertilized eggs in which the gamete-nuclei have been prevented from union (p. 447). When, however, the butyric treatment is followed by hypertonic sea-water cytasters make their appearance, and *one of these is said to become associated with the monaster to form the first cleavage-amphiaster.* Herlant believed that he had followed this process step by step both in sections and in the transparent living eggs of *Paracentrotus (Strongylocentrotus).*

This account is not so anomalous as it first appears; for many cases have been described in which amphiasters are formed synthetically by the secondary union of asters previously separate, for instance, the first cleavage-spindle of *Crepidula* according to Conklin (p. 443), or the first polar spindle in eggs of some animals,[1] and even in ordinary mitosis of the second type the original spindle seems wholly to disappear, to be replaced later by a new spindle found between the separate centers (p. 148). Herlant's result would also explain the fact, which long puzzled the writer ('01), that the cytasters seem only to divide at the close of the first mitosis instead of at its beginning. Herlant's account of the phenomena in the sea-urchin is, however contradicted by Chambers's careful study of the transparent living eggs of *Echinarachinas* ('21) and is thus rendered still more improbable.

On the whole it seems most natural to assume that the cleavage-centers in all these cases arise by the division of a single original center closely associated with the nucleus and that the cytasters represent a kind of epiphenomena which may often modify the process of division but do not form an essential part of it. Every egg, we may assume, is capable of producing the complete apparatus of mitosis in response to adequate activation. In natural parthenogenesis and fertilization alike, this reaction is complete; but in the former case the egg plays the sole rôle, while in the latter the sperm takes a leading share, providing from the start a focus, as it were, in which the reaction centers and which inhibits in greater or less degree certain other activities *which would otherwise take place* in the egg (*e. g.,* the formation of an ovo-center and "egg-aster"). In artificial parthenogenesis we are dealing with activating agents which are admittedly of vary-

[1] See Mead ('95, '98), Griffin ('99), Lams ('10).

ing degrees of efficiency and which call forth varying types of reaction by different species of eggs. Experimentally it has in some cases been found possible to supplement the defective activation of one agent by that of another and thus to bring the reaction of the egg more nearly to the normal. To the cytologist the processes called forth by fertilization or parthenogenetic activation offer the appearance of a single train of connected events, more or less plastic in each individual case and varying materially in its details from species to species.

LITERATURE V

(For abbreviations see General Literature List.)

Bataillon, E., '10. Le problème de la fécondation, etc.: *A. Z. E.*, VI, 5.
    '12. La parthénogénèse des Amphibiens et la fécondation chimique de Loeb: *A. S. N.*, 9th series.
Blackman, V. H., '04. On the Relation of Fertilization to "Apogamy" and "Parthenogenesis": *N. P.*, III.
Boveri, Th., '92. Befruchtung: *Merkel und Bonnet's Ergebnisse*, I.
    '95. Ueber das Verhalten der Centrosomen bei der Befruchtung, etc.: *V. P. M. G.*, Würzburg, XXIX.
Brauer, A., '93. Zur Kenntniss der Reifung des parthenogenetisch sich entwickelden Eies von *Artemia salina: A. M. A.*, XLIII.
Buller, A. H., '02. Is Chemotaxis a Factor in the Fertilization, etc.? *Q. J.*, XLVI.
Conklin, E. G., '02. (II.)
    '04. Experiments on the Origin of the Cleavage Centrosomes: *B. B.*, VII.
Delage, Yves, '01. Études expérimentale sur la maturation cytoplasmique, etc.: *A. Z. E.*, IX.
Delage and **Goldsmith,** '13. La parthénogénèse naturelle et expérimentale: *Flammarion*, Paris.
Farmer and **Digby,** '07. Studies in Apospory and Apogamy in Ferns: *A. Bot.*, XXI.
Haecker, V., '12. Befruchtung: *H. Nw.*, I.
Held, H., '16. Untersuchungen über den Vorgang der Befruchtung: *A. M. A.*, LXXXIX.
Herlant, M., '11. Recherches sur les œufs di- und tri-spermiques, etc., *A. B.*, XXVI.
    '13. Étude sur les bases cytologiques du méchanism de la parthénogénèse expérimentale chez les Amphibiens: *A. B.*, XXVIII.
Hertwig, G., '13. Parthenogenesis bei Wirbeltieren, etc.: *A. M. A.*, LXXXI.
Hertwig, O., '75, '77, '78. Beiträge zur Kenntniss der Bildung, Befruchtung und Teilung des tierischen Eies, I: *M. J.*, I, II (*Ibid.* III); III (*Ibid.* IV).
Hertwig, O. and **R.,** '87. Ueber die Befruchtungs- und Theilungs-Vorgänge, etc.: *J. Z.*, XX.
Hertwig, P., '20. Haploid und Diploid Parthenogenese: *B. C.*, XL.
Hertwig, R., '06. Eireife und Befruchtung: In O. Hertwig Handbuch d. Vergl. und Experim. Entwickelungslehre. I, 1, *Fischer, Jena*.

Just, E., '19. The Fertilization Reaction in *Echinarachnius:* I, II, III, *B. B.*, XXXVI; '20, IV, *Ibid.*, XXXIX; '23, VI, VII, VIII; *B. B.*, XLIV.

Korschelt and Heider, '03. Eireifung, Samenreifung und Befruchtung: *Lehrb. d. vergl. Entwicklungsges. Allg. Th.*, II, 1, 2.

Kupelwieser, H.,'12. Weitere Untersuchungen über die Befruchtung, etc.: *A. Zf.*, VIII.

Lefevre, G., '07. Artificial Parthenogenesis in *Thalassema: J. E. Z.*, IV.

Lillie, F. R., '01. The Organization of the Egg of *Unio:* etc.: *J. M.*, XVII.

'12–'15. Studies on Fertilization: III (Morphology), *J. E. Z.*, XII, IV, V: *Ibid.*, XIV, VI: *Ibid.*, XVI, VII: *B. B.*, XXVIII.

'19. Problems of Fertilization: *Univ. Chicago Press.*

Lillie, R. S., '17. The Conditions, etc., and the general Relation of Changes of Permeability to Activation: *A. J. P.*, XLIII.

Loeb, J., '12. Ueber den Mechanismus der heterogenen Befruchtung: *A. Entwm.*, XL.

'13. Artificial Parthenogenesis and Fertilization: *Univ. Chicago Press.*

Mark, E. L., '81. (Int.)

Mead, A. D., '98. The Origin and Behavior of the Centrosomes in the Annelid Egg: *J. M.*, XIV, 2.

Meves, F., '11. Ueber die Beteilung des Plastochondria an der Befruchtung des Eies von *Ascaris: A. M. A.*, LXXVI.

'14. Verfolgung des Mittelstückes des Echinidenspermiens, etc.: *A. M. A.*, LXXXII.

Moore, C., '17. On the Capacity for Fertilization after the Initiation of Development : *B. B.*, XXXIII (see also XXXI).

Mottier, D., '04. Fecundation in Plants: *P. C. I.*

Nemec, B., '10. Das Problem der Befruchtungsvorgänge: *Berlin.*

Strasburger, E., '77. Ueber Befruchtung und Zelltheilung: *J. Z.*, XI.

'84. Neue Untersuchungen über den Befruchtungsvorgang bei den Phanerogamen, etc.: *Jena.*

'09. Zeitpunkt der Bestimmung des Geschlechts, Apogamie, Parthenogenesis, etc.: *Hist. Beitr.*, VII.

Van Beneden, E., '83-'84. (See Int.)

Van Beneden, E., and Neyt, A., '87. Nouvelles recherches sur la fécondation et la division cellulaire chez l'Ascaride mégalocéphale: *B. A. B.*, VII.

Vejdovský, F.,'88. Entwickelungsgeschichtliche Untersuchungen, Heft I. Reifung, Befruchtung und Furchung des Rynchelmis-Eies: *Prag.*

Vejdovský and Mrazek, '03. Umbildung des Cytoplasma während der Befruchtung und Zelltheilung, etc.: *A. M. A.*, LXII.

Vines, S. H., '11. Reproduction in Plants: In *Enc. Brittanica, 11th Ed.*

Weismann, A., '85. Richtungskörper bei parthenogenetischen Eier: *Z. A.*, IX.

Wilson, E. B.,'01. A Cytological Study of Artificial Parthenogenesis in Seaurchin Eggs: *A. Entwm.*, XII.

Wilson and Mathews, '95. Maturation, Fertilization and Polarity in the Echinoderm Egg: *J. M.*, X.

Winkler, H., '08. Parthenogenesis and Apogamie im Pflanzenreiche: *P. R. B.*, II, 3.

'13. Apogamie und Parthenogenesis: *H. Nw.*, II.

'20. Verbreitung und Ursache der Parthenogenesis im Pflanzen- und Tierreiche: *Jena.*

CHAPTER VI

MATURATION AND REDUCTION. MEIOSIS

"There must be yet another kind of karyokinesis, in which the primary equatorial loops are not split longitudinally, but are separated without division into two groups."

WEISMANN. [1]

We have now to examine the far-reaching vistas of inquiry opened by Van Beneden's fundamental discovery that the gamete-nuclei, and hence the two parents from which they are respectively derived, contribute each a haploid or single group of chromosomes to the fertilized egg. Each act of fertilization doubles the gametic number of chromosomes; yet the number characteristic of the species remains constant from generation to generation. Somewhere in the course of the life-cycle, accordingly, the diploid or so-called "somatic" number must be reduced by one-half to the haploid or gametic. When and how is this accomplished?

The first guess (Van Beneden, Boveri, Rückert, Van Bambeke, Van der Stricht) was that reduction might be effected by some process of degeneration or casting out of half the chromosomes from the nucleus; but subsequent research showed that the process is of very different type.[2] Reduction results from a regrouping of the chromosomes of the diploid group and their segregation into two single or haploid groups corresponding in a general way to those that originally came together in the egg. So far as the chromosomes are concerned this process may be regarded broadly as the reverse of nuclear union or karyogamy. Its fundamental interest for the problems of genetics has made it the object of innumerable cytological researches, and the main facts now seem well established. Its critical study offers, however, many intricate and difficult questions of detail, some of which are still matters of controversy. We shall here consider only the cytological problems of meiosis, deferring to later chapters an account of their relation to the genetic phenomena for the explanation of which they provide the key.

I. GENERAL SURVEY

Reduction or *meiosis* takes place at a particular part of the life-history, known as the *meiotic phase*, the preliminary operations of which some-

---

[1] *Essays on Heredity*, '87, p. 360.

[2] A review of the earlier history of this question will be found in the work of Maréchal ('07) and more recently of O. Hertwig ('17).

times take place very early in the individual life; for instance, in the eggs of higher vertebrates the process begins about the time of birth or earlier, though not completed until near the time of sexual maturity. In higher plants it takes place in a different generation (sporophyte) from that which

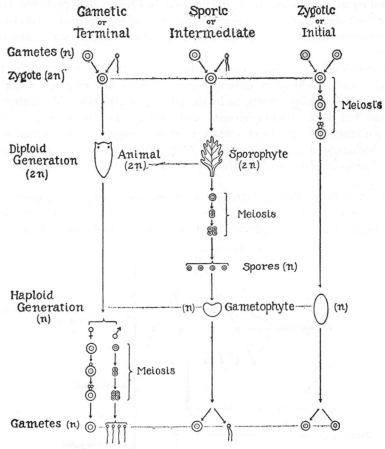

Fig. 230.—Diagram comparing the three known types of meiosis.

produces the gametes. Its climax appears in two peculiar mitoses called the *meiotic* or *maturation-divisions* during which the actual sorting out of the chromosomes into two haploid groups is completed; hence these divisions are often designated as *segregation-divisions*. In general aspect they are of mitotic type; but they are distinguished by certain special peculiarities in the history of the chromosomes, and in some instances also in the character of the achromatic figure. Meiosis seems to be accomplished by two divisions, neither more nor fewer, throughout nearly the whole of the plant and animal kingdoms. The only seeming exceptions to this are offered by a few cases in which but one division has been identified, or in which the meiotic divisions are closely associated with one or more additional equation-divisions (*e. g.*, in ciliates or in *Fucus*). It is probable, however, that these exceptions are only apparent, and that the meiotic divisions under many disguises everywhere have the same fundamental characteristics.

The period at which meiosis takes place, though constant in the species, differs widely in different groups, in a few cases even within the limits of smaller groups, as in the conjugate algæ (desmids, diatoms), in the red algæ (Rhodophyceæ), and perhaps in the Sporozoa. The known cases fall into three clearly marked groups or types, which may be characterized as (1) *Gametic or Terminal*, (2) *Zygotic or Initial*, and (3) *Sporic or Intermediate Meiosis*. These are shown in diagram by Fig. 230.

(1) *Gametic or Terminal Meiosis* is characteristic of animals generally, including all Metazoa and many Protozoa (Figs. 230, 282). It occurs in a few lower plants (Thallophyta), the best known examples being found per-

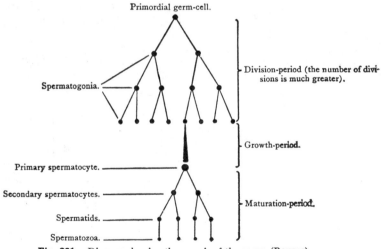

Fig. 231.—Diagram showing the genesis of the sperm (BOVERI).

haps in the Fucaceæ (*Fucus*) and the diatoms. Meiosis of this type takes place during the last two divisions by which the gametes (or their nuclei) are produced. The meiotic divisions here form part of the general process of *oögenesis* in the female and of *spermatogenesis* in the male; and since the gametes result from two successive divisions they are typically formed in quartets or groups of four.[1] Externally a marked contrast exists between the sexes in respect to these quartets (p. 493), but internally the phenomena are fundamentally alike in both, as was first indicated by Platner in 1889 and brilliantly demonstrated in detail by O. Hertwig in the following year.

(2) *Zygotic or Initial Meiosis* is a rare but interesting form which stands at the opposite extreme from the gametic type (Figs. 230, 297). At present it is known only in a few of the algæ (*Spirogyra, Zygnema*, desmids and certain diatoms, *Coleochæte, Nemalion* and *Scinaia*), and in certain Sporozoa (*Diplocystis, Aggregata*). Here the meiotic divisions occur just after instead of just before the union of the gametes, *i. e.*, they are the initial divisions of the zygote and take place at the beginning of the sexual lifecycle. The products of the zygote (ordinary vegetative cells), therefore, possess nuclei of haploid instead of diploid organization, the latter condition appearing only in the zygote as a transitory result of syngamy. From a theoretical point of view there is some reason to suspect that this condition may be a very primitive one (p. 617).

(3) *Sporic or Intermediate Meiosis* is characteristic of all the higher plants (cormophytes) and also occurs in some of the thallophytes, but is thus far

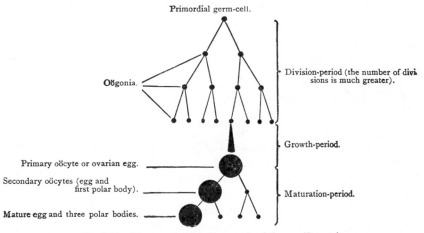

Fig. 232.—Diagram showing the genesis of the egg (Boveri).

unknown among animals (Fig. 230). The meiotic divisions here take place at some point in the diploid organism intermediate between the zygote and the formation of the gametes, and their products are not gametes but asexual spores (tetraspores, embryo-sacs, pollen-grains, etc.). Here, therefore,

---

[1] These groups are sometimes called "tetrads," but this term causes confusion with the chromosome-tetrads (p. 505), which may be avoided by use of the word quartet.

the meiotic divisions form part of the general process of *sporogenesis*, and involve an alternation of generations, as follows: [1] The spores (being the products of meiosis) receive the haploid number of chromosomes and develop without fertilization into a haploid, gamete-producing "sexual" generation, known as the *haplont* (in plants the *gametophyte*) which intervenes between meiosis and the gamete-formation. From this organism arise the gametes by ordinary mitosis; and by their union is produced the zygote from which arises a diploid, asexual spore-producing *diplont* (in plants the *sporophyte*), thus completing the life-cycle. This process, typically illustrated by the alternation of the diploid leafy fern-plant and the haploid prothallium, is now generally designated as *antithetic* in contradistinction to *homologous* alternation in which both generations have the same number of chromosomes.[2] In all the higher plants, from bryophytes to seed-plants, and even in some of the algæ (*Cutleria*), the two generations are of markedly different appearance and morphological type. On the other hand, in some of the algæ (*Dictyota, Polysiphonia*, etc.), the investigations of Williams, Yamanouchi, Svedelius and others have shown that the haplont and diplont generations are of nearly or quite identical morphological type (p. 627).

Why meiosis should require two divisions is wholly unknown; as far as we can see one division should equally well accomplish the result. A key to the problem is perhaps to be sought in the diploid type of animal parthenogenesis (p. 468), where but a single maturation division takes place and reduction fails to occur.

II. EXTERNAL ASPECTS OF MATURATION

1. In Animals

The origin of the germ-cells, and the general character of the germ-track have already been considered (p. 310). During the growth-period following the final gonial divisions (which like their predecessors are diploid) the auxocytes undergo a marked growth and are designated, in the female as primary *oöcytes*, in the male as primary *spermatocytes*, and in plants generally as primary *sporocytes*, or spore-mother-cells. The auxocytes of the two sexes are at first nearly or quite indistinguishable (p. 329), and both

---

[1] See also p. 617.

[2] This distinction was first clearly recognized, without knowledge of the cytological relations, on the basis of the vegetative characters by Celakowsky ('74, '77), later by Bower ('91). Homologous alternation was said to take place between sexual and asexual generations of similar morphological type (*e. g.*, in *Vaucheria*), antithetic alternation between generations of essentially different type, as in all cormophytic plants. The distinction first acquired precision when placed upon a cytological basis by the discovery of Dixon ('91), Overton ('93), and Strasburger ('94) that the spore-producing divisions are meiotic, and that the nuclei of the resulting gametophytes are haploid.

alike undergo extensive enlargement during the growth-period. In the female this growth takes place on a far greater scale than in the male, so that the fully grown oöcytes may thus become thousands of times larger than the spermatocytes. In some degree this difference is correlated with the length of the growth-period, which is in general much more prolonged in case of the oöcyte; but this is subject to wide variations in different cases; the growth-period of the oöcyte may last for only a few days (some

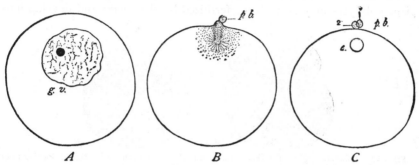

Fig. 233.—Formation of the polocytes before entrance of the sperm, as seen in the living ovarian egg of the sea-urchin, *Toxopneustes* (× 365).

of the Diptera) or may be continued throughout months or even years (mammals). But, obviously, the great size of the oöcyte is not determined by this alone. The prolonged growth-period in the placental mammal, for instance, does not lead to a growth comparable in degree to that occurring in Ornithodelphia or Sauropsida. Fundamentally, the differential factor forms a part of the general mechanism of heredity; and the size of the egg is correlated not alone with the length of the growth-period but also with the conditions of embryonic and larval development, and other unknown factors.

To the same primary cause is traceable the division of labor that has taken place among the cells of the maturation-quartets. In the male, speaking generally, all four of these cells (sperms) are of minute size and are structurally and functionally alike (Fig. 231);[1] and the divisions take place as a rule in the testis. In the female, on the other hand (Figs. 232, 234), but one cell (the ovum) is functional, and it is enormously enlarged at the cost of the others (polar bodies or polocytes) thus becoming a store-house of active protoplasm and of passive food-materials for the use of the developing embryo (p. 256). Here we find ground for the conclusion that the polocytes must be regarded as vestigial gametes, or rudimentary eggs[2]

---

[1] An important exception to this occurs in the spermatogenesis of rotifers, aphids and phylloxerans, and of bees, ants and other Hymenoptera (p. 797).

[2] This view was first suggested by Mark ('81), and later emphasized by Bütschli ('84).

which have lost the power of development. This conclusion is supported by the fact, reported by Fol ('79) and Platner ('86), that the polocytes may be penetrated by sperms; and by the still more striking fact that by an occasional abnormality of division one or both polocytes may be abnormally large, in extreme cases even as large as the remainder of the egg (Fig. 235). This occurs as a spontaneous abnormality in platodes and gasteropods; [1] and in the former case Francotte has found (in *Prostheceræus*) that such giant polocytes may actually be fertilized by the sperm and develop into

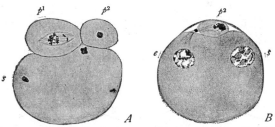

Fig. 234.—Polocytes and fertilization in the mouse (*A*, from KIRKHAM; *B*, original drawing from a preparation by KIRKHAM).

A, earlier stage, both polocytes, the first in division, egg-nucleus and sperm-nucleus (*s*); *B*, later stage, first polocyte not shown.

actively free-swimming dwarf larvæ, two larvæ being thus produced by one egg.[2]

Extrusion of the polocytes from the egg sometimes takes place in the ovary (*e. g.*, in sea-urchins) but commonly is deferred until the egg leaves the ovary or is discharged from the body; not infrequently it does not begin until after the sperm has actually entered the egg, maturation and fertilization being in this case closely associated (p. 398).

In typical cases the first polocyte divides while the second one is being formed (Figs. 183, 199); but frequently this fails (Fig. 198). As a rule the polocytes are extremely minute, and in the case of large, heavily yolk-laden eggs, like those of fishes or reptiles, are thousands of times smaller than the egg. An example of relatively large polocytes is shown in Fig. 198 (*Pterotrachea*), and of very large ones in the mouse (Fig. 234), where according to the measurements of Kirkham the first polocyte may attain to nearly 1/20 the volume of the egg. In some cases, espe-

---

[1] See Francotte ('97), Lams ('08), and Conklin ('17).

[2] The writer has observed the same in *Leptoplana*. Conklin found that in *Crepidula* giant polocytes (which are readily induced by centrifuging the eggs) never develop. This is no doubt due, as Conklin points out, to the fact that in *Crepidula* the sperm normally enters the egg before formation of the polocytes, so that the latter, like the egg, have passed the "second critical period" (p. 420) and become immune to additional sperms. In the platode, on the other hand, the sperm does not enter until after extrusion of the first polocyte, which like the egg has not yet passed the second critical period.

cially in eggs heavily laden with yolk (insects, crustacea), the polocytes fail
to be actually extruded from the egg, their nuclei remaining in the egg-
protoplasm near the periphery (Fig. 194). Here we can hardly speak of
polar bodies or polocytes but rather of polar nuclei; but as usual two polar
divisions typically occur, a group of three polar nuclei thus being formed
near the periphery of the egg. In many such cases among the insects the

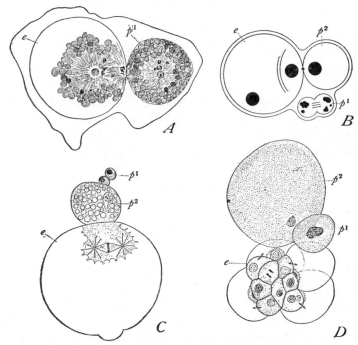

Fig. 235.—Giant polocytes in the eggs of platodes and snails.

A, egg of *Thysanozoön*, with giant first polocyte and second polar spindle (VAN DER STRICHT);
B, Arion, with both polocytes abnormally large, schematic (LAMS); *C, D, Crepidula*, after centrifuging the egg, showing various degrees of giantism of the polocytes; in *D* the second polocyte is as
large as the diminished egg; the latter has segmented normally (CONKLIN).

second polar nucleus fuses with the inner one of the pair arising by division of the first; in other cases all three polar nuclei fuse together. In
either case the fusion-nucleus may then progressively divide for a considerable time. An example of this is described by Silvestri ('06–'08) in the
parasitic hymenopter *Litomastix*, where this nucleus thus gives rise to
a mass of cells that finally almost surrounds the embryo (Fig. 142).[1]

[1] This has superficially the appearance of a gametophore generation analogous to the gametophyte
in plants, but the resemblance is of no significance and the cells in question must be triploid instead
of haploid.

Most commonly the meiotic divisions take place in rapid succession, often without the formation of a resting nucleus during the interkinesis, or interval between them.   In such cases the telophase-chromosomes of the first division pass directly into the equatorial plate of the second (Figs. 238, 239, etc.).   More commonly a nucleus is reconstructed during the interkinesis; but in many of these cases the chromosomes do not completely break up, the nucleus attaining only to a "semi-resting" stage in which the chromosomes, or at least a spireme-like condition, can still be recognized (p. 532).   At the close of the second division a true "resting-nucleus" is almost always formed, which in the oögenesis is always much smaller than the original oöcyte-nucleus or "germinal vesicle" (Fig. 189, 237).

During the foregoing process the number of chromosomes has been reduced to one-half, i. e., from the diploid to the haploid number.   The only exceptions to this occur in the diploid type of parthenogenesis and in the spermatogenesis of haploid animals (pp. 789, 797).

2. In Plants

Externally meiosis in plants offers a more involved aspect owing to the complications introduced by the alternation of generations (p. 492). Among the thallophytes, as later described (p. 627) there are cases in which the haploid and diploid generations are separate plants, closely similar in general appearance and differing little save in respect to the reproductive organs and the number of chromosomes (p. 627).   In higher plants a progressive series can be traced in the reduction of the sexual generations (gametophyte) until it becomes a vestigial structure.   In the seed-plants it wholly loses its chlorophyll and becomes a minute and as it were parasitic structure within the sporophyte, represented by the products of the embryo-sac (megaspore) or of the pollen-grain (microspore), and in the higher forms loses in greater or less degree its internal cell-walls so as to become syncytial, at least in its earlier stages.   The reduction of the male gametophyte goes much further than that of the female, and in the seed-plants it is represented only by the pollen-tube, containing a few nuclei.   The climax is reached in the angiosperms, where previous to fertilization the female gametophyte commonly contains but eight nuclei and sometimes but four, including that of the egg, and the male but three, including two generative or sperm-nuclei (Figs. 216, 308).[1]   A slight further reduction would lead to the disappearance of the gametophyte or

[1] By some botanists the male gametophyte is regarded as having been reduced to a single antheridium which produces two gametes.

haploid generation as such and thus produce a condition essentially like the gametic reduction seen in animals.[1]

The foregoing series in respect to the evolution of the gametophyte is accompanied by an interesting parallel series in the spore-formation. Like

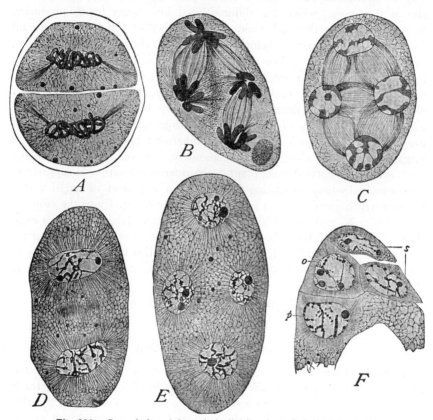

Fig. 236.—General view of the meiotic divisions in seed-plants (MOTTIER).

A–C, in the pollen-formation; *D–F*, in the embryo-sac. *A*, the two secondary sporocytes (pollen-mother-cells) just after the first division (*Lilium*); *B*, final anaphase of second division (*Podophyllum*); *C*, resulting telophase, which by division of the cytoplasmic mass produces four pollen-grains; *D*, embryo-sac after completion of the first nuclear division (*Lilium*); *E*, the same after the second division; *F*, the upper four cells resulting from the third division *o*, ovum; *p*, upper polar cell; *s*, synergidæ.

the gametes the spores are typically formed in quadruple groups or quartets. Lower plants generally (*e. g.*, algæ, bryophytes or ferns) are *isosporic, i. e.*, the four members of each quartet show no morphological differences; but even here the work of Blakeslee, the Marchals and others has proved that

---

[1] This comparison is further developed at p. 621.

in some cases the spores are physiologically already predetermined as male-producing or female-producing (p. 746). In higher plants, beginning in some of the pteridophytes (*Selaginella, Isoëtes, Marsilia*) isospory gives way to heterospory, in which a sexual predetermination appears in the size of the spores, which are differentiated into larger female-producing megaspores and smaller male-producing microspores.[1] Of this type are all seed-plants, the megaspore being represented by the primary embryo-sac, the microspore by the pollen grain. In the evolution of the heterosporic forms we find, finally, a pretty analogy to the egg with its three polocytes; for here, too, one cell of each quartet becomes larger than the others and it alone becomes a functional spore.[2] Typically the mother-cell (primary megasporocyte) undergoes two meiotic divisions to form a linear series of four cells, of which, as a rule, only the innermost becomes the functional megaspore or embryo-sac. Not uncommonly, however (as in *Lilium* and some other monocotyledonous plants), the quartet-formation is suppressed, the meiotic divisions producing no more than a quartet of nuclei within the primary sporocyte, which is itself directly converted into the embryo-sac (Figs. 236, 308). In this case a third and last division produces eight nuclei (cells) of which one is the egg while the other seven give rise to the synergidæ, polar nuclei and antipodal cells. In this case, too, but one of the four original products of the meiotic divisions normally gives rise to the egg.[3]

III. INTERNAL PHENOMENA OF MEIOSIS

A. INTRODUCTION

1. Historical and Theoretical

We need not here consider the earlier and unsuccessful attempts to interpret meiosis (in case of the polocyte-formation in oögenesis) as a factor in sex-production.[4] Of greater interest was the view of Weismann ('87) that only the second meiotic division is concerned in reduction, based on the fact that in diploid parthenogenesis (as in the daphnids or aphids), where no reduction takes place, the second polocyte fails to be formed (p. 468). The first polocyte, Weismann therefore argued, plays no part in reduction, but merely removes from the egg an "histogenetic" plasm, so as finally to transmit only germ-plasm. This hypothesis evidently breaks down in the case of spermatogenesis and is also disproved by more recent cyto-

---

[1] This presents an interesting analogy to the differentiation of the eggs of certain animals (rotifers, phylloxerans, *Dinophilus*) into larger female-producing and smaller male-producing forms. *Cf.* p. 806.

[2] For a further development of this comparison see p. 620.

[3] See p. 496.

[4] See Minot ('77), Balfour ('80), Van Beneden ('84) and for criticisms Nägeli ('84), Strasburger ('84) and Weismann ('85).

logical observations which show that both meiotic divisions may be concerned in reduction (p. 573).   Nevertheless it is quite possible that Weis-

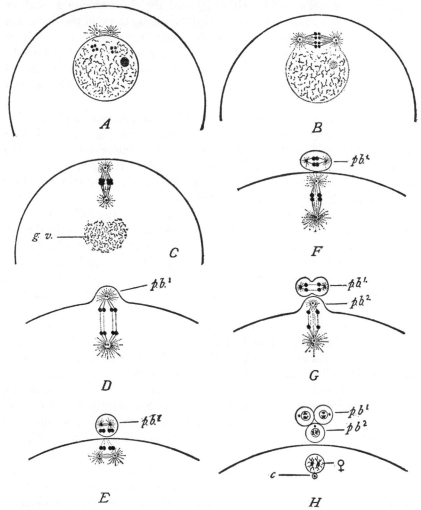

Fig. 237.—Diagrams showing the essential facts in the meiosis of the egg. The diploid number of chromosomes is supposed to be four.

A, initial phase; two tetrads in the germinal vesicle; *B*, *C*, the first polar spindle; *D*, *E*, formation of the first polocyte; *F*, *G*, the second division; *H*, final result; three polocytes and the egg-nucleus (♀), each containing two single chromosomes (half the diploid number); *c*, the egg-center which now disappears from view.

mann's suggestion contained a nucleus of truth; for we have thus far no
other clue to the meaning of "diminution" (p. 323), nor have we as yet

any more satisfactory explanation of why two meiotic divisions should take place instead of one.

Many of the earlier writers either ignored the chromosomes as such or relegated them to a position of comparative unimportance in the discussion of the reduction-problem. Some of them treated the problem as merely or mainly a quantitative one; but this position quickly proved untenable. As will later be shown, however (Chap. XII), modern research has proved the hopeless inadequacy of any analysis that does not reckon with the chromosomes as leading factors in the problem.

The first fruitful attempt to analyze the internal phenomena of reduction was made on purely theoretical grounds by Weismann ('87) in one of those brilliant essays on heredity which contributed in so important a way to the enlargement of our views concerning cytological research. Roux had argued ('83) that the transformation of the nuclear substance into long threads, and their division by longitudinal splitting can only mean that in some sense or other this substance must embody many different "qualities" that assume a linear alignment in the threads. Splitting of the threads thus insures not merely a mass-division of the nucleus as a whole, but beyond this a meristic division of all its constitutional "qualities." Upon this highly fruitful thought Weismann built an elaborate speculative system of pangenesis and development of which the basic assumption was that the nucleus consists of self-propagating units or "biophores" aggregated to form "ids," that are aligned like Roux's "qualities" in linear series in the spireme-threads and undergo division by splitting of the threads. Each "id" was assumed to possess the complete architecture of the germ-plasm, the "ids" differing slightly from each other in a manner corresponding to individual differences within the species. Each chromosome, therefore, represents a linear group of complete but slightly different germ-plasms. We now know that these particular conceptions concerning the "ids" were untenable; for the experimental work of Boveri on multipolar mitosis (p. 916) demonstrated that the whole chromosome group is necessary to the integrity of the germ-plasm even of a single individual. In principle, nevertheless, Weismann was right in urging that a process of reduction must periodically occur to counteract "the excessive accumulation of different kinds of hereditary tendencies or germ-plasms" which otherwise would so soon result from the periodic process of doubling in fertilization.[1] He was also right in the prediction that "there *must* be a form of nuclear division in which the ancestral germ-plasms contained in the nucleus are distributed to the daughter-nuclei in such a way that each of them receives only half the number contained in the original nucleus." Weismann indicated two

[1] *Cf.* Nägeli ('84, p. 224).

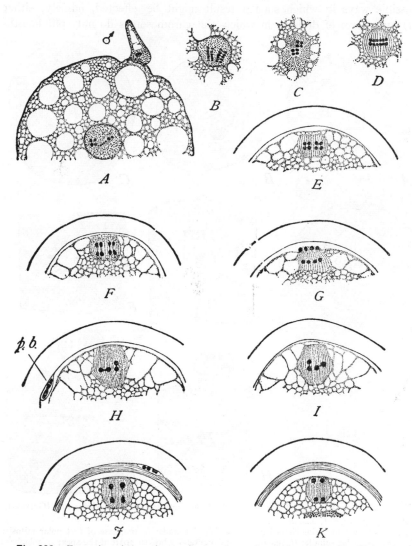

Fig. 238.—Formation of the polocytes in *Ascaris megalocephala*, var. *bivalens* (BOVERI).

A, the egg with the sperm just entering at ♂; the germinal vesicle contains two rod-shaped tetrads (only one clearly shown), the number of chromosomes in earlier divisions having been four; *B*, the tetrads seen in profile; *C*, the same in end view; *D*, first spindle forming (in this case inside the germinal vesicle); *E*, first polar spindle; *F*, the tetrads dividing; *G*, first polocyte formed, containing, like the egg, two dyads; *H, I*, the dyads rotating into position for the second division; *J*, the dyads dividing; *K*, each dyad has divided into two single chromosomes, completing the reduction.

possible ways in which such a result might be effected, namely, either
(1) by a form of division in which the chromosomes do not split length-

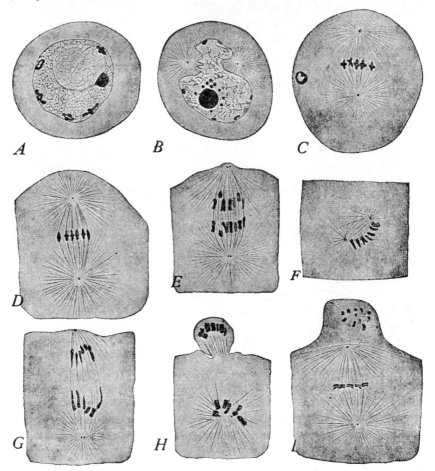

Fig. 239.—Meiosis in eggs of the pelecypod *Zirphæa* and the annelid *Thalassema* (Griffin).
A–E, Zirphæa; F–I, Thalassema.
A, unfertilized egg, ring-shaped and cross-shaped tetrads; B, prophase of first polar mitosis;
C, D, E, first polar spindle; G, ensuing stage; daughter-V's broken apart at the apex; H, telophase
of first, early prophase of second, division; F, later prophase of second division; I, second polar
spindle in metaphase.

wise but are sorted out, without division, into two corresponding groups,
or (2) by a transverse instead of a longitudinal division of the chromosomes.[1]
For either process (both were at that time purely theoretical postulates)

---

[1] A reduction of the "ids" or "ancestral germ-plasms" would result from either process; but the
second suggestion offers no explanation of the reduction in the number of chromosomes.

he proposed the term *reduction-division* in contradistinction to the ordinary type or *equation-division,* in which longitudinal division of the whole chromosome takes place. In the case of the female he believed the reduction division to coincide with the second of the two maturation-divisions, and predicted that a corresponding type of division would also be found in the male.

The fulfillment of Weismann's prediction is one of the most interesting results of modern cytological research, though opinion is not yet unanimous in respect to the details of the process. From the start investigation of the problem has been confused by the emphasis that Weismann laid upon the supposed theoretic significance of a transverse division of the chromosomes, thus implying that a longitudinal division is *ipso facto* an equation-division. Some of the leading early investigators, such as O. Hertwig, Boveri and Brauer, found both maturation-divisions to be longitudinal, and were thus led to deny the occurrence of a reduction-division. The fallacy of this was demonstrated as it gradually became clear, especially through the work of Winiwarter ('00) and his successors, that what seems to be a longitudinal split may in reality be the separation of two chromosomes that have been associated side by side; and conversely, that a division that seems to be transverse may be only the final separation of such a pair (*cf.* p. 133). The apparent contrast between longitudinal and transverse division in meiosis thus in large measure loses its significance; and it becomes evident that the problem of the reduction-division cannot be solved by study of the actual meiotic-divisions alone but involves also the whole series of preceding events in the meiotic prophases.

2. Preliminary Outline

It is now widely held that reduction is initiated by a preliminary process or *synapsis* or *syndesis* in the course of which the chromosomes conjugate —or otherwise become closely associated—two by two to form *bivalents* or *gemini* (Figs. 102, 105). The two chromosomes of each pair, called *synaptic mates,* are in general alike in size and form (though there are some exceptions to this). There is the strongest ground for the conclusion that in each case the synaptic mates are respectively of paternal and of maternal descent (Montgomery) and that they are homologous (Montgomery, Sutton, Boveri). Conjugation of the chromosomes does not, however, in itself effect reduction. It is no more than a preliminary coupling or *pseudo-reduction* (Rückert) producing a haploid group of bivalents; and since each of these represents a pair of chromosomes the total number remains unchanged. Actual reduction first occurs in the course of one or the other of the meiotic divisions, when the two synaptic mates are disjoined by the "reduction-division." and pass into different germ-nuclei.

Thus far all is clear. The process just outlined is, however, complicated by the fact that sooner or later after synapsis each of the synaptic mates itself undergoes a "secondary" longitudinal split which represents a future equation-division. The bivalent thus becomes a quadripartite body or

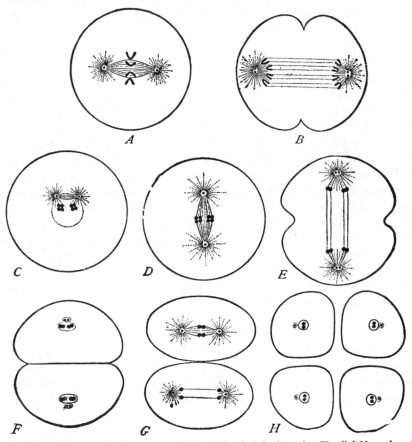

Fig. 240.—Diagrams showing the essential facts of meiosis in the male. The diploid number of chromosomes is supposed to be four.

A, *B*, division of the spermatogonia; *C*, primary spermatocyte preparing for division; the chromatin forms two tetrads; *D*, *E*, *F*, first division; *G*, *H*, division of the two second spermatocytes to form four spermatids. Each of the latter receives two single chromosomes and a centriole.

tetrad, divided into four parts or *chromatids* by two clefts at right angles to each other, one representing the future reduction-division, the other the equation-division. Since each tetrad later divides successively along these two planes, the final result is its separation into its four component chromatids one of which enters each of the four resulting nuclei. Each of the latter thus receives a haploid group of single or univalent chromosomes (Figs. 237, 238, 240).

This process is readily made clear when schematized as follows: Let us designate the chromosomes of the diploid group by the letters A, B, C, D, a, b, c, d, etc., capitals representing chromosomes of maternal descent, and small letters those of paternal. Synapsis of the homologous chromosomes produces the bivalents Aa, Bb, etc., the number of which is of course half the original chromosome-number. By equational splitting of these arise

the tetrads $\dfrac{Aa}{Aa,}\ \dfrac{Bb}{Bb,}$ etc., or (indicating the plane of apposition or synapsis)

$\dfrac{A}{A}\Big|\dfrac{a}{a}$—Division of such a tetrad along the vertical plane gives the two dyads

$\dfrac{A}{A}$ and $\dfrac{a,}{a,}$ which then separate into the four single chromosomes A, A, a, and

a, which finally enter four different gametes.

It is evident that if the original synaptic mates retain their identity during this process *each of them actually divides but once during the maturation-process*, namely, along the horizontal plane (second division) in the above diagram. This division, clearly, is an equation-division quite comparable to an ordinary somatic division. The other "division" of the tetrad, on the contrary, involves no actual division but only disjoins the two associated mates—a process which obviously meets all the theoretical demands of Weismann's postulate. This process takes place in every bivalent, and is not affected by variations affecting the order of division, the time at which the equational split makes its appearance, or of the particular mode in which the mates of each pair are connected. We can thus understand how tetrads of the most diverse forms give the same result in the course of the two divisions. This interpretation finds a striking confirmation in the maturation-divisions of organisms having only a haploid group of chromosomes, or of those in which the diploid number of chromosomes is odd; for example in certain types of mutants (p. 874), in the males of many insects (p. 750) or in forms having unpaired supernumerary chromosomes (p. 844).

So far as the actual divisions are concerned, and apart from all questions of hypothetical interpretation, the main facts concerning the structure of the tetrads and their history during the meiotic divisions are now perfectly well established. Existing differences of opinion relate almost solely to their earlier history. In particular the following questions demand critical examination: (1) Is the conception of synapsis and bivalence valid? Do corresponding chromosomes become associated two by two to form double chromosomes or bivalents? (2) If such be the fact, is the reduction-division also a fact? Do the two conjugants or synaptic mates subsequently disjoin or separate? (3) Do they retain their identity throughout these operations? Each of these questions has long been debated. The reality of the whole conception of synapsis, bivalence and the reduction-division

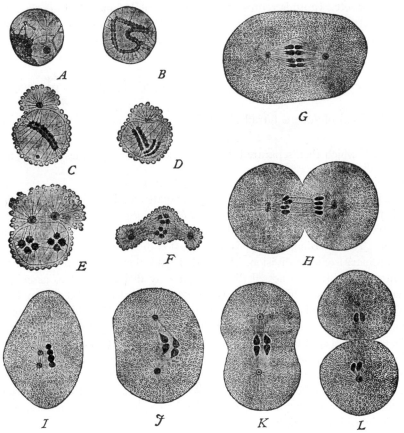

Fig. 241.—Reduction in the spermatogenesis of *Ascaris megalocephala*, var. *bivalens* (BRAUER).

A–G, successive stages in the division of the primary spermatocyte. The original reticulum undergoes a very early division of the chromatin-granules which then form a doubly split spireme-thread, *B*. This shortens (*C*) and breaks in two to form the two tetrads (*D* in profile, *E* viewed endwise); *F*, *G*, *H*, first division to form two secondary spermatocytes, each receiving two dyads; *I*, secondary spermatocyte; *J*, *K*, the same dividing; *L*, two resulting spermatids, each with two single chromosomes.

has been in effect denied (Meves, Fick, Della Valle, Champy, Regaud). Other cytologists, while accepting the fact of synapsis, have maintained that conjugation results in a complete fusion of the mates to form new chromosomes or *mixochromosomes* (Winiwarter, Bonnevie). Were this correct, the conception of the reduction-division, in its original form, would fall to the ground. These negative conclusions, however, far overshot the mark; for both synapsis and disjunction (reduction-division) have now been demon-

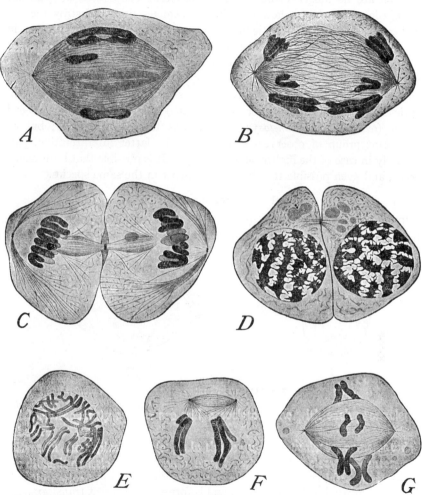

Fig. 242.—Spermatocyte-divisions in *Salamandra* (*E*, from FLEMMING, the others from MEVES). *A*, first (heterotypic) division in metaphase, showing heterotype rings; *B*, anaphase; longitudinal splitting of the daughter-loops; *C*, telophase, *D*, ensuing pause; *E*, early prophase of second division with longitudinally divided segmented spireme; *F*, later prophase; *G*, metaphase of second division.

strated in the case of certain particular chromosomes with a clearness that leaves nothing to be desired. On the other hand, genetic evidence has of late given the strongest grounds to conclude that definite exchanges of material often take place between the synaptic mates (by "crossing over," p. 942) during the period of their close association in synapsis. To whatever extent this occurs the chromosomes separated by the reduction division are no longer identical with those that conjugated in synapsis. As will later be shown, however, these exchanges do not destroy the homology between the synaptic mates nor the principle of disjunction in meiosis. For the moment, therefore, they may be disregarded.[1] An important question, still to a certain extent in doubt, concerns the mode of synapsis. Evidence has steadily accumulated to show that in a large class of cases synapsis involves a side-by-side union of the synaptic mates (*parasynapsis* or *parasyndesis*) instead of an end-to-end union (*telosynapsis* or *metasyndesis*) as was formerly supposed; but an important group of observers still hold to the latter interpretation, particularly in case of the higher plants (p. 557). It is possible that both modes occur, and even possible that both may coexist in the same species.

3. General Characteristics of the Divisions

The meiotic divisions are distinguished from the ordinary somatic mitoses by certain marked peculiarities of the chromosomes and sometimes also of

A   *B*

Fig. 243.—Anastral polar spindles.

A, first polar spindle with tetrads, in *Heterocope* (HÄCKER); *B*, second polar spindle in *Triton* (CARNOY and LEBRUN).

the achromatic figure. Among the latter may be mentioned the fact earlier referred to (p. 150) that in the eggs of certain animals the polar mitoses are of the anastral type. In these cases the spindle is typically barrel-shaped, having truncated or rounded ends, and is formed by a direct transformation of the substance of the germinal vesicle (Figs. 238, 243). Such spindles are seen in the oögenesis of *Ascaris* (Van Beneden, Boveri) of copepods (Haecker, Rückert), insects (Henking), tunicates (Crampton, Golski, Conklin), *Amphioxus* (Sobotta), and many vertebrates.[2] The absence of asters is a

---

[1] *Cf.* p. 572.

[2] See Van Beneden ('87), Boveri ('87, '88), Haeckel ('95a), Rückert ('94), Henking ('92), Sabotta ('97), Conklin ('05a), etc.

noteworthy feature of these spindles because in these same forms the cleavage-figures, somatic divisions, and the spermatogenetic divisions of the male, are characterized by the presence of conspicuous asters and central bodies. Such anastral spindles are somewhat exceptional; and in many forms (platodes, annelids, mollusks) the polar mitoses offer very fine examples of the amphiastral type (Fig. 239, etc.). In higher plants, also, differences often appear between the meiotic and the somatic divisions in respect to the achromatic figure, the former being in general characterized by the multipolar type of spindle-formation, the latter, as a rule, by the formation of polar caps (p. 153). Of the meaning of these differences nothing as yet is known.

For the problems of meiosis the important peculiarities of the meiotic divisions appear in the chromosomes, especially during the prophases and later stages of the first division, and are so marked as to have led to the designation of this division as *heterotypic* (Flemming, '87). In the second or *homeotypic* division the chromosomes approach much more closely in type to those of the somatic divisions.[1]

The most salient peculiarities of the heterotypic division are as follows:

(1) The number of heterotypic chromosomes [2] is seemingly haploid; but when we consider the composition of these chromosomes, it becomes evident that this appearance is deceptive. The actual reduction has not yet occurred; for each heterotypic chromosome represents two gonial chromosomes (synaptic mates) in close association. The total number of originally single chromosomes is therefore still diploid.

(2) In most cases, perhaps in all, each of the synaptic mates thus associated in pairs is now itself longitudinally split. Each bivalent as already explained, has thus become a quadripartite *tetrad*, consisting of four components or *chromatids*. The total number of chromatids is therefore tetraploid or double the diploid number, precisely as is the case in an ordinary somatic metaphase, when each chromosome of the diploid group is longitudinally split. This split is generally regarded as the forerunner of the equation-division. It makes its appearance early in the meiotic process— sometimes soon after synapsis, in some cases possibly even earlier—but often becomes obscured in later stages so that it is sometimes not clearly evident before the heterotypic metaphase, or even the anaphases. The earlier history of these chromosomes indicates, however, that they are probably always

---

[1] Flemming employed these terms in a purely descriptive sense without regard to the problem of meiosis in the modern sense. Since then the heterotypic division has been so widely identified with the reduction-division that the two terms have come to be used almost as synonyms. As will later appear (p. 572), this usage is inadmissible; and the word heterotypic will here be used, as it was by its author, merely as a convenient descriptive term to designate the first meiotic division.

[2] For the sake of brevity each separate chromatin-mass in this mitosis will be spoken of as a "chromosome," whatever be its actual composition.

quadripartite in internal structure even when this escapes the eye. We shall therefore speak of them indifferently as bivalents or tetrads as may be convenient, the former term indicating their mode of origin, the latter their prospective value and in most cases their visible structure.

(3) The bivalents (or tetrads) are of many different forms, some of which differ widely from those seen in the somatic divisions. They result from

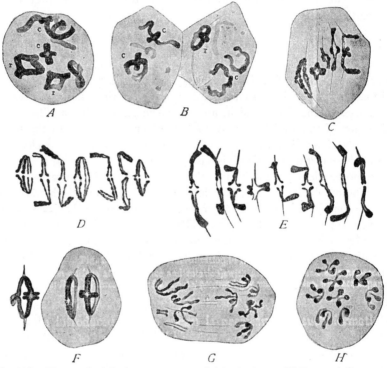

Fig. 244.—The tetrads of the first spermatocyte-division in the annelid *Tomopteris* (SCHREINER).
A, first spermatocyte prophase-nucleus, showing early rings (*r*) and double crosses (*c*); *B*, two slightly later nuclei; *C*, five of the tetrads of the first spindle, showing ring, double cross, transverse rod-tetrads and *E* figure; *D*, seven of the tetrads from another spindle; *E*, all of the nine tetrads from another spindle, showing various forms of rod-tetrads and double-crosses; *F*, three varieties of the rings at metaphase; *G*, anaphase of first division, showing various forms of anaschistic dyads; *H*, interkinesis, with dyads.

processes that begin early in the prophases (diakinesis) and undergo various modifications as the divisions proceed. The most characteristic of these forms are rings (especially emphasized by Flemming) and cross-shaped figures; but V-shaped and hook-shaped figures and a great variety of others may also appear, differing more or less from species to species and to a certain extent characteristic of particular tetrads (Figs. 242, 244, 255). The analysis of these various figures has proved a laborious and protracted task but, in the main, order has now been brought out of the former chaos.

B. The Heterotypic Division

Introductory [1]

It is now generally agreed that the heterotypic chromosomes are always derived from more or less elongated spireme-threads that are longitudinally double from an early period (*diplonema*, p. 544), and sooner or later longitudinally quadripartite (Figs. 268, 436, etc.). The primary longitudinal cleft is generally regarded as representing the synaptic plane along which two synaptic mates have conjugated side-by-side, and the secondary cleft as an equational splitting of each of these mates. In the later stages of the growth-period the double (or quadruple) threads condense, shorten, become intensely basophilic, and typically tend to take up a peripheral position near the nuclear membrane. The period thus marked is generally called the *diakinesis* (Haecker), and in a broad sense it corresponds to the later prophases of an ordinary somatic mitosis. It is important to bear in mind that the process of condensation varies widely both in rate and in degree among different species. For instance, in *Tomopteris* (Fig. 244) it never proceeds as far as in *Ascaris* (Fig. 238) or in Hemiptera (Fig. 369), while intermediate conditions are found in the urodeles (Fig. 242) or in many of the seed-plants (Fig. 252). In *Tomopteris*, therefore, the tetrads enter the metaphase group at a stage which in *Ascaris* or the insects only appears at a much earlier period, during the prophases. Cases of the *Tomopteris* type are of great importance for an exact analysis of the mode of division of the tetrads, for in many cases this is impracticable without tracing the whole earlier history of the bivalents. It will be understood, therefore, that the following account of the bivalents takes into account the earlier stages as well as the metaphase.

1. The Heterotypic Chromosomes. Forms and Spindle Attachments

The diversity of form displayed by the heterotypic chromosomes arises early in the diakinesis and becomes more marked as the prophases advance. It is due to two distinct causes. One of these is correlated with corresponding differences in mode of attachment to the spindle-fibers. The studies of many observers have made it clear that these differences are approximately constant and result from corresponding differences present already

---

[1] This introductory sketch is based on the conditions observed in animals generally, leaving out of account for the moment the process of synapsis by loop-formation advocated especially in the case of higher plants by Farmer and Moore, Mottier and their followers. For an account of this, see p. 557.

in the diploid groups (somatic or gonial).[1] Thus in the case of any particular pair of synaptic mates the attachment as seen in the gonial groups whether terminal, median or intermediate, is found also in the tetrads resulting from their synaptic union, and in the resulting dyads of the second or homeotypic division (Figs. 245, 247, etc.). Remarkable examples of

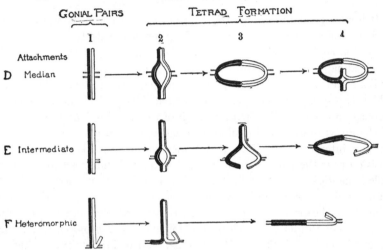

Fig. 245.—Atelomitic types of attachment.

D, median producing atelomitic or tangential ring (*Tomopteris* type); E, intermediate, producing unequal anaschistic Vs or J-shaped figures; F, heteromorphic, with both terminal and non-terminal attachment (*Trimerotropis* type).

this are offered in cases of chromosome-linkage (pp. 779, 879) or in heteromorphic tetrads (p. 571).

It is important to bear in mind the fact that some of the forms thus correlated with the spindle-attachments are assumed long *before the actual spindle-attachments have been established* (for instance in certain types double crosses and rings). We are thus led to recognize a second type of diversity due to various displacements of the tetrad-components (chromatids) with reference to one another, which in extreme cases completely alter their original form of association.[2] Rings, for instance, arise by the separation of the chromatids along the middle-region of one cleft while the ends remain united (Figs. 246, 257), double crosses by a related but different process (Fig. 254). The differences arising from both these causes appear

[1] For a discussion of this point see especially McClung ('14) and other works referred to in the following footnote.

[2] These changes have been studied by numerous observers, prominent among them Flemming ('87), Farmer and Moore ('95), Meves ('96), Janssens ('01, '03, '05, etc.), Sinéty ('01), Allen ('05), Grégoire ('99, '05, '10), the Schreiners ('06, etc.), Mottier ('03, '14, etc.), more recently by Robertson ('08, '16, etc.), Wilson ('12), McClung ('14), Mohr ('14), Wenrich ('16, '17), and others.

not only in the form of the heterotypic chromosomes but also in their apparent modes of division in the second or homeotypic mitosis. The feature common to all alike is the division of the bivalent (or tetrad) into two daughter-chromosomes or dyads, each of which is itself double, or soon becomes so, in preparation for the second division.

The various forms assumed by the heterotypic chromosomes are not merely haphazard fluctuations. Within certain limits they are character-

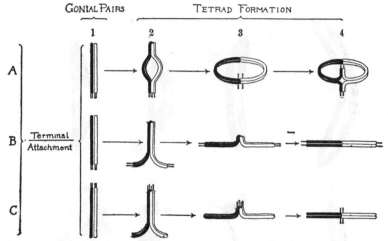

Fig. 246.—Terminal spindle-attachments in meiosis. In each case 1 represents the original gonial pair (synaptic mates) in parasynaptic association.
A, the formation of telomitic or equatorial rings (*Hippiscus* type); B, formation of transverse rod-tetrads with biterminal attachment (diaschistic) readily converted into double cross (Fig. 254); C, transverse rod-tetrad with apparently median attachment (diaschistic, *Mecostethus* type) convertible into diaschistic V by median flexure.

istic of particular bivalents as urged by Baumgartner ('04), Moore and Arnold ('05) and many later observers. Numerous cases have been observed in which certain individual bivalents are at once recognizable both by their size and form (p. 834). On the other hand, it has been clearly shown, by studies especially on insects (Orthoptera, Hemiptera) that a considerable range of variation often exists in the external form of particular tetrads. Robertson, McClung and others have shown that sometimes the number of rings may vary materially in different cells of the same individual. Rings and V's are, however, closely related forms, as is proved by their mode of formation; and all the facts point to the conclusion that each bivalent conforms to its general type, *provided its whole history be taken into account*. Many examples of this will hereafter be given in connection with various related topics such as the spindle-attachments (p. 516), random assortment (p. 931) and the individuality of the chromosome (p. 828).

In comparing the various forms of tetrads as seen in the late diakinesis or metaphase it is convenient to recognize two types that *seem* to differ widely in respect to the relation of the two cleavage-planes along which they are destined to divide. These may be designated as A and B. In A (*Ascaris*, vertebrates generally, many higher plants) both divisions are plainly longitudinal with reference to the spireme-thread (diplotene) from which the tetrad arises (Fig. 249); while in B (common among insects) but one division

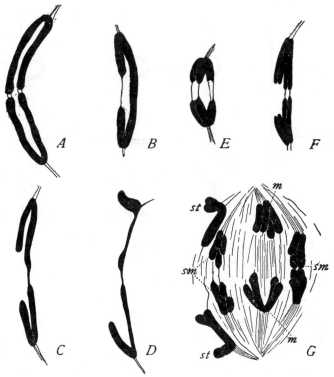

Fig. 247.—Metaphase and anaphase-chromosomes in urodeles (*E, G,* in *Plethodon* original), the others in *Salamandra*, from FLEMMING.

A, ring with median attachment; *B, C,* sub-median attachments; *D,* nearly sub-terminal attachment; *E,* ring, median attachment with secondary (equational) split; *F,* similar form, submedian attachment; *G,* anaphase-figures, non-terminal attachments, giving anaschistic V's and J's (*s, t,* sub-terminal; *s, m,* sub-median; *m,* median).

is longitudinal and the other apparently transverse (Fig. 251). This difference, now known to be of quite secondary importance, was overemphasized by earlier writers because of the emphasis laid by Weismann on transverse division as a possible mode of reduction (p. 502). By Korschelt and Heider ('03) the two types were distinguished as *eumitotic* (A) and *pseudo-*

mitotic (B); by Farmer and Moore ('05) more appropriately as *anaschistic* (A) and *diaschistic* (B). The former terms are obsolete. Those of Farmer and Moore have never come into general use but nevertheless have a certain utility for descriptive purposes. They must not, however, be taken to imply any important distinction; for it is now certain that in a large class of cases the so-called transverse or cross-suture of the tetrad in type B *only marks the final separation-point of chromatids that originally lay side-by-side.* In this respect such tetrads are precisely analogous to the later stages of somatic rod-shaped chromosomes having terminal attachments (p. 133). Whether this is true of all tetrads of this type is still an open question. With this distinction in view we may briefly review some of the more important forms of tetrads, and their modes of division.

2. Course of the Division

a. Rod-tetrads. These forms, widely distributed among both plants and animals, have the form of rods or threads, always longitudinally double, the two longitudinal halves sometimes more or less separate, sometimes united at one or both ends to form loops or elongate compressed rings, in either case sometimes more or less twisted about each other (a remnant of the strepsinema, Fig. 250). They may be of either type A (anaschistic) or B (diaschistic) showing, in the first case two longitudinal clefts, in the second one longitudinal cleft and one transverse suture at the middle point. These two cases may conveniently be distinguished as "longitudinal" and "transverse" rod-tetrads.

(*a'*). *Anaschistic or Longitudinal Rod-tetrads.* Tetrads of this type are widely distributed in both animals and plants and may be treated as the fundamental form from which most others may readily be derived. The classical example of such tetrads is offered by *Ascaris megalocephala*, made known by the pioneer works of Van Beneden ('84), Boveri ('88), O. Hertwig ('91) and Brauer ('93), in which the tetrads at first consist of four parallel threads or rods (Figs. 238, 241) which later condense to form very compact quadripartite bodies [1] in which the original long axis cannot be distinguished. More important for our analysis are the forms, often seen in *Tomopteris* higher plants, and in the urodeles and some other animals, which retain their elongate form at the time they pass upon the spindle. In these cases the secondary split is often obscure, so that the bivalent appears longitudinally double; the two halves are often separate throughout, but may be united at

---

[1] Various futile attempts were formerly made to treat tetrads of this type as pathological formations, as artifacts, as optical illusions, as exaggerated cases of conditions that exist also in the somatic chromosomes, etc.; but all this belongs to a bygone period.

one or both ends and sometimes twisted more or less about each other (Figs. 248, 250).

The history of these bivalents, which is of the most instructive nature, very clearly illustrates the diversity of form resulting from different modes of attachment to the spindle. Like those of the somatic chromosomes (p. 130), these attachments may be either median, intermediate or terminal, and in each case separation of the two halves always begins at the point of attachment, proceeding thence along the chromosome. This process leads

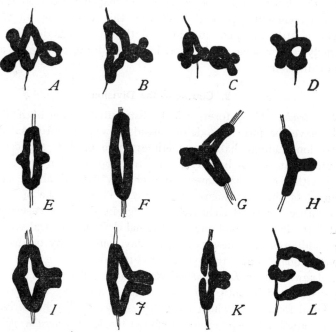

Fig. 248.—Metaphase figures, heterotypic division, in spermatogenesis of urodeles. (*A–D, L*, from JANNSENS, the others original.)

A–D, in *Triton*, twisted figures with free ends and non-terminal attachments; *D*, twisted loop, with two ends free; *E, F, Plethodon*, ring-figures; *G, H*, modification of ring-figure, giving cross-shaped figure with median attachment, in *G* seen obliquely, in *H* from one side; *I–K, Amphiuma*, ring-figures with sub-median attachments; *L, Triton, E-figure* resulting from forms like the preceding.

during the late metaphase and early anaphases to characteristic forms analogous to those seen in the somatic divisions modified in the heterotypic division only by the secondary split that is present in each half or makes its appearance as the division proceeds, as follows:

Median Attachment. In this case (as in the somatic divisions) the separating halves have the form of V's or U's connected by their ends to form ◊-shaped or ring-shaped figures (Figs. 249, 251). These tetrads readily become converted into V-shaped forms by flexure at the point of attachment (Figs. 250, 253); and they differ from atelomitic ring-shaped forms only in that in the latter the separation of the two halves occurs already in the diakinesis (p. 547). Since their history during the anaphases is essentially the same in all these cases they need not at this point be separately described. As the apices draw apart in the initial anaphases the tetrads are drawn out into ◊-shaped or elongate ring-shaped figures which commonly show a transverse suture at the points where the two halves arc connected; and often develop on one or both sides a prominent

LONGITUDINAL TETRADS

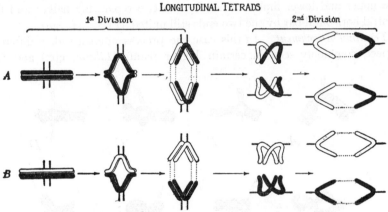

Fig. 249.—Diagrams of longitudinal or anaschistic rod-tetrads. The attachment is in both cases median (giving longitudinally cleft V's in the first anaphases and simple V's in the second). The A series shows post-reduction; B, pre-reduction. Compare Fig. 247.

projection longitudinally double and sometimes twisted; this represents the peripheral portions of the limbs of the two V's still closely associated, and often swollen to form knobs at the ends. These projections or "lugs" often stand out at a considerable angle both from the central portion (ring) and from the spindle, so as to give in profile view somewhat the aspect of a bird with outstretched wings (Figs. 256, 248). As the division proceeds the two V-shaped (or U-shaped) halves progressively draw apart and finally separate to form two daughter-V's with their apices turned towards the poles *and always, sooner or later, longitudinally cleft,* owing to the development in each of the secondary split (Figs. 252, 256).

With many minor variations rings of this type are of common occurrence in most of the main groups of plants and animals. When fully formed they are often not to be distinguished from early anaphase rings produced by

V-shaped bivalents, or from the atelomitic ring-tetrads, later to be described, which are formed during the early diakinesis (p. 527).

Intermediate Attachment (sub-terminal or sub-median). In this case the daughter-chromosomes, as they separate, have the form of unequal V's or of J's or hooks, in each case longitudinally double (Figs. 247, 245, 252). In this case, too, rings are often temporarily formed as the two halves separate (Figs. 252), the opening being nearer one end of the tetrad, and the ring usually first breaks at this point to form J-shaped sister-chromosomes. Not infrequently as the two halves separate the united ends at the opposite side, standing out at a considerable angle (as above mentioned) give the tetrad as seen in side view the appearance of an E-shaped figure, the upper and lower limbs formed by the two separating halves and the central horizontal bar by the two ends still united (Figs. 244, 248).

Terminal Attachment. In this case the process offers a widely different aspect, commonly seen in certain higher plants (*Lilium*, etc.) and fre-

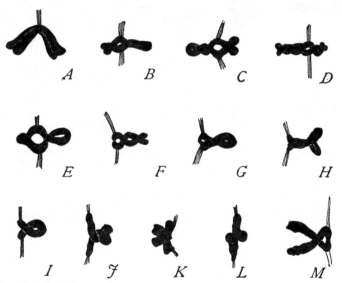

Fig. 250.—Metaphase-chromosomes in heterotypic division of seed-plants, showing various attachments.

(*A, D, F, I*, from Grégoire; *B, E, C, G, H*, from Mottier; *J–L*, Allen; *M*, Strasburger). *A*, median attachment (*Trillium*); *B–E*, sub-median, bivalents more or less twisted (*Lilium*); *F–H*, terminal attachments bivalents twisted (*Lilium*); *I–K*, terminal crossed attachment; *L*, later stage of same, *en face*; *M*, sub-terminal crossed attachment.

quently in animals. Here again, as in the somatic mitoses, the two halves each individually split, draw apart apong the spindle from their point of attachment towards the poles (*cf.* Figs. 246, 252), until they lie end-to-end and finally break apart at the equator by an *apparently* transverse division. In the anaphase the resulting dyads sometimes retain the form of straight rods, longitudinally split, but very commonly their longitudinal halves diverge more or less widely at their free equatorial ends, remaining united only at their attached (polar) ends. The anaphase rod is thus converted into a simple V attached by its apex (Fig. 252, G, H). Such V's do not split lengthwise, like those which result from a median attachment; *the whole chromosome is already split*, and the two halves (diverging limbs of the V) are destined to separate at the apex of the V. This again illustrates how widely tetrads may seem to differ in mode of division merely because of a difference of spindle-attachment; for precisely the same original type of tetrad (the anaschistic rod-type) gives in one case (median attachment) anaphase V's that are anaschistic or longitudinally dividing, and in the other (terminal attachment) anaphase V's which superficially regarded *seem* to be diaschistic or transversely dividing. Fundamentally, the two cases are identical, the tetrads undergoing in both two longitudinal divisions and differing only in the minor details of their distribution.[1]

This is conspicuously shown in cases of terminal attachment in higher plants (*Lilium*, etc.) in which the rod-tetrad clearly shows in certain cases both longitudinal clefts at the metaphase or even earlier.[2] Both clefts may open already in the metaphase before the dyads have separated, the equatorial cleft from the spindle outwards, the axial cleft from the free end inwards (Fig. 252, B, C). The result of this process (as in case of median attachment is a <> shaped figure or ring, very similar in general appearance to those resulting from a median attachment but having a quite different history in the anaphase, the daughter V's in the former case apparently dividing cross-wise at the apex (diaschistic), in the latter case splitting lengthwise (anaschistic).

Crossed Insertion. This mode of terminal attachment, described by Grégoire, Mottier, Allen, Strasburger and others in plants and by Sinéty, Montgomery, Davis and others in animals, is still a matter of dispute. According to the usual account, the two halves of the rod in this case cross one another in the metaphase in such a manner that each is connected with the opposite spindle-pole instead of that on its own side (Figs. 248, 250). The two rods may be free at both ends or united at one end to form a loop (Fig. 250); and in the latter case may be so widely separated as to form a nearly closed ring (Fig. 248, D). In all these cases attachment is at the free ends; and as the halves separate, accordingly, they slide past one an-

---

[1] The elucidation of this fact is due especially to the work of Grégoire ('99, etc.) and Strasburger ('95, '00, '04, etc.), on higher plants. Grégoire's conclusions on this point have been confirmed by many later observers.

[2] Strasburger ('95), Mottier ('08), Guignard ('08), Grégoire ('90), etc.

other so that each half passes to the pole opposite to that towards which it originally lay.

Assuming the correctness of this account, it seems clear that the crossed insertion is essentially the result of an earlier twisting of the two halves about one another, *i. e.*, is a last remnant of the strepsinema (Fig. 273). It is doubtful whether this account is valid for all cases. In the Orthoptera, for example, McClung ('14) has shown that some supposed cases of this type are due to a misinterpretation of the equatorial rings (described below) as seen in slightly oblique side view. Such an error does not, however, seem possible in the case of crossed rods with both ends completely separated,

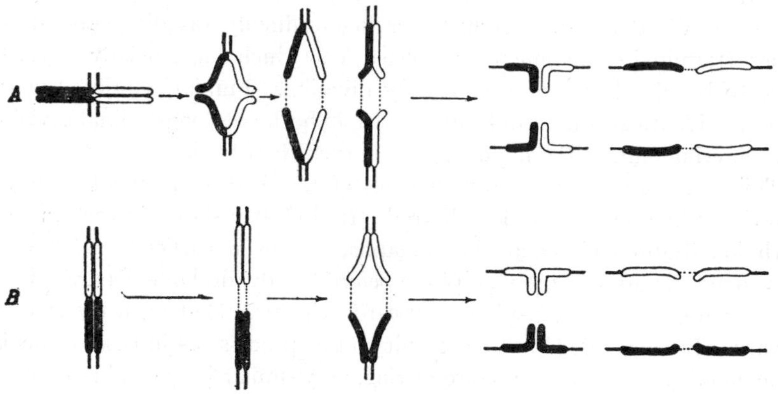

TRANSVERSE TETRADS

Fig. 251.—Diagram of the transverse or diaschistic rod-tetrads. In the *A* series attachment is median if the tetrad be considered as whole (terminal with respect to the component chromatids) giving simple anaphase-V's and post-reduction; in *B* it is biterminal with pre-reduction, giving anaschistic anaphase-rods or diaschistic simple V's.

such as are described for instance by Strasburger, Mottier, Allen or Grégoire in the higher plants.

(*a²*). *Diaschistic or Transverse Rod-tetrads.* Rod-tetrads of this type are of common occurrence in insects and some other animals but are less well known in plants. These tetrads almost invariably divide first across the median cross-suture, and since they are often constricted at this point are commonly referred to as "dumb-bell shaped"; they may, however, show forms transitional to the double crosses described below.

Tetrads of this type most commonly lie parallel to the spindle-axis with the median suture or constriction in the equatorial plane, the spindle-attachments being bi-terminal, *i. e.*, at both ends of the rod (Figs. 251, 367, 369). They then divide crosswise at the middle-point, separating into two longitudinally split rods which pass together to the poles, often in close association and without opening out to form simple V's, thus contrasting markedly with the longitudinal tetrads described under a^1. Such tetrads formerly seemed to support Weismann's conception of reduction by cross-division (p. 502). This was subsequently proved to be fallacious by the demonstration that such tetrads arise, in many cases at least, by the open-

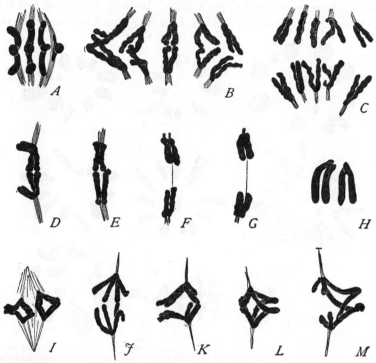

Fig. 252.—Metaphase- and early anaphase-chromosomes in heterotypic division of seed-plants. (*A–E*, from MOTTIER; *F, G*, ALLEN; *H*, GRÉGOIRE; *I–M*, STRASBURGER.)

A, metaphase-figures, terminal or sub-terminal attachments (*Podophyllum*); *B*, early anaphase, terminal attachments giving diaschistic V's (*Lilium*); *C*, later stage of same; *D, E*, sub-median and sub-terminal attachments (*Podophyllum*); *F, G*, anaphase figures, diaschistic V's, terminal attachment (*Lilium*); *H*, similar figure in *Trillium; I*, metaphase-figures, sub-median attachment (*Allium*); *J–K* (*Lilium*), late metaphase, showing "secondary" split; *J*, median attachment; *K, L*, sub-median, *M*, sub-terminal.

ing apart from one end of two tetrad-halves that originally lay side-by-side until they are connected only at the opposite end (Figs. 244, 254). Such tetrads are exactly comparable to the final metaphase-form of anaschistic rod-tetrads with terminal attachment. They differ only in the fact that, in the former, the opening-out process takes place already in the diakinesis before the spindle has been formed (p. 547).

The two types of tetrads next to be considered are readily derivable from rod-tetrads and are actually such during their earlier stages in a large number of cases. The simpler of the two includes:

b. *V-shaped Tetrads.* This form appears to be less frequent than the foregoing one, though common in certain groups, such as the Orthoptera. It differs from the rod-tetrad only in being flexed at the middle point, where the V is ultimately attached to the spindle. We may distinguish two types of such tetrads, derived respectively from the anaschistic and the dias-

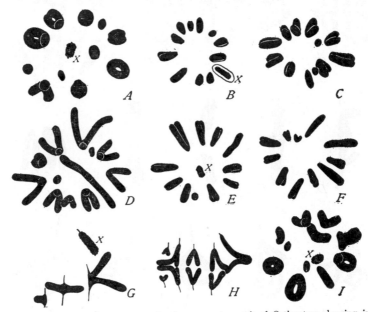

Fig. 253.—Maturation-chromosomes in the spermatogenesis of Orthoptera showing in polar view equatorial rings and other forms (*A, I*), rod-shaped anaschistic tetrads with terminal attachment (I) and diaschistic V's and rod with median attachment (D) (McClung).

A, polar view, first spermatocyte-metaphase, *Hippiscus; B*, second spermatocyte, 12 chromosomes X-class; *C*, same, 11 chromosomes, no X-class. *D, E, F*, corresponding stages in *Mecostethus; G, H*, side-views of same, first division; *I*, polar view, first spermatocyte metaphase, *Tropidolophus.*

chistic rod-tetrads. In general, anaschistic V's can hardly be distinguished from anaschistic rods with median attachment; and they have the same later history, the anaphase-dyads having the form of V's longitudinally split (Fig. 247). Diaschistic V's are common among Orthoptera, where they have been studied in various grasshoppers by McClung and his followers.[1] Such V's are essentially diaschistic rod-tetrads, flexed at the middle-point and attached to the spindle at that point (Fig. 246). This is shown with especial clearnesss in the genus *Mecostethus* (Fig. 253), where they are

[1] See Sutton ('02), McClung ('14), Pinney ('08), Robertson ('16), Wenrich ('16).

more extended than in most other forms and sometimes almost straight (McClung, '14).

V's of the diaschistic type divide along their longitudinal split in the first division, giving daughter-V's like the original tetrad but not longitudinally split. In the second division the two limbs of these V's break apart at the apex. From the foregoing it will be seen that simple anaphase V's, dividing diaschistically at the apex, may be produced in two wholly different ways, namely (1), as a result of the terminal attachment of longitudinal or anaschistic rod-tetrads (Fig. 252, B, C) or (2), as just described by the median attachment of diaschistic rod-tetrads commonly flexed at the point of attachment to form V's (Fig. 253). This illustrates once more the purely provisional and secondary nature of the distinction between

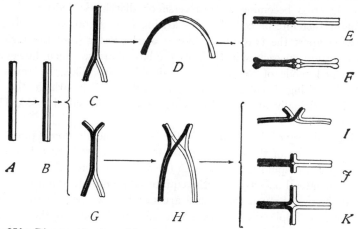

Fig. 254.—Diagrams showing origin of transverse or diaschistic rod-tetrads, and of double crosses. The synaptic mates in black and white.

A, diplotene thread; *B*, longitudinally quadripartite stage, common to both forms of tetrads; *C*, *D*, opening apart of the rod from lower end along the reduction-plane, leading to *E*, *F*, tetrad rods of slightly differing type; *G*, *H*, opening apart along the reduction-plane from lower end and the equation-plane from upper end; *I*, result of further divergence at lower end side-view; *J*, *K*, resulting double crosses in face view after complete straightening out.

the anaschistic and diaschistic modes of division; and it also indicates a prolific source of confusion in the earlier literature of the subject.

c. Double Crosses. By still another modification of the rod-tetrads arise the so-called double crosses, which are among the most interesting and, in animals, the most widespread forms of tetrads. They are perhaps most frequent among the insects and annelids.[1] These tetrads have the form of a rectangular cross, each of the four arms being longitudinally cleft (Figs. 254, 259). As the figures show, four chromatids lie in

[1] See Paulmier ('99), Sutton ('02), Montgomery ('01, '06), Janssens ('01), Schreiner ('06), Wilson '05, '06, '12), Mohr ('14).

one plane, each bent at a right angle and symmetrically grouped about a common center. Each arm of the cross is thus formed by the close approximation of corresponding portions of two chromatids, the cleft between them passing straight through the arm. At the center often appears a considerable open space with which the clefts are continuous. Peripherally the latter may extend completely through to the ends of the arms, but often seem not to do so.

In their fullest development the four arms are equal, but more frequently we may distinguish two longer "axial" arms and two shorter "lateral" ones (Figs. 254, 268). In this respect all gradations occur from equal-armed crosses down to those in which the lateral arms are only just distinguishable (Fig. 244). A step further and these arms would disappear, the double cross becoming a transverse or diaschistic rod-tetrad. The cross might therefore be conceived as arising from a transverse rod-tetrad by drawing apart the two lateral halves of the latter from the region of the cross-suture on each side to form the lateral arms. Such, however, is not its usual mode of formation, the double cross, like the transverse rod-tetrad, arising from a longitudinal rod-tetrad in which the four chromatids originally are straight, lying parallel and side by side (Figs. 244, 268).

The later history of these tetrads in the heterotypic division is practically identical with that of the transverse rod-tetrads. They form a biterminal attachment to the spindle, usually with the axial arms parallel to the spindle-axis and the lateral ones lying in the equatorial plane. In the first division they split in two through the lateral arms and draw apart in the form of double rods or simple V's that subsequently break apart at the apex. If the lateral arms be very short, or disappear entirely it becomes obvious that the first division corresponds to the diaschistic or cross-division of the rod-tetrad (Fig. 259).

d. Ring-tetrads. These are among the most interesting forms of tetrads because of the emphasis laid upon them by Flemming in his first character-ization of the heterotypic division, and also because of the numerous elabo-rate studies of their transformations that have since been made. As we have seen, figures more or less clearly ring-shaped are often temporarily offered by other forms of tetrads (rods, V's) as they draw apart in the late metaphase and early anaphase, especially after median or sub-median spindle-attachments. The rings now to be considered differ only in degree from these, but show the phenomena in more spectacular fashion because of their much earlier origin in the early prophase or diakinesis at a time when the chromosomes are in more extended form, and have no visible connection with the spindle (Figs. 244, 268). Such rings are seen to particular advantage in insects (Orthoptera, Hemiptera), annelids (*Tomopteris*, *Allolobophora*) and lower vertebrates (Amphibia), where they have been the object of investigation by many observers.[1]

With some possible exceptions these rings are actual tetrads, being longi-

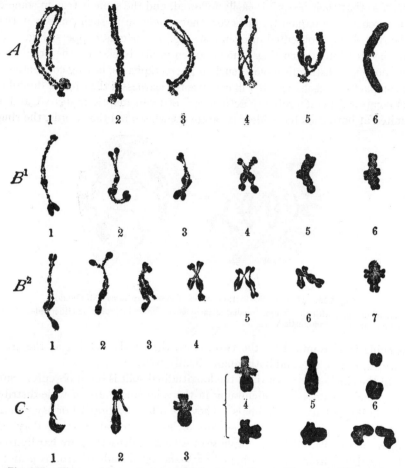

Fig. 255.—History of three selected tetrads in the grasshopper *Phrynotettix* (WENRICH).

A, bivalent "A," equal type; 1-6, successive stages in the growth-period; first appearance of the equation-split in 3; *B¹*, bivalent "B," equal type, leading to symmetrical double cross (6); *B²*, the same, unequal type, leading to asymmetrical cross (7); *C*, bivalent *C*, unequal type, which may divide either pre-reductionally (4-6 above) or post-reductionally (4-6, below).

tudinally cleft in the plane of the ring and showing two transverse sutures at opposite points 180° apart (Fig. 259). One of the ensuing divisions

[1] See Flemming ('87), Henking ('91), Meves ('97), Paulmier ('98, '99), Sutton ('02), McClung ('14), Schreiners ('06), Mohr ('14), etc.

thus divides the ring lengthwise, the other transversely through the two cross-sutures into two half-rings. They may therefore be characterized as diaschistic. They differ widely in degree of condensation at the time they enter the metaphase. In *Tomopteris* (Fig. 244) they remain still widely open so that their history is easily followed, and the same is true in some of the urodeles. Frequently, however, they condense to such an extent that the ring-shape is obscured or even lost, *e. g.*, in the grasshoppers (Fig. 253). In the Hemiptera such rings, though often perfectly clear in the prophases, are no longer distinguishable as such in the metaphases, having condensed to a compact tetrad-shape. It will conduce to clearness if the ring be described as composed (as it probably actually is) of two synaptic mates (A and a) united at both ends but widely separate elsewhere; in other words, the ring-

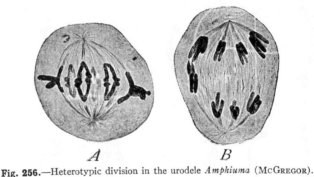

A   *B*

Fig. 256.—Heterotypic division in the urodele *Amphiuma* (McGregor).

A, metaphase, with ring-figures (median attachments) shown in profile at either side; *B*, anaphase-figure with anaschistic V's.

opening is surrounded by the two mates, their ends meeting at the cross-sutures, 180° apart, and both longitudinally split.

In the simpler types of rings the longitudinal split is often obscure. Such rings, first described by Flemming in the salamander are of wide distribution in both plants and animals. They are often compressed or asymmetrical (Figs. 247, 248) and may be more or less twisted at the time they pass upon the spindle. In the metaphase or early anaphase they are hardly to be distinguished from the rod-shaped or V-shaped tetrads of groups *a* and *b*. More commonly the ring shows a lateral prominence or "lug" at one or both cross-sutures, often drawn out into arm-like processes (Figs. 244, 257), longitudinally split, each half being continuous with a corresponding half of the ring. The arms are thus seen to result from the fact that the two synaptic mates have still not fully opened apart but remain in contact for a certain distance from their ends (Figs. 244, 259).[1] In many of these cases

---

[1] Some observers (*e. g.*, Janssens, '01, '05) have described the lateral arms as twisted, a remnant of an earlier twisted condition of the whole tetrad.

as shown in the figures the lateral arms are converted into cross-shaped figures, by a drawing apart of the two halves of the longitudinally split ring on each side of the cross-suture and at right angles to the plane of the ring. Instead of a single arm at this point (as in the preceding case) we now have two arms extending in opposite directions at right angles to the ring, and forming a cross-shaped figure comparable with the four double cross-tetrads. Such figures may appear at both of the cross-sutures or only at one (Fig. 244). In the latter case the close relationship between rings of this type and the double crosses of group c is evident, particularly when (as occasionally happens) the ring is incomplete on the side opposite the cross (Fig. 244, B). We may indeed think of the ring as a double cross with one short and one long pair of arms, the latter being bent around until their free ends have joined. This was in fact the original conception of the origin of such rings as conceived by Paulmier, Sutton and other earlier observers; but such is not their actual origin (p. 548).

A remarkable further development of this type, discovered by McClung ('02) and confirmed by Granata ('10) and later observers (Robertson, Wen-

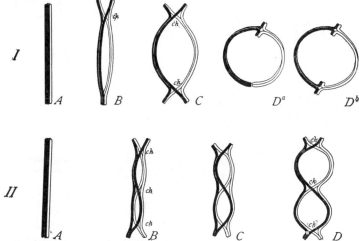

Fig. 257.—Diagram, drawn in perspective from clay models, to show the origin of the single ring, double rings and double cross types of tetrads. In each case the starting-point is a pair of synaptic mates (black and white) both longitudinally split, and lying side by side to form a quadripartite rod.

rich) is offered by double or even triple rings, in connected series. This results from a still greater elongation of the lateral arms of the cross which curve towards each other until they form a second ring at right angles to the first (Figs. 257, 258); and if this occurs on both sides of the primary ring a third ring may arise, the two or three (possibly a larger number) forming a connected series. The rings in these cases are successively at right angles to each other and the double (or triple) ring involves an "exchange of partners" (Sutton, McClung), the longitudinal halves of each secondary half-ring consisting of one from each of the original half-rings, as will be made plain from Figs. 453, 454.[1]

Behavior in the Heterotype Division. During the heterotypic division the rings are of two types which result respectively from non-terminal (usually median) and terminal attachment (applying these terms to the component chromatids of the tetrad). With non-terminal or atelomitic attachment (typically seen in *Tomopteris*, Figs. 244, 259) the ring lies vertically, or tangential to the spindle with the spindle-fibers attached to each half ring midway between the two cross-sutures, or at some intermediate point. Such

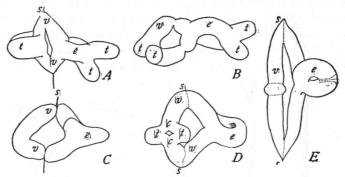

Fig. 258.—Double ring tetrads in the grasshopper *Chorthippus* (ROBERTSON).

All are shown in side-view, attached to the spindle-fibers at the points *s, s* (atelomitic attachments). The drawing out of the attached (tangential) ring has begun in *A, C* and *D*, and is more advanced in *E*. All of these cases, except *A*, show a cross-suture at the point of attachment, indicating the probably compound nature of these rings.

In each case *e* marks the horizontal or equatorial ring (seen from the side, or obliquely), *v*, the vertical or tangential ring (seen *en face*), *t* the terminal arms. In *D*, the double-cross figure formed by these arms is seen in oblique view at *c*.

rings have conveniently been characterized by McClung ('14) as *axial* or atelomitic. These rings draw out towards the poles and are cut in two crosswise through the cross-sutures, and also through the lateral arms when present. They are thus divided into two half-rings, each longitudinally split (anaschistic), which in the anaphases assume the form of split V's, quite as in the case of longitudinal rod-tetrads (Fig. 259).

The telomitic ring, with terminal attachment, lies in a position at right angles to the atelomitic, *i. e.*, in the equatorial plane, so that its opening is only seen in polar view (hence *equatorial* in contradistinction to *axial* or

[1] These curious facts, of much interest for the chiasmatype theory, are more fully considered at p. 959.

tangential), as shown in Figs. 253, 259. Such rings first divide along the longitudinal cleft, the lateral arms or lugs drawing out towards the poles at the expense of the ring, the latter decreasing as the former increase (Fig. 259). The daughter-chromosomes have the form of single V's or (by close approximation of the two limbs) double rods, each limb being formed from one of the quarter-rings. Their later history is essentially the same as that of the double rods or diaschistic V's resulting from the telomitic rod-tetrads or double crosses, or the V's of *Mecostethus* (Fig. 253).

The axial or atelomitic ring is by far the most common, being widely distributed among both invertebrates and vertebrates and not uncommon in plants. Of this type are the rings of urodeles as originally described by Flemming ('87) and his followers (Meves, Carnoy and Lebrun, McGregor, Janssens, etc.), and remarkable examples of it are seen in annelids (*Tomopteris, Allolobophora*).[1] The telomitic or equatorial ring, on the other hand, seems to be of relatively limited occurrence, our knowledge of it being almost wholly confined to the orthopteran family of Acrididæ (*Hippiscus, Brachystola, Chortophaga, Syrbula*, etc.)[2] It is interesting that even within the limits of this family rings of both types occur. Most commonly they are of the telomitic type (as in *Hippiscus, Brachystola, Syrbula*, etc.), but axial or atelomitic rings are found in *Stenobothrus, Chorthippus, Chloëaltis* and a few other forms. That species so nearly related should differ in respect to the ring-tetrads is of general interest because the two types, though precisely similar in morphological composition, seem to be reversed with respect to the order of division; if, for example, the *Hippiscus* ring (telomitic) be post-reductional, as believed by McClung, the *Stenobothrus* ring is pre-reductional, and *vice versa* (Fig. 259).

The two extreme types are connected by many intermediate forms. Not infrequently, for example, the atelomitic or axial ring has a sub-median instead of a median attachment. In such cases the ring breaks first on one side and thus gives asymmetrical anaphase V's, or more or less E-shaped figures, as already explained in case of the metaphase-rings of rod-shaped tetrads (p. 518). Many such figures no doubt arise from incomplete rings or loops, as was first pointed out by Janssens ('01) in the case of *Triton* (*cf.* Meves, '97, Flemming, '87). Such loops offer many degrees of transition from complete rings to straight double crosses (Fig. 244), and in another direction graduate insensibly into longitudinal rod-tetrads which give rise to metaphase rings and related figures. In the anaphases the daughter-chromosomes are U's, V's or J's, in each case of course longitudinally double.

---

[1] See especially Henking ('91), Paulmier ('98, '99), McClung ('14, etc.), Sutton ('02), Granata ('10), Davis ('08). Robertson ('08, '16), Foot and Strobell ('10), Wenrich ('16, '17), etc.
[2] See especially McClung, '14.

The ring-tetrads strikingly illustrate the correlation between the gonial chromosomes and those of the meiotic divisions in respect to the spindle-attachments. The axial or atelomitic ring of *Tomopteris* or the urodele is

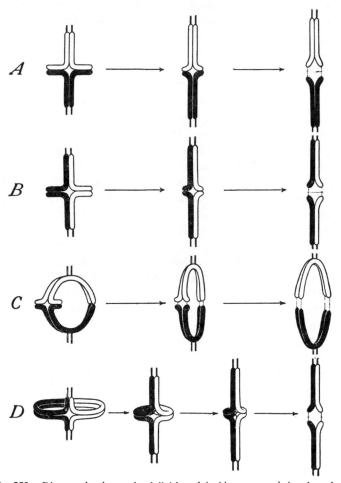

Fig. 259.—Diagram showing mode of division of double crosses and rings in meiosis.

A, double cross with pre-reduction; *B*, the same with post-reduction; *C*, tangential ring with median attachment and pre-reduction (as in *Tomopteris* or urodeles); *D*, equatorial ring with terminal attachment and post-reduction (as in *Hippiscus* type of grasshoppers).

Note that in *A*, *B* and *D* the longitudinal halves of the anaphase-chromosomes often separate more widely from their free ends than is here shown, thus giving diaschistic V's.

obviously correlated with the non-terminal attachments of the gonial chromosome-pair from which it arises. Nearly all the gonial chromosomes in these animals are of V-shaped or similar form, with non-terminal or median attachments. The union of two such V's side-by-side, followed by their separation in the middle region while the ends remain united obviously produces an atelomitic ring represented by two V's placed base to base, with the attachments at the apices; hence the axial or tangential position of the ring on the spindle (Fig. 259). On the other hand, the telomitic or *Hippiscus* type of ring results from a rod-shaped pair of gonial chromosomes with terminal attachments. When two such chromosomes unite, side-by-side, subsequently opening apart to form a ring, the terminal attachments still persist as such at one of the cross-sutures (or lateral arms) of the ring (Fig. 259). Hence, obviously, the ensuing equatorial position of the ring on the spindle, and its post-reductional division.

That this is the true explanation is demonstrated by the atelomitic or axial rings of *Stenobothrus*, *Chorthippus*, *Chloëaltis*, etc.; for all such cases offer an exception to the rule among the Acrididæ in that certain of the gonial chromosomes are V-shaped, having non-terminal attachments; and it is precisely from these chromosome-pairs, as is proved by their size, that the atelomitic rings arise.[1]

It is the same with the rod-tetrads, or the double crosses. The longitudinal or anaschistic rod-tetrad may have any attachment, its resulting form in the early anaphase varying correspondingly (whether a rod, V, J, E-shaped figure or ring). The typical diaschistic or transverse rod-tetrad and the double crosses both arise from gonial rods with terminal attachments; and since these tetrads arise by the spreading apart of the two from this end while remaining united at the other these forms typically have a biterminal attachment. The diaschistic V-tetrads, so common in Orthoptera, arise in a similar way, but spread apart from the free instead of the attached ends and do not fully open, the V-shape being more or less retained (Fig. 253). Such V's (like the atelomitic rod-retrads of *Mecostethus*) commonly open out in the early anaphase to form axial ring-shaped tetrads (Fig. 253); but differ from the axial rings of *Tomopteris*, etc., in that they are diaschistic, *i. e.*, break across at the middle-point of each half ring during the anaphases (Fig. 259). Prophase-rings of the same type, showing four instead of two cross-sutures, seem to occur also in certain copepods as described by some of the earlier observers (Rückert, Haecker), and are probably open to a similar interpretation.

Such facts emphasize the fact that the tetrads have a quite definite and characteristic organization that is maintained at every state throughout

---

[1] This is strikingly shown in Mohr's ('16) study of *Locusta viridissima* in which there are (in addition to the X-chromosome) 28 spermatogonial chromosomes, of which 26 are short rods and two large V's (Fig. 394). All of the resulting tetrads arise from double crosses or rod-tetrads excepting one much larger one which is a typical atelomitic ring, the size of which proves it to represent the large V-pair of the spermatogonia. See also especially Robertson ('16).

their history and in which the genetic continuity of the chromosomes remains unbroken throughout.[1] This finds a remarkable confirmation in the heteromorphic tetrads of *Trimerotropis* and *Circotettix* (p. 571) in which certain of the somatic chromosome-pairs differ in mode of attachment of the synaptic mates, one being rod-shaped and terminal, the other hook-shaped and non-terminal (Fig. 439). The crucial proof is given by the fact that the number of non-terminal attachments, though constant in the individual, differs from one individual to another. Close comparison by Carothers has demonstrated that whatever be the number of non-terminal attachments in the gonial groups *the same number reappears in the tetrads of the same individual* (p. 934).

C. THE INTERKINESIS AND THE HOMEOTYPIC DIVISION

The concluding phases of meiosis offer a much simpler problem than the earlier ones. In the anaphases of the heterotypic division, as we have seen, the daughter-chromosomes are typically double, forming dyads each of which is destined to separate into two single chromosomes during the second or homeotypic mitosis. Externally the second division is in this respect closely similar to an ordinary somatic mitosis; its only noticeable peculiarity in many cases, indeed, is the shorter and more compact form of the chromosomes, and even this is sometimes but slightly marked. Nevertheless this division may differ in a very important way from the somatic divisions; for there is now no doubt that at least some of the chromosomes may divide reductionally, as will later be shown.

That the anaphasic duality of the heterotypic division is the forerunner of that which appears in the metaphase-chromosomes of the second division is often readily seen and is practically certain even when not directly demonstrable. The two divisions are separated by a pause or interkinesis usually of short duration, though wide differences in this respect exist between different species. Some of the observed conditions are brought together in Fig. 260 so arranged as to show a progressive series. At one extreme are cases in which no vesicular nucleus or "resting stage" is formed, the dyads persisting as such and passing directly upon the second spindle with only slight change of form and without the formation of a vesicular nucleus. This condition is common in the polar divisions in the animal egg generally, typical cases being given by such forms as *Ascaris* (Fig. 238), the insects, mollusks and annelids (Figs. 194, 239). The same condition is also often seen in the spermatocyte-divisions, *e. g.*, in *Ascaris* (Fig. 241) and in many insects (Fig. 369); and in some of these cases the dyads not only retain their identity as such but also their characteristic anaphasic grouping only slightly

---

[1] Modified only by the exchanges of material in crossing-over (p. 950).

changed as they enter the second metaphase (Fig. 260, D). All such cases are probably conditioned by a very short pause between the two divisions.

With a longer interkinesis the dyads become inclosed by a nuclear membrane and become less regular in outline, but may still visibly retain their identity and double structure in many forms. In such cases the two halves of the dyads often become partially separated, flexed or displaced so as to produce characteristic X-shaped, V-shaped or other figures. This condition seems to be rare in plants (Fig. 260, E), but is common in animals (annelids,

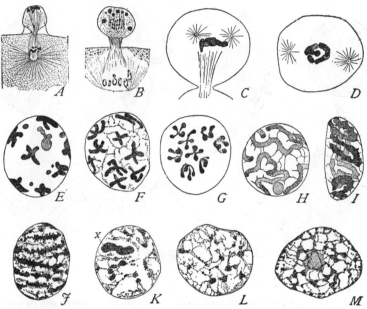

Fig. 260.—Nuclei during the interkinesis, from various plants and animals.

A, oögenesis in the gastropod *Crepidula* (CONKLIN); B, in the annelid *Rhynchelmis* (VEJDOVSKÝ) C, telophase and D, interkinesis in the hemipter *Oncopeltus* (WILSON); E, sporogenesis in *Œnothera* (DAVIS); F, spermatogenesis in the salamander *Desmognathus* (KINGSBURY); G, spermatogenesis, in the annelid *Tomopteris* (the SCHREINERS); H, sporogenesis, *Podophyllum*, not yet at full rest (MOTTIER); I, *Trillium* (ATKINSON); J, spermatogenesis in the salamander *Amphiuma* (MC-GREGOR); K, L, spermatogenesis in the grasshopper *Phrynotettix* (WENRICH); at X, the X = chromosome; M, sporogenesis in *Galtonia* (DIGBY).

insects, some vertebrates); examples are shown in Fig. 260, F, G.[1] In such cases likewise it is easy to prove that the dyads pass directly upon the second spindle, and are separated into their two components. With a longer interkinesis the dyads undergo more extensive changes, during which the anaphasic duality is often obscured or lost to view. This condition

[1] See Kingsbury ('02), Vejdovský and Mrazek ('03), the Schreiners ('06), Bonnevie ('08), Morse ('09), Kornhauser ('15), etc.

appears, for example, in *Salamandra* (Meves, '98), *Amphiuma* (McGregor,
'99), *Lilium* (Strasburger, '00, Mottier, '03) or *Paris* (Grégoire, '05), etc.
In such cases the nucleus commonly shows a spireme-like structure (Fig. 260,
H–J), but in some forms it may advance almost as far as the "resting" or
reticular condition (Fig. 260, K, L, M). Such cases offer the same problem
as the somatic nuclei generally. Since, however, these cases are connected
by all possible intergradations with those in which the chromatids as such are
never lost to view, the conclusion seems fully justified that the two original

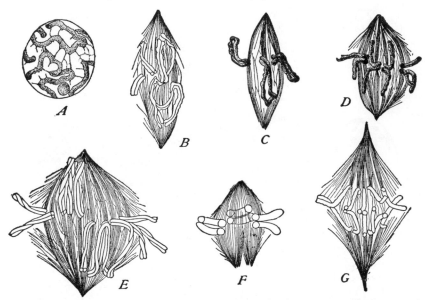

Fig. **261.**—The second meiotic division in seed-plants. (*B*, STRASBURGER and MOTTIER; the
others from MOTTIER.)

   A, nucleus of secondary microsporocyte (*Podophyllum*); *B*, prophase of second division (*Lilium*,
male) with longitudinally divided chromatin-threads; *E*, corresponding stage in the female; *F*,
metaphase of second division (*Podophyllum*, male); *G*, initial anaphase (*Lilium*, female); *C*, *D*,
illustrate Mottier's earlier conclusions; *C*, second division (*Lilium*, male) with chromosomes
bent together so as to simulate a split; *D*, slightly later stage (*Fritillaria*, male), showing stage
supposed to result from breaking apart of the limbs of the U at point of flexure.

cleavage-clefts of the tetrads are the forerunners of the two actual divisions
respectively.

   At the end of the interkinesis the chromosomes are bipartite bodies which
separate into two single chromosomes in the course of the second division.
In the case of compact tetrads they are commonly of a short, dumb-bell
shape, and often do not differ markedly in outline from the tetrads of the
first division (*e. g.*, in Hemiptera, Fig. 369). When more elongate they have
the form of simple rods, J's or V's, longitudinally double, often closely simi-

lar in appearance to the somatic chromosomes (Figs. 242, 261). These forms, as indicated in the preceding section, correspond closely to the original spindle-attachments of the gonial chromosomes, and to those of the tetrads.[1] These facts constitute very strong evidence in favor of the individuality or genetic continuity of the chromosomes; and demonstrate that a complete continuity of organization is maintained throughout the whole process of meiosis and segregation from the diploid gonial groups down to the haploid groups of the gametes.

D. Growth Period of the Auxocytes

1. Introductory

In the foregoing account theoretic prepossessions have, as far as possible, been laid aside except in so far as they might be useful in following an objective description of the observed phenomena. We have thus far simply assumed that the bivalent represents two gonial chromosomes (synaptic mates) in close synaptic association and sooner or later longitudinally split. On what actual evidence does this interpretation rest; and if it be well founded, when and how does the association take place? An immense amount of effort has been put forth in the search for decisive answers to these questions. It has been fully demonstrated that in higher plants and animals the formation of the bivalents occurs during the growth-period of the auxocytes. Most observers are also agreed that the process takes place at a very early period, before the auxocytes have entered upon their most active growth, during the so-called *synaptic period* or *synaptic phase*. It is not yet certain whether synapsis always takes place at this time—certain special exceptions are indeed known (pp. 769, 839)—and some differences of opinion still exist concerning the nature of the process itself. Its effects, however, are unmistakable, as shown by a vast array of evidence, direct and indirect. To its survey we now address ourselves by an examination of the earlier history of the bivalents, and their genetic relations to the gonial chromosomes.

Comparative studies have shown that the events of the growth-period may be grouped in a series of stages which, with many minor variations, display a broad similarity in both sexes of animals and in the spore-formation of plants. The most conspicuous fact in all cases is the formation of a spireme, analogous in many respects to the early prophase of a somatic mitosis, but not at first longitudinally double and not leading directly to a mitosis. This is followed at an early stage by a coupling (synapsis, syndesis) of the spireme-threads or their products two-by-two to form bivalent chro-

---

[1] For striking examples of this see the observations of Davis ('08), McClung ('05, '14, '17), and Carothers ('17) on *Orthoptera*, and of Agar ('11, '12) on *Lepidosiren*.

mosomes; and the association of synaptic mates thus effected typically persists throughout the whole growth-period until they or their products are disjoined in the reduction-division.[1] It is a remarkable fact, still unexplained, that synapsis and disjunction should be separated by so long a period—in some cases it is measured by years—and by so many cytological events concerned not with meiosis but with the growth and differentiation of the gametes or spores.

2. Outline of the Stages

The stages of meiosis during the growth-period differ appreciably in different species and some of the differences may be of major importance. For the purposes of a preliminary survey we may, however, conveniently recognize eleven successive stages, beginning with the final gonial telophase and extending up to the heterotypic division. Some of these stages may fail to appear in particular cases; others may differ in an important way from that here indicated; but the following outline may serve as a useful guide to the terminology and to the general order of the stages as commonly described. They are illustrated by the accompanying diagram (Fig. 262) based primarily on the conditions observed in animals generally, but also broadly applicable to those of plants. The terminology is based on that of Winiwarter ('oo). There is reason to believe that beneath all differences, real or apparent, a fundamental uniformity exists in the most essential of the phenomena, and that the seeming contradictions which in some measure still exist will be cleared up by further investigation.

Of the following stages those inclosed in brackets, including *c*, *d*, *h*, *i*, and perhaps *b*, may be omitted in particular cases.

a. The final gonial telophase. In this, the initial stage of the growth-period, the nuclei are vesicular, rather small, and still show the individual telophase-chromosomes, still more or less compact and deeply-staining (Fig. 265, B, E). It is possible that in some cases this stage passes directly over into Stage *c*; but as a rule it is followed by

b. A "resting" or net-like stage, commonly of rather short duration (as judged by the size of nucleus and cytosome), in which the individual chromosomes are temporarily lost to view in a net-like framework, approaching in this respect to the condition of a somatic nucleus (Fig. 263, A–C). These nuclei (slightly enlarging the application of Winiwarter's term) may be called *protobroch* nuclei. In their later condition, as they prepare to enter the following (leptotene) stage, they were called by Winiwarter *deutobroch* nuclei, but this term, like the preceding one, is not yet in general use. It

---

[1] Certain special exceptions to this are elsewhere indicated (p. 563, etc.).

is possible that this stage, though of widespread occurrence in both plants and animals, may be suppressed in some cases.

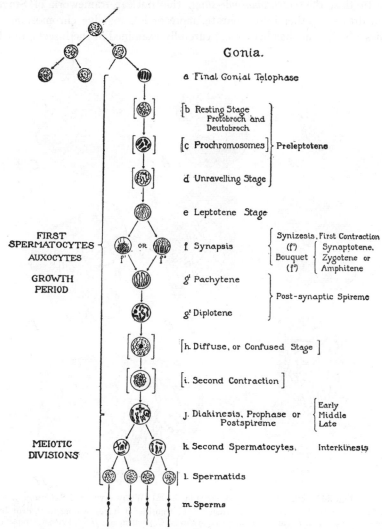

Gonia.

a Final Gonial Telophase

[b Resting Stage
Protobroch and
Deutobroch

[c Prochromosomes] ⎫ Preleptotene

d Unravelling Stage

e Leptotene Stage

FIRST
SPERMATOCYTES
AUXOCYTES

f Synapsis   Synizesis, First Contraction
(f¹)   Synaptotene,
Bouquet   Zygotene or
(f²)   Amphitene

GROWTH
PERIOD

g¹ Pachytene

Post-synaptic Spireme

g² Diplotene

[h. Diffuse, or Confused Stage]

[i. Second Contraction]

j. Diakinesis, Prophase or   Early
Postspireme   Middle
Late

MEIOTIC
DIVISIONS

k Second Spermatocytes.   Interkinesis

l. Spermatids

m Sperms

Fig. 262.—Diagram of the stages of maturation and meiosis, to show their order of succession. Stages inclosed in brackets may be lacking in certain cases. The synaptic stage (f) is represented of two different types (f¹ and f²). Terminology based on that of Winiwarter. Cytological detail roughly indicated in the key-figures.

The changes taking place in the two following stages (*c, d*) result in the formation of a fine spireme, the *leptonema* or *leptotene-stage* (Stage *e*); but in many cases (*e. g.*, in vertebrates generally) the leptonema may be formed directly from the network of Stage *b*, Stages *c* and *d* being omitted.

c. In this, the *prochromosome-stage*, the nuclear framework of Stage *b* again draws together into separate, more or less massive chromosome-like bodies. This stage has been most carefully examined in the insects, but has

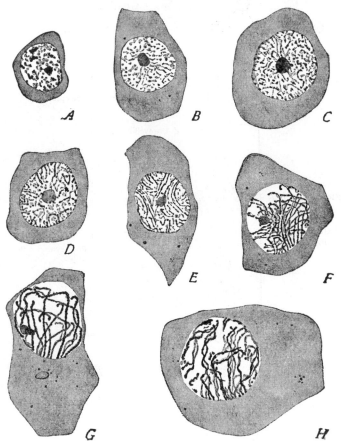

Fig. 263.—Early stages of oögenesis in the cat (WINIWARTER and SAINTMONT).
A, protobroch nucleus, or "resting" stage; *B*, *C*, transitional stages leading to *D*, deutobroch nucleus; *E*, leptonema; *F*, early synaptonema, synapsis; *G*, pachynema; *H*, diplonema, strepsinema.

also been described in some other cases. The form of the prochromosomes varies in different species, but in some degree approaches that of the gonial chromosomes. In the Orthoptera, for instance, they are often elongated and more or less distinctly polarized (Fig. 265, G–I); in the Hemiptera or Coleoptera they are commonly much shorter, often spheroidal, tend to take up a peripheral position, and are not definitely polarized (Figs. 266, 267). Many careful observers have found that their number is nearly, in some cases exactly, equal to the gonial or diploid number; and sometimes they clearly show the same size-relations. Clearly, therefore, these bodies represent ·a *diploid group of chromosomes corresponding with those of the gonial divisions.* In many cases no trace of this stage has yet been found; typical examples are offered by the vertebrates (urodeles) and platodes (*Dendrocœlum,* Fig. 279).

d. *The unravelling stage,* during which each prochromosome resolves itself into a closely convoluted or irregularly coiled fine thread which then

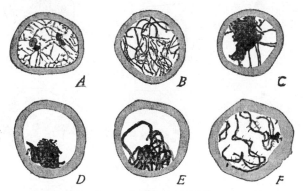

Fig. 264.—Oögenesis in the rabbit (WINIWARTER).

A, early deutobroch nucleus; *B,* leptonema; *C,* synaptic stage (early synizesis); *D,* complete synizesis; *E,* pachynema; *F,* diplonema.

unravels or uncoils to form a single leptotene-thread (Figs. 265, 267). The evidence, though rather scanty, makes it highly probable that only one such thread is formed from each prochromosome [1] and this has been clearly proved in the case of particular prochromosomes, *e. g.,* the large M-chromosome pair in the beetle *Blaps* (Nonidez). This point is of great theoretic interest in contributing to the demonstration that, in some cases at least, *the number of leptotene-threads is diploid* (p. 541).

e. *The leptonema or leptotene-stage.*[2] This stage is a fundamental and all but universal one from which all later ones take their point of departure. The nuclear substance has now resolved itself into delicate threads which typically show no sign of longitudinal splitting. They are at first irregular, contorted, and when preceded by prochromosomes often clumped in masses corresponding to the bodies from which they have arisen. As above stated,

[1] See especially Davis ('o8), Wilson ('12), Nonidez ('20), etc.

[2] It is customary to use the first of these forms as a substantive and the second as the corresponding adjective form; and similarly with pachynema, pachytene, etc.

however, the threads may be formed directly from the nuclear framework of Stage *b* by a process similar to the early spireme-formation in many somatic mitoses (Figs. 263, 279). This has been circumstantially described by various observers in both animals and plants.[1] In a large class of cases

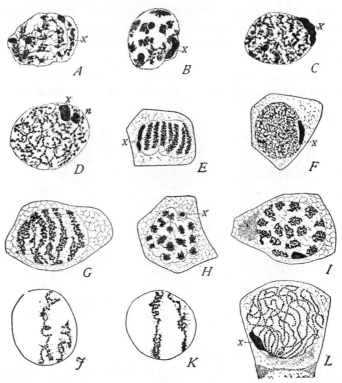

Fig. 265.—Presynaptic stages of meiosis in grasshoppers.   (*A–D*, from ROBERTSON, the others from DAVIS).

A–D, Syrbula; A, spermatogonial nucleus, separate X-vesicle at X; *B,* spermatocyte-nucleus, just after last spermatogonial telophase, condensed X-chromosome; *C, D,* origin of spireme-like structure (leptonema) from same; *E,* last spermatogonial telophase in *Dissosteira,* stage *a; F,* net-like "stage *b*"; *G,* formation of massive polarized prochromosomes (stage *c*) in *Chortophaga; H,* same from pole; *J, K,* unravelling of leptotene-threads (stage *d*); *L,* leptonema, in some degree polarized, *X,* the chromosome-nucleolus or X-chromosome (monosome).

the threads gradually become more even and often form loops that are more or less definitely polarized with their ends turned towards that pole of the nucleus near which the centrioles and idiozome lie (Figs. 263, 265, 279).   The nucleus thus enters the initial "bouquet-stage," which attains its full development in the ensuing stage.

[1] *E. g.,* in mammals (Winiwarter, '00, Winiwarter and Saintmont, '09), urodeles (Janssens, '01), elasmobranchs (Maréchal, '06) and platodes (Gelei, '13, '21), and in the seed-plants (Mottier, '97, '05, '09, etc., Berghs, '04, '05, Allen, '04, Grégoire, '04, '05, '07, '10, etc.. Digby. '10, '14, etc.).

In the case of animals generally evidence has steadily accumulated that *the leptotene-spireme is not continuous but consists of separate segments; and in most well-determined cases these are of the diploid number;* their union to form bivalents has therefore not yet taken place (p. 556). This may be determined with a high degree of probability in Type f^1 by counting the number of prochromosomes from which they arise, in Type f^2 by polar views of the polarized threads, or in certain cases by counting them in side-view (*Dendrocœlum*, p. 555). Among plants, on the other hand, it has not yet been found possible to count the leptotene-threads at this time, and many observers have concluded that the spireme is continuous, only breaking into shorter pieces or segments at a much later period.[1]

The foregoing five stages are preparatory in character and are often designated as *pre-synaptic* or *pre-syndesic*. Now ensues

f. The *synaptic stage* during which, in a large class of cases, occurs the actual association or conjugation, of the chromosomes (in the form of leptotene-threads) two by two to form the bivalents. This process we shall designate as *synapsis* (or syndesis).[2] Nuclei in this stage are of two types, as follows:

f^1. In one of these, widely distributed in higher plants, in arthropods and in various other invertebrates, the leptotene-threads commonly show no definite polarization and become massed together into a more or less dense, intensely staining knot, usually situated towards one side of the nuclear cavity and often inclosing a nucleolus (Figs. 264, 267). This is the contraction-figure or *synizesis* (often called the "synapsis"), which greatly increases the difficulties of observation at this time. Even nearly related forms may differ in respect to the synizesis; for example, it is conspicuously present in Hemiptera or Odonota but absent in most Orthoptera. The synizesis has been supposed by many writers to be an accidental artifact or coagulation product (Meves, Janssen, McClung, Schreiner and others) due to defective fixation; but such is not always the case as is proved by the oft-repeated observation (Sargent, Overton, Grégoire, Vejdovský, Œttinger, Wilson and others) that the contraction-figure may be observed in the living or fresh unfixed material, though it may be accentuated, or even in

---

[1] See, for instance, the works of Strasburger, Grégoire, Berghs, Allen, Mottier and Digby, cited above.

[2] The term synapsis as thus used is open to some objection, for an important group of cytologists have disputed the conjugation of the chromosomes at this time. The terms *synaptenic* (Winiwarter, '00), and *zygotenic* (Grégoire, '10) are open to the same objection. Janssen's term ('03) *amphitenic* avoids this particular difficulty but is not sufficiently inclusive. A second source of confusion lies in the double meaning attached to the word "synapsis" itself. Though originally applied by Farmer and Moore ('05) to "the temporary union in pairs of premeiotic chromosomes," it later became confused with the contraction figure (synizesis) often associated with this process, so that the word has been widely applied to this figure instead of to the process itself. In the opinion of the writer, the original use of the word should be retained (*cf.* Wilson, '12, p. 349).

some cases artificially produced, by coagulation.[1] Of much interest is the
fact that in a few cases the synizesis is foreshadowed already in Stage *c* by
a migration of the prochromosomes towards one pole where they become

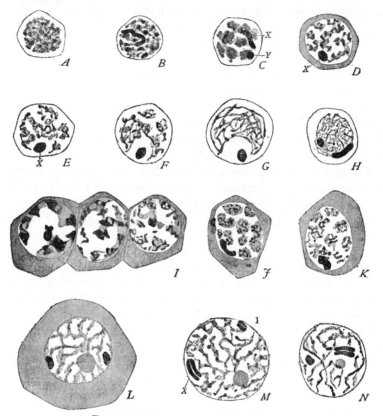

Fig. **266.**—Earlier stages of meiosis in insects.

A–C, H, M, N, from the hemipteron *Lygæus bicrucis; D–G*, from *Largus cinctus; I*, from the
dragon-fly, *Anax; J, K*, from the grasshopper, *Achurum; L*, the hemipter, *Oncopeltus.*

A, Stage *b*, net-like condition; *B*, appearance of the X and Y-chromosomes; *C*, stage *c*, prochromosomes; *D–F*, stage *d; G, H*, leptonema; *I*, prochromosomes at left, unravelling at right; *J, K*,
stage *d*, unravelling; *L, M*, stage *h*, diffuse stage; *N*, stage *j*[1], very early diakinesis.

closely aggregated before the leptotene-threads are spun out from them,[2]
so that the synizesis is indicated from the first stages of leptotene-formation.

  Many observers, among both botanists and zoölogists, have produced

----

[1] Sapĕhin ('15) has published photographs of the synizesis from living cells of the mosses *Fissidens*
and *Catherinea*. Taylor ('22) has on the other hand found that in *Gasteria* the synizesis may be almost completely eliminated by proper fixation.

[2] This was demonstrated by Nonidez ('20) in the beetle, *Blaps*, though earlier observers had seen
something of the sort (Arnold, '08, in *Hydrophilus*).

evidence that as the leptotene-threads draw together to form the synizetic knot they become associated two-by-two and side-by-side (Fig. 264) to form threads that are thicker and at first longitudinally double, thus constituting the bivalent chromosomes. The evidence for this process is, however, less convincing in this case than in the following type.

f^2 In a second type, widely distributed among animals but apparently rare among plants, a contraction-figure or synizesis is usually lacking (there are some exceptions) and the spireme-threads, now having the form of loops, show a more or less pronounced polarization with their ends turned

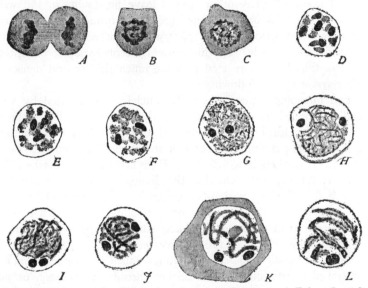

Fig. 267.—Earlier stages of meiosis in spermatocytes of Hemiptera; A–K, from *Oncopeltus fasciatus; L*, from *Largus cinctus*.

A, B, stage a, spermatogonial telophase; C, stage b, net-like or "resting " stage; D, stage c, prochromosomes; E–G, stage d, unravelling of the leptotene-threads; H, stage e, leptonema; I, J, stage f^1, synizesis, here not greatly marked; K, stage g, post-synaptic spireme, pachynema; L, diplonema.

From D onwards the X and Y-chromosomes distinguishable by their compact form (chromosome-nucleoli).

towards the pole of the nucleus near which lie the centrioles surrounded by the idiozome. The polarized threads now progressively thicken and shorten by a process that begins at their polar (free) ends and proceeds towards the opposite pole, so that in the middle part of the period the polar region of the nucleus is occupied by polarized thick threads (*pachytene*), the antipolar by thin ones (*leptotene*), the latter often still irregular in arrangement (Figs. 269, 271, 272). This is the stage often called the *bouquet* (Eisen) or *amphitene* (Janssens),—the latter name in allusion to the presence

of two kinds of threads, thick and thin. The former, growing at the expense of the thin threads and still retaining their polarized grouping, finally
occupy the entire nucleus, which thus enters the following or pachytene
stage.

The nature of the foregoing process has been examined with particular care in the mammals (Winiwarter), urodeles (Janssens), elasmobranchs (Maréchal, Schreiners), and has also been minutely studied in
some of the invertebrates, especially in the annelid *Tomopteris* (Schreiners),
in the Orthoptera (Wenrich, Robertson), and in the platode *Dendrocœlum*
(Gelei). These and many other studies leave no doubt, in the writer's
opinion, that the thick or pachytene threads are formed by a union of the
thin ones (leptotene) side-by-side (*parasynapsis*) which proceeds from the
pole towards the antipole. By this process the pre-synaptic or leptotene-
spireme has thus been converted into the much thicker and denser *post-
synaptic spireme* of the following stage.

The two foregoing types of synaptic nuclei are connected by various
intermediate conditions which prove that they are essentially of the same
nature. The polarization, so striking and regular in the forms enumerated
above, is much less definite in many of the Orthoptera and disappears in
certain of the Hemiptera in which the synizesis is but slightly marked (Montgomery, '11, Wilson, '12). On the other hand, a more or less definite polarization is described by various observers in synaptic nuclei which show
a decided synizesis.[1] We are therefore probably dealing with two divergent modifications of a single type, accentuated in some cases, perhaps,
by the coagulating effects of the fixatives employed in their study.

g. The *post-synaptic spireme* (sometimes called the *auxospireme*) consists of conspicuously shorter and thicker threads (*pacyhnema*, or *pachytene-spireme*) *of half the original number* (*i. e.*, of the haploid number). In
many cases the thick threads show no external sign of duality (Figs. 263,
267, 268, 269), as if a complete fusion of the synaptic mates to form a
single pachynema had taken place (*Tomopteris*, urodeles, mammals).
In others they seem always to show at least some indication of longitudinal
duality (Turbellaria, Orthoptera); and it is probable that such a duality is
always present in their internal structure even when they seem externally to
have fused (p. 951). Sooner (*Dendrocœlum*) or later (urodeles), however, the
threads are plainly longitudinally double (*diplonema*); and the two threads,
especially in the later stages, are often spirally twisted about each other to
form the *strepsinema* or *strepsitene* (Figs. 272, 273). These various conditions cannot as yet be very logically separated as distinct stages and may
better be classed in a single group (*g*, as above).

[1] *E. g.*, by Mottier ('98) in *Lilium*, or by Morse ('09) in the cockroach.

h. Diffuse stage. Wide variations exist in respect to the stage that follows the pachytene or early diplotene; but all agree in the fact that the nuclei recede in greater or less degree towards the condition of a "resting" nucleus. This is shown by a more or less diminished basophily, a loosening up of the spireme-threads during which they acquire rougher contours, often branch more or less, and in extreme cases may thus be lost to view in a general nuclear network. These changes, undoubtedly, are correlated with the processes of cytoplasmic growth; for in general the longer the growth-period and the greater the growth of the auxocytes the greater the nuclear diffusion. The deconcentration of the spireme-threads is thus correlated in some measure with the size of the auxocytes, and goes further in the oöcytes than in the spermatocytes. In some cases the pachytene or diplotene is never lost to view (*Tomopteris*, urodeles, various Orthoptera, copepods, platodes, etc.), the "diffuse" stage being slightly marked or hardly distinguishable as such. The extreme diffuse stage is most typically seen in large oöcytes, heavily laden with deutoplasm (p. 351), but the same condition occurs in the spermatocytes of certain animals (some insects, Fig. 266). Even in auxocytes, that approach the extreme type, however, the chromosomes are sometimes distinguishable at every stage, though in a state of great deconcentration (Figs. 161, 312). It is a noteworthy fact that in some of these cases, probably in all, the diffuse chromosomes are distinctly double, with the halves widely separated but still arranged in pairs.[1] Probably, therefore, the diffuse stage should be regarded as a highly modified diplotene in which the duality of the early diplotene, however it may be obscured, in some manner persists throughout.

The preceding stage, whether in the form of a true diffuse stage or of a more or less evident double spireme, is in some forms succeeded by:

i. The second synizesis or contraction-figure, in which the nuclear substance is again contracted in some degree. This condition, rather rare in animals, more frequent in plants, is most marked when it follows a condition of great diffusion, as is seen for instance in some of the Hemiptera (such as *Pyrrochoris* or *Alydus*) where the second synizesis is almost as marked as the first. In plants the contraction is less marked, the spireme-threads being thrown into loops that radiate irregularly from a central mass in which a plasmosome usually lies (Fig. 275).[2]

j. The *diakinesis,* or prophase in the narrower sense. In this, the final

[1] This fact was first observed by Rückert ('92) in the oöcytes of elasmobranchs (p. 269) and has since been found in many other cases.

[2] A somewhat similar stage occurs in certain fishes (Fig. 277) and other animals, which also show a typical amphitene or bouquet stage. It is at this stage, or that which immediately follows, that Farmer and Moore and their followers believe the equivalent of synapsis to take place, *i. e.*, the establishment of the definitive bivalents. It is important to bear in mind, therefore, that in some cases, (*e. g.*, in many insects) no trace of a second contraction-figure seems to exist.

stage, the bivalents assume their final forms by a rapid process of condensation, during which their quadripartite or tetrad structure usually becomes
evident, and the chromatids undergo those various shiftings of position
and form by which the different types of tetrads are produced (p. 548).
The bivalents or tetrads now appear as unmistakably separate bodies,
commonly peripheral in position, and *haploid in number* (there are some
special exceptions to this). It is conveniently subdivided into the early,

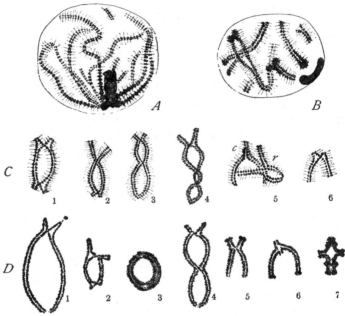

Fig. 268.—Prophase-tetrads in the spermatogenesis of grasshoppers. (*A, B, C,* from GRANATA;
D, from WENRICH.)

A, diplotene stage, *Pamphagus; B,* early diakinesis, beginning of the opening-out process; *C,*
later diakinesis, *Pamphagus;* 1, early ring with two pairs of lateral arms; 2, the same with one long
pair of lateral arms and one short; 3, double ring; 4, twisted ring; 5, *r,* ring with very long lateral
arms; *c* doubled cross, 6, double cross, in process of opening out.

D, similar figures from *Phrynotettix;* 1, early single ring, with one pair of arms; 2, ring similar to
C_2; 3, condensed ring, no arms; 4, double ring; 5, 6, double cross, opening-out; 7, completed double
cross, not yet fully condensed.

middle and late diakinesis (j^1, j^2, j^3). In the early diakinesis (j^1) the
bivalents appear in the form of separate more or less elongate spireme-
threads, *longitudinally* double and usually from an early period *longitudinally
quadripartite*, owing to the appearance of a so-called "secondary split,"
at right angles to the first (p. 505). The time at which this cleft first becomes
evident seems to vary widely in different cases. In *Dendrocœlum* Gelei's
careful study ('21, '22) shows that it is first indicated in the early diplotene,

soon after synapsis (Fig. 428, A), though later for a time lost to view. In *Phrynotettix* Wenrich ('16) finds it first appearing in the early diakinesis (Fig. 255, A, 3). In many cases, however, it has not been clearly seen before the anaphases of the heterotypic division.

The shiftings of the chromatids sometimes begin even in the early diakinesis (j ^{1}) and are continued during the middle period (j ^{2}) at a period

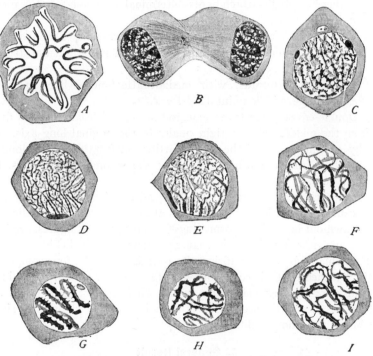

Fig. 269.—Synapsis in the annelid *Tomopteris* (SCHREINER).

A, spermatogonial metaphase; *B*, telophase of last division; *C*, preleptotene; *D*, leptonema; beginning of conjugation; *E*, slightly later stage, amphinema; *F*, late amphinema, the conjugation nearly completed, one Y-figure clearly shown; *G*, pachynema; *H*, *I*, diplonema stages.

when the bivalents are rapidly concentrating; at this time, therefore, many of the characteristic forms of tetrads are seen (rings, double-crosses, transverse tetrad-rods, etc.) in their highest development (Figs. 255, 268). These figures often persist, sometimes in great perfection (*Tomopteris*, etc.) until the late diakinesis (j ^{3}); but in many cases their relations to the earlier figures are obscured or lost (*Ascaris*, many insects, etc.). All these various forms may be, and in a large number of cases are known to be, derived from threads or rods that are at first longitudinally double (primary or reductional cleft) and later longitudinally quadripartite by the appearance of a second cleft (secondary or equational) at right angles to the first.   To summarize, the principal forms arise as follows:

(1) Longitudinal or anaschistic rod-tetrads by simple shortening of the threads. Spindle attachments terminal, median or intermediate (Fig. 245).

(2) Diaschistic or cross-rod-tetrads, by separation of two halves from one end (most usually along the primary cleft) while remaining attached at the other.   Spindle-attachments biterminal or (superficially) median (Figs. 251, 246, 254).

(3) Anaschistic V-tetrads, with median attachment, like anaschistic rods flexed at the middle point (Fig. 250). With subterminal attachment give J-figures (Fig. 252).

(4) Diaschistic V-tetrads, with median attachment, like diaschistic rods flexed at the middle-point (Figs. 251, 253).

(5) Double-crosses, like transverse rod-tetrads with lateral arms drawn out from the middle-point at right angles to the original long axis, often arise by opening apart of the quadripartite rod from one end along the primary cleft, from the other end along the secondary one (Figs. 244, 255, 254, 268).

(6) Single rings by separation of the quadripartite rod along one plane in the central region, leaving the halves attached by their ends; the latter often drawn out laterally to form "lugs" or cross-shaped figures. Spindle-attachments either terminal (Figs. 246, 259) or non-terminal (Figs. 245, 259).

(7) Double rings, from quadripartite rods in which the four components remain attached by their ends but separate along the primary cleft in one half and along the secondary cleft in the other (Figs. 257, 268, etc.).

Other less clearly defined types of tetrads arise by changes of similar type but with minor modifications.

3. General Result

The foregoing facts constitute a solid basis for our earlier assumption (p. 503) that the bivalents or tetrads do, in fact, arise by the association of chromosomes two by two, in pairs, and in many cases side by side; and that the two chromosomes of each such pair persist as the two longitudinal halves of the diplotene-spireme thread.   Further, as earlier indicated (p. 505), all the curious shapes and transformations of the tetrads are readily explicable when regarded as modifications of such an original double thread, which has become quadripartite by a longitudinal splitting of each synaptic mate, and has undergone various shiftings of the four chromatids of the tetrad $\frac{A|a}{A|a}$ thus produced.   These processes are not a matter of inference but of observed fact.   Nevertheless, before we can unreservedly accept the foregoing interpretation of meiosis, it will be necessary to look more critically at the cytological evidence.

IV. SYNAPSIS AND DISJUNCTION

The Problem of Synapsis

1. Introductory

In its earlier and (superficially) simpler form the theory of synapsis assumed no more than a segmentation of the spireme-thread into the haploid instead of the diploid number of pieces. This conception, which originated with Rückert ('92–'94), Haecker ('92, '95), and Vom Rath ('92), assumed that in mitosis and meiosis alike the chromosomes become aligned end-to-end in a continuous spireme which later segments, in the one case into the diploid number of univalent chromosomes, in the other into the haploid number of bivalents. In meiosis, such a process evidently would involve a primary end-to-end association (telosynapsis or metasyndesis) of the chromosomes but no actual conjugation other than that involved in the spireme-formation. To those who rejected the individuality of the chromosomes accordingly the whole problem of reduction seemed to involve no more than the mode of segmentation of the spireme. This notion has persisted almost down to the present day;[1] but long ago this too simple solution of the problem became untenable.

This theory, obviously, assumed the reduction-division to be a transverse division of the bivalent at the point where the synaptic mates are connected. Evidence quickly was produced, however, demonstrating that both meiotic divisions are often longitudinal (*Ascaris*, urodeles, seedplants, etc.); hence the earlier scepticism concerning the reduction-division (p. 503). In this conception, nevertheless, investigation of the subject for a long time largely centered, and as remodeled by Farmer and Moore ('03, '05) it is even now upheld by a considerable group of observers. Meanwhile, observations began to accumulate showing that in many cases the chromosomes of the early auxocytes appear at the beginning as separate univalents and of the *diploid number* (as in somatic mitosis) and later conjugate two-by-two in synapsis to form the bivalents.[2] This view later took the dominating position that it now holds. Such a conjugation might conceivably be either end-to-end (telosynaptic) or side-by-side (parasynaptic), and each of these possibilities has been energetically defended.

[1] " In my view, the germ-cells, that is to say their nuclei, inherit the specific peculiarity of producing only the half-number of chromosomes as they enter the growth-period " (Meves, '11, p. 296; also '96, etc.). See also Brauer ('92), Regaud ('10), Champy ('13).

[2] This view first suggested by Henking ('91) and considered by Rückert ('92) and Boveri ('93), first took well-defined shape in the work of Montgomery ('99, '00) and Winiwarter ('00).

On the whole, however, the theory of *parasynapsis* has steadily gained ground since 1900, when the possibility of such a process was first seriously considered. Parasynapsis has, however, been attacked even by recent writers; [1] and we are by no means in a position as yet to assert its universal occurrence.

The issues here raised may conveniently, if not quite logically, be considered under the two heads of *parasynapsis* and *telosynapsis*.[2]

2. Parasynapsis or Parasyndesis

If we except certain casual references by earlier writers (see Fick, '92) the first definite suggestion of a side-by-side conjugation of leptotene-threads came from Winiwarter in 1900, as the result of a study of mammalian oögenesis (rabbit, man), though he did not fully commit himself to this conclusion until several years later (Winiwarter and Saintmont, '09). In the meantime the theory of parasynapsis was placed upon a firm basis, in both animals and plants, by the work of many observers, prominent among them Janssens and A. and K. Schreiner.[3] Since then the theory of parasynapsis has been adopted by many other observers, among them some who, like Montgomery ('11) or Robertson ('16) had long been convinced advocates of telosynapsis.[4]

These observations leave no doubt of the fact that in a large number of cases a side-by-side association of leptotene spireme-threads takes place during the synaptic stage. The general aspect of this process shows wide differences, correlated especially with the presence or absence of a contraction-figure or synizesis. When such a figure is present (most insects and higher plants), the leptotene-threads usually show little or no polarization, and the difficulties of observation are much increased; but even in this case the leptotene-threads are often seen to lie side by side in pairs as they draw

---

[1] See for example the recent works of Stieve ('18, '20) on *Proteus*.

[2] As will later appear, parasynapsis does not necessarily imply the side-by-side conjugation of single pairs of chromosomes (though it is so described by nearly all zoölogists). It might equally well take place between two continuous spiremes, maternal and paternal, the product later segmenting to form bivalents; and the parasynaptic theory has in fact been advocated in this form by some botanists.

[3] See especially Schönfeld ('01) on the bull, Janssens and Dumez ('03), and Janssens ('01,'05), Wilson ('12), Snook and Long ('14) on urodeles; the Schreiners on *Myxine* ('04, '05) *Salamandra* and *Spinax* ('06a), *Ophyrotrocha* ('06b), and especially on *Tomopteris* ('06, '08); of Bonnevie ('06), *Enteroxenos* ('07); of Maréchal on selachians and other forms ('04, '05, '09); of Vejdovský on annelids ('07) and insects ('11, '12); of Gérard ('09), Morse ('09), Agar on *Lepidosiren* ('11), Montgomery ('11), Vejdovský ('11, '12), Wilson ('12), Stevens ('12), Wenrich ('11, '17), Robertson ('15, '16), Mohr ('16); Hogben ('20, '21) on insects, of Gelei on *Dendrocœlum* ('21, '22), and others; on the botanical side by Berghs ('04, '05), Allen ('04, '05), Grégoire ('04, '05, '07), Rosenberg ('05, '07, etc.), Strasburger ('05, '07, '08, '09), Cardiff ('06) and others. For a nearly complete list of the literature down to 1910, see the extended review and critique of Grégoire ('05, '10).

[4] For a general critique see Grégoire ('10), Wilson ('12), Gelei ('21, '22).

together (often around the nucleolus) to form the synaptic knot, while their more peripheral portions are still separate. Examples of this are seen in some of the mammals (Fig. 264, Winiwarter) and higher plants. (Berghs, '04, Allen, '04, Cardiff, '06, Digby, '20); and in some of these the paired grouping is more or less clearly seen even before the contraction

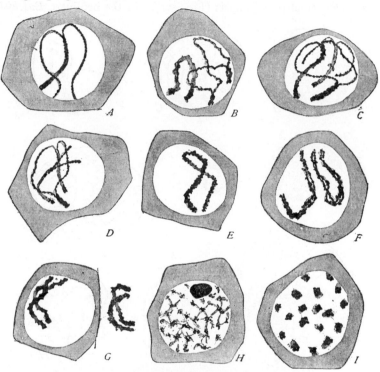

Fig. 270.—Details of synapsis in *Tomopteris* (SCHREINER).

A–D, parallel conjugation; *E*, single pachytene-thread; *F*, diplotene; *G*, the same, later stage; *H*, presynaptic stage in cross optical section, showing about 36 threads (18 loops); *I*, similar section of post-synaptic pachynema, 18 threads (9 loops).

begins. By some writers this has been ascribed to accident; but the weight of opinion is now opposed to this.

A more or less marked synizesis occurs in some of the polarized forms of synapsis, and these are also less favorable for observation,—for instance in some of the mammals (Winiwarter, '00) in the cockroach (Morse, '09, Hogben, '20b) or in the fern *Osmunda* (Grégoire, '07). In forms having no synizesis the leptotene stage is almost always more or less distinctly polarized (bouquet-stage) and the process of synapsis is more readily observed since it begins at one pole and progresses towards the opposite one. The most typical and convincing examples of this are seen in the urodeles (Janssens) and some of the annelids (*Tomopteris*, Fig. 270) and platodes (*Dendrocœlum*, Figs. 279, 280). In the mammals (Fig. 263) the polarization is somewhat less evident and the process less regular. The same is true in the Orthoptera, though this group has lately offered some of the clearest evidence of parasynapsis (Fig. 271). In the hemipter *Euschistus*,

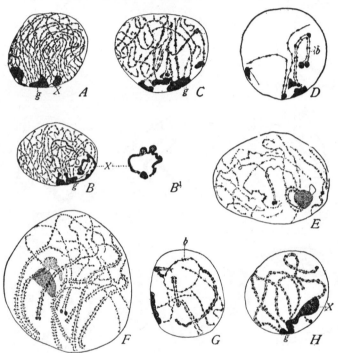

Fig. 271.—Parasynapsis in grasshoppers (WENRICH).

(*E* in *Chorthippus; F* in *Trimerotropis;* the others in *Phrynotettix.*)
A, B, leptotene stages, *g* the polar granules, X, the X-chromosome, the latter in greater detail at *B¹; C,* early synaptic nucleus, a few double threads; *D,* detail from similar nucleus, pairing completed in *B; E,* Y-figure and many unpaired letoptene-threads; *F,* amphitene-nucleus, conjugation in full progress; *G,* detail of similar stage, showing at *b* bivalent open in middle region; *H,* completed pachytene-diplotene stage.

as described by Montgomery ('11), neither synizesis nor polarization is present and the process proceeds very irregularly.

With an open and clearly-marked bouquet-stage the process of conjugation advances with considerable regularity from the nuclear pole, nearest the central bodies and idiozome, so that a very definite amphitene-stage may be recognized (Figs. 269, 271). Among the finest examples of this are those offered in the spermatogenesis of the urodeles *Batrachoseps* and *Plethodon* and of the annelid *Tomopteris*, made classical by the works of Janssens and of the Schreiners, as cited above. Even more striking are the phenomena as shown in the oöcytes of *Dendrocœlum lacteum* of which Gelei ('21) has made a detailed and careful study.[1] In cases of this type the spireme-threads are most commonly, and perhaps always, loop-shaped with both free ends directed towards the pole. In either case side-by-side union of the threads begins at their free ends, nearest the pole, and proceeds thence step by step towards the opposite pole. Thus arise char-

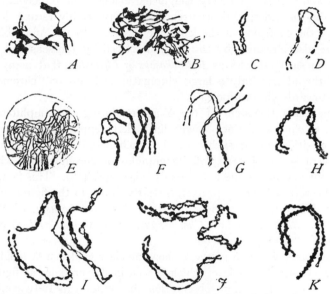

Fig. 272.—Earlier stages of meiosis in plants (mainly from GRÉGOIRE).

A, B, formation of leptotene-threads in *Lilium; C, D,* parasynaptic pairing of the threads; *E,* synaptic nucleus, *Osmunda; F,* early diplonema; *G–K,* twisted or strepsitene stages in *Lilium* (*K* from BERGHS).

acteristic Y-shaped figures, with thick longitudinally double stems, from which diverge the two halves to form the single branches of the Y. In many cases this process advances with considerable regularity, so that in its middle stages one-half the nucleus is occupied by thick and more or less parallel double threads, the other by single, thin and often contorted single threads; hence Janssens' term *amphitene.*[2]

When, as is usually the case, the two leptotene-threads have the form of

---

[1] See also Bordás, '21.

[2] Gelei ('21) has clearly shown that in *Dendrocœlum,* though a typical polarized bouquet is present, conjugation takes place irregularly, often being completed in some bivalents at a time, when in others it has only just begun.

loops, the conjugation proceeds from the free ends towards the middle point,[1] giving rise to the curious figures shown in Figs. 270, B–D; 271, G; 280 E, F; which may be likened to a pair of Y-figures united by their divergent branches.   These forms, obviously, represent two leptotene-loops, united for a certain distance near their free ends, but still wide apart in the central region.   Such forms have been clearly demonstrated by several observers, in particular by the Schreiners in *Tomopteris,* by Wenrich in *Phrynotettix,* by Robertson in *Chorthippus,* Mohr in *Locusta* and Gelei in *Dendrocœlum.*   They offer very convincing evidence of parasynapsis and are probably of widespread occurrence, but may readily escape detection because of the confusion of the leptotene-threads.   In the Amphibia these figures are also obscured by the fact, described by Janssens and readily verifiable in such urodeles as *Batrachoseps* or *Plethodon,* that many of the leptotene-threads run into a large chromatin-nucleolus or "chromoplast" situated towards the antipole.[2]

In some cases the stem of the Y-figure, during the amphitene-stage continues to show a distinct longitudinal cleft representing the plane of lateral apposition; and in such cases the two halves, in some cases at least, show each a series of very definite granules or chromomeres, which lie opposite one another in the two threads (Figs. 271, 428).   This fact, of the highest theoretical interest (p. 952), is clearly shown in the figures of many observers, for instance in those of Mohr ('16), on *Locusta,* of Wenrich ('16, '17) on *Phrynotettix* and *Chorthippus,* or of Gelei ('21 '22) on *Dendrocœlum.*[3]

In other cases the stem of the Y shows no clear evidence of longitudinal duality, a classical example of which is seen in the urodeles as figured especially by Janssens, whose observation the writer can fully confirm in both *Batrachoseps* and *Plethodon.*   This appearance may be due to an intimate fusion of the conjugants, to inappropriate fixation, or to other causes. Many interesting possibilities in this direction are suggested by Gelei's studies on *Dendrocœlum,* a very favorable object.   This work, carried out with an improved technique, offers a remarkable demonstration of parasyn-

---

[1] An exception to this seems to occur in *Chortippus* and *Trimerotropis* according to Wenrich ('17) who found some reason to conclude that pairing of the V-shaped and other atelomitic chromosomes here first begins at the apices of the V's and proceeds thence towards the free ends. A similar conclusion was earlier indicated by Gérard ('09).

[2] It seems possible that some of the figures here described do not belong to the synaptic period but to the early diakinesis and are early stages in the formation of rings; *i. e.,* the threads are not coming together but separating at this time. In such cases the central regions of the threads may have remained separate from the beginning.

[3] This fact has been urged by opponents of the theory of parasynapsis in favor of the contention that the two opposed threads result from longitudinal splitting of a single thread; but many facts are opposed to this. Wenrich has emphasized the fact, which may be clearly seen in Fig. 428, that the two opposed granules are sometimes unequal in size, a fact hard to reconcile with such an interpretation.

apsis. The number of leptotene-threads (which are of different lengths) is definitely 14, the diploid number, and of post-synaptic bivalents, 7. The pre-synaptic threads show very clearly a beaded structure, consisting of definite basichromatic granules (chromomeres) in a single series connected by a more lightly staining substance (linin?). During the conjugation the threads are brought together two by two in parasynaptic association and in outward appearance completely fuse to form a pachytene. *The chromomeres, however, remain distinct* and after suitable extraction of the dye are found lying in two distinct and separate series, *lying opposite each other two by two* in the pachytene thread and afterwards in the diplotene (Figs. 279, 280, 428). This makes it probable that the seeming fusion of the conjugants

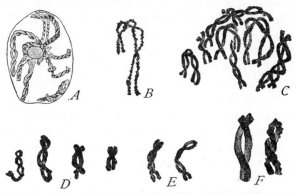

Fig. 273.—Later stages of meiosis, especially strepsinema stages (*A*, from OVERTON, *B, D, F,* from BERGHS, *C* from JANSSENS).

A, second contraction-figure in *Podophyllum; B*, earlier strepsinema in *Lilium; D, F*, later stages, twisted loops and double rods; *E*, similar figures, *Convallaria; C*, late strepsinema in the salamander *Batrachoseps.*

is deceptive, and that in internal structure the bivalents are always double structures.

Another interesting possibility is that the apparent fusion of the conjugants may in some cases be due to a close twisting together of the two leptotene-threads, a process which is clearly indicated (though not described) in Janssens' figures of *Batrachoseps* ('06). Other observers who have figured or described a similar torsion at this time include Grégoire ('07) in *Osmunda* and *Allium*, Agar ('11) in *Lepidosiren*, Bolles Lee ('11) in *Helix*, and Gelei ('21) in a few cases in *Dendrocœlum*. This point calls for the closest investigation because of its bearing on the chiasmatype-theory (p. 954); but the evidence in its support is very inadequate. Both Stevens and Lee believed the double spiral to persist from the time of synapsis through all the ensuing stages up to the period of diakinesis, but this is urgently in need of confirmation.   Most observers, including Winiwarter, the Schreiners, Wenrich, the writer, and many others, have found no evidence of a synaptic twisting.   In *Dendrocœlum*, Gelei found twisting only in rare cases (Fig. 428); and it seems possible that this may be an accidental product of the technique.   On the whole, therefore, there is little to support the hypothesis of a synaptic twisting.

In any case the result of the synaptic process is the complete replacement of the leptotene-threads by the pachytene.   There is no doubt in many cases that the number of pachytene-threads is haploid, *i. e.*, that the pseudo-reduction has been accomplished during the synaptic stage, as is demonstrated with certainty by endwise or polar views or the polarized loops during the bouquet-stage.   In *Tomopteris*, for example (as is clearly figured by the Schreiners, '08) the post-synaptic or pachytene-bouquet shows 18 threads, the pre-synaptic twice this number (Fig. 270).   Since each loop-shaped thread appears as two in polar view the actual numbers are 9 (18) and 18 (36) corresponding to the haploid and the diploid numbers respectively.   An example of the facts in species showing a synizesis is shown by the hemipter *Largus cinctus*, in which the male diploid number is 11, including an unpaired X-chromosome and five autosome-pairs.   Here the number of post-synaptic pachytene-threads is five (with one unpaired condensed X-chromosome, Fig. 267, L), while the pre-synaptic number (of prochromosomes) is 11.[1]   A considerable number of such cases have now been determined.

The evidence thus briefly reviewed seems to the author to leave no doubt that in a large class of cases pseudo-reduction is accomplished during the synaptic stage by a side-by-side union of leptotene threads, each of which represents a single or univalent chromosome.   This conclusion has, however, met with energetic opposition on the part of some recent writers, even in case of the urodeles.   Champy ('13) could find no evidence of any kind of synapsis and, like Fick, Meves, Della Valle and others practically abandons the whole problem of reduction as insoluble.   Stieve ('20), in two lengthy papers on *Proteus*, contradicts all of the essential results of Janssens, Schreiner, Snook and Long, the writer, and other observers of the urodeles, finding a continuous spireme up to and through the pachytene bouquet; the diploid number of loops throughout both the leptotene and pachytene bouquet; complete absence of an amphitene stage or of other evidence of parasynapsis; the segmentation of the pachytene-spireme into the *diploid* number of univalent chromosomes; and finally a telosynaptic union of the latter two-by-two to form the bivalents.   The present writer, who has examined the original preparations of the Schreiners (*Tomopteris*)

---

[1] Wilson, '12.

and of Janssens (*Batrachoseps*),[1] supplemented by subsequent repeated study of other preparations of urodele material, is of the opinion that Stieve's results on all of these points are erroneous.

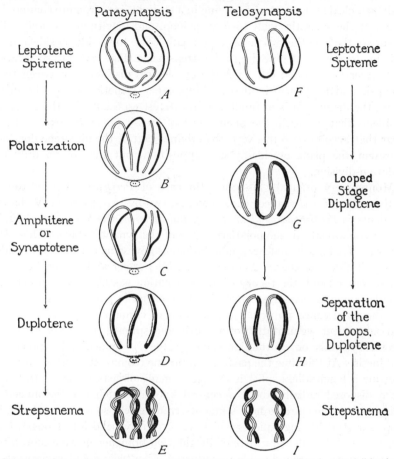

Fig. 274.—Diagram showing the relation between parasynapsis and "telosynapsis" by loop-formation. In the parasynaptic series one pair of loops and one pair of rods are shown. The final stages are much alike in effect (parasynaptic association of the synaptic mates), but the early stages are widely different.

3. Telosynapsis or Metasyndesis.   End-to-end Union and the Theory of Loop-formation

Though telosynaptic conceptions have lost ground in recent years they still have the support of some competent observers.   The theory of Rückert and his followers received its first detailed development by Montgomery

[1] *Cf.* Wilson ('12).

('oo, '03, '05) and by Farmer and Moore ('03, '95). Though differing somewhat in detail, these interpretations (like Rückert's) alike assume primarily
that upon segmentation of the spireme the synaptic mates of each pair remain attached at one end, either lying in a straight line, or, more commonly,
flexed at the synaptic point to form a loop, and longitudinally split. By
closure of the loop the two mates may finally come to lie side by side and by
twisting together may give rise to the strepsinema (Fig. 275). In such cases,
as Farmer has pointed out ('13) the cytological distinction between telosynapsis and parasynapsis almost disappears. Genetically, on the other
hand, the distinction is of fundamental interest especially for the group of
problems that center in the phenomena of crossing-over (p. 955). It is
clear that according to this view the original cleft of the diplotene does not
represent the plane of side-by-side apposition, but that of an ordinary
equation-division.

Montgomery originally assumed (in case of *Peripatus*) an end-to-end
conjugation of rod-shaped chromosomes two-by-two to form V-shaped
bivalents *in the telophases of the last gonial division*, the V's thus produced
giving rise directly to the polarized loops of the synaptic stage. This view
never received much credence, though there is now some reason to reconsider
its possibilities (p. 562).[1] As developed by Farmer and Moore ('03, '05)
on the other hand, the theory of loop-formation has had many adherents,
especially among investigators of the phenomena in plants.[2] In this form
the theory assumed no actual conjugation of chromosomes but a looping
and subsequent segmentation of a continuous spireme; taking place in the
second synizesis or contraction-stage (Stage *i*) immediately preceding
diakinesis. At this time the pachytene spireme (commonly, but not always,
showing a longitudinal split) is in fact in many objects thrown into loops,
often disposed radially about a central knot in which lies the nucleolus
(Fig. 275). The spireme now segments transversely so as to separate the
loops (or straight single pieces which subsequently bend into loops) which
constitute the bivalents. Meanwhile the two branches of each loop often
approximate until they lie side by side and often twist about each other to
form 8-shaped figures or short double spirals. The bivalents thus formed
may subsequently undergo the various changes of form already described.

This interpretation agrees with the parasynaptic in the conclusion that
the synaptic mates in many cases *ultimately* do come to lie side by side but

[1] Montgomery's conception of the composition of the synaptic loops, apart from their mode of
origin, was the same in principle as that adopted by Paulmier, McClung, Sutton, Wassilieff, Stevens
and some other investigators of the time.

[2] See Strasburger ('04) and especially Mottier ('05, '07, '14) on *Lilium, Podophyllum, Acer,* and
other forms; Gates ('08, '09), B. M. Davis ('09, '10, '11), Geerts ('08), and Cleland ('22) on *Œnothera;* Lewis ('08) on *Pinus* and *Thuja;* Digby ('10, '14, '20) on *Galtonia, Crepis,* etc.; Frazer and
Snell ('11) and Sakamura ('14) on *Vicia.*

through a secondary process. In all other respects it involves a fundamentally different conception of the organization of the spireme; for the longitudinal cleft of the diplotene is considered as a simple equational split (like

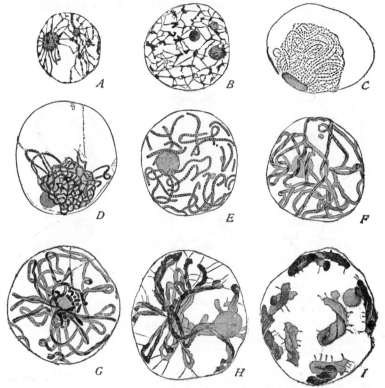

Fig. 275.—Meiosis by loop-formation in the pollen mother-cells of *Lilium*, as described by MOTTIER (FARMER and MOORE mode).

A, B, presynaptic net-like stages; *C,* early synizesis ("synapsis") of the leptotene-threads; *D,* loosening of the synizesis, spireme longitudinally double (diplonema); *E,* "hollow," segmented, double spireme (diplonema); *F,* similar or slightly later stage, twisting; *G,* looping of the twisted and longitudinally double threads; *H,* later looped stage, second contraction, segmentation of the threads in progress; *I,* diakinesis, loops separate, shorter and thicker, near periphery.

that of a somatic prophase) instead of the apposition-plane of two synaptic mates (or spiremes).

If therefore we accept the conclusion that the synaptic mates in each pair are respectively of maternal and paternal ancestry (p. 505) it must be assumed that in the original spireme paternal and maternal chromosomes regularly alternate and in such a way that synaptic mates always adjoin. In apparent harmony with this are the facts described in *Œnothera*, where just prior to the diakinesis the full diploid number of chromosomes (14) are said to be visible, most of them aligned end to end in the pachytene spireme (Fig. 276), though a few may already be free. By segmentation of the spireme seven bivalents are formed, each consisting of two synaptic mates attached end-to-end. During the diakinesis the two mates usually fold together so as to lie side by side, or even to form rings; but they may remain end to end in telosynaptic union. A similar alignment in the spireme is seen in *Bufo* (King, '07) and in *Carex* by Stout ('12) though these observers leave the mode of synapsis undetermined. Too much importance

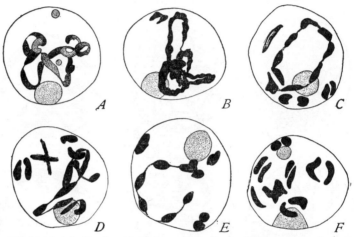

Fig. 276.—Meiosis in *Œnothera* (*A*, *Œ. lamarckiana*, DAVIS; *B–F*, *Œ. rubrinervis*, GATES).
A and *B* partly segmented pachynema; *C–E*, later stages, serial alignment of chromosomes with several pairs separate; *F*, the chromosomes separate and in part paired.

should not be ascribed to these facts, however, in view of the diakinetic phenomena later to be described.

Farmer and Moore's interpretation still has the support of some able observers,[1] but has of late lost ground. In case of the cockroach, for instance (Moore's object), both Morse ('09) and Hogben ('20) have produced strong evidence in favor of the parasynaptic theory, while Digby ('20), still a convinced supporter of the loop-theory, has recently admitted the side-by-side union of leptotene-threads at the synaptic stage. In *Spinacea, Smilacina* and some other seed-plants according to Stomps ('10) and Lawson ('12) the spireme is not continuous at any period, but consists of separate *univalent* threads, each of which is longitudinally split from an early period.

---

[1] "In the entire history of the nucleus from the stage of rest to the formation of the twelve bivalents, nothing is clearer to the writer than the fact that all of the bivalents are derived from the spireme; that no spireme is formed previous to synapsis (synizesis); that there is no union of spiremes, either before, during or after synapsis, and that the spireme is composed of the somatic chromosomes placed end to end " (Mottier, '14, p. 120).

These threads, according to Lawson's very specific account, conjugate side-wise in pairs at a stage nearly corresponding to the second synizesis or the early diakinesis, the original longitudinal fission of the threads meanwhile becoming less evident or wholly obscured. With this may be compared the phenomena in *Euschistus* (according to Montgomery, '11) where the spireme is likewise segmented from the very beginning and the parasyn-aptic pairing of the chromosomes occurs step by step in rather irregular fashion as the growth-period advances. Were this process deferred until a later period a condition much like that described by Lawson would exist.[1]

4. Synapsis in Relation to the Anaphasic Duality

Certain attempts have been made to reconcile the side-by-side association of leptotene-threads in the synaptic stage with telosynaptic conceptions. It is hardly necessary to consider seriously the earlier crude notion that this association is merely an accidental result of the drawing together of polar-ized leptotene-threads towards one pole. More careful consideration is due to the conception of Meves ('98) that it represents a kind of precocious longitudinal fission, in which the spireme is formed progressively as a double structure from the beginning. Advocates of the loop-theory of telosynapsis have given a certain vogue to the related notion that parasynapsis is no more than a reunion of sister-threads that have resulted from an earlier longitudinal fission and have temporarily separated. This fission has for the most part been referred to the final gonial anaphase, the sister chromo-somes then produced, often widely separated, being assumed to have per-sisted throughout all the following stages until their reunion in the synaptic stage.[2] The meiotic prophase is thus treated as merely a special modi-fication of the anaphasic splitting in the somatic mitoses (p. 138), and the parasynaptic pairing of leptotene-threads loses all significance for the reduction-problem.

Advocates of the loop-theory of synapsis have thus sought to reconcile their own conclusions with the positive observation of parasynaptic pairing described by so many competent observers.[3] To cite Brunelli: "Step by step the two longitudinal halves of the individual chromosomes place them-selves side by side; wherefore the intermediate appearances that have been described as the fission of a single thread or as the reunion of two threads having the value of two separate chromosomes (zygotene hypothesis)"

---

[1] For more recent accounts of telosynapsis see Nothnagel, '16 (*Allium*), Nakahara, '19 (*Perla*) Gates and Rees, '21 (*Lactuca*).

[2] This possibility is clearly suggested by Rückert ('92a, p. 149, '92b, p. 51) in his remarkable papers on elasmobranch oögenesis, in which are foreshadowed so many later conclusions concerning the his-tory of the chromosomes (p. 924).

[3] See especially Digby ('10) on *Galtonia* and ('19) on *Osmunda*, Fraser and Snell ('11) and Frazer ('14) on *Vicia*, Brunelli ('11) on *Trixalis*.

(*op. cit.*, p. 9). This interpretation deserves careful attention but has encountered fatal difficulties. The *status* of the so-called anaphasic "splitting" in the somatic mitoses has itself become extremely dubious (p. 139); but a still more serious difficulty appears in the numerical relations. Since the gonial number is diploid the anaphasic split should give the tetraploid number, and parasynapsis should reduce this number again to the diploid (of pachytene threads); but both these demands of the hypothesis are contrary to fact,[1] at least in some cases. Direct counts of the leptotene-threads are sometimes practicable; and when such is not the case, accurate counting of the prochromosomes from which the threads arise may still be possible. Both methods show conclusively that the number is *diploid*. Especially clear cases of direct counting are offered by the Schreiners' studies on *Tomopteris* ('96, '08) (haploid 9) and the more recent ones of Gelei ('21) on *Dendrocœlum* (haploid 7). Enumerations of the prochromosomes are especially convincing when certain of them are recognizable individually by their size or otherwise. In *Lygæus bicrucis*, for example, their number, like that of the spermatogonia, is 14; and two of these are at once recognizable by their denser and more basophilic character and their unequal size (p. 542). Again, in the beetle *Blaps lusitanica* Nonidez ('20) found 33 spermatogonial chromosomes including constantly three large ones, readily recognizable. In Stage *c* the prochromosomes show the same number and character; and as in other cases one leptotene thread is formed from each.

Finally, Robertson ('19), who himself accepts the anaphasic splitting, has briefly announced that in grasshoppers of the family Tettigidæ the presynaptic-threads in the male are of the diploid number (13) and *longitudinally split*, the 12 autosomes pairing side-by-side to form six bivalents, each of which is presumably already a tetrad. This, if well founded, is evidently fatal to the interpretation of Digby, Brunelli and others as above indicated. Still a different condition (still unpublished) has been found by McClung in the grasshoppers (*Leptisma* and *Mecostethus*)[2] in which the number of prochromosomes is *haploid*. Here the chromosome-conjugation seems to be at least initiated in the gonial telophases or a little later, the telophase-chromosomes becoming associated side by side in pairs. Such a mode of synapsis, evidently, approximates to Montgomery's original conception of an anaphasic conjugation. These observations evidently are no more favorable to the interpretation in question than are those of Robertson.

Taken together the foregoing facts appear to be decisively against the theory of anaphasic duality as applied to parasynapsis, and equally opposed to the earlier telosynaptic conception of Montgomery.

---

[1] Wilson, '12.
[2] The writer has had the privilege of examining the original preparations. See McClung, '24.

5. Late Conjugation. Diakinetic Synaptic Phenomena

Certain accounts of chromosome-conjugation taking place late in the growth-period, or even at its close, open interesting possibilities concerning the phenomena already considered. That excellent observer Henking ('91) found evidence in *Pyrrhocoris* of a diakinetic conjugation following the second contraction-figure; and a similar phenomenon has been described more in detail by Gross ('04, '06) in *Syromastes* and *Pyrrhocoris*. In the elasmobranch *Pristiurus* Rückert ('92, '93) found the full diploid number

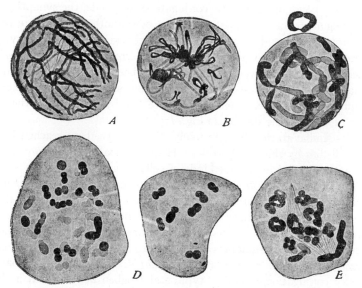

Fig. 277.—Later stages of spermatogenesis in *Lepidosiren* (AGAR).

A, late pachynema, with haploid number (19) of loops; *B*, second contraction-figure, strepsinema, loops formed by separation of the ex-conjugants; *C*, diakinesis, shortening, thickening and separation of the ex-conjugants, a ring-tetrad shown separately above; *D*, final diakinesis (in two sections), nuclear membrane disappeared, 38 univalent chromosomes, each transversely constricted; *E*, late prophase, secondary pairing of the chromosomes to form rings or tetrad-shaped bodies.

of chromosomes (36), arranged in pairs in the middle growth-period of the germinal vesicle, the haploid number appearing at a later period.[1] A more recent example is offered by the works of Stieve ('18, '20a, '20b) on the spermatogenesis and oögenesis of *Proteus;* but this account as above stated is, in the author's opinion, open to serious question.

There are certain well-established cases of chromosome-conjugation at a late stage—in the diakinesis or even later. For example, the *m*-chromosomes of coreid Hemiptera regularly conjugate in the final prophases of the

---

[1] See also Born ('93), Wilcox ('95), Korschelt ('95).

heterotypic division (p. 839); while the XY-pair of sex-chromosomes of Hemiptera generally do not conjugate until the final anaphases of that division (p. 769). In some of these cases the conjugation in question seems undoubtedly to represent *a secondary coupling that has been preceded by a typical synapsis at the usual time and a subsequent deconjugation.* One of the clearest of these cases is described by Agar ('11) in *Lepidosiren.* In this case the diploid divisions show 38 chromosomes, which give rise in the presynaptic period to typical leptotene-threads. In a typical amphitene or synaptotene bouquet-stage these conjugate side-by-side, the synaptic mates often being more or less twisted about one another. Thus are formed 19 pachytene loops; but after a second contraction-figure or synizesis a disjunction occurs to form short, thick chromosomes of the *diploid* number (38) which show no sign of having been previously coupled. In the final stages of diakinesis, as the chromosomes are actually passing upon the spindle, the univalents again conjugate two-by-two to form the 19 bivalents of the meiotic divisions (Fig. 277).

Results similar to the above in many respects have been reached in some of the gall-flies by the recent work of Hogben ('20a). In *Rhodites* (p. 803), the somatic number in various kinds of cells is uniformly 18. In synapsis the leptotene-threads (presumably also 18 in number) conjugate *parasynaptically* to form 9 bivalents; but in the diakinesis reappear 18 single threads which are said to conjugate *end-to-end* to form the 9 bivalents that pass upon the spindle. The facts reported in *Cynips* are quite similar save that the respective chromosome-numbers are 20 and 10. The diakinetic telosynaptic pairing observed by Hegner ('14) in *Copidosoma* is very probably a secondary conjugation of similar type, and Hogben believes that a similar process occurs also in *Orthopelma.* A similar explanation undoubtedly applies to the above cited case of the elasmobranchs as described by Rückert. Here the later work of Maréchal and of the Schreiners demonstrated a typical parasynapsis at the usual time; and the later appearance of the diploid number is clearly owing to the wide temporary separation of the halves of the diplotene, which finally reunite side-by-side. The meaning of these singular manœuvers of the chromosomes is almost unknown; but they show how readily we may fall into error concerning both the mode of synapsis and the time at which it occurs if every stage of meiosis be not closely scrutinized. They are also of much interest in relation to diploid parthenogenesis, which in some cases is likewise preceded by a process of conjugation and pseudo-reduction, only to be undone by a disjunction prior to the single maturation-division (p. 793).

6. Critical

The parasynaptic and telosynaptic hypotheses, as outlined above, do not differ in respect to the final result of maturation; but from a theoretical point of view it is important to determine the precise *modus operandi* of synapsis because of its bearing on "crossing-over" (p. 952). It is possible that both types of synapsis may actually occur; but to the writer this seems improbable. We may admit that to some extent the time and mode of synapsis may not be the same in all objects; but no explanation can here be found for the contradiction in case of the same objects; in the lily, for example, diametrically opposing results have been reached by such competent observers as Allen and Grégoire on the one hand, and Farmer, Moore, and Mottier on the other. Grégoire ('07, '09) after a critical reëxamination of the phenomena in the seed-plants most positively reaffirmed the parasynaptic conclusions of Allen, Berghs and others in opposition to Farmer and Moore; while the opposing hypothesis in its turn received fresh support from the studies on other seed-plants of Mottier ('14) of Digby ('10, '14, '20), Frazer and Snell ('11), Frazer ('15) and others. In the case of *Œnothera*, as already indicated, a "telosynaptic" association of the chromosomes in early diakinesis seems indubitable. Among zoölogists, on the other hand, the drift of opinion has been steadily towards the parasynaptic conception. Montgomery himself, after a renewed and extended study of the spermatogenesis of *Euschistus* ('11) definitely accepted this conclusion in opposition to his earlier conclusions. The results of Moore ('05) on the cockroach have been shown to be almost certainly untenable by Morse ('09) and Hogben ('20) in later studies on the same object. The present writer ('12) after long study of the problem in the Hemiptera, and especially on original preparations of *Batrachoseps* by Janssens, of *Tomopteris* by the Schreiners, and on numerous additional preparations of *Plethodon* and *Batrachoseps*, likewise became convinced of the reality of parasynapsis. McClung ('14, '20) long favorable to a telosynaptic conception in the case of Orthoptera, has at length accepted as most probable the parasynaptic one, which also finds strong support in the recent work on this group of Robertson ('15, '16), Wenrich ('16, '17) and Mohr ('16), of Gelei on the Turbellaria, and that of Metz and others on the unquestionable side-by-side pairing of the chromosomes in Diptera, even in the somatic divisions (p. 837).

Some of the existing divergence of interpretation has, no doubt, arisen from errors of observation in this difficult field. To the writer, however, it seems probable that the divergence may also be due in part to a failure to reckon with all the cytological phenomena and in particular with possible secondary modifications. Interesting possibilities in this direction are

suggested by the phenomena of diakinetic deconjugation and reunion reviewed in the last section; and it seems possible that important further
light may be thrown on the subject by more adequate studies on the relation between the synaptic stage, the second contraction, and the diakinesis.
There is increasing reason to believe that the serial alignment of chromosomes sometimes seen in the later stages, may in some cases be a secondary
association quite different from the original one.   Perhaps we may find in
this direction a common ground on which parasynapsis, telosynapsis and
loop-formation may come together.   For parasynapsis begins by the union
of the chromosome-ends; and we might further conceive that the looping
process as described in higher plants was originally (perhaps still is) preceded by an early side-by-side association that is undone in later stages
preceding the loop-formation.   The latter process would then restore the
original side-by-side association.

7. The Mechanism of Synapsis

The causes that determine the pairing of the synaptic mates, are wholly
unknown.   We think naturally of a chemical or physical difference of sign
or potential between the maternal and paternal homologues; but every
such hypothesis stumbles against the fact that maternal chromosomes of
one generation may become paternal in the following one (or *vice versa*).
The difficulties increase when we consider synapsis as observed in triploid
or tetraploid cells.   In such cases the process is of especial interest since
three or four synaptic mates are present instead of the normal two.   Certain tetraploid forms, such as some of the *gigas* forms of *Œnothera* or *Primula*,
breed approximately true without splitting up to any large extent into other
forms; and from this we may infer that during meiosis the chromosomes at
least tend to mate in pairs and to disjoin in typical fashion.[1]   It is certain,
also, that such a mode of pairing takes place in the meiosis of particular
lobes or cysts of the testis that are abnormally tetraploid in individuals otherwise diploid [2] (see Bowen, '22).

Such cases would seem to suggest that some sort of "affinity" exists
between the synaptic mates—such as a difference of electric charge or of
chemical nature—that is satisfied by their union; and the same view is suggested by the behavior of certain triploids or other forms having an odd

---

[1] Gates found, however, that the synaptic pairing in *Œ. gigas*, as often in other Œnotheras, is very
loose and irregular in appearance. See Gates, '09, '13, '15, '24.

[2] This gives substantial ground for the conclusion that mutants or species that are "tetraploid"
as compared with original or related forms are really such—*i. e.*, that each specific type of chromosome is present in quadruplicate instead of in duplicate. This conclusion explains the otherwise puzzling fact that in hybrids between diploid or tetraploid forms (as in *Drosera*, p. 846) synapsis produces a number of bivalents equal to the fundamental haploid number, the remaining chromosomes
being univalent.

number of chromosomes, where the unpaired chromosomes find no mates in meiosis (p. 848). Unluckily, however, this seems to be contradicted by the synaptic phenomena in certain other triploid and tetraploid forms where the synaptic mates conjugate by threes or fours. A demonstrative example of this is offered by the trivalent m-chromosome of *Metapodius* (p. 876); and more recently the same fact has been clearly shown by Belling and Blakeslee ('23) in both triploid and tetraploid *Daturas*. In the latter cases synapsis leads to the formation of trivalent or quadrivalent heterotypic chromosomes, followed by a disjunction that involves a random assortment of the chromatids and conscquent splitting up of the original groups. In harmony with this are the results of Holt ('17), Bridges ('22) and Metz ('22) on the association of homologous chromosomes in triploid, tetraploid, and polyploid somatic cells of *Drosophila*, which indicate that in such cells the synaptic mates tend to an association in groups of three, four or more, instead of in pairs as in the normal diploid individuals. In

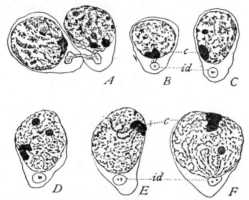

Fig. 278.—Telokinetic movement of the nucleus in very young spermatocytes of the salamander *Batrachoseps* (JANSSENS).

A, early stage, sister-cells still connected by spindle-bridge, chromoplasts near the idiozome; *B*, slightly later stage, chromoplast close to idiozome; *C, D, E*, successive stages in the rotation of the nucleus, leading to *F*, leptotene, already slightly polarized, with chloroplast opposite to the idiozome.

view of all this, we can only record the observed facts, admitting our present inability to find their physical explanation.

Undoubtedly the side-by-side conjugation of long thread-like loops from both ends towards the center involves some difficult mechanical problems. The difficulty is to some extent lessened by the preparation for the process that begins in the pre-synaptic stages and may be more extensive than has been suspected. In animals, at least, the central bodies evidently play an important part in this process; for it is towards them (*i. e.*, the idiozome-pole of the nucleus) that the free ends of the leptotene threads or loops are drawn during the polarization; and it is here that their union two by two typically begins.　Rod-shaped chromosomes with the spindle attachment at one end seem to become looped during synapsis with both ends towards the pole, as clearly seen (for example) in the "conflexion" of the X-chromosome in Orthoptera (p. 761).　The behavior of V-shaped chromosomes (*Tomopteris*, urodeles), is of especial interest; for here the spindle-attachment is at the apex of the V, yet in the bouquet-stage it is the free ends that are turned towards the idiozome-pole (Janssens, '05).　This observer has

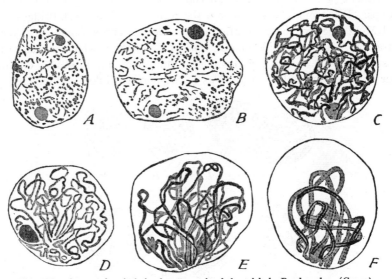

Fig. 279.—Stages of meiosis in the oögenesis of the triclade *Dendrocœlum* (GELEI).

A, netlike stage (protobroch); *B*, beginning of the spireme-formation (deutobroch); *C*, fully formed but still unpolarized leptonema, free ends of the threads marked by crosses; *D*, beginning of the leptotene polarization; *E*, polarized leptotene-bouquet stage, with seven pairs of loops; *F*, polarized diplonema, seven double loops.

produced apparently strong evidence that during the telokinesis of the last gonial division in urodeles the nucleus rotates through 180°, so that the original relations of the loops to the central bodies are reversed (Fig. 278). A similar telokinetic transposition was indicated by the Schreiners ('06) in the case of *Tomopteris*, and is also stated by Gelei ('21) to take place in *Dendrocœlum*, though its exact *modus operandi* was not determined. This clearly shows that the relation between chromosome and center is not due to a persistent attachment between them.

Gelei has demonstrated, further, that before the polarization the free ends of the leptotene loops lie upon the nuclear membrane, at first quite irregularly scattered, but later gliding towards the pole until they finally come into contact with their mates as the conjugation begins (Fig. 279). Gelei believes these movements to result from an active motility of the chromosomes; but this is hypothetical. In any case it is evident that they prepare the way for a conjugation that begins with the free ends and gradually draws the synaptic loops together towards the central points. We can thus in a measure understand how the loops disentangle themselves from the spireme; and we even may suspect that the seeming labyrinth of threads is an orderly system the nature of which is determined at a still earlier period. Of much interest in connection with this is the occasional occurrence of two or even three ring-shaped bivalents linked together like links in a chain, of which several cases have been observed by McClung. This obviously might result from an entanglement of the leptotene-threads such that one or more of them were caught between the two synaptic mates of another conjugating pair. Such conditions actually occur, as is clearly shown by Gelei (Fig. 280, F). This observer believes such entangled threads to be subsequently liberated by pulling through the ring; but the occasional occurrence of interlocking rings shows that such is not always the case. The parasynaptic theory, evidently, gives a simple explanation of such cases.

B. DISJUNCTION AND SEGREGATION

The purely sceptical attitude towards both synapsis and disjunction formerly taken by some writers [1] is now possible only for those who have not troubled themselves with the progress of modern cytological research. On the other hand, the question whether the synaptic mates that couple in synapsis retain their identity as such, to be disjoined as such in the reduction-division, has found a definite answer only in the case of particular chromosomes (p. 571).

1. The Reduction-division

In many objects, including those classical ones *Tomopteris* and *Batrachoseps* (p. 551), it has not been possible to demonstrate with certainty any longitudinal duality in the pachynema for a certain period following synapsis and prior to the appearance of the diplonema (a period very short in *Tomopteris* but extending through a large part of the growth-period in urodeles). An important group of observers (p. 506) were thus led to a position of great reserve concerning the reduction-division, concluding that synapsis leads to a complete fusion of the synaptic mates to form "mixochromosomes" or "zygosomes" in which the identity of the original

---

[1] E. g., Meves, or Fick (p. 506).

conjugants may be wholly lost (Winiwarter, Bonnevie and others). So far as
the visible phenomena in these cases go, there seems externally to be nothing
to distinguish the formation of the diplonema from an ordinary longitudinal or equational split, and hence no ground for assuming the occurrence
of a reduction.   On the other hand, a considerable number of good observers
have emphatically maintained that in some objects the longitudinal duality
produced by parasynapsis is never at any period wholly lost to view,[1]
at least in portions of the pachynema; while, as earlier indicated, Gelei
has shown that in *Dendrocœlum* a union of the synaptic mates that externally seems to involve complete fusion may leave intact the two separate

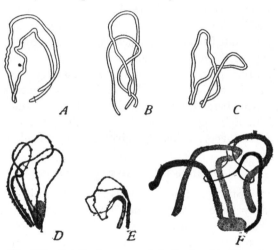

Fig. 280.—Details of parasynapsis in *Dendrocœlum* (Gelei).

A–C, three pairs of leptotene-threads (from one nucleus) at the beginning of conjugation; *D,
E*, middle stages of conjugation, entanglement of the loops in *D; F*, diagram showing entanglement
of the loops during conjugation.

series of chromomeres derived from each (Fig. 428).   But apart from
this direct evidence the indirect evidence from other sources is so strong
as to remove every doubt concerning the reality of the reduction-division
or the fact that in some sense or other a duality of the post-synaptic spireme
persists throughout the pachytene stage.

The special and indirect evidence of the reduction-division is of widely
varied nature.   It is most demonstrative in the case of certain kinds of
chromosomes which do not spin out into leptotene-threads before synapsis
but conjugate and disjoin at a late period in the form of condensed chromosomes of the ordinary type.   An example of these is offered by the micro-

---

[1] See especially Grégoire ('07, '10), Montgomery ('06, '11, etc.), McClung ('14, etc.), Wenrich
('16, '17).

chromosomes or "*m*-chromosomes" of certain Hemiptera (p. 839). These chromosomes ordinarily remain separate in the diakinesis and only couple to form a bivalent as the chromosomes are actually grouping themselves to form the equatorial plate.[1] Their conjugation is always immediately followed by disjunction, the process being one of "touch-and-go" which seems merely to serve the purpose of ensuring a definite segregation of the synaptic mates. Not the smallest doubt can here exist of the reality of synapsis and disjunction without intervening fusion of the synaptic mates or loss of their identity.

In this case the process might indeed be merely a secondary one, preceded by an earlier primary synapsis and disjunction (p. 793). This possibility is, however, excluded in a second case offered by the XY-pair of sex-chromosomes in certain Hemiptera, which are recognizable already in the pre-synaptic period (Stage *c*) by their condensed form which is retained throughout all the succeeding stages. In some of these cases, it is true, these chromosomes conjugate, deconjugate, and again conjugate at a later period (p. 769), though their identity never is wholly lost.[2] In others conjugation often wholly fails in the earlier stages, and both synaptic mates fully retain their identity at every period without the least sign of fusion.[3] In all cases these chromosomes divide separately in the heterotypic mitosis, though usually lying side by side, and conjugate in its final anaphase to form a bivalent in most cases unequal or heteromorphic (Fig. 369). Without fusion of its two components this bivalent enters the second mitosis and immediately disjoins. In this case, which may be taken as a crucial one, both synapsis and reduction-division are plain to demonstration. This is even more strikingly shown in case of the compound sex-chromosomes (p. 772).

A third decisive demonstration of the reduction-division is offered by the so-called *heteromorphic* chromosome-pairs in which the synaptic mates are visibly distinguishable by the eye by differences of size, form, mode of spindle-attachment or structure. The most remarkable cases of this kind are offered by the XY-pair, just referred to, in which Y is almost always smaller, often much smaller, than X (p. 767). This case is of crucial importance, because we know that the Y is of paternal ancestry and the X of maternal (p. 767), this case having first substantiated Montgomery's general hypothesis that the synaptic mates are respectively of maternal and paternal origin.[4] Since this case was made known heteromorphic pairs of ordinary chromosomes (autosomes) have been demonstrated by Carothers, Robertson and Wenrich in several genera of *Orthoptera*. In some of these

---

[1] Gross, '04, Wilson, '05b, etc.
[2] Wilson, '05b, etc.
[3] *Oncopeltus*, Wilson, '12.
[4] Stevens, '05, Wilson, '05.

cases the synaptic mates differ only in size (*Arphia, Phrynotettix*), in others in mode of spindle-attachment, as in *Trimerotropis* or *Circotettix*, where one may have a terminal attachment, the other a non-terminal (p. 934).

In the face of such facts scepticism must give way to the conviction that whatever changes of reorganization the synaptic mates may undergo during the meiotic cycle their identity is not lost.   The cytological phenomena of synapsis in these cases have not yet been sufficiently followed out.   Wenrich ('16) carefully studied the earlier history of an unequal autosome-tetrad in *Phrynotettix* and found that the unequal mates originally lie side by side in the *diplonema* (Fig. 255),[1] subsequently opening apart to form an unequal double cross.   If this is correct, it seems fatal to the assumption that synapsis is followed by total fusion and a subsequent new splitting of the mixochromosome thus produced.

We here again emphasize the striking fact that while every bivalent (or tetrad) resulting from the conjugation of synaptic mates, undergoes two divisions during meiosis, a chromosome having no synaptic mate *divides but once*.[2]   Remarkable examples of this are offered by the maturation-divisions of organisms having only a haploid group of chromosomes, such as the males of Hymenoptera (p. 797) or the haploid mutants of *Datura* recently described by Blakeslee and Belling ('22).   In such cases synapsis fails to occur, and the univalents pass singly upon the spindle.   Though each is at this time longitudinally double (equation-split) the halves do not separate in the first division but in the second.   In the first division of these *Daturæ* the twelve double chromosomes (dyads) are distributed at random to the poles (3 and 9, 8 and 4, etc.) *without division;*[3] while the second division is quite normal apart from the diminished number of chromosomes.   In the bee or wasp the first division is abortive and though the spindle forms, the dyads do not pass to its poles.   The second (equational) division, as before, is normal.   Evidence of the same type, though less spectacular, is afforded by organisms having an odd number of chromosomes, such as various mutants of *Œnothera* or *Datura* (p. 942), the males of many insects (p. 751), or individuals having supernumerary chromosomes (p. 872).   The validity of the conceptions of synapsis and disjunction is thus fully demonstrated; for obviously the "reduction-division" is not properly such but only the separation of two associated synaptic mates (p. 505).

2. Order of the Divisions

In the foregoing pages no attempt has been made to discuss the order of succession of the reduction- and the equation-divisions.   An answer to

---

[1] *Cf.* also Robertson.   [2] Certain exceptions to this statement are considered at pp. 847, 852.
[3] All pollen grains with less than twelve seem to be abortive.

this long-disputed question must obviously rest upon our means of identification of the reduction-division and, as will be evident from the foregoing,
*such identification can only be made with complete certainty in cases where the
synaptic mates are visibly distinguishable* by differences of form, size, structure, or mode of attachment. A sufficient number of such cases are now
known to demonstrate that *the two divisions do not in all cases follow the
same order, and that even in the same division the bivalents may differ individually in this respect.* Weismann's early assumption that the first division, considered as a whole, is equational, and the second reductional ("post-reduction") led to a tedious controversy as to the order of the two divisions.
Weismann's conclusions were adopted by Rückert, Haecker, Van der
Stricht, Griffin, McClung and many others. The reverse order ("pre-
reduction") was advocated by Henking, Korschelt, Paulmier and Montgomery, and ultimately by Strasburger, Mottier, Farmer and Moore, the
Schreiners and most of the later students of the problem. As recently
as 1910 Grégoire, in an important review, leaned strongly towards the
conclusion that pre-reduction would prove to be the prevailing and perhaps
the universal order of division. This conclusion was based especially on
the conclusion that the first division takes place through the "primary"
longitudinal cleft of the bivalent, and that this represents the plane of
parasynaptic conjugation on either side of which lie the homologous conjugants or synaptic mates. This interpretation seemed to be supported
by the strong tendency of the two primary halves to early separation (as
early emphasized by Flemming) and the consequent formation of rings,
crosses and other peculiar forms.

There is some strong additional special evidence in favor of a general
pre-reduction. In the haploid *Datura* mutants or in male Hymenoptera,
as indicated above (p. 572) it is obviously the first division that represents
the reduction-division. In the heteromorphic tetrads of *Trimerotropis*
and other Orthoptera, it is always the first division in which disjunction
of the synaptic mates occurs (p. 933). In 15-chromosome mutants of
Œnothera (*lata* type, p. 944) or in 25-chromosome mutants of *Datura*
(p. 944), it seems to be always the first division in which the unequal distribution occurs.

Nevertheless it is certain that this order is not invariable, as is proved
especially by the sex-chromosomes. The heteromorphic XY-pair, for example, always divides pre-reductionally in Coleoptera and Diptera, so far
as known, while in the Hemiptera heteroptera, it follows the reverse order.
The same is true with the unpaired X-chromosome (p. 756). A remarkable
demonstration of such differences is seen in the heteropter *Metapodius*,
where, in the first spermatocyte-division, the *m*-chromosome pair and the

XY-pair may be seen side-by-side in the same mitosis, the former manifestly dividing reductionally, the latter equationally. Finally, in the grasshopper *Phrynotettix* one of the heteromorphic bivalents ("pair C") was found by Wenrich ('16) to divide in either order, even in the same individual.

From the foregoing we may conclude that pre-reduction probably constitutes the general rule, but that changes in the order may readily occur. In such cases both divisions may be of mixed type, and the old distinction between the reduction- and the equation-divisions can only apply to the tetrads considered individually. This fact, evidently, has an important bearing on the genetics of parthenogenetic animals (p. 962). In practice, however, it is often difficult to distinguish between the "primary" and "secondary" clefts of the tetrads and hence between the reduction-division and the equational. In the formation of the double crosses for instance, both clefts open out nearly or quite at the same time, though from opposite ends (p. 523); so that in the fully formed cross it is often impossible to distinguish certainly between the two. The case is precisely similar with the double rings (p. 527) which arise by the opening out of the primary cleft in one-half of the original rod, of the secondary cleft in the other; or in case of the transverse rod-tetrad (which is equivalent to a double cross devoid of lateral arms). The Schreiners ('06, *Tomopteris*), Montgomery ('11, *Euschistus*), Robertson ('16, *Syrbula*) and most others have concluded that the original quadruple rod opens out along the primary cleft, the resulting "cross-division" being reductional. Wenrich ('16) on the other hand produces some evidence in grasshoppers (*Phrynotettix*) in favor of the contrary conclusion that the primary cleft closes up while the secondary one opens so that the "cross-division" is here equational. It is entirely possible that both sides are right and that different species may vary in this respect as they undoubtedly do in the order of the divisions (p. 572).

V. INDIRECT EVIDENCE. GENERAL ASPECTS. SUMMARY

The general conception of synapsis and reduction is supported indirectly by a great body of indirect evidence, of which the cumulative force is irresistible and leads us to the confident expectation that the remaining difficulties will sooner or later be overcome. The most convincing of this evidence includes the size-differences and pairing of the chromosomes in the diploid groups, and their relation to the tetrads; the chromosomes of hybrids; the history of the sex-chromosomes; and the cycle of the chromosomes in the antithetic alternation of generations of plants. Since these phenomena will be more fully considered hereafter we will here only briefly emphasize a few of the more important facts. Prominent among them is the fact that in some plants and animals, notably in Diptera, the synaptic mates of the diploid groups are arranged in pairs in the somatic or diploid divisions (Fig. 396). In some of these cases, as shown especially by Metz ('14, '16), the synaptic mates of each pair are so closely associated in the somatic pro-phases as to appear exactly like the products of longitudinal fission in the spireme-threads; and they have actually been described as such by some observers, but this proved to be an error (p. 837). The fact that paternal and maternal homologues may pair so closely, side-by-side, when in the

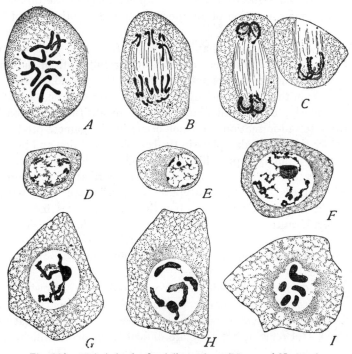

Fig. 281.—Meiosis in the fly *Asilus sericeus* (METZ and NONIDEZ).

A, spermatogonial metaphase, 10 chromosomes; B, last spermatogonial anaphase, pairing of the chromosomes; C, succeeding telophase, close pairing; D, E, spermatocytes, stage a (resting stage); F, early stage of the five bivalents; G, the same, pachytene, five polarized bivalents; H, late prophase of first spermatocyte; I, first spermatocyte-metaphase.

form of long spireme-threads, meets all those *a priori* objections that might be urged against the theory of parasynapsis. That this process as seen in the somatic mitoses is actually comparable to a parasynapsis is shown by Metz and Nonidez ('21) in *Asilus*. Here the chromosomes retain their paired disposition in the final spermatogonial anaphases (as is often the case also in earlier anaphases) and enter the telophases in close association (Fig. 281), then passing into the "resting" conditions (Stage *b*). From this stage *they emerge in the form of typical pachytene-bivalents of the haploid number* (Stage *g*), Stages *c*, *d*, *e*, and *f*, including the leptonema and synaptic stages, being omitted. Here, evidently, pseudo-reduction is initiated by an anaphasic parasynapsis, similar in principle to the anaphasic or telophasic conjugation assumed by Montgomery (p. 558). It seems, therefore, a reasonable view that in animals generally the paired union of chromosomes in synapsis is usually long delayed, but may be foreshadowed by a more or less definite paired association that takes place early in the diploid cycle, thus giving some suggestion of an approach to the zygotic type of meiosis (p. 491).

Another striking fact is that true tetrad-formation and heterotypic mitosis are seen only in bivalent chromosomes resulting from the union of synaptic mates, and hence does not take place in the haploid phase of organisms but only in the diploid, however brief the latter may be. It is for this reason obviously, that in all plants having an antithetic alternation of generations tetrad-formation does not occur in the gamete-producing divisions, since the latter takes place in the haploid generation and by a simple mitosis of the ordinary type, while heterotypic mitosis appears only in the diploid generation during the process of spore-formation (pp. 491, 619). So-called "tetrads" and "heterotypical mitosis," have, it is true, been described in the somatic mitoses; but these appearances have a totally different significance from that so manifest in the meiotic divisions. They do not result from a process of synapsis; they do not lead to a reduction of chromosome-number; and they divide through only one of the tetrad-sutures (p. 904).

In conclusion it may be said that a vast and always growing body of data, both cytological and genetic, supports the general conclusions drawn by Weismann thirty-five years ago. Some perplexing cytological difficulties, indeed, still remain; but they are difficulties of detail which, we may confidently expect, will sooner or later be cleared up. The most obvious effect of meiosis is to sort out the diploid chromosome-group into two haploid ones. Karyogamy and meiosis are thus opposite and complementary processes; but it must be borne in mind that the haploid groups brought together by karyogamy do not remain long separate as such (gonomery), since the paternal and maternal chromosomes soon become indistinguishably mingled; nevertheless the diploid chromosome-group as a whole, when once established, is maintained intact by mitosis throughout the whole diploid cycle.

Meiosis brings about two additional results, less obvious but fundamentally important. One is to establish *new haploid combinations* of the original maternal and paternal chromosomes in the germ-cells. The genetic evidence demonstrates that the haploid groups produced by meiosis are in most cases not purely maternal or paternal (though they may be so). Most of them represent regroupings of the original chromosomes, always such as to retain the essential character of the haploid group but differing in respect to the parental source of the individual chromosomes (Fig. 105). This reorganization of the haploid groups results from a very simple mechanism later to be considered (p. 927).

Not less important is the reorganization of the chromosomes, individually considered, that takes place during meiosis, by means of " crossing-over," *i. e.*, of orderly exchanges of material between the synaptic mates during the period of their association. This process, thus far certainly known only from the genetic evidence, is of unknown physiological significance. As earlier mentioned, and will later be shown in greater detail (p. 956), crossing over is often of such a type as to render both divisions of a given tetrad in part reductional, in part equational (*i. e.*, in the so-called " two-strand chiasma," Fig. 451). In such cases both divisions are necessary for complete reduction of the chromosome-components, and the distinction between reductional and equational division *of the chromosomes as such* cannot strictly be maintained. This, however, leaves untouched the fact that in the processes of meiosis lies the explanation of the main phenomena of Mendelian heredity, including segregation, random assortment of the linkage-groups and recombination by "crossing-over," as will be more fully indicated in Chapter XII.

LITERATURE VI

(See also IV, V, VII, X, XI. For abbreviations see General Literature List.)

Agar, W. E., '11. The Spermatogenesis of *Lepidosiren:* Q. J., LVII.

Dalc, A., '21. La spermatogénèse chez l'Orvet (*Anguis*): A. B., XXXI.

Davis, H. S., '03. Spermatogenesis of Acrididæ and Locustidæ: B. M. Z., LII.

Digby, L., '10. The somatic, premeiotic and meiotic nuclear Divisions of *Galtonia candicans: A. Bot.*, XXIV.

Farmer and **Moore,** '05. The Meiotic Phase in Animals and Plants: Q. J., XLVIII.

Fick, R., '06. Vererbungsfragen, Reduktionstheilung, etc.: E. A. E., XVI.

Gates, R. R., '08. A Study on Reduction in *Œnothera rubrinervis:* B. G., XLVI.

Gates and **Rees,** '21. A cytological Study of Pollen Development in *Lactuca*: A. Bot., XXXV.

Gelei, J., '21, '22. Weitere Studien über die Oögenese von *Dendrocœlum*, II, III: A. Zf., XVI, 1, 3.

Granata, L., '10. Le cinesi spermatogenetiche di *Pamphagus marmoratus: A. Zf.*, V.

Grégoire, V., '05. Les resultats acquis sur les cinèses de maturation dans les deux régnes, I: L. C., XXII.

Grégoire, V., '10. Les cinèses de maturation dans les deux régnes: *Ibid.*, XXVI.

Henking, H., '91. Ueber Spermatogenese, etc., bei *Pyrrhocoris apterus: Z. W. Z.*, LI.

'92. Untersuchungen über die ersten Entwicklungsvorgänge in den Eiern von Insekten: *Ibid.*, LIV.

Hertwig, O., '90. Vergleich der Ei- und Samenbildung bei Nematoden. Eine Grundlage für cellulare Streitfragen: *A. M. A.*, XXXVI.

Janssens, F. A., '01. La spermatogénèse chez les *Tritons: L. C.*, XIX.

'05. Évolution des auxocytes mâles du *Batrachoseps attenuatus: Ibid.*, XXII.

Janssens, F. A., et Dumez, R., '03. L'élément nucleinien pendant les cinèses de maturation des spermatocytes chez *Batrachoseps attenuatus et Plethodon cinereus: L. C.*, XX.

Kœrnicke, M., '04, '05. Die neueren Arbeiten über die Chromosomen-Reduktion im Pflanzenreich und daran anschliessende Karyokinetische Probleme: *B. Z.*, LXII.

Maréchal, J., '07. Sur l'ovogénèse des Selachiens: *L. C.*, XXIV.

Matschek, H., '10. Ueber Eireifung und Eiablage bei Copepoden: *A. Zf.*, V.

McClung, C. E., '14. A Comparative Study of the Chromosomes in Orthopteran Spermatogenesis: *J. M.*, XXV.

Meves, F., '08. Es gibt keine parallele Konjugation der Chromosomen: *A. Zf.*, I.

Mohr, Otto L., '14. Studien über die Chromatinreifung der männlichen Geschlechtszellen bei *Locusta viridissima: A. B.*, XXIX.

Montgomery, T. H., '04. Some Observations and Considerations upon the Maturation Phenomena of the Germ Cells: *B. B.*, VI, 3.

Mottier, D. M., '05. The Development of the Heterotypic Chromosomes in Pollen Mother-cells: *B. G.*, XL.

'07. The Development of the Heterotype Chromosomes in Pollen Mother-cells: *A. B.*, XXI.

'09. On the Prophases of the Heterotypic Mitosis in the Embryo-sac Mother-cell of *Lilium; Ibid.*, XXIII.

'14. Mitosis in the Pollen Mother-cells of *Acer* and *Staphylea; A. B.*, XXVIII.

Platner, G., '89. Ueber die Bedeutung der Richtungskörperchen: *B. C.*, VIII.

Rückert, J., '92a. Zur Entwicklungsgeschichte des Ovarialeies bei Selachiern: *A. A.*, VII.

'92b. Ueber die Verdoppelung der Chromosomen im Keimbläschen des Selachiereies: *A. A.*, VIII.

'93. Die Chromatinreduktion der Chromosomenzahl im Entwicklungsgang der Organismen: *Merkel and Bonnet, Erg.*, III.

Schleip, W., '09. Vergl. Untersuchungen der Eireifung bei . . . Ostracoden: *A. Zf.*, II.

Schreiner, A. and K. E., '06a. Neue Studien über die Chromatinreifung der Geschlechtszellen. I. Die Reifung der männlichen Geschlechtszellen von *Tomopteris onisciformis: A. B.*, XXII.

'06b. II. Reifung der männlichen Geschlechtszellen von *Salamandra maculosa, Spinax niger* und *Myxine glitinosa: A. B.*, XXII.

'08. Gibt es eine parallelle Konjugation der Chromosomen?: *Videnskabs-Selskab. Skrifter.* I. *Math.-Natur. Klasse*, IV.

Stomps, T. J., '10. Kerndeeling en Synapsis bij *Spinacia:* See *B. C.*, XXXI.

Strasburger, E., '05. Typische und allotypische Kernteilung: *J. W. B.*, XLI.

Vejdovský, F., 07. Neue Untersuchungen über die Reifung und Befruchtung: *Königl. Böhmische Ges. d. Wiss., Prag.*

Wenrich, D. H., '16. The Spermatogenesis of *Phrynotettix magnus*, etc.: *B. M. Z.,* LX.

'17. Synapsis and Chromosome Organization in *Chorthippus (Stenobothrus) curtipinnis* and *Trimerotropis suffusa: J. M.,* XXIX.

Wilson, E. B., '12. (See X.) Studies on Chromosomes, VIII: *J. E. Z.,* XIII.

Winiwarter, H. de, '01. Recherches sur l'ovogénèse, etc.: *A. B.,* XVII.

Winiwarter and **Saintmont,** '09. Nouvelles recherches sur l'ovogénèse, etc.: *Ibid.,* XXIV.

CHAPTER VII

REPRODUCTION AND SEXUALITY IN LOWER ORGANISMS

Genealogical Considerations on Syngamy and Meiosis

"There is in Protozoa only one kind of reproduction, namely, cell-division."
R. Hertwig.[1]

We are accustomed to think of sexuality as forming an integral part of reproduction; and such, in fact, it has become in all higher animals. But already in the higher invertebrates, such as insects and crustaceans, and in almost all plants, we find asexual forms of reproduction as well as sexual; while in the *Protista* sexuality and reproduction appear as quite distinct, and in some respects opposite processes. The unicellular protistan has but one mode of multiplication, cell-division, in itself a purely asexual process; and the immediate effect of syngamy, obviously, is not to increase but to decrease the number of cells. The most that can be said is that syngamy in *Protista*, as in higher forms, may initiate a new cycle of growth and cell-division. The widespread occurrence of syngamy in unicellular organisms, and its evident similarity to that seen in higher forms, might be expected to throw light on the sexual processes of higher forms; and to a certain extent this is true. In practice, however, the process in Protista offers many difficulties, which often compel us to interpret the observed phenomena in a measure deductively in the light of our knowledge of higher forms.

In the Bacteria, Cyanophyceæ, and certain other low forms no sexual process has thus far been made known; but most of the main groups of Protista exhibit a process of syngamy effected by a union of gametes that show many degrees of differentiation and in some cases are as unlike as in higher plants and animals. The correlative process of meiosis likewise seems, in some Protista at least, to parallel very closely that seen in higher groups (p. 597). Finally, many of the Protista exhibit an alternation of sexual and asexual cycles analogous to the alternation of generations seen in higher organisms, though it is still unknown whether it is of the antithetic type, *i. e.*, an alternation between haploid and diploid forms.

The Protista have undergone innumerable modifications due to parasitism, degeneration, special adaptation and the like; and it is as difficult here to

---

[1] Arch. Protistenk., I.

distinguish between primitive and highly modified conditions as in higher forms. Nevertheless some of the sexual phenomena in Protista are evidently of simpler and more primitive type than those seen in higher forms, and in some measure help us towards a better understanding of the latter. Only a few illustrative facts can here be indicated; a full account of them would require a large volume.[1]

I. GENERAL SURVEY. TERMINOLOGY

Among unicellular organisms syngamy is accomplished by a process of *conjugation* in the course of which two cells unite, their nuclei fusing to form the nucleus of a zygote which may be considered as the starting point for a new cycle of growth and cell-division, as in multicellular forms. In the latter the cells belonging to each cycle combine to form a multicellular body; in the Protista they remain separate (though they may temporarily form colonies) each to lead an independent life as a physiological individual. *Morphologically*, therefore, the multicellular body may be compared to a succession or cycle of individual Protista. Physiologically the single protozoan is as truly an individual as the metazoan; but morphologically it is comparable both in structure and mode of origin to a single tissue-cell, or a single germ-cell, of a metazoan (pp. 101, 238).[2]

1. Types of Conjugation

In most Protista union of the gametes is complete and permanent, nuclear fusion or *karyogamy* being accompanied by complete protoplasmic fusion or *plastogamy*. In the ciliates, however, complete plastogamy does not take place, the two conjugants merely becoming temporarily united and undergoing an exchange of nuclei. Following the terminology of Bütschli these two types of syngamy are commonly designated respectively as "copulation" and "conjugation"; but it seems preferable to employ the self-explanatory terms *total* and *partial* conjugation. Conjugation is often exogamous, *i. e.*, takes place only between gametes of different ancestry; but there are many exceptions to this, and it is probable that strict exogamy is only one extreme of a series of conditions leading to *endogamy* and finally to *autogamy*. In *Paramœcium aurelia* Calkins ('02) found that descendants of the same cell not more than eight or nine divisions removed would con-

---

[1] See especially the general treatises of Calkins ('01, '09), Minchin ('12), Doflein ('16), West ('16), Oltmanns ('22, '23).

[2] This comparison, due primarily to Siebold (1845), was first clearly stated with reference to the reproductive cycle by Bütschli in 1876 (*cf.* p. 238). It has been widely accepted by modern students of protistology, for instance, by R. Hertwig, Schaudinn, Lang, Doflein, Calkins, Minchin and others, but has also encountered energetic opposition on the part of some writers, *e. g.*, A. Sedgwick ('94), Awerinzew ('10), Franz ('11), Dobell ('11, '14).

jugate (endogamy) and the offspring from such a zygote were able to live through a complete cycle of 379 bipartitions.[1] Carried to an extreme, endogamy becomes *autogamy*, in which the gametes are sister-cells, resulting from the division of a single mother-cell (*e. g.*, in *Actinophrys* or *Actinosphærium*, Fig. 282). In such cases the sister-cells (or nuclei) are known in some cases to undergo a process of meiosis before their reunion (p. 597); the zygote-nucleus, therefore, is not identical with the original mother-nucleus, having undergone a process of reorganization presumably involving a recombination of nuclear elements. As Hartmann has indicated ('09) autogamous conjugation is probably a secondary mode of union, possibly even a degenerate one, the primitive type having been exogamous.

2. Relation of the Gametes to the Vegetative Cells

In considering the structure of the gametes and their relation to the vegetative cells we find it necessary to enlarge the meaning of the term "gamete" as heretofore employed. In case of higher organisms generally we are accustomed to restrict this term to the germ-cells after completion of the meiotic or maturation process; but even here the sperm often enters before the egg has completed the process of meiosis and while it is technically a *gametocyte* (oöcyte). In the Protista, and even in some higher forms, the same is often true of both conjugants (*e. g.*, in ciliates), syngamy and meiosis being more closely associated than in higher forms. If then, we insist on restricting the term "gamete" to haploid conjugants we are driven to the conclusion that in some of the most familiar examples of conjugation true gametes do not exist. In this dilemma it seems preferable to adopt a more elastic usage, designating the conjugating cells as "gametes" whenever we find it convenient to do so, even at some cost of consistency. The difficulty, however, may be avoided by employing the word "conjugant."

In respect to the character of the conjugants, three main types may conveniently be distinguished among Protista:

a. Hologamy or *Macrogamy*. In this case the conjugants are of the same structural type as the original vegetative cells, and do not differ markedly from them in size or external appearance. This condition is seen in various flagellates, rhizopods, ciliates, diatoms, desmids and the Conjugatæ generally. Like the vegetative cells the conjugants may be flagellated, ciliated, amœboid or non-motile, and are often indistinguishable in appearance from the corresponding vegetative cells. In most of these cases, the conjugants are isogamous (*e. g.*, in most diatoms, desmids, Zygnemaceæ, ciliate Infusoria), in others more or less unequal in size (anisogamy) though still

---

[1] Enriques ('08), states that ex-conjugants that have not yet divided may immediately proceed to conjugate again.

structurally alike. This condition is illustrated by certain species of *Spirogyra* (Fig. 283), or by the vorticellid Infusoria. In the latter case different species show anisogamy in various degrees, the microgamete or "male" being a smaller, free-swimming cell of the same general type as the larger attached macrogamete or "female," save that the stalk is absent (Fig. 304). Even when hologamous gametes are alike or closely similar in appearance

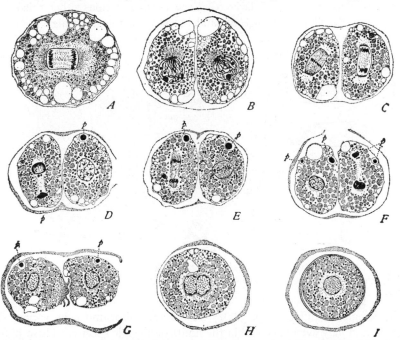

Fig. 282.—Gamete-formation, meiosis and autogamous conjugation in the rhizopod *Actinophrys* (BĚLAŘ).

A, the progamic mitosis, producing two diploid conjugants; *B*, the latter in the polarized synaptic stage; *C*, the first meiotic division, producing in each conjugant (*D*) the first polar nucleus (*p*); *E*, second division; *F*, the two resulting haploid gametes each with two polar nuclei; *G*, *H*, conjugation; *I*, resulting zygote.

they often display definite physiological differences that become evident at the time of conjugation (pp. 585, 586).

b. Merogamy or *Microgamy*. In this type, widely distributed among unicellular organisms and in lower plants, the gametes are much smaller than the vegetative cells, more or less widely different from them in structural type, and commonly motile. They arise from cells of the ordinary vegetative type by a rapid series of divisions, the size of the merogametes thus produced varying with the number of divisions. For instance, in the flagellate *Polytoma uvella* but two such divisions typically take place, giving rise to four relatively large gametes (Dangeard); in *Sphærella* the mother-cell produces 32–64 much smaller gametes; while in such rhizopods as *Polystomella* or *Trichosphærium* the number of the division is still larger, and the gametes correspondingly more minute [1] (Fig. 284). In some cases they are amœboid (*Arcella, Centropyxis,* some *Sporozoa*); more commonly they are flagellated and actively free-swimming, a condition seen in Foraminifera (*Polystomella*), Radiolaria (*Collozoum*), and various other rhizopods; in certain flagellates (*Mastigella*); and in many of the green algæ (*Ulothrix, Cladophora, Pandorina,* etc.). Many of these cases seem to be perfectly isogamous (*e. g.,* in Foraminifera, *Ulothrix, Ulva*), but here, too, often are

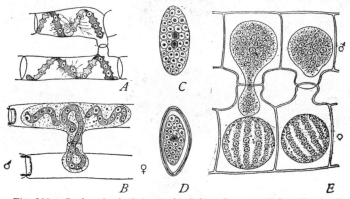

Fig. 283.—Conjugation in *Spirogyra* (*A–D* from OVERTON, *E* from OLTMANS).

A, B, union of the gametes in *S. communis; C, D,* the resulting zygote; *E,* the gametes in *S. heeriana.*

physiologically different (p. 585). Others are anisogamous in various degrees, and may even vary within the limits of a single species. These differences no doubt depend in part on the number of divisions in the mother-cell; but may in part be due to variation in the size of the latter.

c. Heterogamy. A third type, connected with the foregoing by intermediate conditions, is true *heterogamy,* analogous to that seen in the higher forms. The gametes are here widely different from each other and often also from the vegetative cells, the macrogamete (now called the ovum) being of the hologamic type, often larger than the vegetative cells and almost always non-motile, while the sperm is merogamic, and typically has the form of a minute actively motile flagellated cell. In such cases the macrogametes are often called "female," the microgametes "male," but these terms are misleading, since even in higher forms it is inadvisable to speak of the gametes as possessing sex (p. 818). This condition is ex-

---

[1] In the algæ the size of the asexual zoöspores shows similar variations, due to the same cause, sometimes within a single species (*Ulothrix*).

emplified by such forms as *Œdogonium* (Fig. 306), *Volvox* (Fig. 291), *Vaucheria* or *Fucus*. It is not impossible, as Minchin has indicated, that the heterogamic type has arisen from the merogamic by "progressive, and finally complete, inhibition of the divisions that produce the swarm-spores in one sex — possibly also with an enhanced tendency to such divisions in the other sex " ('12, p. 172).

3. Physiological Differences of the Gametes

It is a fact of fundamental interest for the theory of sex that in many lower organisms definite physiological differences often exist between gametes

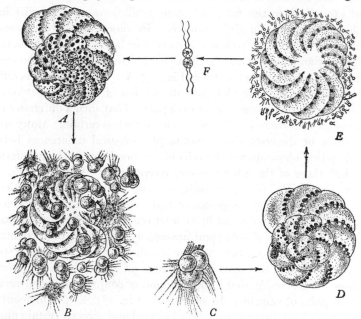

Fig. 284.—Life-cycle with alternation of generations in the rhizopod *Polystomella crispa* (from HARTMANN, after SCHAUDINN and LANG).

A, microspheric (asexual) generation or agamont; *B*, same, producing the asexual agametes, *C; D* macrospheric (sexual) generation or gamont, producing (*E*) biflagellate gametes; *F*, conjugation of the gametes.

which structurally, so far as we can see, are perfectly isogamous. This is seen in both exogamous and endogamous forms. An interesting example of the latter case is seen in the heliozoan rhizopod *Actinophrys*, in which the gametes are sister-cells. Bělař ('21, '23) has shown that although the two gametes are structurally alike one remains a passive rounded cell, while the other puts forth towards the passive gamete a group of pointed pseudopods which play the leading rôle in the subsequent fusion (Fig. 282).

In other isogamous forms exogamy seems to be strictly obligatory, *i. e.*, gametes from the same immediate source will not conjugate with one another, though they conjugate readily with gametes from a different source. For example, in the rhizopod *Polystomella*, a perfectly isogamous, merogamic form, Schaudinn states that only gametes of different parentage will conjugate with one another; and the same is true, according to Dodel and Klebs, of the isogamous flagellated gametes of the simple alga *Ulothrix* (Fig. 287).

Various interesting conditions exist among the green algæ and the fungi. In the group Zygnemaceæ exogamy is the rule, conjugation usually taking place between the cells of different filaments (Fig. 285, D); but there are important exceptions to this rule, and many gradations seem to exist in the physiological specification of the gametes. In some species of *Zygnema*, for example, they show no difference of structure or behavior, both gametes being migratory and meeting halfway between the two conjugating filaments to form a zygote in the connecting tube (Fig. 285, A). In this case it is difficult to determine whether a physiological distinction of sex exists between the two filaments or the two gametes of each pair. That such a difference exists in other isogamous forms in this group is nevertheless certain. Many species of *Spirogyra* or *Zygnema* show definite physiological differences between the conjugating filaments, all the cells of the one being actively migratory or "male," those of the other passive, receptive, or "female" (Fig. 285). In these cases "male" filaments conjugate only with "female" and the filaments may appropriately be spoken of as diœcious. Most such species are morphologically isogamous, but in at least one case (*Spirogyra tenuissima*) a considerable degree of structural anisogamy is said to be recognizable, the male gamete being smaller than the female (Fig. 285, F). Some species that usually show a well-marked difference of sexual behavior now and then show "cross-conjugation," the direction of conjugation being reversed by certain pairs of gametes. In such cases (Fig. 285, E) the filament as a whole is physiologically to some extent bisexual and shows a certain analogy to the hermaphroditic condition of higher forms, though the cells may individually be "male" or "female." Finally, at the opposite extreme from the exogamous forms are strictly endogamous species, such as *Spirogyra longata* (Fig. 285, C) in which the adjoining cells of the same filament unite by "lateral" conjugation, through a connecting tube formed between each pair, a condition which offers perhaps an analogy to the self-fertilizing types of hermaphrodites in certain higher plants and animals (*e. g.*, in some of the cestodes and nematodes).[1]   In *Spirogyra inflata*, and a few others both

---

[1] Many hermaphrodites in higher forms are strictly exogamous. A remarkable example of this is offered by the ascidians, in which the eggs are fertilized in the sea-water and are infertile to sperms of the same individual though readily fertilizable by the sperms of any other individual (p. 421).

lateral and the ordinary or "scalariform" types of fertilization occur; and in this or a nearly related species Cunningham ('17) [1] found all three modes, the most common being the typical exogamous scalariform process, in which

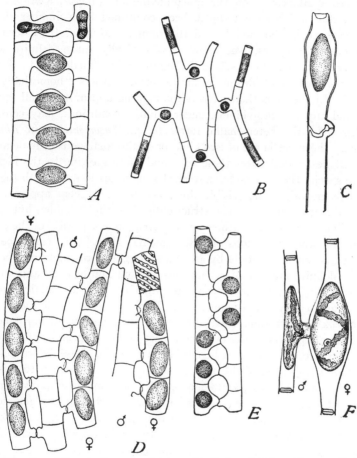

Fig. 285.—Sex-relations in the conjugate algæ. (*A*, *B*, *C*, and *E* from HASSALL, *D*, *F*, from WEST.)

A, *Zygnema stagnalis*, "scalariform" conjugation; *B*, *Debarya nummuloides* with several conjugating filaments; *C*, *Spirogyra quadratum*, with "lateral" conjugation; *D*, *Spirogyra nitida*, several conjugants showing sexuality of the filaments; *E*, *Zygnema insignis*, "cross-conjugation"; *F*, *Spirogyra tenuissima*, with slight anisogamy.

conjugation takes place in only one direction; but both lateral and cross-conjugation are occasionally found, sometimes in the same pair of filaments. These facts suggest that in this group of algæ as a whole the distinction

[1] This author has given a useful review and critique of the literature.

between the bisexual and unisexual condition, and possibly also that between the sexes, has not yet become very firmly established.

Phenomena of analogous type have been made known by the illuminating researches of Blakeslee,[1] on the mucorine moulds (*Mucor, Rhizopus, Phycomyces*, etc.) which have recently been confirmed by a number of other observers both in the moulds and the smuts.[2] Most of these forms are structurally isogamous, but show physiologically quite definite sexual characteristics, some species being "heterothallic" (analogous to the diœcious or unisexual condition in higher forms) others "homothallic" or bisexual. In the homothallic forms the mycelia appear to be all sexually alike, and any two individuals, under suitable conditions, may conjugate together. In the heterothallic forms (*e. g.*, *Mucor mucedo* or *Rhizopus nigricans*) the mycelia are of two kinds or strains analogous to male and female. Blakeslee designates these as + and – forms, owing to the fact that in some species the + form has a somewhat more luxuriant growth than the –; though in others no visible difference between them appears. The two strains produce gametes structurally indistinguishable, but the + forms will conjugate only with – and *vice versa*, independently of the culture medium or other conditions of environment. If the two strains be kept separate and cultivated only by asexual sporangiospores they may be bred for an indefinite number of generations without conjugation and without modification of their sexual type; but when the two are finally brought together again they readily conjugate. The two strains must therefore be characterized by constant sexual differences, though often no morphological sign of them appears in the external aspect of the mycelia or the gametes which they produce.[3] We are here led to suspect that these differences may lie in the organization of the nuclei, such as are now known to exist between the male-producing and female-producing gametes of many animals; and (in at least two cases) between the male-producing and female-producing spores of plants (p. 746). These differences are in some cases known to be quantitative (p. 812), which points to a similar type of sexual difference in these lower plants. To a certain extent this is borne out by the experiments of Blakeslee and his collaborators on *Mucor* and *Cunninghameila*[4] which indicate that the strength of the + and – sexual activity in different races varies markedly in degree. In *Cunninghamella* there appears to be a graded series in this respect, ranging from "sexually strong" races down to those that are "sexually weak," perhaps even

---

[1] '03, '04, '06, '15, '20, etc.
[2] See Burgeff ('14–'15) on *Phycomyces*, Kniep ('19) on *Ustilago*.
[3] *Cf.* Chapter X.
[4] Blakeslee ('20), Blakeslee, Cartledge and Welch ('21).

to sexually neutral forms which thus far have shown no tendency to conjugate.[1]

4. Structure of the Gametes

Gametes of the hologamic type require no special description; they have in general the same structure—flagellated, amœboid, or non-motile—as the

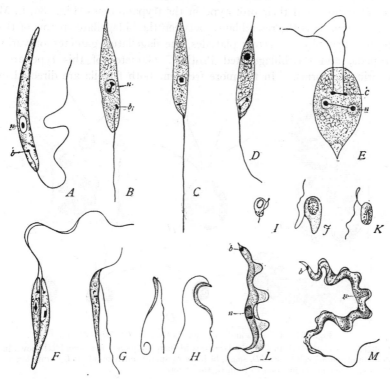

Fig. 286.—Some gametes and gamete-like flagellates.

A, Leptomonas jaculum (LÉGER); *B–E*, stages of longitudinal fission in *Leishmannia* (WENYON); *F*, final stage of fission in *Leptomonas* (LÉGER); *G, Bodo gracilis* (STEIN); *H*, microgametes of *Coccidium* (SCHAUDINN); *I*, microgametes of the radiolarian *Collozoum* (R. HERTWIG); *J*, macrogamete, and *K*, agamic swarmspore of same; *L, Trypanosoma tincæ* and *M, Trypanosoma granulosum* (MINCHIN).

vegetative cells of the species. The most interesting of such gametes occur in the flagellates; for the widespread occurrence of flagellated gametes in plants and animals generally leads to the conclusion that these probably

---

[1] Some observers have considered such gradations as sex-intergrades (*cf.* Burger, '19, etc.), but the work of Blakeslee and others indicates that they should not be so considered. There is, however, some evidence that true intergrades may exist in some of these fungi. (See Blakeslee, Cartledge and Welch, *op. cit.*)

represent the most primitive form; and many of the principal forms of flagellated sperms are paralleled with astonishing closeness among the adult forms of existing flagellates. The ordinary uniflagellated animal sperm is represented by various uniflagellated species, in particular by slender and elongated forms, such as *Leptomonas* or *Herpetomonas* (Fig. 286). Sperms that are provided with undulatory membranes, such as those of *Bombinator* or *Darwinia*, find their prototype in the trypanosomes (Fig. 286, L, M). Not less striking is the resemblance between the biflagellate sperms of thallophytes, bryophytes, certain platodes, the flagellated gametes of various rhizopods, and the biflagellated Protista. Gametes of this type are of two principal forms. In the more frequent both flagella are directed for-

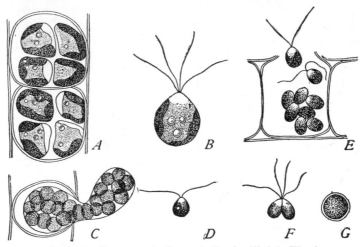

Fig. 287.—Gametes and zoöspores in the alga *Ulothrix* (WEST).

A, division of mother-cell to form the large quadriciliate zoöspores (macrogonidia) shown in *B; C*, division of mother-cell to form *D*, small, biciliate zoöspores (microgonidia); *E*, formation of the biciliate gametes; *F*, conjugation to form *G*, the zygote.

wards; this is seen in the rhizopods (*Polystomella, Trichosphærium, Paramœba*), in certain Sporozoa (*Aggregata*), and is widely prevalent in the green algæ (*Volvocaceæ, Ulothrix, Bryopsis*, etc.), where the gametes are closely similar to the sexual zoöspores or swarmers (Figs. 287, 290). In a second type, exemplified in various brown algæ (*Fucus, Cutleria*) one flagellum is directed forwards while the other trails behind (Fig. 311). Both these types also are paralleled by the adult or vegetative form of flagellates. The first type, with two forwards-directed flagella, is seen in such forms as *Chlamydomonas, Polytoma* or *Spongomonas* (four flagella are present in some forms, Figs. 290, 292). The second type, with one forward and one trailing flagellum is seen in *Bodo, Trypanoplasma,*

Trypanosoma, and their allies, and by a modification of this are formed such sperms as those of *Coccidium* (Fig. 286,H) with one anterior and one posterior flagellum. The resemblance is heightened by the fact that in flagellates generally the flagellum (or flagella) is attached at its base to a basal granule or *blepharoplast* from which it grows forth during its formation and which is, in some cases at least, identical with a central body and division-center (p. 690). The parallel between the flagellated gametes and the asexual swarmers or "zoöspores," which occur in certain rhizopods and Sporozoa and in many of the lower algæ, is even more striking; they possess, indeed, the same essential internal structure and may even be indistinguishable externally.[1] These resemblances point to the derivation of gametes from asexual zoöspores and more remotely from flagellated Protista. The most primitive forms, as has been indicated especially by Strasburger ('92, '00) are commonly isogamous, *e. g.*, *Ulothrix* (Fig. 287), *Carteria*

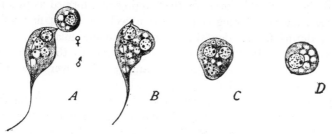

Fig. 288.—Fertilization in the gregarine *Stylorhynchus* (LÉGER).
A, pyriform sperm attached to the small spheroidal ovum; *B*, *C*, plastogamy; *D*, zygote.

(Fig. 290) or *Hydrodictyon*. These forms are more or less pear-shaped and pointed at one end at or near which are borne two flagella. Such gametes commonly contain a chromotophore and also a red "eye-spot" or "stigma" both of which are probably to be regarded as plastids or products of such bodies. The clear anterior region from which the flagella arise is considered by Strasburger to be largely composed of "kinoplasm" ; and in the case of the closely analogous swarm-spores a localized blepharoplast may often be seen at the base of the flagella, (Strasburger, '92, '00, Timberlake, '02, etc.). In some cases the gametes contain pulsating vacuoles (*Hydrodictyon*, according to Klebs) as is also the case in certain zoöspores. A good example of micro-gametes of this type is offered by *Sphæroplea*, save that the flagella are attached at some distance from the anterior end. In Volvox (Fig. 291) the sperms are similar. This gives a transition to the type seen in *Cutleria* (Fig. 311) and other forms, where the two flagella are attached at one side

[1] Strasburger ('92, '00), Dangeard ('99), Timberlake ('02), Davis ('02, '04), West ('16), Oltmanns ('22, '23).

of the cell, or *Vaucheria*, where one is attached near the anterior end, the other backwards, reminding us of such flagellates as *Bodo* (Fig. 286, G). In the Charales appears a type of biflagellate sperm that is closely similar to that characteristic of the bryophytes generally (p. 307), and parallel to those of certain Turbellaria.

The transition from isogamy to heterogamy is shown by various intermediate stages in the simpler forms of both animals and plants, particularly in the merogamic Protozoa and in various groups of algæ. Among the merogamic rhizopods some forms are perfectly isogamous (*Polystomella, Trichosphærium*), others anisogamous in various degrees (*Arcella, Collozoum*) (Fig. 286, I, K). In Sporozoa nearly all gradations exist between complete isogamy (*Gregarina*) and a typical heterogamy such as appears in *Coccidium;* but many of these forms are non-flagellate. Here may be mentioned the case of *Basidiobilus* (one of the phycomycetes) as described by Fairchild ('97). In this form the two conjugants, formed as bud-like protuberances from neighboring cells of the mycelium, are at first alike (Fig. 289), but during fertilization the "female" gamete enlarges greatly, and after reception of the "male" nucleus gives rise to the zygote ("zygospore"). Here we see an original isogamy passing over into anisogamy during the act of fertilization.

The most complete series of transitional forms is seen among the algæ, exemplified by the series *Carteria, Monostroma, Pandorina, Bryopsis* (Fig. 290) and *Aphanochæte* (Fig. 292). In the last-named form the macrogamete, formed singly in the mother-cell (oögonium) is still flagellated but has lost the free-swimming habit, moving but feebly within its surrounding capsule and coming to rest as soon as fertilized. It is but a step from this condition to true heterogamy, where the egg has lost its flagella, is non-motile, and is fertilized without discharge from the oögonium. The latter condition, of widespread occurrence in lower plants, is exemplified by *Eudorina, Volvox, Vaucheria, Coleochæte, Fucus*, etc., and occurs in typical form in the coccidian Sporozoa. A curious exception to the usual rule in heterogamy is offered by the flagellate *Mastigella vitrea*, where, according to Goldschmidt ('07), the microgamete is non-motile, the macrogamete flagellated.

Attention has earlier been drawn to the widespread presence of plastids in the eggs of plants (p. 306). In the algæ plastids are commonly present in the gametes of both sexes, and also in the closely similar asexual swarmers or zoöspores. For example, in *Cutleria*, according to Yamanouchi ('12), the zoöspore contains upwards of 20 plastids, the macrogametes 30 or more, the microgametes usually but two (Fig. 311). In each the motile germ-cell contains a red stigma or "eye-spot." This structure appears in the motile zoöspores and gametes of many other algæ (*e. g.*, in *Ulothrix, Ectocar-*

pus and *Pandorina*) and also in the microgametes of various forms, such as *Eudorina, Volvox,* or *Fucus*.[1] From the bryophytes upwards plastids seem to be present only in the egg.

All these facts tell in favor of the view that the gametes of plants were originally flagellated, motile cells, closely similar to zoöspores and to the phytoflagellates. The existing types of hologamic non-flagellates, gametes such as appear in the diatoms, desmids and other Conjugatæ, have probably

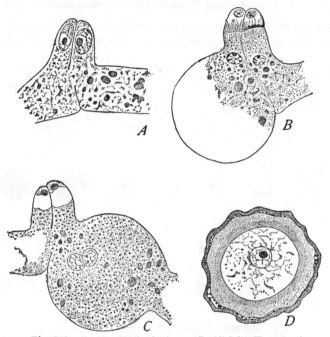

Fig. 289.—Fertilization in the fungus *Basidiobolus* (FAIRCHILD).

A, the two conjugants associated; *B*, two small sterile cells cut off, enlargement of one gamete; *C*, karyogamy; *D*, the zygote.

been derived secondarily from flagellated forms. A similar conclusion is indicated for animals, though the evidence is here less extensive.

In true heterogamous forms the macrogamete becomes a large, non-motile cell, essentially of the same type as in higher plants, but often highly colored through the presence of pigmented plastids or chromatophores. The microgametes or sperms are most commonly biflagellate and of varied type. In *Fucus* Retzius ('06) showed that the biflagellate sperm contains a "nebenkern-organ" apparently comparable to that seen in the middle-piece of certain types of animal sperms (p. 287); and the more recent work

[1] See especially Oltmanns ('22, '23).

of Meves ('18) establishes the correctness of this comparison by showing that it is composed of chondriosomes. Non-motile microgametes are found in the red algæ in the form of small, colorless, spheroidal, uni-nucleated cells constricted off from the vegetative cells and known as *spermatia;* and non-motile forms are all but universal among fungi. In many cases, however, the homology of the "gametes" of fungi is doubtful.

5. Gametes and Gametocytes. Cœnogametes

In certain Protista, and even in some of the multicellular plants, a preliminary conjugation takes place between cells that are not yet gametes

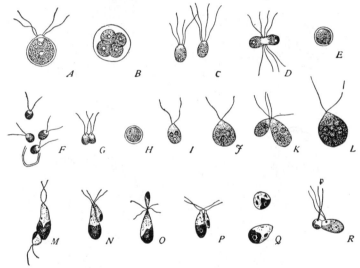

Fig. 290.—Isogamy and anisogamy in algæ.

A–E, isogamy in *Carteria* (West); *F–H,* anisogamy in *Monostroma; I–L,* anisogamy in *Phyllobium; M–Q,* anisogamy in *Bryopsis* (Oltmans); *R,* in *Pandorina* (Klebs).

A, vegetative cell; *B,* its division to form *C* the gametes; *D,* syngamy; *E,* zygote; *H,* zygote; *I,* microgamete; *J,* macrogamete; *K,* syngamy; *L,* zoöspore (zygote); *M–P,* various forms of syngamy; *Q,* zygotes.

in the strict sense but *gametocytes* which later give rise by division to the true gametes or gamete-nuclei. This is mostly clearly shown, perhaps, by the phenomenon in the gregarines, where conjugation is typically of this form, the primary union taking place between two "sporonts" or "gametes" (gametocytes) which become closely associated and inclosed in a common cyst but without fusion ("pseudo-conjugation"). The nucleus of each gametocyte now divides successively to form a number (often very large) of gamete-nuclei which pass to the periphery and here are budded off, together with a small quantity of protoplasm, to form minute true gametes.

The latter then unite two by two, one member of each pair being derived from each of the original conjugants, as is made evident in the anisogamous forms. The distinction between the gametocytes and the true gametes is here obvious; and it is also evident that the original "pseudo-conjugation" of the gametocytes is no more than a prelimary to the true syngamy of the gametes.[1]

Closely analogous to this are the phenomena in some of the fungi, where the primary conjugants are large cells which are multinuclear like the mycelium from which they arise, and constitute the so-called *cœnogametes*. In *Mucor* they are nearly or quite isogamous and fuse completely. In *Pyronema* and *Albugo* they are unequal, the male conjugant ("antherid-

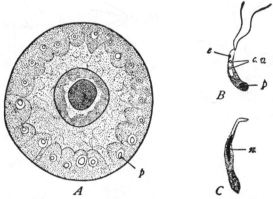

Fig. 291.—Germ-cells of *Volvox* (OVERTON).

A, Ovum (oösphere) containing a large central nucleus and a peripheral layer of chromatophores (plastids); *p*, pyrenoid; *B*, spermatozoid; *c*, *v*, contractile vacuoles; *e*, "eye-spot" (chromoplastid); *p*. pyrenoid, *C*, spermatozoid stained to show the nucleus (*n*).

ium") being much smaller than the female ("oögonium"), and sending into the latter an in-growing "antheridial" tube, the contents of which enter the oögonium. In *Pyronema* the numerous nuclei which it contains conjugate two by two with those of the oögonium (Fig. 293), and the same is true in some species of *Albugo*. In *A. candida*, on the other hand, only a single antheridial nucleus enters and conjugates with one nucleus of the oögonium, and the remaining nuclei ultimately disappear (Fig. 294).[2] Analogous to this are the phenomena in the ciliates, where each conjugant produces at least five nuclei, and sometimes a larger number, of which only two take part in conjugation (p. 609). In all these cases, evidently, the

[1] All doubt concerning this interpretation seems to be removed by Nusbaum's ('03) observations on *Schaudinella*, where pseudo-conjugation of the gametocytes does not take place, though the gametes are formed as usual.

[2] See Harper ('00), Stevens ('99, '01), review in Davis ('04).

original conjugants can be called gametes only by courtesy; and even in case of the animal ovum the sperm often enters before the polar divisions have been formed while the egg is still technically a gametocyte or oöcyte (p. 398).

6. The Chromidial Formation of Gametes. Chromidiogamy

A remarkable phenomenon said to occur in certain Protista is the formation of gamete-nuclei from chromidia extruded from the nuclei, or even, it is said in certain cases, a union of chromidia from the two conjugant-nuclei without preliminary formation of gamete-nuclei. The first of these condi-

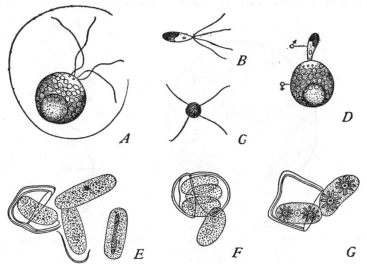

Fig. 292.—Reproduction in green algæ (*A–D*, from HUBER; *E–G*, from DeBARY).

A, macrogamete of *Aphanochæte* ready for conjugation; *B, C*, different views of microgamete; *D*, conjugation; *E*, germination of the zygote in the desmid *Mesotænia*, producing four functional products (zygotic meiosis); *F*, similar process in *Mesotænium*; *G*, the same in *Cylindrocystis*, two functional products.

tions was described by Schaudinn in the Foraminifera *Polystomella, Centropyxis* and *Chlamydophrys*, later by several observers especially in rhizopods and gregarines.[1] In these rhizopods the scattered chromidia are said to enlarge to form the nuclei of minute flagellated or (in *Arcella*) amœboid gametes that conjugate in pairs. In the gregarines an interesting series of conditions leading up to such a condition has been observed. In most of the gregarines the gamete-nuclei are formed by repeated division of the original nucleus of the gamont (gametocyte) to produce minute gamete-nuclei. In certain

[1] R. Hertwig ('99); Schaudinn ('99, '00, '04); Elpatiewsky ('07) (*Arcella*, flagellates, gregarines); Kuschekewitsch ('07); Swarzewsky ('10, '12) (gregarines), etc. See Fig. 342.

cases,[1] the primary nucleus is said to break down into, or to give off, chromidia from which is re-formed a single nucleus, which divides progressively to form the gamete-nuclei. In *Gregarina cuneata* and *Lankesteria sp.* the primary nucleus breaks down into a mass of chromidia from which are said to arise many small nuclei (as in the Foraminifera) each of which divides twice to form four gamete-nuclei.[2] The climax is offered by *Difflugia areolata* (a multinucleate species) in which, according to Sülzer ('04) after fusion of the two conjugants (gametocytes) the nuclei give off most of their chromatin in the form of chromidial granules which become closely intermingled and supposedly fuse (chromidiogamy); and from the products are said to arise new nuclei for the new generation.

None of these accounts, especially the last one, seems to the writer to be sufficiently demonstrated; and they have in fact been viewed with considerable scepticism by specialists in this field.[3] In any case all call for the most careful reëxamination.

II. ILLUSTRATIVE EXAMPLES

1. Hologamy and Isogamy with Gametic Meiosis

A striking example of this is offered by the heliozoan rhizopod *Actinophrys sol*, in which the cytological phenomena have been made known in greater detail than in any other recorded case. An extended account of these phenomena, illustrated by numerous excellent figures, is given by Bělař ('21, '23).[4]

As above stated (p. 582) the conjugants are in this case (Fig. 282) sister-cells, arising by a "progamic" mitosis, the two cells thus produced becoming surrounded by a common cyst. In this mitosis, as in the vegetative mitoses, appear 44 chromosomes (the diploid number) which arise from elongate spireme-threads, split lengthwise, and show marked size-differences. In each conjugant the nucleus now undergoes two meiotic divisions, producing successively two small reduction-nuclei or "polar bodies," which approach the cell-periphery and quickly degenerate. *In the course of this division the number of chromosomes is reduced from 44 to 22.* The remaining nucleus in each gamete now enlarges, becomes reticular; and this is followed by complete fusion of the gametes. Fusion of the cytosomes (plastogamy) is followed by that of the two gamete-nuclei, thus completing the formation of the zygote which, after a period of rest within the cyst,

---

[1] Léger et Dubosc, '09.

[2] This suggests a process of gametic meiosis; and such a process had actually been described in *Monocystis* by Mulsow ('11). On the other hand, in *Aggregata* and *Diplocystis* Dobell has found meiosis to be zygotic (p. 491).

[3] See Doflein, '19, Kofoid, '21.

[4] See also Schaudinn, '96, Keysselitz, '08, Distaso, '08, Prowazek, '13.

escapes and assumes the ordinary vegetative form. It is here evident that the original conjugants are not gametes but gametocytes (p. 582). According to the account of Bělař, the history of the chromosomes, during meiosis shows a very exact parallel, which extends to many of the finer details, to that seen in higher animals. In the early prophase of the first meiotic division the nucleus of each conjugant develops a leptotene spireme which quickly becomes polarized, and passes through a typical amphitene stage in the course of which the threads conjugate side-by-side. Thus arises a polarized pachytene which later loses its polarization, becomes longitudinally double (diplonema) and twists to form a strepsinema. A typical diakinesis now ensues, in which may be seen some of the tetrad forms occurring in higher animals (transverse rod-tetrads, double crosses) and showing some

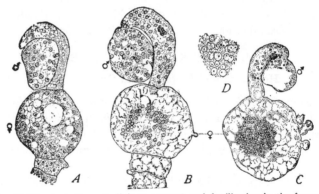

Fig. 293.—Multinucleate "gametes" (gametocytes) and fertilization in the fungus *Pyronema* (HARPER).

A, the multinucleate "oögonium" (♀), to which is attached the male gametocyte (♂); *B*, entrance of sperm-nuclei into the trichogyne; *C*, intermingling of sperm-nuclei and egg-nuclei; *D*, conjugation of nuclei in pairs, in various stages.

of the same variations in mode of spindle-attachment. The resemblance extends even to the interkinesis, which clearly shows the single crosses, so often seen in higher forms. In this rhizopod, accordingly, it would seem that the *entire mechanism of meiosis exists substantially in the same form as in a fish, a salamander or a mammal.*

No other case is so completely known as this; but many less complete observations indicate that an essentially similar process may take place in other Protista. An example of this in a flagellate is described by Dobell ('08) in *Copromonas subtilis*. The conjugants are here typical flagellates, indistinguishable in size or appearance from the vegetative cells or from each other. Union of the conjugants is followed by complete fusion, during which the flagellum first of one gamete and then of the other is lost. Before union of the nuclei each divides twice by a simple type of heteropolar promitosis, thus giving three nuclei in each gamete, of which two quickly degenerate as "reduction-nuclei" while the third persists as the gamete-nucleus or pro-nucleus. Karyogamy now follows the two nuclei completely fusing into one, after which the zygote may at once resume its ordinary free-swimming type, or may first undergo a period of rest while encysted.

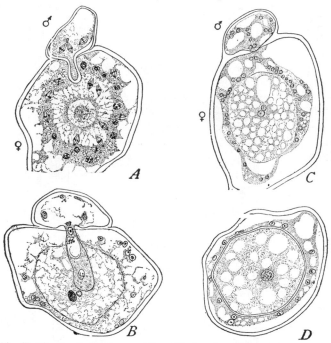

Fig. 294.—Fertilization in the fungus *Albugo* (*Cystopus*) *candidus*. (*A*, *B*, from Davis, *C*, *D* from Wager.)

A, antheridial tube from male gametocyte (♂) penetrating the oögonium or female gametocyte (♀); *B*, later stage, ovum formed, with single nucleus (near it the cœnocentrum); one sperm-nucleus in antheridial tube; *C*, union of gamete-nuclei; *D*, zygote.

The history of the nuclear elements is not known; but these observations suggest that the nuclei are originally of diploid organization, and that the two divisions preceding karyogamy are meiotic in character and effect a reduction of the nuclei to the haploid condition.[1]

A third example of this type, with certain interesting modifications, is seen in the diatoms, among which three different conditions have been described. In *Surirella* (Karsten, '00) the phenomena are essentially as

[1] Some doubts have been expressed as to whether the cycle described by Dobell may not represent stages of fission rather than of conjugation. Berliner's results on *C. major* ('09) are, however, in harmony with Dobell's, though in some respects less complete.

in the foregoing cases; the nucleus of each conjugant divides twice, producing four nuclei, of which one becomes the gamete-nucleus while three degenerate as reduction-nuclei. More complicated conditions are found in a number of other diatoms [1] where the phenomena are of particular interest since *two of the products of the maturation-divisions are functional instead of one.* In *Rhopalodia*, as described by Klebahn (Fig. 295) the process begins as in

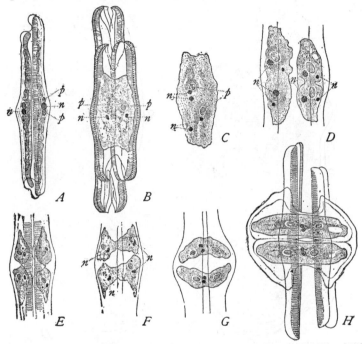

Fig. **295.**—Conjugation and gametic meiosis in the diatom *Rhopalodia* (KLEBAHN).

A, union of the conjugants in side-view, each having one nucleus (*n*) and two pyrenoids (*p*); *B*, later stage, from above, showing two nuclei (result of first division) in one conjugant; *C*, protoplast of one conjugant after second division, four nuclei, two pyrenoids; *D*, later stage of the two conjugants, side-view, each with four nuclei, two large and two small ("polar bodies" or reduction-nuclei); *E*, division of each conjugant, to form two gametes, each with one functional nucleus and one reduction-nucleus; *F*, *G*, fusion of the gametes two by two, disappearance of the reduction-nuclei; *H*, the two resulting zygotes, gamete-nuclei not yet fused.

Surirella, each nucleus dividing twice to form four nuclei, but is later complicated by the fact that in each conjugant two of the four nuclei enlarge and become functional while two degenerate as reduction-nuclei; and the protoplast now divides into two gametes each of which receives one of the functional nuclei. Thus arise four gametes which now fuse two by two, the two gametes of each pair being derived respectively from the two original con-

[1] Karsten, *op. cit.*, Klebahn, '96, '02, Oltmanns, '22.

jugants, so as to effect an exogamous union. The final result is to produce two zygotes instead of one (Fig. 295, H).

The process is essentially similar in *Epithemia*, *Amphora*, *Navicula* and some other forms. It is here perfectly clear that the original conjugants are not gametes but gametocytes (p. 582), and the same conclusion follows, strictly speaking, for all cases of gametic meiosis in which the meiosis first takes place after union of the conjugants, even when only a single gamete-nucleus results from the process.[1]

A remarkably interesting case is offered by *Amœba diploidea* as described by Hartmann and Nägler ('09).[2] In this rhizopod the ordinary vegetative individuals are visibly diploid (though the chromosome-number is not known), being regularly binucleate, precisely as in the sporophytic genera-tion of the *Uredinales* and some other fungi (p. 624), the two nuclei being closely appressed and dividing side by side by "conjugate division" (Fig. 296). This condition arises from the fact that in conjugation the two gamete-nuclei become closely associated during this process but do not actually fuse until near the end of the vegetative cycle—an ideal example, as Hartmann has said, of gonomery (p. 433). In conjugation (Fig. 296) these *Amœbæ* first become associated two by two, and without immediate fusion become inclosed in a common cyst. Subsequently the two nuclei in each conjugant at last fuse to form a single diploid nucleus. This is followed by complete plastogamy, the two diploid nuclei still remaining separate (Fig. 296, F). Now, as in *Actinophrys* or *Copromonas*, each of these nuclei is said to undergo two successive heteropolar divisions of simple promitotic type, three of the products in each case being abortive reduction-nuclei while the fourth is the gamete-nucleus. The two gamete-nuclei thus pro-duced finally conjugate with each other without fusion to form the double zygote-nucleus for a new vegetative cycle (Fig. 296, H). If this account is correct it seems clear that the case is one of gametic meiosis quite compar-able to that seen in other rhizopods (*Actinophrys*, *Actinosphærium*). Owing, however, to the complete autonomy of the two gamete-nuclei throughout the vegetative cycle, the phenomena offer a superficial resem-blance to the zygotic type, since the meiotic divisions take place just after final fusion of the original gamete-nuclei. In reality the two cases are radically different; for in zygotic meiosis the cells of the vegetative cycle are haploid, in *Amœba diploidea* diploid. The final fusion of the nuclei

---

[1] *Cf.* p. 597. Among the pelagic diatoms a number of forms have been described in which the phenomena are widely different, conjugation being of the merogamic type, and *followed* by meiosis. In *Corethron*, for example (Karsten, '04), the protoplast divides to form numerous small gametes which fuse in pairs with those from other cells to form zygotes. Two nuclear divisions now follow, the zygote dividing into two cells each containing two nuclei of which one degenerates. This proc-ess is closely parallel to that seen in the desmids.

[2] See also Nägler ('09) and Erdmann ('10, '13).

just preceding maturation in the latter case is in a broad sense comparable
to synapsis, and like the latter may be regarded as "the final step in the
conjugation of the germ-cells" (Montgomery, '01, p. 223).

In none of the foregoing cases have the chromosome-numbers been determined; but it seems probable that all belong to the gametic or terminal
type of meiosis. It is a fact of much theoretic interest that in *Rhopalodia*

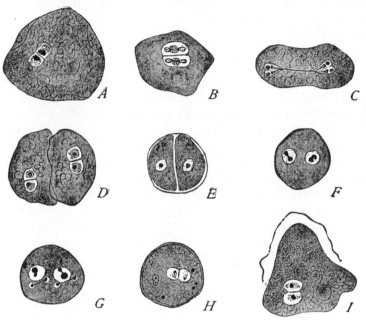

Fig. **296.**—Nuclear cycle in *Amœba diploidæ* (Hartmann and Naegler).

A, binucleate individual of ordinary vegetative type; *B*, *C*, ordinary mode of division, by conjugate promitosis; *D*, conjugation; *E*, fusion of nuclei (= synapsis) in each conjugant; *F*, *G*,
supposed meiotic divisions of simple type; *H*, union of the gamete-nuclei without fusion; *I*, escape of zygote from cyst.

two of the products of meiosis are functional gamete-nuclei, instead of only
one (as in the animal egg) or all four (as in the animal sperm).

2. Hologamy and Isogamy with Zygotic Meiosis

In the cases now to be considered meiosis is initial or zygotic, immediately following syngamy and karyogamy instead of preceding them.
Among animals this type is known only in certain gregarines (p. 605),
but it is more frequent in lower plants, and is well illustrated in
the conjugate algæ (Conjugatæ). An interesting series of forms here
exists.

In the Zygnemaceæ (*Spirogyra, Zygnema*) conjugation is typically holo-gamic, any or all of the cells of the linear cell-aggregates being able to con-jugate with little visible alteration of structure beyond a contraction of the protoplast into a rounded form. Complete plastogamy or fusion of the gametes is at once followed by complete fusion of the nuclei in karyogamy; and only after the completion of this process do the meiotic divisions take place. In both cases there are, as usual, two of these divisions,[1] producing four nuclei, of which one enlarges to form the initial functional nucleus while three remain of small size, forming reduction-nuclei that finally degenerate

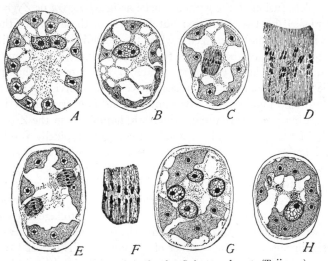

Fig. 297.—Zygotic meiosis in the alga *Spirogyra elongata* (Tröndle).

A, zygote, gamete-nuclei uniting above (the peripheral dark bodies are pyrenoids); *B*, fusion of gamete-nuclei; *C*, first (heterotypic) resulting division; *D* (from *S. neglecta*) tetrads in this division; *E, F*, second division; *G*, resulting 4-nucleate stage; *H*, later stage, one functional and three de-generating nuclei (polar bodies?).

(Fig. 297). This condition, evidently, is comparable with that seen in animal ova generally, excepting that meiosis occurs at the beginning of the vegetative cycle instead of at the end. This interpretation seems to be placed beyond doubt in the case of *Spirogyra* by the chromosome-number, which is said to be in the second division but half that present in the first, the numbers found by Karsten in *S. jugalis* being 28–14, while Tröndle found in *S. neglecta* 24 and 12, in *S. longata* 20–22 and 10–11, and in *S. colo-spora* 18–9. The primary functional nucleus is therefore haploid, as are also the nuclei of the filament developed from the zygote. *The ordinary vegetative or "adult" plant is therefore a haploid organism or haplont*, like the

[1] See for *Spirogyra*, Karsten ('00) and Tröndle ('11) and, for *Zygnema*, Kursanow ('11).

haploid or gametophyte generation of higher plants, and the diploid number exists for only a brief period in the unicellular zygote. This condition
is unknown in higher plants and animals.

In the Zygnemaceæ but one of the four nuclei resulting from the meiotic
divisions is functional, and but one embryo is produced from the zygote
(zygospore) upon its germination. The same condition is said to exist in
certain of the desmids (Gonatozygæ, according to De Bary);[1] but more
usually two or even four embryos are produced from a single zygote. In
Closterium and *Cosmarium*, as shown by Klebahn ('90), meiosis follows
upon complete fusion of the gamete-nuclei as in *Spirogyra* or *Zygnema;* and
is accomplished by two divisions; but the first of these divides the zygote
into two complete and equal cells, while the second is merely a division of
the nucleus in each of these forms to form one functional nucleus and one
small reduction-nucleus (Fig. 298). Each of the two cells thus produced
forms the starting point for a new vegetative cycle of division; and although
the chromosome numbers are not known, there is every reason to believe
that the ordinary vegetative individuals are haploid as in the Zygnemaceæ.
In certain of the Mesotæniaceæ, finally, the zygote typically produces four
functional embryos, though sometimes two (species of *Mesotænia, Spiro-
tænia,* and *Cylindrocystis,* Fig. 292). Here again the cytological detail is not
yet known, but it seems probable that in all these cases alike meiosis is
zygotic, and is accomplished by two divisions.[2] This is supported by the
more recent observations of Pascher ('16), on the phytoflagellate *Chlamydomonas* in which total conjugation is said to be followed by a process of zygotic meiosis during which the number of chromosomes is reduced from 20 to
10. The interesting fact here is that even in this simple unicellular form
meiosis is effected by two divisions, all four of the products being functional,
flagellated swarm-spores, each of which initiates a haploid cycle of successive
cell-divisions that ultimately ends with conjugation.[3] This leads to the
suspicion that zygotic meiosis may occur in various other cases among algæ
in which the zygote produces four swarm-spores (*e. g.,* in *Œdogonium* or
Bulbochæte, Fig. 306), and that this type of meiosis may be of widespread
occurrence in the lower plants.

We may conveniently consider here the only known cases of this type
among animals, though both these belong to the merogametic forms, and
one of them is heterogamous. These cases are offered by the coccidian

[1] See West, '16, p. 375.

[2] See Hartmann ('14), Kaufmann ('14), Oltmanns ('22).

[3] That this is the correct interpretation is indicated by the fact that different species of *Chlamydomonas* may be crossed and the offspring reared until the next enduring conjugation According
to Pascher the offspring of the zygote show varying combinations of the gamete-characters which
point to a segregation during the spore-producing (meiotic) divisions of the zygote like that seen in
higher forms (p. 930).

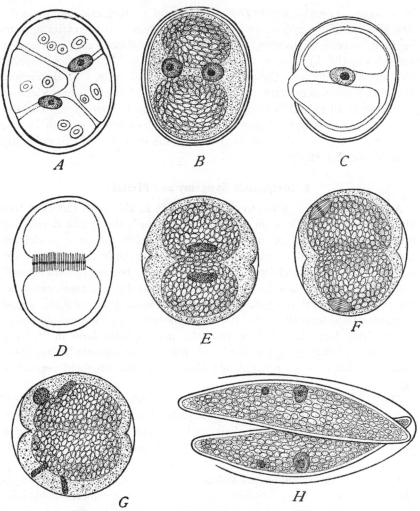

Fig. 298.—Conjugation and zygotic meiosis in *Closterium* (KLEBAHN).

A, soon after union, four chromatophores; *B*, chromatophores reduced to two, nuclei distinct; *C*, fusion of the nuclei; *D*, first cleavage of the zygote; *E*, resulting 2-cell stage; *F*, second mitosis; *G*, resulting stage, each cell bi-nucleate; *H*, separation of the cells; one of the nuclei in each enlarging to form the permanent nucleus, the other degenerating.

sporozoan *Aggregata eberthi* and the gregarine *Diplocystis schneideri*, as described by Dobell and Jameson ('15) [1] in both of which the chromosomes can readily be counted. The diploid and haploid numbers are respectively

[1] These results are contrary to those of several earlier observers, who described more or less definitely a process of gametic reduction. The most important of these is that of Mulsow ('11) who described such a process in the gregarine *Monocystis rostrata*.

in *Aggregata*, 12 and 6, and in *Diplocystis*, 6 and 3. Reduction occurs in the first division of the zygote, and the haploid number (6) thereafter appears in each succeeding division, producing the sporoblasts and sporozoites, and also in the divisions of the resulting schizonts. The haploid number thus occurs during both the asexual and the sexual cycle, *i. e.*, throughout the entire life-history with the single exception of the zygote-nucleus—a condition in all essentials identical with that seen in *Spirogyra*. The two cases are noteworthy in that meiosis *seems* to be effected in both by one division, in *Aggregata* the first, in *Spirogyra* the second—but this evidently calls for further study.

3. Merogamic Syngamy and Meiosis

A typical example is given by *Polystomella*.[1] In this form there is a true alternation of generations (in the zoölogical sense), the zygote developing into an asexual form (microspheric type) in which numerous nuclei are produced by progressive division. These nuclei (which in the meantime are said to break up into a chromidial form) ultimately become centers of small amoeboid asexual germ-cells or *agametes*, formed by a fragmentation of the protoplasm; and these develop, without conjugation, into the sexual or macrospheric form (Fig. 284, E), which likewise contain numerous nuclei progressively formed. When mature the macrospheric form in its turn fragments, producing a multitude of minute, uninucleate biflagellated gametes which have no resemblance whatever to the amoeboid vegetative type.[2]

Theses gametes are perfectly isogamous, but Schaudinn states that gametes from the same macrospheric individual will not unite with one another. Conjugation is therefore exogamous, and one may infer that some sort of physiological difference exists between "male" and "female" individuals as in the moulds (p. 588).

The chromosome-numbers are unknown; but it seems clear that the zygote in this case must be of diploid organization and the gametes of haploid. The point at which meiosis takes place is not certain. Schaudinn, Lister and Winter state that the last two divisions, leading to the gamete-formation, differ in type from those which precede them and may perhaps be meiotic; but this question still remains undecided. The same gap exists in our knowledge of the rhizopod *Trichosphærium*, which has a life-history closely parallel to that of *Polystomella* (Schaudinn, '03) save for the fact that the small gametes are not flagellated and are somewhat unequal in size. Similar

---

[1] Schaudinn ('03), Lister ('05), Winter ('07).

[2] Lister has shown, however, that the macrospheric individuals may produce amoeboid agametes instead of gametes. The alternation is therefore not strictly obligatory.

doubts hang over many other cases of merogamic conjugation in plants (*e. g.* among the green algæ) as well as in animals.

4. Partial or Temporary Conjugation

There is now a general agreement among protozoölogists that conjugation of this form is a secondary process that has been derived from a more primitive total type. It possesses, nevertheless, a high interest, especially

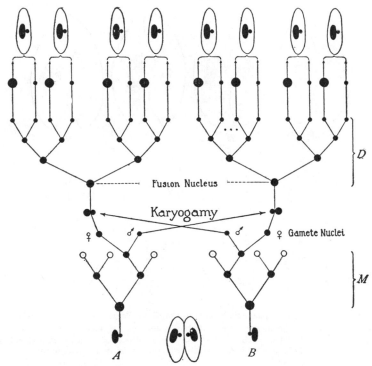

Fig. 299.—Diagram showing history of the nuclei in the conjugation of *Paramœcium caudatum.* (Following Maupas and Calkins.)

A and *B* represent the nuclei of the two conjugants, *M* the supposed meiotic divisions of the micronucleus in each, and *D* the division of the zygote-nucleus in each conjugant (*cf.* Fig. 300, *I–M*); the final result of the three divisions gives four reconstructed ex-conjugants as show above.

because of its historical association with the experimental and cytological researches of Bütschli, Engelmann, Maupas, R. Hertwig, and their successors, on the general problem of senescence and rejuvenescence in unicellular organisms.

Partial conjugation is known only in the ciliates, is always hologamic, and usually isogamous. The general course of the process is largely conditioned by the fact that the ciliates typically possess two kinds of nuclei, a large macronucleus and much smaller micronucleus, the former generally regarded as a vegetative or somatic nucleus, the latter as a reserve or generative one. Both nuclei divide at each mitosis; but in conjugation the micronucleus alone is concerned.[1]

We select as a type the classical object *Paramœcium caudatum*, in which a single macronucleus and micronucleus are present. In all cases the macronucleus degenerates and disappears during the process, and in species

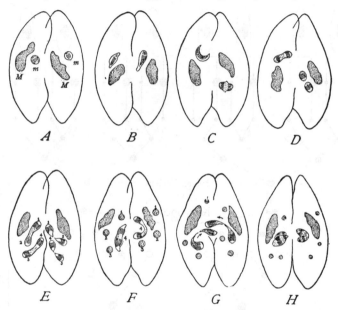

Fig. 300.—Conjugation and gametic meiosis in the ciliate *Paramœcium caudatum* (CALKINS).

A, the two conjugants (gametocytes) united; *M* macronucleus; *m*, micronucleus; *B–E*, division of each micronucleus into four (meiosis); *F*, third division of one micronucleus in each conjugant 4 and 4) to produce the pronuclei, leaving three reduction-nuclei in each conjugant.

possessing more than one micronucleus all of them save one likewise degenerate. Although conjugation is here of the hologamic type the conjugants are measurably smaller than in ordinary vegetative forms, a fact noted by many observers and demonstrated by Pearl ('07) by extended statistical studies. Two such individuals become attached by their oral surfaces and partially fuse over a rather small area. This is followed by two successive divisions of the micronucleus, a little later by a fragmentation and final disappearance of the macronucleus, which becomes

[1] In many forms more than one micronucleus is present, and not infrequently more than one macronucleus.

irregular in shape (Figs. 299–301) and finally breaks up into large spheroidal granules, which finally disappear leaving no trace. Meanwhile three of the four products of the micronucleus in each conjugant degenerate as "reduction-nuclei" (or "polar bodies"), while the fourth remains as the only persistent derivative of the old nuclear apparatus.

A third division now ensues to form two spindle-shaped gamete-nuclei in each conjugant. One of these, formerly called the "female pronucleus"

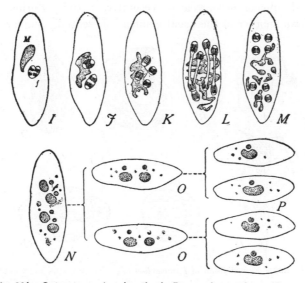

Fig. 301.—Later stages of conjugation in *Paramœcium caudatum* (CALKINS).

I, ex-conjugant (zygote), with fusion-nucleus (*f*) and macronucleus (*M*); *J–M*, division of fusion-nucleus to form eight small nuclei; breaking up of macronucleus; *N*, differentiation of four new macronuclei and four micronuclei; *O, P*, distribution of the products, by two fissions, to four resulting individuals of ordinary vegetative type.

and now usually designated as the *stationary nucleus* remains in the conjugant; the other or *migratory nucleus* ("male pronucleus") passes over into the opposite conjugant and there fuses with the stationary nucleus of the latter, after which the two conjugants separate. By this process the two conjugants have reciprocally fertilized each other, each now containing a single fusion-nucleus or zygote-nucleus, equally derived from the original micronucleus of the two. From this nucleus a new nuclear apparatus is rebuilt as follows: Separation of the conjugants is followed by three successive divisions of the fusion-nucleus in quick succession, producing in each ex-conjugant eight nuclei, of which four enlarge to form new macronuclei, while four remain small as micronuclei (Fig. 301). By two ensuing fissions of the entire cell the four new macronuclei are distributed, one to each of the resulting individuals. In some species the four micronuclei seem to be distributed in the same way, but in *Paramœcium caudatum* (Maupas) [1] three of the four degenerate, to be replaced by derivatives of the fourth. In either case the final result is a group of eight individuals, each containing a micronucleus and macronucleus derived from the fusion-nucleus, and hence equally from the micronuclei of the original conjugants. The original macronucleus has meanwhile disappeared, and the cells have now entered upon a new cycle of vegetative activity during which one fission follows another in the usual manner. Essentially similar facts have

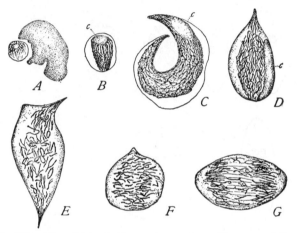

Fig. 302.—First division in *Paramœcium caudatum* (CALKINS and CULL).

A, macronucleus and micronucleus, initial stage; *B*, micronucleus elongating, with "division center"; *C*, crescent stage of same; *D, E*, later stages, formation of (bivalent?) chromosomes; *F, G*, anaphases.

been observed by many observers in a large number of forms. In cases of permanent conjugation, as in *Vorticella*, where a smaller microgamete unites with a larger macrogamete, the process is essentially the same, though the details are more complex.

Maupas and Hertwig concluded that the first two divisions of the original micronucleus (preceding karyogamy) are comparable to the maturation-divisions; and this is to a considerable extent borne out by more recent observations. Calkins and Cull ('07) offer a careful study of these divisions in *Paramœcium caudatum*, showing that in the early prophase the micronucleus first assumes the form of a spindle near the end of which appears a large, nucleolus-like body or "division-center," and then bends into a

[1] Maupas's conclusions on this point are confirmed by Klitze ('14) and (in *P. pritinum*) by Doflein ('07), but have been questioned by some observers. See Woodruff and Erdmann ('14).

characteristic crescent or sickle (as already described by Maupas and Hert-wig), regarded by Calkins and Cull as the synaptic stage (Fig. 302). Still later the crescent is converted into a mitotic anastral spindle by elongation in an axis at right angles to that of the crescent, while the "division-center" disappears from view, and the chromatin network of the nucleus gives rise to numerous elongate chromosomes, which show many of the characteristic forms of bivalents, such as rings, 8-figures, and Y's, and divide to form two groups. These observations seem clearly to show that the first division is heterotypic in form.

The third division is of especial interest because of the fact, first clearly made out by Prandtl in *Didinium* and confirmed by Calkins and Cull in

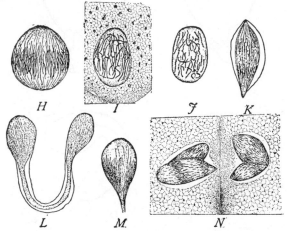

Fig. 303.—Later stages of maturation and syngamy in *Paramœcium caudatum* (CALKINS and CULL).

H, I, stages in the second division; *J, K,* the third division; *L,* telophase of third division, showing heteropolar condition; *M,* the larger pronucleus after the third division; *N,* karyogamy, showing size-difference of the gamete-nuclei.

Paramœcium, that it is in some cases heteropolar (Fig. 303), producing a larger and a smaller nucleus, of which the former is the stationary or "female" gamete-nucleus, the latter the migratory or "male." [1] Thus, although the conjugants appear to be isogamous the gamete-nuclei are distinctly anisogamous, a fact which sustains the view that the conjugating ciliate is a gametocyte (p. 582) and emphasizes the analogy between the conditions seen in ciliates and the hermaphroditism of higher forms. The third division, here obviously correlated with the reciprocal fertilization

[1] Dogiel ('23) has recently found, in the parasitic ciliate *Cycloposthium,* that the migratory nucleus in each conjugant is accompanied by a long cytoplasmic structure (derived from the spindle) so as closely to stimulate a flagellate sperm.

of each other by the conjugants, is unknown in higher animals and has no precise parallel in the total conjugation of most Protozoa (the Vorticellids are an exception). As will later appear (p. 616) it raises the question of an antithetic alternation of generations in the Protozoa. The facts also obviously suggest that the infusorian conjugant should be regarded as a gametocyte, derived from a form having merogamic conjugation and producing a large number of small gametes.[1] This view, now widely held,

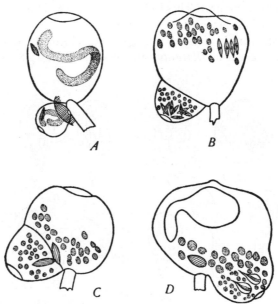

Fig. 304.—Conjugation of Vorticellids (MAUPAS).

A, attachment of the small free-swimming microgamete to the large fixed macrogamete; micronucleus dividing in each (*Carchesium*); B, microgamete containing eight micronuclei; macrogamete four (*Vorticella*); C, all but one of the micronuclei have degenerated as polar bodies or "corpuscules de rebut;" D, each of the micronuclei of the last stage has divided into two to form the pronuclei; two of these, one from each gamete, have conjugated to form the zygote-nucleus seen at the left; the other two at the right, are degenerating.

is supported by the fact that in the micro-conjugant of *Vorticella* (Maupas) and *Carchesium* (Popoff) the three divisions produce eight (instead of five) nuclei, while a fourth division of one of these gives rise to the gamete-nucleus (Fig. 304). In the multinucleate form *Opalina*, conjugation is actually merogamic in type, the vegetative cell dividing up into many small uninucleate or binucleate gametes (Metcalf, Neresheimer); but the significance of this is doubtful in view of the parasitic habit of *Opalina* and its wide divergence from the typical forms of ciliates.

[1] Lühe ('02), Popoff ('08), Hartmann ('09, '14).

To sum up: the most essential result of the process is to bring about in each conjugant a radical reorganization of the nuclear apparatus of both conjugants as follows:

(1) In each ex-conjugant the old macronucleus is wholly lost, to be replaced by one equally descended from both of the gamete-nuclei.

(2) The new micronucleus in each is likewise equally derived from both of the gamete-nuclei.

(3) The gamete-nuclei, though derived from the original micronuclei, are not identical with them, each of the latter having undergone the maturation divisions, during which, if we may accept an analogy with higher forms, a re-grouping of nuclear elements has probably taken place. This conclusion must, however, be accepted with some reserve.

5. Endomixis and Parthenogenesis

As earlier indicated (p. 243), nuclear reorganization may be accomplished by a process of *endomixis* in a single individual without any process of conjugation or amphimixis. This process is analogous to the asexual process of parthenogenesis in higher organisms, and bears a similar relation to the sexual process of conjugation. The cytological changes in *Paramœcium aurelia* (which possesses two micronuclei) are in broad outline as follows (Fig. 305).[1]

As in conjugation, the macronucleus disintegrates and finally disappears. Meanwhile the two micronuclei migrate away from their normal position beside the macronucleus, and towards the end of the macronuclear disintegration undergo two successive divisions, thus producing eight micronuclei in all. This, again, is precisely as in conjugation, but is not followed by the third division which in the latter case gives rise to the gamete-nuclei (p. 609).

The reconstruction is now initiated by the disappearance of all but one or two of the eight micronuclei. Most commonly each of these divides twice to form four products, of which one enlarges to form a new macronucleus, the other persists as a micronucleus. These are then distributed by one or two cell-divisions in such a manner that each resulting cell receives one macronucleus and one micronucleus, the latter finally dividing to form two which thereafter persist. This is closely analogous to the reconstruction following conjugation, as may be seen from the diagram (Fig. 305), which shows, at the right, one of the four variants of endomixis, recognized by Woodruff and Erdmann, for comparison with the conjugation-process, as shown at the left.

From a cytological standpoint the most noteworthy features of endo-

[1] Woodruff and Erdmann ('14).

mixis are: (1) the occurrence of two "maturation divisions" of the micronucleus which seem to be quite comparable with those that take place in
conjugation; and (2) the lack of the third division which in the conjugating
cell gives rise to the gamete-nuclei.   At first sight this seems analogous to
the diploid type of parthenogenesis in such animals as the aphids, or daphnids (p. 467); but further consideration reveals difficulties that can only
be cleared up by further research.   If we adopt the current assumption
that reduction takes place during the first two micronuclear divisions we

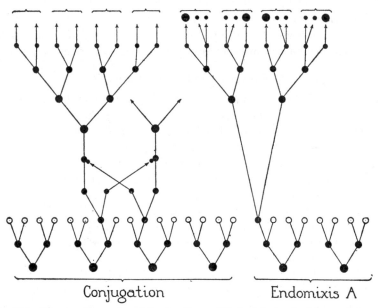

Conjugation   Endomixis A

Fig. 305.—Diagram, Comparison of Conjugation and Endomixis showing history of the micronuclei (after WOODRUFF and ERDMANN).

fall into the following dilemma.   If the two divisions in endomixis likewise
effect reduction, then the reorganized *Paramœcium* and all of its descendants should be of haploid nuclear constitution, which contradicts the
primary assumption concerning the maturation divisions.   The alternative
to this is to suppose either that a process of autogamous syngamy has been
overlooked in endomixis, or that a compensatory doubling is effected.   All
difficulties would disappear under the conclusion that it is the third division by which reduction is effected; but this is in contradiction with the
results of all previous cytological investigation of the problem (p. 610).
This whole question must therefore be left open for the present.

As a supplement to the foregoing brief outline, attention may be called to the possibility that endomictic reorganization may be widespread among Protozoa in connection with the process of encystment. The latter process, common in Protista, offers a means of protection against or recovery from the effects of unfavorable conditions, and is often accompanied by changes in the consistency of the protoplasm and nucleus and the loss and subsequent redifferentiation of various specialized cell-organs, such as cilia. Encystment may or may not be preceded by a process of conjugation, and in either case it may be followed by a marked renewal of vitality as shown by the division-rate; in *Didinium nasutum*, for example, Calkins ('16) found that encystment (without conjugation) is followed by a division-rate from five to seven times that of the same rate prior to encystment. A number of the earlier observers described marked changes in the nuclear apparatus at this time; and more recently it has been shown that these changes involve a nuclear reorganization of the same general type as that effected by endomixis or by conjugation. In *Stylonychia* (Fermor, '13) and in *Didinium* (Calkins, *op. cit.*) it was found that the old macronucleus breaks up and degenerates while a new nuclear apparatus arises by the division of the micronucleus and subsequent differentiation of its products.[1] Many interesting possibilities for further researches on encystment are here raised; though this process and endomixis are of course not necessarily connected.

III. GENEALOGICAL CONSIDERATIONS

The phenomena of reproduction in lower organisms bring to our attention three closely connected historical problems, namely, the origin of syngamy, the primitive relation between syngamy and meiosis, and the origin of antithetic alternation of generations. None of these has yet been completely solved, but certain interesting possibilities may here briefly be considered.

1. The Origin of Syngamy

This question still remains in the stage of more or less plausible guess-work. It has been suggested that syngamy first arose as a process of reciprocal cannibalism or "autophagy," two unicellular organisms devouring each other to the refreshment and advantage of both. This notion, suggested by Van Rees ('87), is developed in a suggestive manner by Dangeard ('99). In his view the gametes are "hungry cells" which lack sufficient energy to continue their development, but are rescued by a union of their resources. Such a speculation is more picturesque than convincing; never-

---

[1] According to Fermor the reorganization in *Stylonychia* is preceded by a conjugation of the two micronuclei. If this is correct endomixis here would seem to approach autogamous conjugation.

theless, as an historical explanation of syngamy it makes a certain appeal to the imagination. More plausible, perhaps, is the assumption of some kind of quantitative difference between the primitive gametes, the prototype of which appears in the suggestion of Bütschli [1] that syngamy and the primitive gametic differentiation resulted from imperfections in the mechanism of cell-division and consequent inequalities of distribution of the nuclear components. Thus arose some cells having an excess of chromatin, others a deficiency; and by the union of such contrasting individuals (now gametes) the normal balance was restored.

By later writers this hypothesis was given a different direction in accordance with certain views concerning the dualism of the cell-substance. Strasburger ('92, '98) assumed that the primitive gametic differentiation arose through variation in the relative amounts of trophoplasm and kinoplasm (p. 723), the female gamete containing an excess of the former, the male gamete of the latter. Syngamy, the result of a chemotactic interaction between the two, restored the normal balance and thus became a condition of survival. This conception emphasized the cytoplasmic differences of the gametes rather than the nuclear. On the other hand, the hypothesis of Schaudinn ('05) and his followers, assumed the primitive gametes to have differed in respect to "kinetic" and "trophic" chromatins, the former relatively in excess in the male, the latter in the female (p. 726).[2] More recent cytological studies on sex have in fact given some reason to suspect that the primitive sex-differentiation may have taken its origin in a quantitative difference of chromatin—perhaps a particular kind of chromatin—a difference at first irregular and fluctuating, later regular and constant, as is now the case in many higher animals (p. 816). "The sexual differentiation may therefore be rooted in a simple principle of plus and minus that holds true of all sexual organisms and may be an expression of a fundamental principle of metabolism." [3] The weak point in this hypothesis is its failure thus far to give us a clear view of the origin of hermaphroditism and its relation to diœcism.[4] To spin theories concerning this inaccessible field of inquiry is, however, no part of our purpose.

2. The Origin of Meiosis and Its Primitive Relation to Syngamy

This question is closely bound up with that of the origin of antithetic alternation, from which it is here separated only as a matter of convenience. By Weismann and other earlier writers meiosis was treated teleologically as an adaptive process, though which the gametes are "prepared" for their

[1] ('87–'89.)
[2] See Prowazek ('07), Hartmann ('09); also the critical reviews in Doflein ('11), and Minchin ('15)
[3] Wilson, '10 '11), p. 266.
[4] *Cf.* Doflein ('11), Minchin ('12, '15).

subsequent union in syngamy and the summation of the germ-plasms in successive generations prevented. This view involved, tacitly at least, the assumption that the diploid number was historically the original and fundamental one, and the haploid a derivative from it. Great difficulties stand in the way of such a view; for it provides us with no explanation of the double character of the diploid groups or the mechanism of meiosis. The problem suddenly took on a new form with Strasburger's ('94) [1] illuminating suggestion that the reverse conclusion is more likely to be, the correct one, namely that the haploid condition was the original one, inherited from an early prototype in which conjugation or fertilization had not yet arisen. Thus regarded, the periodic doubling of chromosomes appears as a secondary or derived phenomenon, a consequence of syngamy. "The morphological cause of reduction and the equality of chromosome-number in the germ-cells of each species is, according to my view, a phylogenetic one. I consider the process as a return to the original generation from which, through the development of the sexual process, first arose forms possessing the double chromosome-number . . . . The reduction of this number to one-half represents the restoration of the original number present in the nuclei of those organisms in which the sexual process first took its origin" (*op. cit.*, p. 523). This conclusion was suggested by the fact that the gametophyte and sporophyte generations in plants are characterized respectively by the haploid and diploid numbers of chromosomes respectively (p. 492). Its plausibility was increased by the later discovery of haploid parthenogenesis even in bees and other animals of relatively high grade of organization (p. 794). There is, therefore, nothing unreasonable in the hypothesis that the primitive organisms were asexual (as appears still to be the case in the Bacteria and Cyanophyceæ), that they were of haploid constitution, and that the diploid condition was a later acquisition.

It is of course unknown at what period in the life-history the process of reduction primitively took place. Theoretically, we might perhaps expect meiosis to have been originally of the zygotic type, *i. e.*, to have followed soon after syngamy as a kind of regulative process by which the original haploid condition was quickly restored; and it is interesting to note that the only cases of this type occur in very simple forms such as the algæ and the Protozoa.

3. Antithetic Alternation of Generations

Before the announcement of Strasburger's conclusions botanists had begun to turn towards the early view of A. Braun (1877) that the gametophyte or sexual generation of higher plants represents the older and preëxistent

---

[1] This remarkable work abounds in fruitful suggestions bearing on the whole series of problems here involved.

generation, and that the sporophyte is a neomorph, secondarily interpolated into the life-history. This view, developed in detail and with much ingenuity by Bower ('90, '94, '19) and later writers, has been widely accepted by botanists. The origin of the sporophyte was sought in a division of the zygote to produce spores, such as still occurs in certain of the algæ.

"The gradual development of this generation (the diploid) from the sexual product of the first generation can be actually traced step by step phylogenetically. The first indication of this development is apparently to be found in the Algæ; at least the life-history of *Œdogonium*, *Coleo-*

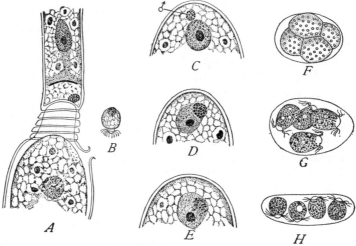

Fig. 306.—Fertilization in the alga *Œdogonium* (*A–E*, from KLEBAHN; *F*, *G*, from JURANYI; *H*, from PRINGSHEIM).

A, oögonium (below), just after opening, containing single ovum; *B*, sperm-cell; *C–E*, union of gamete-nuclei in the egg; *F*, *G*, division of zygote (possibly zygotic meosis) to form four zoöspores; *H*, corresponding quartet in *Bulbochæta*.

chæte, and the *Floridæ*, may be interpreted in this sense. In *Œdogonium*, four swarm-spores are formed from the fertilized ovum (see Fig. 306); whilst in *Coleochæte* a small multicellular body is developed from the cells of which swarm-spores are formed; in both cases the swarm-spore gives rise to the first generation. In the Floridæ the cystocarp is developed from the fertilized ovum, and the spores of the cystocarp give rise to individuals of the first generation. The Muscineæ and the Pteridophyta can readily be traced to the Chlorophyceæ: in the Muscineæ the fertilized ovum gradually developed into a sporogonium, and, in the Pterodophyta, into a sporangium-bearing cormophytic plant." [1]

[1] Strasburger ('94, p. 285). *Cf.* the discussion of Klebs ('98), Campbell ('05), Lotsy ('05), Cook and Swingle ('05).

Following strictly the logic of his theory, Strasburger adopted a similar interpretation of animal evolution, suggesting that in animals the haploid or gamete-producing generation has all but disappeared, its last vestiges *being represented by the three polar bodies or polocytes formed during the maturation of the egg.*[1] *This hypothesis assumed more definite shape in* the development given it by Chamberlain ('05, '08) and his followers, who

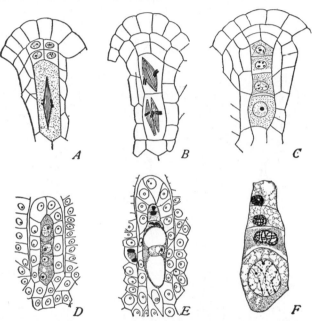

Fig. 307.—The megaspore-quartet in seed-plants.

(*A–C*, from Schniewind-Thies; *D*, *E*, from Merrill; *F*, from Ferguson.)

A–C, division of megaspore mother-cell (primary sporocyte) of *Galtonia* to form the four mega-spores; *D*, early megaspore-quartet in *Silphium;* *E*, later stage of same, enlargement of inner cell to form functional megaspore; *F*, early stage of megaspore-quartet in *Pinus*.

have pointed out the close analogy between the animal egg with its three polocytes and the megaspore-quartet and its products in the higher plants. In both cases, only one of the four cells is functional (in the animal, this cell is the egg, in the plant the embryo-sac), while the other three are reduced in size and sterile (Fig. 307). In both cases the four cells of the

---

[1] Conclusions more or less akin to this have been suggested by a number of other writers. Whitman ('78) early suggested that the polar bodies might be the remnant of a former sexual generation, though the chromosome relations were at that time unknown. Beard ('95a), following out the suggestions of Strasburger and the earlier ones of Bower ('87) on apospory, endeavored to show that metazoan development actually involves an antithetic alternation. Lotsy ('05) considers that the animal body is an asexual phase or diploid generation, while the sexual phase or haploid generation is confined to the germ-cell. These views are well criticised by B. M. Davis ('05).

quartet result from the two meiotic divisions, in the course of which the number of chromosomes is reduced from diploid to haploid. The analogy between the three vestigial megaspores and the polocytes is obvious.

How the condition seen in animals might have been reached is clearly shown by an almost continuous series of intermediate conditions still exist-

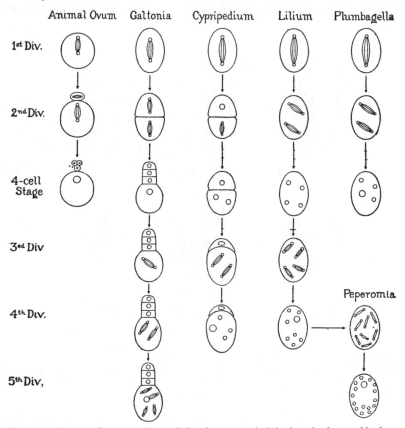

Fig. 308.—Diagram illustrating the parallelism between meiosis in the animal egg and in the megaspore (or embryo-sac) in angiosperms. Based on diagrams by CHAMBERLAIN, PACE and others. *Galtonia* shows the typical condition in angiosperms, with three abortive megaspores and one functional (embryo-sac) the latter producing eight nuclei (one egg, seven prothallial cells). In *Cypripedium* but two actual megaspores are formed; in *Lilium, Peperomia* and *Plumbagella* the primary mother-cell is directly converted into the embryo-sac. The total number of divisions varies, as shown.

ing in the seed-plants. In all cases reduction is effected by the first two divisions of the spore-mother-cell (typically producing the megaspore-quartet), and in nearly all these are followed by a certain number of additional divisions in which the haploid chromosome-number persists, thus giving origin to a more or less reduced haploid generation or female gametophyte. The number of these divisions in different species varies (Fig. 308), and with it the degree of the reduction of the female gametophyte. In many gymnosperms, e. g., in *Pinus* (following Chamberlain's discussion) the embryo-sac produces thousands of nuclei, in *Gnetum* they are numbered by hundreds, while in the angiosperms the number is usually reduced to eight. A slight further reduction would produce a condition closely analogous to that seen in animals, and such a case has actually been reported recently by Dahlgren ('15) in *Plumbagella*, a form in which (as in *Lilium*) both megaspore-producing cleavages have been suppressed and the primary sporocyte is directly converted into the embryo-sac. The nucleus of this cell divides but twice altogether (meanwhile undergoing reduction), one of the four resulting nuclei becoming the egg-nucleus, one an antipodal cell, while the remaining two fuse to form the endosperm-nucleus (*cf.* p. 454). Here the whole haploid generation (other than the egg) is reduced to three cells, just as Strasburger conceived to be the case in animals. The relation of this case to the more typical ones in the angiosperms is indicated by the diagram (Fig. 308), as explained in the subjoined footnote.[1]

From a merely logical standpoint, clearly, the general comparison, as above outlined, is quite admissible; but it rests upon a mere analogy, and one that probably indicates no real genetic relationship between the two cases. Among the Metazoa there is no trace of such a mode of evolution.

---

[1] This relation can only be fully grasped when we take into account the total number of divisions involved, including those by which the megaspores are formed. This number is typically five, of which the first two are always the meiotic divisions (heterotypic and homotypic respectively) however the external aspect of the process may vary otherwise. Typically (as in *Galtonia*), these two divisions produce four actual megaspores (one functional and three vestigial), while the remaining three take place within the functional megaspore (now the embryo-sac) to produce eight nuclei; one of the latter is that of the egg while the other seven constitute the vestigial gametophyte (p. 496). This process may be modified and abbreviated in two ways, namely, (1) by the suppression of one or both megaspore *cleavages* (the nuclear divisions taking place as usual), and (2) by reduction of the total number of divisions from five to four, three or finally to two. When both megaspore protoplasmic cleavages are omitted (as in *Lilium*) the primary sporocyte or megaspore mother-cell is directly converted into the embryo-sac and the meiotic divisions take place as the first two nuclear divisions within it. One or both megaspore-producing divisions may thus, as it were, be telescoped into the embryo-sac; and by the continuation of this process, together with a reduction in the total number of divisions, have arisen many curious modifications of the typical process, some of which are shown in a schematic form in the diagram (Fig. 308). The typical process is here illustrated by *Galtonia*, where the meiotic divisions produce one functional and three vestigial megaspores, followed by three other divisions in the embryo-sac. In *Cypripedium* (Pace, '07) the number of divisions is reduced to three, the first meiotic division producing one vestigial macrospore and one functional (the embryo-sac), while the second and third take place in the embryo-sac. The latter, accordingly, contains but four nuclei, one of which is the egg-nucleus. In *Lilium* and some other cases the number of divisions is likewise reduced to three; but the result is different, since the spore-mother cell is directly converted into the embryo-sac; and the three divisions take place within the latter, thus producing eight nuclei. In *Plumbagella*, the process is the same as in *Lilium*, but only two divisions take place, giving a result like that in *Cypripedium*, but again by a different process. In *Peperomia*, finally, the process begins as in *Lilium*, but is followed by a fourth division, producing 16 nuclei.

The lowest Metazoa (sponges, cœlenterates) show precisely the same conditions as the highest; and nowhere in the great series of forms between these extremes do we find an antithetic alternation between haploid and diploid generations, unless we choose so to regard the case of the Hymenoptera and Rotifera, where the males are haploid, the females diploid. With these very special exceptions alternation of generations in Metazoa, in particular in the Cœlenterata, is of the homologous type, *i. e.*, both sexual and asexual generations are diploid; and this is even true, as Hartman has shown, of the Dicyemids, which are among the simplest of the Metazoa, though probably degenerate forms. By the zoölogist, accordingly, the view that the condition existing in animals generally has resulted from the gradual loss of a haploid generation, or gametozoön, can hardly be taken seriously. At best such an hypothesis can only have application in the earliest stages of sexual evolution, and in Protista.

Strasburger's view clearly implies that meiosis was originally of the zygotic or initial type; and this has met with some support in the demonstration that this type of meiosis has been more or less clearly demonstrated, or made probable, in a considerable number of forms that are unicellular or represent simple types of cell-aggregates. This type of reduction seems also to occur in various other simple algæ, including *Coleochæte*, desmids, certain diatoms, the Zygnemaceæ, in some of the red algæ (*Scinaia*, *Nemalion*, *Batrachospermum*) and possibly in some other cases. That the zygotic type may be still more widely prevalent is suggested by the formation of four swarm-spores from the zygote in *Œdogonium*, *Bulbochæte* (Fig. 306) *Hydrodictyon* and other cases, and also by the frequent formation of four spores in the Basidiomycetes, or of four (and then of eight) spore nuclei in the Ascomycetes, in each case preceded by a process of nuclear fusion.[1] It must, however, be borne in mind that the sexual phenomena in fungi are believed to be in many cases of highly modified or quite secondary nature.

The foregoing cases may well be cited in favor of the view that zygotic reduction is a very primitive and perhaps original type. On the other hand, some studies in this field lead us to consider the possibility that antithetic alternation may likewise have been a very early type. It seems admissible to assume that the primordial process of syngamy may from the first have been followed by a considerable series of diploid divisions before reduction took place, thus producing immediately an antithetic succession of haploid and diploid cycles.[2] Such a primitive succession, we may surmise, is likely to have been at first irregular and facultative, only later becoming estab-

---

[1] See Blackmann ('04), Harper ('10), Guilliermond ('13), Bower ('19), etc..

[2] The view here suggested is essentially in harmony with that advocated by W. H. Lang ('09) in his suggestive discussion on the origin of alternation in the archegoniate plants.

lished as a regular alternation. Such a succession may well have formed
the starting point from which arose all the existing types of meiosis, the
sporic by persistence of both haploid and diploid cycles, the zygotic by the
reduction and final disappearance of the diploid cycle until only the zygote
remained, the gametic by a similar disappearance of the haploid cycle, until
nothing remained but the two meiotic divisions.

Some such hypothesis as this, I venture to think, claims our attention
because of the fact, now apparently well established, that antithetic al-

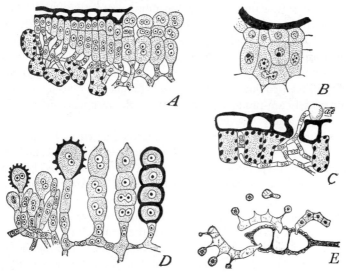

Fig. 309.—Alternation of generations in the rusts (Uredinales) slightly schematized (*A–D*,
GUILLERMOND; *E*, SAPIN-TROUFFY).

(All the figures from *Phragmatobium violaceum*.)

A, portion of the æcidium formed by the uninucleate mycelium with binucleate æcidiospores
above (products of the diploid zygote); *B*, supposed fertilization in cells of the uninucleate mycelium (gametophyte) by migration of nucleus; *C*, germination of the binucleate æcidiospore (*æ*),
producing binucleate mycelium (sporophyte), here entering stoma of wheat; *D*, formation of binucleate teleutospores in which fusion of the two nuclei (? synapsis) finally takes place; *E*, three
teleutospores germinating to produce promycelium and four basidiospores by two divisions, believed to be of meiotic type; from these spores arises the original uninucleate mycelium (*A*) or
gametophyte.

ternation between independent and equally well developed generations
already exists in certain of the algæ and fungi (p. 626).[1] Though the fungi
are perhaps too far removed from the direct line of evolution of higher
plants to bear very directly upon our general problem they display a highly

[1] No attempt will here be made to consider the problems of sexuality in the fungi generally, for
the homologies of the gametes, and the relations of the phenomena to those seen in algæ are too
doubtful to be discussed profitably by a botanical layman. See Harper ('10). An interesting review
of this subject is given by Guilliermond (Les Progrès de la Cytologie des Champignons) in *Progressus
Rei Botanicæ*, IV, 3, 4, 1913.

suggestive series of nuclear phenomena certain of which may here be illustrated by the life-history of the rusts (*Uredinales*), which has been the object of numerous cytological studies. These fungi show a regular antithetic alternation between haploid and diploid mycelia, similar in general morphological type but readily distinguishable by their nuclei, which are single in the haploid and double in the diploid. In this respect the cells of the diplont are quite analogous to those of *Amœba diploidea* (p. 601).[1] The general life-history is briefly as follows (Fig. 309). Fertilization takes place in the *œcidium* (a structure produced by the uninucleate mycelium) [2] but is not followed by fusion of the nuclei, the zygote remaining binucleate (quite as in *Amœba diploidea* and giving rise by "conjugate division" to cells that are binucleate like itself (Fig. 309, *A*). These cells give rise to a series of binucleate "æcidiospores" which are set free, and upon germination give rise by continued conjugate division to a binucleate mycelium. From the latter ultimately are produced binucleate "teleutospores" in each of which the two nuclei finally fuse into one.

By the earlier observers this fusion was considered as the act of fertilization. The work of Maire and Blackman makes it probable, however ,that this fusion is the preparatory act of meiosis, and is compared by Blackman to synapsis, again as in *Amœba diploidea* (p. 602). After fusion of the nuclei the teleutospore (now uninucleate) undergoes two divisions producing a "promycelium" which quickly forms four uninucleate spores ("sporidia"); and by germination of the latter arises the uninucleate mycelium which ultimately produces the *œcidium*, the starting-point. The number of chromosomes cannot be certainly determined, but there is now a fairly general agreement that the two divisions of the teleutospore are identical with the meiotic divisions. If this be correct the case is clearly one of sporic meiosis, the teleutospore being analogous to the primary sporocyte, the sporidia to the spores, the uninucleate mycelium to the haploid gametophyte, and the binucleate mycelium to the diploid sporophyte.

Among the algæ we find many forms that are primitive in respect to both gametes and the fertilization process; and they are of especial interest because many botanists have held that the nearest approach to the ancestors of the cormophytic plants are probably to be sought among the green algæ or Chlorophyceæ. Unluckily, the relations of the chromosomes in these particular algæ are unknown, save in a few cases (Zygnemaceæ, Desmidia-

---

[1] See especially Sapin-Trouffy ('96), Maire ('98, '00, '03, '10), Blackman ('04), etc.

[2] The details of fertilization seem to vary considerably in different species, being effected in some cases by a migration of the nucleus of one cell into an adjoining cell (*Phragmidium violaceum, Uromyces Poæ*), in other cases by a lateral fusion of cells (*Ph. speciosum, Uromyces Caladii*, etc.), but in every case the result is a binucleate zygote. The exact homologies of the conjugants is uncertain, and it is doubtful whether they are morphologically comparable to the "true" gametes of algæ.

ceæ), and these give no clue to the origin of antithetic alternation. On the other hand, among the brown algæ (Phæophyceæ) and red algæ (Rhodophyceæ) are conditions which prominently raise the question of an origin of antithetic alternation differing materially from the one adopted by Bower, Strasburger and their adherents.

It seems to be clearly established that in some of these cases no antithetic alternation exists; further, that in some of them meiosis is of the gametic type (as in animals generally) in others of the zygotic (as in *Spirogyra*). An example of gametic meiosis is offered by the brown alga *Fucus* (Phæophyceæ) where reduction takes place in the course of the first two divisions

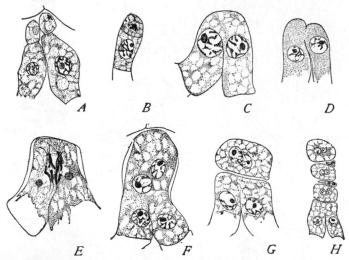

Fig. 310.—Sexual process in the rusts (CHRISTMAN). (All the figures from *Phragmidium speciosum*, except *D* from *Uromyces*.)

A, gametes ready to fuse after cutting off two sterile cells; *B*, single gamete and sterile cell; *C, D*, fusion of gametes without karyogamy; *E*, conjugate division following fusion; *F, G*, resulting binucleate æcidiospores; *H*, series of æcidiospores and sterile intercalary cells.

of the primary oöcyte (oögonium), quite as in animals (Yamanouchi, '09), though a complication arises from the fact that these two divisions are followed by at least an additional one, producing (usually) eight mature ova. The egg, after fertilization, develops with the diploid number of chromosomes (64 in *F. vesiculosus*) and the same number persists in the resulting thallus. In this case, accordingly, there is but one generation, and this is diploid, as in animals. At the opposite extreme are the Zygnemaceæ (p. 603) in which meiosis is zygotic, following immediately upon syngamy; so that the only existing generation is haploid, like the gametophyte of higher forms. It is a remarkable fact that in certain groups both types coexist; for instance in the diatoms, the ordinary forms (*Surirella, Navicula*) display meiosis of the gametic type, the pelagic forms the zygotic (p. 599). Here, accordingly, the ordinary vegetative individuals appear to be in some species of diploid constitution, in others of haploid.

In a third class of cases appears a typical antithetic alternation, highly interesting for the general problem because of the fact that the haploid and

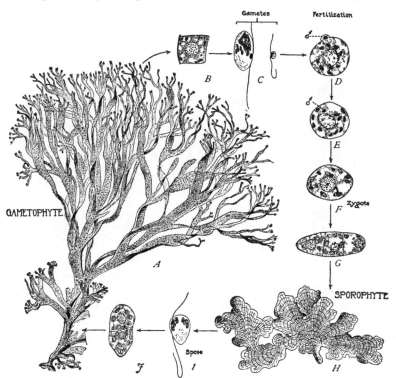

Fig. 311.—Alternation of generations in the alga *Cutleria-Aglaozonia* (*A*, from THURET and JANCEWSKI; *H*, from FALKENBURG; the remaining figures from YAMANOUCHI).

A, mature *Cutleria*, the haploid gametophyte; *B*, cell of female gametangium, 24 chromosomes; *C*, gametes; *D*, *E*, fertilization; *F*, zygote, 48 chromosomes; *G*, embryo; *H*, mature *Aglaozonia*, the diploid sporophyte; *I*, motile spore (zoöspore); *J*, embryo, 24 chromosomes.

diploid generations are of similar, and in some cases of identical, morphological type save in respect to the reproductive organs. In most of these cases the diplont or sporophyte produces its spores (either motile or non-motile) in groups of fours, hence known as *tetraspores*, by two meiotic divisions, as in higher forms).

An example of these cases is offered by *Cutleria-Aglaozonia* (Phæophyceæ), a form in which the two generations are separate plants both of thalloid type but differing so considerably in external appearance that they were originally described under different generic names. The main features of this life-history are shown in Fig. 311. An interesting feature of this case is the fact that all the germ-cells, whether gametes or asexual spores, are of primitive biflagellate type, and all contain plastids and a red pigment-spot associated with one of the plastids. The haploid gametophyte or sexual generation (*Cutleria*) is a more or less branched thallus (Fig. A), while the diploid sporophyte, or asexual generation (*Aglaozonia*) is an irregularly lobed encrusting form (H). The following facts are from the important paper of Yamanouchi ('12).

Cutleria multifida (usually diœcious), shows 24 chromosomes in the division of all its cells and the same number is delivered to the gametes (B, C). The latter are typical, biflagellate, free-swimming forms, very unequal in size, but of exactly similar type, except in regard to the number of plastids, of which the macrogamete contains 30 or more, while the microgamete has but two (Fig. 311). By their union (D E,) is formed a zygote (F), which contains 48 chromosomes, and germinates to give rise to the diploid *Aglaozonia* (H), the cells of which likewise divide with 48 chromosomes. At maturity the *Aglaozonia* produces numerous zoöspores (1) closely similar in type to the gametes, but varying in size with the number of divisions of the mother-cell by which they are produced (as is often the case in other algæ). The spores usually contain 20 or more plastids. Without conjugation the zoöspore germinates to produce the haploid *Cutleria*, thus completing the cycle. The reduction of the chromosome-number is effected, in the first two divisions within the zoöspore mother-cell in the zoösporangium and is accompanied according to Yamanouchi by the occurrence of a polarized synaptic stage and the formation of 24 heterotypic chromosomes. Reduction is therefore complete after completion of the second division; but from one to three additional divisions take place, thus producing from 8 to 32 zoöspores, from each of which (Fig. 311) a haploid *Cutleria* plant may develop.[1]

Another step brings us to forms in which the alternation appears in still more generalized form, the diploid and haploid generations being entirely similar in general type. Among the brown algæ this condition is known only in *Dictyota*, where the generations differ only in the fact that the diploid one produces *tetraspores*, by the germination of which arise the haploid sexual individuals which produce the gametes. In these algæ both tetraspores and ova are large, non-motile cells, while the sperms are minute

---

[1] This is analogous to the multiplication of the primary oöcyte in *Fucus* (above described), though the starting-point is in the one case a zygote, in the other case the terminal product (oöcyte) of a zygote.

and flagellated. The work of Mottier ('oo) and of Williams ('04) proved that meiosis here takes place in the two tetraspore-forming divisions, the diploid or sporophytic number being 32, the haploid number (found in the tetraspore and the gametophyte to which it gives rise) 16.

The essential facts (disregarding certain complications of detail) are essentially similar in certain of the red algæ, as shown especially in *Polysiphonia* by Yamanouchi ('07) whose results have been confirmed in other forms particularly by Svedelius. Yamanouchi proved, in the case of *Polysiphonia vidolacea* that the two tetraspore-forming divisions are of meiotic type and effect a reduction of the chromosome-number from 40 to 20; and this has been confirmed in several other red algæ by other observers.[1] The life-history of *Polysiphonia* is therefore as follows: The tetraspore-producing plant, of diploid constitution (40 chromosomes), corresponds to the *Aglaozonia* generation (sporophyte) of *Cutleria*. By this plant are produced tetraspores, each containing 20 chromosomes; and from such a spore arises a haploid sexual plant quite similar in general structure and appearance to the diploid generation. From these plants are formed the gametes (*carpogonium* = ovum, and *spermatium* = sperm), each of which receives 20 chromosomes, and by their union is produced the zygote, containing 40 chromosomes, from which ultimately arises the diploid sporophyte. All the essential features of this account, even the same chromosome-numbers, are confirmed in the related form *Delesseria* by Svedelius; and important confirmatory evidence has also been contributed by the studies of Lewis on *Griffithsia* and of Kylin on both this form and *Rhodomela*.

It is remarkable that in another series of red algæ (*Scinaia, Batrachospermum, Nemalion*) no tetraspore-bearing plants appear, the tetraspores being replaced by monospores, which are formed singly on the sexual plants and develop directly into new sexual plants. This case formerly offered a cytological puzzle which was solved by Svedelius ('15) in his studies on *Scinaia* by the surprising discovery that meiosis is here of zygotic type, and no diploid generation exists. Svedelius showed that the monospores are of haploid constitution and, like the gametes, are produced by ordinary somatic (non-meiotic) mitosis from the haploid sexual plant. Fertilization is immediately followed by meiosis in the zygote (as in *Spirogyra*).[2] The formation of monospores thus seems analogous, broadly speaking, to the vegetative apogamy of higher forms.

We have here a remarkable example of the readiness with which the type of meiosis may change, even as between rather closely related forms. The extreme plasticity of these phenomena shown in the red algæ and the dia-

---

[1] Lewis ('09, '12), (Svedelius ('11, '12, '14), Kylin ('14, '16).

[2] For the nearly similar case of *Nemalion* see Davis ('10) and Kylin ('16).

toms (p. 599) is emphazised by the classical experiments of Klebs ('96, '99, etc.) which show how readily the sexual processes of the green algæ may be modified by change of external conditions such as light, temperature, chemical medium and the like. In case of the red algæ, Svedelius considers the *Scinaia* type, with zygotic meiosis, to be the more primitive and suggests that the *Polysiphonia* type, with antithetic alternation, may have arisen suddenly by a postponement of the meiotic divisions, the diploid number of chromosomes having been carried forward into the carpospores which accordingly give rise to a diploid generation or true sporophyte. It seems, however, at least equally plausible to assume with Lang (p. 622) the correctness of the reverse view, *i. e.*, that the *Polysiphonia* type, with alternation of equally developed haploid and diploid generation, was the primitive one.

The origin of the internal phenomena of meiosis is still wholly unknown. What led to the conjugation of the chromosomes and their subsequent disjunction in orderly system, and what part this process may have played in the physiological activities of the cell can only be conjectured. It is easy to offer hypothetical teleological answers to such questions. We may say that only through these processes could the normal organization and activities of the species be maintained, the "summation of ancestral germ-plasms" prevented, the species held true to its type, or (conversely) provided with a fruitful source of variation and natural selection; but such "explanations" leave us no wiser than before. If the cytological problems here involved remain unsolved they are none the less real and offer an interesting field for further inquiry.

LITERATURE VII

(See also III, V, VI. For abbreviations see General Literature List.)

Bělař, K., '23. Untersuchungen an *Actinophrys sol*. I: *A. Zf.*, XVI.

Bensaude, M., '18. Recherches sur la cycle evolutif et la sexualité des Basidiomycetes: (See *B. G.*, LXVIII.)

Blackman, V. H., '04. On the Fertilization, Alternation of Generations and General Cytology of the Uredineæ: *A. Bot.*, XVIII.

Blakeslee, A. F., '04. Sexual Reproduction in the Mucorineæ: *P. A. A. A. S.*, XL, 4.
'06. Differentiation of Sex in Thallus, Gametophyte and Sporophyte: *B. G.*, XLII.
'15. Sexual Relations between Hermaphroditic and Diœcious Mosses: *B. B.*, XXIX, 2.
'20. Sexuality in the Mucors: *Sci.*, LI.

Bonnet, J., '14. Reproduction sexuée et alternance des génération chez les algues: *P. R. B.*, V.

Bower, F. O., '89-'91. On Antithetic as distinguished from Homologous Alternation of Generations in Plants: *A. Bot.*, IV.
'19. The Botany of the Living Plant: *Macmillan, London.*

Burgeff, '14–'15. Untersuchungen über Variabilität, Sexualität und Erblichkeit bei *Phycomyces: Flora,* CVII, CVIII.

Calkins, G. N., 'o1. The Protozoa: *New York.*
    'o9. Protozoölogy: *Philadelphia.*

Campbell, D. H., 'o5. The Structure and Development of Mosses and Ferns: *The Macmillan Co., New York.*

Christman, A. H., 'o7. The Alternation of Generations, etc., in the Rusts: *B. G.,* XXXIX.

Coulter, J. M., '14. Evolution of Sex in Plants: *Chicago.*

Cunningham, B., '17. Sexuality of the Filament of *Spirogyra: B. G.,* LXIII, 6.

Davis, B. M., 'o1. The Origin of Sex in Plants: *Pop. Sci. Monthly,* LX.
    'o3. The Evolution of Sex in Plants: *Ibid.,* LXII.
    '10. Nuclear Phenomena of Sexual Reproduction in Algæ: *A. N.,* 44.

Dobell, C., 'o9, '14 (III, IX).

Doflein, F., '16. Lehrbuch der Protozœnkunde: 4 Auflage, *Jena.*

Enriques, P., 'o7. La coniugazione, etc., negli Infusori: I, *A. P.,* IX.
    'o9. La sexualité chez les Protozoaires: *Rev. di Scienza.*
    '16. *Mem. R. Accad. Sci. Bologna,* VII, 3.

Farmer and **Williams,** '98. Contributions to our Knowledge of the Fucaceæ: *P. T., B.,* 190.

Fortpflanzung der Gewächse, in *Handwört. der Naturw. Jena,* 1913. *Algæ,* F. Oltmanns; *Fungi,* E. Fischer; *Archegoniata,* F. O. Bower; *Mosses,* G. Tischler; *Ferns,* F. O. Bower; Intermediate Forms, between Ferns and Seedplants, N. Arber; Seed-plants, A. Ernst; Physiology, G. Klebs.

Guilliermond, A. '10. La sexualité chez les champignons: *B. S. F. B.,* 44.

Harper, R. A., 'oo. Sexual Reproduction in *Pyronema confluens,* etc.: *A. Bot.,* XIV.
    '10. Nuclear Phenomena of Sexual Reproduction in Fungi: *A. N.,* XLIV.

Hartmann, M., 'o9. Autogamy bei Protisten, etc.: *A. P.,* XIV.
    '13. Flagellata: *H. Nw.,* III, *Fischer, Jena.*
    '14. Der Generationswechsel der Protisten, etc.: *V. D. Z. G.,* XXIV.
    '18. Ergebnisse und Probleme der Befruchtungslehre im Lichte der Protistenforschung: *Die Naturwissenschaften,* VI.
    '21 (III).

Hartmann and **Schilling,** '17. Die Pathogenen Protozoa: *Springer, Leipzig.*

Hertwig, R. '89 (III).
    'o2. Die Protozoen und die Zelltheorie: *A. P.,* I, 1.

Jennings, H. S. (III).

Jollos, V., '21. Untersuchingen über Varietät und Verebung bei Infusorien: *A. P.,* XLIII.

Klebs, G., '96, '12, (III).
    '99. Ueber den Generationswechsel der Thallophyten: *B. C.,* XIX.

Kofoid, C. A., '23 (III).

Marchal, Élie et Émil, 'o6, 'o7. Aposporie et sexualité chez les mousses: *B. A. B.,* 'o9, *Ibid.* (see also XI).

Maupas, E., '88, '89 (III).

Minchin, E. A., '12. An Introduction to the Study of the Protozoa: *London.*

Oltmanns, F., '22, '23. Morphologie und Biologie der Algen, I, II, III. 2nd Ed.: *Fischer, Jena.*

Prowazek and **Nöller,** '20. Handbuch der Pathenogenen Protozoa: *Barth., Leipzig.*

Svedelius, N., '11. Ueber den Generationswechsel bei *Delesseria sanguinea: Svensk. Bot. Tidskrift*, V.

'15. Zytologisch-entwicklungsgeschichte Studien über *Scinaia furcellata*, etc.; *Nova Acta Reg. Soc. Sc. Upsaliensis*, Ser. 4, IV.

West, G. S., '16. Algæ, I: *Cambridge Univ. Press, Cambridge.*

Woodruff and **Erdmann,** '14 (III).

Yamanouchi, S., '06. The Life-History of *Polysiphonia: B. G.*, XLI, XLII. Also Univ. Press, *Chicago,* '07.

'12. The Life-History of *Cutleria: B. G.*, LIV, 6.

CHAPTER VIII

SOME ASPECTS OF CELL–CHEMISTRY AND CELL–PHYSIOLOGY

"The synthetic act by which the organism maintains itself is at the bottom of the same nature as that by which it repairs itself after undergoing a mutilation, or by which it multiplies and reproduces itself. Organic synthesis, generation, regeneration, reintegration, the healing of a wound, are but different aspects of a single phenomenon."

CLAUDE BERNARD. [1]

"The morphologist, on the one hand, strives to elucidate the structure of protoplasm down to its finest details; the biochemist, on the other, with his apparently ruder yet still more searching methods, seeks to determine the chemical functions of the same protoplasm; broadly speaking, they are only dealing with two different sides of the same thing."

HOFMEISTER. [2]

No attempt will here be made to consider the general chemistry and physiology of the cell; such a task, manifestly would lie far beyond both the scope of this work and the competence of its author. In practice, however, the modern study of cytology, cellular embryology and genetics, especially on its experimental side, passes insensibly into that of cell-physiology and cell chemistry. We cannot for instance, intelligently employ the modern technique of cytological staining without some knowledge of its chemical and physical basis. Such topics as the structure of protoplasm, the mechanics of cell-division, or the phenomena of fertilization cannot adequately be discussed without keeping in view at least some elementary notions concerning the chemical basis of protoplasm and the properties of colloidal systems. Again, we can only skirt the margin of the problems of development and heredity so long as we deal only with their morphological aspects. As the study of embryology, cytology and genetics goes forward we see more and more clearly that it can only approach its final objectives through a close alliance with biophysics and biochemistry. Even a work that deals primarily with cytology must therefore attempt in some degree to orient itself with respect to these other sciences. As such an attempt, and no more, the following brief discussion is offered.

[1] *Leçons sur les phénomènes de la vie*, p. 517, 1878.
[2] *Die chemische Organization der Zelle*, p. 29, 1901.

I. GENERAL VIEW

1. The Cell a Colloidal System

Physico-chemically regarded, as has been indicated (pp. 60, 73) the cell appears as a complex system largely composed of colloidal material. That it may profitably be treated from this point of view is proved by many of the most important physiological advances of our time; life as we know it is indeed inseparably bound up with matter in the colloidal state.[1] This conception seems likely to prove as fruitful in cytology as it has been in physiology. Under its influence many of the leading problems of cytology took on a widely different aspect when once the subject had thrown off the dominance of those earlier conceptions of the cell-substance that found expression, for instance, in reticular theories of protoplasmic structure and the nearly allied hypothesis of fibrillar contractility in mitosis. More modern attempts to consider the structure and transformations of protoplasm, the mechanism of mitosis, the nature of fertilization, the nature and function of the cell-membrane and the physiological relation between nucleus and cytoplasm, have for the most part taken the colloidal nature of protoplasm as a common starting point; and numerous recent observations on both living and fixed cells tend to demonstrate that we are here on the right track. On the physiological side of the subject this is even more obvious, and many striking cell-phenomena have in a measure been imitated in artificial colloidal systems: for instance, the properties of surface-films or membranes, the antagonistic effects of inorganic salts on the nature and stability of the system, or the changes of viscosity in the living cell-substance.

Obviously, however, the cell-substance is not to be thought of as a simple diphasic system. The cell is a highly heterogeneous or polyphasic system, in which the disperse phases are represented by many different kinds of suspended particles of all degrees of magnitude, differing among themselves more or less widely in degree of aggregation, physical consistency, chemical nature, and physiological activity, and varying endlessly from species to species. The system also contains various inorganic salts, either in combination or in solution, which play a most important part in controlling the equilibrium of the system. Protoplasm considered as a colloidal system thus offers a problem of extreme intricacy, alike from the morphological, physiological and the physico-chemical point of view.

To the cytologist one of the most interesting parts of this problem concerns the nature of the ultra-microscopical dispersed particles, both in the hyaloplasm and in artificial colloidal solutions of protein and related sub-

---

[1] *Cf.* Loeb ('06, '22), Bechold ('12), etc.

stances; but the questions here raised are still too largely a matter of controversy among students of colloidal chemistry to be profitably discussed at length by a non-specialist. Until recently it has been the prevalent opinion that in colloidal solutions (*e. g.*, of proteins) the dispersed particles are not ions or molecules but larger molecular aggregates, to which have conveniently been applied the term *micellæ*, adapted from Nägeli's earlier use of the word (p. 718).[1] Important recent researches, however, point to the conclusion that the degree of dispersion may often be molecular, and that even protein solutions differ from true solutions only in the greater size of the dispersed molecules and of the ions into which they may break up.[2] That the dispersed particles, though still below the horizon of microscopical vision, are relatively of very large size is shown by the extremely slow rate of diffusion of protein solutions, by their viscosity and often by their opalescence (Tyndall effect); and by the fact that by the use of the "ultra-filter" [3] the particles of egg-albumin, gelatin, various albumoses, and even of dextrin, may be separated from their watery solutions (Bechold). The opalescence of certain protein solutions shows that the suspended particles are large enough to disperse and reflect part of the transmitted light; and it has been shown that the smallest particles capable of thus scattering light are from 50 to 100 times smaller than the mean wave length of light (0.5μ). They must, therefore, have a diameter of at least $5-10\mu\mu$ ($0.005-0.010\mu$) and this is believed to be about the size of the smallest particles revealed by the ultra-microscope (p. 33). According to the calculations of Robertson ('18), the diameter of a molecule of casein, which has a molecular weight of nearly 16,000 (based on Nernst's estimate of the diameter of the CO_2 molecule) is less than half this ($\pm 2.4\mu\mu$). It can not be concluded from this alone that the dispersed particles are necessarily molecular aggregates; on the contrary Robertson has urged the view that not only the Tyndall effect and non-filterability of the particles in protein solutions but also their viscosity may be due to an association of the protein ions with a large amount of water to form complexes of great size.[4] Apart from all this, however, it is evident that the hyaloplasm of living protoplasm, though apparently structureless, is not merely a solution of colloidal material. Many facts indicate that in addition to proteins, carbohydrates, salts, and other substances in true solution, it may contain great numbers of larger molecular aggregates[5] which form the original source of many of the still larger

---

[1] For a presentation of this view see Zsigmondy ('18).

[2] See especially Robertson ('18), Loeb ('22).

[3] Bechold, 1906.

[4] *Op. cit.*, p. 344, etc.

[5] This is admitted by Robertson, who also holds that many proteins enter into true solution, becoming molecularly dispersed in accordance with Avogadro's law ('18, p. 341). See also Bayliss ('11, '21, '23), Bechold ('12), Höber ('14), Mathews ('15), Maclendon ('17), Zsigmondy ('18), etc.

bodies that emerge into microscopical view as the smallest visible formed components of protoplasm. At this point we only emphasize from the cytological point of view the conclusion of Bayliss that "no hard and fast line is to be drawn between matter in pieces visible to the naked eye, down through ultra-microscopic particles to molecules."[1] The field open to the cytologist forms the middle portion of this series, ranging from the largest formed elements of the cell down to those just perceptible by the highest powers of the microscope (p. 720); but we may regard it as certain that the diminishing series does not end at the purely artificial boundaries determined by the working limit of our instruments.[2]

2. The Cell a Chemical Machine

Modern physiology unhesitatingly accepts the fundamental conclusion that all vital energies are traceable to the chemical energy of food-stuffs that have been incorporated into the cell-substance and are there set free by oxidations and other destructive chemical processes of metabolism. Physiologically, therefore, the cell may be regarded as an apparatus for the transformation and application of chemical energy. In the phrase of Loeb, it is a chemical machine.

Within certain well-defined limits the activities of every cell are of specific type—the muscle-cell, the nerve-cell or the gland-cell displays its own characteristic performance just as the egg of each species has its own mode of development, or each species of protozoön its own specific forms of behavior. We assume, as our fundamental working hypothesis, that the specificity of each kind of cell depends essentially upon what we call its *organization, i. e., upon the construction of the cell-machine,* in some sense or other—morphological, physical or chemical. Even the most superficial acquaintance with the cell-activities shows us that this conclusion cannot be taken in any crude mechanical sense—the difference between the cell and even the most intricate artificial machine still remains too vast by far to be bridged by present knowledge. Nevertheless we accept the hypothesis that the difference is one of degree rather than of kind because it has proved itself fruitful in discovery and has kept us moving in the right direction (p. 1116).

Fundamentally the cell-system is a *reaction-system,* which responds to a multitude of *modifiers* (Bechold) by activities that differ with the nature both of the system and of the modifier. Some of these agents are *activators,* which incite or accelerate action; others *inhibitors,* which suppress or retard it; still others *transformers,* which change the character of activities in progress. Some modifiers are external to the cell, and include those agents which effect the coördination of action between different tissues and cells and the

[1] Bayliss, '11, p. 20.   [2] Wilson, '99, '23.

maintenance of the general organic equilibrium. Some of these (such as the nerves) belong to the obvious mechanical structure of the body as a whole. Others are soluble chemical substances, such as the enzymes and hormones, that are independent of fixed structural relations and hence capable of being transported from one part to another in the blood or lymph or by diffusion from one cell to another. This subject is too large to be entered upon here; but we may emphasize the interest for the student of the development of the hormones or related soluble substances that call forth or maintain character- istic structural relations, sometimes of a very complicated type. It must here suffice merely to mention such well-known hormones as thyroidin, or the pituitary hormone, both of which powerfully affect growth and metabolism. The sex-hormones, produced by certain cells of the repro- ductive organs, bring the subject conspicuously into relation with our con- ceptions of development and heredity, especially in the production of the secondary sexual characters. The remarkable morphological, physiological, and even psychical reactions of the organism to castration have long been familiar; and equally striking effects are often produced by the trans- plantation of the gonads of one sex into the body of the other sex. These effects are now known to be due to specific hormones produced by the in- terstitial cells or other non-germinal cells of the gonads; the growth and functional activity of the mammary gland in the female, for example, is incited by a hormone derived from the fœtal cells. An interesting dem- onstration of the action of the sex-hormones is made by F. R. Lillie ('16) in his solution of the long-standing puzzle of the "free-martin" twin. In this case, the female characters of a female twin are more or less completely suppressed, and certain male organs may develop, as a result of anastomosis of the placental blood vessels with those of the associated male twin. This apparently can only be due to the influence of soluble substances derived from the male, and transferred to the female by the blood.

Loeb ('16) points out the manifest analogy between such phenomena and the effects of food in inciting the production of the sexual forms in the poly- morphic social insects,[1] or in the rotifers, as demonstrated by Whitney and Shull (p. 229). These effects too must be due to a reaction of the organism to substances in the blood, either introduced as such in the food or produced by its transformation, and having effects analogous to those of hormones, even though not technically so called. Loeb has suggested that in the same category with the hormones should be placed the "formative stuffs " of Sachs, suggested by so many facts of regeneration and development (p. 1065); and this view is supported by a number of recent investigations.[2]

[1] See Caullery, '13.   [2] See Bayliss, '18.

This conclusion may open the way to a more adequate conception of localization than has hitherto been possible (p. 1062).

A similar view may be taken of the individual cell, if only for the reason that the organism as a whole is a single cell at an early period of its existence (*cf.* p. 1). The intracellular coördinations, like the intercellular, may be effected by structural relations, in some cases of high complexity, as seen, for instance, in the neuro-motor apparatus of the flagellates and ciliates (p. 695) or in the relations between the central bodies, the astral formations, and the movements of the chromosomes. Other internal modifiers undoubtedly are soluble enzymes or hormones. A probable example of this is offered by the fact (p. 405) that so long as the germinal vesicle of the egg is intact, the cytoplasm is in general incapable of aster-production under the influence of either the sperm or of parthenogenetic agents. As soon as the germinal vesicle breaks down and nuclear substance mingles with the cytoplasm, the latter becomes capable of fertilization, and is able, upon appropriate stimulus, to produce an astral system, and to proceed with its development (p. 405). The effect of the sex-chromosomes and of other chromosomes on development may be thought of in the same way (p. 815). We may emphasize, lastly, the fact that since the reaction of the cell to its modifiers is of specific type it must somehow depend upon its own specific type of organization. In the words of Bechold, "The order maintained among the activities of the vast number of modifiers in the body must itself be referred to an organization of the body as a whole, and ultimately to that of the germ-cell from which it has been derived" ('12, p. 31).

The cell, like the whole organism, thus appears to us as a delicately balanced moving equilibrium, offering a picture that is continually changing yet always remains within the boundaries of a specific type. Nothing is more remarkable than that a thing so delicate and plastic should run so true to form through countless generations. How this is possible we can hardly imagine. We can but record the observed fact that it is effected by an inherent power of adjustment or self-regulation that holds the cell fast to its own type; and by processes of assimilation, growth, and cell-division that ensure an unbroken protoplasmic continuity between successive generations.

II. CHEMICAL RELATIONS

1. General

As has often been remarked, the chemical conditions existing in living cells are of necessity imperfectly known, because every attempt to examine them by precise methods kills the cell. In the main, therefore, our statements concerning these conditions are limited to inferences based on the chemical behavior of dead cells or their components. Even as thus circumscribed, investigation is beset with formidable difficulties. Neither protoplasm nor nucleus consists of a single substance of fixed composition. Both are made up of a great number of different chemical components, themselves often highly complex, and in a continual flux of chemical transformation. Only in very restricted degree is it possible to isolate these components for accurate chemical analysis; and our so-called "micro-chemistry"—i. e., observation by the microscope of the effect of treatment by dyes, and other reagents—is still in too rudimentary a state of development to give us more than a few rough qualitative indications. There is good reason to conclude, further, that many of the most significant of the chemical properties of the cell-components (for instance, the nucleo-proteins) are too subtle to be recognized by our present methods of analysis; we know nothing, for example, of the chemical differences between different chromosomes of the same group; yet the experimental evidence makes it certain that such differences exist (p. 916). In these considerations we find sufficient explanation of the fragmentary and unsatisfactory existing state of our acquaintance with the chemical physiology of the *cell* as such, and the great distance by which our knowledge of this subject is still separated from that of the chemistry of organic substances.

Regarded from a purely chemical point of view the cell-substance is a complex mixture of substances, of which a large percentage (60 to 90%, or more) consists of water, while 1%, more or less, is formed by various inorganic salts. Among the latter the compounds (mainly chlorides and phosphates) of sodium, potassium, calcium and magnesium preponderate; but small quantities of iron are probably also always present and sometimes manganese, silicon, copper and other elements. It is an interesting fact, that the chief inorganic constituents of the living body (as indicated by the salt-composition of the blood) are the same as those of sea-water; and this has ingeniously been conjectured to indicate that living matter first appeared in the sea and has thus from the first maintained an adjustment or colloidal equilibrium with its characteristic salts or their ions (Macallum, '04). This is supported by the familiar fact that in marine invertebrates both the osmotic pressure of the blood and the nature and proportions of the inorganic salts are approximately the same as those of the sea-water.[1] In higher forms the osmotic pressure of the blood is much lowered and the Mg-content largely decreased. M. R. Lewis ('16) has shown that the embryonic tissues of vertebrates (birds) may be successfully grown in sea-water diluted until isotonic with the normal blood-plasma of the

[1] See Höber ('14),

animal; it is well known also, that some of the most useful of the "normal fluids" employed for culture-fluids (such as the solutions of Locke or of Ringer) approximate in salt-proportions to sea-water, though of different concentration. The notion, therefore, that the similarity of salt-content between the cell-substance and sea-water has a real historical significance is hard to escape, even though it be (as Loeb has said) no more than a "poetical dream."

However this may be, the work of many observers, prominent among them Herbst, Loeb, Osterhout and R. S. Lillie, has shown that the salts of the sea-water and those of the blood or lymph alike form "physiologically balanced" solutions, *i. e.*, they are present in such proportions as to maintain a normal equilibrium with the cells of the organism. Some of these salts are actually poisonous when acting alone, but their injurious effect is counteracted or antagonized by the presence of other salts; sodium chloride, for instance, is thus antagonized by calcium chloride, and a similar balance exists between magnesium and calcium. A wide vista here is opened of the fundamentally important rôle played by the inorganic salts in protoplasmic action, and even in animal behavior,[1] but this subject lies outside the scope of this work.[2]

The organic constituents of the cell [3] are for the most part compounds of carbon with oxygen, nitrogen and other elements, and some of these are the most complicated of known chemical compounds. The time-honored classification of these substances is into (1) *carbohydrates* (2) *fats*, and (3) *proteins*, the first two being non-nitrogenous compounds of carbon, hydrogen and oxygen, while the third contain also nitrogen, and commonly small quantities of sulphur and sometimes of phosphorus. Many recent writers, however, include the true fats and oils in a larger group of *lipins* to which are assigned various other fat-like bodies such as lecithin or cephaline which contain nitrogen and phosphorus in addition to carbon, hydrogen and oxygen. All the substances of this group agree in their solubility in chloroform and other fat-solvents, and their insolubility in water.

[1] *Cf*. Loeb ('06, '16).

[2] According to Macallum ('08), the nucleus contains no potassium, no chlorides and no phosphates, and probably no sodium or magnesium; but iron and calcium appear to be generally present. Macallum believes that inorganic salts are in general absent from the nucleus and that when such substances as calcium, or iron are present, they are always in organic combination. This fact is ascribed by him to the impermeability of the nuclear membrane to inorganic salts; and he makes the interesting suggestion that it may thus serve to protect the intra-nuclear nucleins, or nucleo-proteins from the action of inorganic salts contained in the cytoplasm and thus to insure their stability. The osmotic properties of the nuclear membrane may thus be a factor in heredity (*op. cit.*, p. 650). *Cf*. Mathews, p. 176.

[3] *Cf*. Mathews, *Physiological Chemistry*, 1915, and Halliburton, *Essentials of Chemical Physiology*, 9th Ed., 1916.

2. The Proteins and their Derivatives

The proteins are of especial interest since they are the most complex and varied of the cell-components, and there is also reason to believe that they form the main chemical basis of the apparatus of heredity. Recent research, it is true, has emphasized anew the importance of both the carbohydrates and the lipins in the fundamental operations of the cell; nevertheless it seems certain that in most cases the proteins (together with water) constitute the main bulk of the active cell-substance and of its more constant structural components, including the hyaloplasm and many of the formed elements such as plastids, many forms of granules, fibrillæ, chromosomes and nucleoli, and the material of the astral rays and spindle-fibers. A great number of proteins are known. A large and increasing body of evidence shows that some of them differ characteristically from species to species [1] and even indicate that they may constitute the fundamental chemical basis of heredity.

a. General Nature. The proteins habitually appear in the colloidal state, and some of them have the largest and most complex of known molecules, as is shown by their high molecular weight, low diffusibility, and the great number and complexity of their cleavage-products. Chemical formulas for the proteins have little meaning apart from the structure of the protein molecule as revealed on the one hand by its breaking up by means of **hydrolysis** into simpler components (the building-stones or " Bausteine" of Kossel), on the other by the progressive artificial recombination or synthesis of these components to form more complex substances. Some of the compounds thus artificially produced, such as the polypeptids, are in the view of Emil Fischer actually proteins, or at least would have been classed as such had they first been met with in nature (Robertson, '18).

By these methods it has been established that the protein molecule is in general built up from a series of the *amino-acids*, familiar examples of which are *glycin* ($C_2 H_5 NO_2$), *leucin* ($C_8 H_{13} NO_2$), and *tyrosin* ($C_9 H_{11} NO_3$). The smallest number of component amino-acids occurs in the protamines, which therefore may be regarded as the simplest of proteins; and it was especially their study which led Kossel to his general hypothesis concerning the constitution of the protein molecule in more complex forms. Proteins vary with the nature, number and proportions of these component units and also with their mode of linkage; hence the immense number of possible combina-

---

[1] This is shown, for instance, by the fact that the hæmoglobins of different species differ characteristically in form of crystallization (Reichert and Brown, '09); by the remarkable specific precipitin-reactions of blood-sera from different animals (Nuttall, '04); by the phenomena of anaphylaxis; and by the differences shown by the protamines from the sperm-nuclei of different fishes. (See tables in Mathews, '15, pp. 128, 129). An interesting discussion of the general subject is given in Loeb's *The Organism as a Whole*, Chap. III, 1916.

tions and the corresponding diversity which distinguishes the proteins above all other known substances. To employ a figure of Kossel's, just as the letters of the alphabet may be variously grouped to form an immense multitude of words, so a comparatively small number of amino-acids (about a score of them are known) may by different combinations and groupings build up a practically unlimited number of distinct proteins. Kossel even went so far as to maintain that every peculiarity of the species and every occurrence affecting the individual may be indicated by special combinations of these "building stones" or molecular components; and physiologists have shown a growing readiness to accept the conclusion that the specificity of organisms generally may have its root in that of their component proteins.[1]

In the "simple proteins" the molecule on being treated by enzymes or by acids breaks up wholly into the amino-acids or their derivatives; such proteins are the protamines, histones, albumins or globulins. These proteins readily combine with other substances to form salt-like compounds, thus giving rise to still more complex "compound" or "conjugated" proteins. The substances with which such unions may take place are of varied nature; they include many acids, bases and salts, both organic and inorganic, various lipoids, and perhaps such substances as toxins, anti-toxins, hormones and enzymes.[2] Proteins readily combine with other proteins, and many of the proteins of the tissues and tissue-fluids are believed to be thus united, forming complexes which, as a number of biochemists have suggested, may be characteristic of these several tissues and thus offer a key to their physiological individuality. Many proteins or their components will unite with *dye-stuffs* to form colored compounds—a fact of fundamental importance for the theory of cytological staining, though the precise nature of the combination is still under discussion (p. 646). It is also of cytological interest that some of the natural pigments (*e. g.*, hæmoglobin or the phycoerythrin of plants) are conjugated proteins.

A remarkable peculiarity of the proteins, especially interesting for the theory of cytological staining, is their *amphoteric* character, *i. e.*, the capacity of one and the same protein to form a salt-like compound with either an acid or a base. This property is due to varying electrical charges, the protein-radical being in the one case electro-positive, in the other electro-negative. Some proteins, such as protamine, are predominantly basic, others predominantly acid, such as casein, or the "nucleins." It

---

[1] "There can be no doubt that on the basis of our present knowledge proteins are in most or practically all cases the bearers of this specificity" (Loeb, '16, p. 61). "The specific character of every animal or plant may be determined ultimately by the specific characters of their structure-forming proteins" (R. S. Lillie, '18, p. 77).

[2] Robertson, '18, p. 156.

was demonstrated experimentally by Hardy ('oo) that the charge of the suspended particles in a simple protein solution is determined by the reaction of the medium; in an acid medium (*i. e.*, in the presence of an excess of H-ions) they become electro-positive and behave as bases, while in the presence of alkali (with an excess of OH-ions) they become electro-negative and behave as acids.[1] At an intermediate point, which is neutral or isoelectric, they are chemically indifferent and unable for the time being to enter into combination. The extreme importance of these facts for the practical use of staining agents will later be indicated (p. 649).

b. The Nucleo-proteins. Among the compound proteins a special interest is offered by the nucleo-proteins since they form the principal chemical basis of the nuclear substance and by earlier writers were identified with the "chromatin" of cytologists. Substances related to nucleo-proteins occur, however, also in the cytoplasm, and it should also be borne in mind that the word "chromatin" is no longer employed to denote a single or definite chemical compound (p. 88). It was shown by Miescher in 1871, that when cells can be obtained of practically unmixed type and in large quantity (*e. g.*, pus-cells, fish-sperm, or yeast-cells, etc.) and are treated with artificial gastric juice (hydrochloric-pepsin) the cytoplasm is digested, leaving only the nuclei. Nuclear substance ("chromatin") thus obtained in large quantity and practically pure for quantitative analysis was found to consist largely of a complex protein, rich in phosphorus, which Miescher called "nuclein," giving to it the formula $C_{29}H_{49}N_9P_3O_{22}$. By Altmann, it was later shown (1889) that Miescher's "nuclein" may be split into a protein base, rich in nitrogen (protamine or histone in case of the sperm-nucleus) and a complex organic acid containing phosphorus to which he gave the name of nucleic acid: further, that "nuclein" may be synthetically re-formed by recombination of these two substances. It thus became clear that in some cases "nuclein" or nucleo-protein is a salt-like compound in which a simpler protein plays the part of a base (*i. e.*, is electro-positive),[2] and this was confirmed by many later workers.

The simplest and best-known of the nucleo-proteins have been obtained from the sperm-nuclei in fishes which the work of Kossel and his followers showed to be a protamine in salt-like union with nucleic acid; and Kossel likewise demonstrated that the nucleo-proteins of the thymus gland and of the erythrocytes of birds is a salt-like compound between histone and

---

[1] For the explanation of this see p. 649. *Cf.* Robertson ('09), Loeb ('04, '22), Mathews ('15,) Bayliss ('18.)

[2] Since the amount of phosphorus in nucleic acid is constant, the total amount of this substance in nucleo-proteins may be taken as a measure of the relative proportions of nucleic acid in the nucleo-protein compound. It was at first assumed that "chromatin" might in some cases even be pure nucleic acid (Kossel, Halliburton), but this has not been substantiated.

nucleic acid. In sea-urchin sperm Mathews found the basic component to be *arbacin*, a substance related to both protamine and histone. In general, however, the nucleo-proteins are of more complex composition, containing a larger proportion of protein, and a greater number of protein radicals; and much evidence exists to show that a large number of such protein bases and their combinations may exist, among which may possibly be organic enzymes and hormones, though this is conjectural.[1] The components of the nucleo-proteins in general, and the order of their disassociation upon hydrolysis are shown in the following scheme.[2]

Nucleo-protein

Protein   "Nuclein"

Protein   Nucleic Acid

Phosphoric Acid   Nucleosides

Carbohydrate   Nuclein Bases
a. Pentose in plants   *Purine Bases*
a. Hexose in animals   Adenine
                       Guanine
                       Pyrimidine Bases
                       Cytosine
                       Thymine (in animals)
                       Uracil (in plants)

As is here shown, the nucleic acid itself splits into phosphoric acid and nucleosides, which are compounds of various bases with carbohydrate. The nucleic acids are, however, of two types, characteristic respectively of animals and of plants. In percentage composition the two are not dissimilar, as may be seen from the formulas $C_{43}H_{57}N_{15}O_{30}P_4$ for animal thymus nucleic acid (Steudel), and $C_{38}H_{55}N_{15}O_{32}P_4$ for that from yeast (Levene), and both alike yield as cleavage products the purine derivatives guanine and adenine,[3] and also the pyrimidine derivative cytosine. On the other hand, plant nucleic acid yields uracil in place of thymine, and a carbohydrate pentose group in place of a hexose.[4] Miescher showed that nucleoproteins are more or less resistant to pepsin-hydrochloric digestion, a fact

---

[1] Mathews, p. 180.

[2] From Sherman ('18), based on the works of Wells and of Jones, and the earlier results of Kossel.

[3] In this respect, according to Kossel, the true nucleic acids of the nucleus differ from the nucleoproteids or "pseudo-nucleins" of the cytoplasm (prepared from egg-yolk or milk). Some biochemists have concluded, accordingly, that nucleic acid and true nucleo-proteins are found only in the nucleus (Mathews, '15, p. 174).

[4] These statements are given on the authority of Jones ('14).

of importance when taken in connection with the staining-reactions as an indicator of nucleo-proteins ("chromatin") in the cell (p. 652). It has been commonly assumed that the variations shown in respect to this resistance are due to varying proportions between the nucleic acid and the protein component; but Kossel's later work has shown that another factor probably lies in varying degrees of the firmness of the union between them.[1] The peptic digestion test of "chromatin," like the staining tests (p. 650), is therefore by no means a trustworthy one. To some extent, both these tests are supplemented by the nuclease test, introduced into cytological technique by Oes in 1908–10 and more recently extended by Van Herwerden.[2] Nucleic acid is readily split up by the nucleases (enzymes found in the pancreas and many other kinds of cells) and most nuclei thus treated lose more or less completely their basophily. This test, too, is defective; the sperm-nuclei of mammals, for example, resist nuclease-digestion as they do peptic (Van Herwerden, '16). It must be admitted, therefore, that we still have no certain means of identifying "chromatin" in the cell apart from its morphological history. Opinion among biochemists as to whether true nucleo-proteins (i. e., such as contain true nucleic acid) occur in the cytoplasm seems to be somewhat conflicting. Since nuclear substance is discharged into the cytosome at every mitosis (p. 126) we should expect to find nucleo-proteins there; and there is some direct evidence that such is the case—for instance, Masing's ('10) studies on the amount of nucleic acid in sea-urchin eggs at the end of cleavage as compared with that in the unsegmented egg. Indications in the same direction are offered by the observation of Van Herwerden ('13) that the basophilic microsomes of these eggs are dissolved by nuclease, as is also basichromatin.

It is an interesting fact, which has been emphasized by biochemists, that apart from the characteristic differences between animals and plants, referred to above, the nucleic acids of the nucleus are on the whole remarkably uniform, showing with present methods of analysis no differences in any degree commensurate with those from the various species of cells from which they are derived. In this respect they show a remarkable contrast to the proteins, which, whether simple or compound, seem to be of inexhaustible variety. It has been suggested, accordingly, that the differences between different "chromatins" depend upon their basic or protein components and not upon their nucleic acids.[3] Interesting questions are here raised

---

[1] For instance, the sperm-nuclei of various fishes and echinoderms examined by Kossel are readily attacked (so as to lose their basophily) by 1% hydrochloric acid, while those of mammals are but slightly affected. See Burian, '06; Kossel, '13, '14; Van Herwerden, '16.

[2] See Oes ('10); Van Herwerden ('13, '14, '16).

[3] See Mathews ('15), Levene ('17).

concerning the qualitative differences of the chromosomes and of their changes of staining-reaction at different periods of the nuclear cycle (p. 652).

3. Staining-Reactions of the Cell-Substance [1]

Staining agents are indispensable adjuncts to our microscopical analysis of the cell; but experience has shown that they may form a prolific source of error when employed as tests for the chemical nature of the cell-components or even for their morphological identification. Certain elementary sources of error must first be excluded.

First, color in itself is devoid of all significance. For example, by the use of methyl-green and eosin the nucleus is typically stained green and the cytoplasm red; but the same cell gives the reverse color effect if stained by safranin and light green, the nucleus now being red and the cytoplasm green.

Secondly, the most diverse structures may often be stained alike by the same dye. In cartilage, for example, both the basichromatin of the nuclei and the inter-cellular matrix (a non-protoplasmic product of the cell) are alike stained by methyl green, though unrelated chemically. Again, many kinds of granules and other formed cytoplasmic elements resemble the nuclear basichromatin in staining-reaction, and hence have actually been regarded as "cytoplasmic chromatin"; but we cannot for this reason alone conclude that they are of nuclear origin or chemically similar to the nuclear "chromatin." The naïve conclusion, without further evidence, that similarity in staining-reaction necessarily indicates similarity of chemical or morphological nature has indeed been one of the most frequent sources of error in cytological work.

Thirdly, the character of staining-reactions, as every cytologist knows, is profoundly affected by the reaction of the medium and by the processes of fixation, mordaunting, and the like. This applies especially to treatment by metallic salts, which may enter into combination with the organic components of the cell so that they cannot be removed by simple washing. This process, which is really a kind of mordaunting, may be favorable to certain stains, and unfavorable to others. The effects and nature of staining are therefore best examined after fixation by non-electrolytes, such as alcohol or heat, which produce a minimum of chemical change in the organic cell-constituents; but in other respects, unluckily, such agents are usually far inferior.

Even when all such sources of error have been eliminated the nature of

[1] A useful discussion of this subject is given by Mann ('02). Among other important works may be mentioned those of Mathews ('98), Heidenhain ('02, '07, '14) and earlier works, Michælis ('09, '10, '20), Bechold ('12), and Bayliss ('21, '23).

the process of staining offers a complicated problem that has been but incompletely solved; for it is still uncertain how far dyeing is a chemical process and how far a physical one, *i. e.*, in what measure it involves a chemical union between the dye-stuff and the stainable material, and in what measure a merely physical process or adsorption of the dye by surface-action. Nevertheless, it now seems certain that the effect is often to a considerable extent conditioned by the chemical relation between the dye-stuff and the dyed material. Cytological staining methods may, therefore, have a certain value as *indicators;* but since the physical phenomena of adsorption also may play an important part in the process, we must admit that for the present *the main use of cytological staining processes is to make the cell-components more clearly distinguishable by the microscope.*[1]

The foundation of the chemical theory of staining was laid by Ehrlich ('77, '91, etc.). Cytologists long since classified coloring agents as "nuclear" and "plasmatic" (or "plasma") dyes, the former (such as carmine or hæmatoxylin) displaying a marked tendency to stain the nucleus, the latter (such as eosin) staining more especially the cytoplasm.[2] Ehrlich first pointed out, in case of the coal-tar or "anilin" dyes, that this difference is correlated with a definite difference of chemical composition. These dyes are in general organic compounds in which (to state the matter in the most general way), a color-determining radical (chromatophore) is united with another radical to form a salt-like compound. In the various dyes thus formed, the color radical plays the part sometimes of the anion (acid), sometimes of the kation (base)—*i. e.*, in some cases is electro-negative, in others electro-positive; hence Ehrlich's designation of these dyes as "acid" and "basic" respectively. These terms do not refer to the reaction of the dye itself, but only to the nature of the color-determining component; an "acid" dye may indeed actually have a neutral or alkaline reaction, and *vice-versa*.[3] It seems preferable, therefore, to designate the "acid" dyes as *acidic*.

A typical example of an acidic dye is eosin, which is a sodium salt of the color-acid tetrabrom-fluorescein; and of a basic dye, methylen-blue, which is the chloride of a color-base, tetramethyldiphenthiazin.[4] As already indicated, this distinction bears no relation to actual color. Basic dyes may be blue (methylen-blue, gentian violet), red (safranin, basic fuchsin),

[1] *Cf.* Bayliss ('21).

[2] The history of the subject from 1850 to 1880, is considered in Mann's work, above cited, and also in the interesting articles by Gierke in early volumes of the *Zeitschrift für wissenschaftliche Mikroskopie*. Here we only refer to the introduction of the use of carmine by Hartig and Gerlach (1854–58), of double staining by Schwarz and Ranvier (1867–68), of hæmatoxylin by Waldeyer (1863) and Böhmer (1865) and of the coal tar-colors by Beneke, Frey and Waldeyer (1862–63).

[3] Ehrlich also distinguished as "neutral" dyes those in which a color-base and a color-acid are united in the same compound; but these need not here be considered.

[4] From Mann.

green (methyl green), or yellow (Bismarck brown). Similar differences are shown by the acidic stains. Examples are methyl-blue, eosin, Congo red, light green and orange. In some cases the same color-group may play the part of either a base or an acid, an example of which is fuchsin, a red dye of which the color-determining component is rosaniline. By appropriate chemical treatment this may appear in either the "basic" or "acidic" form, being in the former case a hydrochloride of the base rosaniline, in the latter a sodium salt of sulphonic acid (a derivative of rosaniline).

The most convincing demonstration of these distinctions is offered by the simultaneous use of basic and acidic dyes in a mixture,[1] the one most commonly employed containing basic methyl-green and acidic red (acid fuchsin), which acts electively on the cell in such a manner as to stain the nucleus (basichromatin) green and the cytosome red. As Ehrlich pointed out, however, both nucleus and cytoplasm usually contain elements of opposite staining-capacity to that of their principal components. Thus, the cytoplasm, while predominantly *oxyphilic* (*i. e.*, showing an affinity for acidic stains) nevertheless often contains granules or other structures that are intensely *basophilic*. Again, in the case of the nucleus only certain constituents are basophilic ("chromatin" in the older sense, karyosomes) while others are strongly oxyphilic (plasmosomes, "linin" in the older sense); hence Heidenhain's distinction between "basi-chromatin" and "oxychromatin" (p. 88).

These various facts led Ehrlich to conclude that staining results from a chemical union between dyes and the tissue-elements; and this conclusion has been supported by many later students of the subject. On the other hand, it has been demonstrated also that many dyes are energetically taken up from their solutions by powdered charcoal, filter paper, silk, and other inert substances in a state of fine subdivision. Doubts, therefore, were early raised concerning the chemical theory of staining by Gierke ('99), Rawitz ('97) and others, above all by A. Fischer ('99), who brought forward a large body of evidence demonstrating the important effect upon cytological staining of the physical processes of adsorption and the like.

Fischer showed that in combinations of different stains the effect is largely influenced by such factors as the relative size of the granules or other stainable elements, the order in which the dyes are used, their relative concentrations, and their differences in rate of diffusion. He showed that the double staining of granules of coagulated proteins by the simultaneous use of an acidic and a basic dye, or even of two acidic or two basic dyes,

---

[1] Similar results can of course be produced by their separate and successive action, but the interpretation is here always more doubtful because of the artificial factor introduced by the manipulation of the two dyes.

may be thus wholly determined. If these granules be stained with a suitable mixture of picric acid and acid fuchsin, or of eosin and light green (all acidic dyes) the large granules are in the first case yellow and the small red, while in the second case, the large ones are red and the small ones green. The double staining is here due to different rates of diffusion, the more rapid dye taking possession of the granule before the slower has had time to act; but in the end all the granules ultimately stain alike, since the slower dye finally displaces or covers the faster. More recently, Bechold ('12) has shown by accurate studies that the density of the stainable object has an important effect upon the rate of diffusion of the dye, and hence on the staining-capacity.

Such facts clearly show that physical factors play an important part in cytological staining-reactions; nevertheless the evidence now seems to indicate that with certain reservations the chemical theory of staining is still tenable. It has been clearly demonstrated by Heidenhain, Michælis, Bechold, and others that the adsorption of dyes by insoluble substances in fine suspension (or otherwise finely divided) is conditioned by the chemical nature of those substances. Substances that are electro-negative (*e. g.*, kaolin, siliceous marl, silicic acid) adsorb in general only basic dyes; those that are electro-positive (clay, iron hydroxide) adsorb only the acidic; while the amphoteric substances are stainable by both kinds of dyes, and the indifferent faintly by both.[1] All this indicates that the staining-process is here not one of adsorption alone but involves a chemical reaction; and this seems to be proved in certain cases by the fact that products of the chemical exchange are later found in the liquid (Michælis, '20).

To return to the chemical theory of staining, it was shown by the early work of Miescher (1874) that isolated nucleic acid will form insoluble intensely colored precipitates with basic tar colors. Malfatti ('91) and Lilienfeld ('93, '94) observed that in a mixture of basic methyl-green and red acid fuchsin free nucleic acid stains intensely green while albumen is stained red. The same observers demonstrated that compounds of metaphosphoric acid and albumin in various proportions stain bluish red graduating into pure red as the percentage of phosphorus diminishes. Observations of this type indicate that the differences of staining capacity displayed by different forms of nuclei, or by different conditions of the same nucleus, may be interpreted as due to varying proportions between the nucleic acid and the basic protein components, the former being at a maximum during mitosis when the chromosomes are so markedly basophilic. In harmony with this are the later experiments of R. Lillie, Pentimalli, and others on the behavior of nuclei and chromosomes in the electrostatic

---

[1] See table in Bechold ('12, p. 29).

field, which demonstrate their electro-negative or acidic character (p. 189). It has been supported by numerous more direct experiments on staining reactions, and especially those of Mathews ('98), Mann ('02), Heidenhain ('02, '03, '07, etc.), and Loeb ('18).

Mathews found that acidic dyes (used in the form of neutral salts) have no effect upon solutions of albumin or albumose until a small amount of free acid is added when an intensely colored insoluble precipitate (a combination of the color-acid and protein) is at once thrown down. With basic dyes the opposite result is obtained. If added to neutral or acid solutions of albumose they produce no effect; but if the solution be made slightly *alkaline* a deeply colored insoluble compound is precipitated. In like manner, egg-albumin coagulated by heat or alcohol fails to stain in neutral solutions of either acid or basic dyes [1] but is instantly and intensely colored by acidic dyes if the latter be acidified, in basic dyes if these be rendered slightly alkaline. Conversely, no effect, or but a slight one, is produced by acidified basic dyes or by acidic ones rendered slightly alkaline.

It is the same with the staining of cells (from the liver, pancreas, and muscles) fixed in neutral or acid alcohol. When such preparations are treated with neutral solutions of basic dyes (such as methyl green, safranin or thionin) a pure "chromatin stain" results, but if the section be first treated, even for a very short time, in a weak alkaline solution (of sodium carbonate), or if the staining fluid itself be made slightly alkaline, not only the chromatin but also the *cytoplasm* is intensely and permanently stained. In this way the cytoplasm of these cells may be given a powerful "plasmastain" by the use of various typical "nuclear" (basic) dyes. With acidic dyes, on the other hand, the cytoplasm is stained only in acid solutions.

These results, confirmed fully by the work especially of Heidenhain, are explained under the chemical theory of staining by the amphoteric nature of the proteins. After treatment by acids (which are ingredients of most cytological fixing agents), or upon staining in acidified solutions, the cytoplasmic proteins are in general oxyphilic, *i. e.*, they behave as bases and hence combine with acidic dyes. In alkaline solutions they show the reverse behavior, becoming acid and hence combining with basic dyes. The nuclear proteins, on the other hand, are for the most part electro-negative or acid, because of the large proportion of nucleic acid which they contain; and in general, therefore, are basophilic. Quite similar are the results of Loeb ('18) on gelatine. Stained in neutral red (a basic dye) it gives off its color in acid solutions; stained in acid fuchsin the color is given off in alkaline solutions. For in the first case gelatine becomes electro-positive or basic, in

---

[1] A temporary physical imbibition of the dye may take place, but the color thus produced may readily be washed out in water.

the second electro-negative or acid and fixes (*i. e.*, combines with) or gives off the dye accordingly.

The simplest interpretation of these results, evidently, is that staining involves an actual chemical combination to form a salt-like combination; and this explanation has been adopted by Heidenhain as a result of his above-cited extended experiments and by Bechold, Michælis, Loeb and many others. Bayliss ('21, etc.) has made an interesting attempt to interpret results of the foregoing type in terms of surface-action and electrical charges; but at the same time he emphasizes the fact "that the physical properties of a surface ultimately depend on its chemical nature" ('23, p. 27). Bechold, Michælis and others have recognized the probability that the part played by the physical process of adsorption is a preliminary one, the dissolved or finely suspended dye-stuffs being first taken up by a process of surface-action on the part of the protoplasmic particles and then more intimately combined with them by a process which to say the least approaches a true chemical union.

All this makes it highly probable that the oxyphilic or basophilic staining-reactions of the cell-components are in greater or less degree determined by chemical conditions; and the possibility is here undoubtedly offered of achieving ultimately a rational micro-chemistry of the cell, such as Ehrlich always had in mind. It must, however, be admitted that we are still very far indeed from its realization. It may again be emphasized that mere similarity of staining-reactions is always an unsafe guide either to morphological or chemical nature. Basic dyes, for example, are not in any sense specific tests either for "chromatin" (basichromatin) or for nucleo-proteins. For, as Mathews' experiments showed, even the basic or neutral cytoplasmic proteins readily become basophilic in alkaline solution; and there are also a number of strongly basophilic compound proteins known to be of cytoplasmic origin and to contain no nucleic acid. Examples of these are offered by mucin or the inter-cellular substance of cartilage, both of which are conjugated proteins containing a complex organic acid (chondriotic) other than nucleic. The basic dyes are therefore merely indicators for proteins in the acid state, or for basic proteins linked with acids.

With these results in mind it will be instructive to glance at certain problems concerning the staining-reactions of the cell-components which first took on definite form with the classical studies of Heidenhain on leucocytes ('93, '94) by the use of simultaneous staining with mixtures of acidic and basic dyes. Heidenhain emphasized the conclusion that the periodic changes of staining-reaction on the part of the nuclear structures may largely be due to changing properties between the basic (protein) and the acid (nucleic acid) components of the "chromatin." Basichromatin and oxychromatin ("chromatin' and "linin" in the older sense), as was earlier emphasized by Van Beneden, are by no means to be regarded as permanent or fixed bodies, but may change their color-reactions by combining with or giving off phosphorus (nucleic acid), according to varying physiological conditions of the nucleus or of the cell. Many examples of such changes of chromatophily have been given in the foregoing pages, for example: the intense increase of basophily on the part of the chromo-

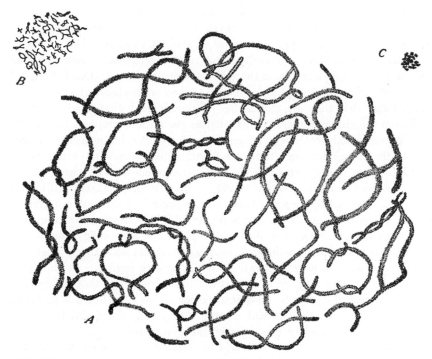

Fig. 312.—Chromosomes of the germinal vesicle in the shark *Pristiurus*, at different periods, drawn to the same scale (RÜCKERT).

A, At the period of maximal size and minimal staining-capacity (egg 3 mm. in diameter); *B*, later period (egg 13 mm. in diameter); *C*, at the close of ovarian life, of minimal size and maximal staining-power.

somes during the prophases of mitosis, the corresponding decrease following its final phases in ordinary somatic cells, and the still more marked decrease so often seen in the auxocytes, particularly in the germinal vesicle of the animal ovum (p. 351). The decrease of basophily is accomplished by marked, and often extremely striking processes of growth on the part of these structures (Fig. 312). Not less striking is the fact that their later resumption of basophily is accompanied by a marked decrease in size, very often also by a giving off or leaving behind of a quantity of residual oxyphilic or but slightly basophilic material (p. 355).

All this falls in line with the assumption that during the vegetative activities of the cell the protein bases of the nucleus increase in quantity, the acidic character of the chromatin (and hence its basophily) correspondingly diminishing as the affinities of the nucleic acid radical are more completely satisfied. Whether this means an actual increase in the protein components, or a diminution of the nucleic acid, can only be surmised. Perhaps both may be true; for the enormous growth of the chromosomes, accompanied in some cases by a complete reversal of their staining-reactions seems to indicate a progressive accumulation of protein-components and a giving up, or even a complete loss, of the acid component (p. 650). One is tempted to suspect that the basophily of the nucleoli so often observed at this time may mean that they are storehouses of nucleic acid that has been given off from the chromosomes; further, that as the nucleus prepares for mitosis the accumulated protein-components are in considerable measure set free while the remainder are left in combination (or recombine) with nucleic acid to form the spireme-threads and chromosomes. The chromatin is thus restored to its original basophilic condition in preparation for division, only the essential components being carried over into the next cell-generation. From the point of view thus suggested it is interesting that the cast-off material (which may contain both oxyphilic and basophilic components) is often thrown out into the cytoplasm as "residual substance" when the nucleus breaks down in preparation for the ensuing mitosis. In part, perhaps, this process may be a mere discarding of material that has played its part during the growth and differentiation of the cell,[1] but it is probable that in some cases the residual substance plays an active and important part in the constructive processes of the cytoplasm.

An important, little explored field of inquiry is here opened. At this point we may mention the hypothesis that the various nucleo-proteins (or chromatins) are determined by their protein rather than by their nucleic-acid components (p. 644). Mathews suggested that in a chemical sense the nucleic-acid component may be regarded as "a colloidal, gelatinous substratum in the nature of an organic skeleton to which the specifically active, more labile albuminous constituents, possibly of a catalytic nature, may be attached.[2]" Goldschmidt emphasized the biochemical evidence that certain enzymes (oxydases, hydrolytic ferments) are often linked with nucleo-proteins. "The thought is thus suggested that it is the function of

[1] Cf. the "histogenetic plasm" of Weisman, p. 498.
[2] Mathews, '15, p. 176.

chromatin to adsorb the heredity-enzymes and to serve as their skeleton." [1]
This suggestion is of much interest, but to the cytologist it seems to reverse
the conditions as actually observed. For, as has been indicated (p. 351),
in some cases the chromosomes may become nearly or quite oxyphilic
without loss of their identity; and in others, the nuclear network to which
they may give rise undergoes a similar change; hence the conclusion of
certain observers that the "chromatin" may wholly disappear from the
nucleus. So far as the staining-reactions show, therefore, it is not the basophilic component (nucleic acid) that persists, but the so-called "achromatic" or oxyphilic substance. The nucleic acid component comes and goes
in different phases of cell-activity, and it is the oxyphilic component that
seems to form the essential structural basis of the nuclear organization.
This would accord perfectly with the "achromatin hypotheses" of chromosome continuity (p. 895) and also with the accumulation of basophilic
material ("chromatin") in the nucleoli while the chromosomes lose their
basophily, and often also, in appearance, their identity in the general nuclear framework. Mathews seems to have overlooked these facts in his
criticism of theories of heredity "based on the behavior of the nucleic
acid of the nucleus, *that is, the behavior and number of the chromosomes*"
(italics by the writer).

III. GENERAL PHYSIOLOGICAL RELATIONS BETWEEN NUCLEUS AND CYTOSOME

1. General

In his celebrated work, *Leçons sur les phénomènes de la vie* (1878), Claude
Bernard grouped the constructive processes of the cell in the two categories
of *chemical synthesis* by which specific organic substances are formed, and
morphological synthesis by which these substances are built into a specifically organized fabric. Bernard was one of the first clearly to see that the
two categories represent fundamentally only different phases or degrees
of the same general phenomenon. The primary agent in both he believed to
be the nucleus, considering the cytoplasm to be characterized by the predominance of the destructive operations by which energy is set free. This
highly fruitful generalization now rests on a solid basis of known fact; but
it was orginnally stated in too simple a form. All physiologists, probably,
will agree that the principal arena for the liberation of energy is the cytoplasm, and that this process may for a time go on in the absence of a nucleus (p. 659). It is equally certain that the nucleus plays an important
part in organic synthesis. It is impossible, however, to consider the nu-

[1] Goldschmidt, '17a, p. 94. See also '17b, p. 608.

cleus as the sole agent in synthesis, as is made obvious by the fact, among many others, that the photosynthesis of carbohydrates from H_2O and CO_2 (the most fundamental of all organic syntheses) takes place only in the chloroplasts, which are strictly cytoplasmic structures; and it has further been shown that photosynthesis continues in chlorophyll-containing masses of protoplasm from which the nucleus has been removed (Klebs, '79, '87), and according to Molisch ('04) even in isolated chloroplasts.[1] There is now indeed little or no evidence to show that the nucleus is the actual formative center of the cell.

The influence of the nucleus upon organic synthesis nevertheless remains a fundamentally important fact. How this influence is exerted still remains almost unknown; but it is probably connected with exchanges of material between nucleus and cytosome which continually or intermittently take place. This fact is most obvious in the cyclical reproductive processes of the cell. At the time of mitosis, when the nuclear membrane breaks down, a considerable and sometimes very large amount of nuclear material is directly set free into the cytoplasm. Conversely, at the close of mitosis the nucleus undergoes extensive growth, the material for which process, obviously, must be taken into the nucleus from the surrounding cytoplasm. But there is other ground for the conclusion that exchanges of material between nucleus and cytoplasm likewise go on during the vegetative state of the cell, whether by processes of osmosis or, as some observers maintain, by an actual extrusion of formed elements through the nuclear membrane. The opinion has steadily gained ground that the nucleus may be a storehouse of enzymes, or of substances that activate the cytoplasmic enzymes, and that these susbtances may be concerned with synthesis as well as with destructive processes.[2] To cite Hopkins "We have arrived, indeed, at a stage when, with a huge array of examples before us it is logical to conclude that all metabolic tissue reactions are catalyzed by enzymes, and, knowing the properties of these, we have every right to conclude that all reactions may be so catalyzed in the synthetic as well as in the opposite sense." Too little is known as yet concerning this subject to justify its extended discussion here; but it may be pointed out that the suggestions which it offers have already opened interesting possibilities concerning the problems both of genetics and cytology.

2. Nuclear Size and Cytoplasmic Growth

We may here again refer to observations and experiments which prove that artificial increase in the size of the nucleus leads to a corresponding increase

[1] Jost ('07), p. 107.
[2] See, for example, Bayliss ('13, '18). An interesting discussion of the enzymes is given by Loeb ('18). See also Loeb and Chamberlain ('15) and Goldschmidt ('16, '17, '20).

in the size of the cytosome by a compensatory growth of the cytoplasm (pp. 100, 729). Especially convincing is the demonstration of this offered by Gerassimoff's experiments on *Spirogyra* (Fig. 313).[1] Since these experiments involve no disturbance of the cytoplasm other than that which results from the nuclear change, they seem to afford decisive proof that the

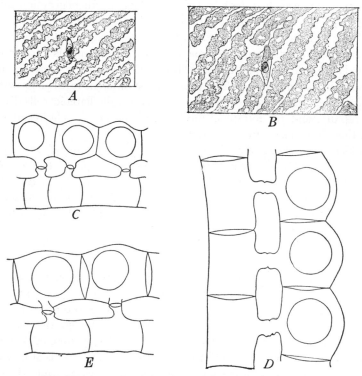

Fig. 313.—Normal and giant forms of *Spirogyra bellis* (GERASSIMOFF).

A, cell from a normal (haploid) plant; *B*, cell from an artificially produced giant (diploid) plant of the same species; *C*, part of two conjugating normal filaments; *D*, corresponding view of conjugating diploid filaments, forming tetraploid zygospores; *E*, conjugation of normal (haploid) and giant (diploid) filaments, to form triploid zygotes. *C*, *D*, and *E* drawn to the same scale.

nucleus is the *primary* agent in the constructive processes of cytoplasmic growth. The experiments of Boveri, the Marchals, and others (p. 729) though in some respects less direct, have placed this conclusion on a broader basis by the demonstration that within a given cell-type the cytoplasmic volume varies with the number of chromosomes that enter the nucleus (p. 729). In the mosses the relation seems to be essentially the same as

[1] See p. 25.

Spirogyra; for the Marchals found (p. 730) that in diploid or tetraploid gametophytes the cells, both somatic and germinal, are approximately two or four times that of the normal (haploid) forms. This applies to nucleus and cytosome alike (as in *Spirogyra*), the normal karyoplasmic ratio being thus retained. In sea-urchin eggs, the proof is less evident because the cell-size is here affected by compensatory changes in the rate of cell-division. The segmenting eggs may here be either haploid (parthenogenetic), diploid (normal, fertilized eggs) or tetraploid (fertilized monaster-eggs, p. 729) and the size of the resulting cells differs correspondingly. In each of these cases the ratio of cytoplasmic volume to nuclear is the same as in the normal egg (as is the case in the tetraploid cells of *Spirogyra* or the mosses). Here, however, the size-differences do not result from different rates of growth (as in *Spirogyra*), but from different rates of cleavage, the haploid cells dividing most rapidly, and the tetraploid most slowly (p. 728).[1] The result is the same, though here seen from a different angle.

Winkler ('16) shows that in tetraploid *gigas* mutants of the tomato (*Solanum*), not only are the cells (including the pollen-grains, Fig. 350 A-H) larger than those of the normal diploid form but *also the chloroplasts* (I, J). This seems clearly to show that the increase of nuclear content affects the growth not merely of the cytosome as a whole, but also that of its formed components (*Cf.* p. 732).[2]

The relation between chromosome-number and nuclear size is well shown in larvæ (usually abnormal) from dispermic eggs, in which cleavage is typically multipolar and usually leads to an irregular distribution of the chromosomes to the cells of different embryonic regions. The size of these cells, and their nuclei, is likewise larger or smaller according to the varying number of chromosomes that they receive (**Fig. 432**) though the numerical relations cannot here be so exactly determined. In dispermic or trispermic eggs of frogs, as shown by Brachet and by Herlant, the case is still clearer; for here but one sperm-nucleus unites with the egg-nucleus, while the other one (or two) divides separately (p. 418). Both the diploid and the haploid nuclei thus produced continue to divide, finally producing larvæ in which the cells of certain regions (sometimes in one-half of the body) contain diploid nuclei, while in the remaining regions they are haploid. Both nuclei and cytosomes, as might be expected, are much smaller in the haploid regions than in the diploid (Fig. 314).

In the foregoing cases we are dealing with only quantitative effects.

---

[1] This difference is due to the fact that the cleavage-cells do not grow noticeably, cytoplasmic growth for these stages having already been accomplished by the egg before cleavage begins.

[2] It should, however, be recalled that the polymegalous spermatocytes of Hemiptera, though all alike diploid, likewise show corresponding variations in the size of the cytoplasmic components (p. 304). Perhaps, therefore, another factor may be concerned, as in certain diploid giants (p. 101).

In later chapters we shall become acquainted also with qualitative effects in the cytoplasm due to the influence of the nucleus; but attention may here briefly be drawn to them. Boveri's celebrated experiments on multi-polar mitosis ('02, '07), demonstrated that normal development and differentiation are dependent on the presence of the normal combination of chromosomes in the nucleus. When this combination is impaired or modified without disturbance of the cytoplasmic substance development is correspondingly impaired or modified, leading to the production of asymmetrical, incomplete, pathological or monstrous forms. This can only mean that constructive morphological processes of the cytosome are conditioned by the nucleus in a qualitative as well as a quantitative sense (p. 920).

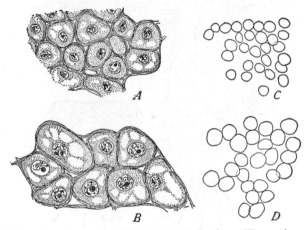

Fig. 314.—Cells and nuclei from trispermic frog-larvæ (HERLANT).

A, cartilage-cells from right side, B, from left side, larva of 10 days; C, nuclei from central nervous system, right side, D, from left side, larva of 54 days.

The same conclusion follows from the relations of the chromosomes to sex, as will be shown in the tenth chapter; for it is now known that the production of the male or female characters in many animals, and in a few plants, is dependent upon the nature of the chromosome-combination (pp. 816, 817, etc.).

3. Nucleated and Non-nucleated Cell-fragments

Equally convincing, if less direct, is evidence drawn from the remarkable contrast between nucleated and non-nucleated cell-fragments in respect to synthetic processes. The earliest observations on this subject were the classical ones of Waller (1852) on the regeneration of nerve-fibers, which proved that this process only takes place when the axis-cylinders remain in connection with the nucleated cytosomes of the nerve-cells. When a nerve-fiber is severed the distal portion degenerates, while the proximal portion (still connected with the nerve-cell and its nucleus) may readily grow forth until the missing portion is restored. This observation, repeatedly confirmed by later observers, was not wholly decisive, but nevertheless gave the first clear indication of the necessity of the nucleus for growth, regeneration and differentiation. Conclusive evidence was later obtained by experimental studies on the cells both of Protista and of higher forms.

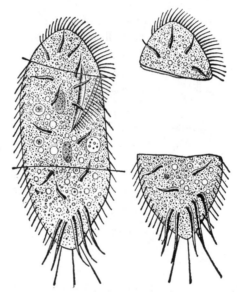

Fig. 315.—Regeneration in *Stylonychia* (VERWORN).

At the left an entire animal, showing planes of section. The middle piece, containing two nuclei regenerates a perfect animal. The enucleated pieces, shown at the right, swim about for a time, but finally perish.

Brandt ('77) long since observed that enucleated fragments of *Actino-sphærium* soon die, while nucleated fragments heal their wounds, and continue to live. The first decisive comparison between nucleated and non-nucleated masses of protoplasm was, however, made by Moritz Nussbaum in 1884 in the case of a ciliate, *Oxytricha*. If one of these animals be cut into two pieces, the subsequent behavior of the two fragments depends on the presence or absence of the nucleus or a nuclear fragment. The nucleated fragments quickly heal the wound, regenerate the missing portions, and thus produce a perfect animal, while enucleated fragments, consisting of cytoplasm only, quickly perish. Gruber ('85) obtained a similar result in the case of *Stentor*, another ciliate (Fig. 316). Fragments possessing a large fragment of the nucleus completely regenerated within twenty-four hours. If the nuclear fragment were smaller, the regeneration proceeded more slowly. If no nuclear substance were present, no regeneration took place, though the wound closed and the fragment lived for a considerable time. The only exception was the case of individuals in which the process of normal fission had begun; in these a non-nucleated fragment in which the formation of a new peristome had already been initiated healed the wound, and completed the formation of the peristome. Lillie ('96) later found that *Stentor polymorphus* may be shaken into fragments of all sizes, and that nucleated fragments as small as $1/27$ the volume of the entire animal are still capable of complete regeneration. In all the foregoing cases all non-nucleated fragments perish.[1] In *S. cœruleus* Morgan ('01) showed that nucleated fragments not more than $1/64$ the normal size might still produce a complete individual.

These studies were extended to the rhizopods by other observers. Verworn ('88) proved that in *Polystomella*, one of the Foraminifera, nucleated fragments were able to repair the shell, while non-nucleated fragments lack this power. Balbiani ('89) found that although non-nucleated fragments of ciliates had no power of regeneration, they might nevertheless continue to live and swim actively about for many days after the operation, the contractile vacuole pulsating as usual. Hofer ('89) found in *Amœba*, that non-nucleated fragments might live as long as fourteen days after the operation (Fig. 317). Their movements continued, but were somewhat modified, and little by little ceased, but the pulsations of the contractile vacuole were but slightly affected; they lost more or less completely the capacity to digest food, and the power of adhering to the substratum. Verworn's later experiments ('89) on various Protozoa confirmed the accounts of his predecessors, and added many important results. Non-nucleated fragments both of ciliates (*e. g.*, *Lachrymaria*) and rhizopods (*Polystomella*, *Thalassicolla*) may live for a considerable period (Fig. 315), performing perfectly normal and characteristic movements, showing the same susceptibility to stimulus, and having the same power of ingulfing food, as the nucleated fragments. *They lack, however, the power of digestion and secretion.* Ingested food-matters may be slightly altered, but are never completely digested. The non-nucleated fragments are unable to secrete the material for a new shell (*Polystomella*) or the slime by which the animals adhere to the substratum (*Amœba*, *Difflugia*, *Polystomella*.)

These results have been confirmed in their main features by the work of many later observers.[2] With certain variations of detail they establish

---

[1] As Calkins has pointed out, the phenomena in ciliates are less demonstrative than in rhizopods, owing to the difficulty of making sure of the presence or absence of micronuclei in the fragments.

[2] Lists and reviews of the literature will be found in K. Gruber's work on *Amœba* ('13) and especially in that of Sokoloff ('24), received too late for further mention here.

the fact that destructive processes and the liberation of energy, as manifested by coördinated forms of protoplasmic movement, may go on for some
time undisturbed in a mass of cytoplasm deprived of a nucleus.   On the
other hand, the building up of new chemical or morphological products by
the cytoplasm is only initiated in the presence of a nucleus, and soon ceases in
its absence.   The nucleus must, therefore, play an essential part both in the
operations of synthetic metabolism or chemical synthesis, and in the *morpho-*

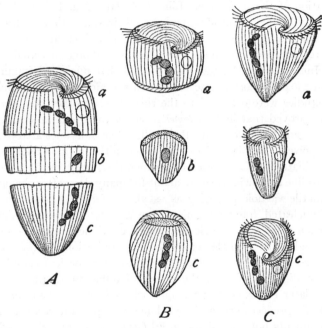

Fig. 316.—Regeneration in the unicellular animal *Stentor* (from GRUBER after BALBIANI).

A, animal divided into three pieces, each containing a fragment of the nucleus; *B*, the three fragments shortly afterwards; *C*, the three fragments after twenty-four hours, each regenerated to a perfect animal.

logical determination of these operations (*i. e.*, the morphological synthesis of
Bernard)—a point of capital importance for the theory of inheritance.

Convincing experiments of the same character and leading to the same
result have been made on the cells of plants.   Francis Darwin ('77) long
since observed that movements actively continued in protoplasmic filaments,
extruded from the leaf-hairs of *Dipsacus*, that were completely severed
from the body of the cell.   Conversely, Klebs ('79) showed that naked
protoplasmic fragments of *Vaucheria* and other algæ were incapable of
forming a new cellulose membrane if devoid of a nucleus; and he afterward
showed ('87) that the same is true of *Zygnema* and *Œdogonium*.   By plas-

molysis the cells of these forms may be broken up into fragments, both nucleated and non-nucleated. The former surround themselves with a new wall, grow, and develop into complete plants; the latter, while able to form starch by means of the chlorophyll they contain, are incapable of utilizing it, and are devoid of the power of forming a new membrane, and

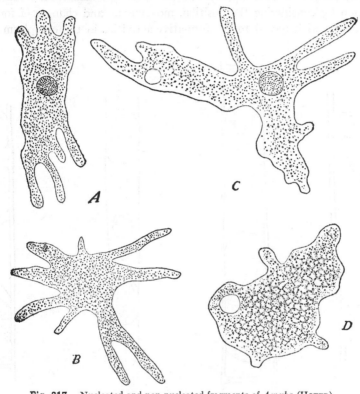

Fig. 317.—Nucleated and non-nucleated fragments of *Amœba* (Hofer).

A, B, an *Amœba* divided into nucleated and non-nucleated halves, five minutes after the operation; *C, D,* the two halves after eight days, each containing a contractile vacuole.

of growth and regeneration. A striking confirmation of this was given by Townsend ('97), who found in the case of root-hairs and pollen-tubes, that when the protoplasm is thus broken up, a membrane may be formed by both nucleated and non-nucleated fragments, by the latter, however, *only when they remain connected with the nucleated masses* by protoplasmic strands, however fine. If these strands be broken, the membrane-forming power is lost. Of great interest is the further observation (made on leaf-hairs in *Cucurbita*) that the influence of the nucleus may thus extend from cell to cell, an enucleated fragment of one cell having the power to form a membrane if connected by intercellular bridges with a nucleated fragment of an adjoining cell (Fig. 318).

4. Form, Position, and Movements of the Nucleus

Many observers have approached the same problem from a different direction by considering the position, movements, and changes of form in the nucleus with regard to the formative activities in the cytoplasm. To

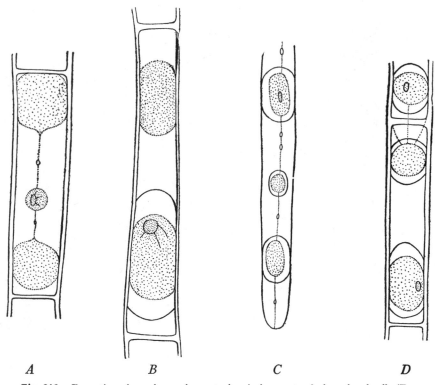

| A | B | C | D |

Fig. 318.—Formation of membranes by protoplasmic fragments of plasmolyzed cells (TOWN-SEND).

A, plasmolyzed cell, leaf-hair of *Cucurbita*, showing protoplasmic balls connected by strands; *B*, calyx-hair of *Gaillardia;* nucleated fragment with membrane, non-nucleated one naked; *C*, root-hair of *Marchantia;* all the fragments, connected by protoplasmic strands, have formed membranes; *D*, leaf-hair of *Cucurbita;* non-nucleated fragment, with membrane, connected with nucleated fragment of adjoining cell.

review these researches in full would be impossible, and we shall limit our consideration to the well known researches of Haberlandt ('77) and Korschelt ('89). Haberlandt's studies related to the position of the nucleus in plant-cells with especial regard to the growth of the cellulose membrane.

He determined the very significant fact that local growth of the cell-wall is always preceded by a movement of the nucleus to the point of growth. Thus, in the formation of epidermal cells, the nucleus lies at first near the center, but as the outer wall thickens, the nucleus moves toward it, and remains closely applied to it throughout its growth, after which the nucleus

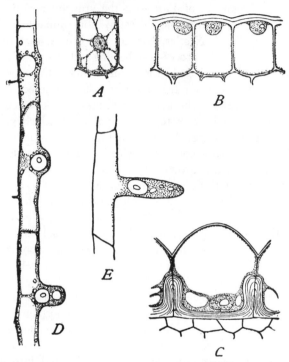

Fig. 319.—Position of the nuclei in growing plant-cells (HABERLANDT).

A, young epidermal cell of *Luzula* with central nucleus, before thickening of the membrane; B, three epidermal cells of *Monstera*, during the thickening of the outer wall; C, cell from the seed-coat of *Scopulina* during the thickening of the inner wall; D, E, position of the nuclei during the formation of branches in the root-hairs of the pea.

often moves into another part of the cell (Fig. 319, A, B). That this is not due simply to a movement of the nucleus toward the air and light is demonstrated in the coats of certain seeds, where the nucleus moves, not to the outer, but to the inner wall of the cell, and here the thickening takes place (Fig. 319, C). The same position of the nucleus is shown in the thickening of the walls of the guard-cells of stomata, in the formation of the peristome of mosses, and in many other cases. In the formation of root-hairs in the pea, the primary outgrowth always takes place from the immediate neighborhood of the nucleus, which is carried outward and remains near the tip of the growing hair (Fig. 319). The same is true of the rhizoids of fern-prothallia and liverworts. In the hairs of aërial plants this rule is reversed, the nucleus lying near the base of the hair; but this apparent exception proves the rule, for in this case growth of the hair is not apical, but proceeds from the base! Very interesting is Haberlandt's observation that in the regeneration of fragments of *Vaucheria* the growing region, where a new membrane is formed, contains no chlorophyll but numerous nuclei. Again it was shown by Tangl, Nestler, Nemec, and others, that after injury to the epidermis of plants the processes of healing and regeneration are initiated by a movement of nuclei and protoplasm towards the wounded surface. The general result, based on the study of a large number of cases, is, in Haberlandt's words, that "the nucleus is in most cases placed in the neighborhood, more or less immediate, of the points at which growth is most active and continues longest." This fact points to the conclusion that "its function is especially connected with the developmental processes of the cell" and that "in the growth of the cell, more especially in the growth of the cell-wall, the nucleus plays a definite part."

Korschelt's work dealt especially with the correlation between form and position of the nucleus and the nutrition of the cell, and bore more directly on chemical than on morphological synthesis. The results showed that there is a definite correlation, on the one hand, between the position of the nucleus and the source of food-supply; on the other hand, between the size of the nucleus and the extent of its surface and the elaboration of material by the cell. In support of the latter conclusion many cases are brought forward of secreting cells in which the nucleus is of enormous size and has a complex branching form. Such nuclei occur, for example, in the silk-glands of various insect larvæ (Meckel, Zaddach, etc.), which are characterized by an intense secretory activity concentrated into a very short period. Here the nucleus forms a labyrinthine network (Fig. 31), by which its surface is brought to a maximum, pointing to an active exchange of material between nucleus and cytoplasm. The same type of nucleus occurs in the Malphigian tubules of insects (Leydig, R. Hertwig), in the spinning-glands of amphipods (Mayer), and especially in the nutritive cells of the insect ovary (p. 665). Here the developing ovum is accompanied and surrounded by cells which there is good reason to believe are concerned with the elaboration of food for the egg-cell. In the earwig *Forficula* each egg is accompanied by a single large nutritive cell (Fig. 320), which has a very large nucleus rich in chromatin. This cell increases in size as the ovum grows, and its nucleus assumes the complex branching form shown in the figure. In the butterfly *Vanessa* there is a group of such cells at one pole of the egg, from which the latter is believed to draw its nutriment (Fig.

153). A very interesting case is that of the annelid *Ophryotrocha* (p. 333). Here, as described by Korschelt, the egg floats in the perivisceral fluid, accompanied by a nurse-cell having a very large chromatic nucleus, while that of the egg is smaller and poorer in chromatin. As the egg completes its growth the nurse-cell dwindles away and finally perishes (Fig. 151).

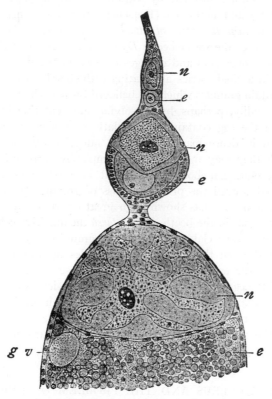

Fig. 320.—Upper portion of the ovary in the earwig *Forficula*, showing eggs and nurse-cells (Korschelt).

Below, a portion of the nearly ripe egg (*e*), showing deutoplasm-spheres and germinal vesicle (*g v*). Above it lies the nurse-cell (*n*) with its enormous branching nucleus. Two successively younger stages of egg and nurse are shown above.

In all these cases it is scarcely possible to doubt that the egg is in a measure relieved of the task of elaborating cytoplasmic products by the nurse-cell, and that the great development of the nucleus in the latter is correlated with this function.

Regarding the position and movements of the nucleus, Korschelt reviews many facts pointing toward the same conclusion. Perhaps the most suggestive of these relate to the nucleus of the egg during its ovarian history.   In many of the insects, as in both the cases referred to above, the egg-nucleus at first occupies a central position, but as the egg begins to grow, it moves to the periphery on the side turned toward the nutritive cells.   The same is true in the ovarian eggs of some other animals, good examples of which are afforded by various cœlenterates, e. g., in medusæ (Claus, Hertwig) and actinians (Korschelt, Hertwig), where *the germinal vesicle is always near the point of attachment of the egg.*   Most suggestive of all is the case of the water-beetle *Dytiscus*, in which Korschelt was able to observe the movements and changes of form in the living object.   The eggs here lie in a single series alternating with chambers of nutritive cells. The latter contain granules which are believed by Korschelt to pass into the egg, perhaps bodily, perhaps by dissolving and entering in liquid form. At all events, the egg contains accumulations of similar granules, which extend inward in dense masses from the nutritive cells to the germinal vesicle, which they may more   or   less completely surround.   The latter meanwhile becomes amœboid, sending out long pseudopodia, which are always directed toward the principal mass of granules (Fig. 153).   More recently Wiemann ('10) has shown with great clearness, by the use of differential stains, that in the beetle *Leptinotarsa* the nutritive cells of the end-chamber of the ovary elaborate basophilic granules that flow downward into the eggs through the protoplasmic pedicles by which the latter are connected with the end-chamber (p. 335).   These granules flow into the main body of the egg, and towards the germinal vesicle, around which they form a characteristic broad zone (*cf.* Fig. 155).   Their precise fate is uncertain, but undoubtedly they provide material at the expense of which the egg grows.   The similar observation of Nussbaum-Hilarowicz are elsewhere reviewed (p. 336).

IV. THE NUCLEUS AND THE PROBLEM OF HEREDITY

The close relation between the nuclear activities and the synthetic processes of the cell points unmistakably towards its important relation to heredity, which, as Darwin long ago remarked, may be looked upon as a form of growth (p. 1035).   The theory that hereditary characters are transmitted by the nucleus, as independently advanced by O. Hertwig and by Strasburger (1884), was based originally on the history of the gamete-nuclei in fertilization.   The conclusions of both were reached through direct observation, but were considerably influenced by more theoretical considerations on heredity developed by Nägeli in his notable work on the idioplasm, which appeared earlier in the same year (p. 722).   Nägeli himself did not attempt definitely to localize the idioplasm or germ-plasm in the cell, but emphasized the equal parts played by the gametes in heredity, despite their enormous difference in size. Hertwig and Strasburger transferred this argument to the nucleus, contrasting the exact equivalence of the gamete-nuclei in fertilization (as demonstrated especially by Van Beneden) with the extreme disproportion between the gametes in respect to the cytoplasm. In respect to the chromosomes, which embody the primary essential and fundamental nuclear substance, the parent germ-cells make equivalent contributions to the offspring (with the special exception of the sex-chromosomes), while with respect to the cytoplasm a very great discrepancy exists— a significant difference when we consider that so far as can be determined by experiment the two parents contribute equally, on the whole, to the hereditary endowment of the offspring. Additional weight was brought to this consideration by the wide contrast between nucleus and cytosome during mitotic division. The nucleus undergoes an exactly equal and a meristic division, effected by the spinning out of its substance into fine threads, and the longitudinal splitting of the thread; hence the conception of Roux ('83) that the nucleus consists of numerous smaller elements or "qualities," each of which must be transmitted unimpaired to the daughter-nuclei (p. 908). The cytosome, on the other hand, offers the general aspect of a mass-division, and is often unequal, sometimes in an extreme degree. There is, it is true, increasing evidence that the cytoplasm may contain numerous independently dividing bodies, such as plastids, central bodies, and possibly chondriosomes and other formed components; but in none of these cases is there evidence of exactly ordered distribution of the division-products, such as is so strikingly displayed in the division of the nucleus.

General considerations of this type long since caused the widespread acceptance of the nuclear theory of heredity; but its complete demonstration only came through the close coöperation of genetic experiment and cytological studies on the chromosomes which followed the rediscovery of Mendelian heredity in 1900.[1] This must not be taken to mean that the cytoplasm is without significance for these phenomena, as some opponents of the nuclear theory have pretended; it is indeed probable that in a large sense the whole cell-system is involved in the production of every hereditary trait. Most adherents of the nuclear theory have gone no further than to treat the nucleus as an essential, but not the exclusive, factor in heredity.[2] The point of view thus indicated will later be made clear (pp. 637, 916).

[1] See Chapters X, XII.
[2] See for instance Godlewsky ('06), Wilson ('12, '14).

LITERATURE VIII

(For abbreviations see General Literature List.)

Aberhalden, E., '09. Abbau der Proteine: *Handbuch der Biochemie,* I.
'14. Defensive Ferments of the Animal Organism: 3d Ed., Eng. Trans., *London.*

Adami, J. G., '08. Principles of Pathology: *Lee and Fibiger, Philadelphia and New York.*

Bayliss, W. M., '11. The Nature of Enzyme Action: *Longmans, Green & Co.*
'18. Principles of General Physiology, 2d Ed.: *Longmans, Green & Co.*
'21. Staining. Chap. XI, in *Lee's Microtomist's Vade-mecum; 8th Ed., London.*
'23. The Colloidal State: *London.*

Bayliss and **Starling,** '06. Die chemische Koordination der Funktionen des Körpers: *E. P.,* I, 2.

Bechold, H., '12. Die Kolloide in der Biologie und Medizin: *Dresden.*

Bernard, Claude, '78. Leçons sur les phénomènes de la vie; 1st Ed.: '78; 2d Ed., '85. *Paris.*

Burian, R., '06. Chemie der Spermatozoen: *E. P.,* V, 1.

Clowes, G. H. A., '16. Protoplasmic Equilibrium: *Journ. Phys. Chem.,* XX, 5.

Cohnheim, O., '11. Chemie der Eiweisskörper: 3 Aufl. *Braunschweig.*

Czapek, F., '11. Chemical Phenomena of Life: *N. Y.*

Dakin, H. D., '12. Oxidations and Reductions in the Animal Body: *Longmans, Green and Co.*

Furth, O. v., '12. Probleme der Physiologischen und Pathologischen Chemie: *Leipzig, Vogel.*

Haberlandt, G., '87. Ueber die Beziehungen zwischen Funktion und Lage des Zellkerns: *Fischer, Jena.*

Halliburton, W. D., '16. The Essentials of Chemical Physiology: 9th Ed., *Longmans, Green & Co.,*

Hammarsten, O., '09. A Textbook of Physical Chemistry. 5th Ed., *N. Y.*

Hardy, W. B., '13 (I).

Hatschek, E., '22. An Introduction to the Physics and Chemistry of Colloids: 4th Ed. *Philadelphia.*

Heidenhain, M., '02. Ueber chemische Umsetzungen zwischen Eisweiskörpern und Anilinfarben: *A. Ph.,* XC, III, 4.
'10. Färbungen: *Handbuch d. Mikr. Tech.,* 2te Aufl. I.

Höber, R., '14. Physikalische Chemie der Zelle und der Gewebe. 4te Aufl.: *Engelmann, Leipzig and Berlin.*

Hopkins, F. G., '13. The Dynamic Side of Biochemistry: *Nature,* XCII.

Jones, Walter, '14. Nucleic Acids: *Longmans, Green & Co.*

Kanitz, A., '09. Biochemie der Zelle: *Handb. der Biochemie des Menschen und der Tiere,* I.
'10. Das Protoplasma als chemisches System: *Ibid.,* II, 1.

Korschelt, E., '89. Beiträge zur Morphologie und Physiologie des Zellkerns: *Z. J.,* IV.

Kossel, A., '12. The Proteins, Herter Lecture: *Johns Hopkins Hospital Bulletin, Baltimore.*

Lillie, R. S., '18. Heredity from the Physico-Chemical Point of View: *B. B.,* XXXIV.

Loeb, J., '18. Amphoteric Colloids: I, *J. G. P.,* I, 1; II, *Ibid.,* II, 2.

Macdougal, D. T., and **Spoehr, H. A.,** '20. The Components and Colloidal Behavior of Plant Protoplasm: *Proc. Am. Phil. Soc.,* LIX.

Mann, G., '02, '06. Physiological Histology: *Clarendon Press, Oxford.*

Mathews, A. P., '98. A Contribution to the Chemistry of cytological Staining: *A. J. P.,* I, 4.

'15. Physiological Chemistry: *Wood & Co., New York.*

Molisch, H., '13. Mikrochemie der Pflanze: *Jena.*

Nuttall, '04. Blood Immunity and Blood Relationships: *Cambridge Univ. Press.*

Ostwald, W., '09. Die wichtigsten Eigenschaften des Kolloiden Zustandes der Stoffe: *Handbuch der Biochemie,* I.

Pratje, A., '20. Die Chemie des Zellkerns: *B. G.,* XL.

Reichert and **Brown,** '09. Differentiation and Specificity of Corresponding Proteins and other vital Substance in Relation to Biological Classification and Organic Evolution: *Carnegie Inst.*

Schittenhelm, A., '11. Der Nukleinstoffwechsel: *Handbuch der Biochemie,* IV, 1.

Sokoloff, B., '24. Das Regenerationsproblem bei Protozoen: *A. P.,* XLVII.

Spaeth, R. A., '16. The Vital Equilibrium: *Sci.,* XLIII.

Spiro, K., '09. Physikalische Chemie der Zelle: *Handbuch der Biochemie,* I, 2.

Verworn, '91. Die physiologische Bedeutung des Zellkernes: *A. Ph.,* LI.

'03. Die Biogenhypothese: *Jena.*

'09. Allgemeine Physiologie, 5te Aufl: *Fischer, Jena.* (Eng. Tr. by Lee, from 2nd German Ed., London, Macmillan, '99.)

'15. Zellphysiologie: *H. Nw.,* X, *Fischer, Jena.*

Warburg, '13. Ueber die Wirksamkeit der Strukturen auf die chemischen Vorgänge in Zellen: *Jena.*

Zacharias, E., '10. Die chemische Beschaffenheit von Protoplasma und Zellkern: *P. R. B.*

Zsigmondy, R. '20. Kolloidchemie, 3te Auflage.

CHAPTER IX

SOME PROBLEMS OF CELL–ORGANIZATION

"We must therefore ascribe to living cells, beyond the molecular structure of the organic compounds that they contain, still another structure of different type of complication; and it is this which we call by the name of organization."   BRÜCKE. [1]

Whether structure or function is the primary determining factor in vital phenomena is a question that has been a subject of debate for many generations of biological philosophers. As thus stated, however, the question has proved barren, for all students of the problem have in the end had to admit that structure and function are inseparable. It is certain that vital action is not known to us apart from an organized material basis, and equally certain that vital structures exist only as products of protoplasmic activity. Thus has arisen a dilemma which belongs to the fundamental philosophy of biology and may here be left aside as practically insoluble. The fact of importance to the cytologist is that we cannot hope to comprehend the activities of the living cell by analysis merely of its chemical composition, or even of its molecular structure alone. Many investigators, it is true, including Pflüger, Verworn, Adami and other physiologists have tried to formulate vital activities in terms of the properties of large molecules or *biogens* of which the "living substance" is assumed to be built; and this conception has rendered important service in physiological analysis. Modern investigation has, however, brought ever-increasing recognition of the fact that the cell is an *organic system,* and one in which we must recognize the existence of some kind of ordered structure or *organization.*

The necessity for such a postulate has been as clearly recognized by physiologists and biochemists as by morphologists and cytologists. The eminent investigator, Ernst Brücke was one of the first of a long line of physiologists to insist upon this necessity; and it has not been set aside by conceptions of the cell as a colloidal system, or by modern investigations in biochemistry. "One cannot help assuming," says Jost, "that the mode of arrangement of the ultimate parts of the organism is of greater importance than the chemical nature of these parts " ('07). "It is clear," says F. G. Hopkins, '13, "that the living cell as we now know it, is not a mass of matter composed of live molecules, but a highly differentiated system." Mathews emphasizes the enormous contrast between living protoplasm and the same

[1] Elementarorganismen, p. 386, 1861.

670

protoplasm after it has been ground up in a mortar without altering its merely chemical or molecular properties. "The orderliness of the chemical reactions (in the cell) is due to the cell-structure, and for the phenomena of life to persist in their entirety that structure must be preserved." [1] The whole mechanistic interpretation of vital processes rests, indeed, upon the assumption that their specific character, and particularly their orderly localization in the system, must somehow depend on what we call their "organization" in Brücke's sense; and even the vitalistic theories cannot free themselves from the same conception. "No one, not even the vitalist, doubts that the organism is a Gibbs system." [2] We cannot, it is true, say precisely what organization is, but we can hardly think of it as other than some kind of material configuration of the protoplasmic substance, and one that involves both a differentiation of parts and their integration to form a whole, as Herbert Spencer long since urged. [3] When, therefore, Loeb (to cite still another physiologist) characterizes the living organism as a chemical or colloidal *machine* ('06) he employs a word that implies the existence of such a configuration; Loeb specifically maintains, indeed, that "without a structure in the egg to begin with, no formation of a complicated organism is conceivable." [4] The same implication lurks behind every attempt to formulate the unity and order of the individual in purely physiological terms, *e. g.*, by ascribing it to "definite relations in both space and time among the reactions occurring in protoplasm." [5] That such a configuration exists is made evident first of all by the fact that "living matter" is known to us only in the form of cells or their products. To a limited extent we are able to see special configurations or structures within the cell correlated with specific modes of action, but such structures are for the most part of secondary origin; they are products of differentiation during embryological development. Since, however, they are hereditary, such specific cell-structures must somehow be predetermined in the germ-cells. Of what nature is this predetermination? Is there in the cell a *primary* or fundamental organization that is handed on from one cell-generation to another without essential change to form the source of the *secondary* or derived organization that may appear anew in each cell-generation? This question, evidently, belongs as much to embryology as to cytology and as such will further be discussed in the closing chapters of this work. Here we are more directly concerned with certain cytological aspects of the problem, which come to a focus in the phenomena of growth, division,

---

[1] Mathews ('15), p. 11.
[2] Henderson ('17), p. 131.
[3] *Cf*. Conklin, '24.
[4] Loeb, ('16), p. 39.
[5] Child ('15), p. 17.

and differentiation, as displayed by the various formed components of the cell.

Superficially regarded, many of these components *seem* to arise *de novo*, as in case of the chromosomes and chromomeres, and of various forms of cytoplasmic granules, fibrillæ or other structures. Undoubtedly, however, there are many cases in which this impression is not correct. It has long been known that chromosomes are transmitted from cell to cell by division, and recent studies in this field increase the probability that the same is true of smaller bodies or chromomeres of which the chromosomes are in part at least built up (p. 906). We have long been familiar with the fact that certain of the cytoplasmic components, such as the central bodies or the plastids, may likewise be transmitted from cell to cell by growth and division. Nothing is more noteworthy in recent studies on protoplasmic structure and histogenesis than the increasing tendency of cytologists to extend the same conclusion to other cytoplasmic components, such as chonriosomes, chromidia, and possibly the Golgi-bodies and fibrillar structures. It is certain that in some cases the formed components do not arise *de novo* but are largely built up from preëxisting elements or their products derived from earlier generations of cells; examples of this are conspicuously seen in the important part played in the genesis of the egg and sperm by the central bodies, the chondriosomes, and apparently also by the Golgi-bodies associated with the idiozome and astral apparatus.[1] To what extent may the genetic law of continuity, now so strongly supported in case of the nuclear components, likewise apply to those of the cytosome? To this question we shall return after consideration of certain more specific problems of cell-morphology.

I. THE CENTRAL APPARATUS. THE DIVISION–CENTERS AND THEIR DERIVATIVES

There is now no doubt that in many cases the central bodies of the daughter-cells arise by the division of those of the mother-cell; and we must admit that there is a certain presumption in favor of the conclusion of Van Beneden, Boveri and their followers that the division-center (centriole) may be regarded as a permanent and autonomous cell-organ that arises only by the division of a preëxisting body of the same kind. Doubt has been thrown on this conclusion by apparently strong evidence that in certain cases it may arise *de novo*. In the very fact of such a double mode of origin (if it can be accepted) lies the peculiar interest of the central bodies in their relation to the protoplasmic metastructure. We shall later meet with the same problem in relation to the origin of mitochondria and of plastids; but

[1] (Pp. 357, 385).

in case of the central bodies it is made more accessible by their small number and by the frequent presence of a surrounding aster which, as it were, isolates them for observation.

1. The Central Body and Its Relation to the Astral Formations

Much confusion still exists in the literature concerning the terminology and relationships of the central body. Its discoverer, Van Beneden ('76), first called it the "polar corpuscle," later "central corpuscle" ('87). Boveri

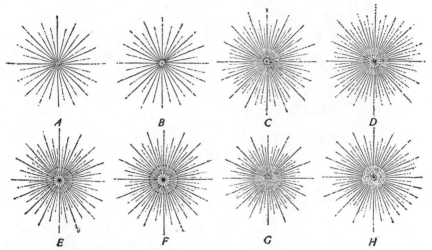

Fig. 321.—Diagrams illustrating various accounts of central bodies and aster.

A, central body a simple granule at the center of the aster; *ex*, sperm-aster in various animals; *B*, "centrosome" a sphere enclosing a central granule or centriole; *ex*, Brauer's account of spermatocytes of *Ascaris;* *C*, like the last, but "centrosome" surrounded by a clear zone; *ex*, Boveri's account of the centrosome of the *Ascaris* egg; *D*, centriole surrounded by a radial sphere ("centrosome") bounded by a microsome-circle, and lying in a clear zone; *ex*, polar spindles of *Thysanozoön*, Van der Stricht; *E*, centriole surrounded by medullary and cortical radial zones, each bounded by a microsome-circle; *ex*, polar spindle of *Unio*, LILLIE; *F*, Van Beneden's representation of aster of the *Ascaris* egg; like the last, but the "corpuscule central" consisting of a group of granules; *G*, central body a group of granules surrounded by a clear zone; *ex*, the echinoderm-egg; *H*, "centrosome" a large reticulated "centrosphere" containing a new centrosome within which lies the centriole; *ex*, *Rhynchelmis* (VEJDOVSKÝ) or *Arion* (LAMS).

('88) applied to it the term *centrosome*, later describing it as consisting of a specific centroplasm ('01, p. 204), and as forming the central point of attachment for the astral rays. Within it is a much smaller body which Boveri ('95) called the *centriole, which is first of all to divide* and thus to initiate division of the whole astral system and of the cell. This fact, first clearly recognized in *Ascaris*, has received repeated confirmation by later observers.

Boveri at first considered the centrosome as an individualized body that is distinct from the aster, and held that both centriole and centrosome are persistent structures that grow and divide without loss of their identity; and such may perhaps sometimes be the case. Subsequent studies by many observers, prominent among them Vejdovský and Mrázek ('03), Yatsu ('09) and Lams ('10), demonstrated that in many cases the centrosome is but a transitory structure which, like the surrounding aster, may form, disappear and re-form in successive phases of mitosis. The whole prob-

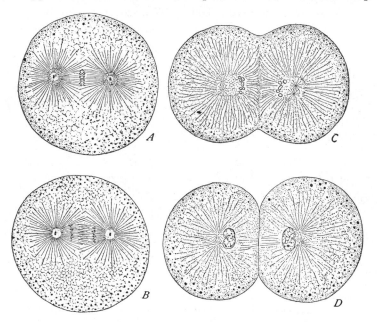

Fig. 322.—First cleavage of the ovum in the nemertine *Cerebratulus* (COE).

A, initial anaphase, center double; *B*, middle anaphase; *C*, early telophase; daughter-amphiaster; *D*, late telophase.

lem thus comes to a focus in the centriole, a consideration of which demands some account of its relations to the centrosome and aster.[1]

In its simplest forms (Fig. 321) the central body appears under the highest powers as a single granule of extreme minuteness, staining intensely with iron-hæmatoxylin, crystal violet and some other dyes, and often hardly to be distinguished from a microsome save by the fact that it lies at the

---

[1] For the literature of the subject see especially the works of Boveri on sea-urchins and *Ascaris* ('95, '01), Van der Stricht on Turbellaria ('98), MacFarland on gasteropods ('97), Lillie on pelecypods ('98), Griffin on annelids ('99), Wilson, general ('00), Meves, critical ('02), Vejdovský and Mrázek ('03), and Vejdovský ('07) on annelids, Heidenhain on leucocytes, etc. ('92, '94, '07), Yatsu on nemertines ('09), and Lams on gasteropods ('10). Also Van Beneden ('93, '87), Boveri ('88) Brauer ('93), Kostanecki ('97), and Kostanecki and Siedlecki ('97) on *Ascaris*, Francotte ('97) and Schockaert ('01) on Turbellaria, Coe on nemertines ('99), Byrnes ('99), Conklin ('03), Smallwood ('04) and Linville ('00), on mollusks.

focus of the astral rays. In this form it appears, for example, in the very young sperm aster during fertilization (Fig. 207) or in its very early prophases during ordinary mitosis, often also in the "resting" or vegetative cells (Figs. 8, 42). In all such cases these bodies are probably to be identified as centrioles, though they are often erroneously called "centrosomes."[1] In the vegetative cells they may be surrounded by a "centrosome," "sphere" or idiozome" (p. 329); but in these cases this surrounding structure usually

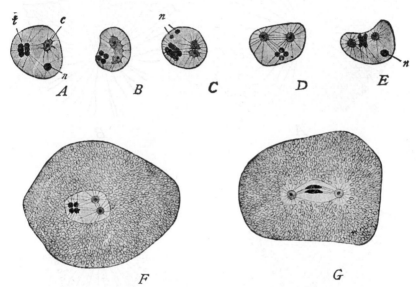

Fig. 323.—Mitosis with intra-nuclear central body in the spermatocytes of *Ascaris megalocephala* var. *univalens* (BRAUER).

A, nucleus containing a quadruple group or tetrad of chromosomes (*t*), nucleolus (*n*), and centrosome containing a centriole (*c*); *B*, *C*, division of the centriole and centrosome; *D*, *E*, *F*, *G*, transformation of the mitotic figure, centrosomes escaping from the nucleus in *G*.

breaks up or degenerates in the early prophases of mitosis, so that the centrioles alone form the focus of the ensuing operations (Figs. 8, 328).

---

[1] The word "centrosome" will be found in the literature in at least four different senses, namely:

(1) In a general physiological sense as the division-center of the cell.

(2) As the innermost differentiated body at the center of the aster, the only persistent element of the whole system, equivalent to the central granule or centriole (earlier works of Heidenhain, Kostanecki, Coe, Griffin, Wilson, Conklin, etc.).

(3) In Boveri's original sense as a larger body surrounding the centriole, having a persistent identity and independent of the aster.

(4) As a transitory structure, representing the innermost astral zone and thus equivalent to Van Beneden's "medullary zone" (Brauer, Erlanger, Van der Stricht, Lillie, Vejdovský and Mrázek, Lams, and most other recent writers).

It was this ambiguity that led Flemming ('91), and later Heidenhain and many others, to adopt the more inclusive and non-committal terms *central body*, *division-center* or simply *center* in all cases where the genesis of the central apparatus is not fully known.

At a slightly later period during the prophases the centriole (now usually double) is found to be surrounded by a centrosome, which steadily enlarges as mitosis proceeds, while the centrioles remain very minute.

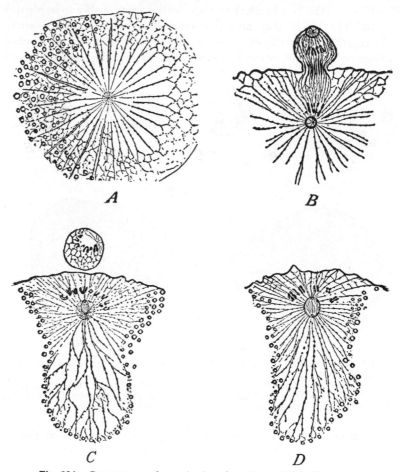

Fig. 324.—Centrosome and aster in the polar mitoses of *Unio* (LILLIE).

A, aster of the first polar figure; central granule (centriole) surrounded by medullary (entosphere) and cortical (ectosphere) zones; *B*, late anaphase of second polar mitosis; radial entosphere bounded by continuous membrane; *C*, *D*, prophases of second mitosis; formation of central spindle within and from the substance of the old entosphere.

Growth of the centrosome continues throughout the whole mitotic process up to the late anaphase or early telophase, when in some cases it attains an enormous size, particularly in cells richly laden with yolk, such as segmenting eggs (Figs. 322, 330).

At its highest development the centrosome is of several different types, as follows:

(1) In the simplest case (Figs. 321, B, 323, 327) it is a spheroidal body of moderate size, homogeneous structure, and definite contour, and not traversed by the astral rays, which are inserted on its periphery. Examples of such centrosomes are offered by *Ascaris* as described in the cleavage of the egg by Boveri ('88, '01, etc.) and by Kostanecki and Siedlecki ('97), and in the spermatocytes by Brauer ('93).

(2) In a second type (Figs. 321, G, 58) often seen in the eggs of sea-urchins (Wilson, '01a, etc.), the centrosome offers a similar appearance but contains

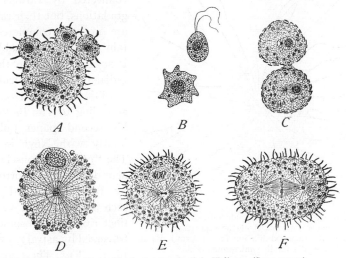

Fig. 325.—Central body (centroplast) in Heliozoa (Schaudinn).

A, Acanthocystis, bud-formation, producing *B,* swarm-spores, devoid of central bodies; *C,* swarm-spores preparing for division, new central bodies arising from nucleus; *D,* vegetative cell of *Sphær-astrum* with nucleus, central body and aster; *E,* division of central body in *Acanthocystis; F,* metaphase.

a group of irregular granules so as to give almost the appearance of a small nucleus in which the centrioles cannot be distinguished. These have been called "pluricorpuscular" centrosomes; but Boveri ('01) considers them as artifacts and gives a description of the centrosome in sea-urchins approaching that of the first type (Fig. 327).

(3) In a third type, exemplified in the polar divisions of platodes and molluscs (Fig. 321, D–F), the centrosome, or at least its outer zone, is traversed by the basal portions of the astral rays, so as to assume a radial structure. This type affords convincing evidence that the centrosome is to be regarded as the innermost zone of the aster.

(4) In a fourth type, well shown in the early cleavage-stages of annelids and nemertines (Figs. 205, 329, 330), the centrosome becomes greatly enlarged, shows a finely alveolar or netlike structure, and often has a somewhat vague boundary. In this enlarged condition it was early described by Vejdovský ('88) under the name of *periplast* (later *centroplasm*) and by many later observers was called by Strasburger's ('92) term *centrosphere* (Wilson, Mead, Coe, Griffin, Meves, etc.). It was, however, made clear in the extended works especially of Boveri ('01) and of Vejdovský and Mrázek ('03) that this term should give way to the earlier one, *centrosome*.[1]

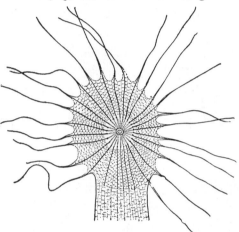

Fig. 326.—Astral system (pseudopods, axopodia, and central granule or centroplast) of the vegetative ("resting") cell in the rhizopod *Wagnerella* (ZUELZER). Basal granules of axopodia forming microsome-circle.

The above four types are connected by various intergradations, but their relations are not yet completely certain. The most probable view is suggested by the third or radial type, in particular the conditions in the *Ascaris* egg according to Van Beneden in his second paper published jointly with Neyt in 1887. The "central corpuscle" was here described as surrounded by two well-defined zones, each bounded by a very distinct ring of microsomes and traversed by astral rays (Figs. 76, 321, F). These zones obviously arise as differentiations of the inner region of the aster and were designated by Van Beneden respectively as "medullary" (inner) and "cortical" (outer), which together form the "attraction sphere."[2] Boveri considered his "centrosome" to be the equivalent of Van Beneden's "central corpuscle." Brauer ('93) suggested on the other hand that the central corpuscle was in reality the centriole and that *Boveri's "centrosome" corresponds to Van Beneden's "medullary" zone of the "attraction-sphere";* and this view, adopted by numerous later observers, became the prevalent one. This conclusion sets aside the apparent anomaly offered by the fact that in the second type of mitosis (p. 148) the new amphiaster is formed *inside the old centrosome* (Fig. 47); for the centroplasm consists of the same material from which the old aster was formed. In some cases this zone is bounded

---

[1] See also Yatsu ('09).

[2] By Ziegler ('99), the two zones were called the *entosphere* and *ectosphere* respectively.

by a definite ring of microsomes; in others this ring later is transformed
into an apparently continuous envelope (*e. g.*, Fig. 324), as in the second
polar spindle of *Thysanozoön* (Van der Stricht) or of *Unio* (Lillie), and the
facts seem to be similar in *Arion* (Fig. 328). In some cases the rays within
this zone disappear, partially or wholly, (possibly in some cases as an
effect of the reagents), thus giving the appearance seen in Type I. It is
apparently the breaking up of these rays that gives rise to the large reticu-

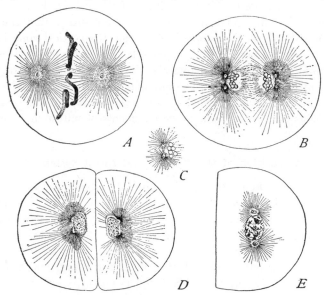

Fig. 327.—The central bodies during mitosis (BOVERI).

A, in *Ascaris megalocephala*, metaphase of first cleavage, centriole, centrosome and aster; *B–E*,
in the sea-urchin *Echinus; B, C*, early telophase, karyomeres, division of centrioles; *D*, late telophase;
E, "resting" stage.

lated or alveolar "centrosphere," "periplast" or "centroplasm" of the
fourth type.

Van Beneden's "cortical zone," as Brauer pointed out, probably corresponds to the clear zone which in all four types is often seen surrounding
the centrosome, sometimes without a definite boundary (sea-urchins, Fig.
58), sometimes sharply marked by a definite microsome circle (polar asters
of *Unio*, Fig. 324). Some of these various conditions are show in the diagram, Fig. 321, which calls for no further explanation. Additional reason
for accepting Brauer's comparison is perhaps given by the fact, that in
some cases additional concentric microsome-circles seem to occur in the
asters outside the clear zone; but the interpretation of this is still somewhat
doubtful (p. 682). In any case the facts indicate that the particular

type of configuration in the centrosome is a matter of secondary importance, and that the centriole constitutes the most stable and constant feature of the whole astral system of which it forms the center.[1]

It is an interesting fact that the structure of the central apparatus and aster in higher forms is to a certain extent paralleled by the central granule and axopodial system in the heliozoan rhizopods. This may be seen in Schaudinn's figures of *Sphærastrum* (Fig. 325), in Dobell's of *Oxnerella* (Fig. 85) and still more clearly in Zuelzer's of *Wagnerella* (Fig. 326), in all of which medullary and cortical zones may be seen surrounding the central granule towards which the axopodia converge, the cortical zone bounded by a ring of microsomes. When we consider that the astral systems and central granules here play the same rôle during division as in the mitosis of higher forms (p. 203) we must admit that the conception of the amphiastral system as a fibrillar structure, and even as a contractile structure, may not be as baseless as some modern students of mitosis have assumed (p. 184).

2. Division of the Centers and Astral System

The centrosome and aster present certain further complications that may best be considered in connection with the division of the centers generally. The amphiaster was formerly supposed to arise by the division of a single mother-aster following division of the central body; and this led to attempts to follow out Rabl's early conception (p. 829) by the assumption that division of the center initiated a splitting of the astral rays and hence a meristic division of the whole aster; hence the aphorism *omnis radius e radio*.[2] This assumption proved to be erroneous and the division of a single aster into two was found to be a relatively rare process.[3] In most cases the old aster degenerates and the amphiaster appears as a new formation within its remains, even while the old aster is at the height of its development (Figs. 322, 328).

Many variations of this process have been observed.[4] In the most typical cases (*e. g.* in *Thysanozoön* or *Arion*) the young amphiaster is of quite typical structure, having a central spindle and asters whose rays show the usual equatorial crossing. Since this whole structure is formed inside the enlarged but still intact centrosome, the new astral rays and spindle-fibers, obviously, are differentiated from the centroplasm, and have *no*

---

[1] For accounts diverging more or less from the above see Bonnevie('06) (*Enteroxenos*), and Conklin ('01, '04, '05) (*Styela, Ciona* and especially *Crepidula*).

[2] Kostanecki and Siedlecki ('97).

[3] An undoubted example of such a division is offered by the division of the sperm-aster in the fertilization of the egg (p. 400).

[4] These are reviewed by Yatsu ('09) in his paper on *Cerebratulus*.

direct relation to the old rays. As the process advances the old centrosome, continually enlarging, sooner or later loses its definite boundary, and the new astral rays now extend themselves more or less widely into the region of the old aster, while the latter sooner or later degenerates and disappears. The new asters, in such cases, are clearly new formations, not formed directly from the old ones but endogenously within them. Wide variations

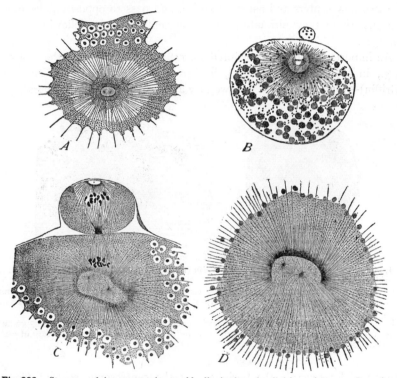

Fig. 328.—Structure of the asters and central bodies in the polar divisions of the egg. In each case the aster shown is the inner one of the first polar spindle (*A, C, D*, in the snail *Arion*, from LAMS; *B*, in the platode *Thysanozoön*, from VAN DER STRICHT).

A, polar view of aster at metaphase, early stage of new astral system; from the center outwards, (1) the centrioles; (2) centrosome (clear); (3), radiate cortical zone; (4) mitochondrial zone; (5) clear zone and (5) outer granular zone.

B, side view of inner aster, with daughter-amphiaster and medullary and cortical zones; *C, D*, telophases, breaking down of old centrosome, development of new astral system.

exist in respect to the details. In *Thysanozoön* (Van der Stricht) or in *Limax* (Byrnes) the new astral rays seem actually to traverse the microsome-circle that bounds the centrosome and to thread their way through the old rays outside it (Fig. 328). In *Arion* (Lams) the wall of the centrosome, here continuous, first dissolves at one side thus setting free the new astral rays, which then become intermingled into the old ones (Fig. 328). In *Thalassema* (Griffin) the centrosome seems to lose its boundary at an early period and the new astral rays are intermingled with the old (Fig. 205). In *Rhynchelmis* (Vejdovský and Mrázek), where the centrosome assumes an enormous size, the original central spindle quickly disappears, and the two asters lie separately within the centrosome (Fig. 330). In all of these cases the two new centers and asters separate, and pass to opposite poles of the nucleus where they ultimately form the centers of the following mitosis (p. 438).

An important point, earlier noted (p. 148) is that in some of these cases— *e. g.*, in the trout (Henneguy), in *Cerebratulus* (Coe), or in *Thalassema* (Griffin)—the formation of the two new asters is preceded by a migration of

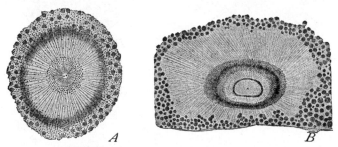

A   *B*

Fig. 329.—Structure of asters and centers.

A, inner polar aster in the egg of the snail *Arion* (LAMS); *B*, aster from 4-cell stage of the annelid *Rhynchelmis* (VEJDOVSKÝ and MRÁZEK).

In *A*, from the center outwards, (1) the two centrioles; (2) the clear centrosome; (3) the inner astral zone (= cortical layer of the "sphere"); (4) granular (mitochondrial) zone; (5) outer astral zone, (6) mitochondria and yolk.

In *B*, from the center outwards (1) centriole; (2) granddaughter-centrosome bounded by granular layer; (3) inner astral zone (cortical layer); (4) outer granular layer, marking boundary of earlier centrosome.

the centrioles towards the periphery of the centrosome, so that *the new astral system does not center in the old focus* (Figs. 205, 322). This affords evidence that the centriole is indeed an active division-center which causes the formation of the aster and is not itself created by the aster.

An interesting feature of the aster is the above mentioned fact (p. 146) that it sometimes shows more or less definite concentric zones outside the centrosome and clear zone. These were observed in *Ascaris* by Van Beneden, by Heidenhain ('92, '94) in giant cells and leucocytes (Fig. 10), by Braus ('95) in the segmenting eggs of *Triton*, and especially by Drüner ('94) in the spermatogonia of urodeles, in which no less than nine such concentric zones were found. By these authors the zoned appearance was believed to be due to the presence of concentric circles of microsomes upon the astral

rays; and such perhaps may sometimes be the case. The studies of Vejdovský and Mrázek ('03) on cleavage in the annelid *Rhynchelmis* (Figs.
329, 330), and of Lams ('10) on the snail *Arion* (Fig. 329) seem to show that

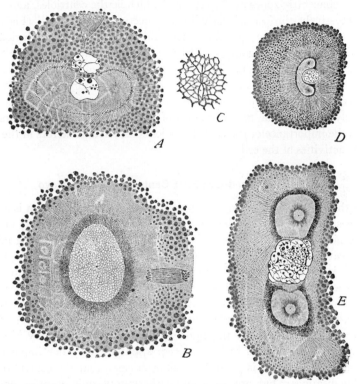

Fig. 330.—Relations of centers and astral systems in fertilization and first cleavage of the annelid
Rhynchelmis (VEJDOVSKÝ and MRÁZEK).

A, conjugation of gamete-nuclei, prophase of first cleavage-amphiaster (sperm-amphiaster).
At the center of each aster is a single centriole, surrounded by the clear second centrosome not
traversed by astral rays. Outside of this the enlarged original centrosome (centroplasm) traversed
by the astral rays and bounded by the dark granular zone; *B*, aster and spindle of early first cleav-
age-telophase (with karyomeres); centrosome greatly enlarged, granular zone (mitochondria)
thickened; *C*, appearance of daughter-amphiaster within the old centrosome; *D*, resulting telophase-
nucleus in 2-cell stage, division of daughter-centrosome; *E*, later stage of same, daughter-centro-
somes enlarged and separate.

the appearance in question may be produced by a zoned massing around
the centers, and between the astral rays, of other formed bodies (granules,
etc.), the concentric zones thus produced being designated as *periplasms*
or *centroplasms*. Vejdovský believes the zones to arise from the fact
that after each division the peripheral portion of the old centrosome,
continually enlarging and passing further away from the center, may

persist long after the daughter-centroplasms have formed within it, and even after a third generation has appeared within the second, a fourth within the third, and so on. The old centroplasms thus give the appearance of a series of concentric zones at the center of which lie the centrioles, and which are successively thrown off, as if by a process of "moulting" (Figs. 329, 330).[1] The interesting questions here raised await further elucidation.

Lastly the fact may again be recalled (cf. p. 30) that even in the "resting" cell, when the asters may be much reduced or even wanting, the central bodies are sometimes surrounded by zones of specific cytoplasmic bodies, such as the chondriosomes, Golgi-bodies, yolk-granules, etc. This fact, strikingly shown in the growth-period of the auxocytes (p. 329) bears witness to the importance of the central bodies considered as factors in the non-mitotic activities of the cell.

3. The Supposed Origin of Central Bodies de Novo

Whether central bodies may arise *de novo* as well as by division is a difficult question. Very often they are lost to view in the interphase or non-mitotic phase of the cell, reappearing in the prophase of the ensuing mitosis as if created *de novo* out of the protoplasmic substance. A conspicuous example is given by the heliozoön *Acanthocystis*, where the central body persists as an extra-nuclear body through many generations but seems to disappear in the budding individuals, to be re-formed in the nuclei of the buds and subsequently extruded into the cytoplasm (Fig. 325). Again, in the process of fertilization, the egg-center disappears from view after the completion of maturation to be replaced, apparently, by one imported by the sperm (p. 440). It is possible in all such cases that the centers do not actually disappear, but are lost among the cytoplasmic granules or have become reduced to sub-microscopic size; but this is merely hypothetical. Fortunately, however, the question may be approached by experimental methods; and these have afforded important if not yet wholly conclusive evidence. Reference has earlier been made to the accessory asters or cytasters (Figs. 331, 335) sometimes formed in the prophases of normal mitosis or fertilization, and often in eggs dividing under the influence of various physico-chemical agents (p. 481). The cytasters (in artificial parthenogenesis) often contain very definite central bodies (Morgan, '96–'00), and, as may be seen, both in living eggs and in sections they may multiply by division (Wilson, '01a). Division of the cytaster is initiated by that of the central body, the formation of a central spindle and of a typical amphiaster (Fig. 333); and during mitosis the cytasters actually operate as centers of

[1] See Yatsu, ('09).

division though the cleavage-furrows formed around them often are not permanent (Fig. 332). These facts indicate, if they do not prove, that the central bodies within these asters are true division-centers; and, since they are often seen developing simultaneously and independently in large numbers in all parts of the egg, that they are formed *de novo*.

This conclusion could not safely be drawn from such evidence alone; for the cytasters might result from a very rapid multiplication of a single

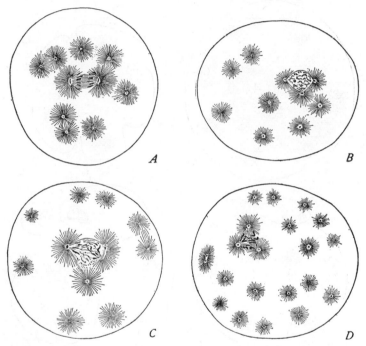

Fig. 331.—Cytasters in the artificial parthenogenesis of *Toxopneustes*, after treatment with hypertonic sea-water.

A, dicentric cleavage-figure in anaphase, cytasters and cyto-amphiasters; *B*, earlier stage, early tripolar figure; *C*, slightly later stage, following last; *D*, tripolar figure, cytaster dividing at left.

original egg-center, either before or subsequent to the development of the astral rays.[1] A crucial experiment was, therefore, attempted by shaking unfertilized eggs to pieces and treating the fragments with the same agent (sea-water rendered hypertonic by the addition of $MgCl_2$) that calls forth the production of cytasters in entire eggs. Under this treatment the *egg-fragments, whether nucleated or non-nucleated, were found to develop cytasters which are capable of multiplication by division, and which contain*

<hr/>

[1] Such a mode of origin was in fact afterwards maintained by Meves ('02), Wassilieff ('02), Petrunkewitsch ('04), and Buchner ('11); but on insufficient grounds.

central bodies (Wilson, 'oia).   Single cytasters maybe formed in fragments
as small as 1/150 the volume of the entire egg, but the cytasters only divide
in larger fragments.   Their history in the enucleated fragments as observed
in life, is closely similar to that in entire eggs; the cytaster moves towards
one side, elongates, its rays become much reduced, the hyaloplasm sphere
at its center assumes an hour-glass shape, and the whole aster then divides

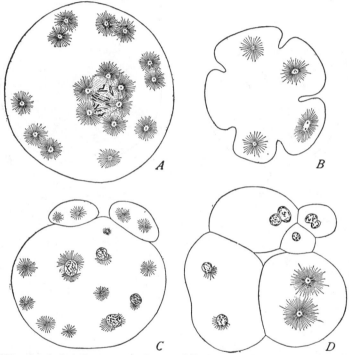

Fig. 332.—Cytological phenomena in the eggs of *Toxopneustes* after treatment with hypertonic
sea-water.
    A, polycentric figure, cytasters and cyto-amphiasters; *B*, tangential section at the time of first
cleavage, showing furrows between cytasters; *C*, syncytial cleavage-stages showing complete
cleavage about cytasters; *D*, abnormal cleavage-stage with cytasters in non-nucleated blastomere.

into two (Fig. 333).   In these experiments *such enucleated fragments, despite
the division of the aster,* never showed any sign of cytoplasmic cleavage.   In
entire eggs, however, one or more of the cytasters may come into association
with the nuclear asters to form a triaster or polyaster, and in such case
multipolar cleavage may take place (Fig. 332).   From all these facts the
conclusion was drawn that in their fullest development the cytasters are not
to be distinguished from cleavage-asters either structurally or functionally;
that the central bodies ("centrosomes") are true division-centers of the

same nature as those of entire, normal eggs; and that these bodies are formed *de novo* from the protoplasmic substance.

A confirmation of these results was given by the works of Yatsu ('05) and McClendon ('08) which exclude certain possibilities of error in the mass-cultures. Yatsu operated with the eggs of the nemertine *Cerebratulus lacteus*, which, upon discharge into the sea-water, and *without fertilization*, form the first polar spindle; and this remains in the metaphase-stage until

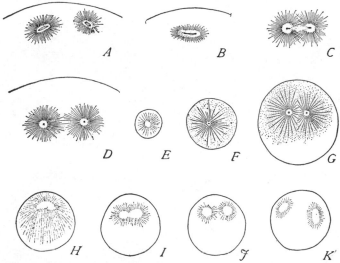

Fig. 333.—Division of cytasters in artificial parthenogenesis from entire eggs and egg-fragments of *Toxopneustes*.

A–C, various stages of division, from peripheral region, sections of entire eggs; F, G, from sections of enucleated egg-fragments; E, cytaster in very small living egg-fragment; H–K, successive stages in the division of a cytaster in a single, living, non-nucleated egg-fragment, elapsed time 25 minutes.

fertilization (p. 403). In this condition the eggs may readily be cut in two individually with a scalpel [1] and both fragments isolated for further observation. If the nucleated fragment be fixed and stained it is easy to demonstrate in it the presence of the polar spindle, at the poles of which are the two normal polar asters and central bodies (Fig. 334). On the other hand, the enucleated fragment, when treated with a parthenogenetic agent (in this case a solution of $CaCl_2$ in sea-water), readily develops a varying number of cytasters in all respects like those seen in the entire egg (Fig. 334). In some cases they are scattered through the fragment, in others occur only in a central large clear area. They show typical astral rays and a rather large and irregular centrosome or centroplasm within which is a group of

[1] Wilson. '03.

centrioles forming a pluricorpuscular center. No evidence of division was found in these asters or their centers.

In this experiment, obviously, the cytasters and their central bodies must have arisen without connection with the original egg centers; *i. e.*, they must have been formed *de novo*. Some doubts arise as to whether these cytasters are of the same nature as the corresponding ones in normal eggs because of the fact that the centrioles are multiple and that neither they nor the asters were found to divide; but this condition may very well be an effect

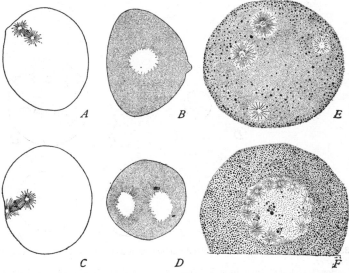

Fig. 334.—Formation of cytasters and centers in enucleated egg-fragments in the nemertine *Cerebratulus* after treatment with hypertonic sea-water (YATSU).

A and B, nucleated and non-nucleated pieces of a single egg cut in two with scalpel; A the nucleated half; D the non-nucleated, with large aster; C, D, similar pair from another egg; E, fixed and stained section of a non-nucleated piece, with four cytasters; F, section of a non-nucleated fragment showing central clear area with numerous cytasters.

of the reagent, since the same is seen in the polar asters of entire eggs after the same treatment, while in the writer's experiments the cytasters likewise often failed to divide. In the case of starfish eggs (*Asterias*) McClendon ('08), was able to suck out the polar spindle by means of a capillary pipette and then treated the enucleated egg with carbonated sea-water (Delage's method). Such eggs, deprived of both centers and chromatin, developed numerous cytasters, about which appeared cleavage-furrows and finally complete cleavage. Thus were formed non-nucleated "cells" devoid of nuclei, each containing one or more cytasters; and such "cells" were seen subsequently to divide again into two or more "cells." More recently

Herlant also ('18, '19) has been led to the conclusion that the cytasters are formed *de novo* and that one of them joins with the "nuclear aster" to form a synthetic amphiaster. In view of the difficulty of determining this point by direct observation the writer is, however, disposed to lay greater weight on the evidence derived from egg-fragments.

Unfortunately the foregoing experiments are not completely demon-

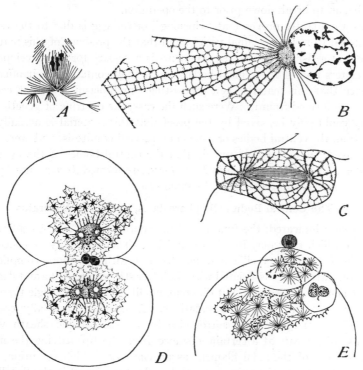

Fig. 335.—Astral formations in early cleavage under various conditions; *A–C;* in *Asterias* (YATSU); *D, E,* in *Crepidula* (CONKLIN).

A, "parasitic asters" formed on astral rays of polar amphiaster (normal egg); *B,* structure of aster in nucleated blastomere of parthenogenetic egg; *C,* amphiaster in enucleated blastomere of slightly etherized egg; *D,* 2-cell stage in hypertonic sea-water, with cytasters attached to astral rays (*cf. A*); *E,* scattered asters in abnormal 3-cell stage.

strative. It has been suggested that the asters and their central bodies may be of two kinds—"artificial" asters and centers, formed *de novo*, and "true" asters and centers which arise only in connection with the egg-nucleus; [1] but in view of all the facts this seems improbable.

Conklin endeavored to save the doctrine of genetic continuity as applied to the central bodies by assuming their common derivation from the nuclear

[1] Boveri '(01), Conklin ('02, '12), Petrunkewitsch ('04).

substance. As earlier indicated, a non-nucleated egg-fragment acquires the power to develop a sperm-aster only when the egg has been cut in two subsequent to the dissolution of the nuclear wall (p. 405); and Yatsu ('05) added the fact that when unfertilized egg-fragments (of *Cerebratulus*), thus obtained, are treated with hypertonic sea-water cytasters do not appear in the non-nucleated pieces unless the germinal vesicle has at least begun to break down prior to the operation.

This abundantly proves that "ripening" of the egg is due to the escape of material from the germinal vesicle, and that the presence of this material in the protoplasm of enucleated fragments is necessary for the development of cytasters and of the central bodies which they contain; but it offers no evidence that this material is a preëxisting "archiplasm," or that central bodies are formed from it. Were such the case, the doctrine of genetic continuity could only be saved by the proof that this material is actually derived from the central bodies or asters of a preceding mitosis; and were even this proved, the fact would remain that the central bodies of the cytaster, considered *as visible individualized structures*, are formed *de novo*, not by the division of preëxisting bodies of the same kind.[1]

4. The Central Bodies, Blepharoplasts, and Basal Apparatus

As earlier indicated, the function of the central bodies is not confined to the part which they play in mitotic division. They also may be concerned with the formation of cilia and flagella and with the more complicated basal apparatus often associated with the latter structures. Cilia and flagella, as is generally agreed, are but different modifications of a single type and are connected by many intergradations. A flagellum typically consists of a delicate *axial filament* surrounded by a protoplasmic sheath which typically disappears at a certain distance from the tip, leaving the naked terminal part of the axial filament as an *end-piece*. This condition, conspicuously shown in the animal sperm, has also been found in the flagellated Protista, *e. g.*, in *Euglena* (Bütschli), *Trachelomonas* (Plenge), or *Bodo* (Fischer), and is probably of general occurrence. The internal structure of cilia is more difficult to analyze, owing to their extreme tenuity; nevertheless the presence of an axial filament and a surrounding sheath seems to have been clearly demonstrated in certain cases.[2] At the base of the axial

---

[1] A possible source of error in some of these experiments is indicated by Boveri's posthumous work ('18) in which it is shown that when eggs are shaken to pieces the nuclei are readily altered or even disorganized, so that it may be impossible to distinguish certainly between nucleated and non-nucleated fragments; all results based on this method, therefore, require further evidence. Such an error is eliminated by cutting experiments on individual eggs (as in Yatsu's experiments). In the writer's judgment, therefore, the origin of true central bodies or division-centers *de novo* has been rendered at least probable; but the questions here involved are too fundamental to be accepted unreservedly without additional proof.

[2] See Maier ('03), Koltsoff ('06, '09), Erhard ('10), Khainsky ('10), Saguchi ('17), etc.

filament is a *basal apparatus* consisting in its simplest form of a single basal body (Fig. 341) but often of much greater complexity.

Both cilia and flagella, as a rule, are secondary and often temporary structures, though in certain flagellates they may actually divide by longitudinal fission and thus be handed on from one cell-generation to another (Fig. 336). The axial filament originally grows forth from a basal body or blepharoplast which in some cases plays the part of a division-center during mitosis

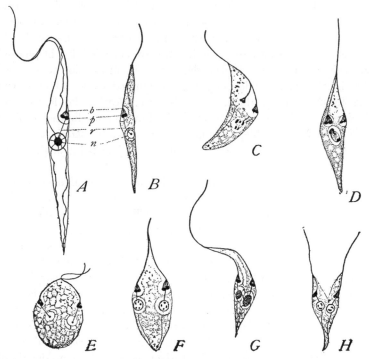

Fig. 336.—Basal apparatus and longitudinal fission in the flagellate *Crithidia leptocoridis* (Mc-Culloch).

A, B, vegetative individuals; *b,* basal body or blepharoplast; *n,* nucleus; *p,* parabasal ("kineto-nucleus"); *r,* rhizoplast; *C–H,* stages of fission, longitudinal fission of the flagellum, division of blepharoplast and parabasal without relation to the nuclear spindle.

and hence is identical with a centriole. This phenomenon is now conclusively established in the spermatogenesis of some animals and plants (p. 357) and among the flagellated Protista. In the latter case, however, a more complicated type of basal apparatus is often present, the blepharoplast being sometimes quite distinct from the centriole, while in addition a *parabasal* body and other structures may also be present. The relations between these various basal structures have not yet been completely elucidated; and the same may be said of the basal bodies in the ciliates and ciliated tissue-cells of higher Metazoa. That a close analogy exists between all these various basal structures can harldy be doubted, but the morphological problems here involved still await adequate analysis.

a. Centriole and Blepharoplast in the Sperm-formation. In animal spermiogenesis it is probable that in all cases the centriole is the lineal descendant of the centrioles of earlier cell-generations, possibly even back to the fertilized egg. On the other hand, in higher plants (bryophytes, pteridophytes, cycads, *Ginkgo*) division-centers seem to be absent in both the somatic cells and in those of the earlier germ-line; nevertheless in the closing spermatogenous divisions the spindle-poles are occupied by blepharoplasts which in many cases show all the characteristics of division-centers, arising by the division of a single body and surrounded by astral rays, while a spindle forms between them. In this case, clearly, the law of genetic continuity as applied to these structures is of much more limited application, and the central bodies (blepharoplasts), considered *as individualized bodies*, must apparently be formed *de novo* at a certain late point in the germ-line (p. 387).

The fact has earlier been emphasized that in animal spermatogenesis the original spermatid centriole divides into two products of which only one (the distal) forms the blepharoplast, while the other (the proximal) has no direct connection with the axial filament (p. 381). Further, the distal centriole itself frequently divides into two portions, of which only one remains in connection with the axial filament while the other in the form of a ring or otherwise, undergoes a displacement varying widely in different species of sperms, and in some cases apparently is cast out altogether (p. 376). In these facts we find reason to conclude that the centriole itself may be a compound, or at least dual body, *of which only one component is concerned with the functions of a blepharoplast.* This is supported by facts in the flagellated Protista, now to be considered, which prove that centriole and blepharoplast may be completely separate structures.

b. The Basal Apparatus in Flagellated Protista. The basal apparatus of the flagella in Protista shows many interesting complications of which only a few illustrations can here be offered.[1] In its simpler forms the basal apparatus has been described as a single basal granule (blepharoplast), or a small group of such bodies, from each of which a flagellum grows forth; but in most if not in all cases other basal structures are associated with it. Typically it lies near the cell-periphery at the base of the flagellum (Figs.

[1] See Prenant ('14), Kühn ('15), Kofoid and Swazey ('15), Doflein ('16, '18), Swezy ('16), Kuczynski ('18), Bělař ('21).

337, 338), but often more deeply, sometimes near the nucleus or even within it. In the amœbo-flagellate *Nägleria* the basal granule is said to be originally within the nucleus, apparently inside the karyosome, later escaping from it to form a blepharoplast from which the flagella grow forth (Fig. 337). Probably in all these various cases it gives origin peripherally to the axial filament of the flagellum. Centrally, a delicate fibrilla or rhizoplast extends

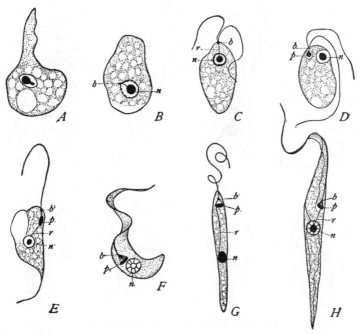

Fig. 337.—The basal apparatus in flagellates, after Swezy. (*A–C*, from C. W. Wilson; *D–G*, from Swezy; *H*, from McCulloch.) *b*, basal body or blepharoplast; *n*, nucleus; *b*, parabasal body or "kinetonucleus;" *r*, rhizoplast.

A, Nägleria, an amœbo-flagellate, blepharoplast arising as a bud from the karyosome; *B*, its escape from the nucleus; *C*, the developed flagellate form with blepharoplast but no parabasal body; *D, Prowazekia* a flagellate, with both blepharoplast and large parabasal; *E, Trypanoplasma; F, Schizotrypanum; G, Herpetomonas; H, Crithidia;* in each of these (*E–G*) a conspicuous parabasal, with a well developed rhizoplast and, in *F–G*, a cone of fibrils connecting the blepharoplast with the parabasal.

inwards to the nucleus and sometimes beyond it, and is also connected with other components of the basal apparatus (Figs. 336, 338). The rhizoplast closely suggests the proximal or "intra-cellular" portion of the axial filament in the animal spermatid.

Most frequently the basal apparatus is complicated by the presence of other structures. In some cases the basal body seems to have no relation to the division-figure while definite centrioles have in addition been described in some cases at the spindle-poles (*e. g.,* in *Collodictyon* (Fig. 341). In addition to the foregoing there is often a larger and more conspicu ous *parabasal body* typically connected by fibrillæ (rhizoplasts) with both blepharoplast and nucleus. In a few cases this is said to be a tempo-rary structure, indistinguishable in certain phases of the life-history; but it is typically persistent, often being handed on by division like

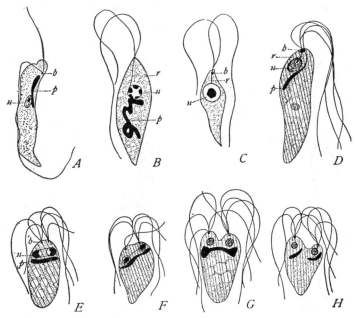

Fig. 338.—The basal apparatus in flagellates.

(*A,* from MARTIN; the rest from SWEZY.)

A, Trypanoplasma; B, C, Prowazekia; D–H, Polymastix. Small letters as in Fig. 337.

A, B, vegetative individuals (trophozoites) with large parabasal; *C,* individual without para-basal, ordinary trophozoite; *E–H,* stages of mitosis, division of both blepharoplast and parabasal independently of the nucleus.

the blepharoplast (Figs. 336, 338) and showing a great variety of forms. In some species it is a rounded body connected peripherally with the blepharoplast by a single fibrilla (*Trypanoplasma,* Fig. 337, E) or by a cone of such fibrillæ (*Herpetomonas, Crithidia,* etc., Fig. 336) and centrally by a single fibrilla with the nucleus, from which one or more such fibrillæ may also extend towards the basal region of the cell. In other cases it is a more or less elongate and sometimes convoluted rod. This structure, still of doubtful significance, has received many names (*chromidial body, reserve-body, blepharoplast,* etc.). By Schaudinn ('96–'03) and his successors, even to a recent date, it was called the "blepharoplast," and was regarded as a second nucleus or "kinetonucleus" (Woodcock, '06); and out of this grew the so-called "binuclearity theory" of the protistan cell (Hartmann, '07, '11) (p. 726).

More recent studies have failed to support this view, giving no evidence of the nuclear nature of the parabasal, pointing rather to the conclusion that it has arisen as a derivative of the basal body; further, that both bodies,

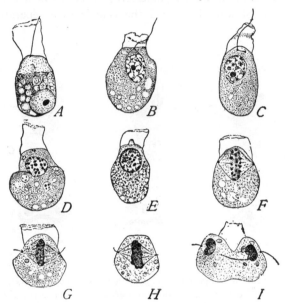

Fig. 339.—Mitosis of the choanocytes in the sponge *Clathrina* (MINCHIN).

A, B, vegetative cells; *C, D,* division of blepharoplast, disappearance of flagella; *E, F,* separation of blepharoplasts, spindle-formation; *G, H, I,* later stages of mitosis, outgrowth of new flagella.

together with the connecting rhizoplasts, belong to a "neuro-motor" apparatus [1] concerned with the motor activities as well as with the operations of division. This apparatus reaches its highest development in the ciliates, where it is sometimes of great complexity.[2] We are here concerned only with its relation to the phenomena of division, as yet definitely known only in the flagellates.

Still other structures, of unknown significance, may be found in connection with the basal apparatus. One is a basal ring of unknown origin, encircling the rhizoplast below the blepharoplast (Fig. 340) [3] which recalls the ring derived from the distal centriole in the spermatids of mammals and some other animals (p. 377).

[1] Kofoid and Christiansen ('15).
[2] Sharp ('14), McCulluch ('15), Yocom ('18), Taylor ('20).
[3] See Kuczynski ('18), Bělař ('21).

c. Blepharoplast and Centriole in Protista.   The foregoing conditions may offer a clue to the fact that in some of the flagellates the blepharoplast seems to play the part of a centriole during mitosis while in others it is a quite distinct structure, not lying at the spindle-poles, but handed on by division from cell to cell.   The contradiction disappears under the view that the centriole in some cases unites the functions of a division-center and a blepharoplast while in others the centriole has separated into two

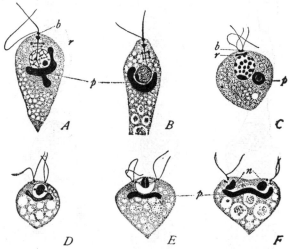

Fig. 340.—Basal apparatus and centriole in *Bodo lacertæ* (BĚLAŘ).

A, B, normal vegetative individuals, with blepharoplast (*b*), basal ring (*r*), and parabasal (*p*); *C,* initial stage of division; *D,* later stage, with supposed intra-nuclear spindle and centrioles; *E,* metaphase; *F,* telophase.

corresponding distinct structures.   Examples of the first case seem to occur in species of *Bodo*,[1] *Copromonas*,[2] *Ochromonas* [3] and *Trichomonas;* [4] and similar conditions are described by Jahn ('04) in the flagellated swarm-spores of myxomycetes and by Minchin and Robertson ('10) in the collar-cells of calcareous sponges (Fig. 339).   In some of these cases the old flagella disappear in the earlier stages of mitosis, new ones growing forth at a later period; in others the old flagella seem to persist throughout.   In *Bodo lacertæ*, for example, Bělař found two basal bodies, close together and each bearing a single flagellum.   As they separate in the prophases each divides into two parts, one bearing the old flagellum while a new flagellum grows forth from the other, the double blepharoplasts and flagella then persisting throughout

[1] Prowazek ('04), Alexeieff ('14), Kuczinski ('18), Bělař ('21).
[2] Dobell ('08).
[3] Doflein ('19).
[4] Kofoid and Swezy ('15), etc.

all the later stages (Fig. 340). In *Trichomonas* the facts are similar (Fig. 86) though somewhat more complicated. Upon division of the single blepharoplast two of the three free flagella remain attached to one half and one to the other, while the normal number is in each case restored by a new formation, as in *Bodo*. The fourth or intra-cytoplasmic flagellum is said to split lengthwise throughout, half remaining connected with each half of the blepharoplast.[1]

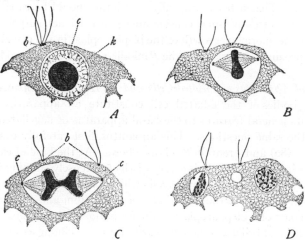

Fig. 341.—Blepharoplast (basal granule) and centriole in the flagellate *Collodictyon* (Bèlàr).
A, vegetative nucleus, with karyosome (*k*), centriole (*c*), and blepharoplasts (*b*); *B*, metaphase with intra-nuclear spindle; *C*, anaphase figure; *D*, telophase.

The most conspicuous fact here is that during the whole process the blepharoplasts, still bearing their flagella, occupy the spindle-poles, as in case of the Lepidoptera; but there are two important additional facts. In *Trichomonas* several observers have found indications that the blepharoplast-centriole is a double body, at least in certain stages, the flagella being attached to one of these, while the other is connected with its fellow by the paradesmose (p. 204). Kofoid and Swezy, accordingly, consider these two components to represent, respectively, the blepharoplast and the centriole, here so closely associated as often to appear as a single body. Such a condition might readily lead into one in which the two components are wholly separate and divide independently. Bĕlař found that in *Bodo* the blepharoplasts are at first quite separate from the centrioles at the spindle-poles but later move towards the latter to a position just outside the centrioles (Fig. 340), later assuming their typical position at the cell-periphery,

---

[1] The latter observation by Kofoid and Swezy ('15) was not confirmed by Kuczinski ('18) and Wenrich ('21).

From such a condition it would be only a step to one in which the blepharoplasts divide and separate at the periphery without approaching the spindle-
poles as in *Polytoma* (Doflein, '16), *Polymastix* (Fig. 338), *Crithidia* (Fig.
336), or *Collodictyon* (Fig. 341).

Swezy ('16) has developed in an interesting way the view that the whole
basal apparatus has developed by the growth and differentiation of a
simple original basal granule comparable with the centriole-blepharoplast of
higher forms. That a body originally so minute should be capable of producing an apparatus of such considerable size need not surprise us when
we consider the enormous growth of the blepharoplast in the cycads (p. 389),
or of the proximal centriole in the "middle-piece" of the urodele sperm
(p. 379).

The Basal Apparatus of Ciliated Cells and the Henneguy-Lenhossék Theory.
The basal bodies of the ciliated cell constitute an apparatus obviously
similar in its general features to the basal apparatus of flagellated cells and
involving the same questions. This apparatus, first carefully examined by
Engelmann ('80) and Frenzel ('86) is as follows. At the base of each cilium,
near the periphery of the cell, is a very distinct, intensely staining *basal body*,
often clearly visible in the living cell, which has the same morphological
relation to the cilium as the basal body of a flagellum and appears likewise
to play the part of a blepharoplast in the formation of the cilium. From this
body a delicate fibrilla extends outwards into the cilium as an axial filament, while inwardly it is prolonged into the cytosome to form the so-called
ciliary root or basal filament, which is no doubt comparable to the rhizoplast of the flagellate. These filaments are often gathered together centrally
to form a more or less conical bundle, extending downwards towards the
nucleus and sometimes beyond it (Figs. 17, 18). The basal body is typically a minute rounded granule and in the simplest case is single (a common
condition); but there are many complications of this simple type.[1] The basal
body is often rod-shaped, sometimes dumb-bell-shaped, and in many
cases is divided into a superficial or distal, and a central or proximal
part; these are connected by the axial filament, often more or less thickened, which form the "basal rod" or "intermediate piece" of the cilium.
In some cases the basal apparatus even consists of three basal bodies connected by the axial filament or basal rod. In addition to the foregoing, which
belong to the basal apparatus proper, there is often a swelling of the free
portion of cilium near its base, forming the so-called "ciliary bulb."

The analogy between the basal apparatus of ciliated cells and of flagellates or sperm-cells is so close as to raise the question whether here too the
basal bodies may not be central bodies or their derivatives. That such

---

[1] *Cf.* Frenzel ('86), Böhming ('91), Heidenhain ('99), and references at p. 699.

is actually the case was urged by Henneguy ('97) and Lenhossék ('98), whose conclusions have since been generally known as the "Henneguy-Lenhossék theory." In columnar ciliated epithelium (epididymis of mammals) these observers found non-ciliated cells intermingled with the ciliated, closely similar to the latter in general type but containing a peripherally placed "diplosome" or pair of centrioles in place of the group of basal bodies characteristic of the ciliated cells. In the latter, diplosomes were not found; and the above-named observers could find no evidence of mitosis in the ciliated cell. They therefore concluded that the basal bodies represent a group of centrioles, probably derived by the multiplication of an original pair. Centrioles, blepharoplasts and basal bodies were thus regarded as homologous structures. This was supported by Meves' studies on the ciliated or multiflagellate oligopyrene sperms of *Paludina* (p. 300). Benda ('oo) described the origin of basal bodies from centrioles in the ciliated cells of the ependyma and the epididymis of man; and similar results have been reached by several later observers, in particular Moreaux ('10, '12). Others likewise failed to find diplosomes in ciliated cells,[1] while many observers have been struck with the rarity of mitotic divisions in these cells, though it now seems to be established that such divisions may occur.

On the other hand, it seems now to have been conclusively proved that ciliated cells may contain a true microcentrum in the form of a pair of centrioles, situated in the outer region of the cell (as in epithelia generally) in addition to the peripheral group of ciliary basal bodies;[2] and some of these observers have produced evidence that the diplosome gives rise to the centrioles of the division-figure of such ciliated cells in mitosis, and that the basal bodies take no part in the process. The best evidence of this is offered by the work of Wallengren ('05) and Erhard ('10); but these observers differ as to the behavior of the ciliary apparatus, the former maintaining that both cilia and basal bodies disappear before mitosis, while Erhard asserts their persistence. These observers and others have considered these facts as decisive against the Henneguy-Lenhossék hypothesis, so far as ciliated tissue-cells are concerned; and another adverse argument has been based on the occurrence of basal bodies in the cilia of the ciliate Infusoria,[3] organisms in which mitosis seems to take place in the absence of either asters or clearly individualized central bodies. In spite of these apparent difficulties the writer shares the opinion of Prenant[4] that the last word had not yet been spoken on this subject. It seems entirely possible that in the ciliated cell,

[1] See Zimmerman ('98), Heidenhain ('99), Fuchs ('04), Joseph ('03), etc.
[2] Studnička ('99), Fischel ('oo), Benda ('01), Gurwitsch ('01, '02), Wallengren ('05), Ikeda ('06) schassownikoff ('13).
[3] See Maier ('03), Mitrophanow ('03, '04), Hamburger ('03), Schuberg ('05).
[4] '12, p. 608.

as is so clearly seen in some of the flagellates, the basal bodies (blepharoplasts) though still retaining the power of multiplication by division, have
wholly separated from the division-centers, so as no longer to take direct part
in mitosis. Yocom ('18) has suggested that the blepharoplast of the flagellate is represented by the *motorium* of the hypotrichous ciliates, a body
regarded as a probable center of coördination and connected by delicate
fibrillæ with the bases of the anal cirrhi and the membranelles;[1] but there is
no evidence to connect this structure with a division-center. The homologies between the basal apparatus of the ciliates and of flagellates thus remain
in doubt.

II. CHROMIDIA, CHONDRIOSOMES AND GOLGI-BODIES

Both chromidia and mitochondria formerly belonged to that miscel-
laneous assemblage of granules known as "microsomes" (p. 32). Up
to rather a late period the two were often confused, and even now considerable uncertainty exists concerning their identification. Theoretically
an essential distinction lies in the fact that chromidia are of nuclear origin
and are composed of "chromatin" while mitochondria are considered by
nearly all recent students of the subject as strictly cytoplasmic; but in practice the determination of the origin of these bodies is not an easy task.

1. Chromidia

In the form of scattered or "distributed" nuclei chromidia were observed in
various Protista (rhizopods, flagellates, bacterioid forms) by Gruber, Brandt,

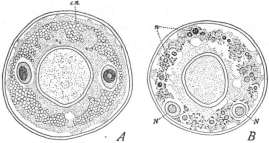

A B

Fig. 342.—The rhizopod *Arcella*, showing nuclei and chromidia (R. HERTWIG). In each figure
the large central circle represents the opening of the shell.
  A, vegetative state with two nuclei and scattered chromidial net (*c. n.*); *B*, supposed secondary
gamete-nuclei forming from chromidia (*cf.* Fig. 343).

Schewiakoff, Lister, Calkins and others some time before they attracted
wider attention. Their theoretical interest was first fully recognized in the

---

[1] See also Taylor ('20).

so-called "chromidia hypothesis," founded by R. Hertwig and developed especially by Goldschmidt and others [1] who endeavored to extend it to the cells of vertebrates and gave to it a far-reaching theoretic elaboration. These later developments of the hypothesis, it must be said, have in considerable measure failed to meet the test of subsequent investigation. On its physiological side the most important development of the hypothesis has been the theory of nuclear dualism, which will be considered under a later heading (p. 725).

R. Hertwig first showed in certain heliozoan rhizopods, that the cytosome contains numerous intensely basophilic granules believed to be given off from the nucleus—hence his term "chromidia" (1902). In *Actinosphærium* during conditions of hunger or overfeeding the vesicular nuclei may break up completely into chromidia ("physiological degeneration"), the cell now being filled with chromidial granules, often forming a "chromidial net." If some of the nuclei remain intact the *Actinosphærium* cell is capable of complete recovery; if all the nuclei break down this seems to be impossible and the animal dies. In *Arcella* and other Thalamophora chromidia are given off in large quantities from the nuclei, without fragmentation, and give rise to a chromidial network; and Hertwig found that from this may be formed numerous small "secondary nuclei" (Fig. 342) which according to Schaudinn ('03), become the nuclei of minute gametes which conjugate in pairs.[2]   More or less similar observations have since been made by a considerable number of observers, [3] who have found that in various Protista the nucleus may thus break down into chromidia, or give them off into the protoplasm by a process of emission; and that from such scattered chromidial formations new nuclei may reform. In some cases these nuclei are said to arise by the aggregation of chromidia, for instance, in the spore-formation of various bacteria; [4] in others by the enlargement (and multiplication?) of single chromidial granules. A good example of this is offered by the life-history of *Arachnula*, a primitive rhizopod originally described by Cienkowski ('76) as devoid of a nucleus and hence referable to Haeckel's "Monera." Dobell's recent studies of this form ('13) show that in its ordinary or vegetative condition it contains a variable number of vesicular nuclei. During encystment the nuclei are said to give off numerous chromidia to the cytoplasm and finally wholly to disappear as such, now being represented only by the scattered chromidial granules (Fig. 343).

---

[1] See especially R. Hertwig ('99, '00, '02, '04), Goldschmidt ('04, etc.), Goldschmidt and Popoff ('07), Popoff ('07), Schaudinn ('03, '07). For critique see Dobell ('09), Prenant ('10), Kofoid ('21).
[2] In the rhizopods *Polystomella, Centropyxis, Chlamydophrys* and *Entamœba*. The same was afterwards described by Elpatiewsky ('07) in *Arcella*, flagellates, gregarines, and other forms.
[3] Goldschmidt ('07), Schouteden ('07), Prowazek ('04, '05), Guilliermond ('07), Dobell ('13).
[4] See Schaudinn ('02, '03), Guilliermond ('08), Dobell ('08).

The cell thereupon breaks up to form a brood (10–20) of small daughter-cells, containing chromidia which give rise to a number of vesicular nuclei each of which seems to arise by the growth (and multiplication?) of a single granule.

If such accounts can be accepted it seems clear that the chromidial substance undergoes extensive growth, and that the number of granules largely increases in the course of the life-cycle. It is possible that this takes place by growth and division of the individual granules; and this view has been maintained by some observers, in particular by Schewia-koff ('93) who long since gave a careful description and figure of the

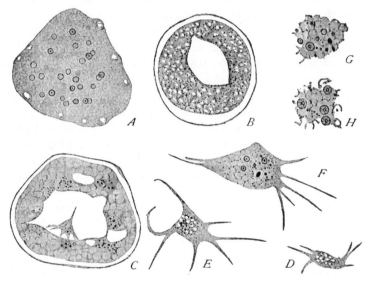

Fig. 343.—Chromidia and nuclei in the rhizopod *Arachnula* (DOBELL) (from fixed and stained specimens).

A, Individual ready for encystment, with many nuclei, no chromidia; *B*, encysted individual with large vacuole, nuclei broken down into scattered chromidia; *C*, endogeneous formation of daughter-cells; *D*, *E*, young chromidial daughter-cells, recently escaped; *F*, older form with nuclei forming, *G*, detail from individual similar to last, stages in formation of vesicular nuclei form chromidia; *H*, detail from mature specimen, nuclei and chromidia.

dividing chromidia in the large bacterium-like *Achromatium* (Fig. 32). This has never been sufficiently confirmed by later observers, either in bacteria or other Protista; nevertheless, there has been a rather general, more or less tacit, assumption that the chromidia are endowed with such powers.

The chromidia hypothesis underwent a sudden expansion with the works especially of Goldschmidt, Popoff and still later of Buchner and of Schaxel by whom an attempt was made to extend it to the Metazoa and to elaborate a general theory of the chromidia. Goldschmidt ('04) described in the epithelial, muscular, glandular and connective-tissue-cells a "chromidial apparatus" consisting of basophilic granules and fibrillar formations which were assumed, mainly because of a general similarity of staining-reactions, to be extruded basichromatin destined to play a particular rôle in the trophic functions of the cell (p. 726); and Goldschmidt accepted the probability of a similar origin of many other well-known cytoplasmic structures, including the mitochondria, the yolk-nucleus, nebenkern, pseudochromosomes, reticular apparatus, ergastoplasm and cytomicrosomes. These conclusions were extended to the germ-cells by Wassilieff ('07), Popoff ('07), and Buchner ('09, '10), all of whom concluded that the cytoplasmic granules and filaments aggregated near one pole of the nucleus, of the auxocytes, in the early growth-period (p. 330), are chromidia extruded from the nucleus, at or near the time of the synaptic or "bouquet" stage of maturation (p. 543). An actual extrusion of chromatin from the free ends of the threads at this time was in fact described by Buchner ('09, '10) and Jörgensen ('10); but these results have either been contradicted or have failed of sufficient support by later observers. The nuclear origin of Goldschmidt's "chromidial system" in nematodes was specifically denied by later workers,[1] and it was made clear that many of the other elements of the so-called "chromidial system" in Metazoa are of mitochondrial and not of nuclear origin.   In case of the germ-cells it was clearly demonstrated by Duesberg ('11), Fauré-Fremiet ('10), Van der Stricht ('05, '11, etc.) and others, that the granules and fibrillæ aggregated at the nuclear pole in the bouquet stage are typical cytoplasmic chondriosomes, already present before the polarization of the spireme-threads and derived from chondriosomes of the spermatogonia.

Widespread scepticism thus arose concerning the whole conception of chromidia as applied to the Metazoa. Some observers still hold to the view that chromidia and mitochondria coexist in the cell as independent though often closely similar structures. Schaxel[2] in particular has devoted an interesting series of papers to the general thesis that differentiation or cytomorphosis is largely brought about by a periodic emission of chromatin from the nucleus, beginning already in the unfertilized egg and continuing during cleavage and development. Schaxel's figures of the supposed chromatin-emission are among the most careful in the literature (Fig. 344). If they do not seem to the writer conclusive it is because of the extreme difficulty of arriving at a certain conclusion from the study of sections

---

[1] See Vejdovský ('07), Bilek ('09. '10), Hirschler ('12) and especially Kemnitz ('12).
[2] See especially ('10, '11, '12, '13, '15).

alone.[1] On the other hand, it is important not to lose sight of the fact, which has been emphasized by many observers,[2] that at every mitosis residual nuclear material is set free into the cytoplasm; and in case of the germinal vesicle of the ovum this material, very large in amount, may play

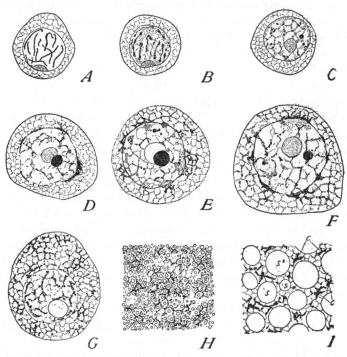

Fig. 344.—Supposed chromidia-formation in the animal egg (SCHAXEL); (*A–F*, in the annelid *Aricia; G* in *Holothuria; H, I,* in the medusa *Pelagia*).

A, B, early oöcytes; *C,* reticular stage; *D–F,* stages of "chromatin-emission"; *G,* cytoplasmic "chromasia" following emission; *H,* cytoplasmic detail in later oöcyte, small yolk-spheres appearing with chromidial granules scattered between them; *I,* from mature egg, with yolk-spheres (*s. s.*) and inter-vitelline chromatin-remnants (*c*).

a direct and important part in building the body of the embryo.[3] F. R. Lillie ('06) showed that in the annelid *Chætopterus*, the nuclear granules (microsomes) of this substance are visible in the living eggs; that upon their liberation, as the wall of the germinal vesicle breaks down, their staining-reaction changes from acidic to basic (with thionin and orange); that they

[1] Beckwith ('14) who has carefully reëxamined the phenomena in the oöcytes of hydromedusæ was unable to confirm Schaxel's account. See also the work of Dantschakoff ('16), and of Van Herwerden ('13).

[2] See Wilson ('95, etc.), Conklin ('02, etc.).

[3] See especially Conklin ('05) and Lillie ('06).

can still be distinguished as basic-staining "microsomes" during early cleavage and undergo a fairly definite distribution to the embryonic cells. Lillie also observed the liberation of another and larger type of granules at each cleavage-mitosis, in addition to the setting free of oxychromatin, emphasized by earlier writers.

The facts, apparently, are here well determined, and there seems to be no valid reason why the granules thus derived from the nucleus should not be called "chromidia." The possibility is here opened that such bodies, once set free, may long retain the powers of growth and division, and be capable of definite chemical transformations, and that they may even give rise to bodies indistinguishable from mitocondria which, unless their whole history be followed out, would appear to be of strictly cytoplasmic origin.

Further interesting possibilities are offered by the recent work of K. E. Schreiner who has produced evidence that certain types of secretory granules arise by the extrusion from the nucleus of fragments of the true nucleolus. In a first paper ('15) this conclusion is reached in case of the subcutaneous fat-producing gland-cells of the epidermis in *Myxine;* in later works ('16, '18) it is extended to the remarkable slime-producing gland-cells of the epidermis. These cells contain numerous intensely fuchsinophilous granules and fibrillæ, called by Schreiner *plasmosomes* (following Arnold and Held), and are identified by him with Altmann's plasma-elements (granules and their products). Schreiner believes that, in some cases at least (the small mucus-producing cells) the plasmosomes are capable of independent growth and division, and that they may thus be handed on from cell to cell in mitosis. The filaments may arise from the granular forms either by elongation or by linear alignment, and conversely the filaments may break up into granules, a process that always precedes mitosis. By the transformation of these bodies are said to arise both the fat-drops or lipoid granules and the long, spiral threads of mucus-producing material in which form the secretion is discharged from the cell; and Schreiner further concludes that in the sensory cells the neurofibrils may arise by direct transformation of the "Altmann threads."

All this is in harmony with the results of Altmann himself (pp. 74–77) and of those who have ascribed a similar physiological rôle to the chondriosomes (Benda, Meves), as described beyond (p. 708). The point which especially interests us here is Schreiner's conclusion that the Altmann elements (granules and fibrillæ) originally arise *by extrusion of fragments of the true nucleoli*, either in the basal cells or in their products.[1] Could this result be accepted it would go far towards a reconciliation of the chromidia hypothesis and that of the chondriosomes. The conclusions of so experienced

---

[1] See also p. 345 for an account of the formation of yolk-spheres from nucleolar fragments.

and competent an observer carry great weight; neverthless it must be said that they still await more convincing evidence than has yet been produced.

2. The Chondriosomes

Most of the bodies now called chondriosomes were described by the earlier cytologists under other names (p. 46); and even the theoretical aspects of the "chondriosome-theory" were in most essentials worked out by Altmann and others some time before the more modern development of the subject. This development was due, first to technical improvements by Benda ('97–'01) and his successors, which made it possible to fix and stain the chondriosomes with greater certainty and brilliancy; and secondly, to a theoretical treatment by Benda and Meves nearly akin to Altmann's but avoiding many of the errors into which that writer had fallen. With these authors arose a new terminology, which, as has so often happened before, contributed to the impression that the chondriosomes represented a newly discovered cell-component. But, as most of the leading investigators in this field have clearly recognized, what was new was not the thing itself or even its theoretical treatment but only an impulse to its further investigation. Due in the first instance to Benda, this was carried forward especially by Meves and Duesberg, and more recently by Regaud, Fauré-Fremiet, Guilliermond, Bensley, Cowdry, the Lewises and many others.

The most salient histological characters of the chondriosomes have earlier been indicated (pp. 45–47). In their broader bearings they are of general interest in relation to the phenomena of histogenesis and considered as possible factors in differentiation and heredity.

a. Chondriosomes and Histogenesis. As applied to the phenomena of histogenesis the chondriosome-theory is essentially a modernized development of Altmann's granule-theory (p. 74). It began with the identification of mitochondria in the germ-cells, and was followed by Benda's demonstration of their presence in both egg and sperm and in the blastomeres of the sementing egg (*Triton*), and of the fact that they are handed on from cell to cell without loss of their identity during the processes of mitosis (p. 163). These facts, repeatedly confirmed by more extended observation in later years, led Benda to suggest that mitochondria introduced into the egg by the sperm may take part in the process of fertilization; further that they may be handed on by division to the embryonic cells; that from them during histogenesis may arise more specialized structures, such as the myofibrils, the basal bodies of the cilia, etc.; and finally, that the mitochondria must be regarded as definite and permanent cell-organs, identical in part with the "microsomes" of earlier writers and the "bioblasts" of Altmann,

which play a definite part in heredity.[1]   Benda thus offered, in brief outline
a general far-reaching hypothesis of the chondriosomes, about which
quickly gathered numerous more detailed studies supporting his main conclusions.

The lead in this movement was taken by Meves, who has contributed
many interesting works in support of Benda's general conclusions; but an
important part in it was played by Duesberg, Regaud, Hoven, Fauré-
Fremiet, Guilliermond and many others.   The demonstration, it must be
confessed, still leaves much to be desired and a considerable group of excellent observers, e. g., Retzius, Vejdovský, Cowdry and Mottier, have
taken a sceptical attitude towards the whole hypothesis.   In some directions, clearly, the chondriosome-theory has far outrun the facts; in others
it has met with direct contradiction by observation.   But if it is not yet
fully ripe for discussion it has too many facts in its favor to be lightly dis-
missed.[2]

Meves ('08) found numerous chondriosomes, in the form of mitochondria
and chondrioconts, in all kinds of embryonic cells (in vertebrates) up to a
stage when histogenesis is well advanced, and pointed out that these bodies
are in all probability identical with Altmann's granules and fibrillæ; further,
that the chondrioconts represent the *fila*, or separate fibrillæ of Flemming
('82).   By the transformation of these embryonic chondriosomes, in the
view of Meves, arise various other formed bodies, including the myofibrils
of both smooth and striated muscles, the neuro-fibrils, the fibrillæ of the
neuroglia- and connective-tissue-cells, the basal filaments of ciliated cells,
the fibrillæ of glandular epithelia and many forms of granules, including
the secretory, the pigment-granules, and the yolk-spheres.   A long series
of later works were devoted by Meves to the support and extension of these
conclusions, including the proof that during fertilization the sperm brings
into the egg mitochondria which mingle with those of the egg (p. 435) thus
providing a biparental store of these bodies to be drawn upon during development as material for histogenesis of the formed components of the tissues.

The foregoing conclusions have formed the subject of numerous special
investigations since 1908 without having led as yet to any general agreement
among cytologists.   There are few of the cytoplasmic formed bodies that
have not been supposed to be products of chondriosomes; but few of these
conclusions have not been contradicted by other observers.   For example,
both Benda and Meves believed the myofibrils to arise by direct transformation of the embryonic chondrioconts (Fig. 345).   This was supported by the

[1] Benda, '03, pp. 749, 781.
[2] General reviews of the literature are offered by Benda ('03), Meves ('08), Prenant ('10), Duesberg ('12, '20), the Lewises ('15), Guilliermond ('14, '19, etc.), Schreiner ('16), Meves ('18), Cowdry
('18, '24) and Nassonov ('23).

accurate and detailed studies of Duesberg ('09, '10), later by those of Leplat ('12), Luna ('13), Brück ('14), Torraca ('14) and others, and has been adopted by a number of leading histologists, including Prenant ('11) and Schäfer ('12).   On the other hand, this conclusion is sceptically regarded by Heidenhain ('11), Gurwitsch ('13) and Cowdry ('19), who have pointed out various difficulties and sources of possible misinterpretation.   The case is similar with the neurofibrils and other fibrillar formations.   Hoven ('10), for example, brought forward detailed evidence that the neurofibrils are derived from embryonic chondrioconts, but this too has been strongly opposed, particularly by Cowdry, who has devoted particular attention to the problem ('12, '14, etc.).

Interesting possibilities in this direction are offered by the relation of the chondriosomes to secretion and related chemical processes in the cell, and to the formation of plastids.   Altmann, Arnold, and other advocates of the granule-theory believed that the secretory granules or "zymogen-granules"

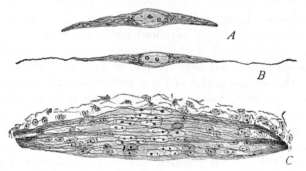

Fig. 345.—Supposed transformation of chondriosomes into myofibrils, from embryo chick (DUESBERG).

A, myoblast, about 60 hours, with chondrioconts; B, myoblast of 76 hours; C, frontal section of myotome; 96 hours, with developing myofibrils.

are not formed *de novo*, as earlier observers had supposed, but arise from preëxisting protoplasmic granules ("bioblasts" or "plasmosomes"); and this conclusion has been accepted by many competent histologists (*e. g.*, M. Heidenhain, '11) some of whom likewise believe them to be products of the chondriosomes.[1]   This conclusion appears in a somewhat different light in view of Nassonov's recent conclusions concerning the possible relation of the Golgi-apparatus to secretion, to be considered in the following section. Here we only emphasize the fact that not only the secretory granules proper but many other specific types of granules have by many observers

[1] See Regaud ('09), Hoven ('10, '11), Grynfelt ('12, '13), Laguesse ('11), Dubreuil ('13), Saguchi ('20), etc.

been assumed to arise from chondriosomes. Among these may be mentioned granules of fat (see especially Dubreuil '11, '13); yolk-granules (Fig. 348) (Van der Stricht, Loyez, Russo, Fauré-Fremiet, Hirschler); pigment of various types (Arnold, Meves, Ciaccio); the granules of leucocytes (Meves) and of connective-tissue-cells (Prenant, Dubreuil). Some of these observers believe the granules to arise by the direct morphological transformation of original mitochondria or chondrioconts; others, that they are secondary products of mitochondrial activity. In either case the chondriosome is regarded as a *localized center of specific chemical transformation*, a view urged especially by Regaud ('09, '11), who compared the chondriosomes in this respect to the plastids of plant-cells, which undoubtedly are such centers of action. Physiologically, in Regaud's view, the chondriosomes are "electosomes" which have a specific selective action upon the surrounding cytoplasm and are centers of specific chemical elaboration and accumulation.

Support is brought to this conception by the conclusion that *plastids themselves are enlarged and transformed chondriosomes*. This conclusion, first reached by Levitsky and Pensa, was later supported particularly by Guilliermond and others and still more recently by Meves and by others [1] who have described, in a very detailed manner and in a considerable variety of objects, the transformation of the chondriosomes into plastids in the embryonic tissues and their products. That the plastids in these tissues are often very small and numerous has long been familiar (p. 43). Levitsky, Guilliermond, Meves and Twiss show that in their earliest stages they are indistinguishable from chondriosomes (Fig. 19) and that all intermediate stages may be traced between them as histogenesis proceeds. Most commonly the chondriosomes have originally the form of chondrioconts (rods or threads), but in some cases they are granules or mitochondria, as described for instance by Guilliermond in the parenchyma where they give rise to amyloplasts (Fig. 346). As the cells grow older these chondriosomes are gradually transformed into plastids, producing chlorophyll in case of the chloroplasts, anthocyanin in that of the chromoplasts, starch in the amyloplasts, or fat in case of the elaioplasts. Guilliermond's observations seem to afford strong evidence that some of these substances (in particular starch) are originally laid down as solid deposits within the chondriosomes, others (pigments) are dissolved in their substance. In either case the chondriosome enlarges in later stages to form the body of the plastid, meanwhile undergoing various changes of form. During this process the power of division may be retained (as in case of the chloroplasts) or finally lost (apparently in case of the amyloplasts).

[1] Levitsky ('10, '11), Pensa ('10, '14), Guilliermond ('12, '13, '14, '1?, '20), Forenbacher ('11), Maximow ('13), Cavers ('14), Meves ('17), Twiss ('19), Nassonov ('20), Ernberger ('20).

These results seem to give substantial ground for accepting the derivation of plastids from chondriosomes, and indirectly lend greater probability to the hypothesis that the latter may have the powers of independent growth and division, at least in some stage of their history. On the other hand, the foregoing conclusions concerning the origin of the plastids have been contested, in particular by Rudolph ('12), Sapĕhin ('13, '15) and Mottier

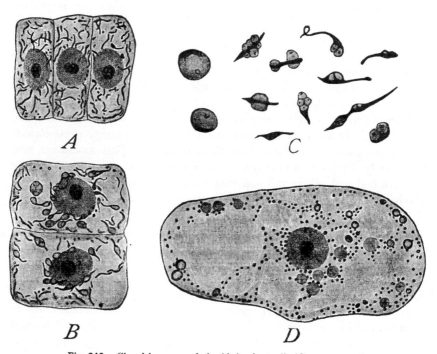

Fig. 346.—Chondriosomes and plastids in plant cells (GUILLIERMOND).

A, cells from growing root-tips of barley, with chondriosomes; B, older cells from same, starch-grains forming inside the chondriosomes (now amyloplasts); C, more enlarged amyloplasts; D, cell from potato-tuber, mitochondria (small granules), leucoplasts, and starch-granules.

('18), who hold that the embryonic plastids are from the first distinct from the chondriosomes, just as has been maintained in case of the myofibrils, neuro-fibrils and secretory granules. It is not disputed, however, that in the embryonic tissues the smallest plastids are hardly if at all distinguishable from chondriosomes.

The evident difficulty of settling this question by direct observation has led to many attempts to approach it indirectly by study of the relative number of chondriosomes at successive periods of histogenesis; for, if the embryonic chondriosomes are converted into differentiated elements of the tissue-cells, their number should progressively diminish as histogenesis proceeds. Such a diminution was in fact observed by Meves ('08) during histogenesis in chick-embryos and now seems to be well established, both for plants and animals, and also by the fact that in old and senescent cells the mitochondria may nearly or quite disappear. In the salivary glands, for instance, Regaud and Mawas ('09) found the number of mitochondria to be inversely proportional to that of secretory granules; the number of the former progressively decreasing as that of the latter increases. A similar relation was found by Guilliermond ('12) in respect to chondriosomes and plastids in embryonic plant-cells. This question has been carefully examined in the development of animals especially in *Ascaris* by Held ('12) and Romeis ('13) and in mammals by Rubaschkin ('10) and Levi ('15). All these observers have found, though with some variations, that the number of chondriosomes ultimately diminishes as development proceeds, though in *Ascaris*, Romeis described a progressive multiplication of mitochondria during the cleavage stages. In the bat, on the other hand, Levi's detailed studies clearly show that the mitochondria, very small and numerous in the fertilized egg, steadily become less numerous during cleavage, since at each division their number is halved. As this process advances they increase in size and are gradually transformed into the chondrioconts with which the embryonic cells are filled and which are said to form the source of the various intra-cellular differentiations. Beyond this point no further diminution occurs—a fact supposed to be due to a resumption of the power of division by the chondriosomes. It thus comes to pass that undifferentiated chondriosomes may still persist, in greater or less degree in the most highly differentiated cells, such as nerve-cells (Cowdry), striated muscle-cells (Benda, Regaud) or in the chloroplast-containing cells of plants.

Convincing as some of these observations seem it must be recognized that the subject is still in too confused a state to warrant any very definite conclusions concerning the rôle of the chondriosomes in histogenesis. Researches in this field have nevertheless opened many interesting possibilities which to say the least should not be rejected until they have been far more thoroughly examined. In particular the supposed origin of plastids from chondriosomes deserves the most critical further examination; for should it finally be established it would tell strongly in favor of the general chondriosome-hypothesis as developed by Benda, Meves and their followers and also of the general conception of protoplasmic organization advocated by Altmann, Arnold and other adherents of the granule-theory.

b. Growth and Division of the Chondriosomes. The chondriosomes undoubtedly possess remarkable powers of growth, as is seen for example in the auxocytes of many animals (p. 364). Whether such growth is followed or accompanied by division—as is the case, for example, with plastids or chromosomes—is, however, by no means clear; and the question is complicated also by the fact that smaller chondriosomes may fuse or closely unite to form larger ones until the whole chondrioma may be condensed into a single massive body (pp. 364, 371).

As earlier indicated, the behavior of the chondriosomes during mitosis (chondriokinesis), as seen particularly in the spermatocytes, is of two apparently widely different types (p. 163) in one of which these bodies become distinctly aggregated about the spindle,[1] while in the other they remain scattered through the cytosome.   In the first of these cases it seems certain that some of them, at least, are cut through transversely during mitosis; though this may be a merely passive or mechanical result of cytokinesis.   In the second case it seems equally certain that many if not all of them pass undivided towards the poles (p. 163).   When (as in *Centrurus*, p. 364) all the chondriosomes unite into a single dividing body, there is no evidence that its components undergo division during mitosis; the reverse conclusion seems more likely.   Such cases make it certain that the actual distribution of chondriosome-material is not necessarily effected by a process of fission at the time of mitosis; but neither do they exclude the possibility that the chondriosomes may have arisen by division at an earlier period.

In the protozoa a number of observers (Künstler, Wallengren, Prowazek and others) have observed granules, spherules, or rods in the form of dumb-bells and have interpreted them as forms of division.   Fauré-Fremiet (1907–08) followed, in the living object, the actual division of such bodies synchronously with that of the nucleus, and showed that in sections they are not to be distinguished in their staining reactions, or otherwise, from the chondriosomes of higher forms (Fig. 346a).   Here also they show all stages of constriction, dumb-bell and diplococcoid forms.[2]   On the whole, nevertheless, the direct evidence of division on the part of the mitochondria still remains very deficient; and to this extent the whole theory is insecurely based.   Its strongest support is offered by the history of the plastids; but even here, it must be admitted, the case is far from closed.[3]

There is still no satisfactory evidence that the chondriosomes play any part in fertilization.   Not the slightest proof has been produced of a fusion between the paternal and maternal chondriosomes.   It is not even certain that those brought into the egg by the sperm do not degenerate as main-

[1] See Meves ('00, '03, '07, etc.), Benda ('03), Meves and Duesberg ('08), Giglio-Tos and Granata ('08), Duesberg ('10, '11), Fauré-Fremiet ('10), Terni ('11), Levi ('13), Lewis and Robertson ('16), Bowen ('20), etc.

[2] See Rubaschkin ('10), Romeis ('13), Meves ('16, '17).

[3] Wallin ('22, a, b, c) has emphasized the close similarity, both in structure and in staining-reaction, between chondriosomes and bacteria, and has even suggested that they may actually be bacterial symbionts.   For criticism see Cowdry ('23), Bowen ('23).

tained by Vejdovský ('11) and Retzius ('11); and this is admitted even by Meves himself ('13, p. 235). On the other hand, Held ('18) believes that by the use of molybdate hæmatoxylin and acid fuchsin the less dense paternal mitochondria may be stained red while the maternal ones remain deep black, and that it may thus be shown that the sperm-mitochondria grow

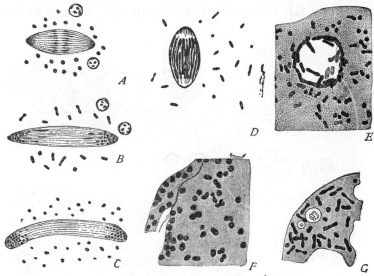

Fig. 346a.—Mitochondria in Protozoa (FAURÉ-FREMIET).

A–C, three successive stages, observed *in vivo,* showing supposed division of the mitochondria synchronously with the micronucleus; *D*, the same in *Urostyla*, from a fixed preparation; *E*, division-stages of the mitochondria surrounding the contractile vacuole in *Carchesium* (fixed preparation); *F*, mitochondria from *Opisthonecta; G*, dividing mitochondria, *Campanella.*

and rapidly multiply by division without the occurrence of a process of fusion during fertilization or up to the first cleavage.

Without entering upon all the doubtful questions here involved we only emphasize once more the fact, determined by Meves himself, as well as by others, that in some animals the mitochondrial formations derived from the sperm do not enter all of the cells of the embryo. In the sea-urchin, Meves found ('11, '12, '14) that the mitochondria-containing middle-piece remains intact and almost unmodified during the first five cleavages, being found in only one blastomere up at least to the 32-cell stage. In order to save his hypothesis Meves was therefore driven to the improbable assumption that the adult sea-urchin is formed only from cells which receive the spermatic chondriosomes, while those which fail to receive them are concerned only with the formation of larval structures which sooner or later degenerate in the course of the ontogeny.[1]

[1] See Meves (18)

3. The Golgi-Apparatus

Too little is known of the Golgi-apparatus, morphologically and physiologically, to warrant extended discussion at this time. Whether the Golgi-bodies have a persistent identity and multiply by growth and division is unknown; but their history in cell-division (p. 165) leads us at least to

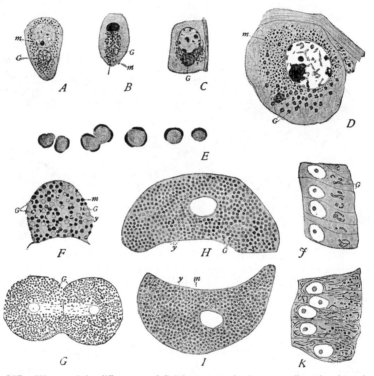

Fig. 347.—History of the diffuse type of Golgi-apparatus in the germ-cells and embryonic cells of the pulmonate snail *Lymnæa.* (*A–G*, from GATENBY; *H–K*, from HIRSCHLER.) *G*, Golgi-bodies; *m*, mitochondria; *y*, yolk.

A, spermatocyte; *B*, young spermatid; *C*, very young oöcyte with localized Golgi-apparatus; *D*, later oöcyte, with Golgi-apparatus breaking up; *E*, supposed division-stages of the Golgi bodies in the egg; *F*, portion of the cytoplasm of nearly mature oöcyte, to show yolk (*y*), mitochondria (*m*) and scattered Golgi-bodies (*G*); *G*, first cleavage of the ovum, showing scattered Golgi-bodies; *H*, more enlarged view of 2-cell blastomere, after sublimate-osmic, showing yolk and Golgi-bodies; *I*, the same after Champy's fluid and stained by Altmann's method, showing yolk and mitochondria; *J*, cells from the shell-gland, showing Golgi-bodies (technique as in *H*); *K*, the same, showing chondriosomes (technique as in *I*).

consider the possibility that the Golgi-material is in some sense self-perpetuating. If such be the case it may thus play a definite part in the genetic continuity of the cytoplasmic cell-system comparable in principle

to that shown by the chondriosomes, the plastids or even the central bodies,
The all but universal presence of this material in all types of animal cells,
and the remarkable uniformity of behavior which on the whole it displays,
point to its fundamental importance in the activities of cells generally.
Its possible relation to the secretory processes, suspected by various earlier
observers,[1] has been emphasized by the recent work of Nassonov, who

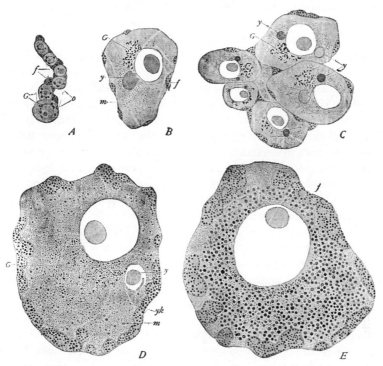

Fig. 348.—Yolk-nucleus, Golgi-bodies, mitochondria and yolk in oöcytes of the tunicate *Ascidia*
(Hirschler).

  A, very young oöcytes, (*o*) with follicle-cells (*f*) and scattered Golgi-bodies (*G*); *B*, *C*, older oöcytes,
showing yolk-nuclei (*y*); scattering of the Golgi-bodies and mitochondria (*m*); *D*, *E*, still older
stages, with diffuse Golgi-bodies, mitochondria and yolk-spheres, the latter (pale) more peripheral
in position.

has closely studied the question in the pancreas, epididymis and other
glands by the use of new and improved methods. This work seems clearly
to show that the secretory granules first make their appearance in close
relation to the Golgi-apparatus in close contact with or actually imbedded
in its meshes, and are subsequently set free into the general cytoplasm where

[1] *E. g.*, Fuchs ('o2), Biondi ('11), Golgi ('o9), Zawarzin ('o9), Cajal ('14), Deineka ('16), Cowdry
('22). Lit. in Nassonov ('23).

they enlarge to form the definitive zymogen granules, while the Golgi-apparatus resumes its compact appearance.[1]   Nassonov does not deny that the chondriosomes may play some part in the process, perhaps as an intermediary between the dissolved materials of the secretion and the actual secretory granules formed by the activity of the Golgi-bodies. "The zymogen-granules first appear in the form of minute bodies inclosed in the osmophilic substance of the Golgi-network. The meshes of the network thus appear as the matrix of the secretion in the cell. . . . After attaining a certain size the granules separate from the network and lie free in the cytoplasm . . . until they dissolve and pass as a liquid secretion into the lumen" (*op. cit.*, p. 431). Bowen ('23) has confirmed the most essential features of Nassonov's account; and we may also recall here the evidence produced by Hirschler and by Gatenby (p. 345) that the Golgi-bodies may be directly concerned in the production of the yolk-spheres (Fig. 347). In view of all this it is hardly to be doubted that the Golgi-apparatus plays an important part in secretion and related processes; but the presence of this structure in non-glandular cells such as nerve-cells, muscle-cells, connective-tissue-cells, and above all in the sperm-cells (p. 361), indicates that it possesses a much broader significance.   Bowen has pointed out the close analogy between the formation of the acrosome in the animal sperm and that of a secretory granule, and has suggested that in both cases the Golgi-apparatus may be a center for the formation of enzymes which in case of the acrosome may play a part in the activation of the egg (p. 435). This at least suggests a new angle from which the puzzle of the Golgi-apparatus may be viewed.

4. Summary and Critique

In their fundamental aspects, evidently, the problems presented by the chondriosomes and Golgi-bodies are still in a somewhat confused state; and the same may be said of the cytoplasmic granules generally. The evidence is still too conflicting to allow us to draw a sufficiently clear line between the objective and the theoretical sides of the subject; and in this respect students of the cytoplasmic structures are at a disadvantage as compared with those of the nucleus because of the almost total lack of genetic evidence. Modern genetic experiment has given an overwhelming demonstration not only of the leading rôle played by the nucleus in heredity but also of its particulate or corpuscular organization, in the sense that it is composed fundamentally of small entities ("genes," "factors," or the like), that are self-perpetuating and within certain limits independent

---

[1] In these glands, as is the rule, the Golgi-complex lies always between the nucleus and the lumen of the gland. In the thyroid Cowdry ('22) found it often also in the basal region, a fact which he correlates with the supposed secretion of these cells either into the lumen or into the blood.

of one another. We have very little such genetic evidence in case of the cytosome; but the fact that it is available in case of the nucleus predisposes us to adopt a similar conception of the cytoplasm. We are likewise predisposed in favor of the theory of chromidia, which is in harmony with De Vries's theory of intracellular pangenesis (p. 11) and if true would enable us clearly to visualize the nuclear "control" of the cytoplasm. Undoubtedly, however, the theory of chromidia has been in large measure discredited by studies on the chondriosomes. This work does not indeed exclude the possibility, even the probability, that visible granules given off from the nucleus may play an important part in the formative processes. The most important of the evidence in this direction seems to the writer to be that produced by Lillie, Conklin and their predecessors in case of the germinal vesicle of the oöcyte. Nevertheless, so far as the Metazoa are concerned it cannot yet be said with assurance that granules having such an origin play an essential part in histogenesis or in other constructive processes of the cell.

The case of the chondriosomes seems much stronger so far as their relation to histogenesis is concerned, though it is still far short of demonstration. That they are independent, self-propagating bodies remains in the main an assumption, supported by a certain amount of definite evidence, but hardly more as yet than a theoretical postulate like Altmann's theory of granules, of which it is no more than a modern development. We should not, therefore, accept the hypothesis of the autonomy of the chondriosomes, still less that of the chromidia and Golgi-bodies, save as an incentive to further cytological study of the phenomena.

III. PROTOPLASMIC STRUCTURE AND METASTRUCTURE

It is an old question whether we may in any measure advance our understanding of the cell-activities by the assumption of an ultra-microscopical organization or metastructure [1] of protoplasm as distinguished from its chemical and molecular constitution. In a speculative form this question long antedates cytology and even the cell-theory itself. The history of our subject impresses us with the great number of eminent investigators, engaged with the most diverse aspects of biological inquiry, who have been driven to the assumption that such a metastructure must exist. Almost without exception this structure has been conceived as having a meristic or particulate character (pangenesis, micromerism, panmerism, etc.), the living substance being assumed to contain, or to be built up from, a multitude of minute discrete corpuscles, which have commonly been assumed

[1] This term is from Heidenhain ('07).

to be of a higher order of complexity than the molecules of proteins and other organic compounds.

The long history of these conceptions can here be indicated only in the most cursory manner.[1] Their prototype appears in Buffon's celebrated theory of "organic molecules," (1804, and earlier) while subsequent to the promulgation of the cell-theory, Henle (1841), and Brücke (1861) seriously considered the possibility that cells might be composed of elementary vital units ranking in degree of complexity between cells and molecules. The first detailed elaborations of such a conception in accordance with more modern scientific ideas include Spencer's theory of *physiological units* (1864), Darwin's celebrated theory of pangenesis (1868), and Nägeli's theory of *micellæ* (1884) which has been widely adopted by botanists. Their climax was reached in De Vries's remarkable and closely reasoned work *Intracellular Pangenesis* (1889), in Wiesner's theory of plasomes (1892), and in Weismann's still more detailed and speculative theory of biophores and the architecture of the germ-plasm (1892). In the nature of the case the primary assumption in all these theories was of purely hypothetical character; for the primary units were in every case assumed to lie beyond the reach of the microscope. Nevertheless numerous investigators in the most diverse fields of biological inquiry were driven to the adoption of the same general type of assumption. We find it in the works of experimental physiologists like Pfeffer, Engelmann, Verworn, or Foster; of students of growth, reproduction and development like Nägeli, Wiesner, O. Hertwig, or Whitman; of investigators in heredity and genetics, such as Darwin and De Vries; of cytologists such as Altmann or Heidenhain; and of more speculative writers such as Spencer, Haeckel and Weismann.

Corpuscular or micromeristic hypotheses of living systems have met with much opposition which, up to a certain point has been justified.[2] Such hypotheses, it has been cleverly said, would make of the world (or the cell) a mere puzzle-picture which we take to pieces only to put it together again, having explained nothing. The emptiness of such a criticism is

---

[1] A valuable review of them is offered in Delage's *Structure du protoplasma et les théories sur l'hérédité*, etc., Paris, 1903. See also Heidenhain, *Plasma und Zelle*, 1010-11. For earlier reviews and critiques see especially De Vries ('89) and Wiesner ('92). The hypothetical units have received a great variety of names, among which may be mentioned: *Physiological units* (H. Spencer), *gemmules* (Darwin), *pangens* (De Vries), *plastidules* (Maggi, Haeckel, Elsberg, Zoja), *micellæ* (Nägeli) *tagmata* (Pfeffer), *inotagmata* (Engelmann), *microzymas* (Béchamp, Estor), *plasomes* (Wiesner), *biophores* (Weismann), *bioplasts* (Altmann), *gemmæ* (Haacke), *idioblasts* (O. Hertwig), *idiosomes* (Whitman), *somacules* (Foster), *chondria* (Rohde), *protomeres* (Heidenhain). These various names are not strictly synonymous: they represent many different special developments of the general conception; but all agree in the fundamental assumption that "living" matter is an aggregate or congeries of ultra-microscopical bodies which are themselves not molecules but molecular aggregates, in most cases (gemmules, pangens, biophores) assumed to possess the powers of growth and division.

[2] For a criticism of such hypotheses see Yves Delage ('03), Ritter ('19).

obvious in view of the enormous advances of physics and chemistry due to corpuscular conceptions of non-living matter, or of the revolution in biology that resulted from the cell-theory. The reaction against such conceptions of the cell took place because too much was claimed for them, not alone by their advocates but also by critics who wished to destroy them.[1] Opposition was directed especially against the assumption that the "ultimate" particles of protoplasm may be regarded as primary vital "units," capable of autonomous growth or division, as if the cell itself were built up as an assemblage of more elementary organisms. Such opposition is still widespread among competent and critical students of the cell. "The structure of protoplasm," says one of these recently, "is the structure of the cell. The search for some ultra-microscopic structure of living substance as such, and more deep-seated than cell-structure, has so far proved as vain as the older attempts to demonstrate the existence of a vital force."[2]

So far as direct cytological evidence goes such statements are of course well founded. Nevertheless the indirect evidence which both cytology and genetics have been accumulating demonstrates that particulate conceptions of cell-structure, sometimes offer the simplest and most effective means of formulating the observed facts. The experimental study of genetics, for instance, most clearly demonstrates that the germ-plasm must contain great numbers of separate, differential "factors" or "genes," which may independently combine, segregate and recombine; which are self-perpetuating; and which may be transmitted unchanged from generation to generation, subject only to occasional sudden mutations. This was in principle precisely the argument mainly relied on by De Vries thirty years ago in developing his ingenious hypothesis of intracellular pangenesis. More modern hypotheses of this type have in fact become indispensable as a practical means of laboratory analysis, prediction and verification. Attempts have been made, it is true, to explain the phenomena in other ways (e. g., by assumptions of isomerism, molecular regroupings, side-chains, and the like). None of these has been found adequate; and in point of accuracy, simplicity and fruitfulness of method the formulas employed in modern genetic analysis based on the particulate hypothesis almost rank with the atomic and molecular formulas of the physicist and chemist.[3]

The cytologist finds himself constrained by a similar, if less pressing

[1] Cf. Wilson ('23).

[2] Harper ('19), p. 274.

[3] These statements are based mainly on the remarkable analysis of Morgan and his co-workers of the immense mass of intricate data collected by them in case of the fruit-fly *Drosophila melanogaster*. See especially Morgan, *The Physical Basis of Heredity*, 1919, and Morgan, Sturtevant, Muller and Bridges. *The Mechanism of Mendelian Heredity*, 1915

necessity. What rational conception can be formed (as Roux long since urged) of the process of mitosis, with its spinning out of the nuclear substance into long spireme-threads, and their *longitudinal fission*, if this be not a device by which different nuclear elements are aligned in orderly series and equally divided? Were division the merely physical separation of colloidal threads into equal parts we should, assuredly, expect them to divide transversely. How shall we draw any logical line of demarcation between dividing plastids, which are often of considerable size, and still smaller bodies that may have similar powers? Centrioles, for example, are known to have the power of self-perpetuation by growth and division though they are so minute as to lie almost at the limit of microsopical vision. When, therefore, they seem to make their appearance *de novo* in the hyaloplasm it is entirely possible that they may preëxist in a form too minute to appear above the horizon of visibility. The reality of the question here raised is attested by the ultra-microscope, which demonstrates the existence of numerous particles suspended in the protoplasmic substance (as in a colloidal solution) and beyond the reach of direct microscopical vision; further, by the supposed existence of ultra-microscopical germs, such as those of measles, the foot and mouth disease of cattle, and others which will pass through a fine Berkefeld filter and are invisible by the microscope, yet are capable of indefinite multiplication without loss of their specific character (as proved by laboratory cultures and inoculations).[1]

Altmann at first identified the essential, living structural components of the cell-substance with the *visible* granules or "bioblasts" (p. 75). Later, as a result of studies on the history of the granules, especially in gland-cells, he extended this view:

"Evidence has been obtained from many sources to show that the larger granules lying in the meshes of the network take their origin from smaller ones which lie in the substance of the net itself, and may there arise from still smaller forms which, perhaps because of their minuteness and other properties, have not yet been made visible. As the small granules in the course of their vital metabolism (assimilation) give rise to and store up in themselves proteins, fats, carbohydrates, they increase in size and change their staining reactions through the reduction of their own living substance. They thus effect the transportal of nutritive substances in the process of reabsorption; in secretion they are cast out as secretory granules which form the essential component of the secretion; while in the intermediate stages of transformation they often constitute deposits of reserve substance. This we see most conspicuously in the fat cells and in the nutritive yolk of the egg, but in less extreme degree the same may be observed in almost all forms of cells." [2]

Somewhat akin to this was the conception of the alveolar structure of protoplasm suggested by the work of G. F. Andrews ('97) [3] who recognized

---

[1] Cited from Jordan ('11).
[2] 94, pp. 16, 17.
[3] See also Wilson, '99.

in the alveolar protoplasm of the sea-urchin that the interalveolar or "continuous" substance (hyaloplasm) is itself alveolar on a smaller scale, *i. e.*, contains numerous minute granules or drops ("microsomes") which graduate in size down to the limits of microscopical vision, as is seen with especial clearness during the progressive development of the alveolar structure (p. 73). Manifestly, however, the limits of microscopical vision are purely artificial. The cytologist, therefore, finds it difficult to escape the conclusion that in respect to their size and degree of dispersion the visible and the invisible components of the protoplasmic system form a continuous series.

The conception of Heidenhain is very similar to Altmann's: "We must logically conclude that these (the secretory granules) do not arise *de novo* in the cell-body by a kind of *generatio equivoca* . . . but must themselves be derived from (preëxisting) components of the cell-substance. But since the primary granules appear at the limits of visibility we are necessarily again brought back to Altmann's view, that the granules in their first beginnings have their origin in the protoplasmic matrix (*i. e.*, hyaloplasm), of the cell. . . . The granules, accordingly, take their first origin from the smallest, meta-microscopic living particles, which acquire a certain degree of independence, and by assimilation, growth and corresponding metathesis of their substance become converted into the histological (visible) granules." [1]

In this conception the fundamental problem of protoplasmic structure passes over into that of the colloidal state. It should not be taken to imply that the dispersed particles of the hyaloplasm necessarily are self-perpetuating, elementary living "units" or "protomeres" as postulated by earlier micromeristic theories. To the writer, however, it would seem a backward step wholly to reject the possibility that some or many of these particles may have the power of perpetuating their own specific type, as is known to be the case with some of the visible formed components of the cell. Could we accept such a view we could more readily meet some puzzling difficulties such, for example, as the apparent contradiction between the origin of a centriole *de novo*, and its origin by division of a preëxisting body of the same kind. [2]

The alveolar structure of protoplasm is obviously an emulsoid or suspensoid formation, which repeats on a large scale some of the features of a "homogeneous" colloid. In this visible structure we are not dealing with a simple diphasic system but with a compound or polyphasic system, often of great complexity, the discontinuous or disperse phase being represented

[1] '07, p. 396.
[2] Wilson ('99, '23).

by bodies of great chemical and physical diversity. Some of them are independent organellæ, active elements, such as plastids, centrioles or mitochondria, possessing the powers of independent assimilation and growth, and in some cases also of division. Others are in various degrees more passive, having arisen perhaps by the direct transformation of more active elements, and in extreme cases converted into true metaplasmic, ergastic or paraplasmic structures, such as drops of water or fat, starch grains, or yolk-spheres.[1] Somewhat like this larger picture in miniature we may perhaps imagine the metastructure of the hyaloplasm which lies below the horizon of our microscopical vision. That it is not wholly imaginary seems to me to be indicated alike by the ultra-microscope, by studies on the protoplasmic colloids, and by cytological observation. We should not emphasize unduly the analogy between such a metastructure and the cellular structure *of the tissues* (as has often been done by earlier writers on the speculative side of this subject). It is a highly theoretical question whether we can rightly speak of protoplasm (hyaloplasm) as being "built up" of self-perpetrating protomeres; and it must be borne in mind that protoplasm is not, like most tissues, a relatively rigid system, but is in a state of continual flux. The conception that has been indicated may be of practical value in so far as it aids practically in investigation,[2] and may serve to put us on guard against too simple a formulation of these problems from the standpoint of physical and colloidal chemistry.

IV. DUALISTIC CONCEPTIONS OF THE CELL-SUBSTANCE

We may here briefly consider certain dualistic conceptions of the cell-substance that have considerably influenced the development of modern cytology. If none of them have been entirely successful they are none the less of interest considered as efforts to bring together the physiological and the morphological aspects of cell-phenomena.

The earliest attempts in this direction, of very general character, did not distinguish specifically between nucleus and protoplasm. Here belongs Beale's distinction (p. 58) between living, formative or "germinal" substance (bioplasm) and secondary or formed products (*formed matter*). Here too may be placed Nägeli's theory of the idioplasm (1884) which has exercised an important influence on our conceptions of heredity. Nägeli conceived the organism as composed fundamentally of two living substances or plasmas. One, constituting the main bulk of the protoplasm, is a vegetative or nutritive *trophoplasm* ("*Ernährungsplasma*"), in which are carried

---

[1] *Cf.* A Meyer's grouping of the cell-components as protoplasmatic, alloplasmatic and ergastic (p. 58).
[2] H. V. Wilson ('16, p. 14).

on the main operations of nutrition and metabolism.   The other, present in much smaller quantity, is a generative *idioplasm* that plays a leading rôle in reproduction and development and constitutes the physical basis of heredity (p. 1037).   This hypothesis was elaborated with an acuteness and skill that still commands our admiration, and though it cannot be upheld in the original form it has proved itself to be one of the most fruitful conceptions of modern biology.

1. The Cytoplasm.   Archiplasm, Kinoplasm, Morphoplasm and the " Superior Protoplasm "

The first clearly formulated hypothesis of cytoplasmic dualism appears in Boveri's much discussed conception of the *archiplasm*.   By this term (originally written *archoplasm*) Boveri designated the material of the spindle-fibers and astral rays, at first conceived as a permanent substance, distinct from the general cytoplasm of the resting cell but scattered through it in the form of specific granules.[1] Subsequently ('95) this view was modified by the conclusion that neither the archiplasmic fibrillæ nor the granules are permanent structures but formations which come and go with different phases of the protoplasmic activity.[2]   Boveri still held, however, that the archiplasm might preëxist as a specific, homogeneous substance which, though not ordinarily visible, may become so by taking on the form of granules or fibrillæ that crystallize, as it were, in the preëxisting protoplasmic framework.   In this form the hypothesis is close to the *kinoplasm* hypothesis of Strasburger ('92 and later) which has enjoyed a wide repute among botanists.

Strasburger conceived protoplasm to consist of—or to have a marked tendency to transform itself into—two distinct substances, *trophoplasm* and *kinoplasm*, which differ characteristically both physiologically and structurally.   The kinoplasm (earlier called "formative protoplasm") was assumed to be an especially active and irritable substance that forms the astral rays and spindle-fibers, the central bodies, the plasma-membrane, and the contractile material of cilia and flagella.   Morphologically, it shows a marked tendency to assume a fibrillar structure; hence the term *filar plasma*. On the other hand, the trophoplasm (which, like Nägeli's trophoplasm, constitutes the main mass of protoplasm) is the seat especially of the nutritive processes and tends to assume an alveolar structure.

---

[1] '88, 2, p. 80.

[2] It has been shown, especially by Meves, that the archiplasmic granules, as described by Boveri in *Ascaris*, were probably nothing other than mitochondria. Meves clearly shows, further (here confirming Boveri's later account), that these granules do not give rise to the astral rays or spindle-fibers but lie between them.   Lams ('10) contributes interesting details concerning the concentric zones of mitochondria in the snail *Arion* (*cf.* p. 683).

Later writers extended the conception both of archiplasm and of kino-plasm so as to include a great variety of other cell-components.   In the meantime arose a third related conception, that of the *ergastoplasm*, due to Garnier ('97, 98) and P. and M. Bouin ('98, '00) and subsequently devel-oped by Maziarsky ('03), Prenant ('04) and others.   This term was applied to the substance of the fibrillar formations characteristic of many gland-cells and also to certain flocculent masses or other formations, described under this name by the Bouins ('98) in the embryo-sac of the lily, in the oöcytes of the starfish, the spermatocytes of *Lithobius* ('99) and elsewhere. Ergastoplasm was regarded by these observers as a specific and dominant protoplasm (*"d'essence supérieur"*), of which the most characteristic property is its power of elaborating and transforming the various substan-ces laid down in the cell.

Out of the foregoing conceptions grew the more general one developed by Prenant ('98, '99, '10) of a "superior protoplasm" which plays a leading rôle in the cell-activities generally.   Archiplasm, kinoplasm, ergastoplasm were conceived as closely related but slightly differing forms of this sub-stance, which is physiologically the dominating and most active element. Its tendency to assume the fibrillar type of structure (spindle-fibers, astral rays, glandular fibrillæ, myofibrils, neurofibrils, fibrillæ of ciliated cells, etc.) and to stain energetically with basic dyes, led Prenant to speak of it as a kind of "cytoplasmic chromatin" or "cytochromatin."   We need not follow the development of this conception in detail since in Prenant's final develop-ment of the subject ('10) the formed components of the cytoplasm generally are excluded from the "superior protoplasm."   "Is the really primitive and superior protoplasmic substance that which exhibits a particular structure and staining reactions?   Is not the superior protoplasm, on the contrary, represented by the formless and non-staining substance, that of which we know least, yet in which take place the most intimate phenomena of life?"   In common with so many other cytologists, therefore, Prenant is finally driven to seek the fundamental basis of the protoplasmic system in the "structureless" hyaloplasm, and the theory of superior protoplasm becomes hardly distinguishable from Beale's early conception of the living "bioplasm" as distinguished from the "formed" components of the cell-substance.

To the writer, the history of modern cytology seems clearly to show the futility of all dualistic hypotheses of the protoplasm, save as convenient descriptive devices.   Every such hypothesis has broken down when based upon the postulate of two fundamentally and permanently different sub-stances.   For the purpose of description it is often convenient to employ such terms as "trophoplasm," "archiplasm," "kinoplasm," "ergastoplasm" and the like; but in view of the theoretical connotation of all these terms it seems preferable to avoid their use wherever practicable.

2. The Nucleus. Trophochromatin and Idiochromatin

Dualistic conceptions of the cytoplasm have been paralleled by analogous ones concerning the nucleus, based on the frequent appearance of two different forms of "chromatin," which may even be contained in separate nuclei. The two substances in question are assumed to be concerned, respectively, with the metabolic, vegetative or trophic activities, and with the generative or reproductive. Various names have been applied to them; for instance *trophochromatin* and *idiochromatin* (Lubosch); *somatic* and *propagatory* chromatin (Goldschmidt); *trophic* and *gametic* chromatin (Dobell) etc. This conception shows a certain analogy to Nägeli's above-mentioned distinction between trophoplasm and idioplasm; but its real germ appears in Weismann's early distinction between "histogenetic" or "ovogenetic" plasm and "idioplasm," considered as two different forms of nuclear substance or "karyoplasm." [1] Later the hypothesis gradually took more definite shape along two somewhat different lines of development, one starting from the history of the nuclear substance in mitosis and maturation and the phenomena of "diminution" in the formation of the germ-cells in higher organisms (p. 323), the other from studies on the general history of the chromatin in Protista.

We first consider an hypothesis of chromatin dualism especially associated with the names of R. Hertwig, Schaudinn, Goldschmidt and Popoff, though many others have contributed to it. Many observers have laid stress on the fact that in the prophases of mitosis, and especially in the prophases of the egg-nucleus in preparation for the maturation divisions, a considerable quantity of the nuclear material is eliminated from the nucleus, either becoming transformed into spindle-fibers or being cast out bodily into the protoplasm. As earlier indicated (p. 269) the definitive chromosomes are often differentiated from the general network at a very early period in the growth of the egg; and a large part of the network is cast out as a residual substance into the body of the cell when the nuclear membrane breaks down (p. 355). This naturally suggests that the residual substance is especially concerned with the trophic functions of the egg during its long period of growth (the "ovogenetic plasm" of Weismann) while the "true chromatin" or idioplasm is passively awaiting the formation of the spindle. [2] The two constitutents of the germinal vesicle would thus be comparable respectively to the two forms of nuclei in the ciliates, *i. e.*, the macronuclei,

[1] P. 498, Essays, II, IV.
[2] See Rückert ('92, '93), Gardiner ('98), Griffin ('99), etc.

mainly concerned with the metabolic and vegetative activities of the animal, and the micronuclei, which constitute a reserve of "idioplasm" or generative chromatin. A similar conclusion is strongly suggested by the phenomena of "diminution" during the history of the germ-cells (p. 323). It seems impossible to doubt that in these cases the nucleus for the time being contains two different substances, a primary and essential component which alone is transmitted by the chromosomes, and a derived and secondary one the functions of which have come to an end.

A related conception grew out of the researches of R. Hertwig, Schaudinn and others on the formation of chromidia in the rhizopods as above described (p. 700). Schaudinn considered the principal nucleus (or nuclei) in the rhizopods as a "vegetative" nucleus consisting of "metabolic nuclear substance," which represents the macronucleus of ciliates, and like the latter degenerates with the onset of the sexual activity (p. 608), while the chromidia given off from it, and from which the gamete-nuclei arise, are composed of "sexual" or generative chromatin, and correspond in this respect to the micronucleus.[1] In the ciliates the two substances are contained in separate nuclei throughout the whole vegetative cycle; in other forms they are united in a single nucleus and only separate under pathological conditions or in the stages preceding conjugation. Thus arose the much discussed "binuclearity hypothesis" of Goldschmidt and his followers,[2] according to which every cell may be regarded as containing a "somatic" nucleus, composed of *trophochromatin* and a "generative" or "propagatory" nucleus composed of *idiochromatin*. As a rule the two are united to form an "amphinucleus." Their separation is commonly affected by a giving-off to the cytoplasm of chromidia which may be either generative (*idiochromidia*) or somatic (*trophochromidia*).[3] In the cells of Protozoa the chromidia may be of either type; for example, those of *Actinosphærium* formed during periods of starvation are somatic, while those of *Arcella* (p. 701) are *generative*, ultimately giving rise to the gamete-nuclei. In metazoan cells only somatic chromidia were assumed to occur, the generative chromatin being confined to the formed nuclei. Complete separation of the two kinds of chromatin in different nuclei is seen only in Protozoa (ciliates). In Metazoa the separation is but temporary and rarely complete. This hypothesis was given a still broader development in a later paper by Goldschmidt and Popoff ('07).

This hypothesis is open to the same general criticism as the hypotheses of cytoplasmic dualism already considered. It was much weakened by

---

[1] '03, p. 553.
[2] See especially Goldschmidt ('04), Goldschmidt and Popoff ('07).
[3] Mesnil ('03).

later studies proving that many of the so-called "chromidia" in metazoan cells are mitochondrial formations having no connection with the nucleus (p. 703). Further, unless the assumption that "every animal cell is by nature binucleate" be taken as a mere figure of speech, or in a purely transcendental sense, it must imply that the generative and trophic chromatins are definite and distinct entities. Such an assumption, however, collapses in face of the fact that both chromatins originally arise from the chromosomes which, by the hypothesis, consist of generative chromatin. At best, therefore, trophic and generative chromatins can only be regarded as different phases or modes of activity of one original substance.[1] Another development of the hypothesis of binuclearity with reference to the historical origin of the division-centers is considered in a following section (p. 735).

V. THE KARYOPLASMIC RATIO

We digress at this point for some further consideration of the quantitative relations between nuclear mass and cytoplasmic mass which have been briefly reviewed in Chapters I, III and VIII. The development of the theory of the karyoplasmic ratio by Hertwig ('03, '08, etc.) and his followers was undoubtedly carried too far; but there remain well-determined facts concerning this ratio that are of interest for many cell-problems. It is important not to confuse the maintenance or modification of the karyoplasmic ratio under normal conditions with that due to artificially induced changes. The maintenance of the normal relation is well illustrated in the cleavage of the ovum in such forms as annelids or gasteropods, where very marked inequalities of division often occur. In all such cases nuclear division is exactly equal so that all the cells receive equal amounts of chromatin. After the nuclei are re-formed, however, the nuclei grow to a size that is roughly proportional to that of the cytosome.[2] In cases of this type the size of the nuclei is obviously regulated by that of the cytosome. A conclusion similar in principle was afforded by certain experiments on dwarf larvæ of sea-urchins arising from isolated blastomeres or egg-fragments in sea-urchins.[3] In dwarf larvæ of different size, arising from isolated blastomeres of the 2- or 4-cell stages, the cells are of nearly or quite the same size but differ in number, the ½-larvæ containing about one-half, and the ¼-larvæ about one-fourth the normal number characteristic of an entire egg at the corresponding stages. Conversely, in giant larvæ produced

[1] An effective criticism of the hypothesis is given by Dobell ('09), Cf. also Minchin ('12), Duesberg ('12), and Swezey ('16).
[2] This was first clearly indicated by Conklin ('02) though, as he later especially emphasized ('12), wide variation exists in this relation.
[3] Morgan ('95, '01. '03), Driesch ('98, '00), Boveri ('05).

from two fused eggs, the number of cells is double the normal number (Driesch). In all these cases the result is brought about by an adjustment of the cleavage-process to the size of the embryo; the smaller the original piece the fewer the cleavages required to produce cells and nuclei of the proper size. Morgan and Driesch thus reached the conclusion that the cleavage is so regulated as to produce a fixed or typical cell-size at a given

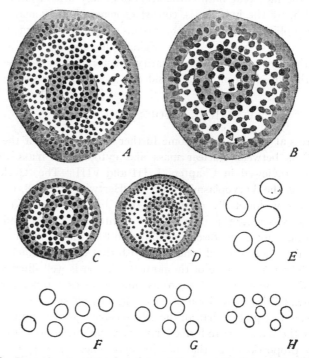

Fig. 349.—Karyoplasmic relation in embryos of the sea-urchin *Paracentrotus* (BOVERI)

A, normal diploid (amphikaryotic) gastrula, from upper pole; B, corresponding view of tetraploid (diplokaryotic) gastrula at the same stage (from a monaster-egg); C, normal diploid dwarf gastrula, from an egg-fragment; D, corresponding stage of haploid (hemikaryotic) dwarf, from merogonic egg-fragment; E–H, more enlarged nuclei from larvæ of various types drawn to the same scale; E, tetraploid (from B); F, diploid (from C); G, diploid (from A); H, haploid (from D).

stage rather than a fixed number of cells; and this was afterwards confirmed by Boveri.

In the foregoing cases the volume of the nucleus varies primarily with that of the cytosome or cytoplasmic mass. Equally interesting is the reverse case in which the primary variable factor is the nuclear mass. Typical cases are offered by the tetraploid giant forms of *Spirogyra*, *Œnothera*, *Primula* and *Solanum*, already mentioned (p. 656), in which the nuclear volume is doubled as a result of a doubling of the number of chromosomes, and the normal karyoplasmic ratio is restored by a corresponding growth of the cytosome to twice its former size. The classical experiments on this subject are those of Boveri ('05, '07) on sea-urchin eggs in which the number of chromosomes may readily be altered experimentally in several ways, as follows: (1) In artificially parthenogenetic eggs (p. 476), or in merogony (p. 465) the number of chromosomes is haploid; (2) in the normal fertilized egg the nucleus is diploid; (3) by shaking the normal egg near the time of the first cleavage the first mitosis of the egg is often rendered monocentric,

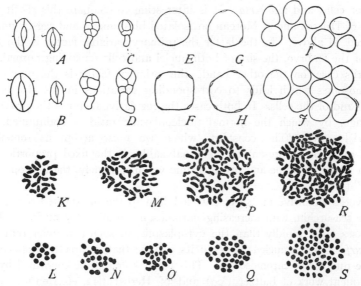

Fig. 350.—Chromosome-number and cell-size in *Solanum* (WINKLER).

A, stomata from normal diploid nightshade (*Solanum nigrum*); *B*, from *gigas tetraploid* mutant of same; *C*, *D*, corresponding views of calyx-hairs from the two forms; *E*, *F*, and *G*, *H*, pollen-grains of the two forms; *I*, chloroplasts from the tomato (*S. lycopersicum*) and *J* from its *gigas* mutant; *K*, somatic diploid chromosome-group from normal tomato (*S. lycopersicum*), 24 chromosomes. *L*, pseudo-haploid group (heterotypic division) from *S. Koelreuterianum* (*Lycopersicum* type) 12 bivalents; *M*, normal tetraploid somatic group from root-tip, *gigas* form (from *S. Koelreuterianum*); 48 chromosomes; *N*, pseudo-haploid group (heterotypic division), 24 chromosomes; *O*, haploid group of same, second sporocyte-division, 24 chromosomes; *P*, normal haploid somatic group of *S. tübingense* (*nigrum* form), 72 chromosomes; *Q*, pseudo-haploid group of the same (heterotypic) 36 bivalents; *R*, normal tetraploid somatic group of *gigas* form of last, 144 chromosomes; *L*, pseudo-haploid group of same (heterotypic division) 72 bivalents.

and the number of chromosomes is doubled without division of either nucleus or cell-body (p. 168). Such eggs may later divide normally and produce larvæ in which the chromosome-groups are tetraploid; (4) in dispermic eggs the number is originally triploid, but by the resulting multipolar mitosis the larval nuclei usually come to have varying numbers of chromosomes (p. 919).

Boveri demonstrated with great clearness that the size of the nuclei at any given stage is directly proportional to the number of chromosomes that they contain; they are smallest in the haploid larvæ, largest in the tetraploid, and of varying size in the dispermic ones (Fig. 349). Here again, however, as in *Spirogyra*, the normal nucleoplasmic ratio may sooner or later be restored by a regulative process, effected in this case by modification in the number of cleavages, this number being increased in the one case, decreased in the other (p. 727) so that larvæ with smaller nuclei have also smaller cells, and *vice versa*. It is interesting to compare this result with those of Driesch and of Morgan on isolated blastomeres and egg-fragments, referred to above. In the latter the primary variable factor is the total size of the embryo, the size of both nuclei and cells remaining normal. In Boveri's case, on the other hand, the primary factor is the number of chromosomes which leads to corresponding variations in the size of the nuclei and of the cells. In both cases the regulative factor is the process of cleavage, by which the normal nucleoplasmic ratio is maintained. In Boveri's words: "The constant, which we must accept as something given and not at present further analyzable, is the fixed proportion between nuclear volume and protoplasmic volume, namely, the karyoplasmic ratio " ('05, p. 68).

Boveri's extensive measurements led him to the unexpected result that in the sea-urchin, with increasing chromosome-number the nuclear volume increases more rapidly than the cytoplasmic, in such a manner that it is the *surface* of the nucleus and not its volume that is directly proportional to the number of chromosomes. This result seems to be confirmed by the subsequent work of Baltzer ('09) and of Herbst ('12, etc.) on sea-urchin eggs, and also by that of Artom ('11a, '11b, '12) on the phyllopod *Artemia salina*. Two races of this species are known, *A. salina uni-* and *bi-valens*, the former having 42 chromosomes (diploid number), the latter 84 (p. 231). Here again the surface-area of the nucleus was found to be approximately proportional to the number of chromosomes.

On the other hand, Gerassimoff found in *Spirogyra* (Fig. 313) that in the giant forms both nucleus and cell-body have approximately double the volume of the normal, though a considerable range of variation exists; and the same result has been reached by a number of others. An interesting example is offered by the studies of É. & É. Marchal ('09, '11), on artificial apospory in mosses (Fig. 407). Haploid nuclei are found in the normal gametophyte, diploid in the aposporic gametophyte generation derived by regeneration from the diploid sporophyte (p. 746). In the diœcious mosses such diploid gametophytes are completely sterile, but in some of the monœ-cious forms (*e. g.* in *Amblystegium repens*) they are fertile, producing diploid gametes, which unite to form tetraploid zygotes and sporophytes. From the latter finally by regeneration (artificial apospory) are obtained tetraploid gametophytes.[1] Measurements of these various cases show that the mean *volume* of both nuclei and cells is directly proportional to the number of chromosomes. This applies alike to somatic cells (of the leaves and of the antheridial tissues) and germ-cells, including both spores and eggs; in each case the diploid nuclei and cell-bodies are approximately twice, and the tetraploid four times the volume of the haploid. It does not appear from the Marchals' memoir that the same rule applies to the plant as a whole, *i. e.*, giant races seem not to be formed. Nevertheless, the reproductive organs (antheridia, archegonia) conform approximately to the rule. In *Amblystegium*, for instance, the length and breadth of the archegonia, in microns, are in the normal haploid race 248:46, in the diploid race 306: 50, and in the tetraploid 456:83.

A somewhat similiar result was reached by Gates ('09) in a study of the tetraploid giant *Œnothera gigas*, in which the nuclei are on the average twice the volume of those of the diploid parent from *Œ. lamarckiana*, the plant as a whole being likewise larger in nearly all its parts, including the seeds.[2] Results similar in type have been reported by Tischler ('10) in races of bananas having respectively 8, 16, and 24 chromosomes, by Nemec ('10) in artificially produced tetraploid cells of root-tips, by Winkler ('16) in giant tomatoes and night-shades (Fig. 350) and by other observers. [3]

It is however, certain, that in some forms the karyoplasmic ratio is subject to wide variation, as is strikingly shown by Conklin ('12) in the cleavage-stages of *Crepidula*. In this case, it is true, large cells usually have larger nuclei than small; but the ratio varies widely with the length of the inter-kinesis and in the amount of yolk material. In *C. plana*, for example, the ratio of cytoplasmic to nuclear volume in protoplasmic cells free from yolk, and measured at their maximum size, varies from 14.5 to 8.7, or from 35.7 to 7 when measured at their mean size. In *Fulgur* at mean size it varies from 127.7 to 3.6. Conklin also showed that the nuclear volume varies not with the total volume of the cytosome but only with that of its active proto-plasm. This is proved by eggs centrifuged during cleavage, in which a sharp separation takes place between the heavier yolk and the lighter proto-plasm, so that their volumes may readily be determined. In such eggs,

---

[1] The experiment cannot be carried beyond this point owing to the complete sterility and general weakness of the tetraploid plants.

[2] Gates found the relative volumes of the cells to vary considerably, those of the giant ranging from 1.44 to 3.84 times the normal diploid.

[3] *Cf.* p. 10?.

during cleavage, it may readily be seen that the largest nuclei appear in blastomeres that contain the largest amount of active protoplasm, *irrespective of their total size*. This is shown in Fig. 351, where the largest nuclei are actually situated in the smallest cells.

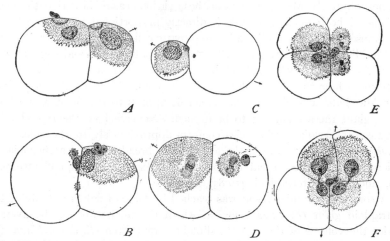

Fig. 351.—Karyoplasmic relation in segmenting eggs of *Crepidula* after centrifuging. Direction of the centrifugal force shown by arrows (CONKLIN).

In each of these 2-cell and 4-cell stages the nuclear size is proportional to the amount of active protoplasm (stippled), not to that of the cell as a whole.

These various facts, together with those earlier considered show that although the karyoplasmic ratio is a real and important cell-constant it results from a complex of factors often difficult to analyze. It calls, therefore, for critical treatment in all attempts to employ it as a factor in age, cell-division or the like or as a guide to the number of chromosomes that have entered into the composition of the nucleus (p. 236, etc.).

Finally, the remarkable fact may be emphasized that not only the nuclear size but also that of the formed components of both nucleus and *cytosome* often varies proportionately to that of the cytoplasmic mass. This is seen in the mitotic figures of dividing blastomeres and the centrosomes or "centrospheres" of the interphase (Conklin, '02, '12); in the centrioles, chondriosomes, acroblast and chromatoid bodies (p. 304); and in the plastids (p. 656). These differences evidently result from the increased size of the cytosome, however caused; for they appear in the polymegalous spermatocytes of insects, which are diploid (p. 304) as well as in the tetraploid cells of *gigas* forms (p. 656). The fact may also here be recalled that the size of the plasmosomes varies with that of the cytosome and nucleus (Montgomery), and that the same is true in certain cases of the chromosomes (during cleavage, p. 237), though this seems not to be invariable (*cf.* p. 304). The interesting problems here offered should repay further study.

VI. HISTORICAL PROBLEMS OF THE CELL [1]

Cells, like the more complex organisms that they may build up, undoubtedly owe their existing characteristics to an historical process of transformation; they too have undergone a process of evolution. Of its early course we have no direct knowledge; nevertheless, we may permit ourselves certain harmless conjectures concerning their later development.

In some directions, as has briefly been indicated in the foregoing pages, a certain amount of light has been thrown on the probable evolution of cells. Evidence has been cited to show, for instance, that mitosis of the more complicated forms has been derived from simpler types; that the central bodies were originally intra-nuclear; that fertilization in higher plants and animals is probably a survival of a process of conjugation in remote ancestral unicellular forms; that the highly differentiated types of gametes have arisen from more generalized ones, probably motile and of similar external form in both sexes; that the vesicular and massive types of nuclei have probably arisen from those of scattered or chromidial type; and so on. Degressive as well as progressive changes have undoubtedly taken place: examples of this are offered by the loss of asters and central bodies in the anastral types of mitosis in higher plants and animals; the production of non-motile sperms in various groups; the loss of chlorophyll in the gametes of higher plants.

It is now rather generally accepted that the more primitive types of cells were very probably devoid of an *individualized* nucleus, *i. e.*, that the nuclear materials were originally scattered through the cell in the form of chromidia-like bodies which only at a later period became aggregated to form a nucleus of the ordinary massive or vesicular type.[2] This view finds its support in the present existence of various forms among the Protista in which the nuclear material is actually thus distributed through the cell, and by the fact (if existing accounts are correct) that in some of these forms individualized nuclei may arise either by enlargement of the individual chromidia or by their aggregation into a granular mass, in the processes of gamete-formation, mitosis, or spore-formation (bacteria).[3] We may plausibly assume that this first occurred as a temporary process preparatory to

---

[1] The author acknowledges his indebtedness in the preparation of this section to the interesting discussions of Strasburger ('09) and of Minchin ('15). Some of the problems here considered may more readily be understood after a reading of Chapters XI and XII.

[2] *Cf.* Strasburger ('09), p. 115, Minchin, ('12, '15, p. 22), etc.

[3] *Cf.* pp. 83, 700.

reproduction, later becoming established as a more permanent feature of the cell though still capable of returning to the chromidial state, as seems still to be the case in some Protista. If this be correct it seems probable, further, that the scattered chromidia from which individualized nuclei arose were self-perpetuating, *i. e.*, that the chromidial substance maintained itself by some process of growth and division referable to the granules as such.

Minchin in particular ('12, '15) has developed in some detail the view that the most primitive of existing nuclei were simple aggregates of chromatin-granules (forming the so-called "karyosome" of protozoan nuclei) surrounded by a protoplasmic vacuole, but not bounded by a definite membrane other than the surface-film or plasma-membrane such as probably forms the boundary of all vacuoles. Such a nucleus, exemplified by those of various small *Amœbæ* of the *limax* type, has been called a "protokaryon." From it as a point of departure may plausibly be derived vesicular nuclei, bounded by a well-marked nuclear membrane, inclosing a large chromatin-nucleus and surrounded by a nuclear cavity containing chromatin. In the earlier stages all the chromatin (or chromosomes) may be assumed to have been confined to the karyosphere, later to have extended into the peripheral zone (originally the vacuole); and by a final step to have abandoned the karyosphere entirely, the latter now forming an intra-nuclear division-center or "nucleolo-centrosome." All these stages, as earlier indicated, exist among *Amœbæ* of the *limax* type (p. 207).

The incipient nucleus may be assumed to have been traversed by an achromatic (*i. e.*, *cytoplasmic*) framework in which the chromioles were suspended; and from this arose the linin network and the nuclear membrane, while the enchylema filling its interstices became the nuclear sap. The nucleus may thus be conceived as arising from a limited area of the cytoplasm, into which are crowded the original chromidia, surrounded by a membrane produced from the cytoplasmic substance. It may be assumed that at this stage chromosomes and mitosis in the strict sense of the words had not yet arisen, and that nuclear division was of simple type, involving no more than division of the chromioles and the separation of the products into two approximately equal groups by an amitotic process such as may still exist in many of the simpler types of Protista.

It was, perhaps, at this stage of the evolution, perhaps earlier, that the process of syngamy arose, as a consequence of inequalities in the distribution of the cell-substance compensated by subsequent processes of cell-fusion (p. 616); but this is purely hypothetical. In any case we may assume the next step to have been the origin of mitosis, which involves two major problems. One of these is the origin of chromosomes, a process which undoubtedly occurred during the unicellular stage of evolution. We may conjecture that this first involved a linear aggregation of chromioles to form spireme-threads; and we are driven to the further assumptions that with the appearance of syngamy and the consequent phenomena of meiosis the chromioles underwent a progressive qualitative differentiation and gradually assumed a definite serial order. To cite Strasburger: "So long as a simple mode of division suffices to ensure the proper distribution of all the units, it is not noticeably complicated. This changes with increased diversity among the units and attains its climax when each unit is devoted to a single function. An equal, qualitative division of the nucleus now demands that during division the units assume a linear alignment in threads, separation of the products being effected by longitudinal splitting of the thread. This must have been the only possible way to the goal; otherwise animals and plants would not show so complete a correspondence in this respect in the higher stages of their evolution" ('09, p. 116). How such linear aggregates can have arisen is not easy for us to picture. A rough analogy may perhaps be offered by the familiar linear aggregates of Protista and other simple organisms, though such aggregates do not divide by longitudinal fission.

It would be unprofitable to speculate concerning how the chromioles came to assume their fixed serial order in each species; how the linear aggregates (chromosomes) became fixed in number; how they learned to conjugate during synapsis with due regard to law and order, to make definite exchanges of material, and to separate in orderly fashion. Merely to state such problems is to force a confession of abysmal ignorance. We may, however, venture the surmise that in some degree the primitive linear aggregates or chromosomes were from the first in some measure qualitatively different, and that their differences grew with the evolution of the nucleus; but even in their most highly differentiated condition, it seems probable that the chromosomes in any given species still consist largely of the same materials, and that their differences affect only certain components.[1]

Somewhat more accessible is the second main historical problem of mitosis, namely, the origin and evolution of the achromatic figure; and here we are brought to the hypothesis of binuclearity in another form.[2]

Its starting point was the assumption of Hertwig that primitively the cell contained two nuclei of which one has retained its "chromatin" to form the ordinary nucleus of the metazoan cell, while the other has lost its chromatin and become converted into a division-center. Bütschli and Heidenhain suggested that this differentiation is foreshadowed in the cil-

---

[1] Cf. Wilson ('12, '14).
[2] See Bütschli ('91), R. Hertwig ('92), Heidenhain ('94), Lauterborn ('95, '96), Schaudinn ('96, 05), and Hartmann and Prowazek ('07).

iates by the presence of the macronucleus and micronucleus, the former representing the trophic, the latter the kinetic nucleus and the incipient central body. This view is manifestly improbable, for all available evidence indicates the highly specialized nature of the ciliates as a group. Lauterborn, on the other hand, assumed the starting point to have been a cell containing two equal and similar nuclei, as is the case, for instance, in *Amœba diploidea* (Fig. 296). The intra-nuclear division-center so common in Protozoa was thus left unexplained.

The hypothesis underwent a further development with Schaudinn's discovery ('05) of the parabasal body in the trypanosomes, which he called the "blepharoplast" and considered as the derivative of a second nucleus. The trypanosome was thus considered, like the ciliates, as binucleate, containing a larger vegetative or trophic nucleus and a smaller kinetic nucleus (the "blepharoplast"), concerned especially with the production of the flagellum, near the base of which it lies.[1] Both "nuclei" were believed to contain "chromatin" and to divide mitotically; but later observers have found no evidence of either conclusion in case of the "blepharoplast" (parabasal body).[2]

Meanwhile Schaudinn's conception was further elaborated by Hartmann and Prowazek (*op. cit.*) by the assumption that the "kinetonucleus" or "blepharoplast" of the trypanosomes is represented in many Protista by the "endosome" or "karyosome," the nucleus being in such cases (as was hinted by Schaudinn in 1896) an "amphikaryon" in which a kinetic nucleus is included within a trophic and often in its turn includes a central granule or centriole. These authors cite many cases in which the karyosome plays the part of an intra-nuclear division-center (*e. g.*, the "nucleolocentrosome" of *Euglena*, p. 206) and others in which the division of the karyosome is said to be initiated by division of a centriole within it—*e. g.*, in *Amœba froschi* or in the genus *Entamœba*. By loss of its chromatin the karyosome becomes a true intranuclear "centrosome," which may escape from the nucleus (as in the budding of *Acanthocystis*, Fig. 325) to form an extra-nuclear body that may persist as such through many divisions. It was thus sought on the one hand to reconcile the binuclearity hypothesis with the views of R. Hertwig ('98), and of Boveri ('00), who assumed the division-

---

[1] By Laveran and Mesnil ('02), followed by French writers generally, the kinetic nucleus was called a "centrosome." Schaudinn's term blepharoplast was previously applied by Senn ('00) to the basal granule of the flagellum in flagellates, still earlier by Webber ('97) to the cilia-forming body in cycads; and in this usage he was followed by German writers generally. Woodcock's term "kinetonucleus" for this structure was adopted by Minchin, Dobell and other English writers, who reserved the name "blepharoplast" for the basal granule alone, and considered it to be homologous with a "centrosome." Its designation as the "parabasal body," has earlier been indicated (p. 694).

[2] See for instance Novy and McNeal ('05), E. and E. Sergent ('05, '07), Woodcock ('10), Minchin and Woodcock ('11), Werbitzki ('10), etc.

center to have been originally differentiated as an intra-nuclear body in a single nucleus.

This much discussed assumption, in the words of one of its critics, strove to make a second nucleus appear in many Protozoa where to the unaided imagination but one such structure is actually present; [1] and it has failed to convince most investigators of its correctness or even of its convenience. It becomes at once untenable if we admit the identity of the parabasal body with the "blepharoplast" or "kinetonucleus" of the trypanosomes and other forms; for in many of the flagellates a typical karyosome is also present (Figs. 337, 338). That an intra-nuclear structure like the karyosome was the forerunner of the division-center of higher forms has been made very probable by many investigations upon Protista, heretofore considered (p. 204). To consider this body as a nucleus within a nucleus is, however, to allow the supposed exigencies of an hypothesis to close our eyes to plain facts; this was indeed admitted by Hartmann who, in a later work ('11) withdrew this portion of his conception though still adhering to it in more restricted form. To the writer it seems simpler and more plausible to consider the original condition as having been a uninucleated one with an intra-nuclear division-center, which may very well have been similar to the karyosome of many existing Protozoa.

If we turn finally to the nature and origin of the cell-components in their earliest forms we find ourselves reduced to purely speculative considerations. We have considered the possibility that the protoplasmic basis or hyaloplasm may contain numerous minute self-propagating dispersed bodies lying beyond the limits of microscopical vision and forming a possible source of many of the visible formed components of the cell. Accepting some such view, for the sake of argument, we might raise the question as to which came first, the corpuscles or the apparently homogeneous basis in which they are suspended? Did corpuscles arise as secondary differentiations of a "continuous" protoplasm, or was the latter (like the matrix of a zoöglœa) a product of corpuscles originally capable of separate and independent existence? It seems legitimate to ask this question in view of the supposed existence to-day of living organisms of this order of magnitude in the form of the filterable pathogenic microörganisms, of which nearly 40 species are said to be known.[2] Some of these still lie above the limits of microscopical vision, e. g., the germ of poliomyelitis in man and of pleuropneumonia in cattle;[3] others are invisible, or as yet have not been seen. The experiments of Esmarch ('02) and others suggest that this may in some cases be due to the extreme tenuity of elongated forms, such as spirochætes; but it is at least possible that forms exist whose linear dimensions lie

---

[1] Swezey ('16), p. 180. [2] Lipschütz ('13). [3] Cf. Jordan, p. 510.

below the present range of visibility. The organisms here in question are parasitic (pathogenic); but it is also possible, as Minchin has especially urged, that many non-parasitic organisms of equal minuteness may now exist unknown to us, since we have no means of perceiving their effects.[1]

Such an hypothesis is of course unverifiable, and for this reason will to many appear worthless. As a purely speculative construction, however, it seems to the writer to offer possibilities concerning the early evolution of the cell that are worth considering, even though it brings us no nearer to a conception of the origin of life or a comprehension of organic individuality. This view was implied in Altmann's original development of his granulum-theory (p. 720) and has been developed by various later writers.[2] By Minchin the earliest living organisms were conjectured to have been minute, possibly ultra-microscopic particles to which he applies Mereschkowsky's term *biococci;* and which were assumed to be composed of "chromatin," the cytoplasm of higher forms being considered a secondary product, constituting a "ground-substance" in which the biococci were suspended in the form of chromidial granules ('15, p. 19). On the other hand, Mereschkowsky ('10), in an entertaining fantasy, has developed the hypothesis that the dualism of the cell in respect to nuclear and cytoplasmic substance resulted from a symbiotic association of two types of primordial microorganisms, that were originally distinct, one including primitive non-nucleated Monera composed of "amœboplasm," the other ultra-microscopical bacteria-like "biococci." By ingestion of the latter by the Monera arose a symbiotic association of the two forms, the cocci becoming chromidial granules and thus ultimately forming the nucleus. In further flights of the imagination Mereschkowsky suggests the origin of the whole group of fungi from bacteria independently of other plants, and of the green plants by a symbiotic union of between colorless nucleated cells and minute Cyanophyceæ, the latter giving rise to the chloroplasts. The latter speculation cannot be considered as totally baseless in view of the symbiotic association of unicellular green algæ with fungi in the lichens, the presence of chlorophyll-bearing bodies in many Protozoa and lower Metazoa (*e. g.*, in *Hydra*) which still form a subject of discussion, *i. e.*, as to whether they are likewise symbiotic algæ or products of the animal itself, with the evidence on the whole favoring the former alternative.[3] Even so cautious an observer as Pfeffer once considered the possibility that the cell may have been the product of a symbiosis between nucleus and cytosome, while Boveri

---

[1] *Cf.* Miehe ('23). This observer's attempts to determine (by the method of "ultrafiltration") whether ultramicroscopical organisms are of widespread occurrence in nature were negative.

[2] See especially Mereschkowsky ('10), Minchin ('15), Bridges ('22).

[3] Fulton ('22), etc.

suggested a "symbiosis of two kinds of simple plasma-structures—Monera, if we may so call them—in such fashion that a number of smaller forms, the chromosomes, established themselves within a larger one which we now call the cytosome." [1] More recently Wallin ('22) has maintained that chondriosomes may be regarded as symbiotic bacteria whose association with the other cytoplasmic components may have arisen in the earliest stages of evolution (p. 712). To many, no doubt, such speculations may appear too fantastic for present mention in polite biological society; nevertheless it is within the range of possibility that they may some day call for more serious consideration.

LITERATURE IX

(See also I, III, IV, VI, XI, etc. For abbreviations see General Literature List.)

Altmann, R., '90, '94 (I).

Arnold, J., '14. Ueber Plasmastrukturen und ihre funktionelle Bedeutung: *Jena.*

Baumgärtel, O., '20. Das Problem der Cyanophyzeenzelle: *A. P.,* XLI, 1.

Boveri, Th., '00. Zellenstudien IV: Ueber die Natur der Centrosomen: *J. Z.,* XXV.
    '04. Ergebnisse über die Konstitution der chromatischen Kernsubstanz: *Jena.*
    '05. Zellenstudien V. Ueber die Abhängigkeit der Kerngrösse und Zellenzahl der Ausgangszellen: *Jena.*

Cavers, F., '14. Chondriosomes (Mitochondria) and their Significance: *N. P.,* XIII.

Chambers, R., '17. The Cell Aster. A Reversible Gelation Phenomenon: *J. E. Z.,* XXIII.

Champy, Chr., '11. Recherches sur l'absorption intestinale et le rôle des mitochondries, etc.: *A. A. M.,* XIII.

Conklin, E. G., '12a. Cell Size and Nuclear Size: *J. E. Z.,* XII, 1.
    '12b. Body Size and Cell Size: *J. M.,* XXIII.

Cowdry, E. V., '16 (I).
    '24. Mitochondria, Golgi Apparatus, and Chromidial Substance: In *General Cytology. Chicago.*

Cowdry, N. H., '17. A Comparison of Mitochondria in Plant and Animal Cells: *B. B.,* XXXIII.

Derschau, M. v., '14. Zum Chromatindualismus der Pflanzenzelle: *A. Zf.,* XII.

De Vries, H., '89. Intracellular Pangenesis: *Jena.*

Dobell, C. C., '09. Chromidia and the Binuclearity Hypothesis: *Q. J.,* LIII.

Duesberg, J., '11. Plastosomen, "Apparato reticolare interno," und Chromidialapparat: *E. A. E.,* XX.
    '13. Plastosomes et "organ-forming substances" dans l'œuf des ascidiens: *B. A. B.,* V.
    '15. Recherches cytologiques sur la fécondation des ascidiens, etc.: *P. C. I.,* 223.

Entz, G., '18. Ueber die mitotische Teilung von *Polytoma: A. P.,* XXXVIII.

Erdmann, R., '09. Experimentelle Untersuchungen der Massenverhältnisse von Plasma, Kern und Chromosomen, etc.: *A. Zf.,* II.

---

[1] '04, p. 90.

Erhard, H., '11. Die Henneguy-Lenhosséksche Theorie: *E. A. E.*, XIX.

Escoyez, E., '07. Blepharoplast et Centrosome dans le *Marchantia: L. C.*, XXIV.

Fauré-Fremiet, '10 (IV).

Fischer, A., '05. Die Zelle der Cyanophyzeen: *B. Z.*

Fritsch, F. E., '05, '07. Studies on Cyanophyceæ: *N. P.*

Guilliermond, A., '14a. État actuel de la question de l'évolution et du rôle physiologique des mitochondries: *R. G. B.*, XXVI.

— '19. Observations vitales sur le chondriome des vegétaux, etc.: *R. G. B.*, XXXI.

— '19a. Sur l'origine mitochondriale des plastids, etc.: *Ann. Sci. Nat. Bot.*, X, 1.

Hartmann, M., '13. Flagellata: *H. Nw.*, III, *Fischer, Jena.*

Hartmann and **Prowazek,** '07. Blepharoplast, Caryosom und Centrosom: *A. P.*, X.

Heidenhain, M., '07, '11. (Int.)

Hegner, R. W., '19. Quantitative Relations between Chromatin and Cytoplasm in the Genus *Arcella: P. N. A.*, V.

Henneguy, L.,'98. Sur les rapports des cils vibratiles avec les centrosomes: *A. A. M.*, I.

Hertwig, R., '08. Ueber neue Probleme der Zellenlehre: *A. Zf.*, 1.

Hoven, H., '10. Sur l'histogénèse du système nerveux, etc.: *A. B.*, XXV.

— '11. Du rôle du chondriome de l'élaboration des produits de la gland mammaire: *A. A.*, XXXIX.

Lams, H., '10. Recherches sur l'œuf *d'Arion: Mém. Acad. roy. d. Belg. Classe d. Sci.*

Maier, H. W.,'03. Ueber den feineren Bau der Wimperapparate der Infusorien: *A. P.*, II.

Meves, Fr., '16. Die Chloroplastenbildung bei den höheren Pflanzen: *B. D. B. G.*, XXXIV.

— '17, '18a (I).

Meyer, A., '12. Die Zelle der Bakterien: *Jena.*

Miehe, H., '23. Sind ultramikroskopische Organismen in der Natur verbreitet?: *B. Z.*, XLIII.

Minchin, E. A., '15. The Evolution of the Cell: *Brit. Ass. Ann. Rept.:* Pres. Address, Sect. D.

Morgan, T. H., '96. The Production of Artificial Astrospheres: *A. Entwm.*, III.

— '99. The Action of Salt Solutions on the . . . Eggs of *Arbacia: Ibid.*, VIII.

Mottier, D. M., '18. Chondriosomes and the Primordia of Chloroplasts and Leucoplasts: *A. Bot.*, XXXII.

Pappenheimer, E. M., '16. The Golgi Apparatus, etc. (L): *A. R.*, XI, 4.

Prenant, A., '98–99. Sur le protoplasma supérieur (archiplasme, kinoplasme, ergastoplasm): *J. A. P.*, XXIV–V.

— '10. Les mitochondries et l'ergastoplasm: *Ibid.*, XLVI.

— '11a. Problems cytologiques généraux soulevés par l'étude des cellules musculaires: *Ibid.*, XLVII.

— '13. Les appareils ciliés et leurs derivés: *Ibid.*, XLIX.

Rabl, C.,'99. Ueber den Bau und die Entwicklung der Linse, III: *Z. W. Z.*, XLVII.

Regaud, C., 10. Étude sur la structure des tubes séminifères, etc., *A. A. M.*, XI.

Rhumbler, L., '02. Der Aggregatzustand und die physikalischen Besonderheiten des lebendigen Zellinhaltes: *Zeitschr. Allg. Phys.*, I, II.

— '14. Das Protoplasma als Physikalisches System: *E. P.*, XIV.

Saguchi, S., '17. Studies on Ciliated Cells: *J. M.*, XXIX.

Sapěhin, A. A., '13. Untersuchungen über die Individualität der Plastide: *B. D. B. G.*, XXXI.

Schaxel, F., '11. Plasmastructuren, Chondriosomen und Chromidien: *A. A.*, XXXIX.

Sharp, L. W., '12, '14, '20 (IV).

Strasburger, E., '93.

Swezey, O., '16. The Kinetonucleus of Flagellates and the Binuclear Theory of Hartmann: *Univ. Calif. Publ. Zoöl.*, XVI.

Troland, L. T., '17. Biological Enigmas and the Theory of Enzyme Action: *A. N.*, LI.

Vejdovský and **Mrázek,** '03 [II].

Watase, S., '93. On the Nature of Cell Organization: *Woods Hole Lectures.*

Whitman, C. O., '87. The Kinetic Phenomena of the Egg during Maturation and Fecundation: *J. M.*, 1.

Wiesner, J., '92. Die Elementarstructur und das Wachstum der lebenden Substanz: *Wien.*

Wilson, E. B., '01 (V).

Yatsu, N., '05. The Formation of Centrosomes in Enucleated Egg-Fragments: *J. E. Z.*, II.

Zacharias, E., '07. Ueber die neuere Cyanophyzeenliteratur: *B. Z.*

CHAPTER X

CHROMOSOMES AND SEX

"The cytological evidence has revealed a visible mechanical basis for the production of males and females in equal numbers and irrespective of external conditions. . . .

"Phenomena of this kind seem likely to throw further light on the mechanism of Mendelian heredity as well as of sex-production, for they demonstrate a disjunction of different elements in the formation of the gametes; and this is a fact, not a theory." [1]

The genetic aspects of our subject are most readily approached through the subject of sex-production, to the elucidation of which cytology and genetics have equally contributed. In no other field of inquiry is the close connection between cytological and genetic phenomena so readily demonstrated; nature here offers us, indeed, a series of experiments, systematically carried out on a grand scale, that afford crucial evidence concerning the causal relation between chromosomes and heredity.

I. SEX AND THE GERM–CELLS

Investigations upon the nature of sex were long dominated by the preconceived notion that it is determined by conditions external to the germ,[2] but the inadequacy of this view is now conclusively demonstrated. It is true that many conditions, external or internal, may influence sex-production; and in certain cases may give the appearance of determining sex. For instance, the classical experiments of Prantl ('81), Buchtien ('87) and their successors showed that in the prothallia of *Equisetum* and certain other pteridophytes the production of archegonia is favored by stronger light or more favorable conditions of nutrition while the reverse conditions favor the production of antheridia;[3] and a result similar in principle in respect to soil-conditions has recently been demonstrated by Schaffner in the diœcious *Cannabis* ('21) and *Arisæma* ('22). It seems clear, however, that external conditions here operate merely to incite the development of one set of sexual characters at the cost of the opposite set in an organism that is actually or potentially monœcious or hermaphroditic.[4]

---

[1] Wilson, '09, p. 15; '10, p. 592.

[2] Compare, for instance, the account of this subject given in the preceding edition of this work, 1900, pp. 144–146.

[3] See Klebs ('13).

[4] This is clearly evident in *Arisæma dracontium* where the individuals as found in nature are often actually monœcious. The effect of soil here is to change the monœcious conditions to the staminate or the reverse.

Probably of the same type is the case of the worm *Bonellia*, in which the mature forms show a very pronounced sexual dimorphism. Here the larva, at first alike in both sexes, becomes a female if it fails to become attached (in some cases showing some hermaphroditic characters); while if it becomes normally attached it produces a male.[1] To cite a case of different type, the experiments of Shull ('10, '12) and of Whitney ('14-'17) have shown that in cultures of rotifers (*Hydatina*, etc.) composed exclusively of parthenogenetic females, males may be quickly caused to appear upon a suitable change of diet (p. 229); but this, evidently, is not a change of one sex into another but only the partial appearance of the sexual forms (both males and sexual females) in addition to the parthenogenetic. Still another type appears in the facts observed by R. Hertwig ('12, '21) in frogs, in which over-ripe eggs produce a large excess of males as compared with those from the same female when fertilized immediately.[2] In this case the explanation is not yet evident; but it seems probable that they are due to a modification of the chromosome-mechanism of sex-production.[3]

It is indeed possible—and such a view has in fact often been advocated—that all organisms are potentially hermaphroditic (see p. 819). Nevertheless a real distinction exists between true hermaphroditic and diœcious organisms; and in the latter both the genetic and the cytological evidence demonstrates the existence in the germ-cells of a definite internal mechanism that is adjusted for an automatic production of the sexes under identical external conditions. It is probable, therefore, that in so far as external conditions affect sex production it is in all cases through their influence upon the internal mechanism (p. 819).[4]

Mendel himself suggested the possibility that sex-determination might be a phenomenon of heredity and segregation; and this suggestion (later adopted by Strasburger, '00 and by Bateson, '02, and elaborated by Castle, '03) was ultimately shown to give the true key to a solution of the problem. Definite evidence of its correctness was first brought forward by Correns ('07) in experimental studies on hybrids between monœcious and diœcious species of plants (*Bryonia*). The results indicated that in the diœcious

---

[1] Baltzer ('14).

[2] In one of these experiments 500 eggs, fertilized at once, produced 226 males, 218 females and 4 undetermined. A large number of eggs from the same lot fertilized from 68 to 77 hours later gave 13 females and 673 males, with a large mortality.

[3] Hertwig, assuming the female to be the homogametic sex (XX), conjectures that over-ripeness of the eggs may tend to weaken the action of one chromosome or even to cause its degeneration.

[4] The sexual dimegaly of the eggs long known in the parthenogenesis of rotifers and phylloxerans and in the sexual eggs of *Dinophilus apatris* (pp. 277, 806) early led to the view that sex is predetermined in the germ-cells. Beard ('02, and earlier) urged the hypothesis of four-fold gametes—*i. e.*, that both eggs and sperms are predestined as male-producing or female-producing, a necessary corollary of which is the assumption of selective fertilization; but later researches rendered this particular assumption highly improbable.

species sex is determined by the pollen-grains, all the eggs being sexually of one type, while the pollen-grains, are of two classes, equal in number, one of them male-producing, the other female-producing. This led Correns to compare the sexual cross to the Mendelian "back cross" between a heterozygote, DR, and a corresponding recessive homozygote, RR, the male (which we may call XY) being in a certain sense the heterozygous sex or sex-hybrid, the female XX the homozygous (Fig. 352). In both cases the "homozygous" parent produces but one kind of gamete (R or X); the "heterozygous" parent two equal classes (D and R or X and Y). In either case, therefore, random fertilization will in the long run produce the two parental forms (DR=XY, and RR = XX) in equal numbers. In order, however, not to complicate the use of the terms "homozygous" and "heterozygous" it has been found convenient from the cytological point

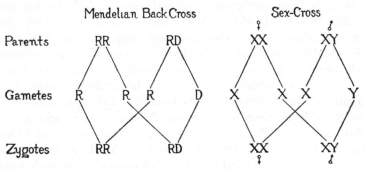

Fig. 352.—Diagram comparing a sex-cross with a Mendelian back-cross between a homozygous recessive (*RR*) and a heterozygote (*DR*).

of view to replace them when applied to sex-heredity by the corresponding terms *homogametic* and *digametic* or *heterogametic*.[1]

Genetic research on the heredity of sex-linked characters (p. 945) has fully borne out the foregoing conclusion and has further demonstrated that either sex may be the homogametic one. Thus, the male has been shown to be the digametic sex in mammals and Diptera, while the reverse condition exists in birds and Lepidoptera. This means that in the former case, all the eggs alike have the constitution X, while half the sperms have the constitution X and are female-producing, and half Y and are male-producing. In the bird or butterfly, on the other hand, it is the sperms that are genetically alike, while the eggs are of two equal classes, female-producing and male-producing. The decisive or differential sex-factor is therefore the sperm in the fly and mammal, and the egg in the butterfly.

The fundamental contribution of cytology to the subject was the dis-

[1] Wilson, '10a, '11.

covery, announced in 1905,[1] that the genetic phenomena are exactly paralleled by certain particular chromosomes; so that the symbols X and Y
may be applied to them in sex-production in precisely the same manner
as to the genetic factors that determine sex. That these chromosomes
bear the differential factors of sex has been proved to be the case by an
irrestistible body of more detailed and concrete evidence drawn from both
genetics and cytology. The chromosomes in question may, therefore,
appropriately be called the *sex-chromosomes*.[2] Thus far the male sex has
been certainly found to be cytologically the digametic one in echinoderms,
nematodes, spiders, myriapods, Odonata, Orthoptera, Hemiptera, Coleoptera, Diptera, Hymenoptera (though with an important qualification),
reptiles and mammals; and there is strong indirect evidence that the same
condition exists in rotifers, ostracodes and Cladocera. On the other hand,
the female has been proved to be cytologically digametic in the Lepidoptera. The birds alone offer a seeming contradiction in that genetically the
female is genetically heterozygous, but cytologically the male has been
described as digametic. This material, however, offers great difficulties
(p. 786).

The facts just outlined mean that a definite relation or predestination
exists between the germ-cells and sex and one that is not dependent upon
external conditions. Examples of such predestination have earlier been
given in case of the rhizopods, algæ and fungi (p. 585, etc.). The evidence
is now conclusive that this predestination of sexual genetic constitution
in the germ-cells is established by the meiotic or maturation-divisions,
i. e., in general during the spore-formation in plants and during the gamete-
formation in animals. In the heterothallic moulds, for instance, the male
(—) and female (+) strains remain perfectly distinct so long as conjugation
does not occur (p. 588). Since, however, conjugation brings together the
+ and — determining factors it seems necessary to assume that they are
segregated or disjoined at a subsequent period. In point of fact Blakeslee
showed ('06), in the case of species of *Phycomyces* that are predominantly
heterothallic, that this disjunction takes place in the formation of the spores;
for if on germination of the zygospores the germ-tube be cut across before
the formation of a sporangium it may give rise by regeneration to a mycelium
of the neutral or homothallic type, which is proved to be bisexual (+ —)
by the fact that branches of such mycelia occasionally conjugate with one
another. The sexual segregation in the spore-formation is, however, in-

---

[1] Stevens ('05), Wilson, '05.

[2] Wilson ('06). Sex-chromosomes are definitely known in sea-urchins, nematodes, arachnids,
myriapods, most orders of insects, reptiles, mammals, and birds. Among plants they have thus
far been found only in the liverwort *Sphærocarpus*, and the seed-plants *Elodea*, *Rumex* and a few
others (p. 812).

complete; for a certain percentage of the spores remain bisexual and give rise to homothallic mycelia.

In higher plants, where the sexes are readily distinguished by the eye, a more definite result has been reached. In *Marchantia*, a strictly diœcious liverwort, the haploid thallus or gametophyte, may be cultivated asexually (by means of gemmæ) through many generations without change of sex, however the external conditions be varied. The spores, however, as proved by isolation experiments, are strictly male-producing or female-producing, and both kinds occur in the same sporangium (Noll, '06).

In a beautiful series of experiments the Marchals ('06, '07) established the same fact in several species of diœcious mosses (*Barbula, Bryum, Cera-todon*). Isolation-cultures proved that each spore is strictly predestined either as male-producing or as female-producing. All efforts to alter this predestination by changes of the external conditions, such as nutrition, light, heat or moisture, failed to produce the least effect. Like the spores from which they proceed, both the primary protonema and the gametophyte (leaf-bearing moss-plant) are of fixed sex, and this applies to every part of the plant. Small fragments of the stem or of the leaves will readily regenerate secondary protonemas from which are budded forth new moss-plants; the latter are always of the same sex as the original plants or spores, irrespective of variations in the environment (Fig. 353). Since the diploid sporophyte (sporogonium) is produced by the zygote it must contain the potentialities of both sexes, and this is directly proved by the fact that it produces spores of both sexes. If, now, small pieces be cut from the sporangium or its stalk they may produce by regeneration (apospory) new gametophytes or moss-plants, quite similar in appearance to the original ones, but diploid in nuclear constitution and *sexually hermaphroditic or bisexual*, a condition otherwise almost unknown in the species under investigation, though common in other mosses.[1]

Experimental demonstration is here given: (1) that male-producing and female-producing factors are brought together in fertilization; (2) that they remain associated in the diploid cells of the sporophyte; (3) *that they are disjoined in the course of the meiotic divisions by which the spores are formed*.[2] This last result received convincing confirmation in the researches of Douin

[1] This fact is not immediately shown by all the plants thus produced; many of them are plainly bisexual, but some are in appearance males, and a few females. These latter forms are, however, in reality also bisexual or hermaphroditic, as is proved by their descendants, again produced by regeneration from fragments of the stems or leaves. It should be noted that mixed or hermaphroditic gametophytes have been recorded in a number of species of mosses that are normally of separate sexes, including one of the species (*Mnium hornum*) examined by the Marchals (see M. Wilson, '15). In this case Wilson showed that such an hermaphroditic gametophyte contained the haploid number of chromosomes (6). It does not seem, however, that the Marchals' results are thus invalidated.

[2] See also Strasburger ('09).

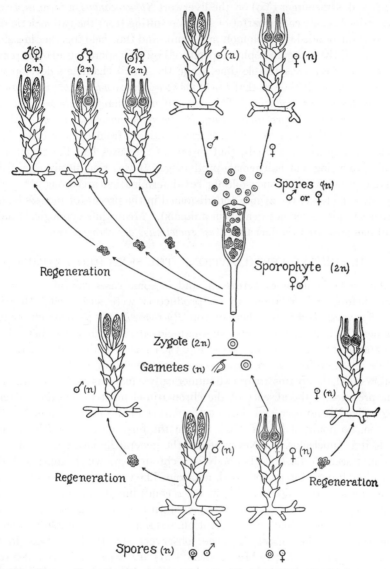

Fig. 353.—Diagram illustrating the experimental results of the MARCHALS on the diœcious mosses).

The male and female haploid gametophytes below, with the diploid sporophyte (sporogonium. above. Regeneration-products of the males or females at either side below; those from the sporophyte are externally male, female or hermaphrodite but in each case may regenerate individuals of different sex.

('09) and Strasburger ('09) on the liverwort *Sphærocarpus*, a form especially favorable because each quartet of spores resulting from the two meiotic divisions is surrounded by a common membrane and thus held together in a single group, and the four gametophytes produced by each spore-tetrad often remain associated for a considerable time, while the sexual characters develop very early. The result showed that *two of the spores in each tetrad are male-producing and two female-producing*.[1] This can only mean that *the male-producing and female-producing factors are disjoined in one of the meiotic divisions.* Almost at the same time genetic evidence was obtained, from the heredity of sex-linked characters in animals, that in one of the sexes half the gametes are male-producing and half female-producing. It was thus firmly established that two *somethings* responsible for sex-determination are brought together by the gametes in the zygote and disjoined in the process of meiosis (sporogenesis in plants, gametogenesis in animals). Meanwhile cytological studies had demonstrated the fact that *these somethings are chromosomes.*

II. SEX AND FERTILIZATION. THE SEX–CHROMOSOMES

The sex-chromosomes were seen, and in some cases carefully described, long before their relations to sex-production were suspected. Henking, in 1891, described in the hemipteron *Pyrrhocoris*, a "peculiar chromatin-element" which in the second spermatocyte-division first lags behind the separating anaphase-chromosomes and then passes undivided to one pole, while all the other eleven chromosomes are equally divided. From this it follows that the sperms are of two numerically equal classes distinguished by the presence or the absence of the chromatin-element in question. Henking arrived at no very clear idea of the nature of this element, and (for this reason, no doubt) labels it "X"; but in the final statement of his results calls it a "nucleolus." [2] Nevertheless, the general implications of his brief account seem to be that this body is a chromosome which appears during the growth-period in a condensed, nucleolus-like form, divides equally in the first division, and fails to divide in the second; but its chromosomal nature was not fully established in *Pyrrhocoris* until long afterwards.[3] All the essential features of Henking's description, so far as it went, were subsequently confirmed in other insects by other observers—by Paulmier ('99) in the hemipter *Anasa tristis*; by Montgomery ('01) in *Protenor, Alydus* and certain other Hemiptera; by Sinéty ('01) in the phasmids *Orphania* and *Dixippus;*

---

[1] The more recent data of Allen ('19) are in harmony with this conclusion (as are also those of Mc-Allister, '15, on *Thallocarpus*) though less extensive. Allen's cytological observations give a remarkable confirmation of the same result, though the actual disjunction of the sex-chromosomes has not yet been seen. (*Cf.* p. 812.)

[2] '91, p. 712.

[3] Gross ('06), Wilson ('09).

by McClung ('02), Sutton ('02) and their followers in many species of grass-hoppers; and a similar type of sex-chromosomes was subsequently found in many other animals. This type has received many names,[1] of which perhaps the most widely employed are the terms *accessory chromosome* (McClung, '02) and *X-chromosome* (Wilson, '09). In the meantime a second, and slightly more complicated type of sex-chromosome was described by Montgomery ('98, '01) in various Hemiptera under the name of "chromatin-nucleoli," but their real nature was not at that time suspected. Still more complicated types were subsequently discovered.

The first suggestion that the X-chromosome is concerned with sex-determination came from McClung ('01, '02b), who emphasized the parallel between the two equal classes of sperm differentiated by the X-chromosome, and the two equal sexual classes of adults. He was thus led to the hypothesis that this particular chromosome is the "sex-determiner"; but the actual proof of this was first produced a few years later.

A. MALE DIGAMETY

This condition, the most frequent and the first to be observed, shows many variations of cytological detail and may be classed in this respect under three main types all of which conform to the same general principle. The first of these, which is the simplest, may be taken as the general basis of our account.

1. The Simple XO–XX or Protenor Type

a. General Outline. In this type half the sperms contain one X-chromosome and are female-producing, while half lack such a chromosome and are male-producing. McClung assumed the X-bearing class of sperms to be male-producing, *i. e.*, that eggs fertilized by them produce males, while the no-X class of sperms are female-producing. This assumption implied that the male should contain one more chromosome than the female, and seemed at first sight to harmonize with Montgomery's discovery ('01) that in several of the Hemiptera having one X-chromosome the diploid (spermatogonial) number in the male is odd (*e. g.*, in *Protenor, Alydus, Harmostes* and *Œdancala*). Sutton ('02) actually described such a condition in the grasshopper *Brachystola;* but this was afterwards proved to be an error. Meanwhile

[1] Some of these are the "special chromosome" (Sinéty), "odd chromosome" (Montgomery), "heterotropic chromosome" (Wilson, '06), "idiochromosome" (Wilson, '05c, and '09), and "monosome" (Montgomery, '06). Montgomery also designated this chromosome as "chromosome X" in the case of *Protenor*, but in other similiar cases called it the "odd chromosome" (*Harmostes, Alydus,* etc.). The general term "monosome" was later proposed by him (in contradistinction to "diplosome") to designate one subdivision of a more general group of specially modified chromosomes called "heterochromosomes," ('04), later "allosomes" ('06). The term X-chromosome was suggested in the interest of a simpler and more consistent terminology, and because of its convenience when transferred to the corresponding genetic phenomena (Wilson, '09).

the whole subject was temporarily thrown into confusion by the erroneous conclusion of Gross ('04, '06), and Montgomery ('04), that in some insects which possess a typical odd or unpaired chromosome both sexes have the same number of chromosomes. An exit from this difficulty was at first sought in the hypothesis, that sperms of the no-X class are non-functional,

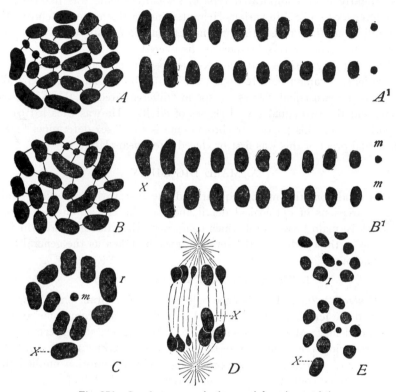

Fig. 354.—Sex-chromosomes in the squash-bug *Anasa tristis*.

A, female diploid group, 22 chromosomes; *A*[1], the same arranged in pairs; *B*, corresponding group in the male (21 chromosomes), one of the largest four (*i. e.*, one *X*) being absent; *B*[1], the same arranged in pairs; *C*, first spermatocyte-metaphase, characteristic grouping, 10 bivalents, one univalent (*X*); *D*, second spermatocyte-anaphase, *X* passing to one pole; *E*, sister anaphase-groups of same division, one with 10 chromosomes (no *X*-class) and one with 11 (*X*-class).

degenerating after the fashion of polocytes, and that either sex may be produced after fertilization by sperms of the X-class.[1]

This confusion was dispelled by the discovery that it is the *female* that possesses one more chromosome than the male, the diploid chromosome-groups of the former containing two X-chromosomes, those of the male

[1] Gross, '04, '06, Wallace, '05.

but one; [1] while in respect to all the other chromosomes the sexes are of identical constitution (Figs. 354, 355). Their total chromosome-number is therefore even in the female and odd in the male.   In *Protenor belfragi,* for example, the female number is 14, the male number 13, and the X-chromosome is immediately recognizable because it is at least twice the size of the next smaller.   It is here seen at a glance that the male contains a single, unpaired large chromosome, the female two such chromosomes (Fig. 356).

In the female, obviously, the diploid groups consist of two similar series of chromosomes; in other words, all the chromosomes may be arranged in symmetrical pairs of synaptic mates (p. 503), one of these being the X-

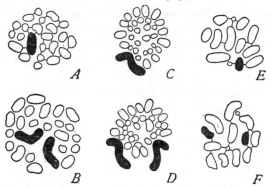

Fig. 355.—Sexual differences of the diploid chromosome-groups in insects (*C* and *D*, from MOHR). The *X*-chromosome black in each case.

A, B, male and female diploid groups of the hemipter *Pyrrhocoris,* 23 and 24 chromosomes; *C, D,* corresponding groups from the grasshopper *Leptophyes,* 31 and 32 chromosomes; *E, F,* from the hemipter *Alydus,* 13 and 14 chromosomes.

pair.   In the male, the conditions are the same except that one member of the X-pair is missing.   With this fact in mind all becomes clear.   In the female synapsis produces, as usual, the haploid number of bivalents, including XX, and all the mature eggs are alike, each receiving a complete haploid series, including one X (Fig. 358).   In the male, on the other hand, the unpaired X-chromosome has no synaptic mate, and hence enters but half the sperms.   The latter, accordingly, comprise an X-class and a no-X class, in equal numbers (Fig. 357).   The sex of the fertilized egg depends therefore upon the class of sperm that enters it in fertilization, as in the following formulas: [2]

$$\text{Egg AX} + \text{Sperm AX} = \text{AAXX} \; (\female)$$
$$\text{Egg AX} + \text{Sperm A} \;\; = \text{AAX (or AAXO)} \; (\male)$$

[1] This was first demonstrated in the hemipteran genera *Protenor, Anasa, Alydus,* and *Harmostes* (Wilson '05, '05a, '05b, '06), later in many other forms.

[2] In this and all succeeding formulas of this type A denotes the haploid group of autosomes or ordinary chromosomes common to all the gametes.

This is also shown in the diagram (Fig. 352) where the no-X class of sperm is designated as Y.

Two additional results of the first importance are made clear by these diagrams. (1) If fertilization take place at random, *i. e.*, if the chances be equal that a sperm of one class or the other will enter any particular egg, then the two sexes should in the long run appear in equal numbers. Departures from such equality are therefore probably to be ascribed to secondary causes, such as different degrees of activity or of viability in the two classes of sperm, or in male and female embryos. (2) *The single X-chromodome of the male is derived from the mother.* This chromosome, therefore, may alternate between the sexes in successive generations; and in fact it always passes from the male to the female in the production of females, and from the female to the male in the production of males.[1] On this fact, as will later be shown, depend some of the most characteristic features of sex-linked heredity.

Two of the conclusions involved in the foregoing interpretation, though firmly based upon our general knowledge of the chromosomes in meiosis and fertilization, were at first inferential, namely, that in maturation each egg receives a single X-chromosome, and that the observed sexual differences in the diploid chromosomes are determined by the class of sperm that enters the egg. Both conclusions were later substantiated by direct observation. The first was established through the work of Morrill ('10) on the maturation of the egg in various Hemiptera (including *Protenor* and *Anasa*); that of Boveri and Gulick ('09) and of Gulick ('11) on the nematode *Heterakis;* and that of Mulsow ('12) on the nematode *Ancyracanthus*, the last a particularly favorable object for study of the entire cycle of the chromosomes. In this form the chromosomes remain separate in the sperm, so that they may readily be counted and are visible even in life (Fig. 357). It was thus possible to establish the entrance into the egg of both classes of sperms; the formation from them of the male pronuclei, containing in one case five chromosomes, in the other six; the presence of six chromosomes in the egg-nucleus; and finally zygotes of two types, containing either 12 or 11 chromosomes (Fig. 358), the respective female and male diploid numbers. So far as its morphological aspects are concerned, therefore, the entire internal mechanism of sex-production in these animals has been clearly demonstrated.

b. Comparative. The simple XO–XX type has since been found in many animals of various groups, though in many individual cases the conditions in the female still remain a matter of inference. The chromosome-numbers in both sexes have been observed in Hemiptera, Odonata, Coleop-

[1] Wilson ('06), p. 28.

tera, Diptera, Orthoptera, sea-urchins, nematodes and mammals, and also in a considerable number of the parthenogenetic forms, such as the Hymenoptera, Hemiptera and rotifers.   The unpaired X-chromosome has

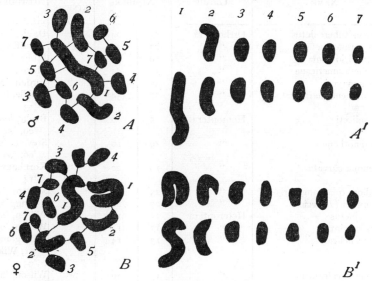

Fig. 356.—Sexual differences of the chromosomes in the hemipter *Protenor.*

A, male diploid group (spermatogonium) and *B,* female group (ovarian cell) with chomosomes numbered in the order of their size; in *A*[1] and *B*[1] the same chromosomes are arranged in pairs according to size.

also been found in the males of myriapods, and spiders; and it is hardly to be doubted that further search will reveal its presence in many other groups.   A partial list of the observed chromosome-numbers follows.[1]

SIMPLE XO–XX OR PROTENOR TYPE

NAME	GROUP	DIPLOID NUMBERS ♂	DIPLOID NUMBERS ♀	HETERO-KINESIS	AUTHORITY
Cerastipsocus venosus	Corrodentia	17	(18)	pr.	Boring, '13
Anax junius	Odonata	27	28	"	Lefevre and McGill, '08
Tettigidea parvipennis	Orthoptera	13	14	"	Robertson, '08, '15
Stenobothrus curtipennis	"	17	(18)	"	Davis, '08
Pamphagus marmoratus	"	19	20	"	Granata, '10
Gryllus domesticus	"	21	22	"	Baumgartner, '04, Gutherz, '07–'09 Meek, '13,

[1] In the fifth column, *pr.* and *po.* mean respectively *pre-heterokinesis* and *post-heterokinesis* (p. 755).

Simple XO–XX or Protenor Type—*Continued*

Name	Group	Diploid Numbers ♂	Diploid Numbers ♀	Hetero-kinesis	Authority
Hippiscus tuberculatus	Orthoptera	23	24	pr.	Davis, '08
Blatta germanica	"	23	24	"	Wassilieff, '07
Locusta viridissima	"	29	30	"	Mohr, '15
Periplaneta americana	"	33	34	"	Morse, '09
Aplopus mayeri	"	35	36	"	Jordan, '08
Diestrammena marmorata	"	57	(58)	"	Schellenberg, '13
Aphis saliceti	Homoptera	5	6	"	Baehr, '08, '09, '12
Aphis œnotheræ	"	9	10	"	Stevens, '05, '06, '09
Euchenopa curvata	"	19	20	"	Kornhauser, '14
Aprophora quadrangularis	"	23	24	"	Stevens, '06
Pœciloptera (2 species)	"	27	28	"	Boring, '07
Largus cinctus	Heteroptera	11	12	"	Wilson, '07
Largus succintus	"	13	14	"	Wilson, '07
Protenor belfragi	"	13	14	po.	Montgomery, '01, Wilson, '05
Archimerus calcaratus	"	15	16	pr.	Wilson, '05
Anasa tristis	"	21	22	po.	Wilson, '05
Pyrrochoris apterus	"	23	24	"	Henking, '90 Wilson, '09
Chariesterus antennator	"	25	26	"	Montgomery, '01, Wilson, '09
Necrophorus sayi	Coleoptera	13	(14)	pr.	Stevens, '09
Limoneus griseus	"	17	(18)	"	Stevens, '09
Photinus consanguineus	"	19	20	po.	Stevens, '09
Diabrotica vittata	"	19	20	"	Stevens, '09
Pachyulus varius	Myriapoda	25	(26)	pr.	Œttinger, '09
Scolopendra heros	"	33	(34)	"	Blackman, '03, '05, '10
Scutigera forceps	"	37	(38)	"	Medes, '05
Epeira scolopetaria	Arachnida	23	(24)	"	Berry, '06
Heterakis dispar	Nematoda	9	10	"	Gulick, '11
Strongylus paradoxus	"	11	12	"	Gulick, '11
Rhabditis nigrovenosa	"	11	12	po.	Boveri, '11
Ancyracanthus cysti	"	11	12	"	Mulsow, '11
Canis familiaris	Mammalia	21	22	pr.	Malone, '18
Felis catus	"	35	36	"	Winiwarter, '14
Equus caballus	"	37	(38)	"	Wodsedalek, '14
Homo sapiens (see XY-list, p. 766)	"	47	48	"	Winiwarter, '12
Mus norvegicus (albino)	"	37	(38)	"	Allen, '18

The size of the X-chromosomes varies widely in different species and shows no correlation with sex.   In some cases X is the largest of all the chromosomes and is thus readily distinguished by the eye, *e. g.*, in *Pyrrhocoris, Protenor* (Fig. 356) *Orphania, Catorintha, Leptophyes* (Fig. 355).   In *Anasa tristis* (Fig. 354) or in *Blaps lusitanica* (Fig. 378) it is one of the two largest pairs of chromosomes.   In many other cases (*Alydus, Largus, Anax*) it is one of the smaller chromosomes, not to be distinguished by the eye

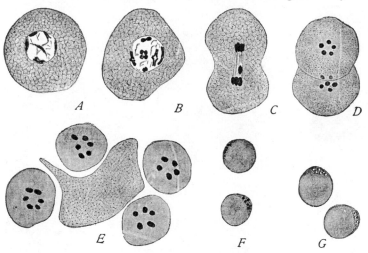

Fig. 357.—History of the *X*-chromosome in the spermatogenesis of the nematode *Ancyracanthus* (MULSOW).

A, spermatocyte in the growth-period; *C*, first spermatocyte-anaphase, with *X* passing to one pole; *D*, products of this division with 5 and 6 chromosomes; *E* (from a smear-preparation), the four spermatids of a quartet (with spermatophore in the center) two of the *X*-class (6 chromosomes) and two of the 1.0-*X* (5 chromosomes); *F*, sperms of the two classes; *G*, the same, from life.

except during the spermatocyte-divisions.   In others, again, X is the smallest of the chromosomes, *e. g.*, in *Philænus* (Boring, '13) or *Photinus* (Fig. 359). In still other cases it is closely linked with one of the other chromosomes and sometimes can only be distinguished under certain special conditions (*Ascaris megalocephala*, p. 779).

Pre-heterokinesis and Post-heterokinesis.   Precession and Succession.   In all the foregoing cases the X-chromosome shows essentially the same behavior in meiosis; it divides equationally in one division and in the second passes undivided to one pole so as to give two equal classes of sperm.   It is an important fact that the differential division or *heterokinesis* [1] (*i. e.*, that in which X passes undivided to one pole) may be either the first or second spermatocyte-division, two cases which for the sake of brevity may

[1] This term is due to Guthera '07.

be spoken of as *pre-heterokineses* and *post-heterokinesis* respectively.   In the Heteroptera post-heterokinesis is the rule; in the Homoptera, pre-heterokinesis, as is also the case in the Orthoptera; but nearly related forms, even species of the same genus, may differ in this respect (Wilson, '05, Gulick, '11).   The key to such variations seems to be offered in the beetle *Photinus*, in which the X-chromosome undergoes its equational division

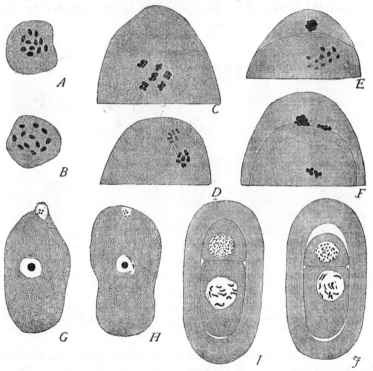

Fig. 358.—History of the X-chromosome in the oögenesis of the nematode *Ancyracanthus* (MUL-SOW).

A, male chromosome-group (spermatogonium), 11 chromosomes; *B*, female group (oögonium) 12 chromosomes; *C*, late prophase of first oöcyte-division, 6 tetrads; *D*, anaphase of same, 6 dyads, to each pole; *E*, second division anaphase, 6 single chromosomes to each pole; *F*, the two polocytes above, 5 chromosomes left in the egg; *G*, entrance of no-X sperm (5 chromosomes) into upper pole of egg; *H*, entrance of X-sperm (6 chromosomes); *H*, same, female (12 chromosomes); *I*, *J*, 2-cell stages, male and female.

with the others in the first mitosis, but very commonly lags more or less behind the others.   In *P. pennsylvanicus* (Fig. 359) the lagging is but slight, but in *P. consanguineus* is so marked that the two halves remain near together and separate from the other chromosomes after completion of the first division.   A slight further retardation of division would cause this chromosome, longitudinally split, to pass without separation of its two halves to one pole in the first division. This is borne out by the case of *Ascaris megalocephala* where, according to Edwards ('10), both conditions *exist in the same species*, the process being in some cases nearly like that in *Photinus*, while in others the two halves of X pass together into one daughter-cell (Fig. 359, H, I). We find here some ground to conclude that originally the differential division was the second.

A second fact, as yet unexplained, is that in the heterokinesis the X-chromosome in some cases precedes the others (*precession*) (Fig. 360); in

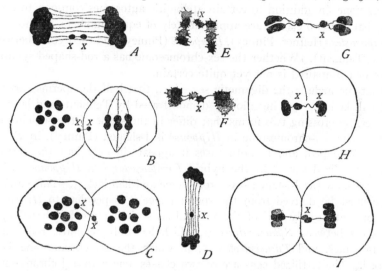

Fig. 359.—The lagging X-chromosome in insects and nematodes (*A–D*, from STEVENS, *G–I*, from EDWARDS).

A, first spermatocyte-anaphase in the beetle *Photinus consanguineus*, lagging division of X; *B*, pair of second spermatocytes of the same in metaphase, with lagging X's at one side; *C*, similar view with one X in the metaphase-group; *D*, second spermatocyte anaphase with lagging X; *E–G*, first spermatocyte-anaphases in *Ascaris megalocephala*, with lagging division of X; *H*, division of same, separating the two X's (leading to post-heterokinesis); *I*, division of same species leaving both X's in one cell (pre-heterokinesis).

other cases lags behind them (*succession*). The first case is the rule among the Orthoptera, the second case in *Hemiptera heteroptera* (an exception is offered by *Syromastes*); while both cases occur in Coleoptera and nematodes. When precession occurs in the first division the X-chromosome in some cases gives rise to a small separate nuclear vesicle in the interphase thus recalling its behavior in the spermatogonial divisions of the Orthoptera. Examples of this are offered by *Stenopelmatus* (Stevens, '05), and *Gryllus* (Gutherz, '07, Brunelli, '09) (Fig. 360).

The sex-chromosomes of sea-urchins are of interest because they were first observed in the early cleavage stages of the ovum without knowledge

of the meiotic phenomena; also because these animals were at first believed
to offer a case of female digamety (Baltzer, '09); but this later proved to be
an error.[1] The critical evidence was obtained from forms in which the
sex-chromosome is characterized by its atelomitic or non-terminal attachment, and has accordingly the shape of a V or U (*Toxopneustes, Parechinus
microtuberculatus*), or of a J (*Paracentrotus, Hipponoë, Moira*). All the
observers named, beginning with Baltzer, have found the segmenting
eggs to be of two kinds, some containing one such sex-chromosome and
others none, in addition to certain atelomitic autosomes common to both;
and that the two classes are approximately of equal numbers, as shown in
Toxopneustes (Heffner, Pinney), *Hipponoë* (Pinney) and the hybrid between
them (Tennent). Whether the sex-chromosome has a rod-shaped synaptic
mate or is unpaired is not yet quite certain.

That the male is the digametic sex—*i. e.*, that half the sperms carry X
and half lack it—was ingeniously demonstrated by Tennent, and later by
Baltzer, by crossing two forms that differ in the shape of the sex-chromosome. The sex-chromosome in *Hipponoë* is J-shaped (Pinney), in *Toxopneustes* V-shaped, and in both cases it appears in only half the straight
(pure) fertilized eggs. In the hybrid *Toxopneustes* ♀ x *Hipponoë* ♂ half
the eggs show the J-shaped sex-chromosome and half lack it. This chromosome must be derived from the sperm (since it is peculiar to *Hipponoë*)
and present in only half of them. Baltzer's similar proof is based upon
the cross between *Sphærechinus* ♀, which has only telomitic rod-shaped
chromosomes, and *Paracentrotus* ♂, in which the sex-chromosome is J-
shaped. The fertilized eggs are of two classes, one with a J-chromosome,
the other without it, thus confirming Tennent's result.

c. Special Peculiarities of the X-chromosome. In the earlier stages of
development, and in the division of the somatic cells generally, the X-
chromosome does not, so far as known, differ in behavior from the others,
nor do the two sexes differ in this respect.[2] In later stages, on the other
hand, the X-chromosome in the male germ-line shows certain special peculiarities of behavior [3] which sometimes appear in the spermatogonia and
are almost always present in the spermatocytes. In the female line these
differences do not exist, or are much less marked.

Heteropycnosis. The most characteristic of these peculiarities is that
during the growth-period of the spermatocytes the X-chromosome becomes
greatly condensed and often rounded in form, stains intensely with basic

[1] Heffner ('10) and Pinney ('11) on *Toxopneustes, Hipponöe, Moira;* Tennent ('11), and Baltzer
('13) on hybrids.
[2] See Morrill ('10), Hoy ('16).
[3] Hence the term *heterochromosomes* or *allosomes* applied by Montgomery ('04, '06) to the sex-
chromosomes and certain other specialized forms of chromosomes (p. 839).

dyes and thus appears as a karyosome or chromosome-nucleolus (Figs. 361, 266, 267, etc.) which shows the sharpest contrast to the thread-like or diffuse, and lightly staining ordinary chromosomes (autosomes or eu-chromosomes, p. 839). This process of *heteropycnosis* [1] was first observed by Henking ('91) in the hemipter *Pyrrhocoris* and found by later observers to be a widespread characteristic of the sex-chromosomes. It shows many variations in respect to the time at which it occurs, the extent to which it

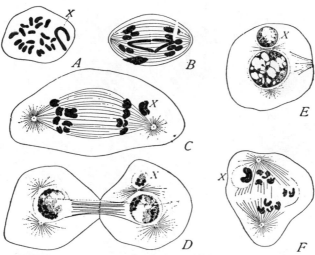

Fig. 360.—The X-chromosome in the cricket *Gryllus* (BRUNELLI).

A, spermatogonial metaphase, 21 chromosomes; *B*, anaphase in side-view lagging X; *C*, first spermatocyte-anaphase, precession of X; *D*, interkinesis, X a separate vesicle; *F*, prophase of second spermatocyte, X-class.

is carried, and the accompanying phenomena; and in a few cases it seems not to take place at any time. [2]

In the greater number of cases heteropycnosis first takes place after the final spermatogonial division (*e. g.*, in most Orthoptera, and in Hemiptera generally) but in a few cases it seems to occur also in the spermatogonia. In *Tryxalis*, according to Brunelli ('10) a "progressive heteropycnosis" takes place, X forming a separate reticulated vesicle in the early sperma-togonia but in the later divisions showing an increasing tendency to remain in a condensed state during the interkinesis (Fig. 362). [3] In Orthoptera most observers have found that the X-chromosome does not (as the other chromosomes do) break up in the telophases but retains its

---

[1] The term is due to Gutherz ('07).
[2] *E. g.*, in the spermatocytes of *Aphis saliceti*, Baehr ('12).
[3] *Cf.* Schellenburg ('13) on *Diestrammena*.

compact form though commonly still surrounded by a separate vesicle (Fig. 265).[1]

On the other hand, there seems to be no doubt that in some forms the final telophase is followed by a net-like stage or "resting-period" in which all the chromosomes are temporarily in a diffuse or reticulated condition. Examples of this are seen in certain of the Hemiptera and Coleoptera.[2] This condition is, however, of short duration, the X-chromosome very soon

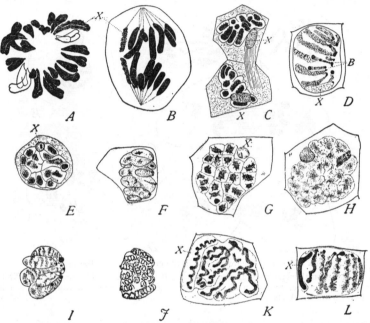

Fig. 361.—Spermatogonial nuclei, prophases and telophases in the grasshopper *Phrynotettix* (*A–D, G, H, K, L*, WENRICH; *E–F, I–L*, PINNEY).

In all the figures *X* designates the *X*-chromosome.

A, spermatogonial metaphase; *B*, side-view of anaphase; *C*, telophase, karyomeres; *D*, later telophase in side-view, chromosome-pair "*B*" and *X* distinguishable; *E*, cross-section of telophase; *F*, side-view, polar granules; *G*, later telophase; *H*, stage of greatest diffusion; *I–K*, spermatogonial prophases; *L*, early pre-synaptic nucleus.

reappearing in a condensed condition, though often more or less elongated (Figs. 266, 267, 361). In the latter case it takes part in the polarization, during the bouquet-stage showing the same orientation as the autosomes.[3] In *Locusta* Mohr has emphasized the fact that during the bouquet-stage the X-chromosome elongates and becomes thickened and sharply flexed

[1] This is well shown in the figures of Robertson ('08), Davis ('08), and Wenrich ('16).
[2] *Cf.* for Hemiptera Wilson ('12), for Coleoptera Nonidez ('12) on *Blaps*.
[3] Compare Moore and Robinson ('05), Buchner ('09), Mohr ('16), etc.

at the middle point, while the two ends, now tapering and pointed, are drawn close together. As a result of this process of "conflexion" it assumes a pear-shape with the narrow end directed towards the synaptic pole and longitudinally double. This cleft is not, however, a longitudinal split, as supposed by earlier observers, but the space between the two approximated limbs of the V. This space soon disappears while the body of the monosome again becomes vacuolated (as in the pre-synaptic stages) and finally assumes once more the form of a compact and open V, which splits lengthwise for the equation-division.

In some cases the chromosome-nucleolus may temporarily undergo a change analogous to the spireme-formation seen in the other chromosomes.

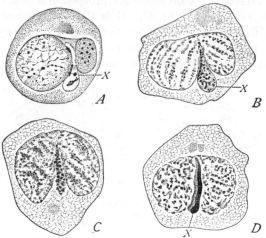

Fig. 362.—Progressive heteropynosis of the X-chromosome in the spermatogonia of the grasshopper *Tryxalis* (BRUNELLI).
    A, *B*, earlier spermatogonia, showing separate X-vesicle; *C*, later, and *D*, penultimate generatior of spermatogonia showing condensation of X.

This was first observed by McClung ('99, '00) in the locustid *Xiphidium*, where the X-chromosome, at first forming a flat, vacuolated plate lying against the nuclear membrane, is in the early prophases converted into a closely coiled spireme, which then uncoils, shortens, thickens and splits lengthwise, to form the rod-shaped accessory chromosome.[1] In the Hemiptera or Coleoptera the history of the chromosome-nucleolus appears to be simpler; but here, too, it is known in some cases to undergo during the diakinesis a process of elongation and loosening that seems to be comparable to that seen in Orthoptera.[2]

[1] See Mohr (*op. cit.*), also Davis ('08) and Wenrich ('16) in *Phrynotettix*.
[2] *E. g.*, in *Anasa* (Foot and Strobell, '07), or *Oncopeltus* (Wilson, '12).

Sooner or later in the course of these changes the X-chromosome becomes double, owing to a longitudinal split that represents the plane of the equation-division. This is often plainly in evidence in the first division, even when the X-chromosome fails to divide at this time, so that it passes to one pole as a longitudinally double body (commonly the case in Orthoptera). At this time it shows no special peculiarities to distinguish it from the other chromosomes, save for the rough contour seen in many Orthoptera (Fig. 361) and sometimes also in the fact that even when it divides in this mitosis it lags somewhat behind them in the division. It is an interesting fact that in some cases the position of the X-chromosome in the equatorial plate is constant, or nearly so. For example, in the coreid Hemiptera almost without exception the bivalents are grouped in a ring with one small bivalent at the center (Fig. 354, C), while the X-chromosome lies outside the ring; but this is characteristic of the first division only.

During the interphase between the two spermatocyte-divisions the X-chromosome commonly retains its compact form and again appears as a

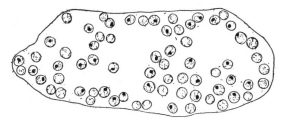

Fig. 363.—Group of spermatid-nuclei of the hemipter *Protenor*, showing 36 of the *X*-class (with chromosome-nucleolus) and 33 of the no *X*-class.

homogeneous, intensely staining chromosome-nucleolus. In the second mitosis it is again closely similar to the other chromosomes, but once more shows its distinctive quality after completion of the division by long retaining its compact and nucleolar-like form in the spermatids.[1] The latter, therefore, are for a considerable period visibly of two classes, equal in number, distinguished by the presence or the absence of the chromosome-nucleolus (Fig. 363).

An interesting feature of the chromosome-nucleolus is its almost invariable intimate relation with the plasmosome. Among many of the Hemiptera the chromosome-nucleolus is in its earlier stages accompanied by a plasmosome forming with it a typical amphinucleolus (p. 94); but in later stages the two commonly separate:[2] and the same has been re-

---

[1] This was described and figured by Henking in *Pyrrhocoris*, and has since been confirmed by many others.

[2] *Cf.* especially Montgomery, '01, '06; Wilson, '05, '06, '09, '12, etc.

corded in many other animals.   At a still earlier period (synaptic and pre-synaptic stages) the plasmosome is usually absent; but in regard to its mode of origin the only safe statement is that it seems in most cases to arise in close connection with the sex-chromosomes.   In the Orthoptera varying accounts of the phenomena have been given.   In *Decticus*, a locustid, Buchner ('09) described the plasmosome as arising by an actual division of the X-chromosome.   In *Blatta* Morse ('10) found the plasmosome as a small sphere, like a bead, attached to the spheroidal X-chromosome.   From a study of *Phrynotettix* Wenrich ('16) is led to suggest a derivation of the plasmosome from one or more of the "polar granules" found at one end of certain chromosomes (p. 910).   This whole subject is thus seen to be in need of further study and can hardly with advantage be followed out here.

The conditions in the female have as yet received comparatively little attention, mainly because of greater practical difficulties.   It has long been known that the germinal vesicle or oöcyte-nucleus often contains one or more intensely staining nucleoli, but only in a few cases is there evidence of any relation between them and the chromosome-nucleoli of the spermatocytes.   Observations on the early oöcytes of various Hemiptera (Wilson, '06), including the synaptic stages and early growth-period, failed to show anything like the chromosome-nucleoli that are so characteristic of these stages of the male; and the later studies of Foot and Strobell ('09), which extended the work to later stages of the germinal vesicle, yielded the same result, as did also those of Payne ('12) on *Gelastocoris*.   On the other hand, a few observers have found a chromosome-like body in the oöcyte-nucleus which they have more or less definitely identified as the X-chromosome-bivalent; though in no case has it actually been traced into either the oögonial or the meiotic divisions.[1]   Until this has been accomplished, judgment on this question will have to be reserved.

In addition to the foregoing the X-chromosome often shows other characteristics, especially in the spermatogonial chromosomes of Orthoptera.   The most important of them were first made known by Sutton ('00) in his studies on the "lubber" grasshopper (*Brachystola*) and with various minor modifications have since been observed in many species, though not all of them al-

---

[1] Among these cases may be mentioned the following.   In the homopter *Aprophora-quadrangularis*, Stevens ('06) describes one or two X-chromosome-nucleoli in the pre-synaptic and synaptic oöcyte-nuclei.   Gutherz ('07) likewise finds a "chromatin-nucleolus," closely similar to that of the male, in the oöcyte-nucleus of *Pyrrhocoris* (as did also Henking); while Buchner ('09) describes in the oöcytes of *Gryllus* a very large "accessory body" that participates in the polarization during the bouquet-stage, gives rise to a large, irregular nucleolus, and finally disintegrates.   There is, however, no reason whatever to identify this body with an X-bivalent, but rather the contrary.   In the cat Winiwarter ('09, '14), describes a chromosome-nucleolus in both sexes and concludes that it is univalent in the male, bivalent in the female.   There is no particular reason to doubt the correctness of this result; nevertheless, it should not be fully accepted until the direct proof is forthcoming.

ways coexist in the same species.[1] These are: (a) In many cases the rough contour of this chromosome, in contrast to the smooth outline of the others (Fig. 361); (b) its tendency, in some species very marked (*Orphania, Gryllus*, etc.) to lag behind the others in the divisions (Fig. 360); and especially (c) its relative independence of the other chromosomes in the spermatogonial interkinesis or resting-stages. In the latter the X-chromosome typically appears in the form of a separate vesicle, showing a reticulated structure often giving precisely the appearance of a small second nucleus lying beside the principal one (Figs. 361, 362).

In some respects this behavior is only an exaggeration of that shown by the other chromosomes; for in these divisions, as Sutton showed, all the karyomeres or chromosomal vesicles are very persistent and fuse but incompletely in the interkinesis or resting-stage (Fig. 361). Nevertheless, the contrast offered by the X-chromosomes is very marked, for the autosome-vesicles usually fuse more or less towards the poles, thus producing a glove-shaped lobed nucleus, while the X-vesicle remains wholly distinct. In structure also this vesicle differs markedly from the others, the X-chromosome breaking up into a finer reticulum than the others, and also lagging behind them in the ensuing transformation of the prophase, when the X-chromosome produces its own spireme, separate from the others, within its vesicle (Fig. 361), and somewhat later. The meaning of these phenomena, and of those earlier considered, is unknown; but they are of far-reaching general interest as demonstrating both the individuality of the X-chromosome and its physiological differences from the other chromosomes.[2]

2. The Simple XY–XX or Lygæus Type

The second type, now to be considered, includes a large number of cases, which almost certainly represent a more primitive condition from which the XO-XX or *Protenor* type has been derived, and is characterized by the presence in the male of a synaptic mate for the X-chromosome known as the Y-chromosome.[3] The sex-formulas thus become $XY = \male$ and $XX = \female$. Since

---

[1] See Sinéty ('01) on the phasmids, *Leptynia, Orphania;* Baumgartner ('04) and Brunelli ('08) on *Gryllus;* McClung ('02), Otte ('07), and Mohr ('14, '16) on Locustidæ; Davis ('08) on various Acrididæ; Robertson ('08) on *Syrbula;* Pinney ('08) and Wenrich ('16) on *Phrynotettix;* McClung ('14) on various Acrididæ; and others.

[2] *Cf.* pp. 839, 920.

[3] Wilson ('09). In earlier papers ('05, 06) this chromosome was called the "small idiochromosome" and X the large "idiochromosome," the terms Y- and X- chromosomes being later proposed ('09) in the interest of simplicity. Sex-chromosomes of this type had earlier been seen by Montgomery ('98, '01) in a number of the Hemiptera and described by him under the name of "chromatin-nucleoli" but without recognizing their relation to sex. The history of the X and Y chromosomes and their distribution to the sperm-nuclei was worked out, and possible relations to sex suggested by Wilson ('05) in the Hemiptera (*Lygæus, Cænus, Podisus, Euschistus*) and Stevens ('05) showed in the beetle *Tenebrio*, that the XY pair of the male is replaced in the female by an XX pair.

the autosomes are alike in both sexes the male diploid number of chromosomes thus becomes equal to that of the female; but the sexual differences are nevertheless often clearly visible since Y commonly differs from X in size, form and structure.   Sex-chromosomes of this type have been demonstrated in a large number of animals, including especially Hemiptera, Coleoptera, Diptera, Orthoptera, nematodes and vertebrates (man in-

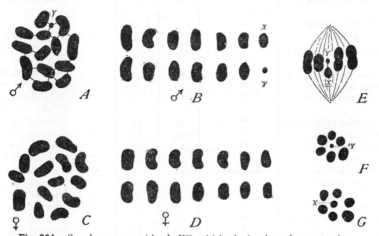

Fig. 364.—Sex-chromosomes (simple *XY*-pair) in the hemipter *Lygæus turcicus*.

A, male diploid group; *B*, the same grouped in pairs; *C*, female diploid group; *D*, the same, in pairs; *E*, second spermatocyte division; *F*, *G*, the resulting sister-groups in polar view one with *Y* (male-producing) and one with *X* (female-producing).

cluded); and they will no doubt be found in many other groups.   An illustrative list follows on page 766.[1]

The relation of this type to the foregoing one is clearly shown in Fig. 364.   It is here evident that the number of chromosomes is the same in both sexes and that all may be arranged in pairs (synaptic mates); but it is only in the female that all these pairs are symmetrical or homomorphic. In the male one pair is asymmetrical or heteromorphic, consisting of a larger member (X) and a smaller (Y).   Should Y become smaller and finally disappear a condition would be produced identical with that of the *Protenor* type. It is extremely probable that such has been the actual origin of the latter.

The phenomena of maturation in this type are precisely such as might be expected from the foregoing facts.[2]   In the male X and Y couple to form

[1] For *Hemiptera*, see Montgomery ('01, '06), Wilson ('05a, b, c, '06, '09b, '12), Payne ('09), Morrill ('10), Browne ('10, '13, '16), Kornhauser ('14); *Coleoptera*, Stevens ('05, '06); *Diptera*, Stevens ('08): Metz ('14, '16), Bridges ('16); *Orthoptera*, Randolph ('08), Stevens ('16), Voïnov ('14); *Nematodes*, Edwards ('11); vertebrates, Stevens ('11), Bachhuber ('16), Painter ('21, '22, '23).

[2] They have been fully and repeatedly worked out in the male, much less completely in the female; but no doubt concerning them in either sex can now exist.

THE SIMPLE XY–XX TYPE

NAME	GROUP	DIPLOID	HAPLOID	HETERO-KINESIS	AUTHORITY
Forficula auricularia	Orthoptera	24	12	pr.	Stevens, '10
Pentatoma senilis	Heteroptera	6	3	po.	Wilson, '13
Œbalus pugnax	"	10	5	"	Wilson, '09
Euschistus crassus	"	12	6	"	Foot and Strobell, '12
Euschistus variolarius ⎫ Cœnus delius ⎬ Nezara hilaris ⎭	"	14	7	"	Montgomery, '01, '06, Wilson, '05, etc.
Lygæus turcicus ⎭	"	14	7	"	Wilson, '05, etc.
Podisus spinosus	"	16	8	"	Wilson, '05, etc.
Oncopeltus fasciatus	"	16	8	"	Montgomery, '01, '06
Metapodius (3 species)	"	22	11	"	Wilson, '09
Notonecta irrorata	"	24	12	"	Browne, '10
Notonecta undulata	"	26	13	"	Browne, '10
Ranatra sp.	"	40	20	"	Chickering, '18
Oryctes nasicornis	Coleoptera	12	6	pr.	Prowazek, '02
Epilachna borealis	"	18	9	"	Stevens, '06
Tenebrio molitor	"	20	10	"	Stevens, '05, '06
Chelymorpha argus	"	22	11	"	Stevens, '06
Listotrophus ungulatus	"	26	13	"	Stevens, '09
Trirhabda canadense	"	30	15	"	Stevens, '06
Drosophila melanogaster	Diptera	8	4	"	Stevens, '08
Scatophaga pallida	"	12	6	"	Stevens, '08
Musca domestica	"	12	6	"	Stevens, '08
Paracentrotus (Strongy-locentrotus) lividus	Echinodermata	36	18		Baltzer, '13
Ascaris felis	Nematoda	(18)	9	"	Edwards, '12
Didelphys virginiana	Mammalia	22	11	"	Painter, '22, '23
Lepus	"	22	11	"	Bachhuber, '16
Cavia	"	56?	28	"	Stevens, '11
Rhesus macacus	Mammalia	48	24	"	Painter, '23
Cebus, sp.	"	54	27	"	Painter, '23
Homo sapiens [1]	"	48	24	"	Painter, '22

[1] The number of chromosomes in man has long been in dispute (more recently also the character of the sex-chromosomes). The recorded diploid numbers include 16, 22, 24, 32, 36, and 48; but most of these are now seen to have been erroneous because of a failure to overcome the technical difficulties. The most careful recent observations, those of Winiwarter ('14, '21) and Painter ('21, '22) leave little doubt that the correct number is 48. Winiwarter believed man to be of the XX–XO type the numbers being 48 and 47, and the more recent work of Oguma and Kihara ('22) confirms this for the male; but Painter's work seems to show clearly that a small Y-chromosome is present in the male and that the number is 48 in both sexes. This result was reached in the case of both the negro and the white man, thus disposing of the suggestion (Guyer, '14, Morgan, '14) that some of the earlier discrepancies might be due to racial differences of chromosome-number. It is of course possible that the Y-chromosome may be absent in some individuals (as in *Metapodius*). For a list of the recorded numbers see Painter ('22).

a heteromorphic bivalent, XY, which in the heterokinesis separates into its two components so that half the sperms receive X and half Y while all the remaining chromosomes (autosomes) are symmetrically distributed. In the female all the mature eggs alike receive a single X. Fertilization of any egg by the X-class of sperm will accordingly produce the female combination

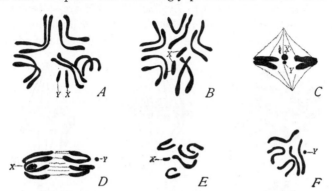

Fig. 365.—The XY-pair in the fly *Calliphora vomitoria* (STEVENS).

A, spermatogonial metaphase, 5 autosome-pairs and the XY-pair; B, corresponding view of oögonial metaphase, with XX-pair; C, first spermatocyte-division, with XY-bivalent; D, anaphase of same; E, metaphase group of X-class second spermatocyte, and F same of Y-class.

XX, by the Y-class of sperm the male combination XY, as will appear from the following formula:

Lygæus Type   Egg AX + Sperm AX = AAXX ($\female$)

Egg AX + Sperm AY = AAXY ($\male$)

Whereas in the first or

Protenor Type   Egg AX + Sperm AX = AAXX ($\female$)

Egg AX + Sperm AO = AAXO ($\male$)

Double proof is thus given that the sex of the zygote depends on the kind of sperm that enters the egg; for both X and Y tell the same story The Y-chromosome is strictly confined to the male line and can be derived only from the Y-class of sperm. On the other hand, in both sexes one X is derived from the egg, while the female zygote receives its second X from the X-class of sperm.

In all certainly known cases the Y-element is a single chromosome which shows no tendency to break up into separate components such as often appears in the case of the X-element (pp. 772, 778).[1] In the most frequent case Y is distinctly smaller than X, sometimes so small as to appear almost

[1] In the remarkable case of the homopter *Pseudococcus* the facts strongly suggest that the male has a Y-element consisting of five components (p. 778). In *Rumex acetosa* the Y-chromosome (so-called) seems to be double (p. 814).

like a vestigial structure. This condition, observed in a number of *Coleoptera* and *Diptera* (Figs. 365, 366), is connected by all intergradations with one in which X and Y are very nearly or quite equal and can be distinguished by the eye only with difficulty or not at all. All these conditions have been observed in the *Hemiptera heteroptera* (Fig. 368). Finally, in *Oncopeltus fasciatus* (a form nearly related to *Lygæus*) X and Y are so nearly equal as often to be indistinguishable by the eye (Fig. 369). Throughout this series, however, the identification of the XY-pair is made certain not alone by

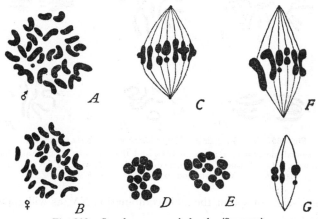

Fig. 366.—Sex-chromosomes in beetles (STEVENS).

A, spermatogonial and *B*, ovarian diploid groups, *Trirhabda virgata*; *C*, first spermatocyte-division; *D*, X-class and *E*, Y-class of second spermatocytes of same; *F*, first spermatocyte of *Chrysochus amatus*; *G*, same of *Photinus*.

the size-relations but by characteristics of behavior in the growth-period and the meiotic divisions, and in the latter also of position.[1]

The extremely small size of Y in some cases, and the additional fact that even nearly related species (such as *Nezara viridula* and *hilaris*) may differ so markedly in the relative size of Y, shows how readily the size-relations may change, and how the total disappearance of Y would leave the X-chromosome without a mate (p. 765). On the other hand, those cases in which Y is as large as X (as in *Oncopeltus*) suggest that an XY-pair (or its representative) may be present in many species which seem to show no differentiated sex-chromosomes.[2]

Most commonly the Y-chromosome (like X) has a terminal attachment

---

[1] In the second division of *Heteroptera* the XY-pair always occupies the center of the group; *cf.* Fig. 369. See Wilson ('05, '06, etc.).

[2] In the hemipteron *Acholla multispinosa* (Payne '10), Y appears to be considerably larger than X (p. 775), and in *Drosophila melanogaster* (Bridges, '13, '16), slightly larger; but these are very exceptional.

to the spindle-fibers; but a few exceptions are known. In the fruit-fly *Drosophila melanogaster* Bridges ('16, etc.) found Y to have a subterminal attachment while X has a terminal one (Fig. 415); and this difference proved to be of great practical importance in analyzing the cytological aspects of non-disjunction (p. 877). In the mantids *Tenodera* and *Paratenodera*, according to Oguma ('21) Y likewise seems to have a sub-terminal attachment, at least in many cases, while in case of the X-chromosomes it is median (Fig. 373).

In the greater number of observed cases X and Y are disjoined in the first or heterotypic division (typically thus in the nematodes, beetles, flies reptiles and mammals) each dividing equationally in the homeotypic division. Such cases offer a spectacular demonstration of pre-reduction for this par-

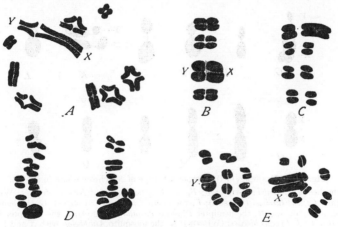

Fig. 367.—Sex-chromosomes in *Ascaris felis* (EDWARDS).

A, prophase of first spermatocyte, showing *XY*-tetrad; *B*, metaphase; *C–E*, anaphases.

ticular chromosome-pair, which in this respect evidently correspond precisely to the pre-heterokinetic forms of the *Protenor* type (such as the Orthoptera), save that in the latter Y is absent. In the Hemiptera heteroptera, on the other hand, the reverse or post-reductional order is almost always followed, the first division being an equational one.[1] No doubt of the facts can here exist because of the remarkable fact that X and Y, though often united during the growth-period, typically separate again during the diakinesis and divide separately as univalents in the heterotypic division lying side-by-side but not in contact (Fig. 369). In the final anaphases of this division they conjugate to form a typical XY-pair that undergoes disjunction in the second division.

[1] Wilson,'05, '06, etc.

During the growth period of the spermatocytes both the X and the Y-chromosomes typically undergo heteropycnosis, assuming a condensed and rounded condition, so as to form chromosome-nucleoli.[1] In most cases (nematodes, Coleoptera, mammals, etc.) they are united to form a single bivalent body, which in the prophases becomes quadripartite to form a tetrad and owing to the smaller size of the Y-component, is commonly asymmetrical (Fig. 367). In Hemiptera, on the other hand, X and Y often

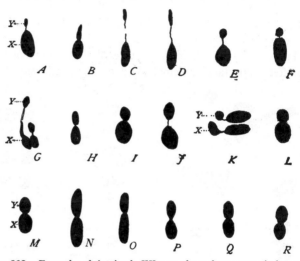

Fig. 368.—Examples of the simple XY-type of sex-chromosome in insects.

A, in the beetle *Trirhabda* (STEVENS); *B, C, D*, the hemipter *Nezara viridula* (WILSON); *E*, the hemipter *Lygæus turcicus* (WILSON); *F*, the beetle *Chrysocus* (STEVENS); *G*, the hemipter *Notonecta indica* (BROWNE); *H*, the hemipter *Thyanta custator* (WILSON); *I*, the hemipter *Euschistus fissilis* (WILSON); *J*, *Lygæus bicrucis* (WILSON); *K*, the mosquito *Anopheles*, with *X* and *Y* linked to one autosome-pair (STEVENS); *L* to *R*, various Hemiptera; *M*, *Mineus*; *N, O, Nezara hilaris; P, Q, R, Oncopeltus fasciatus* (WILSON).

remain separate during the whole growth period, or if united separate before the heterotypic division. This is very clearly seen in *Oncopeltus* (Fig. 266), where the entire history of these bodies may readily be traced (Wilson, '12).

Considerable difference exists (as in case of the unpaired X) in respect to the rate and degree of condensation of X and Y. In many cases the X-chromosome, rarely also the Y, has at first the form of an elongated

---

[1] An exception occurs in the homopter *Euchenopa* (p. 771). Considerable discussion has arisen concerning the chromatin-nucleolus in mammalian spermatocytes. Gutherz ('22) after a careful study of the phenomena in the white mouse, concluded that this body is not a pair of sex-chromosomes. Painter, however ('23), in a still more extended study of the facts in the opposum, has produced apparently demonstrative evidence that here at least the body is in fact a chromosome-nucleolus (XY pair). It forms in this case an irregular knotted ring which resolves into an X-chromosome and a bipartite Y.

rod, in some cases already in the presynaptic stage (Figs. 266, 267). In *Euschistus* (Montgomery, '98) or *Lygeus turcicus* (Wilson, '05) the rods condense completely to a spheroidal form; in *Lygæus bicrucis* (Wilson, '12), both X and Y shorten considerably, but still retain a rod-shape and are often plainly split lengthwise; in *Euchenopa bicurvata* (Kornhauser, '14) an elongate rod-shape is retained throughout the growth-period, by both X or Y which only assume a rounded form in the diakinesis. In this case, which is almost unique, X is always characterized by a denser consistency

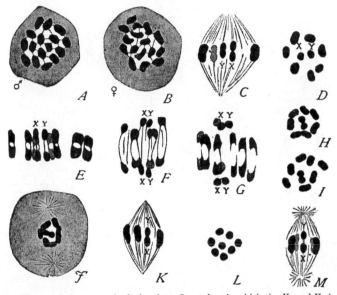

Fig. 369.—The sex-chromosomes in the hemipter *Oncopeltus*, in which the *X*- and *Y*-chromosomes are equal or nearly so.

A, male diploid group (spermatogonial); *B*, female diploid group (ovary), each with 16 chromosomes (*X* and *Y* indistinguishable); *C*, first spermatocyte-metaphase in side-view; *D*, in polar view; *E–H*, anaphases of this division, conjugation of *X* and *Y*; *H*, *I*, sister-groups from the same spindle, *XY*-bivalent near center; *J*, interkinesis; *K*, second spermatocyte in side-view, *L* in polar view; *M*, disjunction of *X* and *Y*.

and deeper staining-capacity, while Y remains more diffuse, in a condition like that of the autosomes.

The relations of the XY-pair to the plasmosome are similar to those seen in case of the unpaired X. When X and Y are united the plasmosome is in contact with the pair; when they are separate the plasmosome is almost always associated with X, to which it may in some cases be seen attached even when the latter has a rod-shape. The plasmosome rapidly increases in size until it is often larger than the chromosome-nucleolus and then as a rule separates from it. In the later prophases it quickly disappears, in some cases undergoing fragmentation.

3. Compound Types. The X-Complex

Under a third type we may place those more complicated cases in which X is represented, not by one chromosome but by a group which during spermatogenesis act together as a compound X-element. The number of X-components, as thus far observed, varies from two (*Syromastes, Fitchia*) to

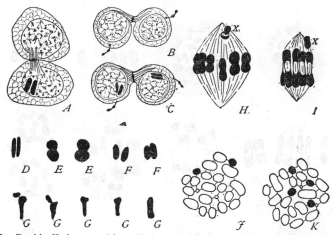

Fig. 370.—Double *X*-element without *Y*, in various species. (*A–D*, from WALLACE; *E*, from WILSON; *F*, *G*, from MORGAN; *H-K* from WILSON.)

A, first spermatocyte-telophase, in the spider *Agalena* with double *X*; *B*, *C*, second spermatocyte-telophases, showing *X* and no-*X* classes; *D*, *X*-chromosome of same; *E*, double *X*-element of the hemipter *Syromastes*; *F*, same of *Phylloxera fallax*; *G–G*, various forms of same in *Phylloxera caryæcaulis*; *H*, *I*, first spermatocyte-metaphase and anaphase in *Syromastes*, precession of *X*-element; *J*, *K*, female and male diploid groups of same, *X*-components black.

eight (*Ascaris incurva*). Whatever be their number, the X-group is single in the male, double in the female; so that these cases, too, conform to the formulas XX = ♀ and X = ♂. In the compound types, likewise, the X-complex of the male may or may not be accompanied by a Y-chromosome; but this is always a simple element. The compound sex-chromosomes, like the simple ones, are thus of two types which correspond, respectively, to the XY–XX or *Lygæus* type and the XO–XX or *Protenor* type. The first such case to be worked out was discovered in the "toad-bug" *Gelastocoris* (*Galgulus*) *oculatus* (Payne, '08) where X consists of four components (Figs. 372, 374). Other cases have since been found in other Hemiptera, in one or two Orthoptera (*Gryllotalpa, Mantis*), in some nematodes (*Ascaris*) and have been described in mammals. Without describing these cases in detail, some of them are given in the two following lists:

XO–XX Compound Types (Y absent)

Name	Group	No. of X-com-ponents	X Sperm	No X Sperm	Diploid No. ♂	Diploid No. ♀	Author-ity
Lepisma domestica	Thysanura	2	18	16	34	(36)	Charlton, '21
Syromastes marginatus	Heteroptera	2	12	10	22	24	Gross, '04, Wilson, '09 a, b
Phylloxera fallax	Homoptera	2	6	4	10	12	Morgan, '08, '12
Phylloxera caryæcaulis	"	2	3(4)	2	5(6)	6(8)	Morgan, '08, '12
Agalena nævia	Araneida	2	27 ±	25 ±	52 ±		Wallace, '05, '09
Anolis carolinensis	Lacertilia	2	18 ±	16 ±	34 ±	(36 ±)	Painter, '21
Sceloporus spinosus	"	2	12	10	22	24	Painter, '21
Ascaris lumbricoides	Nematoda	5	24	19	43	48	Edwards, '10
A. canis	"	6	18	12	30	36	Walton, '16
A. megaloceph-ala [1] univalens	"	(9 ±)	36 ±	27 ±	63 ±	72 ±	Kautzsch, '13
A. megaloceph-ala [2] univalens	"	(8 ±)	30 ±	22 ±	52 ±	60 ±	Geinitz, '15

In all these cases the X-components behave in the diploid divisions as independent chromosomes, scattered at random among the autosomes. In the synapsis of the male they come together in a coherent group, which as a whole splits lengthwise for the equation-division and in the hetero-kinesis passes undivided to one pole (Fig. 375).

Phylloxera caryæcaulis forms a partial exception only in the fact that the two components of X are often indistinguishably fused at every stage in the male and almost always thus fused in the female.[3] Another point of great interest is that the *X-components are constant not only in number but also in size.* In *Syromastes* the two components are always distinctly un-equal, in *Phylloxera caryæcaulis* still more unequal; in *P. fallax* and in *Agalena* they are equal (Fig. 370). In *Ascaris megalocephala* or *canis* the components are equal; in *A. lumbricoides* four of the components of the

---

[1] These numbers represent the components of the original chromosomes linked to form larger chromosomes which are maintained intact as such in the germ-line but break up into much smaller and more numerous bodies in all the somatic divisions. See pp. 323, 879.

[2] Several additional cases of a double X-element have been reported, *e. g.*, in the domestic fowl, Guyer ('09, '16), the pig Wodsedalek ('13) and man Guyer ('10), but all these are doubtful and the last certainly erroneous.

[3] *Cf.* Morgan ('09, '12, '15).

pentad group are small and one large (Fig. 371). The same fact will be still more strikingly shown in some of the cases next to be considered.

Even more remarkable conditions are found among those more numerous cases in which the compound X-element is opposed by a single Y-chromosome which acts as its synaptic mate in the maturation-processes of the male. The more extreme cases of this, such as *Acholla multispinosa* or *Ascaris incurva*, offer a most bizarre appearance in the spermatocyte-divisions, particularly in case of the heterokinesis; but they are perfectly in

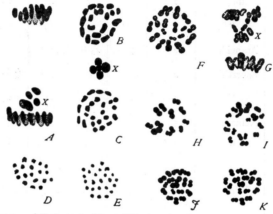

Fig. 371.—Compound *X*-element without *Y* in *Ascaris*. (*A–E, Ascaris lumbricoides,* EDWARDS; *F–K, A. canis,* WALTON).

A, first spermatocyte, anaphase; *B, C,* sister groups from same in polar view, showing the pentad *X*-element between them; *D, E,* the two resulting types of second spermatocyte-groups, one with 19 chromosomes the other with 24; *F,* first spermatocyte-metaphase, of *A. canis,* 18 chromosomes, hexad *X*-group in center; *G,* anaphase of same; *H, I,* sister second spermatocyte-groups, showing two types, one with 12 chromosomes, the other with 18; *J, K,* corresponding sister-groups from second *oöcyte*-division, each with 18 chromosomes.[1]

line with the simple XY-type. A list of the more important known cases follows on page 775.

In all these cases, as in the compound X–XX type, the X-components behave as separate chromosomes in the somatic divisions, only coming together in a coherent group during the maturation-process. It will be observed that in every case the female diploid number exceeds the male by the number of the X-components less one, because in this case the male number is increased by one owing to the presence of Y; in *Gelastocoris,* for example, the female number is $35 + 4 - 1 = 38$; in *Ascaris incurva* it is $35 + 8 - 1 = 42$.

These cases offer remarkable examples of characteristic and constant

---

[1] In this species all the chromosomes appear double, owing to the presence of a median transverse suture: as in copepods, etc. (see p. 904).

XX–XY Compound Types (Y Present)

Name	Group	No. of X-com-ponents	X = Sperm	Y = Sperm	♂ Diploid	♀ Diploid	Authority
Fitchia spinulosa	Heteroptera	2	14	13	27	28	Payne, '09
Rocconota annuli-cornis	"	2	14	13	27	(28)	Payne, '09
Conorhinus san-quisugus	"	2	12	11	23	(24)	Payne, '09
Thyanta calceata	"	2	14	13	27	28	Wilson, '11
Tenodera (Mantis) superstitiosa	Orthoptera	2	14	13	27	28	Oguma, '21
Paratenodera (Mantis) aridifolia	"	2	14	13	27	28	Oguma, '21
Prionidus cristatus	Heteroptera	3	14	12	26	28	Payne, '09
Sinea diadema	"	3	15	13	28	30	Payne, '09
Pselliodes cinctus	"	3	15	13	28	30	Payne, '12
Pnirontis modesta	"	4	14	11	25	(28)	Payne, '12
Gelastocoris oculatus	"	4	19	16	35	38	Payne, '08, '09
Acholla multispinosa	"	5	15	11	26	30	Payne, '10
Sinea rileyi	"	5	17	13	(30)	(34)	Payne, '12
Pseudococcus nipæ [1] and 2 other species	Homoptera	5	5	5	10	10	Schrader, '21, '23
Ascaris incurva	Nematoda	8	21	14	35	42	Goodrich, '16

differences both in number and in size-relations of the X-components in different species, as may be seen in the series displayed in Fig. 372, differences often seen between even nearly related forms. In the pentatomid genus *Thyanta*, for example, the two species *custator* and *calceata* are so closely similar as to have puzzled some of the best systematists, yet in *custator* X is always a single chromosome, in *calceata* always a double element,[2] while the total diploid numbers of the two species are also widely different (see Table). In the reduvioid genus *Sinea diadema* and four other species X consists of three components; in *S rileyi* of five.[3] In *Acholla*, a related genus, the X-complex consists in *A. ampliata*, of three small, equal components, in *A. multispinosa* of five, of which three are small and equal and two very large,[4] the whole group opposed by a very large Y-chromosome. The chromosomal differences between the sexes in this species are perhaps the most remarkable known, since the Y-chromosome is the largest of all the

[1] The interpretation of this form, involving the assumption of 5 Y-components, is still somewhat hypothetical (p. 777).
[2] Wilson ('11), Barber ('11).
[3] Payne ('12).
[4] Payne ('09, '10).

chromosomes and appears only in the male, while of the X-components the male has three small and two large and the female six and four (Fig. 375).[1]

A climax is reached in the nematode genus *Ascaris*. At one extreme is *A. felis* which has a simple XY-pair much like that of many insects.[2] At the other extreme is *A. incurva* with an X-complex of no less than eight components opposed by a single Y, one of the X-components being a very small microchromosome, and one a rather long wedge-shaped chromosome with which the Y-chromosome (here of moderate size)

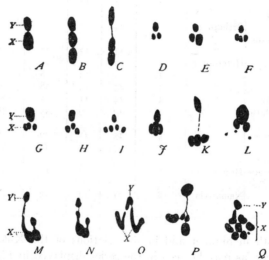

Fig. 372.—Various forms of the compound *XY*-pair. *A* to *N* are from Hemiptera; *O*, from a mantid orthopteran; *P* from a beetle; *Q* from a nematode (*A–C* from WILSON; *D–L* from PAYNE; *M–N* from BROWNE; *O* from OGUMA; *P* from NONIDEZ; *Q* from GOODRICH).

A, Thyanta custator; B, C, Thyanta calceata; D, Fitchia; E, Conorhinus; F, Sinea; G, Pselliodes; H, Prionidus; I, Sinea rilei; J, K, Gelastocoris; L, Acholla multispinosa; M, N, Notonecta indica; O, Tenodera superstitiosa; P, the sex-complex in *Blaps lusitanica,* probably a quadruple *X*-element opposed by a single *Y; Q, Ascaris incurva.*

is always coupled (Fig. 376).[3] In *A. megalocephala* there are eight or nine components closely linked in the germ-cells but separate in the somatic divisions (p. 781).[4] Intermediate between these conditions are *A. canis* with its six components[5] and *A. lumbricoides* with five[6] in each case without a Y: and we may look for the discovery of other species in which X consists of fewer components. In certain nematodes of other genera, such as *Heterakis dispar*[7] or *Ancyracanthus cystidicola*[8] X is a simple chromosome without a Y.

[1] See also *Pselloides*, Fig. 374.
[2] Edwards, '10.
[3] Goodrich ('14, '16).
[4] See Geinitz, ('15) and Kautzsch ('12).
[5] Walton ('16, '18).
[6] Edwards ('10).
[7] Gulick ('11).
[8] Mulsow ('12).

Such facts clearly indicate the conclusion, supported by many other facts, that the X-element is in general a compound and definitely organized but also highly plastic body, consisting of many components that may be closely associated in a single body or may readily appear in the form of separate chromosomes which in meiosis become associated to form a unit-complex. We find here strong ground for the conclusion that other forms of chromosomes are likewise compound bodies, a result supported by numerous additional facts (pp. 903, 906). The conclusion is also indicated that the sex-determining component or "X-chromatin" may form but a small, perhaps a very small, part of the X-element, the remainder of the

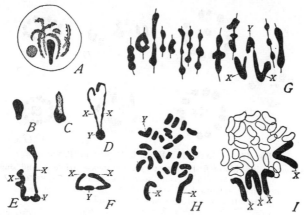

Fig. 373.—Sex-chromosomes in the mantid *Tenodera superstitiosa* (OGUMA).

A, diplotene, with *XY*-chromosome-nucleolus; *B–D*, formation of the *XY*-complex from the chromosome-nucleolus; *E*, *F*, later stages of same; *G*, the chromosomes of the heterotypic division, arranged in serial order; *H*, spermatogonial metaphase; *I*, female diploid group (follicle-cell).

complex consisting of chromatin which has nothing to do with sex as such but may form the basis of sex-linked characters.[1]

It is interesting to compare the foregoing cases with such a one as that of the hemipteran *Notonecta indica*.[2] Here X is in the spermatogonia a single chromosome (the largest of the group), which shows no visible sign of compound structure, but in the later prophases and during the divisions very clearly shows such a structure, consisting of one large and five small components or chromomeres, which remain more or less distinct until the anaphases of the second division (Fig. 426). A slight increase of independence on the part of these components would convert them into separate chromosomes, forming an X-complex consisting of six components (as in *Ascaris canis*) opposed by a single Y.[3]

[1] *Cf.* Wilson ('11). See p. 903.   [2] Browne ('16).
[4] A remarkable case described by Schrader ('21, '23) occurs in certain of the coccids (*Pseudococcus*).

The history of the compound forms in the growth-period has been but partially cleared up; but so far as it has been examined the facts indicate that here, too, the sex-chromosomes undergo a process of condensation or heteropycnosis quite comparable to that seen in the simple types. In some of these cases the X-components unite to form a single spheroidal chromosome-nucleolus accompanied by a plasmosome which later disappears. In others all the components of the XY-complex remain separate, but are imbedded in a large plasmosome.[1]

Peculiar conditions, not yet fully understood, but interesting for the study of the sex-chromosomes, are found in the mantid Orthoptera *Tenodera*

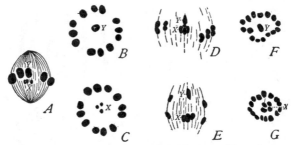

Fig. 374.—Compound *XY*-pair in Hemiptera (PAYNE).

A, Pselloides cinctus, side-view of first spermatocyte-metaphase, triple *X* and single *Y; B*, the *Y*-class and *C* the *X*-class, of resulting second spermatocyte-metaphase-groups; *D, Gelastocoris*, first spermatocyte-metaphase, quadruple *X* and single *Y; E*, anaphase of same; *F*, the *Y*-class, and *G* the *X*-class, of resulting second spermatocyte-metaphases.

and *Paratenodera* (Oguma, '21) and the beetle *Blaps* (Nonidez, '20). In the mantids X consists of two components which early in the growth-period unite with Y to form an apparently single compact chromosome-nucleolus. Later the X-components again become extended to form long threads while the Y-component (assuming its correct identification) remains condensed until it enters the metaphase (Fig. 373). *Blaps lusitanica* shows an X-complex somewhat similar to this but consisting of five components, two small and three large, the latter at once recognizable in

The diploid number in both sexes is here 10, while the X-element seems to be composed of five components. In the male these five remain in a compact group during the spermatocyte growth-period, divide equationally in the first division, and in the second pass together to one pole while the remaining five ("autosomes") pass to the other. In the female all the chromosomes, so far as observed, behave alike, and form five ordinary tetrads. The conclusion seems to be indicated that all the 10-chromosomes of the female here represent X-components while in the male only five such are present. This may mean, as Schrader suggests, that all the chromosomes of the female carry sex-chromatin (X-chromatin). In this case the five autosomes of the male must be confined to that sex and in this respect are analogous to a compound Y-element. It seems possible, however, that only one of the X-components carries X-chromatin, and that only one of the five "autosomes" is comparable to a Y. (*Cf.* the case of *Trialeurodes*, p. 704).

[1] *E. g.*, in *Fitchia spinulosa, Roconota annulicornis, Sinea diadema, Prionidus cristatus*, and one or two others.

the diploid groups by their large size and non-terminal attachments (Fig. 378, from Nonidez, '20). In the heterotypic division these form a pentad element, of which one large component passes to one pole, while two large and two small pass to the opposite one. Though the interpretation of this is uncertain (since the female groups are not known) it is a plausible

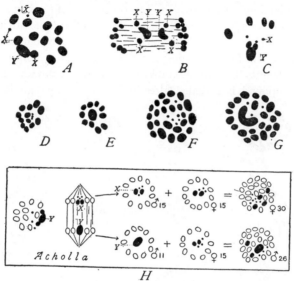

Fig. 375.—The compound XY-pair of sex-chromosomes in the hemipter *Acholla multispinosa* (Payne).

A, first spermatocyte-metaphase, large Y coupled with two large X-components; *B*, anaphase of same division, with lagging Y and 2 X's; *C*, metaphase-figure, showing compound XY-pair; *D, E*, anaphase-groups, the former of the X-class, the latter of the Y; *F*, female diploid group (30 chromosomes, 10 X's); *G*, corresponding male group (26 chromosomes, Y and 5 X's); *H*, diagram showing the general relations of the chromosomes in this species.

assumption that this complex represents a quadripartite X-element (two large and two small components) coupled with a single large Y.[1]

4. Linkage of Sex-chromosomes with Autosomes

The subject of chromosome-linkage in general belongs to a later stage of our discussion (Chap. XI) but must here be considered in relation to the sex-chromosomes. In a considerable number of species the X-chromosome has been found closely linked or united to one end of one of the autosomes, remaining constantly in association with it during the whole chromosome-cycle, including both mitosis and meiosis and no doubt also fertilization. Such a case was first observed by Sinéty ('01) in the orthopteran (phasmid)

[1] Nonidez himself identifies only one of the large components as an X-chromosome considering it to be associated with a large pair (MM) and with two small chromosomes.

genera *Leptynia* and *Dixippus*, where the X-chromosome is coupled with one of the bivalents in the meiotic divisions to form an L-shaped trivalent element. Similar relations were discovered by McClung in *Anabrus*, *Hesperotettix* and *Mermiria* ('05, '17). In all these cases the X-linkage appears to be constant for the individual, being already in evidence in the spermatogonial divisions, where X is linked with one of the larger rod-shaped autosomes to form a V or L attached to the spindle at the angle where the two limbs join (Fig. 377). In synapsis the autosome-component couples with its mate to form an unsymmetrical or heteromorphic trivalent, which splits lengthwise (equation-division) to form a hexad. The identity of the X-compound is revealed already in the spermatogonia by its less

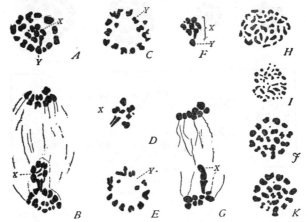

Fig. 376.—The compound *XY*-pair in the nematode *Ascaris incurva* (Goodrich).

A, first spermatocyte-metaphase, 21 chromosomes with octopartite *X* in center and *Y* at margin; *B*, anaphase of same in side-view; *C, D, E*, sister-groups, in polar view, with *X*-complex between them; *F*, the *XY*-pair; *G*, anaphase in side-view; *H*, spermatogonial metaphase, 35 chromosomes; *I*, oögonial division, 40 chromosomes (expected number 42); *J, K*, sister-groups, first oöcyte-metaphase, 21 dyads each.

regular outline and lighter staining-capacity (*Mermiria*) and later, in the spermatocyte, by its more condensed condition while the autosome-compound is diffuse (Fig. 377, F, G). In the first division the hexad divides transversely, so as to separate the two autosome-compounds, which pass to opposite poles with the X-element attached to one of them.

Whether the X-linkage in these cases is permanent, so as to be continued from one generation to another, is not yet certainly known; but there is reason to suspect that such is the case. McClung ('17) found that X is always linked with the same autosome in a given individual but in other individuals may be otherwise linked or may be free. Most often it is joined to the largest of the 11 bivalents, but often also to the fourth or to the fifth largest;

in *Hesperotettix viridis* four individuals out of 37 were found in which X is entirely free, behaving as an ordinary accessory chromosome. Nevertheless it seems probable that when once established the particular mode of linkage may persist from one generation to another as Carothers ('21) has proved to be the case with different modes of spindle-attachment (p. 934).

Certain other cases of this type are of especial interest as examples of linkage so intimate that we are in doubt as to whether it should properly receive this name. In *Culex* (Stevens, '10), the presence of sex-chromosomes

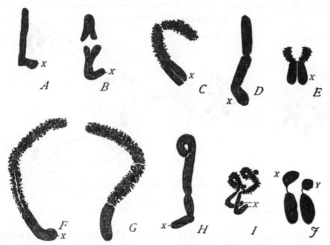

Fig. 377.—Linkage of sex-chromosomes with autosomes. (*A, B*, from SINÉTY, *C–I*, McCLUNG, *J*, STEVENS.)

In all the figure *X* is the *X*-chromosome linked to an autosome.

A, first spermatocyte-division of the phasmid *Leptynia; B*, the same in the phasmid *Dixippus; C–E*, the grasshopper *Hesperotettix, C* in prophase, *D*, metaphase, *E* in the interkinesis; *F–I*, corresponding stages in *Mermiria; J*, from the mosquito *Anopheles*, spermatogonial chromosomes, linkage of both *X* and *Y*.

would not ordinarily be suspected from either the meiotic or the spermatogonial divisions.[1] In a few cases, however, one of the spermatogonial chromosome-pairs was found to be slightly heteromorphic, each consisting of two unequal components, the larger ones equal, the smaller unequal, and the latter are conjectured by Stevens to be the equivalent of an XY-pair intimately coupled with one of the autosome-pairs. Another interesting case is that of the classical object *Ascaris megalocephala*, in which the X-element is usually intimately united to one of the autosomes though in some individuals it appears in the form of a small extra chromosome. In

[1] The later observations of Whiting ('17) are inconclusive on this point.

this case it shows in every respect the behavior of an X-chromosome.[1] In the female the two X-chromosomes in some cases form a bivalent which appears in the form of a typical tetrad and undergoes the usual distribution so that each mature egg receives one X (Frolowa, Geinitz). As will later be shown, the X-chromosome in all these cases is itself a multiple, though this fact is not apparent during the meiotic divisions (see p. 879).[2]

These various cases, together with that of *Blaps* (p. 779), show how difficult it may be to distinguish between a secondary linkage of chromosomes

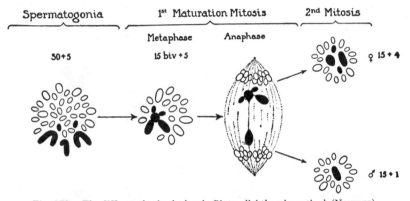

Spermatogonia   1ˢᵗ Maturation Mitosis   2ⁿᵈ Mitosis

Metaphase   Anaphase

30+5   15 biv +5   ♀ 15 + 4

♂ 15 + 1

Fig. 378.—The *XY*-complex in the beetle *Blaps*, slightly schematized (NONIDEZ).
It consists of five components (in black) of which four pass to one pole and one to the other. The simplest interpretation is that it consists of a single *Y* and a quadripartite *X*.

and a primary association; and also indicate the comparative unimportance of the question from a physiological standpoint. It seems to be immaterial, so far as sex-production is concerned, whether the X-material appears in the form of a single separate and readily recognizable chromosome; or as one temporarily or permanently linked to another chromosome; or finally as an indistinguishable component of a chromosome which outwardly seems not to differ from others. Morphologically, however, the questions here raised are of great interest in their bearing on the organization of chromosomes generally and the evolution of the sex-chromosomes (pp. 822, 823).

5. Sexual Dimegaly of the Sperms

In most cases the X- and Y- (or no-X) classes of sperm, when fully matured, do not show any differences that are visible to the eye. Only in

---

[1] The free X-chromosome was first observed in *Ascaris* by Herla ('94), Boveri ('99, '08) and Boring ('09) who found it very rarely present *var. univalens*, but frequently in *bivalens*. Its behavior in the meiotic divisions was elucidated by the work of Edwards ('10), Frolowa ('12), Kautzsch ('13) and Geinitz ('15).

[2] King ('12) describes in *Necturus* an "X-chromosome" that is linked to one of the bivalents in the spermatocyte-divisions, but the identification of this as the X-chromosome is doubtful.

certain nematodes (*Ancyracanthus*, etc., Figs. 357, 358) are the two classes of mature sperm readily distinguishable, since the chromosomes are still visible as such.   Since, however, the nuclei of the two classes commonly receive different amounts of chromatin, and since the sperm-heads consist almost wholly of chromatin, we might expect to find the sperms, or their heads (or nuclei) of two corresponding sizes; and such appears actually to be the fact.   Several observers [1] have made numerous measurements of sperm-heads (or nuclei) and plotted the results in curves of variability to show the distribution of size frequency.   In nearly all cases the curves have been bimodal, indicating the existence of two size-groups.   A test of this result is offered by differences in the relative size of X or (allowing for Y when present) of chromatin-content in different species; for such differences evidently should find expression in corresponding differences in the curves.

In the nature of the case it is difficult to obtain a very precise result; nevertheless expectation and observation show a certain agreement.   In the pig, Wodsedalek found the ratio of head-length in the two maxima to be 11.5:14.25 (1:1.21), in the horse 9.5:11 (1:1.05).   Zeleny and Faust found various ratios in the curves as compared with the expectation derived from measurements of the X-chromosomes.   These and other similar results involve a very considerable, perhaps very large, probable error owing to the relatively small size of the sex-chromosomes and similar causes.   More convincing than any of these is the similar result afforded by *Ascaris incurva*, a form which as above stated, has one of the largest known X-elements, and is also very favorable for exact measurements of the nuclei (Fig. 376).   Clay models of the second spermatocyte metaphase-groups of the X-containing and X-lacking classes, when weighed, gave a ratio between the two of 21:14 (1.5:1) while the bi-modal curve from measurements of 600 sperm-nuclei showed maxima having the ratio 21:15 (1.4:1), a much greater difference than in any other observed case.   This result seems to confirm the conclusion that the two modes of the frequency curves really correspond with the two sex-classes of the sperm.

B. FEMALE DIGAMETY

Digamety in the female is of two widely different types concerning which it is easy to fall into confusion.   One is a digamety in the constitution of the nuclei after meiosis precisely analogous to that seen in the sperm in the cases of male digamety.   The second is a dimegaly of the eggs, which are of two sizes, the larger being female-producing and the smaller male-producing (p. 806).   These two types must carefully be distinguished since they do not

[1] Wodsedalek on the pig ('13) and horse ('14); Faust ('13) on *Anasa tristis;* Zeleny and Faust ('15) and Zeleny and Senay ('15) on various insects and vertebrates; and Goodrich ('16) on *Ascaris incurva*.

parallel each other. At this point we are concerned only with the first of them.[1]

1. Sexual Nuclear Digamety of the Ova

Cytologically this type has been clearly demonstrated only in the Lepidoptera, though the genetic evidence proves that in birds also the female is the heterozygous sex. The Lepidoptera were examined cytologically by several earlier observers [2] but the sex-chromosomes were first made known by the work of Doncaster and especially of Seiler.[3] Seiler's studies, on certain moths of the family of Psychidæ have demonstrated a chromosome-mechanism exactly parallel to that of male digamety but showing a relation to sex in all respects the opposite. In male Lepidoptera all the chromosomes are equally paired and symmetrically distributed, so that but one visibly distinguishable class of sperms is produced. Seiler clearly showed that while the chromosomes are also paired in the female in certain species (*Solenobia pineti*, and *triquetrella*), thus corresponding to the XY–XX type, in other species one member of one pair is missing in the female; while the male has one more. Thus, in *Fumea casta* the diploid groups of the male (spermatogonia) have 62 chromosomes, equally paired (31 + 31), the female but 61 (31 + 30). In *Talæporia tubulosa* the corresponding numbers are male 60 (30 + 30) and female 59 (30 + 29). The meiotic divisions show corresponding relations. In the male all the chromosomes are equally distributed in both spermatocyte-divisions, producing but one class of sperm. In the female, on the other hand, the unmated or odd chromosome passes undivided to one pole (either the inner or the outer) in the first polar division of the egg. The second division, accordingly, is of two types, one showing one chromosome fewer than the other (in *Talæporia* 29 or 30), all the chromosomes dividing equationally. In *Talæporia* Seiler found this chromosome passing to the outer pole in 134 cases, to the inner in 89 cases, a ratio of 1.50:1.00, the observed primary sex-ratio being about 1.75:1. Whether these particular figures are significant or not, the facts as observed make it extremely probable that fertilization by any sperm will produce either a male or a female according to the class of egg which it enters, *e. g.*, in *Fumea casta*

$$\text{Egg } 31 + \text{sperm } 31 = 62 \ (\male)$$
$$\text{Egg } 30 + \text{sperm } 31 = 61 \ (\female)$$

These relations seem to be exactly the reverse of those seen in the *Protenor* type, and it becomes a doubtful question how the sex-chromosomes

[1] For the second see p. 806.
[2] Henking ('90, '92), Grünberg ('03), Stevens ('06), Munson ('07), Dederer ('07, '15), Cook ('10), Federley ('13), etc.
[3] Doncaster ('10–'15), Seiler ('14, '17, '21, '23).

should here be designated.   There are several possible nomenclatures that will satisfy the observed results, both cytological and genetic.   We might simply reverse the symbols employed in male digamety, employing the formulas $XXAA = \male$ and $XOAA = \female$ (Goldschmidt); or the formulas might be written $OOAA = \male$ and $XOAA = \female$ (Castle); or $YYAA = \male$ and $XYAA = \female$ (Wilson).   Evidently, however, in none of these cases does the symbol X have the same meaning as in male digamety.   Some writers, therefore, have preferred to use a different and non-committal terminology by substituting W and Z for X and Y, $i. e.$, $AAZZ = \male$ and $AAZO = \female$; or, in case Z has a mate in the female (*Solenobia* or *Phragmatobia*) $AAZZ = \male$ and $AAWZ = \female$ (Morgan).

To the physiological questions here involved we shall later return (pp. 815, 821).   They do not affect the fact that in a broad sense the same kind of chromosome-mechanism is involved in female digamety as in male.

Earlier work on Lepidoptera, though less decisive, indicates an essentially similar condition.   In *Abraxas* Doncaster ('10, '11) found that all males and most females have 56 chromosomes, and that all the gametes receive 28.   In some individuals, however, and always in a certain strain, the female number is 55, half the mature eggs receiving 27 and half 28.   This result possibly indicates the presence of a supernumerary chromosome, but was interpreted by Doncaster to mean that the 28-chromosome eggs are male-producing, the 27-class female-producing ($28 + 28 = 56\male$, $27 + 28 = 55\female$); further, that typically there is a pair of sex-chromosomes in each sex ($e. g.$, WZ in the $\female$ and ZZ in the $\male$) but that in the female one of these ($e. g.$, W) may be absent.   If this be correct the case would closely parallel that of *Metapodius*, where it is known that the Y-chromosome may be either present or absent in the same species (p. 874).[1]

More satisfactory, though more complex, is the case of *Phragmatobia*, where Seiler ('14) found in the first polar mitosis of the egg one large heteromorphic bivalent, distinguishable by its size, which in the male is replaced by a symmetrical one.   During the heterotypic mitosis in the female one member of this bivalent as it passes to the pole separates into two unequal components, so that the daughter-groups are of two types, one containing 29 chromosomes, the other 28.   Comparison shows that the bivalent in question lies indifferently with the double element turned either outward or inward, $i. e.$, this element may either be retained in the egg or passed out into the polar nucleus.   It thus comes to pass that there are two classes of eggs, one with 28 chromosomes, and one with 29.   In the male on the other hand the corresponding bivalent is symmetrical or homomorphic, and all the sperms receive 28 chromosomes.

Despite some points still obscure, the Lepidoptera thus show a close

[1] Wilson, '09.

general agreement between the genetic facts and the cytological. The case is different with the birds, which still offer a puzzle but incompletely solved. All observers are agreed that genetically the female bird is the sex-heterozygote, but Guyer [1] has brought forward evidence to show that in the common fowl and the guinea hen the sperms are of two classes, distinguished by the presence or absence of an unpaired X-element or accessory chromosome. This element is a large curved body which in many cases passes to one pole in the first spermatocyte division in advance of the other chromosomes, thus producing two classes of second spermatocytes, one with nine and one with eight chromosomes. The second spermatocytes show, as a rule, either four or five chromosomes (the autosomes having secondarily coupled two by two),[2] all of which divide equally. Half the sperms receive eight chromosomes (apparently four) and half nine (apparently five). Guyer believes, however, that the 8-chromosome or no-X class degenerate; so that all the functional sperms are of the X-class, as in aphids or phylloxerans (p. 792).

In view of these facts it is very remarkable that the diploid groups seem to show in the female but one large curved chromosome (X), while in the male two such elements are present.[3] The diploid groups thus seem to show the expected relation, the female being heterozygous, the male homozygous; but, *per contra*, the gamete-formation of the male seems to show this sex to be cytologically digametic, with one class of gametes non-functional. It is stated, further, that the X-chromosome of the spermatocyte-divisions is a bivalent body (representing the large pair in the spermatogonia) which passes as such to one pole.

If these facts be correctly determined they offer a cytological puzzle with which it is not possible to deal without additional data. This material, evidently, is very unfavorable for an accurate determination and it is greatly to be hoped that other species of birds may prove less difficult. A formal solution of the problem is offered by the hypothesis that the X-element of the male is a true bivalent (or pair of synaptic mates) which, after passing together to one pole in the first mitosis separates into its two components in the second, the equation-division being omitted. The sexes would then be produced according to the formulas: Egg $X +$ Sperm $X = XX$ ($\male$) and Egg $O +$ Sperm $X = XO$ ($\female$); [4] but this involves a constant process of non-disjunction in spermatogenesis, a condition contradictory of all that is elsewhere known of synapsis and reduction.

---

[1] ''09a, ''09b, ''12, etc.

[2] As in the Hymenoptera (p. 797).

[3] The total diploid number could not be determined exactly. In the male it is said to be 16–18.

[4] This suggestion is due to T. H. Morgan.

III. SEX–CHROMOSOMES AND PARTHENOGENESIS

1. General Relations of Parthenogenesis to Sex

The fact that eggs which develop without fertilization may produce either males or females seems at first sight almost a nullification of the conclusions based on the study of fertilized eggs. The truth is far otherwise; the history of the chromosomes in parthenogenesis offers, indeed, a conclusive confirmation of those conclusions and forms one of the most interesting chapters in the whole subject of sex-production. In considering the subject it is necessary to distinguish clearly between parthenogenesis in female homogamety (as in the aphids, rotifers or Hymenoptera) and those cases in which this sex is digametic (Lepidoptera); but as will later be shown, the two cases are in principle in agreement.

a. Parthenogenesis with Female Homogamety. The facts in this case are most fully known in the aphids and phylloxerans; but those presented by the rotifers and Hymenoptera appear to conform to the same type and the same is probably true also of the daphnids and ostracodes. The main facts, earlier briefly outlined (p. 228), are as follows:

In the aphids (Fig. 379) the fertilized eggs produce only females which are strictly parthenogenetic and are the first of a series of similar females multiplying only by diploid parthenogenesis. Later in the summer appear parthenogenetic "stem-mothers," the offspring of which are also parthenogenetic but in most cases are of two physiological types, one producing only sexual females, the other only males. The fertilized eggs initiate a new cycle, producing (in the following spring) a new line of non-sexual parthenogenetic females, as before. A similar life-history is shown in the phylloxerans, the daphnids, and the ostracodes; and in all of these cases parthenogenesis (with the exception of one all-important point) is of the diploid type. Among phylloxerans some species have an "open life-cycle" like that of the aphids, *i. e.*, an indefinite number of parthenogenetic generations before the sexual forms appear. More commonly (*P. fallax, P. caryæ-caulis*) the life-cycle is "closed," the stem-mother arising directly from the zygote (also the case in the gall-flies, p. 799). The offspring of the stem-mother are of two kinds, some producing only large eggs from which females develop, others only small eggs from which males develop, and as before, the cycle ends with fertilization (Fig. 379).

In the bees, wasps, and ants, on the other hand (Fig. 380), parthenogenesis appears to be exclusively of the haploid type, and no alternation takes place. Here all the fertilized sexual eggs produce females, the unfertilized exclusively males. The females, accordingly, are of diploid nuclear constitution, the males of haploid.

In the rotifers both types occur. The earlier part of the life-cycle agrees broadly with that of the aphid; a series of diploid female-producing parthenogenetic generations is followed by a generation the eggs of which may develop either sexually (*i. e.*, after fertilization), or by haploid parthenogenesis. This generation is exactly analogous to the bee or ant in the fact that if the egg be fertilized it produces a female of diploid constitution;

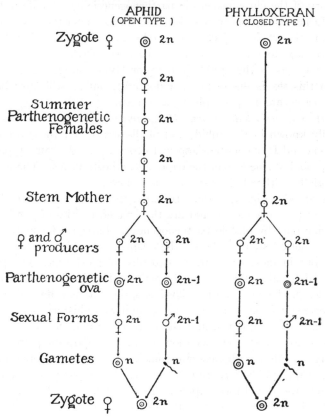

Fig. 379.—Diagram of diploid parthenogenetic life-cycles. Each cycle starts with the fertilized egg and ends with fertilization. The aphid shows a series of parthenogenetic female-producing generations before appearance of the sexual forms, the phylloxeran two such generations.

if it develops parthenogenetically, without fertilization, it produces a male which is of haploid constitution. In the gall-fly (*Neuroterus*) still a different combination appears (Fig. 380). Here, as usual, all the fertilized eggs produce parthenogenetic females, but some of these females produce only sexual females, by diploid parthenogenesis, while others give rise only to males by haploid parthenogenesis, as in rotifers or in the Hymenoptera.

Summing up these various cases we find *that in all of them the fertilized eggs give rise exclusively to diploid females; that in diploid parthenogenesis the offspring may be either male or female (gall-flies, aphids, daphnids) whereas in haploid parthenogenesis only males are produced (rotifers, bees).* In the latter case, obviously, the result is what we should expect; for if the egg develops with only the haploid group of chromosomes it contains but a single X and hence is *ipso facto* of male constitution. On the other hand,

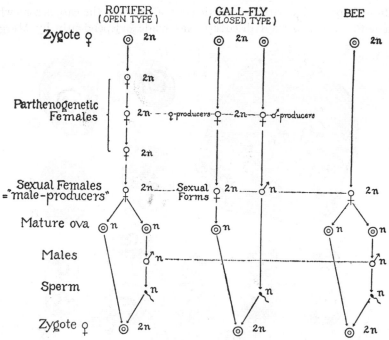

Fig. 380.—Diagram of mixed and of haploid parthenogenetic life-cycles. Each cycle starts with the fertilized egg or zygote and ends with fertilization. The rotifer shows a series of diploid female-producing parthenogenetic generations before appearance of the sexual forms, the gall-fly one such generation, the bee none. In all three cases males are produced from unfertilized mature eggs by haploid parthenogenesis.

the production of males in diploid parthenogenesis is by no means so evident, and its recent complete explanation by Morgan, Stevens, and De Baehr is one of the most interesting discoveries in this field.

2. The Sex-chromosomes in Diploid Parthenogenesis

In typical examples of this form of parthenogenesis the facts are now perfectly clear, though only a few cases have as yet been fully worked out.

In these cases, as earlier stated, but one polocyte is formed, the diploid number of chromosomes appears in the single maturation division (Fig. 223), and no general reduction of the chromosomes takes place. It was at first generally assumed that in this type no reduction of any kind takes place; and such is indeed the case in the production of females (*e. g.*, in the aphids, phylloxerans, ostracodes or rotifers). Without exception so far as known, female-producing parthenogenetic eggs always develop with the diploid number of chromosomes.

In male-producing parthenogenetic eggs of this type the case is somewhat different. The important discovery was made independently by Morgan

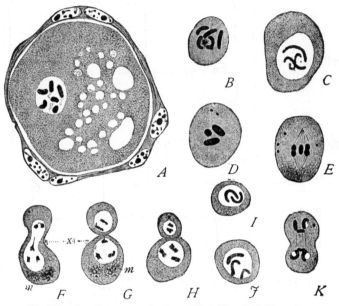

Fig. 381.—Sex-chromosomes in the aphid *Aphis saliceti* (Baehr).

A, polar spindle of the parthenogenetic egg in polar view, with 6 chromosomes (the diploid number); *B*, spermatogonial metaphase, 5 chromosomes; *C*, spermatocyte-prophase; *D*, 1st spermatocyte-metaphase; *E*, the same in side-view; *F–H*, the first division, in side-view; *I* and *J*, the two resulting classes of second spermatocytes; *K*, second division of large second spermatocytes (*X*-class).

('o8, 'o9) and Baehr ('o8, 'o9) that the males of certain aphids and phylloxerans, though having no other mode of origin than by diploid parthenogenesis, nevertheless *have one or two chromosomes fewer than the female*. Thus, in *Aphis saliceti* (the simplest case) the females, according to Baehr, always have six chromosomes, the males five (Fig. 381). In like manner Morgan found in *Phylloxera fallax* 12 chromosomes in the female and but ten in the male; while the corresponding gametic numbers are 6 and 4, the X-element consisting of two separate components, of which the female contains four and the male two.

It is clear from this that the production of the male must involve the elimination of one or two chromosomes; in other words, a reduction does occur *in the case of one or two chromosome-pairs.* This process, earlier suggested as a theoretical possibility,[1] was found actually to occur, in aphids

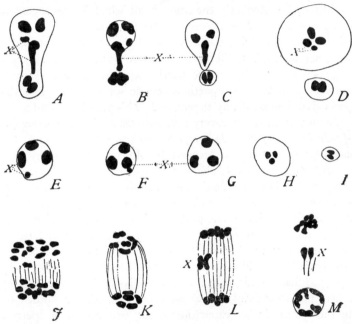

Fig. 382.—Sex-chromosomes in the parthenogenetic hemipter *Phylloxera* (MORGAN).

A, B, C, first spermatocyte-division in *P, caryæcaulis; D* (more enlarged); the two resulting classes of second spermatocytes, one with 4 (or apparently 3) chromosomes, one with 2; *E, F,* 4-chromosome type (2 *X*-components) of second spermatocytes; *G,* 3-chromosome class (with single *X*); *H,* polar view of second spermatocyte-metaphase (3-chromosome type); *I,* 2-chromosome class of second spermatocyte (rudimentary, non-functional); *J, P. fallax,* polar spindle of stem-mother egg 12 chromosomes; *K, P. caryæcaulis,* polar spindle of female-producing egg, six chromosomes to each pole; *L, M,* the same, polar spindles of male-producing eggs, elimination of lagging double *X,* showing five chromosomes left in the egg (the male number).

by Stevens ('10) and, especially by the work of Morgan ('12, '15), in two species of *Phylloxera* in which the X-element consists of two components, usually separate (p. 773). Morgan clearly showed, in these cases, that during the maturation of the smaller (male-producing) parthenogenetic eggs two chromosomes lag behind the others on the spindle during the anaphases, fail to enter the egg-nucleus, and are probably cast out in the polar body (Fig. 382). All is thus made clear; for we can hardly be mistaken

[1] Wilson ('07), Stevens ('09), Baehr ('09).

in the conclusion that the two extruded chromosomes (often closely coupled in *P. caryæcaulis*) represent a double X-element, comparable to that of *Syromastes* or *Fitchia* (p. 772) the mate of which remains in the egg. It thus comes to pass that the parthenogenetic eggs, though of diploid constitution in respect to the autosomes, are of two classes with respect to the X-chromosome, the female-producing egg having the constitution XX, the male-producing, X—obviously the same result which in the sexual process of so many other animals is effected by fertilization.

This is in itself a striking confirmation of the conclusions based on the ordinary sexual forms; but still more conclusive is the evidence given by the sexual reproduction of these same parthenogenetic species. Why should these animals differ from non-parthenogenetic species in the fact that fertilized eggs give rise exclusively to females? This question found a complete and simple answer, in the discovery that *only the X-class of sperms* (*i. e., the female-producing ones*) *come to complete development*. This fact, too, was independently discovered by Morgan in phylloxerans and by Baehr in aphids. In both forms the X-element, as usual, passes to one pole in one spermatocyte division (the first), but the division is markedly unequal. Thus are produced two visibly different classes of second spermatocytes, an X-bearing class of large size, and a no-X class of small size (Fig. 382). The former undergo an equal, equation-division and give rise to two functional sperms of the X-class. The small spermatocytes of the no-X class usually fail to divide and degenerate without giving rise to sperms. The only surviving sperms, therefore, are the X- or female-producing class. Nature here performs daily the precise crucial experiment needed to demonstrate the sex-producing capacities of the two classes of sperms. We may confidently expect that in the daphnids and ostracodes, likewise, the male-producing sperms will be found to be degenerate or non-functional; and also that in the parthenogenetic production of males one X-element is eliminated or rendered ineffective. In all these cases, however, one important point remains undetermined, namely, the mode in which the male-producing and female-producing mothers are differentiated. We look naturally to the origin of these mothers from the stem-mother in the hope of finding evidence of some kind of differential division in the maturation of the eggs from which they arise. Morgan ('12b) has in fact found certain peculiarities of the chromosomes in the male-producing eggs of *Phylloxera caryæcaulis* which suggest that a small component of the X-chromosome is eliminated during the maturation of the stem-mother's egg from which the male-producer arises; but the demonstration of this is still incomplete.

Since parthenogenesis of this type involves no general reduction we might expect to find no evidence of synapsis or the associated phenomena in the oöcytes, and such seems indeed sometimes to be the fact; but there are some notable exceptions. In some cases of diploid parthenogenesis the oöcytes pass through a stage of synizesis indistinguishable from the same stage in the sexual egg, and this may even be followed by *a process of pseudo-reduction and the formation of tetrads*. Woltereck ('98), confirmed by Schleip ('09), found the former condition in the parthenogenetic oöcytes of ostracodes (*Cypris*) but observed no process of pseudo-reduction. This was at first supposed to mean that synizesis has no necessary connection with the process of reduction.[1] Further observation, however, showed that this conclusion was unfounded. Strasburger ('04, '07, '09) found in *Marsilia* that diploid apogamy is preceded by a process of synizesis and pseudo-reduction, but that during the diakinesis the diploid number is restored by a disjunction of the synaptic mates of each bivalent; and indications of a similar process, though less complete, were found in *Alchemilla*. In *Wikströmia* the synaptic phase seems to be entirely absent, and the chromosome-number is diploid from the beginning. Similar variations seem to exist among animals. It was found by Fries ('09) that the sexual eggs of *Branchipus* pass through a typical synaptic stage involving a (probably) parasynaptic conjugation of chromosomes, but in the diploid parthenogenetic eggs of *Artemia* these appearances are wanting and the egg-nucleus gives rise directly to the diploid number of chromosomes. Morgan ('15) likewise found typical synizesis in the sexual eggs of the "bearberry aphid" but never in the parthenogenetic ones, the contrast being so great that ovaries producing the two respective types of eggs can thus readily be distinguished. On the other hand, Baehr ('20) found that the parthenogenetic eggs of *Aphis palmæ* undergo a marked synizesis and give rise to four bivalent chromosomes (the diploid number is eight); but in the diakinesis these are disjoined or "deconjugated" to form eight single chromosomes which undergo a simple longitudinal splitting during the single polar mitosis.

It thus seems to be well determined, as Strasburger ('09) indicated, that parthenogenetic eggs of the diploid type show different degrees of adaption to parthenogenesis. Some of them prepare for complete reduction by the usual process, but this is never fully carried out, the conjugation being undone in the diakinesis so as to restore the diploid number. In others the "deconjugation" is effected earlier (*Alchemilla*), and in still others the synaptic phase seems to have been lost entirely (*Wikströmia*). An indication of how such a series of stages may have had its beginning is possibly seen in the diakinetic deconjugation and reconjugation that takes place in the sexual eggs of *Lepidosiren* as described by Agar (p. 563),

---

[1] Hence also Woltereck's conclusion that synizesis and the associated changes represent an abortive mitosis, a view afterwards advocated by R Hertwig and a number of others.

or in those of certain Hymenoptera (*Rhodites*, *Cynips*, etc.) which may undergo complete reduction and may either be fertilized or develop by diploid
parthenogenesis (p. 803). All these facts point to the conclusion that the
diploid parthenogenetic egg has been derived from a sexual egg which was
originally capable of complete reduction (and perhaps also of haploid parthenogenesis), by the progressive restriction and final loss of the synaptic
phenomena and their consequences.

3. Sex in Haploid Parthenogenesis

The second or haploid type of natural parthenogenesis is at present
known only in Rotifera, Hymenoptera, Thysanoptera, Hemiptera and
Arachnida.

In Hemiptera and Arachnida. Though only a single case is known in each
of these groups the cytological facts seem to be so clear as to form a desirable
introduction to more debatable cases. In the homopter *Trialeurodes va-
porarium*, as earlier indicated (p. 232), virgin females of the English race
produce only females (presumably by diploid parthenogenesis) while those
of the American race produce only males. Schrader ('20) found that in the
latter case the females, produced sexually, are diploid (22 chromosomes) and
the males produced parthenogenetically, are haploid, clearly showing 11
chromosomes. These numbers were found in all stages of development
from cleavage up to late pupæ with gonads in an advanced stage of development. The egg undergoes a typical meiosis with reduction to the haploid
number (11), and in fertilization receives 11 chromosomes from the sperm.
In the male, on the other hand, no reduction occurs and the heterotypic division seems to be entirely suppressed, a result borne out by the numerical relations of the spermatids and spermatocytes. This case will bear
further examination, but the main result seems to be well established. It is
noteworthy that mated females produce offspring of both sexes, which
suggests that the actual fertilization of the egg may be controlled by the
female spermatheca, as in the bee.

In the mite *Tetranychus bimaculatus*, a case also made known by Schrader
('23), the facts are even more demonstrative, since the haploid number
is but 3 and the diploid 6. In this case, also, as shown by several earlier
observers, virgin females produce exclusively male offspring, while mated
females produce offspring of both sexes. Schrader's work proves that all
the eggs subsequent to meiosis have 3 chromosomes; that fertilized eggs
divide with 6 chromosomes, unfertilized with 3; that in the blastoderm-
stages and up to the larval stages, some embryos show 6 chromosomes,
others 3; that the spermatogonial divisions show 3 chromosomes and the
oögonial 6; and that in the male the heterotypic division is suppressed,

while in the oöcytes the meiotic divisions take place normally, with 3 tetrads. All doubt thus seems to be removed that in this species, as in the foregoing case, males arise from unfertilized eggs and undergo complete development by haploid parthenogenesis, while females arise from fertilized eggs, and are diploid.

In *Hymenoptera.* The classical case of haploid parthenogenesis is offered by the honey-bee where the celebrated theory of Dzierzon (1845) long formed a center of controversy. Dzierzon's observations, supplemented by those of Siebold, Leuckart and many later investigators, proved that females alone (queens or workers) are produced from fertilized eggs, males alone (drones) from unfertilized. This condition is now known to be widespread among the Hymenoptera (bees, ants, wasps, chalcids) and so far as the production of males is concerned may be universal in this group. Some doubt, however, still hangs over the cytological side of the subject, since the phenomena are here in a measure confused by the frequent occurrence of double or multiple chromosome-groups in the somatic divisions (p. 803) and also by the frequent secondary coupling of the chromosomes two by two in both the spermatocytes and the oöcytes. This has led to uncertainty as to the number of chromosomes in the diploid and haploid groups, and as to the sexual chromosomal differences. Nevertheless, it may now be stated with considerable confidence that among the Hymenoptera thus far investigated the females, produced from fertilized eggs, develop with the diploid number of chromosomes (or a multiple of it) while the males, produced from unfertilized eggs, develop with the haploid number. The sex-chromsomes have not yet been identified as such. Nevertheless, it is highly probable from the general constitution of the chromosome-groups that the females have the sexual constitution XX, the males X; for the unfertilized eggs, having undergone reduction, should contain one X, and this number is not doubled in the course of development.[1] It must, however, be borne in mind that in case of both bees and ants virgin workers are asserted to have produced female offspring (workers, queens).[2] The workers and queens thus produced should, of course, be diploid; but how this result is produced is unknown. It might be due to a failure of reduction and the formation of but one polocyte in such eggs or to a secondary doubling (*cf.* p. 803). The cytological investigation of such cases should give a crucial test of the XO–XX quantitative theory of sex (p. 816).

We need not here review *in extenso* the rather complicated history of the researches on which this conclusion concerning sex-production in Hymenop-

---

[1] Wilson ('09), Baehr ('09), R. Hertwig ('12), Nachtsheim ('13), Patterson ('17), Whiting ('21), etc.

[2] See Wheeler ('03), on ants. Onions ('12, '14), on bees.

tera is based.[1] A first key to the problem was found by Blochmann ('86) with the discovery that not only the fertilized but also the unfertilized eggs produce both polocytes and hence presumably undergo complete reduction. The possibility was opened that in the bee the parthenogenetic egg (male-producing) might develop with the haploid number of chromosomes. Opposed to this were the observations of Petrunkewitsch ('01, '13) who found that both fertilized and unfertilized eggs developed with 16 chromosomes, though higher numbers (32, 64) were also observed; he concluded, therefore, that 16 is the fundamental diploid number characteristic of both

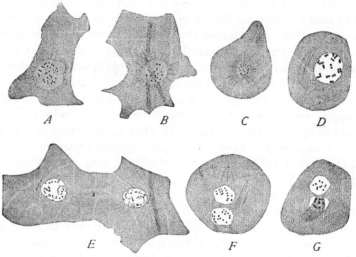

Fig. 383.—Chromosome-groups in the honeybee (NACHTSHEIM).

A, cleavage-cell (anaphase-group) from female (worker) embryo, 32 chromosomes; B, C, similar views, from male (drone) embryos, 16 chromosomes; D, first spermatocyte, diakinesis, 16 dyads; E, telophase, cleavage-cell, drone-embryo; F, G, second spermatocyte telophases, in F about 16 chromosomes, in G about 8.

sexes and 8 the haploid. This result seemed to be supported by the behavior of the chromosomes during maturation; for the polar spindle shows in fact eight tetrads, and the nucleus of the mature egg receives the same number of chromosomes. Petrunkewitsch's conclusion was, however, insecurely based. The studies of Meves ('04, '07) on the spermatogenesis of both the bee and the hornet (*Vespa*), confirmed by those of Mark and Copeland ('06, '07) and other observers, proved that the spermatogonial number in the bee is 16, but also proved *that each sperm-nucleus receives the same number.* Meves therefore concluded that not 8 but 16 is the fundamental

[1] A good review is given by Nachtsheim ('13). See also Schleip ('12), who gives an excellent review of the entire subject of sex-determination.

haploid number, and that the egg must have developed by haploid parthenogenesis. Substantially the same result is reached by Mark and Copeland, and by Doncaster ('07), and especially by Nachtsheim ('13), who made an extended reëxamination of the subject.

Nachtsheim's work clearly shows that the unfertilized egg (male) develops with 16 chromosomes, the fertilized egg (worker) with 32, these numbers occurring both in the cleavage and in later stages (Fig. 383). His observations also show that Petrunkewitsch failed to reckon with a secondary linkage or coupling of the chromosomes first seen in the anaphases of the spermatocyte-division, the 16 chromosomes showing a tendency to unite two by two, so that the spermatid-nuclei often seem to receive only eight chromosomes.[1] In the female the same tendency to couple is seen at still earlier stages. In the female blastoderm 32 chromosomes are present; but in the oögonia the number seems reduced to 16, the chromosomes having already united two by two (p. 869). In the polar spindles appear eight tetrads, and after meiosis the egg seems to receive eight single chromosomes as Petrunkewitsch correctly described. It now seems clear, however, that these chromosomes are bivalent, corresponding exactly to the eight chromosome-couples in the sperm-nucleus; and since the unfertilized egg segments with 16 chromosomes the fertilized with 32 the linkage must be dissolved as soon as development begins.

The foregoing results find a remarkable confirmation in the fact that no reduction of the chromosomes takes place, the sperms receiving 16 chromosomes, the same number shown in the cleavage, and in the spermatogonia. It is, however, a significant fact, discovered by Meves in the bee and hornet, that a kind of vestigial reduction-division takes place, the primary spermatocyte making an abortive attempt to divide, in the course of which an incomplete spindle is formed, and the chromosomes appear, but no nuclear division occurs. The result is the extrusion of a non-nucleated mass of protoplasm or "polar body" (Fig. 384), and this is followed by one complete mitosis in which both nucleus and protoplasm divide normally. A similar condition has been found in many other Hymenoptera.[2]

In these cases, evidently, the formation of a non-nucleated "polar body" is a vestigial process which represents the remnant of a formerly complete reduction-division. The second or homeotypic division is always a complete normal mitosis, involving the division of both nucleus and cytosome. A

---

[1] Earlier observed by Doncaster ('07). Such a secondary coupling in the second meiotic division has been observed in a considerable number of other cases, for instance, in birds (Guyer, '00, '09, G. Smith, '12), man (Guyer, '10) and other mammals (Jordan, '11, Wodsedalek, '13). It is not certain, however, that this may not in some cases be due to an artificial clumping.

[2] In the hornet and bumblebee (Meves and Duesberg, '07, '08; Mark and Copeland, '07); the ant *Camponotus* (Lams, '08); the solitary bees *Xylocopa* (Granata, '07, '13) and *Osmia* (Armbruster, '13); and the gall-flies *Neuroterus* (Doncaster, '10); *Paracopidosomopsis* (Patterson and Porter, '17).

curious and hitherto unexplained fact is that while in some cases this division is equal, and produces two normal sperms (wasps, ants, gall-flies), in others t is markedly unequal, the larger cell alone producing a normal sperm (bees).

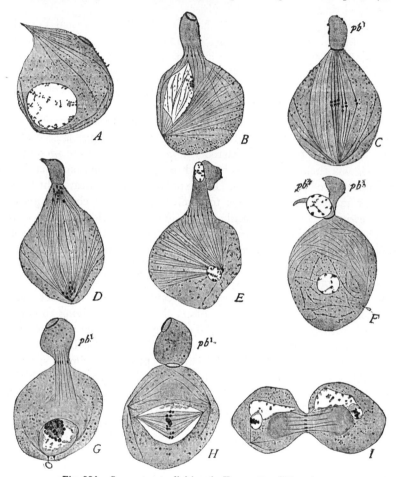

Fig. 384.—Spermatocyte-divisions in *Hymenoptera* (MEVES).

A, first spermatocyte of the honeybee (*Apis*); *B, C,* the first (abortive) division, producing a non-nucleated "polar body" (*pb¹*); *D, E, F,* the second division, producing a nucleated "polar body" (*pb²*) *G, H,* corresponding first division in the hornet (*Vespa crabo*); *I,* second, equal division, producing two spermatids.

The meaning of this is unknown; but it is obvious that the unequal division of the bee must be of wholly different nature from that seen in the spermatogenesis of the aphid or phylloxeran (p. 792). This is proved by the wasps, in which the equal division is obviously identical with the unequal one of the bee, yet both products are female-producing (*i. e.*, of the X-class). In the aphid, on the other hand, the unequal division produces one spermatocyte of the X-class and one (degenerate) of the no-X class.

The general result reached in case of the bee is probably of wide application among the Hymenoptera. Schleip ('08) demonstrated that it holds true for the ant (*Formica*) showing that fertilized eggs develop with 48 chromosomes, unfertilized (male-producing) with 24. Granata (*op. cit.*) found that in *Xylocopa*, a solitary bee, the sperms receive the spermatogonial number (16) without reduction, as in the honeybee or the ant.[1] In the gall-flies, where both diploid and haploid parthenogenesis occur, we may take as a type *Neuroterus (Spathegaster) lenticularis*, which has

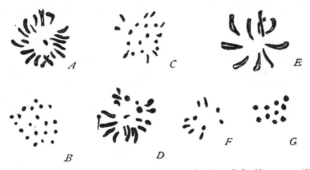

Fig. 385.—Sexual differences of the chromosome-groups in the gall-fly *Neuroterus* (DONCASTER).

A–D, female groups (20 chromosomes); *E–G*, male groups (10 chromosomes).

A, ovarian cell, metaphase; *B*, same, anaphase; *C*, anaphase, larval nervous system; *D*, cleavage-stage, metaphase; *E*, metaphase, larval nervous system; *F*, spermatogonial anaphase; *G*, cleavage-stage, anaphase.

been carefully studied by Doncaster ('10, '11, '16). In this species the diploid number is 20, the haploid 10, the former number characteristic of the females, the latter of the males (Fig. 385). The sexual egg forms two polar bodies, with a reduction of chromosome-number from 20 to 10. The spermatogonia show 10 chromosomes and undergo no reduction, the reduction-division being abortive, while the equation-division produces (as in *Vespa*) two equal spermatids and two functional sperms. The fertilized eggs develop within galls formed on the oak and hatch in the spring to produce exclusively parthenogenetic females, having 20 chromosomes, and constituting the asexual or agamic generation. Their eggs, without fertilization, produce either sexual females or males, in the former case de-

---

[1] Armbruster ('13) believed that in *Osmia* (also a solitary bee) the spermatogonial number was reduced from 16 to 8; but this, as Nachtsheim shows, is no doubt due to a secondary coupling as above described.

veloping with 20 chromosomes (*i. e.*, without undergoing reduction) in the latter case with 10.[1]

Doncaster showed that each individual female produced by the agamic spring generation produces either male or female offspring but not both. These parthenogenetic mothers are therefore exactly comparable to the male-producers or female-producers of the phylloxeran, and the first agamic generation (the product of fertilization) corresponds to the stem-mother generation (p. 787). Doncaster has experimentally ('16) arrived at the further conclusion that each sexual female gives rise exclusively either to male-producing or to female-producing stem-mothers.[2] No explanation of this has thus far been found; it may be due to the existence of two kinds of males, or to differences in the maturation-process of eggs laid by two kinds of sexual females. Until this question (like the analogous one in case of the phylloxerans) has been settled the question of sex-determination in these forms will remain but incompletely solved. Concerning the main point, it seems highly probable, though only a small number of cases are yet known, that the haploid condition of the male is characteristic of Hymenoptera generally; for it is known that males are produced from unfertilized eggs in many Hymenoptera besides those that have been mentioned,[3] and the cytological conclusions are fully borne out by the genetic facts.

The current cytological interpretation of the foregoing cases has already been indicated (p. 795). Since the males are haploid they contain but one X-chromosome, while the diploid females should contain two such chromosomes. There is, however, another possibility, namely, that the haploid group of the male represents a compound X-element, all the chromosomes containing "X-chromatin," while two such groups are present in the female.[4] In case of the bee this seems improbable; but Schrader's remarkable observations on *Pseudococcus* seem to show that such a condition is actually realized, except that a compound Y-element is also present (p. 778).

[1] Doncaster states that the female-producing egg undergoes no maturation-division, the male-producing two divisions, the number of chromosomes remaining 20 in the first case, and in the second being reduced to 10. This suggests the need of further study of the female-producing eggs; but the final result seems to be well determined.

[2] Out of a total of 9574 offspring reared from over 80 galls, produced by 12 isolated females, only 2.09% of exceptions were found and there is good reason to suspect that these were due to accidental contamination.

[3] For a recent discussion of this question see Nachtsheim ('21). An interesting exception to the above statement is found by Whiting ('21) in the parasitic wasp *Hadrobracon*. The genetic evidence (p. 929) proves that males are of haploid constitution but also proves that exceptionally they may arise from *fertilized* eggs. This is demonstrated in crosses between black-eyed males (dominant) and pure-bred orange-eyed females, in which a few of the sons show the black-eyed character of the father. This may mean that the anomalous males are sex-mosaics, or that some of the maternal chromosomes are cast out (*e. g.*, by non-disjunction or the like). See A. R. Whiting, *Genetics*, X, Jan. 1925.

[4] Schrader ('20); see also Gutherz ('23).

3. In Rotifera

In the rotifers, as in the gall-flies or aphids, all the fertilized eggs produce parthenogenetic females, the eggs of which form but a single polocyte and develop by diploid parthenogenesis. This generation may be followed by a long series of others of the same type which in some cases (*Hydatina*) are known to be of diploid constitution (Whitney). Sooner or later appear the sexual forms, characterized by the production of small eggs which, unlike the ordinary parthenogenetic eggs, produce both polocytes and are capable of haploid parthenogenesis but, as in case of the bee are also capable of fertilization. If unfertilized these eggs remain small and develop by haploid parthenogenesis (Whitney) into males. If fertilized, the egg enlarges, secretes a thick membrane about itself, and is thus converted into a "resting" or "winter egg" (Fig. 386). Such eggs contain of course the diploid number of chromosomes; and after a long period of rest, produce parthenogenetic females with which the diploid parthenogenetic cycle begins.

This life-history, evidently, is closely similar to that of the bee, save that a series of diploid parthenogenetic generations precedes the appearance of the sexual forms. The gall-fly (*Neuroterus*) may be considered as intermediate in type, since only one generation of diploid parthenogenetic forms exists, *i. e.*, that produced by the zygotes. In all these cases, obviously, there is but one class of sperm, the female-producing. In case of the rotifer we naturally look for an explanation like that which applies to the bee; but in so doing find ourselves involved in certain difficulties that can only be cleared up by further work. Whitney ('17, '18) has found that there are in rotifers two kinds of sperms, both nucleated, but one much larger than the other and twice as numerous. A solution of the puzzle here offered has not yet been found.

The most interesting point in the life history of the rotifer is the proof that it affords of the fact that *fertilization changes the sex of the egg*. That such is the case in the bee has long seemed nearly certain; nevertheless it might be held that only eggs predestined as female-producing are capable of fertilization. In the rotifer, however, this possibility has now been excluded. Maupas ('90), Nusbaum ('97) and other of the earlier observers found that each individual female rotifer lays but one kind of egg, namely, (1) parthenogenetic (diploid) female-producing eggs or (2) parthenogenetic (haploid) male-producing, or (3) sexual "resting" or "winter" eggs, which develop only when fertilized. Of these three classes of eggs (Fig. 386) the second and third are now known to be identical. Maupas showed that winter eggs are never produced by females that have been isolated from the males, though a certain proportion of males may appear; that females that have had free access to males produce winter eggs in almost exactly the same proportion as that of the males produced by control cultures of females that have been isolated from males. He therefore concluded that

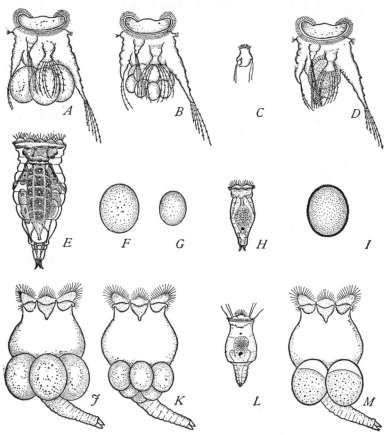

Fig. 386.—Sexual dimegaly of the eggs in Rotifers (WHITNEY).

  A, Pedalion mirum, parthenogenetic female with female-producing eggs; *B,* female with "small male-producing" eggs; *C,* mature male; *D,* sexual female or fertilized "male-producer" bearing female-producing fertilized egg (the latter originally like those of *B*).

  E, Hydatina senta, parthenogenetic female-producer; *F,* egg of same; *G,* male-producing egg; *H,* mature male; *I,* fertilized egg (originally like *G*).

  J-M, Brachionus pala (series exactly corresponding to *A-D*); *J,* female-producing female; *K.* male-producer; *L,* male; *M,* sexual female or fertilized "male-producer."

the sexual or winter egg is simply a "male-producing" egg that has been fertilized. This has been fully confirmed by Shull ('10), who added the decisive observation that the *same female may produce both winter eggs and male-producing eggs,* provided she be fertilized by old or spent males that

contain very few sperms. Since all observers are agreed that all parthenogenetic eggs from one individual are always of the same sex, this observation makes it in high degree probable that the winter eggs are male-producing eggs that have been fertilized. A curious corollary to this conclusion is that the sexual female always appears one generation earlier than
the male; for she is, necessarily, the mother of the male (Shull, *op. cit.*).

4. Problematical Cases

Thus far all the facts are in general accordance with the principle earlier
emphasized (p. 505) that in the course of the two meiotic divisions each
chromosome of the original diploid (gonial) groups divides but once (equationally), the reduction "division" being only the separation of two closely
associated synaptic mates. The cases now to be considered seem at present
explicable only under the assumption either that both divisions are equational
or that two such divisions follow the heterotypic. Such cases, obviously,
call for the closest scrutiny; but unluckily none of them has as yet been
sufficiently worked out to justify more than tentative conclusions. In
most of these cases the egg seems to undergo a complete process of meiosis,
with the production of both polocytes and reduction of the chromosomes
to the haploid number, yet it develops without fertilization with the full
diploid number of chromosomes.[1] Such eggs, so far as known, always
produce females. They have been adequately investigated only in certain
of the Hymenoptera (gall-flies and their allies); but the analogous phenomena in female digamety (Lepidoptera) have been more carefully examined
(p. 805).

The earliest and best-known of these cases is that of the rose gall-fly,
Rhodites rosæ, in which males are almost unknown, reproduction being
uniformly parthenogenetic and producing almost always females. Henking
('92) found in this case that both polocytes are formed; and that during
this process the number of chromosomes is 9; nevertheless the egg segments
with double this number (18–20). He therefore concluded that at some time
subsequent to maturation the haploid number is doubled by a secondary
splitting. The same result is reached in more extended recent studies on
the same species [2] by Hogben ('20a), who shows that the somatic number
is 18 and that the oöcyte undergoes a typical process of pseudoreduction
to form 9 bivalents. The process of doubling subsequent to reduction
has not yet actually been observed but would seem to involve an additional

---

[1] For the similar difficulty concerning the occasionally parthenogenetic production of females in
bees, see p. 795.

[2] Schleip ('09) confirmed Henking in regard to the number of polocytes and also adopted the conception of a second equational split, but was apparently in error concerning the number of chromosomes.

equational division though possibly some other interpretation of the facts may be found.[1]

A very noteworthy feature in this case is the fact, carefully studied by Hogben, that synapsis takes place (parasynaptically) in the usual manner and place but its effect is temporarily undone at a later period (subsequent to the confused period), when *the chromosomes reappear in the diploid number, 18*. This is followed by a *telosynaptic* reunion of the univalents to form again 9 bivalents which pass upon the first polar spindle. A similar phenomenon is described in *Cynips* and in the ichneumonid *Orthopelma* and is believed to be of wider occurrence in the parasitic Hymenoptera, since Hegner also described a late telosynaptic process in the chalcid *Copidosoma* and many other more or less isolated observations fit with the more complete ones on *Rhodites*. A curious additional fact seen in these forms is a clumping together and condensation of the chromosomes of the first polar spindle to form an almost solid mass or "chromatin-nucleus." This has been described by a considerable number of observers,[2] but the relations of this stage to the later stages of maturation have not yet been clearly worked out.

Similar in type to the foregoing is the parthenogenetic phasmid, *Bacillus rossii*, where males are of extreme rarity. Baehr ('07) here found two maturation-divisions, apparently preceded by true tetrad-formation, which makes it very probable that a complete reduction occurs, yet the eggs, with extremely rare exceptions are female-producing, and apparently must restore the diploid number. This case may perhaps be explained, like that of *Rhodites* by assuming the occurrence of an extra equation-division; but it seems at least equally possible that the number may be doubled by reunion of the second polar nucleus with the egg-nucleus or a process of similar type (p. 471). In respect to all these cases, however, we are still on hypothetical ground. The strongest cases for the occurrence of two equation-divisions (here accompanying a partial or complete failure of the reduction-division) is offered by the moth-hybrids of Federley and of Doncaster, and by certain plant-hybrids (p. 852). Further interesting suggestions are offered by the recent work of Seiler ('23) on the cytological phenomena of parthenogenesis in female digamety (Lepidoptera) a brief account of which follows:

a. Parthenogenesis and Sex with Female Digamety. The occasional parthenogenetic development of unfertilized sexual eggs in Lepidoptera (the so-

---

[1] Hogben ('20a) suggests (1) that both polar mitoses may be equational and that the subsequent doubling may be due to a disjunction of the bivalents; but this seems to differ little in substance from the earlier suggestions of Henking and of Schleip.

[2] E. g., by Hegner ('14) in *Copidosoma, Andricus*, and *Apanteles;* by Martin ('14) in *Ageniaspis*, Silvestri ('14) in *Copidosoma;* by Gatenby ('18) in *Trichogramma*, and Hogben ('20) in *Neuroterus*, *Cynips* and *Rhodites*.

called "facultative" parthenogenesis) has been recorded by several observers; [1] and it has long been known that in the family of Psychidæ there are some forms in which parthenogenesis is of regular or even of almost exclusive occurrence (p. 231). The studies of Seiler on *Solenobia*, including both the obligatory or regular parthenogenesis and the facultative or occasional parthenogeneiss of the sexual forms, shows that in the former case parthenogenesis, as in the summer generations of aphids, is strictly female-producing, and the parthenogenetic race was never found to produce males. In the rare facultative parthenogenesis of sexual eggs development is seldom complete and rarely proceeds as far as the adult or even the pupal stage. In these cases both males and females may be produced.[2] Cytologically a striking contrast appears between the two cases. In the facultative process both polar divisions take place, leading to reduction, and the egg begins its development with the haploid number; but in later stages this number is doubled in most of the cells (as often occurs also in the bee, p. 870). The obligatory process, on the other hand, resembles that occurring in the aphids, rotifers or gall-flies (p. 468) in the fact that but one polar division takes place, without reduction. The remarkable fact is, however, that here too the number is doubled, in this case producing the *tetraploid* number, which appears in most if not all of the embryonic cells. It is an interesting fact that in both cases alike the early stages show the typical leptotene, synizesis and diplotene stages leading to the formation of typical tetrads of the haploid number (in *Solenobia triquetrella* and *pineti* approximately 30). In some other respects the two species seem to differ remarkably, in particular in respect to the manner in which the doubling of number takes place.

In *triquetrella* the 30 tetrads first divide equationally giving 30 dyads, which are said *again to divide equationally* in the second mitosis, the 30 dyads thus produced then separating to form at each pole 60 single chromosomes (the diploid number); and this number appears also in the first two cleavages. In later cleavage the number is almost invariably tetraploid ($120\pm$) a result attributed to a fusion of nuclei two by two.[3] In *S. pineti* the early stages are similar; but the tetraploid condition is differently produced, the dyads separating already in the anaphases of the heterotypic division to form 60 single chromosomes which are then doubled in number (to 120) in later anaphases of the same spindle.[4] In the facultative

---

[1] E. g., Platner ('88) in *Liparis dispar*, Henking ('92) in *Bombus mori*, Hartmann ('12) in the first named species and others. See also Goldschmidt ('17).

[2] See Hartmann ('12), Goldschmidt ('17).

[3] This conclusion seems insufficiently based, though such a fusion is actually figured.

[4] The cytoplasmic changes accompanying this doubling are considered by Seiler to represent an abortive second mitosis, the doubling in number at this time being compared to the formation and reunion of the second polocyte in *Artemia* (p. 471).

type (preceded by complete reduction) the mode of doubling to produce the diploid number was not determined.

There are some points in this account that evidently call for further examination; nevertheless the main facts seem clear and contribute in an important way to our understanding of sex-production in parthenogenesis. So far as the obligatory type is concerned the results offer no difficulty; for in the absence of a reduction-division the constitution of the mature ovum does not differ from that of the female that produces it; and since the doubling of the whole group does not affect the balance between the sex-chromosomes and autosomes (p. 817) all such parthenogenetic eggs should be female-producing, as is actually the case. The facultative type with complete reduction is by no means so clear. Seiler's interpretation is as follows. Since complete reduction occurs the eggs should be of the two classes, A + X, and A, which being doubled give the two classes of embryos, AA + XX = ♂ and AA = ♀. The first class obviously should be males and the second are assumed to be females containing no X like those supposed to arise by non-disjunction (p. 877). The difficulties here involved can only be cleared up by further research.

5. Sex and Chromosomes in Artificial Parthenogenesis

The relations of the chrosmomes to sex in artificial parthenogenesis (*cf.* p. 472) are still incompletely known owing to the fact that in very few cases have such parthenogenetic larvæ been reared to a point at which sex could be positively determined. Yves Delage ('12), succeeded in rearing through the metamorphosis six sea-urchin larvæ from parthenogenetic eggs, of which two lived long enough to be identified as males. The chromosome-numbers were not determined; but since the female is homogametic in these animals the sex of such larvæ might be expected to be male if they were haploid (*i. e.*, X-containing), and to be female if of diploid constitution (XX-containing).[1] The second available case is that of the frog, in which out of twenty larvæ reared through the metamorphosis 15 were males, 3 females, and 2 doubtful Loeb ('18). Parmenter ('20) examined 14 individuals out of 65 parthenogenetically produced larvæ reared by Loeb, including one male frog and 13 tadpoles of undetermined sex. In all of these, *the male frog included*, the number was diploid (26) or nearly so; hence it is probable that this number is characteristic of both sexes. (See also Hovasse, p. 479.) Without further cytological examination this result cannot be certainly explained.

6. Sexual Dimegaly of the Ova in Relation to the Chromosomes

We may here conveniently consider with reference to the foregoing account, the sexual dimegaly of the ova earlier referred to (pp. 277, 787).

[1] *Cf.* Shearer and Lloyd, Q. J., '13.

This condition was long since observed in the parthenogenetic eggs of roti-fers of several genera (Fig. 386) [1] and also in those of phylloxerans [2] where they have been more recently studied with care by Morgan ('09). An even more marked sexual dimegaly in sexual eggs (Fig. 117) exists in *Dinophilus apatris* (Korschelt, '82); and sexual dimegaly has also been described in the sexual eggs of mites (Reuter, '07) and spiders (Montgomery, '07). In case of the insects it was likewise supposed by earlier observers that males arise from smaller eggs and females from larger ones; but this result was contra-dicted by the later careful work of Cuénot ('99, '05). In case of the verte-brates Beard ('02) inferred the preëxistence of male-producing and female-producing eggs in elasmobranchs from the fact that at an early stage there are two sizes of blastodisks, the larger containing a number of primordial germ-cells (± 512) about twice that found in the smaller. The former he assumed to be female-producing, the latter male-producing. More recently Riddle ('11, '14, '17, etc.) has maintained in the case of fowls and pigeons that eggs of smaller size, higher water-content and lower energy-content (measured by amount of fat and of phosphorus) are male-producing, while those showing the opposite characters are female-producing.

In all the pronounced cases (rotifers, phylloxerans, *Dinophilus*) the size-dimorphism of the eggs is correlated with a corresponding size-difference between the adult sexes, an extreme case being offered by *Dinophilus apatris*, where the males are stated to be not more than $1/27$ the volume of the females and the male-producing eggs are of correspondingly smaller size (Fig. 117). The sexual dimegaly of the eggs is therefore a true case of promorphology.

It is a very noteworthy and, at first sight, puzzling fact that in many of the foregoing cases (rotifers, phylloxerans) the sexual dimegaly exists in forms where with respect to the *chromosomes* it is the male and not the female that is digametic. This apparent anomaly disappears, however, upon further consideration. In the rotifer, for example, the size of the sexual egg depends upon whether the egg is fertilized or not; in the latter case it remains small and produces a male by haploid parthenogenesis, while if fertilized it enlarges to form a female-producing egg (p. 802). In the phylloxerans the case is different since both the large and the small eggs are parthenogenetic. Here, however, the egg acquires the appropriate chromosome-combination during maturation, the larger eggs retaining the full diploid number, including XX (hence females like their partheno-genetic mothers), while the smaller eliminate one X-element, thus establish-ing the male combination, AAXO (p. 791). In this instructive case the

---

[1] Dalrymple ('49), Ley ig ('54), Cohen ('55), Hudson ('72), Levander ('94), etc.
[2] Balbiani ('73), Lichstein ('76, '78, '79), Buckton ('83), etc.

eggs are *predestined* as male-producing or female-producing irrespective of the chromosome-number; but it is plain that sex is not determined in the egg until the establishment of the chromosome-combination characteristic of the sex in question. There could not be a clearer illustration of the fact that the sex-chromosomes should not be regarded as the sole determiners of sex but only as differential factors in a complex reaction-system[1] (p. 916).[1]

Still a different case is offered by *Dinophilus apatris*. Shearer ('13) endeavored to show that this form is essentially of the rotifer type, *i. e.*, that the size-difference between the eggs results from fertilization, unfertilized eggs remaining very small and producing males, the fertilized ones becoming larger and producing females. The subsequent work of Nachtsheim ('19) proved, however, that this was an error; for virgin females, raised from the egg in complete isolation from the males, produce eggs of both kinds, and unfertilized eggs do not divide at all. Both kinds of eggs, form two polocytes and undergo complete reduction (from 20 to 10 chromosomes), and both are fertilized in normal fashion (Fig. 117).

The explanation of this case is still problematical. The most natural one would seem to be (as in the case of the bird's egg) that the female is here the digametic sex and that the mode of maturation of the egg is determined by its size—as certainly occurs in the parthenogenetic eggs of *Phylloxera*, different as the two cases otherwise are. It is possible that the female is homogametic and that selective fertilization occurs; but this seems less probable. In any case we may probably assume without error that in one way or another these eggs, too, ultimately acquire the chromosome-combination appropriate to their sex.

IV. The Chromosomes in Hermaphrodites, Intersexes, and Gynandromorphs

1. Hermaphrodites and Intersexes

Important light will no doubt be thrown on the sex-producing mechanism by the further study of the group of related phenomena enumerated in the above heading. Unfortunately our actual cytological knowledge in this subject is extremely limited. In hermaphrodites of the usual type, *e. g.*, in oligochætes, leeches, pulmonates or ascidians, there is still no sufficient evidence of the existence of sex-chromosomes or of any connection between the chromosomes and sex-production. There is, however, one case among the hermaphroditic nematodes in which the existence of sex-chromosomes is definitely established by the independent work of Boveri ('11) and of Schleip ('11).

[1] For further discussion of this point, see p. 815.

This case is offered by the nematode *Angiostomum* (*Rhabditis*) *nigrovenosum*, a form characterized by an alternation of generation between a free-living diœcious form and a parasitic hermaphroditic form that lives in the lungs of the frog.[1] In the diœcious generation males and females occur in nearly equal numbers. The fertilized eggs of this generation develop into the parasitic, hermaphrodite form which has the general morphology of a female, possessing an "ovary" which first produces oögonia and somewhat later also spermatogonia, the two being formed in irregularly alternating zones. From the spermatogonia arise spermatocytes which undergo two divisions as usual, and produce functional sperms. The eggs are fertilized by sperms of the same individual (the hermaphrodite is strictly self-fertilizing) and produce the free-living males and females in approximately equal numbers.

Cytological examination shows that in the parasitic (hermaphroditic) generation the diploid number of chromosomes is 12 which in the maturation of the egg is reduced to one-half, each egg receiving six chromosomes (Fig. 387). During the spermatogenesis of this generation, on the other hand, but half the sperms receive six chromosomes, the other half only five owing to the fact that in the second division one of the X-chromosomes remains near the equator, fails to enter the daughter-nucleus and degenerates. It thus comes to pass that one spermatid of each pair receives a complete haploid group of six chromosomes, the other but five.

Schleip demonstrated correspondingly that in fertilization the egg-nucleus contributes always six chromosomes, while the sperm-nucleus contributes in some cases six, in others five, and also found two kinds of embryos containing respectively 12 and 11 chromosomes. Boveri's observations, finally, prove that the males of the diœcious generation have 11 chromosomes, and that half the sperms receive 6 chromosomes and half 5, as we should expect.

A difficulty arises from the fact that we are thus led to expect the resulting zygotes to be likewise of two classes, *i. e.*, females (or hermaphrodites) with 12 chromosomes and males with 11, but in point of fact, all the fertilized eggs produce hermaphrodites (modified females) with 12 chromosomes. The explanation of this is unknown; but both Boveri and Schleip have suggested that the male-producing sperm (*i. e.*, the 5-chromosome or no-X class) of this generation may be non-functional and degenerate. The probability of this will readily be admitted when we recall the analogous phenomena in the aphids or phylloxerans. It is also possible that the 11-chromosome zygotes are not viable. This interesting case can hardly be taken as typical of hermaphrodites generally; for this species is hermaphro-

[1] For further facts concerning the sexual relations in nematodes, see p. 230.

ditic during only a portion of its life-cycle, and the hermaphroditic generation is obviously a modified female.

Another case of supposed sex-chromosomes in a hermaphrodite is described by Zarnik ('11) in the pteropod *Cressus;* but analysis of the results
reveals a number of serious difficulties which Zarnik endeavors to meet by a
number of rather complicated assumptions. These will here be passed over
since the subsequent work of Schitz ('17) has raised serious doubts concern-

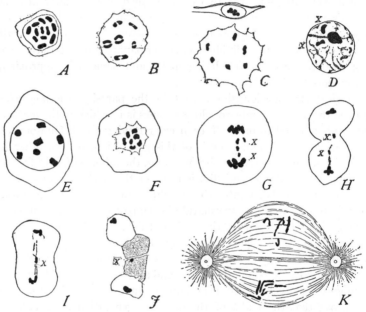

Fig. 387.—Sex-chromosomes in the hermaphroditic nematode *Angiostomum
nigrovenosum* (SCHLEIP).

A, oögonial mitosis, 12 chromosomes; B, first polar mitosis of the egg, 6 tetrads; C, second polar
mitosis; D, spermatocyte, growth-period, two chromosome-nucleoli (X-chromosomes); E, primary
spermatocyte prophase, 5 bivalents and 2 (X and X) univalent; F, polar view, and G, side-view of
first anaphase, the two X-chromosomes (divided) lagging; H, second spermatocyte-telophase, two
lagging X-chromosomes; I, later telophase, one X has passed to the pole, while one lags; J, two
sister-spermatids, with lagging X in one; K, first cleavage-figure of fertilized egg, showing 6 egg-
chromosomes below and 5 sperm-chromosomes above.

ing Zarnik's observations. The whole subject of the chromosomes of hermaphrodites evidently calls for further examination. In such an inquiry it
will be important to bear in mind that the true hermaphrodite should not
be thought of as merely a composite of male and female, but as the result
of a definite genetic complex analogous to that which by the mosaic-like
patterns of pigment ("spotting-factors," etc.) are determined in other organisms; and the same in principle is true of the closely related phenomena
of intersexuality, as shown especially by Goldschmidt ('19). In both these

cases, therefore, it may very well be that the sex-producing mechanism is cytologically unrecognizable.

2. Gynandromorphs

A remarkable opportunity for testing the chromosome-theory of sex-production is offered by sex-mosaics or gynandromorphs, the genetics of which have been carefully examined in hybrid races of *Drosophila* by Morgan and Bridges ('19). Though the cytological phenomena are not yet directly known, important suggestions have been made concerning the underlying chromosome-conditions. One of these was based by Boveri on the facts of partial fertilization in which the sperm-nucleus does not conjugate with the egg-nucleus until the 2-cell stage or even later (p. 458). In such embryos some of the nuclei are of purely maternal origin and hence of haploid constitution containing but one X-chromosome, while those arising from the fusion-nucleus, are of biparental origin and of diploid constitution, and may contain XX. We should expect such diploid regions to show female sex-linked characters and the haploid regions male characters, the particular pattern of the sex-mosaic depending upon the period and place at which the fusion-nucleus is formed. This hypothesis may be tested genetically by the study of hybrid gynandromorphs derived from parents differing in respect to one or more sex-linked characters; and a large number of such gynandromorphs, some of them of most remarkable type, have been obtained in *Drosophila*. The study of these and other forms led to two new hypotheses. One of these assumed gynandromorphs to arise from dispermic eggs in which one sperm-nucleus unites with the egg-nucleus, while the other develops independently in the egg.[1] In the later work of Morgan and Bridges it is shown that a more probable explanation is found in the assumption of an elimination of one X-chromosome at an early division of a cleavage-nucleus of a female (XX) embryo by a lagging or dislocation on the spindle. The effect of this should be the production of larvæ and adults having two kinds of nuclei, some being of XX constitution, others of XO. This hypothesis was tested by the study of many hybrid gynandromorphs combining in each case two or more different sex-linked characters of the two parental races. Since the factors for such characters are known to be borne by the X-chromosomes alone it was thus possible to determine the presumable distribution of these chromosomes by the genetic evidence. A critical test of the hypothesis is given in these cases by non-sex-linked characters, *i. e.*, those borne by autosomes; for these are present throughout, while the sexual characters of the gynandromorph show only in certain regions. It is thus possible, for instance, to obtain gynandromorphs

---

[1] Morgan, '05.

that show a white eye or miniature wing on the male side, and a red eye or normal wing on the female, while both sides alike show dominant auto-somal characters derived from one or both parents. The results seem to prove conclusively that the *Drosophila* cases cannot be explained by either partial fertilization or dispermy and only find an intelligible explanation on the elimination-hypothesis. Apart from the genetic evidence, the hypothe-sis of elimination has in its favor the somewhat analogous elimination of one X-chromosome in *Rhabditis nigrovenosa* above described (p. 809) or in the maturation of the male-producing eggs in the aphids and phyllox-erans, through which the female or XX-condition is converted into the male.

V. The Sex-chromosomes in Plants

The problem of sex-determination in higher plants assumes a some-what different aspect from that offered by animals, since in the former the true sexual generation or gametophyte is a haploid organism while the diploid generation is an asexual sporophyte. Obviously, therefore, the chromosomal relations of the true males and females (*i. e.*, the gameto-phytes) cannot be identical with those of animals; we cannot, for example, suppose the female to be XX and the male XY, since these conditions can only occur in a diploid organism. It is, however, important to bear in mind that in diœcious plants a sexual differentiation is clearly shown already in the diploid sporophyte, the sexual characters being as it were thrown back or impressed upon the asexual generation. In practice, therefore, it is found convenient to speak of the staminate (microspore- or pollen-producing) sporophytes as "male" and of the pistillate or megaspore-producing ones as "female."

If the sex-chromosomes of plants follow the same general scheme as in animals we should look for their segregation in the meiotic or spore-forming divisions; and the sexual predestination of the spores, earlier referred to (p. 746) leads to the same expectation. This expectation is borne out by the history of the sex-chromosomes in the three cases thus far definitely made known. The clearest of these is that of the liverwort *Sphærocarpus*, where Allen ('17, '19) demonstrated the existence of an unequal pair of sex-chro-mosomes similar in a general way to the XY-pair of insects and by him designated by the same names.[1] The number of chromosomes in thalli of both sexes is eight (haploid) one of these being the large "X-chromosome" in the females while in the male its place is taken by the small "Y" (Fig. 388). The diploid groups (of the sporophyte) should, accordingly, include

---

[1] A few earlier observers have recorded in the sporogenesis either lagging chromosomes or such as pass precociously to the poles, Cardiff ('06) on *Salomonia,* Darling ('09) on *Acer*: but there is no evidence to show that these are sex-chromosomes.

16 chromosomes, including seven equal pairs and one unequal XY-pair; and this is clearly the case. The total number is about 16, including a single large X-chromosome. Unluckily the small Y-chromosome has not yet been identified, and does not appear in the figures; this, however, is probably due to an accident of the technique. We should expect that in the sporogenesis X and Y should couple to form an XY-bivalent and then disjoin. Though the proof of this is not complete, it is practically certain that such is the case, since Allen found that the second or homeotypic division is of two types, both showing eight chromosomes, one containing the "X-chromosome" and one the "Y," quite as in the meiosis of the Cole-

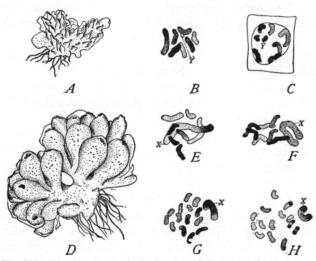

Fig. 388.—Sex-chromosomes in the liverwort *Sphærocarpus* (ALLEN).

A, male gametophytes; *B*, haploid chromosome-group from the same (wall of antheridium); *C*, prophase nucleus from same; *D*, female gametophyte; *E*, haploid group from same (basal cell of archegonium); *F*, similar group (archegonial involucre); *G*, *H*, diploid chromosome-groups from young sporophyte (sister anaphase-groups from the same spindle).

optera or Diptera (p. 768). Apparently, therefore, no doubt can exist that the heterokinesis or disjunction of X and Y takes place in the first or heterotypic division as in Diptera or Coleoptera; this, however, has not yet actually been observed. In any case it is clear that half the spores receive the X-chromosome and half the Y, the former producing female gametophytes and the latter male.

This result is confirmed by the work of Santos ('23) on the diœcious seed-plant *Elodea*, the diploid (sporophytic) groups of which show about 48 chromosomes including one large equal pair and one smaller very unequal one (supposedly an XY-pair). In the heterotypic division X and Y disjoin, so that half the pollen-grains receive X and half Y. Since this agrees closely with Allen's results on *Sphærocarpus* and is in harmony with Correns' conclusions on the sexual predestination of the pollen-grains in *Bryonia dioica* (p. 743) a strong presumption is created that these chromosomes are in fact sex-chromosomes analogous to those observed in animals.

In *Rumex acetosa* Kihara and Ono ('23) report a condition that seems to differ from all other known cases in the presence of a double Y-element. The male diploid number is 15, the heterotypic division showing 6 bivalents and one trivalent element consisting of one large X-chromosome opposed to two Y's. [1] In the heterotypic division this disjoins so as to give second sporocytes with $6+X=7$ chromosomes, and $6+2Y=8$, the resulting pollen-grains being correspondingly of two types. The diploid groups show either one large X ($=\male$) or two (presumably$=\female$).[2]

The foregoing three cases, alike in principle, thus offer a situation hitherto not known in animals. On the one hand, both X and Y are present in the diploid sporophyte, which may nevertheless be either "male" or "female." On the other hand, the male gametophyte contains Y but no X, while the female contains one X. All of these conditions, obviously, are contrary to those observed in animals, and demonstrate that although the mechanism concerned is similar in a general way, the X and Y-chromosomes of the two groups must operate very differently. In *Sphærocarpus* or *Elodea*, it would seem, we must either accept the sex-formulas $X=\female$ and $Y=\male$, as in Allen's terminology, or (if Y be considered as a smaller X) large $X=\female$ and small $X=\male$. The first alternative would lend plausibility to the suggestion of Castle ('09) considered at p. 821, that in female digamety in animals the female constitution may be XO, the male no-X. Under the second alternative the large X might stand for XX (*i. e.*, a double dose of the X-chromatin) and the small one for X (single dose). The sex-formulas for *Sphærocarpus* would thus become identical with those in the Diptera or Coleoptera; but a new difficulty arises from the fact that the sporophyte formula now becomes XXX. At present, therefore, we cannot certainly state the relation between the condition seen in *Sphærocarpus* and that in the XX–XY type of animals generally.[3]

---

[1] This element is closely similar to the XY-triad of the mantids (p. 778) though the X seems here to be single and the Y double.

[2] Winge ('23) reports several additional cases of supposed sex-chromosomes in seed-plants; but the evidence hardly seems adequate to establish their nature.

[3] The segregation of sex in monœcious plants has an interesting bearing on this problem. In the monœcious moss *Funaria hygrometrica* the Marchals found that both male and female gametophytes may arise from the same protonema. Collins ('19, '20) found, however, in this species that gametophytes produced by regeneration from antheridia or the surrounding perigonial leaves of a "male flower" produce only antheridia, while those from the "female flower" produce only archegonia. These facts suggest that there is a kind of separation or "somatic segregation" of sex-factors in the haploid tissue of the gametophyte prior to the gamete-formation and their subsequent reunion in

VI GENERAL CONSIDERATIONS

The combined cytological and genetical investigation of sex has clearly revealed the underlying general mechanism of sex-production but still offers only an incomplete solution of many interesting further problems, both physiological and morphological, which can here only be outlined in a general way.

1. Physiological Problems

How the sex-chromosomes operate in sex-determination is still in large degree an unsolved puzzle which belongs to the larger problem of the determinative action of chromosomes generally. In its discussion we may for the present limit it to the more frequent case in which the male is the digametic sex and the female the homogametic. The problem may also be simplified by excluding the Y-chromosome, since it may be absent without affecting sex-determination. The proof of this is given in the genus *Metapodius*, where a Y-chromosome is usually present but may be absent from certain individuals of the species without in any visible way affecting either sex or the secondary sexual characters (Wilson, '09); and the same is possibly the case also in man (p. 766).[1]

a. Sex-chromosomes and Sex-determination. It has often been urged that the sex-chromosomes may not be determiners of sex but only its cytological accompaniments or indicators ("index-hypothesis") which merely follow sex without playing any part in its causation; but this has not stood the test of critical analysis and has been decisively disproved by Bridges' crucial investigations on non-disjunction (p. 947), and also by those of L. V. Morgan on X-linkage (p. 946). In upholding the contrary view that the sex-chromosomes (X) are true sex-determining factors we must guard against the crude notion that they are such in any exclusive sense. In relation to sex, as to other hereditary traits, the chromosomes form only one part of a larger factorial complex in which are involved other chromosomes (autosomes) as well as cytoplasmic factors (pp. 667, 817). Since, however, they form the visible differentials between the sexes we may for the moment conveniently speak of them as "sex-determiners" or "sex-differentiators."

---

fertilization; but it seems more probable that this is not a true segregation in the Mendelian sense but only an inhibition of one or the other sex-character, such as often appears in hermaphrodites.

[1] The nature of the Y-chromosome is still an unsolved puzzle. As the synaptic mate of X it evidently belongs to a long established mechanism of synapsis and disjunction such as we see in other chromosome-pairs. Bridges' work on non-disjunction shows that in *Drosophila* the absence of Y causes sterility; but the case of *Metapodius* shows that this cannot be general. There are a few sex-linked characters which behave as if borne by the Y-chromosome, being confined to the male line and apparently non-transmissible through the female. One of these is a pigment-spot in a fish (Schmidt, '20), the other the web-toed character in man (Schofield,' 21). See Winge ('22), Castle ('22).

It might be supposed that there are two kinds of X-chromosomes re‐ spectively male-determining and female-determining; but this involves us in numerous difficulties. To give but a single example: In the haploid par‐ thenogenesis of the rotifer or bee the X-chromosome of the mature egg must by the hypothesis contain the ♂ -determining X-chromosome, since, if unfertilized, it always develops into a male.   If fertilized it always produces a female; and by the hypothesis this must be due to the introduction of a dominant ♀-determining X by the sperm; but since the male is haploid its single X must be ♂-determining — a *reductio ad absurdum*. Many other diffi‐ culties of the same type exist. [1] All these difficulties disappear if we assume that in any particular species there is but one kind of X-chromosome, in itself neither male-determining nor female-determining but so adjusted to the general mechanism of development that when single it swings develop‐ ment towards the male side, when double towards the female.   This view, essentially quantitative, ascribes to the egg the capacity to produce either the female or the male, according to the presence of more or less of X-sub‐ stance.[2]   Its correctness in principle is demonstrated by the above-men‐ tioned observations of Bridges and of L. V. Morgan, which prove that the presence of two X-chromosomes in the zygote, however caused, determines such a zygote *ipso facto* as a female whatever be the situation in the gametes. Thus, a normal X-bearing egg gives rise to a male if fertilized by a no-X or Y-bearing sperm; if, however, as a result of non-disjunction or X-link‐ age the mature egg contain XX it produces a female even when fertilized by the no-X or "male-producing" sperm.   The demonstrative proof of this, in which cytology and genetics unite, will be considered later (pp. 947, 948).

With these facts in mind we are in a position to look more closely into the relation of the X-chromosome to the remainder of the factorial complex. That other chromosomes (autosomes) play a part in sex-determination has recently been demonstrated in an interesting way by Bridges' obser‐ vations on triploid mutants in *Drosophila*.[3] Among various heteroploid forms obtained in certain strains of these flies, individuals were obtained with one, two or three X-chromosomes, variously combined with trisomic, disomic or monosomic conditions of the other chromosome-pairs.   Indi‐ viduals that are triploid throughout (including 3 X's) are females scarcely different from the normal diploid females; but those having two X's and

---

[1] See Castle ('03), Wilson ('06, '09).

[2] Wilson ('09, '11). This conclusion was a more specific development of Morgan's earlier sugges‐ tion ('03, '07) that sex might be determined by the relative quantity of nuclear substance. Both cytological and genetic evidence indicates that the X-substance forms but a part, and probably a small part, of the X-chromosomes.

[4] Bridges ('21, '22). Morgan, Sturtevant and Bridges ('21).

otherwise triploid are *inter-sexes* and are also larger and different from the normal in some other definite respects. Here it is plain that the female character depends not alone on the presence of two X's but also on the autosome-combination; *i. e.*, sex must be determined by a certain balanced relation between sex-chromosomes and autosomes. Equally interesting is the fact that individuals with 3 X's but otherwise diploid are sterile females of low viability that differ decidedly in somatic characters from the normal; while one-X individuals otherwise triploid are males, also of peculiar and characteristic somatic type. These facts clearly indicate that the X-chromosome affects not only sex-production but also the somatic characters; while conversely the autosomes as a group, besides their somatic effects, also embody a tendency towards male-production. *The actual performance of the zygote, therefore, is a common effect of the whole group, and is turned this way or that as the result of a quantitative balance between X-chromosomes and autosomes.*[1] This shows specifically that the X-chromosomes should not be thought of as the sole determiners of sex but only as *differentiators;* and in this respect they are to be regarded precisely as we regard other kinds of chromosomes.

Even this conclusion does not go far enough; for it is also clear that the effect of chromosome-combinations during development can only be realized by coöperation with other, presumably cytoplasmic activities. In the hermaphroditic generation of *Angiostomum nigrovenosum*, for example (p. 809), the oögonia and oöcytes are characterized by the presence of XX (as in the females of the diœcious generation), while the males have X. In the hermaphroditic gonad, however, as both Boveri and Schleip have emphasized, the spermatocytes are clearly differentiated from the oöcytes at a time *when both X-chromosomes* are still present. This fact led Boveri and Schleip to the conclusion that the X-chromosomes cannot be primary determining causes of sex; and that they can at most be concerned only with the determination of secondary characters. Upon further consideration, however, the matter will appear in a different light.

The case of the phylloxerans is instructive in connection with this question. Here, as already described (p. 807), the eggs are visibly predestined as male and female before the elimination of one X-element to produce the characteristic male nuclear constitution (p. 791). Morgan concluded from these facts that sex is already determined in these eggs before they are laid, and before the polar spindle has developed; sex therefore is determined in the presence of all the chromosomes ('09, p. 271). This, however, is a question of definition. It seems preferable to say that sex is not actually determined until all the conditions necessary for its production have been

[1] *Cf.* p. 816.

fulfilled, one of these being the establishment of the appropriate nuclear constitution. A similar question is raised by the spermatogenesis of the aphids and phylloxerans. Here, as shown by Morgan, Stevens and Baehr, the first spermatocyte-division is unequal, and it is always the larger of the two products into which the X-element passes in the heterokinesis (p. 792). Baehr shows further that a mass of mitochondria passes into the larger cell, but apparently does not enter the smaller one (Fig. 381). Here, evidently, the pole to which X passes is already predestined as the female-producing or X-pole before heterokinesis takes place. This case clearly brings out the distinction between sex-predestination and sex-determination. Manifestly the X-class of spermatocytes, though normally *predestined* as female-producing, are not predetermined as females. On the contrary could these cells (like the X-bearing ova of rotifers or bees) undergo complete parthenogenetic development they would, presumably, give rise to males because their nuclear constitution is X, not XX.

The analysis enters upon a further stage when we consider hermaphroditism, intersexuality, and the sex of haploid organisms, in all of which cases the simple quantitative interpretation seems to require a more precise physiological formulation. In the Lepidoptera, for example, the chromosome-mechanism is identical with that seen in male digamety, yet its relation to sex-production is exactly the opposite; and so far as visible facts go, we might equally well maintain that in this group XX = ♂ and XO = ♀. In the haploid organism (*e. g.*, *Sphærocarpus*) neither set of formulas can be used. We might here assume a quantitative relation, of simpler type, one sex containing X and the other no-X or less X (p. 814); but this in its turn breaks down in the case of hermaphroditism or intersexuality. Here it is not easy to avoid the conception of more specific male-determining and female-determining factors (*e. g.*, enzymes or hormones), which call forth corresponding reactions in the developing germ.[1] These hypothetical factors have conveniently been designated by Morgan as *M* or *F*, or, correspondingly, as *andrase* and *gynase*.[2] We here consider this hypothesis only in its relation to the chromosome-mechanism.

In the case of male digamety Morgan assumed the M-factor to be present equally in all the gametes, borne presumably by one or more of the autosome-pairs, while the F-factor is borne by the X-chromosome. All the mature eggs, therefore, are FM, while the sperms are either FM or OM (in which F = X). The observed results then follow under the assumption that FF (XX) dominates over MM, while MM dominates over F. Thus:

---

[1] The conception of such opposing sex-factors or sex-substances was suggested by Morgan ('11a, '11b, '13) and by Woltereck ('11), to whom is due the idea that they may be zymogens. It was further developed especially by Goldschmidt ('14, '17, '20) in its application to intersexes.

[2] Goldschmidt ('17), etc.

Egg XA (= FM) + Sperm XA (= FM) = XXAA = FF (MM) ♀.
Egg XA (= FM) + Sperm OA (or YA) = XOAA = (FO) MM ♂.

These formulas must not be taken too literally; they offer merely a convenient symbolism. The X-chromosome, for instance, here stands for the F-factor; but the genetic evidence, derived especially from non-disjunction, seems to prove that zygotes lacking X are non-viable (p. 948). The X-chromosome is therefore necessary for the production of males as well as females.[1]

The conception of Goldschmidt is similar in principle, but suggests that M may be borne by the cytoplasm (or possibly by the Y-chromosome). In the case of female digamety the hypothesis is reversed, the X-chromosome being assumed to carry M, while F is borne by the cytoplasm of the ovum (or possibly by the Y-chromosome) Thus:

Egg XA (=MF) + Sperm XA (=MF) = XXAA = MM(FF) ♂.
Egg OA or YA (=OF) + Sperm XA (=MF) = XOAA or XYAA = (MO) FF ♀.

This hypothesis is ingeniously applied to the explanation of intersexuality in Lepidoptera by Goldschmidt ('16, '17, '20, etc.) by the additional assumption that in some races both sex-factors, M and F, vary quantitatively thus giving different combinations of male and female characters. In case of ordinary hermaphrodites the simplest assumption would be that the M and F factors are equally balanced, and that both are borne by all the gametes, the sexual formula thus becoming MMFF; and from such a starting-point we readily pass to the sex of haploid organisms and to the so-called determination of sex by external conditions.[2]

The foregoing conceptions are in harmony with numerous anatomical facts, such as the frequent presence in one sex of rudimentary structures that are fully developed and functional in the opposite sex, many of which were emphasized by Darwin and other earlier writers. From the cytological standpoint further questions of fundamental interest for the theory of sex-determination are raised by the fact that in some cases the ovary may produce spermatocytes and sperms as well as ova or, contrariwise, the testis may produce, in addition to spermatocytes and sperms, cells resembling oöcytes. An example of the former case is offered by the parasitic nematode *Angiostomum nigrovenosum*, earlier considered (p. 809), in which this condition undoubtedly represents a true hermaphroditism. On the other hand, it is doubtful whether the same can be said of the reverse case. The occasional

[1] *Cf.* Morgan, Sturtevant, Muller and Bridges ('23).
[2] For development of this conception see G. Hertwig ('21).

presence of oöcyte-like cells in the testis of adult diœcious animals has been noted by many observers; [1] in some cases such cells are of regular occurrence in the earlier stages of the testis though they later disappear. A conspicuous case of this is offered in the frog, where the nature of these "ova" is a long debated question. Some observers have considered them as true oöcytes and have in consequence considered the larvæ (of frogs) to be at first hermaphroditic, afterwards developing into either males or females. [2] On the other hand, a different view has been taken by Levi ('15) and especially by Swingle ('20, '21, '22), who have urged that the so-called "oöcytes" are hypertrophied spermatocytes. Swingle has proved in case of the bullfrog *Rana catesbiana* (which has a very long larval period) that they undergo a regular heterotypic mitosis quite like that of the spermatocytes though rarely going further than the anaphase. These cells later degenerate, to be replaced by functional spermatocytes derived from the sex-cords.

In case of the toad (*Bufo*) a further step appears in the fact that the oöcyte-like cells of the testis of the larval male are massed at the anterior end of the testis to form a definite structure, "Bidder's organ" [3] which persists in the adult male toad. The so-called oöcytes *do not, however, become functional ova* but degenerate, to be replaced by others periodically arising by fresh proliferations, but likewise in the end degenerating.

Closely similar to this in principle is the remarkable case of the stone-fly, *Perla*, in which the cytological conditions have been partially worked out. Some species of this genus are ordinary diœcious forms; but in *P. marginata* the upper region of the male gonad, common to both testes, is converted into a structure like that of an ovary and contains numerous large cells closely similar to oöcytes. [4] The resemblance is heightened by the fact that these cells pass through a regular bouquet-stage and undergo synapsis, and form yolk-spherules. As in the case of Bidder's organ, however, the "oöcytes" all degenerate soon after the synaptic stage. The remarkable fact in this case, determined by Junker, is that the " oögonia," from which arise the oöcyte-like cells, divide with the chromosome-number *characteristic of the male*, 22, while the female number is 24. [5] Here, therefore, oöcyte-like cells and a structure closely resembling an ovary, are produced *in the presence of the chromosome-number characteristic of the male*—a condition exactly the reverse of that seen in *Angiostomum nigrovenosum* (p. 809).

Junker himself (a pupil of Baltzer), concludes from this that "the chromo-

---

[1] For example in Crustacea, (Nebeski ('80), Ishikawa ('91) or in scorpions as observed by the writer.

[2] See especially Pflüger ('82), R. Hertwig ('04), Kuschakewitsch ('10), Witschi ('13, '14, '21).

[3] See King ('08).

[4] Schönemund, '12, Junker, '23.

[5] In the male, half the sperms receive 10 chromosomes and half 12, the X-element consisting of two components as in *Syromastes* (p. 773).

ₔomes have nothing to do with the determination of the primary sex-cells"
(*cf.* Boveri and Schleip, above) but this conclusion, to say the least, seems
premature. It is a significant fact that neither in this case nor in that of
Bidder's organ do the "oöcytes" become functional eggs. Even if they really
are oöcytes their invariable degeneration suggests that something is lacking
in their factorial complex, perhaps owing to a disturbance of the normal
balance between the sex-factors. In view, therefore, of the demonstrative
evidence of the determinative effect of the chromosome-combination offered
by non-disjunction, triploids, X-linkage, and other phenomena, we may well
suspend judgment concerning the case of *Perla* until its real meaning has
become clearer.

b. The Relation between Male and Female Digamety. Whether sex-digamety
in the male or in the female is the more primitive type is unknown; but for
the sake of discussion we may assume it to be the former. The transition
from one to the other seems to have taken place readily, and independently
in different groups, but in what manner is still purely conjectural. It seems
clear that both types employ the same general form of chromosome-mechanism, and one that automatically ensures the production of digamety in
one sex in each generation. In order not to prejudice the question some
writers have employed a different symbolism for the two types, employing in the one case $XX = ♀$ and XY (or XO) $= ♂$, and in the other $ZZ = ♂$ and
$ZW = ♀$;[1] the observed genetic results then follow on the assumption that the
factors for sex and sex-linked characters are borne by Z. The latter thus
becomes in all respects the analogue of the X-chromosome save that when
doubled it stands for the male instead of the female condition; and that such
is actually the case seems to be fully established by Seiler's work on the
Psychidæ.[2]

Concerning the possible relation between these two types we have as yet
only guesses. We might assume that the sex-factor and the chromosome-
mechanism are identical in both, in which case the difference would have to
be referred to a reversed reaction of the developing germ (*i. e.*, the remaining
hereditary complex) to that factor; but, as Morgan has pointed out,[3] it
seems simpler to assume that the difference somehow lies in the sex-
chromosomes themselves. Castle ('09) showed that the genetic results
in female digamety can be explained by the assumption that the female
condition is represented by X, the male by no-X; and this led to the further
suggestion that the cytological conditions might be expressed by the formulas XY (or XO) $= ♀$ and $YY = ♂$,[4] which would agree with all the observed
cytological conditions. More recently Castle ('21) has followed this up by

---

[1] See Morgan, Sturtevant, Müller and Bridges ('15), Morgan ('19).
[2] See p. 784 ff., Doncaster ('20).
[3] '19, p. 174.
[4] Wilson ('09b).

the suggestion that such a condition may have arisen through non-disjunction, giving various recombinations in the offspring of which two proved to be stable and self-perpetuating, namely, YY♂ and XXY♀, of which the latter, by permanent union of X and X, becomes XY.

This hypothesis calls for an additional assumption concerning the production of males; for Bridges's work on non-disjunction (p. 948) in *Drosophila* proves that zygotes of the YY (or no-X) class are non-viable. Most attempts to conceive the relation between the two types have in fact assumed neither a change in the reaction-system as a whole nor in the chromosome-mechanism *per se*, but in the sex-factors borne by the chromosomes. This view is taken by Morgan ('19, p. 174), and by Doncaster ('20); it seems also to form the basis of Goldschmidt's assumption regarding the reversal of dominance in the two types, and of the more recent development of his views by G. Hertwig. Whether these various possibilities can be decisively tested by further observation and experiment remains to be seen.

2. Morphological Problems. Evolution of the Sex-chromosomes [1]

The cytological evidence unmistakably indicates that the sex-chromosomes are fundamentally similar to other chromosomes and that they originally formed a pair of synaptic mates indistinguishable in appearance, behavior and visible structure; such a condition, indeed, seems still to exist in many animals (and plants) in which these chromosomes have not yet been identified as such. In this condition they still for the most part remain in the homogametic sex, their most striking peculiarities only appearing in the digametic sex. It is probable therefore that most of their special characteristics have resulted from their constantly heterozygous condition in one sex, which must have existed from a very ancient period. It is evident further that the X-chromosome is a body of complex constitution and that only a part of it, and probably only a very small part, forms the sex-differentiator. This is made plain, first, by the great differences in the size of this chromosome shown by different species, and even by rather closely related ones (p. 768). The complexity of organization of the X-chromosome is indicated in some cases by its visible structure (*e. g.*, in *Notonecta indica* or *Lygæus bicrucis*, p. 777); in others by its appearance as a group of components, constant in number and size-relations, which form separate chromosomes in the diploid groups and even in the meiotic divisions of the female, but are always associated to form a compound synaptic mate for the Y-chromosome in the corresponding divisions of the male. Such an extreme type of this as appears for instance in *Ascaris incurva* (p. 776), is connected by many interme-

[1] The conclusions here outlined were first indicated in Wilson, '11, though they were to some extent foreshadowed in earlier studies ('05 a, b, '06, etc.).

diate conditions with those in which X is always a single body or is linked with one of the autosomes. In all these cases it is probable that most of the X-material, whether in the form of chromosomes or of the separate components that appear in the compound types, has nothing to do directly with sex-determination but is only concerned with sex-linked heredity (p. 939).[1] For the sake of convenience, therefore, we may speak of the sex-differentiator as the " sex-chromatin," which we may think of as a factor or specific substance, perhaps borne by a very minute single body of the same nature as those which carry other Mendelian factors.

To picture the evolution of the sex-chromosomes in detail is not possible at present. There is some reason to suspect that primitively the "sex-chromatin" may have been widely distributed among the chromosomes, perhaps shared by the entire group.[2] All the facts indicate that this chromatin early became localized in one of the chromosome-pairs, originally homozygous in both sexes in respect to all the factors excepting the X-factor. Such a pair would correspond essentially to the XX- and XY-pairs as now generally understood. For our purpose it may be thought of as a YY-pair, one member of which (in the heterozygous sex) contains the X-chromatin.[3] A condition more or less like this may have persisted in many cases with little or no modification; and to this perhaps may be ascribed the failure to find sex-chromosomes in many species. In such cases the heterozygous nature of the sex-pair would give no recognizable cytological sign, as is so often the case also in other heterozygous chromosome-pairs. In many cases, however, the heterozygous pair has become visibly heteromorphic in various ways, some of which are indicated in the diagram, Fig. 389. As this shows, the " X-chromosome," even in the more highly modified forms, may still be conceived as an "XY-chromosome" of which the synaptic mate is a Y-chromosome, the true nature of the pair being indicated in the male by the formula XY–Y and in the female by XY–XY. In one line of change (B) the no-X member of the original pair (the Y-chromosome) has become reduced step by step to final disappearance; in another (C) the no-X member or Y-chromosome has persisted. In either case the X-containing member may have progressively broken up into separate components one of which is assumed to contain the X-chromatin.

As the diagram also shows, linkage of the X-chrosomome produces a condition closely similar to some of those seen in series A (for example in *Thyanta calceata*) and it seems possible that in some cases such linkage is not a secondary union (as has often been assumed) but a more or less direct survival of a more primitive association. In the curious case of *Blaps*, for

---

[1] *Cf.* Wilson ('11). [2] See *Pseudococcus*, p. 778. *Cf.* Schrader ('20, '23), Gutherz ('23).
[3] *Cf.* Stevens ('06), Wilson ('11).

example (Fig. 378), we might conceive the "X-complex" as a YY-pair of larger chromosomes with one member of which are associated one large and two small X-components, the whole forming an XY-complex.

Originally, we may assume, the YY-pair was itself homozygous, in which case no sex-linked heredity would appear. Sex-linkage, and perhaps certain forms of secondary sexual characters, would appear as soon as this pair became heterozygous in respect to factors borne by the Y-chromatin in either synaptic mate. One way in which this has occurred, evidently, has been by reduction and finally disappearance of the Y-chromosome; but even

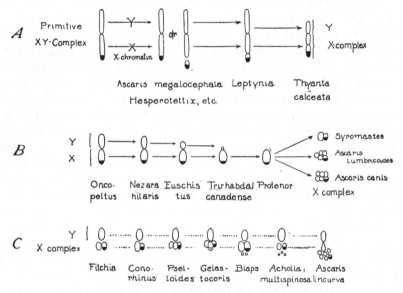

Fig. 389.—Diagram of the possible relations of the *XY*-complex.

A, relations of the primitive complex to linear aggregates; *B*, reduction and disappearance of *Y*, breaking up of *X*; *C*, persistence of *Y*, breaking up of *X*.

when it has persisted we may perhaps infer from its remarkable genetic emptiness, which genetic writers have emphasized, that it has lost many factors even though its main body still remains to play the part of a synaptic mate to the X-chromosome (*cf.* p. 815). The Y-chromosome may, however, have remained homozygous for many factors which have not yet been detected by genetic study.

3. Conclusion

To what extent sex may be determined by an automatically operating nuclear mechanism such as has here been described is unknown; but a mechanism that exists in the same general form in organisms as diverse as bryophytes, nematodes, echinoderms, arthropods and vertebrates is beyond a doubt one of far-reaching significance, and may be as widely distributed as Mendelian heredity generally. The nature of the X-chromatin, its origin and mode of action, are alike unknown, the questions here raised merging into the larger one of the physiological relations of nucleus and cytosome (p. 653). In some manner, no doubt, this chromatin affects the metabolism of the cell; and since one sex differs from the other by a relative excess of this substance we are led to suspect a characteristic and fundamental difference of metabolism between the sexes, and one that is either itself quantitative or has a quantitative basis. This is not to be escaped by the assumption of specific male-determining and female-determining factors (M and F); for, as has been indicated, this assumption can only be worked out under the additional postulate that a quantitative factor plays the decisive rôle in throwing these factors into action. Beyond this we enter a region of pure speculation; but we cannot wholly put aside the thought that sex may be rooted in a simple principle of plus and minus that holds true of all sexual organisms from the lowest to the highest [1] and may perhaps in some manner fit with Bütschli's hypothesis concerning the origin of syngamy (p. 616).

LITERATURE X

(See also II, IV, V, VI, VII, XII. For abbreviations, see General Literature List.)

de Baehr, W., '09. Die Oogenese bei einigen viviparen Aphididen, etc.: *A. Zf.*, III.
Id., '20. Recherches sur la maturation des œufs parthénogénétiques, etc.: *L. C.*, XXX, 2.
Baltzer, F., '14. Die Bestimmung des Geschlechts nebst einer Analyse des Geschlechtsdimorphismus bei *Bonellia: M. Z. S.*, XXII.
Beard, J., '02. The Determination of Sex in Animal Development: *Z. J.*, XVI, 4.
Blakeslee, A. F., '06 (VII).
Boring and **Pearl,** '14. The Odd Chromosome in the Spermatogenesis of the Domestic Chicken: *J. E. Z.*, XVI.
Castle, W. E., '03. The Heredity of Sex: *B. M. Z.*, XL, 4.
'09. A Mendelian View of Sex-Heredity: *Science*, XXI.
Caullery, M., '13. Les problèmes de la sexualité: *Flammarion, Paris.*
Correns, C., '06. Die Vererbung der Geschlechtsformen bei den gynodiöcischen Pflanzen: *B. D. B. G.*, XXIV.
'13. Geschlechterverteilung und Geschlechtsbestimmung (bei Pflanzen): *H. Nw.*, IV.
'13. Selbsterilität und Individualstoffe: *B. C.*, XXXIII.
Correns and **Goldschmidt,** '13. Die Vererbung und Bestimmung des Geschlechtes: *Berlin.*
Cuénot, '99 Sur la détermination du sexe chez les animaux: *B. S. F. B.*, XXXII.
Doncaster, L., '14. The Determination of Sex: *Cambridge Univ. Press*, Cambridge.
Geddes and **Thomson,** '99. The Evolution of Sex: *London.*

---

[1] Wilson ('10a, p. 591).

Goldschmidt, R., '20a. Untersuchungen über Intersexualität: Zeitschr. f. ind. Abst. u. Vererbungslehre, XXIII.

'20b. Mechanismus und Physiologie der Geschlechtsbestimmung: *Berlin, Bornträger.*

Goodrich, H. B., '16. The Germ-Cells in *Ascaris incurva: J. E. Z.,* XXI.

Gulick, A., '11. Ueber die Geschlechtschromosomen bei einigen Nematoden, etc.: *A. Zf.,* VI.

Guyer, M., '16. Studies on the Chromosomes of the common Fowl, etc.: *B. B.,* XXXI.

Hertwig, G., '21. Das Sexualitätsproblem: *B. Z.,* XI.

Hertwig, R., '12. Ueber den derzeitigen Stand des Sexualitätsproblem: *B. C.,* XXXII.

Marchal, É. and É., '06. (VII).

Maupas, M., '00. Modes et formes de reproduction chez les Nématodes: *A. Z. E.* Sér. T, VIII.

McClung, C. E., '01. Notes on the Accessory Chromosome: *A. A.,* XX.

'02a. The Accessory Chromosome—Sex Determinant?: *B. B.,* III.

Meisenheimer, J., '13. Geschlechtsverteilung und Geschlechtsbestimmung (bei Tieren): *H. Nw.,* IV, *Fischer, Jena.*

Mohr, O., '16a. Sind die Heterochromosomen wahre Chromosomen?: *A. Zf.,* XIV.

'14. Studien über die Chromatinreifung, etc., bei *Locusta: A. B.,* XXIX.

Montgomery, T. H., '01, '06. (See XI.)

Morgan, T. H., '09. (See also XII.) A biological and cytological Study of Sex Determination in Phylloxerans and Aphids: *J. E. Z.,* VII, 2.

'13. Heredity and Sex: *Columbia Univ. Press, N. Y.*

Morgan and **Bridges, C. B.,** '19. The Origin of Gynandromorphs: *P. C.,* I, 278, Part I.

Mulsow, K., '12. Der Chromosomencyclus bei *Ancyracanthus, A. Zf.,* IX.

Nachtsheim, H., '13. Cytologische Studien über die Geschlechtsbestimmung bei der Honigbiene: *A. Zf.,* XI.

'19. Zytologische und experimentalle Untersuchungen über die Geschlechtsbestimmung bei *Dinophilus: A. M. A.,* XCIII.

Painter, T. S., '21. Studies in Reptilian Spermatogenesis (Lizards): *J. E. Z.,* XXXIV.

'22a. Studies in Mammalian Spermatogenesis I. (Opossum): *J. E. Z.,* XXXV.

'23. Studies in Mammalian Spermatogenesis II. (Man): *J. E. Z.,* XXXVII.

Payne, F., '08. On the sexual Differences of the Chromosome-groups in *Galgulus: B. B.,* XIV.

'09. Some New Types of Chromosome Distribution and their Relation to Sex: *B. B.,* XVI.

Riddle, Oscar, '16. Sex Control and Known Correlations in Pigeons: *A. N.,* L.

Schaffner, J., '22. Control of the sexual State in *Arisæna: A. J. B.,* IX.

Schleip, N., '12. Geschlechtsbestimmende Ursachen im Tierreich: *Ergeb. Fortschr. Zool.,* III.

Seiler, J., '17. Geschlechtschromosomen-Untersuchungen an Psychiden: *Z. A. V.,* XVIII.

'20, '21, '22, '23. Geschlechtschromosomen-Untersuchungen an Psychiden, I, II, III: *A. Zf.,* XV, XVI; IV (Parthenogenesis): *Z. A. V.,* XXXI.

Shull, A. F., '10, '11. (III).

Shull, G. H., '14. Sex-limited Inheritance in *Lychnis dioica* L.: *Z. A. V.*, XII.

Smith, G., '10, '12. Studies in the Experimental Analysis of Sex, I–IX: *Q. J.*, LIV–LVIII.

Stevens, N. M., '05. Studies in Spermatogenesis with especial Reference to the Accessory Chromosome: *P. C. I.*, XXXVI.

'06. Studies on Spermatogenesis, II: *P. C. I.*, XXXVI.

'08. (See XI.)

'09. Further Studies on the Chromosomes of Coleoptera: *J. E. Z.*, VI.

'11. Further Studies on the Heterochromosomes of the Mosquitoes: *B. B.*, XX.

Strasburger, E., '09 (V).

'10. Ueber geschlechtsbestimmende Ursachen: *J. W. B.*, XLVIII.

Wheeler, W. M., '03. The Origin of Female and Worker Ants from the Eggs of Parthenogenetic Workers: *Science*, XVIII.

Whitney, D. D.,'14 (III. *Hydatina*).

Wilson, E. B., '05a. The Chromosomes in Relation to the Determination of Sex in Insects: *Sci.*, XXII.

'05–'12. Studies on Chromosomes, I–VIII:

I. '05b. The Behavior of the Idiochromosomes in Hemiptera: *J. E. Z.*, II, 3.

II. '05c. The paired Microchromosomes, Idiochromosomes, etc.: *Ibid.*, II, 4.

III. '06. The Sexual Differences of the Chromosomes in Hemiptera, etc.. *Ibid.*, III, 1.

IV. '09a. The Accessory Chromosome in *Syromastes* and *Pyrrhocoris*, etc.: *Ibid.*, VI, 1.

V. '09b. The Chromosomes of *Metapodius: Ibid.*, VI, 2.

VI. '10b. A New Type of Chromosome-combination in *Metapodius: Ibid.*, IX, 2.

VII. '11. A Review of the Chromosomes of *Nezara* with some more general Considerations: *J. M.*, XXII, 1.

VIII. '12. Observations on the Maturation-Phenomena in certain Hemiptera, etc.: *J. E. Z.*, XIII, 3.

'09. Recent Researches on the Determination and Heredity of Sex: *Science*, XXIX.

'10a. The Chromosomes in Relation to the Determination of Sex: *S. P.*

'11b. The Sex Chromosomes: *A. M. A.*, LXXVII.

Zeleny and Faust, '15. Size Dimorphism in the Spermatozoa from single Testes: *J. E. Z.*, XVIII.

Zeleny, C., and Seney, C. T., '15. Variation in Head Length of Spermatozoa in Seven Additional Species of Insects: *J. E. Z.*, XIX.

CHAPTER XI

MORPHOLOGICAL PROBLEMS OF THE CHROMOSOMES

"For every chromosome that enters into a nucleus there persists in the resting-stage some kind of *unit*, which determines that from this nucleus come forth again exactly the same number of chromosomes that entered it, showing the same size-relations as before and often also the same grouping." BOVERI.[1]

I. THE INDIVIDUALITY OR GENETIC CONTINUITY OF THE CHROMOSOMES

In any general account of the history and genetic relations of the chromosomes in the life-cycle, we inevitably find ourselves speaking of them as if their identity were not really lost when they disappear from view in the resting or vegetative nucleus. The vast literature of the subject is everywhere colored by the implication that chromosomes, or something which they bear, have a persistent individuality that is carried over unchanged from generation to generation. This view has met with some determined opposition;[2] but with the advance of exact studies on the chromosomes scepticism has gradually yielded to the conviction that the chromosomes must, to say the least, be treated *as if they were* persistent individuals that do not wholly lose their identity at any period in the life of the cell but grow, divide and hand on their specific type of organization to their descendants. This does not mean that chromosomes are to be thought of as fixed and unchangeable bodies. Beyond a doubt they undergo complex processes of growth, structural transformation and reduction, in some cases so great that not more than a small fraction of the substance of the mother-chromosomes at its maximum development is passed on to the daughter-chromosomes. Whether we can rightly speak of a persistent "individuality" of the chromosomes is a question of terminology. What the facts do not permit us to doubt is that chromosomes conform to the principle of genetic continuity; that every chromosome which issues from a nucleus has some kind of direct genetic connection with a corresponding chromosome that has previously entered that nucleus.

1. Origin of the Theory

A first hint of the conception appears already in Van Beneden's oft-cited work on *Ascaris* ('83–'84) but the modern theory first took definite

---

[1] *Zellen-Studien*, VI., p. 229, 1907.
[2] See, for instance, Fick ('07), Meves ('11), Della Valle ('09, '12).

form in 1885 with Rabl's conclusion that the chromosomes lose neither their identity nor their grouping at the close of the division, but are only lost to view by branching out and anastomosing to form the framework of the resting nucleus.   Rabl believed that traces of the chromosomes could still be distinguished in the conformation of the nuclear framework during the interphase, the nucleus having a "pole" toward which the apices of the V-shaped chromosomes converge and an "antipole" at the opposite point (Fig. 390). During the ensuing prophases the chromosomes again come into view owing to the fact that "the chromatic substance flows back, through predetermined paths, into the primary nuclear threads." The latter (*i. e.*,

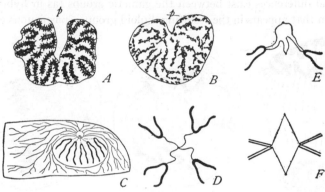

Fig. 390.—Diagrams of chromosome-individuality according to Rabl (*A*, *B*, from Haecker the others from Rabl).

A, earlier, and *B* later telophase-nuclei in epithelial cells of *Siredon* showing branching and vacuolization with retention of polarity; *C*, diagram of interkinesis showing persistent fibrillæ connecting center, chromosomes and general network; *D*, polar view of same (only 4 chromosomes shown); *E*, division of center and of fibrillæ connecting with chromosomes; *F*, fully established spindle.

the chromosomes) accordingly reappear in the same position and number as before.

The further development of this hypothesis was largely due to Boveri, who made it his own by a series of admirable researches extending from 1887 through nearly thirty years. A study of them impresses us both by the solidity of the foundation on which the theory is built and the skill with which its development was worked out. These researches and those that followed showed that the matter is not so simple as it was at first conceived; in principle nevertheless the conclusions of Rabl and Boveri are sustained to-day by a vast and always growing body of data. We need not hesitate, therefore, to accept Boveri's remarkable conclusion, already foreshadowed by Van Beneden, that *in all cells of the offspring produced from the zygote or fertilized egg half of the chromosomes are of maternal ancestry and half of paternal.*

2. General Evidence

Considered as a practical working hypothesis the principle of genetic continuity obviously offers the simplest way of formulating the relations of the chromosomes in the life-cycle generally.   In fertilization or syngamy two haploid groups are brought together to form a diploid group, which perpetuates itself by division until the process of meiosis again resolves it into two haploid groups.   If the germ-cell after reduction develops without fertilization the haploid number [1] may persist, and thus give rise to a haploid individual, as we see with special clearness in the gametophyte generation of plants and in the haploid type of natural animal parthenogenesis.   When numerical differences exist between the gametic groups (as in hybrids) it is their sum that appears in the resulting diploid groups, conspicuous examples

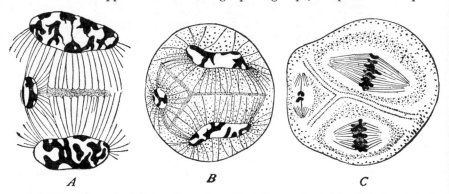

Fig. 391.—Abnormal mitosis in pollen-mother-cells of *Hemerocallis*, showing formation of small nucleus from one or two stray chromosomes and its subsequent division (JUEL).

of which are given by the relations of the chromosomes to sex (p. 751); and here again the diploid group thus established perpetuates itself by division.

The same principle holds for forms which normally have an odd number of chromosomes (irrespective of sex), such as the *lata* types of *Œnothera* with 15 chromosomes.   These, though subject to many irregularities, typically produce gametes with 7 and with 8 chromosomes respectively, the sum of which equals the diploid number (p. 944).   The same is true of forms in which supernumerary chromosomes occur.   Whatever be their number, they appear in the same number in successive generations of cells, both in the diploid groups and during the maturation-process (p. 872). Lastly, when by a natural mutation the number of chromosomes in the zygote is doubled (as in *Œnothera gigas*) this number is retained thereafter.

The foregoing results receive a demonstrative confirmation from the study

[1] In this and other similar statements the occasional formation of double or multiple groups is disregarded (p. 870).

of abnormal deviations from the typical numbers, whether arising spontaneously or produced experimentally; and here belongs some of the most important of the evidence brought forward by Boveri and his immediate followers. In the polar divisions of *Ascaris*, for example, one or both of the chromosomes destined for the second polar body are sometimes accidentally left in the egg. These chromosomes give rise in the egg to a reticular nucleus, indistinguishable from the egg-nucleus. At a later period this nu-

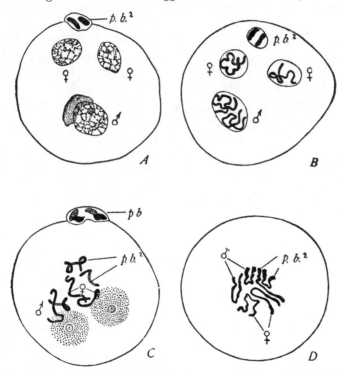

Fig. 392.—Evidence of the individuality of the chromosomes. Abnormalities in the fertilization of *Ascaris* (Boveri).

A, the two chromosomes of the egg-nucleus, accidentally separated, have given rise each to a reticular nucleus (♀, ♀); the sperm-nucleus below (♂); B, later stage of the same, a single chromosome in each egg-nucleus, two in the sperm-nucleus; C, an egg in which the second polar body has been retained; *p. b.*², the two chromosomes arising from it; ♀ the egg-chromosomes; ♂ the sperm-chromosomes; D, resulting equatorial plate with six chromosomes.

cleus gives rise to the same number of chromosomes as those that entered into its formation, *i. e.*, either one or two. These are drawn into the equatorial plate along with those derived from the pronuclei, and mitosis proceeds as usual, the number of chromosomes being, however, abnormally increased from four to five or six (Fig. 392). Again, the two chromosomes left in the egg after removal of the second polar body may accidentally become separated.   In this case each chromosome gives rise to a reticular nucleus of half the usual size, and from each of these a *single* chromosome is afterward formed (Fig. 392).   The same general result was given by Zur Strassen's ('98) studies on the history of giant embryos in *Ascaris*. These embryos arise by the fusion of previously separate eggs, and have been shown to be capable of development up to a late stage.   The embryos from such eggs show an increased number of chromosomes proportional to the number of nuclei that have united.   Thus in monospermic double eggs (variety *bivalens*) the number is triploid (six instead of four); in dispermic double eggs the number is tetraploid, being increased to eight (Fig. 393).

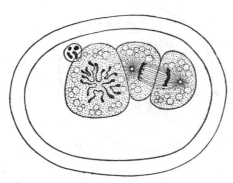

Fig. 393.—Giant-embryo of *Ascaris, var. bivalens,* arising from a double-fertilized double egg, showing eight chromosomes (*Zur Strassen*).

Later researches have afforded a mass of confirmatory data. Among the most striking are the experimental modifications of number in the eggs of sea-urchins and other animals.   It is possible by various methods to cause the egg (after maturation) to develop without union with a sperm-nucleus, for instance by artificial parthenogenesis (p. 472), or by slight etherization of the egg (p. 447).   In such cases the egg-nucleus divides with the haploid number of chromosomes (pp. 447, 476).   In merogonic fertilization the nuclei of the segmenting germ-cell are derived from the sperm-nucleus alone, and as before they divide with the haploid number.[1]   Conversely, the diploid number of the zygote may by artificial means be doubled so as to produce a tetraploid group.   In the resulting embryos, as Boveri showed (p. 729), the tetraploid number thereafter persists.

Essentially the same result is given by the experimental results of Gerassimoff on *Spirogyra* and of the Marchals on mosses, an account of which is given at p. 730.   A parallel to all these cases is given by the recent observations of G. and P. Hertwig ('20), which show that even in animals as highly organized as frogs development is possible with either the haploid (12), diploid (24) or triploid (36) number of chromosomes.   The eggs of the frog *Rana esculenta* fertilized by sperm of the toad *Bufo viridis*, in certain cases produce two kinds of embryos, larger and more vigorous diploid ones and smaller and less vigorous ones which, because of their small nuclei, are believed to be of haploid constitution.   This probably means that both are cases

---

[1] This was first proved by Boveri ('93, '95a) and Morgan ('95d).

of gynogenesis (p. 460), the haploid larvæ arising from eggs that have undergone complete reduction, the diploid from such eggs that have subsequently doubled their number (*e. g.*, by monocentric mitosis). This was tested by fertilizing frog's eggs showing this behavior with sperm of its own species, which produced triploid larvæ (up to 51 days old), in which the chromosomes were actually counted. The original eggs of this type were thus proved to have been diploid after maturation, and to have been fertilized by normal sperm, giving the triploid condition. Even more conclusive are those cases in which different numbers are experimentally produced in different nuclei of the same embryo, as in Boveri's dispermic sea-urchin larvæ or the hybrid sea-urchin larvæ of Baltzer and Herbst (pp. 917, 963). In these cases irregularities of chromosome-distribution, due to multipolar mitosis or the like, produce initial inequalities of chromosome-number which apparently cannot be equalized by regulative processes. The size of these nuclei depends upon the number of chromosomes which they receive (p. 730); and these differences, once established, seem to be irremediable. We thus see in the same larva patches of tissue showing mitoses with different chromosome-numbers and nuclei of different sizes, or larvæ with diploid hybrid nuclei on one side and purely maternal haploid nuclei on the other (p. 966).

Facts of this type demonstrate that *the number of chromosomes issuing from a resting-nucleus is determined by the number of chromosomes that have entered into its formation.* Opponents of the theory of genetic continuity, in particular Fick and Della Valle, have sought to interpret this as a simple quantitative effect, the size of the chromosomes being fixed by the physico-chemical quality of the chromatin and their number by its quantity. Fick urged that chromosomes are merely temporary packets of chromatin, "tactical formations" produced by a process comparable to the manœuvers of a military body. Della Valle compares chromosome-formation to that of liquid crystals and argues that their identity is wholly lost in the resting-nucleus.[1] The weakness of all such views lies in treating the chromosomes *en masse* without regard to their individual characteristics. The constant differences of the chromosomes in size, and often also in form and behavior, persist from one generation to another, whether the chromosome-group be haploid, diploid, triploid or tetraploid or broken up into other numbers by multipolar mitosis (p. 917).

[1] For criticisms of this view see Wilson ('09, '10, etc.), Montgomery ('10), McClung ('17), Tischler ('17), Parmenter ('19), Enriques ('21).

II. DIFFERENTIATION WITHIN THE CHROMOSOME GROUPS

That the chromosomes may show differences of size and shape in the same species was noted by Flemming, Strasburger and other earlier observers, but it did not at first occur to cytologists that such differences were other than fortuitous variations or fluctuations. Montgomery ('01) recognized the constancy of the differences of the chromosomes in respect to size and shape and in some cases also of behavior. His work in this field, carried out especially on the germ-cells of insects, formed the morphological counterpart of Boveri's epoch-making experimental demonstration of the physiological and qualitative differences of the chromosomes (p. 917) and thus contributed in an important way towards the demonstration of the genetic continuity of the chromosomes and the cytological explanation of Mendel's law (p. 926).

1. Differences in Size and Form

Constant differences of size and form among the chromosomes have now been found in so many groups of animals and plants, including even the Protista, as hardly to require enumeration here. They are illustrated by many figures throughout this work, especially in Chapters XI and XII, especially selected examples being shown in Figs. 394, and 395.[1] As before indicated (p. 127) the size-differences are in considerable measure due to the length rather than the diameter of the chromosomes, a point of much theoretical interest for various reasons. Meek ('12) ingeniously endeavored to prove that the transverse diameter of the chromosomes is constant throughout very large animal series, and that the observed variations have a far-reaching phylogenetic significance; but Farmer and Digby ('14) have shown that these relations are much less constant than found by Meek, whether in the individual or in the group; and this is in accordance with the observations of many other cytologists. Nevertheless Meek's observations are of considerable interest in their bearing on the variation of chromosome-number in the individual and in the species (p. 868).

Constant differences of shape among the chromosomes are often correlated with corresponding differences in mode of attachment to the spindle-fibers (p. 130). This is seen among both plants (Figs. 252, 395) and animals (Figs. 394, 396); conspicuous examples are offered by the acridian grasshoppers. In this group all the chromosomes most commonly are rod-

---

[1] For animals, see especially the works of Sutton, McClung, Robertson, Wenrich, Carothers, on Orthoptera; those of Paulmier, Montgomery, Wilson and Morrill, on Hemiptera; of Stevens and Nonidez on Coleoptera; of Stevens, Metz and Bridges on Diptera;—to all of which more special reference is elsewhere made. See also for plants C. Müller ('10, '12) with earlier literature, Stomps ('10), Wisselingh ('10), Strasburger ('10), Tischler ('17), Belling and Blakeslee ('22), etc.

shaped and have terminal attachments (Fig. 413), but in certain species, or even in different individuals of the same species, certain particular chromosomes may be V-shaped or J-shaped. The constancy of these relations has strongly impressed all observers who have studied them critically, not

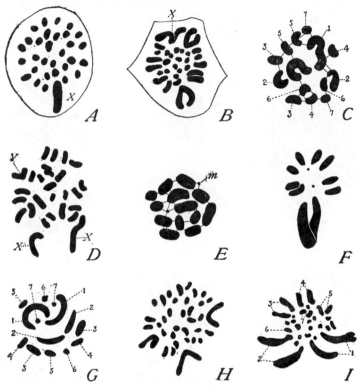

Fig. 394.—Size-differences of the Chromosomes. (All except *E*, *G*, and *I* are spermatogonial metaphases.)

A, the locustid *Orphania denticulata*, 31 chromosomes with one large *X*-chromosome (Sinéty); *B*, *Locusta viridis*, 29 chromosomes with 3 V-shaped (Mohr); *C*, the hemipter *Protenor belgica*, 14 chromosomes; *D*, the mantid *Tenodera superstitiosa*, 27 chromosomes (Oguma); *E*, the hemipter *Pachylis gigas*, with very small *m*-pair (Wilson); *F*, the fly *Drosophila funebris*; *G*, cleavage-nucleus of *Aphis rosæ* (Stevens); *H*, the beetle *Blaps lusitanica*, 33 chromosomes, 3 atelomitic (Nonidez); *I*, root-tip of the seed-plant *Eucomis bicolar* (Müller).

alone in the Orthoptera (Acrididæ, Locustidæ), but in other insects.[1] A remarkable case is that of the grasshopper *Trimerotropis*, as described by Carothers ('17) in which most of the chromosomes are rod-shaped with terminal attachments but a certain number usually are V-shaped or J-

[1] See for example Sinéty ('01), McClung ('14, '17), Robertson ('16), Wenrich ('16), Mohr ('14) Metz ('14, '16). For similar differences in the chromosomes of echinoderms see Baltzer ('09, '10, '13), Heffner ('10), Pinney ('11), Tennent ('11).

shaped.   The number of the latter varies in different individuals *but is constant in the individual, and always affects the same particular chromosomes,* as is demonstrated both by the size-relations and by critical comparison of the diploid (spermatogonial) groups and those of the spermatocyte-divisions (Figs. 439, 440).   Very striking cases of constant differences of both size and shape are also seen among the Diptera, which may be exemplified by *Drosophila melanogaster,* as described by Bridges ('16).   The diploid groups here show eight chromosomes (Figs. 396, 415), four V-shaped (median at-

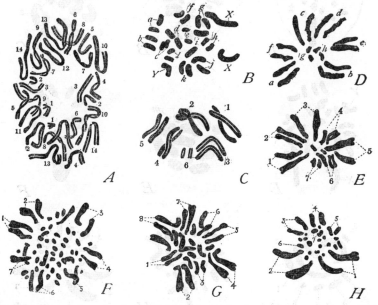

Fig. 395.—Chromosome-pairs in the diploid mitoses of animals (*A–C*), and plants (*D–H*).

In *A* there are 14 pairs, numbered according to size, but not actually grouped in pairs.   The paired grouping is more or less clearly evident in all the others, and is perfect in *C*.

A, prophase of peritoneal cell, salamander, *Amblystoma tigrinum* (PARMENTER); *B,* spermatogonial group of mantis, *Tenodera superstitiosa* (OGUMA), the three sex-chromosomes (*X, X* and *Y*) not symmetrically paired; *C,* oögonial group of fly *Scatophaga pallida* (STEVENS); *D,* from roottip of seed-plant *Galtonia* (STRASBURGER); *E,* same (MÜLLER); *F,* same of *Albuca; G,* of *Bulbina; H, Eucomis* (MÜLLER).

tachment), one rod-shaped with terminal attachment (the X-chromosome), one hook-shaped, with sub-terminal attachment (the Y-chromosome), and two very minute spheroidal ones.   Constant differences of similar type in other species of Diptera have been observed by Stevens, Metz ('14, '16), and other observers.   Differences in the shape of chromosomes are by no means always directly due to differences of spindle-attachment (*cf.* the ring-tetrads of *Tomopteris* and of Orthoptera, p. 530); and the point of

attachment, though on the whole highly constant, is not absolutely invariable.

2. Paired Condition of the Chromosomes in the Diploid Groups

Conclusive proof of the validity of the foregoing conclusions is afforded
by the fact that in all cases where clearly marked differences of size are
shown by the chromosomes the diploid groups contain two chromosomes of
each recognizable size, the haploid groups but one, a fact first indicated by
Montgomery ('01) and more fully studied by Sutton ('02), who found eleven
recognizable pairs of chromosomes in the diploid groups of the male grasshopper *Brachystola* besides one unpaired X-chromosome. In many cases
the chromosomes show no definite order of grouping; in others the synaptic
mates show a certain tendency to approximate two by two in pairs;[1] while
in a few cases *all or nearly all the chromosomes are thus arranged in pairs*.
The most remarkable of these cases occur in the Diptera where all the chromosomes, apart from occasional irregularities, are unmistakably grouped in
symmetrical pairs, the two members being of equal size and lying side by
side, sometimes more or less twisted about each other as in a *strepsinema*
(Figs. 395, 396). In the prophases, particularly, as shown by Metz,[2] the
synaptic mates are so closely associated as to simulate closely the two
halves of a longitudinally split chromosome, and as such they have actually
been described by Lomen ('14) and Dehorne ('14). These observers were
thus led to consider the somatic groups of some of these insects (*Culex,
Corethra*) as haploid instead of diploid. That this is an error has been conclusively proved in *Drosophila* by Metz, and by Taylor, Whiting and Hance
in *Culex*.

Some writers[3] too hastily accepted the probability that an actual pairing
of the chromosomes is a general characteristic of the diploid nuclei; but
this clearly goes too far; the opposite statement indeed would seem to be
nearer the facts. The Diptera thus far stand alone in respect to both the
regularity and the intimacy of the pairing; and even here it often fails in
case of certain chromosomes. The most that can be said of organisms
generally is that there is a rather widespread tendency for such pairing to
take place, though only here and there clearly manifest and often shown by
only a small number of the chromosomes. Little is known as yet regarding
the time at which the pairing takes place. In *Drosophila* Metz found the

---

[1] This condition, so interesting for all the problems of chromosome-individuality, seems first to
have been seen by Montgomery ('04) in the urodeles (*Plethodon*), and in Hemiptera ('06); and by
Strasburger ('05, '07, '08), in certain seed-plants. It was afterwards found in various other animals and plants. See Geerts ('07), Janssens and Willems ('08), Sykes (09), Müller ('09 , '12),
Gates ('12), Stomps ('11), Metz ('14, '16, etc.).

[2] Stevens ('08), Metz ('14, '16, '20); see also M. Taylor ('15, '16), Whiting ('17), Hance ('17),
Holt ('17).

[3] *E.g.*, Strasburger ('09, p. 90).

pairing already in early embryonic stages; and more recently Huettner ('22) has found it even before completion of the first cleavage of the ovum. A similar pairing was described by Hutchinson ('15) in the first cleavage of *Abies*.[1]

The important bearing of the side-by-side pairing of the chromosomes in these cases on the theory of synapsis in general and of parasynapsis in

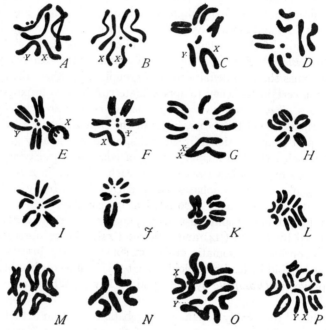

Fig. 396.—The diploid chromosome-groups in various species of *Drosophila* and other Diptera, not schematized. (*A, B*, from BRIDGES, the rest from METZ.)

A, Drosophila melanogaster ♂; *B, the same* ♀; *C, obscura* ♀; *D, melanica* ♀; *E, F, Mulleri* ♂; *G,* the same ♀; *H, virilis* ♀; *I, ramsdeni* ♀; *J, funebris* ♀; *K, immigrans* ♀; *L, Spogostylum simsoni* ♀; *M, Calliphora erythrocephala* ♀; *N,* same, first spermatocyte metaphase; *O, Sarcophaga tuber sarraceniæ* ♂; *P, Anthrax sinuosa* ♂.

particular, has earlier been indicated (p. 575). That the synaptic mates should thus pair in definite order, each with its parental homologue, is indeed an astonishing fact, and one that unmistakably indicates the existence of perfectly ordered qualitative differences among the chromosomes of which their different sizes and forms are outward expressions (p. 927).

---

[1] The pairs thus formed were said to divide *transversely* during the ensuing cleavage; and a similar account was offered by Chamberlain ('16) for *Stangeria* and by Weninger ('18) for *Lilium*. This account was, however. contradicted by Nothnagel ('18) in *Trillium* and by Sax ('18) in *Fritillaria*.

3. Differences in Behavior. Autosomes (Euchromosomes) and Heterochromosomes (Allosomes)

Certain special peculiarities of behavior on the part of particular chromosomes during mitosis and meiosis have been noted in the preceding pages, in particular those due to different modes of attachment to the spindle-fibers, to the lagging of particular chromosomes on the spindle, and the like. There are certain types of chromosomes which differ so widely in behavior from the others as to have received the special name of *heterochromosomes* or *allosomes* in contradistinction to the *autosomes* or *euchromosomes*, which include those of the more usual type.[1]

As first defined by Montgomery, the "heterochromosomes" were characterized by their tendency to undergo "heteropycnosis" during the growth-period of the spermatocytes (p. 758), and sometimes also in the spermatogonia, and hence classed by Montgomery ('98, '01) as "chromatin-nucleoli." Subsequently ('06) the term "allosome" was substituted for "heterochromosome" but has never come into general use. Many recent writers have used the term "heterochromosome" as a synonym of "sex-chromosome"; but this is inaccurate. Montgomery also distinguished between paired and unpaired heterochromosomes, the former being called *diplosomes*, the latter *monosomes*. Later researches showed, however, that the "diplosomes" included two wholly unrelated types, namely, the sex-chromosomes (XY-pair) and the microchromosomes or m-chromosomes which have no relation to sex and are alike in both sexes; while the "monosome" is the unpaired X-chromosome or accessory chromosome as it appears in the digametic sex.[2]

The special behavior of the sex-chromosomes has earlier been indicated. The m-chromosomes are a pair of small and sometimes very minute chromosomes at present known only in the coreid Hemiptera, where they were first described by Paulmier ('99) in *Anasa tristis* and have since been found in all the other Coreidæ thus far examined. They differ widely in size in different species (Fig. 397); in *Pachylis* and *Archimerus* they are excessively minute, in the former case hardly larger than centrioles; in *Anasa, Alydus* or *Syromastes* considerably larger; in *Leptoglossus* only just distinguishable from the smaller autosomes; in *Protenor* usually indistinguishable from the latter save in behavior (Wilson, '11).

Their most noteworthy feature is a marked tendency to delayed synapsis (p. 563) as first noted by Gross ('04) in *Syromastes* and afterwards found to be characteristic of them in many other forms (Wilson, '05, '09, '11). These chromosomes often remain separate, during the whole of the growth-period

---

[1] The first three of these terms are due to Montgomery ('04, '06), the fourth to McClung ('12).
[2] Wilson ('05, '06, etc.).

and only unite to form a bivalent in the final prophases after the nuclear wall has broken down and the chromosomes are passing upon the spindle. Nothing is yet known concerning their physiological significance. Their

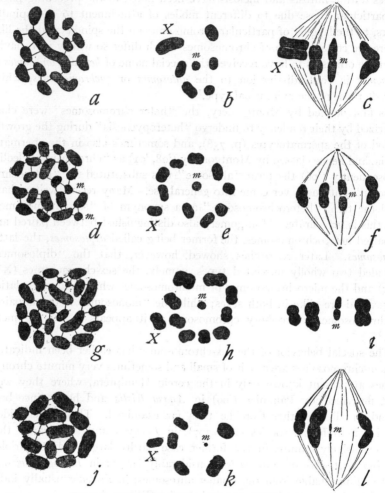

Fig. 397.—The *m*-chromosomes (*m*) in coreid Hemiptera.

In each horizontal row the left figure is a spermatogonial metaphase, the central a first spermatocyte-metaphase, and the right a first spermatocyte-metaphase in side view; *a–c*, in *Protenor*; *d–f* in *Leptoglossus*; *g–i*, in *Anasa*; *j–l* in *Pachylis*.

main present interest lies in the extreme clearness with which they show the processes of conjugation and disjunction (p. 507); in the demonstration which they offer of definite differences of behavior among the chromosomes:

and in their suggestions concerning one possible mode by which the chromosome-number may change from species to species.

III. THE CHROMOSOMES OF HYBRIDS

1. Relation of the Haploid and Diploid Groups

The parental chromosome-groups of hybrids may be alike in respect to both the number and size-relations; such hybrids may be quite fertile and

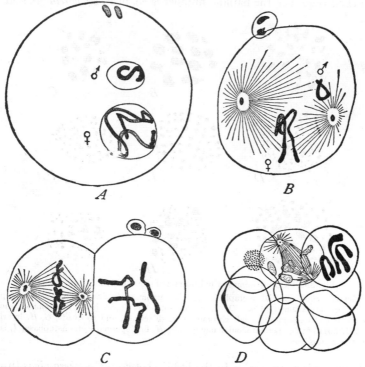

Fig. 398.—Hybrid fertilization of the egg of *Ascaris megalocephala*, var. *bivalens*, by the sperm of var. *univalens* (HERLA).

A, the gamete-nuclei shortly before union; B, the cleavage-figure forming; the sperm-nucleus has given rise to one chromosome (♂), the egg-nucleus to two (♀); C, two-cell stage dividing; D, twelve-cell stage, with the three distinct chromosomes still shown in the primordial germ-cell or stem-cell.

show a normal behavior in meiosis. Of greater interest are those not infrequent cases in which the parental chromosomes differ in number, size, or both, which offer a valuable means of experimental analysis.

With certain definite exceptions the somatic number of the hybrid, as might be expected, is typically equal to the sum of the parental gametic or haploid numbers. The classical case (Fig. 398) is shown in *Ascaris mega-*

locephala (var. bivalens 2 × var. *univalens* 1=hybrid 3). In the sun-dew *Drosera rotundifolia* the gametic number, is 10, in *D. longifolia*, 20, the diploid number in the hybrid 30 (Rosenberg, '04, '09). *Triticum durum* (n=14) × *T. vulgare* (n=21), and two other similar crosses gave hybrids with 2n = 35.[1] In the moth, *Biston hirtarius* the haploid number is 14, in the nearly related *Nyssia zonaria* 56, while the hybrid diploid number is about 70 (Doncaster and Harrison, '14) (p. 851). In the Moth, *Pygæra curtula* (Federley, '13), the haploid number is 29, in *P. anchoreta* 30, and the

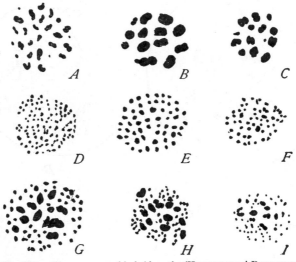

Fig. 399.—Chromosomes of hybrid moths (HARRISON and DONCASTER).

A, *Biston hirtarius*, oögonial metaphase, 28 chromosomes; B, first spermatocyte-metaphase; C, second spermatocyte-metaphase; D, E, F, corresponding stages in *Nyssia zonaria*, showing respectively 100–120 (spermatogonial) chromosomes, 56 tetrads, and 56 dyads; G, H, hybrid *zonaria* ♀ × *hirtaria* ♂; G, spermatogonial metaphase; H, first spermatocyte-metaphase; I, second spermatocyte-metaphase.

hybrid number is 59 (p. 851). In the hybrid between *Œnothera gigas* (n=14) and *Œ. lata* (n usually=7 or 8, but occasionally 6 or 9), most of the hybrids according to Lutz ('09) have, as is to be expected, either 21 chromosomes (14 + 7) or 22 (14 + 8). Interesting exceptions to this rule arise from the fact that in certain crosses some or even all of the paternal chromosomes are unable to sustain themselves in the maternal cytoplasm. The most important of these cases have been observed in the sea-urchins (Baltzer, '09, '10). In *Sphærechinus granularis* the haploid number is 20, in *Paracentrotus* (*Strongylocentrotus*) *lividus* 18, from which we should expect the diploid number of the hybrid to be 38. In point of fact this expectation is realized

---

[1] Kihara ('19). See also Sax ('22).

only in the cross *Sphærechinus* ♀ × *Paracentrotus* ♂. In the reverse cross, *Paracentrotus* ♀ × *Sphærechinus* ♂, the hybrid diploid number varies from 19 to 24, most often 21 or 22. This difference results from the fact that in the first case all of the *Paracentrotus* chromosomes are able to survive and divide normally in the *Sphærechinus* cytoplasm, while in the reverse cross only 3 or 4 of the *Sphærechinus* chromosomes can thus adapt themselves to the foreign environment. The remaining 16 or 17 are eliminated during the first cleavage of the egg (Fig. 455). The cells of these larvæ thus receive the complete complement of maternal *Paracentrotus* chromosomes, but only three or four of the paternal *Sphærechinus;* hence their usual diploid number 21 or 22 (18 + 3 or 4). An elimination of chromosomes more or less similar in type, though varying in the details, has been found in several other sea-urchin crosses, both by Baltzer and by other observers [1] and also by Pinney ('18) in certain teleost hybrids, for example in *Fundulus hetero-clitus* ♀ and *Stenotomus chrysops* ♀ fertilized by the sperm of *Ctenolabrus adspersus*. Here again the reverse cross, *Ctenolabrus* ♀ × *Fundulus* ♂ shows but slight disturbance of the paternal chromosomes, the early mitotic behavior being prevailingly normal. Extreme cases of this type are offered by heterogeneous crosses, such as the fertilization of sea-urchin eggs by the sperm of an annelid or mollusk, in which the sperm serves merely to activate the egg, the nucleus being usually unable to undergo the mitotic transformation, and soon degenerating (p. 970). In these cases the hybrid (if it can so be called) develops with only the maternal chromosomes (*i. e.*, by gynogenesis, p. 460) and with the haploid number (Kupelwieser).

The case for the theory of genetic continuity as applied to the chromosomes becomes still stronger when we consider hybrids in which the gametic groups differ in respect to the size or shape as well as (in some cases) the number of the chromosomes; here, indeed, we find a crucial experimental demonstration of the theory. The classical case of this kind is afforded by the fish-hybrids, described by Mœnkhaus ('04) in the cross *Menidia* × *Fundulus* and by Morris ('14) in the cross *Fundulus* × *Ctenolabrus*. The haploid number is here 18 in each case, but the chromosomes of *Fundulus* are much larger than those of *Menidia*. Both kinds of chromosomes appear in the hybrids, 18 of each as nearly as can be determined, and of characteristic size (Fig. 400) and retain their characteristics throughout the cleavage at least up to the formation of the young embryo. In the moth-hybrids *Biston hirtarius* × *Nyssia zonaria* (Fig. 399), the two types of parental chromosomes, much larger and fewer in one parent than in the other, persist as such during the whole life-cycle up to the time of sexual maturity. Again, in *Datura stramonium* (2n = 24) the haploid group contains six recognizable sizes

[1] See Doncaster and Gray ('12), Tennent ('12).

of chromosomes, including one largest, one smallest and ten of intermediate sizes. Normal (diploid) plants show 12 pairs of corresponding sizes, tetraploid mutants 24 pairs, while the hybrid shows three of each size

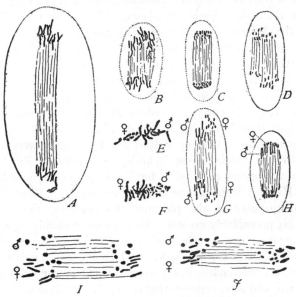

Fig. 400.—Chromosomes in the cleavage of the eggs of hybrid fishes. (*A–G*, MOENKHAUS; *H, I*, MORRIS).

A, first cleavage, *Fundulus; B, C*, later cleavage of same; *D*, first cleavage of *Menidia; E*, first cleavage-metaphase, hybrid *Menidia* ♀ × *Fundulus* ♂; *F*, similar group from the reverse cross, *Fundulus* ♀ × *Menidia* ♂; *G*, anaphase of same hybrid as *E; H*, from same hybrid, later cleavage after loss of the gonomery; *I, J*, anaphases of first cleavage, *Fundulus* ♀ × *Ctenolabrus* ♂.

(p. 567).[1] All such cases offer an irresistible demonstration, indirect though the evidence is, of the genetic continuity of the chromosomes.

2. Meiosis in Hybrids

Many hybrids live through only the earlier stages of development;[2] others cannot be reared to full maturity; still others may attain to sexual maturity but show various degrees of abnormality in the meiotic processes which are certainly in part responsible for the partial or complete sterility so often observed in hybrids. Such abnormalities have been observed by many investigators[3] and are of many kinds and degrees. They may involve irregu-

[1] Belling and Blakeslee ('22).

[2] See Newman ('08, '10, '18), G. and P. Hertwig ('14), Pinney ('18).

[3] E. g., Juel, '00 (*Syringa*), Guyer, '00, '02 (pigeons), Cannon, '03 (cotton), Smith, '13 (pigeons), Smith and Thomas, '13 (pheasants), Cutler, '18 (pheasant × fowl), Wodsedalek, '16 (horse × ass), Rosenberg, '04, '09, '17 (*Drosera, Hieracium*), Täckholm, '20, '22 (roses).

larities in synapsis, spireme formation, and chromosome distribution; in the occurrence of multipolar mitoses; abnormal formation and degeneration of the gametes, and even a complete failure to form them, as is commonly the case in the mule (Wodsedalek). Meiosis may, however, take place quite normally and produce fertile offspring; but such cases seem to be possible only when the parental chromosome-groups are alike in number and other respects.

Hybrids between parental forms differing in respect to the gametic chromosome-groups show three main types of behavior, namely: (1) When more than two synaptic mates are present (as in triploids) all may conjugate in synapsis to form plurivalent instead of bivalent elements. (2) The synaptic mates may conjugate in pairs as far as possible, to form bivalents, while the others remain unmated and enter the heterotypic division as univalents. (3) Synapsis may fail in greater or less degree—in a few cases almost completely—so that many univalents may enter the heterotypic division. Each of these cases shows many variants, some of them of most instructive character.

(1) The first and rarest case is illustrated by certain triploid hybrids between tetraploid and diploid mutants in plants. In certain such hybrids [1] the heterotypic division shows the haploid number (in *Datura* 12) of *triads* (or, if the equation-division be taken into account, hexads), the synaptic mates having united in threes. During the division the elements of each triad break up and separate in such a manner that two components pass to one pole and one to the other. Since the triads show a random or chance orientation on the spindle, various numbers are found in the second division, ranging in *Datura* from 12 to 24, the sum of the numbers in each pair of sister-cells being 36, the triploid number (12 + 24, 13 + 23 . . . . . 18 + 18)—a remarkable example of random assortment in chromosome-distribution (p. 944).

(2) In the second and more frequent case the chromosomes of the smaller gametic group commonly conjugate with a corresponding number from the larger group to form bivalents, leaving the unmated ones as univalents. The heterotypic division therefore shows both bivalents and univalents on the same spindle, the former showing the usual behavior (*i. e.*, as in pure-bred forms) while the latter show numerous irregularities.[2]

The classical case of this type is that of the sun-dew *Drosera* in which,

[1] E. g., in *Morus* (Osawa, '20), *Canna* (Belling, '21) and *Datura* (Belling and Blakeslee, '22).

[2] Attention may here again be called to the interesting fact that in this respect the meiosis of apogamous plants often shows irregularities closely similar to those of hybrids (p. 848); and this, taken in connection with the chromosome-numbers, gives strong reason to conclude that such plants, originally arose as hybrids. See especially the works of Juel, Murbeck, Rosenberg ('17), Osawa, Strasburger, Tischler, Holmgren, Winkler, Blackman and Harrison, and Täckholm ('22). Only a few examples of these facts can here be referred to.

as above mentioned, the diploid number in *D. longifolia* is 40, in *rotundifolia* 20, and in the hybrid (unfortunately sterile) 30 (20 + 10). The heterotypic division shows 20 chromosomes (Fig. 401) of which 10 are obviously double and 10 apparently single.[1] The 10 double (bivalent) chromosomes

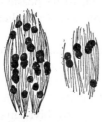

undergo a regular division and distribution to the poles, while the 10 single univalents fail to divide wander irregularly towards one pole or the other, and often fail to enter the daughter-nuclei. The natural interpretation of this, as indicated by Rosenberg, is that the ten *rotundifolia* chromosomes conjugate with ten of the *longifolia* to form bivalents, leaving ten univalent *longifolia* chromosomes without

Fig. 401.—Heterotypic mitosis in the hybrid between *Drosera rotundifolia* (20 chromosomes) and *longifolia* (40 chromosomes) (ROSENBERG).

The chromosome-group (from two sections) shows 10 (hybrid) bivalents and 10 single (*longifolia*) chromosomes.

synaptic mates.[2] In the reduction-division (here the first) the bivalents disjoin as usual while the univalents pass towards one pole like other unpaired chromosomes (supernumeraries, or accessory chromosomes, etc.). The lagging and scattered univalents later vary in behavior. Some seem to enter the daughter-nuclei; others fail to reach the poles and give rise to dwarf nuclei, but apparently some of them may finally fuse with the main nuclei. In any case some, but not all, of them pass upon the second spindle and there (presumably) divide, the observed metaphase-numbers varying from 12 to 18.

Many interesting cases more or less similar in principle have more recently been observed in various plants and a few animals; and we may here include both known hybrids and certain apomictic triploid or other heteroploid forms, which may have originated as hybrids (p. 848). In most cases the unmated chromosomes pass as univalents upon the heterotypic spindle; and further complications not infrequently arise through a partial or even complete failure of synapsis and through varying behavior on the part of the univalents. In Kihara's *Triticum* hybrids (p. 842) with 35 chromosomes, (14 + 21) the heterotypic division showed 14 bivalents and 7 univalents. The former divide equally in both divisions, the latter only in the first, and in the second pass irregularly and undivided towards the poles. A similar result was reached also by Sax ('21, '22). *Papaver somniferum* (n=11) × *orientale* (n=21) gives hybrids with 32 chromosomes, the heterotypic division showing 11 bivalents and 10 univalents which have a behavior like that of *Triticum* (Yasui, '21, Ljungdahl, '22). The 21-chro-

---

[1] Rosenberg, '04, '09.

[2] It is possible that the 20 *longifolia* chromosomes conjugate two-by-two, with each other, leaving the 10 rotundifolia unmated; but this is improbable in view of the facts of meiosis in other hybrids.

mosome hybrids between *Œnothera gigas* (n = 14) and *Œ. lata* (n = 7 or 8) gives hybrids with 21 chromosomes. In the heterotypic division Geerts

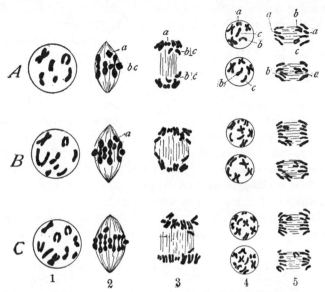

Fig. 402.—Diagrams of meiosis in *Hieracium* (*Pilosella*) hybrids (ROSENBERG)

(The number of chromosomes represented is one-third the actual number.)

First vertical line, (1) diakinesis; second, heterotypic metaphase; third, anaphase; fourth, inter-kinesis; fifth, homeotypic anaphase.

A, of the type *H. auricula* (n = 9) × *aurantiaca* (n = 18), 3 (9) bivalents and 3 (9) univalents. All of these divide excepting one univalent (*a*) which passes double to one pole. In the homeo-typic division the latter divides, while the two other univalents *b*, *c*, are delayed, again split, and pass double to one or both poles. Gametes may thus arise having 4, 5, or 8 chromosomes.

B, partial failure of synapsis in a pure-bred form with 2n = 12 (36) chromosomes, giving 4 biva-lents and 4 univalents, and irregularities resulting in the formation of gametes with 6 or 9 chromo-somes.

C, hybrid with 2n = 16 (48), showing both defective synapsis and irregularities of distribution. In 1 and 2, 7 bivalents and 2 univalents. Gamete numbers, 7, 8, 9, and 10.

('11) found 7 bivalents and 7 univalents, the former dividing regularly, the latter passing without division irregularly to the poles.[1]

A behavior of the univalents similar in principle to the foregoing but often differing more or less in detail, is described in the interesting work of Rosenberg ('17) on hybrids and apogamous species of *Hieracium* (commonly sterile), and those of Blackman and Harrison ('21) and of Täckholm ('20, '22) on the corresponding phenomena in roses. The most important of the deviations appears in the fact, that some of the univalents are said to *split equationally in both mitoses*. In some cases all the univalents, like the

---

[1] Studies on this hybrid by other observers (Lutz, '12, Gates, '09, '13a) gave somewhat different results.

bivalents, divide in the heterotypic division (Fig. 404). In other cases some divide (*b*, *c*, in Fig. 402, A) while others (*a*) pass without division to one pole, becoming double in the anaphase. In the latter case univalents are divided in the homeotypic division; but it is also said that those which have divided in the heterotypic mitosis may *again split lengthwise in the homeotypic mitosis*. In this case, however, the products often fail to separate, passing as double bodies to one pole, and thus causing an increase in the normal gametic number (*b*, *c*, in Fig. 402, A).

In general agreement with the foregoing are the remarkable results of Täckholm ('20, '22) and of Blackburn and Harrison ('21) on many forms of roses, especially of the section *Caninæ*, which are highly polymorphic, some of the so-called species being hybrids, while many others (sterile forms) are believed to have arisen as hybrids and are held constant to type because of their exclusively asexual reproduction (vegetative apogamy, or the like), which is of widespread occurrence in this group.

These investigators revealed a remarkable series of chromosome-numbers in the group, most of the diploid numbers being multiples of 7, namely, 14,

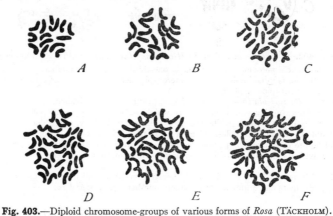

Fig. 403.—Diploid chromosome-groups of various forms of *Rosa* (Täckholm).

A, *R. webbiana*, 14 chromosomes; *B*, *R. chinensis*, 21 ch.; *C*, "Konrad Meyer," 28 ch.; *D*, *Fomentosa cuspidatoides*, 35 ch.; *E*, *R. nutkana*, 42 ch.; *F*, octoploid hybrid, 56 ch.

21, 28, 35, and 42, and in one hybrid form 56 (Fig. 403). Intermediate numbers were rarely found. Forms having 14 chromosomes and some with 28 or 42 undergo a typical meiosis, with reduction to the corresponding haploid numbers, 7, 14, or 21; and these are believed to reproduce only by sexual reproduction and for the most part to be pure bred stable forms. Those with 21 or 35 (and some with 28 or 42) show a behavior analogous to that of the *Drosera* or *Hieracium* hybrids and are maintained exclusively by apogamy. As in the preceding cases the heterotypic divisions show both bivalents and univalents, the former dividing symmetrically in typical fashion and in advance of the univalents which are at first scattered on the spindle and later show varying behavior (Fig. 404). As will appear from the following table the numbers of bivalents and of univalents in each case added together (counting each bivalent as two) equal the diploid number.

Type No.	Somatic No.	No. of Bivalents in Heterotypic Division	No. of Univalents	Constitution
1	14	7	0	diploid
2	28	14	0	tetraploid
3	42	21	0	hexaploid
4	21	7	7	triploid
5	28	7	14	tetraploid
6	35	7	21	pentaploid
7	42	7	28	hexaploid
8	35	14	7	pentaploid
9	42	14	14	hexaploid
10	32–36	Variable	Variable	anorthoploid

All cases in which unmated univalents appear in the heterotypic division fall into line under the assumption that they are hybrids or the descendants of hybrids (some of them are known to be such) between forms having different numbers of chromosomes. As in *Drosera* or *Hieracium* the chromosomes of the smaller parental haploid group (7 or 14 in the above examples) unite in synapsis with an equal number of synaptic mates from the larger group to form bivalents while the remaining univalents are left unmated. In this case, as before, the behavior of the bivalents is typical. That of the univalents shows many variations. In the heterotypic mitosis (pollen-mother-cells) they are as a rule scattered during the division of the bivalents, but later take up a position at the equator and divide equationally (Fig. 404); their distribution to the poles is, however, often irregular. In the second mitosis they usually pass irregularly to the poles, but are said in some cases to undergo a second equational division, as in *Hieracium;* the proof of this latter conclusion seems, however, inadequate.

Except for the supposed occasional second equational division of the univalents the foregoing cases are in the main similar to the *Drosera* hybrids; and in all, the presence of univalents in the heterotypic division is due, obviously, to their failure to find suitable synaptic mates owing to the original difference of gametic number.

(3) Complications due to a partial, or in extreme cases a complete, failure of synapsis are less frequent. An example is offered by fern-hybrids examined by Farmer and Digby ('10). In *Polypodium aureum* the haploid number is

34–36, in *P. vulgare* about 90.   In the hybrid the number of chromosomes in the heterotypic division is commonly 95–105 and sometimes as high as 125; and the chromosomes are of two sizes, large and small.   This indicates that while many of the *aureum* chromosomes find *vulgare* mates with which they

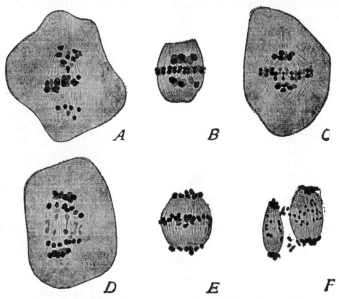

Fig. 404.—Meiosis in the sporocytes of hybrid Roses (TÄCKHOLM).

A, heterotypic metaphase (*R. sicula*) with 7 bivalents at equator and 21 scattered univalents; *B*, later stage (*R. glauca-plebeia*), bivalents in anaphase, univalents dividing in metaphase; *C*, slightly later (*R. Jebei*); *D*, univalents in anaphase (*R. contracta*); *E*, homeotypic division (*R. Desvausii*), univalents at equator; *F*, *recondita*, homeotypic anaphase, with dividing univalents.

pair, certain of them fail to do so; the expected number of bivalents is thus decreased and of univalents increased.

Rosenberg ('17) has more recently described an interesting series of gradations in respect to synapsis in the pollen-formation of triploid apomictic species of *Hieracium* with 27 chromosomes (9 + 9 + 9).   *H. boreale* (Fig. 405, A) shows a considerable but not complete failure of synapsis, the heterotypic division having only 4 to 6 bivalents (instead of 9) and correspondingly larger numbers of univalents (19 to 13).   In *H. lacerum* and *lævigatum* synapsis fails wholly and the first division shows 27 univalents which *without division* pass to the poles in two groups, often different in number, which divide equationally in the homeotypic mitosis.   This type is by Rosenberg called "half-heterotypic" (Fig. 405, B).   By a modification of this arise cases in which the chromosomes split lengthwise without separating into two groups on the spindle but become inclosed in a single membrane

(Fig. 405, C) and undergo an equation-division in the homeotypic mitosis. Finally, in *H. pseudoillyricum* (Fig. 405, D), the reduction-division is wholly suppressed and the primary sporocyte undergoes but one division, equational, and with the full diploid number of chromosomes. This indicates,

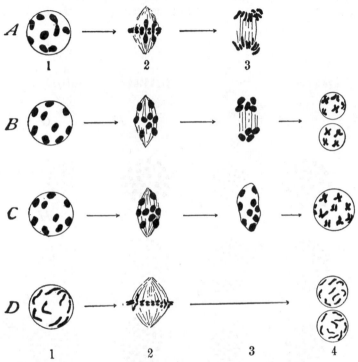

Fig. 405.—Diagram of types of heterotypic divisions in pollen-forming mitoses of apogamous species of *Hieracium* having 18+9 chromosomes (ROSENBERG).

(The number of chromosomes is one-third the actual number.) First vertical row (1) the diakinesis; second and third, heterotypic division; fourth, its products.

A, *H. boreale* type with 2 bivalents (instead of the expected 3) and 5 univalents (instead of 3) (2n = 9, actually 27), all dividing symmetrically.

B, *C*, *H. lævigatum* type, half-heterotypic division, with total failure of synapsis, 9 univalents, either passing undivided to the poles (*B*) or producing a single nucleus (*C*).

D, *H. pseudo-illyricum* type, complete failure of synapsis with one equational division. No heterotypic division.

perhaps, how diploid parthenogenesis may have arisen by a similar suppression of the reduction-division in case of the macrosporocytes.

Among animals remarkable phenomena of the same general type have been observed in hybrid Lepidoptera by Doncaster and Harrison ('14) and by Federley ('13, '14). The first-named observers found in *Biston* 14 pairs of chromosomes (11 large and 3 small), in *Nyssia zonaria* approximately 56 pairs of very small ones. The hybrids (sterile) clearly show both types of chromosomes (Fig. 399), approximately in the expected numbers (14 + 56 = 70). If all the *Biston* chromosomes that persist up to the time of meiosis paired with *Nyssia* chromosomes, the heterotypic division should show approximately 56 chromosomes (14 bivalents + 42 small univalents), but the actual number is 60–65. Not more than 5–10 of the *Lycia* chromo-

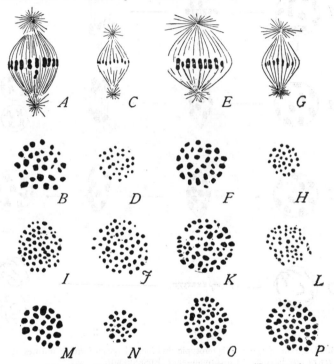

Fig. 406.—Chromosomes of hybrid Lepidoptera (FEDERLEY).

A, B, Pygæra anachoreta, first spermatocyte-metaphores, 30 chromosomes; *C, D*, the same, second spermatocyte-metaphases, 30 chromosomes; *E, F*, and *G, H*, corresponding views of *P. curtula*, 29 chromosomes; *I, J*, hybrid *anachoreta* ♀ × *curtula* ♂, first spermatocytes with 59 and 58 chromosomes; *K*, back-cross *anachoreta* ♀ × (*anch.* ♀ × *curt.* ♂) = ♂, first spermatocyte, 56 chromosomes; *L*, second spermatocyte of same, about 50 chromosomes; *M, Pygæra pigra*, first spermatocyte, 23 chromosomes; *N*, second spermatocyte, 23 chromosomes; *O, P, pigra* ♀ × *curtula* ♂, first spermatocytes, 46 and 48 chromosomes.

somes, therefore, are able to find synaptic mates with which to pair. In the heterotypic division, as in that of the hybrid roses or grasses, all the chromosomes divide (the univalents equationally); but all are said again to divide in the homeotypic division. If correct this means that *the unmated univalents undergo two equation-divisions*, again a contradiction of the rule that in normal meiosis each individual chromosome or synaptic mate divides but once (p. 505). This result receives a very circumstantial confirmation in the extensive work of Federley on moth-hybrids of the genus *Pygæra* which are partially fertile, and also by some of the plant hybrids already considered (p. 848).

In this case the haploid parental numbers are in *P. curtula* 29, in *P. anachoreta* 30, while the hybrids have 59 chromosomes. The heterotypic division often shows nearly the full diploid number, 59 (Fig. 406); *i. e.*, synapsis or pseudo-reduction nearly fails, so that nearly all the chromosomes must be univalent. Nevertheless all the univalents divide *in both mitoses*, so that the gametes (sperms) also receive nearly or quite the full diploid number. This result is borne out by the results of crossing this hybrid (♂) back with the pure *anachoreta* ♀. The resulting secondary hybrids should be triploid or nearly so (59 + 30=89), and do in fact approach this condition, though the number could not be counted precisely. The heterotypic division, however, again shows approximately the *diploid* number (59±), about half the chromosomes being large and double, and half smaller and single (Fig. 406). This means, that the two *anachoreta* chromosome-sets conjugate two-by-two in synapsis, to form bivalents, while the *curtula* chromosomes remain univalent. Federley ('14) reached substantially similar results with crosses of *Smerinthus* and *Dilina*.

The double division of the univalents in these moth-hybrids seems very anomalous; nevertheless Federley's evidence seems conclusive, not only cytologically, but also on its genetic side (p. 929). The questions that it raises relate, however, especially to the mechanism of synapsis and disjunction (p. 505) and do not weaken the strong support obviously given by the chromosomes of hybrids to the theory of genetic continuity.

IV. NORMAL CHROMOSOME NUMBERS

1. Introductory

To speak of the number of chromosomes as a specific constant does not mean that the number is absolutely fixed. Deviations from the typical number are often observed within the species and even in different cells of the same individual; and this fact has led some writers to a premature denial of the constancy of the chromosome-number and even of the genetic continuity of the chromosomes. Such a conclusion, however, could only result from lack of critical consideration of the facts.

It would seem to be a very simple matter to count chromosomes correctly; but the history of the subject abundantly demonstrates the contrary. The fundamental chromosome-number can only be determined with complete certainty *when the whole cycle of the chromosomes is taken into account,* including comparison of the gametic with the zygotic number as shown in the formation of the gametes, their union in syngamy, and the number seen in the diploid or somatic divisions, particularly during the early stages of development.   When these give consistent results, the fundamental number may be established with a high degree of probability, which becomes a practical certainty in all cases where the size-differences of the chromosomes are sufficiently marked to make identification of the individual chromosome-pairs of the diploid groups possible (p. 837).   It must be confessed that only a comparatively small number of cases have been thus completely determined.   In practice, however, the numbers may often be determined with sufficient accuracy by a less exacting standard.

The chromosome-number has been counted, with varying degrees of accuracy, in representatives of all the larger groups of plants and animals and in a very large number of species—according to E. B. Harvey ('16, '20) in nearly 1000 species of animals, while Tischler ('17) lists them for more than 700 species of plants; but the number of thoroughly established cases is very much smaller than these figures indicate.   The limited list which follows is confined almost exclusively to multicellular forms, and excludes many groups concerning which uncertainty still exists.   The selection has been made rather arbitrarily, to illustrate by a few examples the general range and distribution of chromosome-numbers in different groups, in a few cases their relations within single or nearly allied genera in order to indicate the possible modes in which chromosome-numbers may have changed from species to species, and certain other problems discussed in the text.[1]

Supplementary lists are given also at pp. 753, 766, 773, in connection with the subject of the sex-chromosomes.   In order to simplify the lists we shall for the moment lay aside most of the observed deviations from the fundamental numbers, however caused; but an exception is made in certain cases of reduplication (p. 870).   The lists include both haploid and diploid numbers so far as both are known; when only one of these has been directly observed the other (as inferred) is inclosed in parentheses.

---

[1] Its compilation has been much facilitated by several important general reviews, in which will be found fuller data and more detailed references to the literature. See especially those of Tischler ('17), with an excellent critical discussion, and Mrs. E. B. Harvey (Miss E. N. Browne) ('16, '20); also those of Gates ('15), Ishikawa ('16) and Winge ('17). Earlier and less complete lists in Wilson ('00), Enriques ('05), Montgomery ('06) and Haecker ('07). The first accurate counts of chromosome-numbers seem to have been made by Flemming ('82) in the salamander, and by Strasburger ('82) in several species of plants.

EXAMPLES OF CHROMOSOME-NUMBERS IN ANIMALS

Porifera

SPECIES	GROUP	HAPLOID	DIPLOID	AUTHORITY
Sycandra raphanus	Porifera	8	16	Jörgenssen, '09
" "	"			

Cælenterata

Tiara sp.	Hydrozoa	14	28	Boveri, '90
Hydra fusca and viridis	"	6	12	Downing, '05, '09
Campanularia flexuosa	"	10	20	Hargitt, '13
Aglantha digitalis	"	8	16	" '17
Clava leptostyla	"	12	24	Haecker, '92

Chætognatha

Sagitta bipunctata	Chætognatha	9	18	Boveri, '90, Stevens, Buchner, etc.

Nemathelminthes

Gordius tolsunus	Nematoda	2	4	Vejdovský, '12
Paragordius varius	"	7	14	Montgomery, '04
Ascaris megalocephala uni-valens	"	1	2	
	"	(compound)	(compound)	Boveri, '87,
		1 = 27 or 36	2 = 63 or 72	Hertwig, '90, etc Kautzsch, '13
		1 = 22 or 30	2 = 52 or 60	Geinitz, '15 See pp. 323, 869
A. bivalens	"	2	4	
		(compound)	(compound)	Van Beneden, '83–'84, Nussbaum, '84, Boveri, Hertwig, etc.
Heterakis vesicularis	"	4, 5	9, 10	Gulick, '11
Ancyracanthus cystidicola	"	5, 6	11, 12	Mulsow, '11, '12
Ascaris canis	"	12, 18	30, 36	Walton, '16, '18
A. incurva	"	14, 21	35, 42	Goodrich, '14
A. lumbricoides	"	19, 24	43, (48)	Edwards, '10

Platoda

Vortex viridis	Rhabdocæla	2	4	Lepeschkin, '10
Paravortex,	"	4	8	Patterson, '12
Procerodes gerlachei	"	6	12	Böhmig, '07
Dendrocœlum lacteum	Triclada	7	14	Gelei, '13
Leptoplana tremellaris	Polyclada	8	16	Francotte, '97
Thysanozoön ellipticus	"	9	18	Van der Stricht, '97, '98
Eustylochus ellipticus	"	10	20	Van Name, '99

EXAMPLES OF CHROMOSOME-NUMBERS IN ANIMALS—*Continued*

Trematoda

SPECIES	GROUP	HAPLOID	DIPLOID	AUTHORITY
Polystomum integerrimum	Trematoda	4	8	Goldschmidt, '02
Gyrodactylus elegans	"	6	12	Gille, '14
Brachycœlium lanceatum	"	10	20	Goldschmidt, '08

Nemertinea

Lineus ruber	Nemertinea	8	16	Nussbaum and Oxner, '13
Cerebratulus marginatus	"	16	32	Coe, '99

Rotifera

Hydatina senta		10–14	20–30	Whitney, '09
" "		(6)	12	Shull, '21

Annelida

Dinophilus gyrociliatus	Archiannelida	10	20	Shearer, '11, '12
Allolophora fœtida	Oligochæta	11	22	Foot and Strobell, '98, etc.
Enchytræus adriaticus	"		24	Vejdovský, '07
" humicultor	"	16	32	"
Lumbricus herculeus	"	16	32	Calkins, '95
Rhynchelmis limosella	"	32	64	Vejdovský, '07
Saccocirrus major	Archichætopoda	4	8	Hempelmann, '13
" "	"	9	18	Baehr, '13
Ophryotrocha puerilis	Polychæta	2	4	Korschelt, '95
" "	"	4	8	Schreiners, '06
Tomopteris elegans	"	5	10	Senna, '11
" onisciformis	"	9	18	Schreiners, '06
Chætopterus pergam-entaceous	"	9	18	Mead, '98
Phascolosoma gouldii	Gephyrea	10	20	Gerould, '04
Thalassema mellita	"	12	24	Griffin, '99, Lefevre, '06
Nephelis vulgaris	Hirudinea	8	16	Jörgenssen, '08

Mollusca

Paludina vivipara	Gasteropoda	7	14	Meves, '01
Helix pomatia univalens	"	12	24	{ Von Rath, '92 Godlewsky, '97 Prowazek, '02
" " bivalens	"	24	48	{ Bolles-Lee, '96, '11 Murray, '98 Ancel, '02, etc.
Arion sp.	"	16	32	Lams, '10
Carinaria mediterranea	"	16	32	Boveri, '90
Enteroxenus ostergreni	"	17	34	Bonnevie, '05
" "	"	21	42	Schreiner, '07
Crepidula plana	"	30	60	Conklin, '02
Mactra sp.	Pelecypoda	12	24	Kostanecki, '04, '11
Unio. sp.	"	16	(32)	"

EXAMPLES OF CHROMOSOME-NUMBERS IN ANIMALS—*Continued*

Crustacea

SPECIES	GROUP	HAPLOID	DIPLOID	AUTHORITY
Cyclops viridis, var. brevi-spinosus	Copepoda	2	4	Chambers, '12
Cyclops gracilis	"	3	6	Matschek, '09, '10
" signatus	"	4	8	Haecker, '90
" viridis var. americanus	"	5	10	Chambers, '12
Cyclops diaphanus	"	6	12	Braun, '09
" albidus	"	8	16	" "
" dybowskii	"	9	18	" "
" strenuus	"	11	22	Braun, '09, Matschek, '10, Amma, '11
Canthocamptus staphylinus	"	12	24	Haecker, '92, Matschek, Krüger
Diaptomus cœruleus	"	14	28	Krimmel, '10, Amma, '11
" castor	"	17	34	Amma, '11
Branchipus grubii	Phyllopoda	12	24	Brauer, '92, Fries, '09
Artemia salina	"	84	168 or 84	Brauer, '93, '94
" " var. bivalens, parthenogenetic, of Capo d'Istria, etc.	"		84	Artom, '08, '11, '12, etc.
Id., var. univalens, sexual form, Cagliari, etc.	"	21	42	"
Oniscus asellus	Isopoda	16	(32)	Nichols, '09
Idotea irrorata	"	28	(56)	"
Talorchestia longicornis	Amphipoda	18	(36)	"
Eupagurus prideauxii	Macrura	12	(24)	Weismann and Ishikawa, '88
Hippa talpoidea	"	60	(120)	Nichols, '09
Astacus sp.	"	58	(116)	Prowazek, '02
Cambarus virilis	"	100	200	Fasten, '14
C. immunis?	"	104	208	" "
Cancer magister	Brachyura	60	100	" '18

Arachnida

SPECIES	GROUP	HAPLOID	DIPLOID	AUTHORITY
Pediculopsis gramimum	Acarida	2	4	Reuter, '09
Ixodes reduvius	"	14	28	Nordenskiöld, 09
Epeira scolopetaria	Araneida	11, 12	23, (24)	Berry, '06
Agalena nævia	"	25, 27 ±	(52-54) ±	Wallace, '05, '09
Buthus eupeus	Scorpionida	(11)	22	Sokolow, '13
Centrurus exilicauda	"	13	26	Wilson, '16
Euscorpius carpathicus	"	28-40	70-84	Sokolow, '13
Opisthacanthus, sp.	"		80-100 ±	Wilson
Macrobiotus lacustris	Tardigrada	5	10	von Wenck, '14

EXAMPLES OF CHROMOSOME-NUMBERS IN ANIMALS—*Continued*

Tracheata

SPECIES	GROUP	HAPLOID	DIPLOID	AUTHORITY
Peripatus, sp.	Prototracheata	14	28	Montgomery, 'oo
Geophilus linearis	Myriapoda	8	(16)	Bouin and Collin, 'oi
Scolopendra heros	"	16, 17	33, (34)	Blackman, '03, '05, 'io
Scutigera forceps	"	18, 19	37, (38)	Medes, 05
Anurida maritima	Aptera		8	Claypole, '98
Podura aquatica	"		8	Willem, 'oo
Cerastipsocus venosus	Corrodentia	8, 9	17, (18)	Boring, '13
Thysanura domestica	Thysanura	16, 18	34, (36)	Charlton, '21
Termopsis angusticollis	Isoptera	26	52	Stevens, '05
Libellula basalis	Odonata	12, 13	25, (26)	Smith, '16
Anax junius	"	13, 14	27, 28	{ Lefevre and { McGill, '08
Platyplax designatus	Trichoptera	30	55–60	Lutman, 'io
Blatta germanica	Orthoptera (Blattidæ)	11, 12	23, 24	Wassilieff, '07
Periplaneta americana	"	16, 17	33, 34	Morse, '09
Anisolabis maritima	(Forficulidæ)	12	24	Randolph, '08
Forficula auricularia	"	12	24	Sinéty, 'oi Stevens, 'io
Tenodera superstitiosa ⎫ Paratenodera aridifolia ⎭	" (Mantidæ)	13, 14	26, 27	Oguma, '21
Aplopus mayeri	" (Phasmidæ)	17, 18	35, 36	Jordan, '08
Gryllus domesticus	" (Gryllidæ)	10, 11	21, 22	Baumgartner, '04, Gutherz, '07–'09
" assimilis	" "	14, 15	29, (30)	Baumgartner, '04
Gryllotalpa vulgaris	" "	6	12	Payne, '16
" borealis	" "	11, 12	23, 24	" '12
Decticus verrucivorus	" (Locustidæ)	11, 12	23, (24)	Vejdovský, '12
Steiroxys trilineata	" "	14, 15	29, (30)	Davis, '08, Meek, '13
Locusta viridissima	" "	14, 15	29, 30	Mohr, '14
Orphania denticauda	" "	15, 16	31, (32)	Sinéty, 'oi
Xiphidium, sp.	" "	16, 17	33, (34)	McClung, '02, '14
Jamaicana flava	" "	17, 18	35, (36)	Woolsey, '15
Diastremmena marmorata	" "	28, 29	57, (58)	Schellenberg '13
Brachystola magna ⎫				Sutton '01, '02
Hippiscus tuberculatus				Davis, '08
Arphia tenebrosa	" "			" "
Chortophaga iridifasciata				" "
Dissosteira carolina				
Mecosthethus sp.				McClung, '14
Melanoplus (7 species)				" and others
Rhomaleum micropterum	Orthoptera			"
Trimerotropis fallax ⎬	(Acrididæ)	11, 12	23, 24	"
Phrynotettix magnus				{ Pinney, '08, { McClung, Wen-rich
Syrbula admirabilis and nearly fifty additional species of this family. ⎭				Robertson, '08 Meek, '13, Carothers, '13, Nowlin, '08, 12
Stenobothrus biguttulus	" "	8, 9	17, (18)	Gérard, '09 Meek

EXAMPLES OF CHROMOSOME NUMBERS IN ANIMALS—*Continued*

Tracheata—Continued				
SPECIES	GROUP	HAPLOID	DIPLOID	AUTHORITY
Chorthippus curtipennis	Orthoptera (Acrididæ)	8, 9	17, (18)	Davis, '08, Robertson, '16
Circotettix lobatus " radula }	" "	10, 11	21, 22	Carothers, '17
Paratettix leuconotus- leucothorax }	" "			Harman, '15
Acridium granulatus and other species Paratettix, sp. Tettigidea parvipennis }	" Tettigidea "	6, 7	13, (14)	Robertson, '08, '15, 16, '17
Alydus pilosulus Harmostes reflexulus Protenor belfragei }	Heteroptera (Coreidæ)	6, 7	13, 14	Wilson, '05, Montgomery, '06
Anasa tristis Chelinidea vittigera Euthoctha galeator Leptoglossus phyllopus, and others }	" "	10. 11	21, 22	Wilson, '05, '06, McClung, etc.
Margus inconspicuus	" "	(11, 12)	23, 24	Wilson, '09, etc.
Chariesterus antennator	" "	(12, 13)	25, 26	"
Syromastes marginatus	" "	10, 12	22, 24	" " Gross
Largus cinctus	" (Pyrrhorcoridæ)	5, 6	11, 12	" '07, '09
" succinctus		6, 7	13, 14	" "
Pyrrhocoris apterus	" "	11, 12	23, 24	" " (*cf.* Henking '90)
Pentatoma senilis	" (Pentatomidæ)	3	6	Wilson '13
" juniperina	" "	(7)	14	" "
Œbalus pugnax	Heteroptera (Pentatomidæ)	(5)	10	Wilson, '09
Euschistus crassus	" "	6	12	Foot and Strobell, '12
" fissilis, servus " variolarius " etc. }	"	7	14	Montgomery, '01, '06, Wilson, '05
Podisus bractatus	Heteroptera (Pentatomidæ)	(7)	14	Wilson, '09
" placidus	" "	8	16	" "
Thyanta custator	" "	8	16	" '11
" calceata	" "	13, 14	27, 28	" "
Banasa dimidiata	" "	8	16	" '07
" calva	" "	13	26	" "
Aphis saliceti	Homoptera (Aphidæ)	2, 3	5, 6	Baehr, '09, '12
Phyllapis coweni	" "	2, 3	5, 6	Morgan, '15
Aphis ("milkweed, black")	" "	3, 4	(7), 8	Stevens, '09
" œnotheræ	" "	4, 5	9, 10	" '05, '06, '10
" ("golden-rod")	" "	(5, 6)	(11), 12	" '09

EXAMPLES OF CHROMOSOME-NUMBERS IN ANIMALS—*Continued*

Species	Group	Haploid	Diploid	Authority
	Tracheata—Continued			
Aphis ("rose aphid, green")	Homoptera (Aphi-	6, 7	(13, 14)	Stevens, '06, '09
" ("rose, migratory")	" " [dæ)	(8), 9	(17), 18	" '06
Pamphigus pyriformis				
spirotheca	" "	(9, 10)	(19), 20	Baehr, '08, '09
Icerya purchasi	" (Coccidæ)	2	4	Pierantoni, '12, '14
Apis mellifica	Hymenoptera	16	32	Nachtsheim, '13
Osmia cornuta	"	16	(32)	Armbruster, '13
Xylocopa violacea	"	16	(32)	Granata, '09, '13
Paracopidosomopsis sp.	" (Cynipidæ)	8	16	Patterson, '17
Rhodites rosæ	" "	9	18	Henking, '92,
				Hogben, '20
Neuroterus lenticularis	" "	10	20	Doncaster, '09, '11
Nematus ribesii	" (Tenthredini-			
	dæ)	8	16	" '04–'10
Lasius niger	" (Formicidæ)	10	20	Henking, '92
Formica sanguinea	" "	24	48	Schleip, '08
Phyllosamia cynthia	Lepidoptera	13	26	Dederer, '07, '15
Pieris brassicæ	"	14	28	Henking, '90
" "	"	15	30	Doncaster, '12
Callosamia promethea	"	19	38	Cook, '10
Pygæra pigra	"	23	46	Federley, '13
" curtula	"	29	(58)	" "
" anchoreta	"	30	(60)	" "
Lymantria dispar	"	31	62	Seiler, '14
Talæoporia tubulosa	"	30, 29	60, 59	" '17, 19
Fumea casta	"	31, 30	62, 61	" " "
Theophila mandriana	"	27	(54)	Yatsu, '13
Bombyx mori (17 varieties)	"	28	60–50	" " "
Nyssia zonaria	"	56±	112±	Doncaster, '14
Necrophorus sagi	Coleoptera	6, 7	13, (14)	Stevens, '09
Odontola dorsalis	"	8	16	" '06
Coptocycla guttata	"	9	18	Nowlin, '06
Photinus consanguineus	"	9, 10	19, 20	Stevens, '09
Diabrotica vittata	"	10, 11	21, 22	" '08,
	"			Hoy, '14
Coptocycla aurichalcea		11	22	Nowlin, '06
Chrysomela similis	"	11, 12	23, 24	Stevens, '09
Lestotrophus cingulatus	"	13	26	" '09
Trirhabda virgata	"	14	28	" '06
" Canadense	"	15	30	" " "
Lena trilineata	"	16	32	" '09
Doryphora cliricollis	"	17	(34)	" " "
" decemlineata	"	18	36	" '06
Dytiscus marginalis	"	19	38	Schafer, '07
Anopheles punctipennis	Diptera	3	6	Stevens, '11
Culex pipiens	"	3	6	" " "
Drosophila earli	"	(3)	6	Metz, '16
" melanogaster	"	4	8	Stevens, '08
(=ampelophila)				
" amœna and 7 other				
species	"	(4)	8	Metz, '16
" obscura and 3 other	"	(5)	10	" " "
species				
" funebris and 2 other	"	(6)	12	" " "
species				

EXAMPLES OF CHROMOSOME-NUMBERS IN ANIMALS—*Continued*

Tracheata—Continued

SPECIES	GROUP	HAPLOID	DIPLOID	AUTHORITY
Musca domestica	Diptera	6	12	Metz, '16
Asilus notatus	"	7	14	"
Anthrax sinuosa	"	9	18	"
Miastor americana	"	20–24	(40–48)	Hegner, '14

Echinodermata

SPECIES	GROUP	HAPLOID	DIPLOID	AUTHORITY
Parechinus microtubercula- tus univalens	(Echinoidea)	9	18	Boveri, '90, '05 Stevens, '02
Parechinus microtuberoulatus bivalens	"	18	36	Boveri, '90, '05, Stevens, '02, Baltzer, '09–'13
Paracentrotus lividus	"	18	36	Boveri, '02,
	"			Baltzer, '13
Echinus acutus	"	[19]	38 }	Doncaster and
" esculentus	"	["]	38 }	Gray, '13
Sphærechinus granularis	"	20	40	Baltzer, '10
Moira atropus	"	(23)	46	Pinney, '11
Asterias vulgaris	(Asteroidea)	9	18	Tennent, '07
" forbesii	" "	18	36	" " Jordan, '07, '08

Protochordata

SPECIES	GROUP	HAPLOID	DIPLOID	AUTHORITY
Amphioxus lanceolatus	Cephalochorda	12	24	Cerfontaine, '05
Stylopsis grossularia	Tunicata	2	4	Julin, '93
Phallusia mammilata	"	8	16	Hill, '95
Ciona intestinalis	"	9	18	Boveri, '90

Vertebrata

SPECIES	GROUP	HAPLOID	DIPLOID	AUTHORITY
Myxine glutinosa	Pisces (Cyclostomata)	26	52	Schreiner, '04
Lepidosiren paradoxa	Pisces (Dipnoi)	19	38	Agar, '11, '12
Torpedo, sp.	" (Elasmo- branchii)	12	24	Moore, '95
Scyllium canicula	" "	12	24	" "
Pristiurus, sp.	" "	18 ±	36 ±	Rückert '92
Spinax niger	" "		60–70	Schreiner, '07
Fundulus heteroclitus	" (Teleostei)	(18)	36	Mœnkhaus, '04
Menidia notata	" "	(18)	36	" "
Salamandra maculosa				Flemming, '82
Plethodon cinereas				Montgomery, '03
				Janssens, '00, '01
Triton alpestris	Amphibia (uro-			" "
" cristatus	dela)	12	24	" "
Batrachoseps attenuatus				Eisen, '00, Jans- sens, '05, etc.
Desmognathus fuscus and others				Kingsbury, '99 Montgomery '03
Aneides lugubris	" "	14	28	Snook and Long, '14
Amblystoma tigrinum	" "	(14)	28	Parmenter, '19
Pelodytes punctatus	Amphibia (Anura)	6	(12)	Bataillon, '10

EXAMPLES OF CHROMOSOME-NUMBERS IN ANIMALS—*Continued*

Vertebrata—Continued

SPECIES	GROUP	HAPLOID	DIPLOID	AUTHORITY
Bufo vulgaris	Amphibia (Anura)	8–9		Lebrun, '01, Bataillon, '10
Bufo lentiginosus	" "	12	24	King, '02, '07
Alytes obstetricans	" "	16	32	Janssens and Willems, '09
Rana fusca (?)	" "	12	24	Von Rath, 95 Bataillon, '10
" catesbiana	' "	13	26	Swingle
Columba livia domestica	Aves	8	16	Harper, '04
Gallus domesticus	"	9	18	Guyer, '09, '16 (See p. 786)
Phasianus, sp.	"	10–11	20–22	Cutler, '18
Felis catus	Mammalia	17, 18	35, 36	Winiwarter and Saintmont, '09
Canis familiaris	"	10, 11	21, 22	Malone, '18
Didelphys virginiana	"	11	22	Painter, '21
Mus norvegicus albinus	"	18, 19	37 (38)	Allen, '18
Sus scrofa	"	(20)	40	Hance, '17, '18
Bos taurus	"	18, 19	37, 38	Wodsedalek, '20
Homo sapiens [1]	"		47, 48	Winiwater, '12, '21
" "	"	24	48	Painter '21, '22

EXAMPLES OF CHROMOSOME-NUMBERS IN PLANTS

Thallophytta

SPECIES	GROUP	HAPLOID	DIPLOID	AUTHORITY
Ceratiomyxa, sp.	Myxomycetes	8	16	Jahn, '08
Rhopalodia gibba	Diatomeæ	4	8	Klebahn, '96
Surirella saxonica	"	64–65	128–130	Karsten, '12
Closterium Ehrenbergii	Conjugatæ	60 +		Van Wisselingh, '13
Spirogyra neglecta	"	12	24	Tröndle, '11
" calospora	"	8–10	16–20	"
Zygnema stellinum	"	12–14	25–28	Kurssanow, '11
Hæmatococcus pluvialis	Chlorophyceæ	32		Reichenow, '09
Chlamydomonas Dilli	"	10 ±		Dangeard, '98
" monadina	"	30		"
Hydrodictyon uniculatum	"	10		Timberlake, '01
" africanum	"	18		Yamanouchi, '13
Coleochæte sculata	"	32		Allen, '05
Œdogonium cynthigerum	"	19		Van Wisselingh, '08
Chara crinita	"	12	24	Ernst, '18
Cutleria multifida	Phæophyceæ	24	48	Yamanouchi, '12
Fucus vesiculosus	"	32	64	" '09
Dictyota dichotoma	Rhodophyceæ	16	32	Mottier, '00, Williams, '04
Griffithsia bornetiana	"	7	14	Lewis, '09
Nemalion multifidum	"	8 ±	16 ±	Wolfe, '04
Scinaia furcellata	"	10	20	Svedelius, '15
Delesseria sanguinea	"	20	40	" "
Pyronema confluens	Ascomycetes	12	24	Claussen, '12
Humaria rutilans	"	16	32	Fraser, '08, Guilliermond, '11

[1] See note at p. 766.

EXAMPLES OF CHROMOSOME-NUMBERS IN PLANTS—*Continued*

Cormophyta

SPECIES	GROUP	HAPLOID	DIPLOID	AUTHORITY
Riccia lutescens	Hepaticæ	4	8	Lewis, '06
" frostii	"	8	16	Black, '13
Pellia eliphylla	"	8	16	Farmer, '95, Davis, '01
Bryum capillare	Musci	10	(20)	É. and É. Marchal, '11
Sphagnum squarrosum	"	20	(40)	Melin, '15
Mnium hornum	"	6	12	M. Wilson, '08, Arens, '08
Polytrichum juniperinum	"	6	(12)	Arens, '08, Allen, '12
Pteris aquilina	Pteridophyta	32	64	Stevens, '98
Nephrodium molle	"	64–66	128–132	Yamanouchi, '08
Dryopteris (Nephrodium) pseudo-mas	"	72	144	Farmer and Digby, '07
Ceratopteris thalictroides	"	120–130		Gabe and Gasni, '13
Marsilia, 5 sp.	"	16	32	Strasburger, '07
Equisetum limosum	"	45–50		Bönicke, '11
" arvense	"	115		Beer, '13

Gymnospermæ

Cycas revoluta	Cycadales	(12)	24	Ishikawa, '16
Dioön edule	"	12	(24)	Chamberlain, '09
Callitis cupressoides	Coniferales	6	(12)	Saxton, '10
Taxus baccata	"	8	16	Overton, '93, Strasburger, '04
Cephalotaxus drupacea	"	10	(20)	Lawson, '07, Ishakawa, '16
Pinus, 8 sp.	"	12	24	Dixon, '94 Chamberlain, '99 Ferguson, '01
Larix, 5 sp.	"	12	(24)	Strasburger, '92 Juel, '00, Belajeff, '94
Abies balsamea	"	16	32	Hutchinson, '15
Sequoia sempervirens	"	16	32	Lawson, '04

Angiospermæ (Dicotyledoneæ)

Crepis virens	Compositæ	3	6	Rosenberg, '09, Digby, '14
" tectorum	"	4	8	Juel, '05
" lanceolata, var.	"	5	(10)	Tahara and Ishikawa, '11
" japonica	"	8	16	Tahara, '10
" biennis	"		very many	Digby, '14
Lactuca denticulata	"	5	(10)	Ishikawa, '16
" stolonifera	"	8	(16)	" '11
" laciniata	"	9	(18)	" '16
" thunbergiana	"	11 or 12	(24)	" '11
" debilis	"	24	(48)	" '16
Hieracium venosum	"	7	14	Rosenberg, '07, '17
" auricula	"	9	18	" "

EXAMPLES OF CHROMOSOME-NUMBERS IN PLANTS—*Continued*

Angiospermæ (Dicotyledoneæ)—Continued

SPECIES	GROUP	HAPLOID	DIPLOID	AUTHORITY
Hieracium aurantiacum	Compositæ	18	36	Rosenberg '17
" flagellare (apog.)	"	21	42	" "
Chrysanthemum coronarium and others	"	9	16	Tahara, '15, '21
C. leucanthemum, indicum	"	18	(36)	" "
" morifolium	"	27	(54)	" "
" decaisneanum	"	36	(72)	" "
" arcticum, marginatum	"	45	(90)	" "
Spinacia oleracca	Chenopodiaceæ	6	12	Stomps, '10
Chenopodium album	"	9	(18)	Winge, '16
" bonus henricus	"	18	(36)	" "
Viola glabella	Violaceæ	6	(12)	Miyaki, '13
" grypoceras + 5 species	"	10	(20)	"
" okuboi + 2 species	"	12	(24)	"
" diffusa	"	(13)	(26)	"
" japonica	"	24	(48)	"
Vicia faba	Leguminosæ	6	12	Nemec, '04, Strasburger, '11, Sharp, '13, '14
Pisum sativum	"	7	(14)	Cannon, '03, Sakamura, '16
Œnothera lamarckiana (also grandiflora, rubinerois, biennis, etc.)	Œnotheraceæ	7	14	Lutz, '07, Gates, '07, Geerts, '07
Œnothera lata (various forms)	"	7, 8 ±	15	Lutz, '12 Gates, '12
Œnothera semigigas	"		21	Lutz, '12, Stomps, '12, etc.
" gigas	"		28 (27, 29)	Lutz, '07, Gates, '08, etc.
Ribes, 2 sp.	Saxifragaceæ	8	16	Tischler, '06
Solanum lycopersicum	Solanaceæ	12	24	Winkler, '09
" nigrum	"	36	72 ±	"
Drosera rotundifolia	Droseraceæ	10	20	Rosenberg, '04
" longifolia	"	20	40	" '09
Primula sinensis	Primulaceæ	9	18	Gregory, '09
" verticillata	"	12	24	Digby, '12
" kewensis	"	18	36	" "
Thalictrum minus	"	12	(24)	Overton, '09
" purpurascens (apog.)	Rosaceæ	24	48	" "
	"	7	14	Täckholm, '20
		14	21	(see p. 848)
Rosa; various forms (races, species?)			28	
Many apogamous			32–36	
			35	
			42	
			56	
Alchemilla arvensis	"	16	32	Murbeck, '01
" grossidens and others	"	32	64	"
Potentilla rupestris	"	8	16	Forenbacher, '14
Potentilla sylvestris and others	"	16	32	Forenbacher, '14

EXAMPLES OF CHROMOSOME-NUMBERS IN PLANTS—*Continued*

Angiospermæ (*Monocotyledoneæ*)

SPECIES	GROUP	HAPLOID	DIPLOID	AUTHORITY
Naias marina	Naiadaceæ	6	12	Guignard, '99, Müller, '12
Triticum monococcum	Gramineæ	7	14	Sakamura, '18, Sax, '21
" durum	"	14	28	" "
" vulgare	"	21	42	" "
Avena strigosa	"	7	14	Kihara, '19
" barbata	"	14	28	"
" byzantina	"	21	42	"
Zea mays	"	10—	20—	Kuwada, '15
Carex pilulifera	Cyperaceæ	9		Heilborn, '22
" ericetorum	"	15		"
" vaginata	"	16		"
" montana	"	19		"
" diœca	"	26		"
" atrafa	"	27		"
" Helleri	"	28		"
" caryophyllea	"	31		"
" pallescens	"	32		"
" vulpina	"	34		"
" flava	"	35		"
" riparia	"	36		"
" aquatilis	"	37	74	Stout, '13
" rostrata	"	38		Heilborn, '22
" cœspitosa	"	40		"
" vesicaria	"	41		"
Musa sapientia var. "Dole"	Musaceæ	8	16	Tischler, '10
" sapientina var. "Raja Siam"	"	16	(32)	"
" sapientina var. "Kladi"	"	24	(48)	"
Disporum Hookeri	Liliaceæ	5	(10)	Lawson, '11
Trillium grandiflorum	"	6	12	Atkinson, '99
Medeola virginiana	"	7	(14)	Ishikawa, '16
Allium cepa	"	8	16	Schaffner, '98, Miyake, '05
Hyacinthus orientalis	"	8	16	Hyde, '09 Müller, '12
Galtonia candicans	"	8	16	Schniewind-Thies, '01, etc.
Lilium martagon and 9 other species	"	12	24	Guignard, '84, '91, Strasburger, '82, '88, etc.
Iris squalens and 3 other species	"	12	(24)	Strasburger, '00, Miyaki, '05
Smilacina racemosa	" "	24	(48)	McAlister, '13, Woolery, '15
Calopogon pulchellus	Orchidaceæ	13	26±	Pace, '09
Gyrostachys (Spiranthes) gracilis	"	15	(30)	" '14
Gyrostachys cernua	"	30	(60)	"
Listera ovata	"	16	32	Rosenberg, '05

The foregoing list makes evident the fact that the number of chromosomes varies within very wide limits but in far the greater number of cases is relatively small, commonly not more than 36 (diploid) and often less. Among the most frequent diploid numbers in both plants and animals are 16, 18 and 24.[1] The smallest observed diploid number, at the theoretical limit 2, occurs in *Ascaris megalocephala univalens*, but these "chromosomes" represent assemblages of much smaller ones linked together in linear series (p. 879). The next smallest number 4, though rather rare, has been described here and there in several groups of plants, from the fungi (and possibly in the algæ) up to the seed-plants, and among animals in certain platodes (*Vortex*), nematodes (*Gordius*), copepods (*Cyclops*), arachnids (*Pediculopsis*), insects (*Icerya*) and tunicates (*Stylopsis*). Diploid numbers 6, 8, and 10 are also not very frequent; those from 12 to 36 are most frequent, and higher ones rare. The highest numbers have been recorded in some of the radiolarian rhizopods, ranging from 1000 to 1500 (*Aulacantha, Castanidium*); but these undoubtedly represent compound groups formed by many synchronously dividing nuclei in a syncytium.[2] In higher organisms the largest numbers seem to be found in the Filicales (up to 200), the decapod Crustacea (200 or more), and the Lepidoptera (up to 100 or more).

Closer study of the numbers brings out many points of interest. Of these, perhaps the most important is that the chromosome-numbers may differ widely within the limits even of the smaller groups (genus or family) and sometimes even between closely related species. An interesting case is that of the hemipteran species *Thyanta custator* in which were found two "races" previously confused under the same name and morphologically almost indistinguishable, in external appearance, one constantly having the diploid number 16 in both sexes, the other 27–28 (Wilson, '11). Later studies proved the two "races" to be distinct species, the former being the original *custator* of Fabricus, the latter the *calceata* of Say, which had long been buried in the literature as a synonym of *custator* (Barber, '11).

Such cases demonstrate clearly that *the number of chromosomes is per se a matter of secondary significance.* Both cytological and genetic evidence prove that the chromosomes are compound bodies, containing many different components. So long as the sum-total of these remains the same, or nearly so, it seems to be immaterial whether they be grouped to form few or many larger aggregates (p. 903). It is not surprising, therefore, to find no more than a slight degree of correlation between chromosome-numbers and systematic relationships—the numbers 16 and 24, for instance, are found in nearly

[1] *Cf.* Winge ('17).   [2] See Borgert ('01), Haecker ('07).

all the main groups of plants and animals. As far as the larger groups are concerned, therefore. there is little to favor the hope of finding a satisfactory basis of classification in the chromosome-numbers. Nevertheless the fact is not to be overlooked that some groups show on the whole characteristic peculiarities in this respect, and in some cases a number of greatest frequency or "type-number" may be distinguished. Among higher plants, as Tischler emphasizes, the bryophytes are in general characterized by low numbers, pteridophytes by high, and seed-plants by intermediate ones. Among Crustacea low numbers occur in Copepods, high in decapods; among insects relatively low numbers appear in Diptera, much higher ones in Lepidoptera, etc. In the Amphibia the greatest frequency or type-number may be taken as $2n = 24$; in the Acrididæ as 23, 24; in the Pentatomidæ as 14, and so on.[1] So many exceptions exist, however, that figures of this kind do not seem very significant, especially when we consider how small a fraction of the existing species have yet been examined.

It is a striking fact that *higher numbers are often exact multiples of lower ones.* In the simplest of these cases the higher number is double the lower; such cases occur in many genera of animals and plants, for instance in *Cyclops, Gryllotalpa, Aphis, Drosophila, Crepis, Hieracium,* or *Chrysanthemum;* and differences of the same type often appear between species of different genera. The significance of this is, however, made doubtful by the fact that in most such cases intermediate numbers also occur and the problem here raised is more complicated than would first appear. Many attempts have been made to arrange chromosome-numbers in some kind of significant system; but these have not as yet been very successful.

Some writers have assumed that within the limits of particular groups the haploid numbers are either multiples of 2, *e. g.,* 2, 4, 8, 16, or of 3, *e. g.,* 6, 12, 18, etc.; and it has been shown that many of the recorded chromosome-numbers fall into one or the other of these two systems;[2] but many of the series are incomplete or disturbed by the existence of intermediate numbers that cannot be fitted into the system, or by the existence of irreconcilable fundamental haploid numbers such as 5, 7 or 11. Of greater significance, perhaps, is the fact, conspicuously shown by recent investigation especially on the higher plants, that the diploid numbers not infrequently are progressive multiples of a fundamental *haploid* number by 2, 3, 4, and so on in arithmetical progression, sometimes with few or no intermediate numbers,

---

[1] E. B. Harvey ('20) assigns type-numbers to several of the larger groups, *e. g.,* for the Nemathelminthes $n = 6$, Echinoderms $n = 18$, Platyelminthes $n = 8$, Mollusca $n = 16$, etc.

[2] See Haecker ('04), Enriques ('05), Strasburger ('10), Gates ('15), and especially Tischler ('15) and Winge ('17).

so that they are often spoken of as diploid, triploid, tetraploid, etc.[1] The most remarkable examples of this have been found among plants, *e. g.*, in *Chrysanthemum, Triticum, Avena, Musa,* or *Rosa*. Here it may be pointed out that the exceptions in most of these various systems are so numerous as largely to deprive them of significance; for instance in the Copepod genus *Cyclops* and its allies *Diaptomus* and *Canthocamptus,* or in the Coleoptera, where the lowest known haploid number is 3, the second lowest 6, while beyond this point appear all numbers in continuous series from 7 up to 19.[2] Other examples of nearly continuous series are offered by the aphids, the pentatomids, and the seed-plants (*e. g.*, in *Carex*) and further observation seems likely to render many of the existing partial series more complete.

Without further multiplying instances, and with due allowance for incompleteness of the existing data, we must therefore admit the present inadequacy of attempts to reduce the chromosome-numbers to any simple or consistent arithmetical rules. This conclusion, as will presently be seen, forms part of the evidence which indicates that the evolution of chromosome-numbers has not followed a single or consistent course but has taken place on the whole fitfully, irregularly and in various ways.

V. DEVIATIONS FROM THE FUNDAMENTAL CHROMOSOME-NUMBERS

Many of the supposed variations and contradictions of chromosome-numbers as recorded in the literature have been a product of erroneous observation or of theoretic preconception; but apart from these the fact of variation in number, both in the individual and in the species, has been conclusively demonstrated. Some writers have considered this as a disproof of the specific constancy of chromosome-number and have concluded that "not constancy but variability in number of chromosomes is the general rule in all organisms," (Della Valle, '09). Verbally, perhaps, this is not incorrect, though a palpable exaggeration; in substance it is highly misleading.[3]

In general it may be said that variations in the chromosome-number are much more frequent in somatic cells than in those of the germ-line, and are also more frequent in old, highly specialized or degenerating cells. Such variations may be either definite or indefinite. The former are of more fixed type, and may affect not merely one or a few cells of the indi-

---

[1] The use of these terms, though convenient from a phyletic point of view, is somewhat confusing since they were originally applied to reduplication of the haploid groups due to pathological processes, such as polyspermy, fusion of eggs, and the like.

[2] For these cases see preceding lists.

[3] For specific criticisms of Della Valle's conclusions see Wilson ('10), Enriques ('11), McClung ('14, '17), Tischler ('17), Hance ('17, '18), Parmenter ('19), etc.

vidual but often large groups of them, or even all of them, in the same way. In such cases different individuals of the same species may differ definitely in apparent chromosome-number, but the number is constant in each particular individual. Variations of this type take their origin in linkage or in disturbances of mitosis, meiosis or fertilization, giving rise to new combinations which, once established, are thereafter maintained by normal mitosis. Indefinite fluctuations are not ordinarily thus produced but arise in the prophases by a fragmentation or transverse division of one or more of the chromosomes. They are in general inconstant, varying in different cells of the same individual or tissue; and, as will be seen later, some of them differ essentially from definite variations. *Both types, when critically examined, bring strong support to both the theory of genetic continuity and that of the specific constancy of the chromosomes.*

1. Somatic Cells and Germ-Cells

As a rule the chromosomes-groups of somatic mitoses agree closely with those of the germ-line though often with certain minor differences of form.[1] In some cases, however, definite differences of chromosome-number exist between them. The classical example of this is offered by *Ascaris megalocephala* in which cells of the germ-line divide with either two large chromosomes (variety *univalens*), or four (var. *bivalens*), while in all the somatic cells these larger chromosomes break up into much greater numbers of very small ones (Figs. 144, 145).[2] Again, in the honey-bee the fundamental haploid number is 16, as found by all observers. The male-producing (parthenogenetic) egg segments with this number, which is also retained in the spermatogonia, while the female-producing (fertilized) egg divides with the diploid number 32 (p. 797). In later stages the somatic divisions may show multiples of these basic numbers, namely, 32 or even 64; but the oögonial divisions, like the spermatogonial, show 16 chromosomes, probably as a result of coupling.[3]

In the same category, perhaps, we should place the apparent reduction to one-half the *haploid* number in the spermatocytes or spermatids described in certain Hymenoptera and some other animals. The best known example of this is offered by the honey-bee *Apis*. The haploid number (16) appears in the first (abortive) spermatocyte-division and may appear also in the second.[4] In many cases, however, the second division seems to show

---

[1] Morrill, '10, Hoy, '16, etc.

[2] In var. *univalens* this number is about 52 in the male and 60 in the female (Geinitz, '15), somewhat larger according to Kautzsch, '14. *Cf.* p. 855.

[3] Petrunkewitsch ('01), Doncaster ('06, '07), Meves ('07), Granata ('09, '13), Nachtsheim ('12), Armbruster ('13), etc.

[4] Meves ('07), Mark and Copeland ('06).

but 8 chromosomes (Fig. 383); but, as shown by Doncaster ('07) and especially by Nachtsheim ('13), the eight chromosomes are often seen to be double during the anaphases. This is evidently due to a coupling of the chromosomes, two by two, since the metaphase, according to Nachtsheim, shows 16 double chromosomes. A similar coupling seems to take place also in the oögenesis, where Petrunkewitsch ('01) found but 8 tetrads and was thus led to the erroneous conclusion that 8 is the haploid number. Meves, Nachtsheim and others have, however, proved that 16 is the haploid number as shown by the numbers in the gamete-nuclei and in the parthenogenetic development of the males (p. 797). A similar apparent reduction to the semi-haploid condition was found by Armbruster ('13) in the solitary bee *Osmia*, and in several of the vertebrates.[1] There is some reason to suspect that in some of these cases the appearance is due to an artificial clumping by the fixative; but such an interpretation can hardly be generally applicable.

2. Reduplication. Polyploidy

By this term may be designated a rather common form of definite variation in which either the whole diploid chromosome-group, or one of the haploid groups is doubled, or multiplied to give triploid, tetraploid, or polyploid groups. Attention has earlier been directed to the existence in various animals of the so-called "bivalent" (more properly tetraploid) individuals or races in which the normal chromosome-number is doubled but which do not otherwise differ visibly from the usual type (*Ascaris, Echinus, Artemia*, pp. 231, 869). More commonly the doubling (or higher multiplication) of the chromosomes appears only here and there in certain somatic cells, particularly those that are old, highly specialized or degenerating. Such groups are, for instance, common in the connective tissue-cells, fat-cells, investing-cells of the gonads and follicle-cells of insects (Fig. 407) and in the tapetal or investing cells of the sporangia in plants. As above mentioned reduplication is of common occurrence in the somatic divisions of Hymenoptera. It is highly probable that this condition arises from nuclear fusion or from some form of incomplete mitosis, such as monocentric mitosis (p. 168), incomplete separation of daughter chromosome-groups, or a fusion of daughter-nuclei after mitosis. Processes of this type have often been induced experimentally, *e. g.*, in sea-urchin eggs, *Spirogyra* filaments, or growing root-tips of plants that are exposed to the action of cold, CO_2, narcotics, or other poisons during mitosis.[2]

---

[1] In the opossum (Jordan, '11), man (Guyer, '10), pig, horse and bull (Wodsedalek, '13, '14, '20), and in some species of birds (Guyer, '00, '02, '09, '16, Cutler, '18).

[2] See p. 729, O. and R. Hertwig ('87), Demoor ('95), Wilson ('01b), Gerassimoff ('01), Boveri ('05) Nemec ('10), Herbst ('12, '14), etc.

Such cases of reduplication in certain cells of the individual are exactly parallel to those in which the normal diploid numbers of related races or species show constant differences of the same type (p. 867); and are no doubt due to similar causes. Even more interesting are cases in which the aberrant somatic numbers, again as in case of different races or species, do not form a simple geometrical series but are multiples of the fundamental hap-

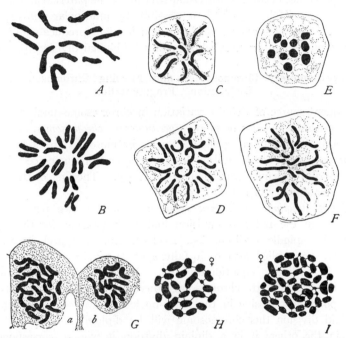

Fig. 407.—Haploid, diploid and tetraploid chromosome-groups in plants and animals (*A*, *B*, from STOMPS; *C–F* from MARCHAL; *G* from NEMEC; *H*, *I*, from WILSON).

A, diploid group from *Spinacea*; *B*, tetraploid group of same, chromosomes paired; *C*, haploid group from gametophyte of moss *Bryum capillare*, 10 chromosomes; *D*, normal diploid groups of the same species from the sporophyte; *E*, heterotypic division of same, 10 bivalents; *F*, diploid group from artificially produced gametophyte regenerated from the sporogonial tissue; *G*, from slightly chloralized root-tip of *Pisum*, *a* with tetraploid group (24 chromosomes), *b*, diploid group (one chromosome missing); *H*, normal diploid group (follicle cell) in the hemipter *Anasa tristis*, showing 22 chromosomes; including 2 small *m*-chromosomes and 4 large ones; *I*, tetraploid group of same, 44 chromosomes, 4 small and 8 large.

loid number in more or less regular arithmetical progression (*cf.* p. 867). Such a case is offered by the mosquito *Culex pipiens* (Holt, '17) in degenerating intestinal pupal cells during the metamorphosis. The normal diploid number is here 6 (often apparently 3, owing to the close paired association of the somatic mates, p. 837). In these cells were found mitoses with 6, 9, 12, 18, 24, 36, and even 72 chromosomes, the most frequent being 12, 24, and 48. These latter numbers ("6-series") may be taken as a result of simple doubling; but those with 9 or its multiples 9, 18, 36, and 72 ("9-series") apparently must have involved, at least in the production of its first term, a reduplication of one of the gametic groups independently of the other. Numbers thus arising are very similar to those seen in highly hybridized groups, such as the roses (p. 848). This might have arisen from an original difference between the division-rhythm of the paternal and maternal haploid groups (Holt, *op. cit.*),[1] or possibly by multipolar mitosis following a bi-nucleate or syncytial condition which might produce many irregularities of number afterwards held constant by bipolar division (p. 917).

3. Supernumerary Chromosomes and Missing Chromosomes. Non-Disjunction. Fragmentation

A frequent source of definite variation in chromosome-number is shown by the appearance of one or more *supernumerary chromosomes*, in addition to the normal chromosome-group.[2] Such chromosomes are of two kinds, differing entirely in nature and mode of origin, and producing certain types of definite and indefinite variation respectively. The first of these result from an abnormality of mitosis known as:

a. Non-disjunction. This process is a failure of two synaptic mates to separate in the reduction-division and their passage together to one pole of the spindle (Wilson, '09, Bridges, '16, etc.) and it may appropriately be applied also to a failure of sister-chromosomes to separate in an ordinary equation-division. In such cases one daughter-nucleus receives an extra chromosome (thereafter a supernumerary) which is correspondingly missing in the sister-nucleus. If it occurs in a meiotic or haploid division this chromosome will be diploid in one nucleus and absent in the other; if in a diploid division it will be correspondingly either triploid or single. In either case the initial modification may be handed on to later descendants of these cells; and when the gametes have been affected may reappear in one or more following generations as a constant character of the individual. Supernumeraries thus arising may therefore lead a kind of wandering life in the species (hence Painter's term *planosome*), passing from one individual to another in successive generations,[3] but forming no necessary part of the chromosome-group as a whole and often

[1] This surmise is based on the fact that the "6 = series" and "9 = series" never appear in the same individual.

[2] These were first recognized in certain species of Hemiptera, viz. *Banasa calva* (Wilson, '05, '07a); several species of *Metapodius* (Wilson, '07b, '09) and in the beetle *Diabrotica* (Stevens, '08). They have since been found in Diptera (Bridges) in Orthoptera (Stevens, Carothers, McClung and others) spiders (Painter) and in many plants (Lutz, Hance, etc.).

[3] This has been proved conclusively by the breeding experiments of Bridges ('16) on the supernumerary X- and Y-chromosomes in *Drosophila* (p. 947).

being absent.   Their inconstancy in the species was the source of confusion in the earlier literature and gave rise to some ill-considered criticism.   In point of fact, however, their behavior is tantamount to an experimental demonstration of the genetic continuity of the chromosomes; and the cytological phenomena also find genetic expression in modified forms of heredity which give an equally cogent demonstration of the determinative action of the chromosomes in heredity (p. 944).

The process of non-disjunction has been directly observed in very few cases;[1] but indirectly both the cytological and the genetic evidence indicate

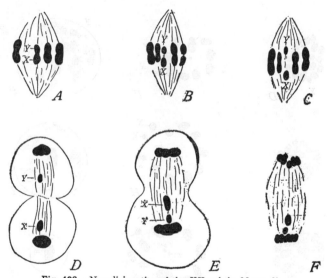

Fig. 408.—Non-disjunction of the XY-pair in *Metapodius*.

A–D, normal disjunction of X and Y, second spermatocyte division (*A–C*, *M. femoratus*; *D*, *M. granulosus*); *E*, non-disjunction, *M. femoratus*; *F*, *M. terminalis*.

its occurrence much oftener.[2]   In *Œnothera* (diploid 14) it results in the production of spore-nuclei having respectively 6 and 8 chromosomes instead of the usual 7.   In this case the minus or 6-chromosome class is believed to be non-viable but the 8-chromosome class is believed to survive and ultimately to give rise to an 8-chromosome gamete-nucleus.   Union of such a nucleus with the normal 7-chromosome type will produce a 15-chromosome zygote, diploid in respect to 6 chromosome-pairs but triploid

---

[1] By Gates ('08) in the heterotypic division of the pollen-mother-cells of *Œnothera*, confirmed by Davis ('10, '11); independently by Wilson ('09) in case of the XY-pair of sex-chromosomes in the hemipter *Metapodius*; more recently by Seiler ('21) in the polar divisions of the moth *Talæoporia*.

[2] Mavor ('21, '23) has reported the experimental production of non-disjunction in Drosophila by X-rays.

in respect to one pair (*i. e.*, with one supernumerary). This condition exists in a considerable group of mutants, of which *Œ. lata* is the type, known to have arisen from 14-chromosome forms such as *Œ. lamarckiana, biennis* or *rubricalyx*.[1] Blakeslee ('20) has recently found similar conditions in the

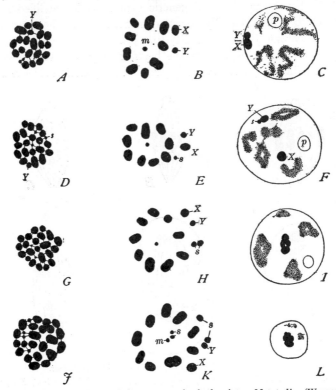

Fig. 409.—Supernumerary *Y*-chromosomes in the hemipter, *Metapodius* (WILSON).

In each horizontal row the left figure is a spermatogonial metaphase, the middle one a first spermatocyte, the right one a spermatocyte nucleus with chromosome-nucleoli (*X, Y, s*) and plasmosome (*p*); *X, Y*, the sex-chromosomes, *s* the supernumeraries, and *m* the *m*-chromosomes. *A–C, M. terminalis*, 22 chromosomes, no supernumerary; *D–F*, the same, 23 chromosomes, one small supernumerary (*s*); *G–I*, the same, two large supernumeraries; *J–L, M. femoratus*, 26 chromosomes, 2 large supernumeraries and 2 small.

jimson-weed (*Datura*). There the diploid number is normally 24 but it is 25 in a series of forms that are comparable with the *lata-group* (p. 945).

In *Metapodius*, likewise, non-disjunction was observed in the meiotic division (spermatogenesis), and the particular chromosome-pair concerned could here be positively identified as the unequal sex-chromosomes or XY-pair (Fig. 408). The supernumeraries thus produced retain all the charac-

[1] See Gates, '15.

teristics of Y-chromosomes, and have been found in varying numbers in different individuals of three species. Some individuals have 22 chromosomes (the normal diploid number) including one Y, others but 21 (Y being missing); still others 23, 24, 25, 26 or (in a single case) 27, both the number and the size-relations being constant in each individual.

In synapsis these supernumeraries usually couple with the normal XY-pair to form compound groups (Fig. 409). During this mitosis they disso-

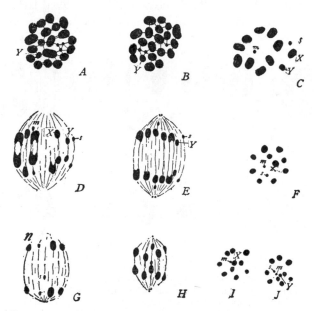

Fig. 410.—Chromosomes of *Metapodius terminalis*, with one small supernumerary Y-chromosome (*s*) (WILSON).

A, *B*, diploid (spermatogonial) metaphases, 23 chromosomes (2 small *m*'s, 1 small supernumerary); *C*, corresponding first spermatocyte-metaphase; *D*, *E*, 1st (heterotypic) spermatocyte division in side-view, division of *X*, *Y* and *s*; *F*, second spermatocyte-metaphase; *G*, *H*, anaphases, *s* undivided; *I*, *J*, sister groups of same, polar view, one with *s* and one without it.

ciate in various ways, X and at least one Y always separating, while the supernumeraries may accompany either X or Y, apparently at random (Fig. 410) so that various combinations therefore appear in the sperm-nuclei. Since those of the X-class (female-producing) may contain also Y the possibility thus exists of introducing supernumerary Y-chromosomes into both sexes at the next fertilization.

By further recombinations the number of supernumeraries might theoretically increase indefinitely; but in point of fact not more than 5 or 6 have yet been found in *Metapodius;* and they are often smaller than Y in various degrees.   Probably, therefore, the supernumeraries sooner or later degenerate and disappear.

Metapodius also afforded the proof that supernumeraries may be of more than one definite type; for a single individual of *M. femoratus* was found having one supernumerary showing none of the peculiarities of a Y-chromosome but all those of an *m*-chromosome (Wilson, '10).   These peculiarities are of such marked type (p. 839) as to preclude all error in the identification and the case is further remarkable because this individual lacks a Y-chromosome (*cf.* p. 815) yet the small *m* does not take its place but behaves

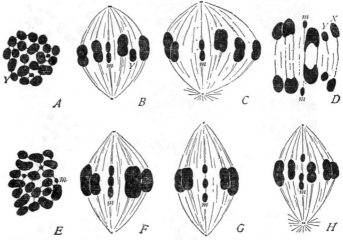

Fig. 411.—Supernumerary *m*-chromosomes in the hemipter *Metapodius femoratus*.

A–D, normal form, for comparison with modified from (E–H).

A, spermatogonial metaphase, 22 chromosomes; 2 *m*'s; B, C, normal metaphases of first spermatocyte, with *m*-bivalent, in side-view; D, anaphase, *m*'s and the X- and Y-chromosomes dividing separately.   The *m*-chromosomes are here disjoining (reduction-division) the X- and Y-chromosomes dividing equationally.

E, spermatogonial group with 23 chromosomes (3 *m*'s); F, G, H, side-views of first spermatocyte-metaphases, *m*-trivalent.

after its own kind and in meiosis couples with the other *m*-chromosomes to form a trivalent element (Fig. 411).   It thus offers a striking example of characteristic differences of behavior between chromosomes which in other respects appear exactly alike to the eye (p. 839).   These cases demonstrate with the utmost clearness the fact that univalent chromosomes typically divide but once in the course of the meiotic divisions, passing undivided to one pole in the other division.   In *Metapodius* it is the first division in which the supernumeraries divide (Fig. 410); in *Banasa*, the second; in *Diabrotica*, according to Stevens, in either division but not in both.[1]

[1] More recently Seiler ('21, '23) has been able to observe non-disjunction directly in the first spermatocyte-division of *Talæporia tubulosa*.

Analogous to the foregoing case is that discovered by Bridges ('13, '14, '16) in *Drosophila*, remarkable because it was purely genetic study that first led him to predict the existence of an extra or supernumerary chromosome in this particular race; and this was fully confirmed by cytological examination. The non-disjunction itself has not yet actually been seen, but the behavior of the sex-linked factors (p. 947) leaves no doubt that it takes place in the meiosis of the egg, and affects the XX-pair. A primary disjunction of this type would give eggs containing either XX or no-X; and fertilization of such eggs by normal sperm would give XXX, XO, XXY and YO. The first and fourth of these classes have not been found in this race and are believed to be non-viable. The XO-class is composed of males, of normal appearance but absolutely sterile, thus demonstrating a connection between the Y-chromosome and fertility (p. 815). From the XXY females (having 9 chromosomes) Bridges raised a race in which the phenomena of "secondary non-disjunction" of the XX-pair is continued in about 4% of cases. Bridges explains this as due to the presence of Y, since in the maturation of eggs containing XXY, Y is always disjoined from one X, while the second X may pass to either pole. Thus may arise four classes of mature eggs, namely: (1) XX, (2) XY, (3) XO and (4) YO; and fertilization of these by normal sperms (X or Y) might give as zygotes the six classes (1) XXX, (2) XXY, (3) XX, (4) XY, (5) XYY and (6) YY. Of these, XXX, XYY and YY are unknown (though the class XYY probably exists); XX and XY are ordinary males and females; while XXY may serve as a starting-point for repetition of the process. The genetic aspect of this interesting case is further considered at p. 947.

More recently Bridges has found in *Drosophila* a supernumerary autosome of the very small fourth pair, which offers a close parallel to the supernumerary *m*-chromosome of *Metapodius* (p. 876). Blakeslee's recent observations on 25-chromosome mutants of *Datura*, make it probable that in that form non-disjunction is of rather frequent occurrence and may effect any one of the twelve chromosome-pairs (see p. 945).

b. Fragmentation. "Deficient" Chromosomes. Fluctuations. In the foregoing cases the normal chromatin-content of the nucleus is increased (or correspondingly decreased) in a definite and constant manner. In a second type supernumeraries arise by a cross-division or fragmentation of one or more of the chromosomes—a process which does not alter the total chromatin-mass but only breaks it up into a larger number of pieces than the normal. The variations thus produced are inconstant, varying in different cells of the same individual and thus having the character of indefinite variations or fluctuations. This is clearly demonstrated by the studies of Hance on the somatic mitoses of the pig ('17) and of *Œnothera scintil-*

lans ('18) in which the typical diploid numbers are respectively 40 and 15. No deviations from these numbers were found in the germ-line; but in the somatic mitoses, along with the typical numbers occur also numbers ranging in the pig from 40 to 58, and in *Œnothera* from 15 to 21, owing to the presence of supernumeraries (Fig. 412).

This seems at first sight a flat contradiction of the specific constancy of chromosome-number; but Hance's careful studies place the matter in a very

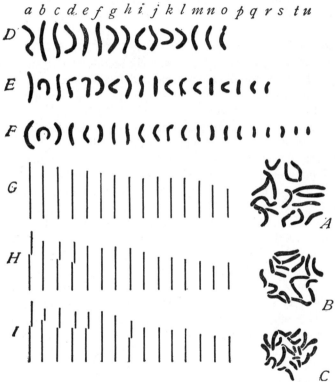

Fig. 412.—Variations of chromosome-number in *Œnothera scintillans* (HANCE).

At the right, *A*, typical somatic group, with 15 chromosome; *B*, one with 19 chromosomes; *C*, one with 21. Above, *D*, *E*, *F*, the chromosomes of such groups arranged in the order of their size, from *a* to *u*. Below, *G*, *H*, *I*, the corresponding chromosome-lengths, similarly graded, so arranged as to bring together the chromosome-fragments and to show the constant total length.

different light. The supernumeraries are always smaller than the normal chromosomes and both their number and size are exactly correlated with corresponding deficiences in the lengths of particular chromosomes; so that when the former are artificially fitted upon the latter the normal size-relations are restored (Fig. 412). *The total length of the chromosomes is thus a specific constant irrespective of their number.* In respect to their mode of origin, therefore, these supernumeraries are evidently not whole chromosomes but pieces, though in behavior they are not to be distinguished from true chromosomes, dividing lengthwise in mitosis, so as to be handed on from cell to cell without loss of their identity.

This conclusion is sustained by many other observations. Carothers ('13, '17) and Robertson ('15) showed that the unequal or heteromorphic chromosome-pairs observed in certain grasshoppers arise in certain cases by the cross-division of one member of the pair; and Carothers shows further that the break takes place at a particular point marked by two large chromosome-vesicles at which the spindle fibers are attached (Fig. 438). This, again, is in harmony with numerous observations which demonstrate the presence of cross-sutures at certain points in the chromosomes, which in some species at least are constant in position. The conclusion that chromosomes may occasionally fragment across the transverse sutures and thus increase the number of chromosomes becomes still more plausible when taken in connection with other evidence concerning the compound nature of the chromosomes (p. 903) and the possible modes by which chromosome-numbers may have permanently changed. The evidence indicates that the position of these cross-sutures is constant for any given chromosome; and hence that if supernumeraries be produced in the supposed manner they probably have a quite definite value.

6. Chromosome-linkage

This subject has already been touched on in case of the sex-chromosomes, the X-chromosome, and possibly also the Y-chromosome, being in some cases attached to one of the autosomes (p. 779). Such linkage constitutes a source of definite variation in number that is the reverse of that caused by the presence of supernumeraries. A similar linkage of autosomes with one another is known to take place in some species, especially among insects; and the evidence indicates that it has probably played an important part in the permanent change of number from species to species.

The classical case is offered by *Ascaris megalocephala,* where the chromosomes of the somatic cells, which are small and numerous, are in the cells of the germ-line united in linear aggregates to form larger and fewer chromosomes (p. 323). We might, it is true, reverse this terminology, designating the breaking up of the long chromosomes into smaller bodies in the primordial somatic cells as a process of fragmentation. This, however, is a mere question of terminology which leaves the fact unaltered, and it is rendered improbable by the numbers in related species of *Ascaris* (p. 855).

Most frequently linkage takes place between the chromosomes two by two to produce so-called "bivalent" elements, each such linkage reducing the apparent chromosome-number by one. Some of the best examples of this are found among the acridian grasshoppers, in which the typical diploid number is 23 or 24, with all the chromosomes rod-shaped and having terminal attachments. This relation is typically shown in *Chortophaga viridifasciata* (Fig. 413, A); but McClung found one male of this species in which

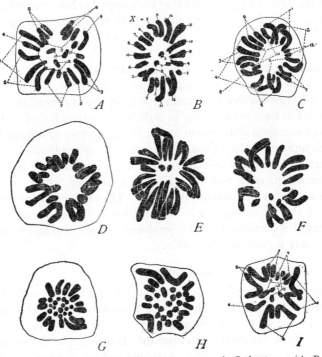

Fig. **413.**—Spermatogonial metaphase chromosome-groups in Orthoptera.   (*A, D, E, F,* Mc-Clung; *B,* Robertson; *C, H, I,* Davis; *G,* Buchner).

The chromosomes in *A–C* numbered according to their size. In *A–C, F, G,* all the chromosomes telomitic with no linkage; in *D,* three atelomitic V's, in *H* two, and in *I* six.

A, Chortophaga, B, Syrbula, C, Arphia, each with 23 rod-shaped telomitic chromosomes; *D, Chortophaga* with 20 chromosomes (3 pairs linked); *E, Mecostethus; F, Tropidolophus* (23 chromosomes); *G, Decticus;* (31 chromosomes); *H, Steiroxys* (29 chromosomes); *I, Stenobothrus* (17 chromosomes).

the number of separate chromosomes was reduced to 19, four of the chromosomes being V-shaped with attachment at the apex of the V (Fig. 413, D). Here, obviously, the apparent reduction in number is due to the linkage of four pairs of the rod-shaped chromosomes, two by two at their inner ends, to form bivalent V's.   This condition was found in every visible spermatogonial chromosome-group of this individual.   Quite analogous is the case found by L. V. Morgan ('22) in a certain strain of *Drosophila melanogaster*, in the females of which the two X-chromosomes, normally rod-shaped, are linked together, end-to-end, to form a single V (Fig. 415). Such a chromosome is never found in the male, since all eggs receiving it develop into females (p. 947).

Still more remarkable are the facts in *Hesperotettix* and *Mermiria* (McClung, '05, '17). *H. brevipennis* and *festivus* thus far have shown only the typical acridian relations (23–24 rod-shaped chromosomes), and these likewise appear in certain individuals of *H. viridis*. In other individuals of the latter species, however, two or more of the rods were found to be linked by their central ends (points of attachment), to form V's (as in *Chortophaga*) attached to the spindle by their apices, thus producing an apparent corresponding reduction of number. The linkage may affect either the X-chromosome or the autosomes, X being rarely free and most commonly linked with the largest autosome (Fig. 414). Whatever be the character of the linkage *it is constant for the individual in all the cells of the germ-line* (spermatogonia, spermatocytes) though varying from one individual to another. Thus far six distinct kinds of classes of individuals have been found, as follows:

CLASS	LINKAGE	APPARENT SPERMATOGONIAL NUMBER	APPARENT NUMBER IN 1ST SPERMATOCYTES
1.	No linkage. All the chromosomes free	23 rods	12
2.	X-linked with No. 12 (the largest)	21 rods; 1 V	11
3.	X-linked with No. 9; 11 and 12 linked	17 rods; 3 V's	10
4.	X-linked with No. 8; 11 and 12 linked; 9 and 10 linked.	15 rods; 4 V's	9
5.	X free; 11 and 12 linked; 9 and 10 linked	17 rods; 3 V's.	10
6.	X free; 11 and 12 linked	19 rods; 2 V's	11

The linked forms ("multiples" of McClung) are at once recognizable in the spermatogonia by their V-shaped or J-shaped form (Figs. 413, 414). In the first spermatocyte-division they are likewise distinguishable in size and form, the X-linkage producing the L-shaped type already described, while the autosome-linkage produces large tangential rings or V's of the " *Stenobothrus* or *Tomopteris* type" (p. 530). The second spermatocytes show corresponding relations.

In *Mermiria*, likewise, certain species show no linkage but in *M. bivittata* X is linked with one of the autosomes, producing a V-shaped multiple, the synaptic mate of which is in this case also V-shaped. In synapsis these two V's unite to form a trivalent element ("hexad") showing a complex appearance which formerly led McClung ('05) to conclude that in the first divi-

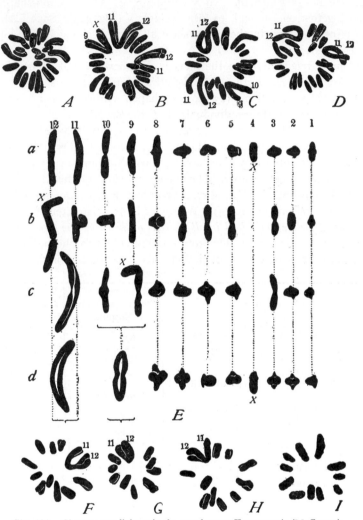

Fig. 414.—Chromosome-linkage in the grasshopper *Hespertotettix* (McClung).

A, H. brevipennis; the others *H. viridis; A,* spermatogonial group with 23 separate, rod-shaped chromosomes (Class 1); *B,* corresponding group of Class 3, 20 chromosomes, linkage of *X* with 9, and of 11 with 12; *C,* the same, Class 5, 20 chromosomes, linkage of 11 with 12 and of 9 with 10; *D,* the same, Class 6, 21 chromosomes, linkage of 11 with 12; *E,* the heterotypic chromosomes of four different classes aligned in the order of their size as numbered above (12 to 1); *a,* Class 1, no linkage; *b,* Class 2 (*X* linked with 12); *c,* Class 3, 11 linked with 12 and *X* with 9; *d,* Class 5, 11 linked with 12 and 9 with 10; *F–I,* second spermatocyte-metaphase of different classes; *F,* Class 6 (11 and 12 linked) *X*-class; *G,* no *X*-class; *H, X*-class, and *I* no *X*-class from individual like *c* (Class 5), with linkage of only one 11 and one 12.

sion whole bivalents (tetrads) passed to one pole.   It is now clear that this
trivalent differs from that of *Hesperotettix* only in the fact that both members
of the trivalent are V-shaped or J-shaped (atelomitic).

Whether the linkage in these cases is permanent or temporary can only
be determined by breeding experiments.   In *Ascaris megalocephala* the linkage is clearly permanent from generation to generation in cells of the germ-
line, but in each generation is broken up in all the somatic cells (pp. 323, 879).
In the moth *Lymantria monacha* the linkage, as described by Seiler and Hanel
('21) is temporary.   Here the diploid number in both sexes, including the
gonia, is 62.   We should expect the heterotypic division, accordingly, to
show 31 bivalent chromosomes; but such is the case only in the female.
In the male both divisions show but 28 chromosomes one of which is much
larger than the others.   The plain inference is that this chromosome represents not one pair but three pairs linked together.   Since the diploid number,

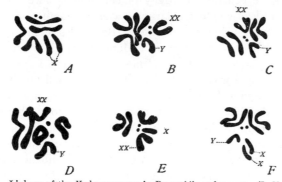

Fig. 415.—Linkage of the *X*-chromosomes in *Drosophila melanogaster* (L. V. Morgan)

A, normal female diploid group, with two separate rod-shaped *X*'s (Bridges); *B, C, D*, from
yellow (sex-linked) females with linked *X*-chromosomes ($= V$) and *Y*-chromosome; *E*, triploid-*X*
($V + X$); *F*, nondisjunctional female, with two free *X*'s $+$ Y (Bridges).

62, uniformly appears in the blastoderm cells, this linkage must be dissolved
at some time, following the formation of the sperm, to be reëstablished at
some time prior to the heterotypic division.   The validity of this conclusion
is established by the conditions seen in the meiosis of the female; for although the first division shows the haploid number (31) of bivalents, *with
no large chromosome*, the second division agrees with those of the male in
showing but 28, *including one large one*.   This can only mean that in the
female the linkage takes place after the first division and before the second,
while in the male it occurs prior to the first division.[1]

It is evident that linkage, whether permanent or temporary, in no wise
alters the nuclear content as a whole.   The same nuclear materials are, as

[1] For the linkage in *Solenobia* see Seiler ('22).

it were, done up in packets of different number—in different individuals, or in different cells of one individual—but so distributed as always to ensure the same essential allotment to the daughter-cells and ultimately to the gametes.   Genetically, such forms of chromosome-linkage might be expected to be expressed in a corresponding linkage of unit-factor groups; but except in the XX linkage of *Drosophila* (p. 880) this particular phenomenon has not yet been recognized.[1]

VI. PERMANENT CHANGES OF CHROMOSOME–NUMBER

We do not yet know with certainty, even in a single case, precisely how the chromosome-number has changed from species to species; but all points to the conclusion that many such changes first took place as variations of the same types as those above described within the species or individual. In respect to the general phylogeny of chromosomes we know still less. It is not even clear whether a large or a small number of chromosomes represents the more primitive condition.   Both sides of this question have been supported by different writers.   Montgomery ('01) accepted, rather doubtfully, the former alternative, Haecker ('04) the latter; but neither conclusion was sufficiently based.   Both large and small numbers are found among Protista, and in higher forms it does not clearly appear that within the limits of particular groups the more primitive forms have smaller or larger numbers than the higher ones.   A study of the facts leads, indeed, to the conclusion that specific changes of number have taken place in both directions, perhaps repeatedly and in many groups; linkage, for example, might cause a decrease, reduplication or fragmentation an increase, non-disjunction a change in both directions.   It may, therefore, often be difficult or impossible to distinguish in any particular case between incipient linkage and fragmentation not yet fully fixed.   With this in mind we may distinguish provisionally not less than six possible modes of change, as follows:

(1) By a gradual reduction in size and final disappearance of individual chromosomes, a process that may be connected with a corresponding dropping out of genetic factors, or a redistribution involving a transfer of their substance to other chromosomes. (Paulmier, '99.)

Very small chromosomes have been described in many forms, in some cases so minute as almost to suggest vestigial structures.   The best known of these cases are the *m*-chromosomes (p. 839) and the Y-chromosomes, in both of which we may trace all gradations from chromosomes of ordinary size almost down to the vanishing point (pp. 768, 823).   In case of the Y.

---

[1] For further remarks on linkage see pp. 887, 938.

chromosome it is almost certain that this process has in many cases culminated in total disappearance, since in a large series of forms the X-chromosome has been left without a synaptic mate. In case of the m-chromosomes the case is not so clear, since they seem always to be present in the *Coreidæ*, though in some cases so minute as to appear like vestigial structures (*Archimerus, Pachylis*).[1] In the nearly related family of *Pyrrhocoridæ* they are absent, so far as known. As shown especially by Metz ('14, '16) a somewhat similar series is shown in *Drosophila* and other Diptera by the two minute chromosomes that commonly lie near the center of the group. (Fig. 396).

(2) A second and probably widespread mode of change has no doubt been by the occurrence of abnormalities of mitosis, such as non-disjunction. Irregularities thus arising often produce combinations that are unstable (since they tend to break up in the next following meiosis). Nevertheless, a single such irregularity occurring during meiosis or at any other point in the germ-line, will if viable be multiplied many times by mitosis during the ensuing development. The chances of producing new and stable recombinations in the course of later processes of meiosis and syngamy are thus greatly increased; and we here see also how the result of an irregularity affecting even a single chromosome may ultimately appear in both gametic groups. In non-disjunction, for instance, the initial effect is to produce haploid groups of the types $n + 1$ and $n - 1$. Union of such groups with the normal will give respectively $2n + 1$ and $2n - 1$. Meiosis of the first of these may give as gametes $n + 1$ or n; and union of two gametes of the former type may give $2n + 2$, a stable combination having one more pair of synaptic mates. We can thus see how not alone non-disjunction but any other irregularity of distribution may readily become a source of permanent change of chromosome-number, provided the new combinations be viable, and above all if they involve new somatic characters of any value in survival. It is possible, as elsewhere indicated, that the 16-chromosome and 22-chromosome mutants of *Œnothera* may have had such an origin (p. 873), and the varying chromosome-numbers in *Metapodius* (p. 875) or *Datura* (p. 874) illustrate the condition of species now actually passing through such a state of transition.

(3) Analogous to the foregoing, but on a larger scale, is the occurrence of series of numbers of which the higher ones are exact multiples of the lower (polyploidy). Specific differences of this type are closely similar to the corresponding ones shown by different races or individuals such as have earlier been noted in the case of *Ascaris megalocephala, Parechinus microtuberculatus, Artemia salina* and other forms (p. 870); and they have probably

---

[1] Wilson ('11).

arisen in the same way. The most striking examples of this occur in plants, e. g., in the species of *Chrysanthemum, Hieracium, Triticum* or *Musa;* but similar cases are not infrequent in animals, e. g., in *Artemia, Asterias,* copepods or sea-urchins. In both cases the higher numbers are often associated with parthenogenesis or apogamy, which in many cases is the only known mode of reproduction, e. g., in certain forms of *Artemia, Hieracium, Rosa,* or *Alchemilla* (p. 230). In some of these cases higher diploid numbers represent exact multiples of lower ones; but most usually intermediate numbers may also occur. In a considerable number of cases higher diploid numbers represent progressive arithmetical series of a fundamental haploid number; for example, in *Hieracium* (fundamental haploid 9) the specific diploid numbers include 18, 27, 36, and 54; in *Chrysanthemum* 18, 36, 54, 72 and 90; in *Rosa,* 14, 21, 28, 35, 42 and 56 (p. 848); in *Musa* 16, 24, 32 and 48. In many such cases, it is true, a certain number of intermediate numbers also occur; but in some of the series (*Rosa*) the progression is so remarkable as to make its origin by reduplication extremely probable.

The precise manner in which such reduplication has arisen is unknown; but there are many ways in which it may readily have occurred (*cf.* p. 870). One of the most probable is by an incomplete or "suspended" mitosis in the zygote, such as has been actually produced by the artificial induction of monaster-formation in sea-urchin eggs (Boveri, Herbst, and others).[1] This view has been adopted by many writers [2] but it is also possible that doubling may have arisen by the union of two diploid gametes (Stomps, '10), or by nuclear fusion. On the other hand, triploids and other forms that do not fall into the diploid series $2 \times 2 \times 2$, etc., must have arisen by a process involving only one of the gametic groups, such as the union of a diploid and haploid gamete, the union of three gamete-nuclei, or the like.[3] In any of these cases the total relative mass of chromatin is thus correspondingly increased; and, in general, cases of this type may be expected to produce larger cells (and often larger individuals) as is the case in *Œnothera gigas,* or in *Artemia;* but there are important exceptions to this (p. 101). It is however equally possible, as both DeVries and Strasburger have urged,[4] that double numbers may also arise by a *transverse* division or fragmentation which would produce chromosomes of double the number but of smaller size, without altering the sum total of chromatin. An example of this, emphasized by Strasburger, is offered by *Rumex acetosella,* which has 32 chromosomes of half the size of the 16 present in *R. acetosa* and several

---

[1] See p. 720.
[2] See Gates ('09, '13), Strasburger ('10), Artom ('11), Winkler ('09), etc.
[3] See Gates ('13, '15, '24).
[4] See Strasburger ('10).

other species (Roth, '06), the nuclei and cells being of the same size in the two cases (p. 101).[1]

(4, 5) A fourth and fifth mode of change, both probably important, are linkage and the opposite process of fragmentation, the former leading to a decrease of number, the latter to an increase. These can best be considered together owing to the practical difficulty in many cases of distinguishing between the two.

(a) That linkage is one important source of definite variations in the number and shape of chromosomes within the species is certain. Whether the same can be said of permanent changes of chromosome-number is less certain; nevertheless, there are some cases that find their most obvious explanation under such an assumption. The clearest of them are found among insects, the inter-specific conditions closely duplicating those produced by linkage within the species, as has been emphasized especially by Robertson ('16). Among the locustids, for example, one of the prevalent diploid numbers is 31 ($\circ\!\!\!\!\!/$), the chromosomes being rod-shaped with terminal attachments. In *Steiroxys trilineata* it is but 29, of which two are V-shaped (Fig. 413). If it be assumed that the latter have resulted from linkage, as in *Chortophaga*, the number becomes 31, as in the related form *Decticus*. Again, in the acridian genus *Chorthippus* (*Stenobothrus*), the male diploid number is but 17 but these include three pairs of V-shaped chromosomes (Fig. 413, I). If each of these be conceived as double, consisting of two rods permanently linked at their central ends (as in *Chortophaga*) the total number becomes 23, the type-number.

Facts of this type make it almost certain that linkage has played an important part in the change of chromosome-number in these animals by the union of rods to form V's, and suggest (as Robertson has especially urged) that the V-shaped chromosomes of other animals may have had such an origin in many cases. Robertson, however, seems to have carried this view too far by overemphasizing the constancy of the point of attachment to the spindle. This is conclusively shown by the recent studies of Carothers ('17) upon *Trimerotropis* and *Circotettix* which demonstrate that in the same species the point of attachment may shift from a terminal (*telomitic*) to a non-terminal (*atelomitic*) point, even in the same chromosome-pair. Thus arise V-shaped chromosomes, of which there may be in *Trimerotropis* from seven to seventeen (Figs. 439, 440), but the spermatogonial num-

---

[1] On the other hand, in the tetraploid mutant *Primula kewensis*, originally from a sterile diploid hybrid form, Farmer and Digby ('13) showed that the chromosomes, though twice as numerous, were but half as large as before, the original chromosomes having presumably fragmented transversely (as assumed by Strasburger). The total chromatin-mass thus remained unchanged; nevertheless the cells and nuclei were larger than in the diploid individuals in the approximate ratio 5:4. This result is ascribed by the authors to the increase of chromosome-surface.

ber remains 23, as in the type-forms. Again, *Circotettix* has but 21 chromosomes; but not merely one pair but from 4 to 7 pairs may be V-shaped. Here the V-shape of these chromosomes can at best be due to linkage in only two pairs. Clearly, therefore, the shape and mode of attachment is not in itself a safe guide in estimating the nature of V-shaped chromosomes in other animals.

(b) Whether fragmentation, like linkage, has been a cause of permanent change of chromosome-number is a question that will appear in a clearer light after considering the chromosomes as compound bodies. Here we only indicate the strong probability that such has been the case. The clearest evidence of this is offered by the X-element, which, as has been shown, may be either a single chromosome or a multiple group of components, ranging in number from two to eight, that behave as independent chromosomes during the diploid divisions but during meiosis are closely associated in a coherent group that behaves as a unit (p. 772). To regard this as a result of linkage involves great difficulties.

All becomes clear, however, if we assume the whole group to have been originally a simple XY-pair, the X-member of which has undergone a progressive segregation of different materials which, by a process of fragmentation, have finally emerged in the form of separate chromosomes.

In case of the autosomes the case is less convincing, owing to the difficulty of distinguishing between linkage and fragmentation. A good example of this is shown in the genus *Drosophila* and its near allies, in which, as shown by Metz ('14, '16), the number in different species ranges from six (*earlei*) to eight (*melanogaster, immigrans*, etc.), ten (*melanica*) or twelve (*funebris*). The diploid groups typically include one pair of very small chromosomes, the others being more or less elongate rods or V's, arranged in pairs, and showing not less than 12 different types in respect to number and shape. Some of these differences may plausibly be explained as a result either of a linkage of rods two by two to form V's or the fragmentation of V's at their apices to form pairs of rods (we know not which). Uncertainty arises, however, from the fact that V's or J's may have arisen from rods (or the reverse process) merely by a change of attachment to the spindle. Such a change certainly has occurred in some species in which the X-chromosome is a V instead of a rod (*Mulleri, obscura, affinis, caribbea* (Fig. 396). Again, *affinis* and *caribbea* are numerically alike in respect to the larger chromosomes; but while both have V-shaped X-chromosomes the former species has in addition three pairs of rods, the latter *three pairs of V's*.[1] The whole case concerning the change of number in *Drosophila* is thereby

---

[1] The difference of attachment in this case is analogous to that discovered by Carothers in *Trimertropis* and *Circotettix* (p. 887).

rendered doubtful; and the same may be said of the pretty case of linkage (so-called) in the species of *Notonecta*, as reported by Browne ('10, '13, '16).

The same question arises in respect to the transverse sutures or constriction at certain points in the chromosomes, referred to beyond (pp. 904, 905). That these sutures may often represent points at which fragmentation may take place, has been made probable by Hance in the case of *Œnothera* (p. 878); but in many cases they may equally well be a consequence of linkage. Both linkage and fragmentation are nevertheless undoubted facts; and they facilitate our understanding of how changes of chromosome-number affecting only one or a few chromosomes have arisen. Here, perhaps, lies the explanation of the almost continuous series of numbers observed in some groups (*e. g.*, in copepods, beetles, or aphids) or the interpolation of intermediate or non-conformable numbers in other series which otherwise show a regular progression.

(6) It seems not improbable that chromosome-numbers may have changed by a sudden mutation. Such a process has already been considered under the head of reduplication (p. 870); and it seems probable that mutation may also have produced suddenly new numbers that are neither exact multiples nor fractions of the old. Such a change is suggested, for instance, by the very closely related two species of *Thyanta* (p. 866) in one of which the diploid number is 16, in the other 27, 28; but for the present such a mode of change is purely hypothetical.

(7) Lastly, it is not improbable that changed chromosome-numbers may have resulted from hybridization through irregularities of chromosome-distribution in the meiotic divisions, such as have earlier been indicated;[1] but little is yet positively known of this.

Conclusion. The evidence clearly indicates that specific changes of number may have been effected in several ways, involving sometimes an increase, sometimes a decrease, and that both processes may have taken place, perhaps many times, within the limits of the same groups, often accompanied with little morphological change. All this sustains the conclusion, that the number of chromosomes is of relatively minor importance. What is essential is the materials of which they are composed. Their number represents no more than a particular configuration assumed by these materials in the process of mitosis and meiosis; it is, in the phrase of Fick (though in a very different sense from his) a *tactical formation* of the nuclear constituents, and one that may change from species to species or even within certain limits from individual to individual, without necessarily producing any other visible disturbance of heredity or development. In view of all

[1] *Cf.* Rosenberg, '17, etc.

this, the surprising and significant fact is the fidelity with which within the species the number and relative sizes of the chromosomes adhere to the type.

VII. DIRECT EVIDENCES OF GENETIC CONTINUITY

Attempts to identify the individual chromosomes as such in the "resting" or vegetative nucleus have been completely successful only in exceptional cases. Among these may be recalled the fact that the chromosomes often visibly persist as such during the interphase between the meiotic divisions (p. 532), and during the growth-period of the auxocytes (p. 350); that the sex-chromosomes often persist in the form of chromosome-nucleoli in the spermatocytes (p. 758); and that the X-chromosome often gives rise to a separate and persistent nuclear vesicle in the spermatogonia of Orthoptera (p. 764). These, however, are special cases. We are here interested in the more general aspects of the question as offered by the nuclear cycle in ordinary forms of cells.

1. Relations of the Chromosomes in Telophase, Interphase and Prophase

Rabl ('85) assumed the chromosomes to retain their relative position in the vegetative nucleus (p. 829). Later observers have not succeeded in establishing this by direct observation, except in the case of very rapidly multiplying cells, such as plant root-tips, in which case several observers have concluded that the telophase-chromosomes, though much branched and vacuolated, may still be distinguished as individualized bodies during the interphase and pass over directly into the prophase-chromosomes without complete loss of their boundaries.[1] A parallel to this is found in the history of the chromosomes in the germinal vesicle of the oöcytes in many forms (p. 350).

One of the most successful attempts to attack the problem was made by Boveri ('88, '09) in his remarkable studies on the blastomere nuclei of *Ascaris megalocephala*. These nuclei commonly show a number of finger-shaped lobes, which are formed during the telophases by the free ends of the V-shaped chromosomes (Fig. 416),[2] thus giving landmarks in the resting nucleus to mark the position in which the chromosomes have entered into it. In the prophase the chromosomes (spireme-threads) always reappear *with their free ends lying in these lobes* and continue to occupy this position until the dissolution of the nuclear membrane.[3] In a general way therefore this fact confirms Rabl's assumption and the case was further strengthened

---

[1] Mano ('04), Strasburger ('07, '08), Grégoire ('06), Bonnevie ('08), Lundegårdh ('12), Schustow ('13), Sharpe ('13, '20), Litardière ('21), Overton ('22).

[2] Van Beneden and Neyt ('87), Boveri ('87, '88).

[3] This has since received repeated confirmation. See Bonnevie ('08, '13), Vejdovský ('12).

by the fact that both the number and the position of the nuclear lobes (and hence of the spireme-threads) vary widely in different cells, *but are alike in sister-cells*. This may readily be observed during the early cleavages of the ovum. In variety *univalens* there are two chromosomes (with four free ends); and the number of lobes varies from one to four, disposed in various ways. In respect to the number and position of these lobes sister-nuclei are mirror-pictures of each other, though with minor variations of

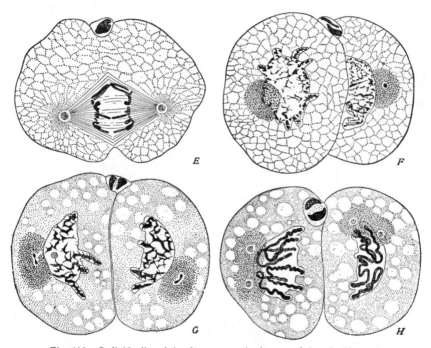

Fig. 416.—Individuality of the chromosomes in the eggs of *Ascaris* (BOVERI).

E, anaphase of the first cleavage; *F*, two-cell stage with lobed nuclei, the lobes formed by the ends of the chromosomes; *G*, early prophase of the ensuing division; chromosomes re-forming, centers dividing; *H*, later prophase, the chromosomes lying with their ends in the same position as before; centers divided.

detail (Figs. 417, 418). Boveri proved, in an elegant demonstration, that *the various observed groupings of telophase-chromosomes and nuclear lobes correspond closely to varying positions of the chromosomes during the prophases and metaphases.* The whole series of facts, therefore, is simply explained by the assumption that whatever be the chance grouping assumed by the chromosomes in the metaphase it is retained with only slight changes through all the subsequent stages, *including the interphase or "resting" nucleus*, until the ensuing prophases. When for example the four free ends are well separated in the metaphase, four nuclear processes are formed, varying in grouping, but always more or less similar in sister-cells (Fig. 418, D). When two, three or even all four ends are very close together they become inclosed in a single process (418, C). Both the number and the grouping of the processes depend, therefore, on the grouping of the chromosomes, which varies continually from one mitosis to another owing to displacements in the later prophases.

Evidence of the same kind, but in some respects more direct, has been found in the spermatogonial divisions of grasshoppers where, as shown by Sutton ('oo, 'o2), in *Brachystola*, the nucleus likewise often shows finger-shaped lobes corresponding to the telophase-chromosomes. In the telophases the chromosomes, without losing their polarized disposition, lose their homogeneous appearance, become granular or alveolized, and are finally transformed into elongate vesicles or karyomeres, which may give

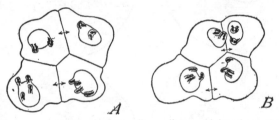

Fig. 417—Chromosome-grouping in sister-cells, 4-cell stages of *Ascaris megalocephala univalens* (Boveri.).

quite the appearance of small separate nuclei.[1] For a time, therefore, the nucleus appears to be composed of separate compartments; and this may persist more or less clearly during the whole interphase. As a rule the vesicles in later stages undergo partial fusion at their peripheral ends, leaving their opposite (central) ends free, in the form of lobes like the fingers of a glove, that are obviously comparable to those of *Ascaris*, as described above. These processes often persist during the whole resting-stage, and even in the main body of the nucleus distinct indications of the vesicles are often clearly visible at every stage (Fig. 361). *In the prophases a single spireme-thread is formed in each vesicle or process*, quite as in *Ascaris*, but the case is here even stronger owing to the partial persistence of the chromosome-boundaries throughout the resting-stage. (Figs. 265, 422.)

Still greater weight is given to this conclusion from the history of the X- or accessory chromosome which passes through essentially the same changes as the autosomes, with the important difference that the telophasic vesicle

---

[1] This account has been confirmed by many later observers (McClung, Davis, Pinney Robertson, Wenrich).

to which it gives rise never fuses with the others but retains its identity
at every stage, giving exactly the appearance of a small independent nucleus lying close beside the principal one and distinguished by its lightly

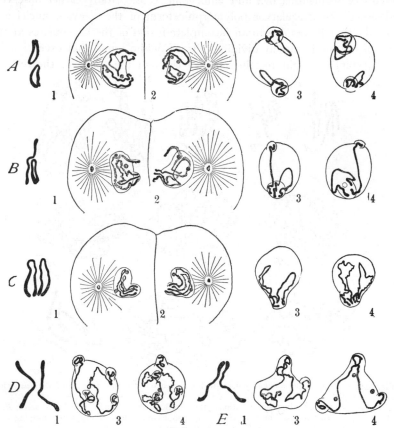

Fig. 418.—Genetic continuity of the chromosomes in the early cleavage of *Ascaris megalocephala univalens* (BOVERI).

At the left (*A, B, C, D, E*) are shown various forms of metaphase-groupings, marked 1 in each
case; at 2 are corresponding telophase-figures showing positions in which the chromosomes enter
the daughter-nuclei; 3 and 4 in each case are corresponding prophase-figures of the daughter-nuclei.

staining appearance (Figs. 361, 362).[1] In the early prophases the X-chromosome is formed as a single, spiral spireme coiled within the X-vesicle (Fig.
361) and may be traced thence uninterruptedly forwards, to the metaphase.

---

[1] This account has been confirmed in a number of other Orthoptera, in particular by Pinney ('08,
Davis ('08), Wenrich ('14, '16). The phenomena appear to be similar in many other grasshoppers
See Mohr ('16) on *Locusta*.

In case of this chromosome, therefore, no doubt can exist as to its genetic continuity throughout many generations of cells.

In agreement with this is the evidence in respect to the chromosomal vesicles of segmenting ova and embryonic cells. Many earlier observers had noted the irregular or polymorphic form of the cleavage-nuclei and showed [1] that it was due to an incomplete fusion of the karyomeres at the close of mitosis in rapidly dividing cells. Conklin found that exceptionally the karyomeres might remain separate through the whole of the resting-

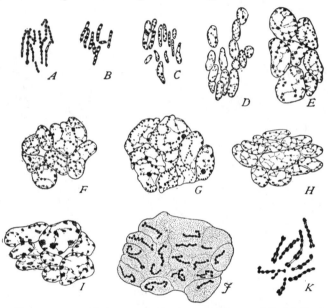

Fig. 419.—Chromosomes and karyomeres in the cleavage of the egg of the fish *Fundulus* (RICH-ARDS).

A–D, successive stages in transformation of the anaphase-chromosomes into karyomeres; E, F, final telophases; G, "resting" nucleus; H, I, early prophases; J, new chromosomes forming separately inside the old karyomeres; K, metaphase-chromosomes.

period, showing the structure and behavior of miniature nuclei. More recently Richards ('17) likewise found that in the cleavage of the teleost *Fundulus* the karyomeres do not at any time undergo complete fusion, but only become closely appressed, the partitions between them being more or less completely retained at every stage up to the ensuing prophases. The new chromosomes arise, each endogenously within one of the vesicles, the latter finally breaking down and disappearing as the prophases advance (Fig. 419). In such cases the karyomeres are seen not only in the telophases but in the *prophases* of mitosis. A striking example of this type

[1] See Conklin ('02), Rubaschkin ('05), Beckwith ('09), Boveri ('07), etc.

occurs in the prophases of the first polar spindle of the gasteropod *Haminea*,[1] where the chromosomes first appear in the form of irregular vesicles within each of which is formed a condensed chromosome (tetrad). Still more remarkable is the case offered by the mite *Pediculopsis* [2] in which the karyomeres remain completely distinct during the early cleavages throughout the whole mitotic cycle, each assuming a spindle-shape during mitosis and developing internally a thread-like chromosome that splits lengthwise and then separates into two parts. In this process (called by Reuter *merokinesis*) and the foregoing ones, the prophase-karyomeres seem clearly to correspond to the alveolized prophase-bands in the root-tips of plants.

When we consider the various intergradations that connect the foregoing cases with less extreme ones we can hardly avoid the conclusion that even vegetative nuclei of the ordinary type must consist of definite areas or regions, each the product of a single chromosome and each the fundamental basis of a future corresponding chromosome (Boveri, '01, '04). These same facts clearly show, however, that the chromosomes are not to be regarded as fixed bodies that persist unchanged from one cell-generation to another. They grow, become vacuolated and often branched, and give rise to linin, nuclear sap, in some cases to the nuclear membrane. Only a small part of the complex thus produced is preserved in the ensuing mitosis. We cannot therefore properly speak of a persistent and unchanged *individuality* of the chromosome, but only of a genetic continuity such that each new chromosome is derived from a portion of its predecessor.

Boveri suggested that the persistent portion might completely lose its colorable (basichromatic) component only regaining it as the next division approaches; and out of this grew a controversy as to whether the basis of chromosome-continuity is "chromatin" (basichromatin) or "achromatin" (oxychromatin or linin). The latter view, adopted by Haecker ('02, '05), Strasburger ('04), Montgomery and others, has received definite support from those cases, earlier referred to, in which the chromosomes undergo a more or less complete loss of basophily during the growth period of the auxocytes without loss of their morphological identity (pp. 350, 545). This, however, is a question of secondary importance; for the theory of the genetic continuity of chromosomes need for the present go no further than to maintain that the old chromosome passes on to the new a portion of its own substance which somehow carries with it the essential features of its own organization. That the continued presence of "chromatin" (*i. e.*, basichromatin) is essential to the genetic continuity of the chromosome has, however, become an antiquated notion (p. 653).

[1] Smallwood. '04.   [2] Reuter ('09).

2. The Chromonema-hypothesis

The most noteworthy fact established by the foregoing observations is the endogenous formation of new chromosomes, each in the form of a fine spireme-thread inclosed within its predecessor; and out of this fact, now conclusively demonstrated in certain cases, grew the chromonema-hypothesis of Bonnevie and Vejdovský (p. 136). The existence of a finely coiled basichromatic thread (chromonema of Vejdovský) during the anaphases and telophases, early reported by Barenecki ('80) in the pollen-mother-cells of *Tradescantia*, was again briefly described in the telophase-chromosomes of the spermatogonia of urodeles by Janssens ('01), who found the thread coiled more or less definitely around the periphery of the chromosome and imbedded in an "achromatic" basis of "plastin." The first germ of the chromonema hypothesis appears in his suggestion that this thread may be identical with the spireme which is seen unraveling from the prochromosomes or chromatin-blocks in early prophases of the ensuing division ('01, p. 58). This idea was developed in greater detail especially by Bonnevie and later by Vejdovský,[1] both of whom believed the telophase chromonema to be converted directly into the nuclear framework and in the ensuing prophase to give rise directly to the early spireme. In evidence of this both found that in *Ascaris* the spiral prophase spireme-threads reappear with their free ends in the nuclear lobes originally formed by the ends of the telophase-chromosomes, as described by Boveri (Fig. 59).

Bonnevie argued from this that "the nuclear network arises . . . from thin, spirally coiled threads, which have arisen endogenously in the old chromosomes; and these threads develop in the prophase directly into the chromosomes of the following mitosis . . . ." ('08, p. 470). In rapidly dividing cells (root-tips) Bonnevie believed that the telophase-spirals may still be distinguished more or less clearly in the vegetative nucleus so that the individuality of the chromosomes is never wholly lost at this time.

The conclusions of Vejdovský ('12), especially in the case of *Ascaris*, were essentially similar. Like Janssens, he gives a circumstantial account of how in the telophases the chromosomes swell up and finally unite, their achromatic axial portions giving rise to the nuclear sap and membrane while the coiled peripheral thread produces the general framework. The thread itself is said to arise by the linear aggregation of originally scattered, minute basichromatic granules or chromioles.[2]

Bonnevie first found the prophase-spiral or chromonema in the anaphases or telophases of the preceding mitosis and believed this spiral to persist as

---

[1] See references at p. 136.
[2] *Cf.* Dobell's account of the formation of the spiral nuclear thread of bacteria from scattered chromidial granules, p. 84.

such during the interphase, uncoiling to form the prophase-spireme, and splitting lengthwise. Vejdovský's conclusion comes to the same in the end, but is complicated by the additional conclusion (in *Ascaris*), that the original chromonema first arises within the *prophase*-spireme. While, therefore, the latter, considered as a whole, splits lengthwise (as concluded by Bonnevie), the same is not true of the new chromonema, the close coils of which seem to break up more or less into rings or discoid chromomeres (Fig. 59). In either case the new chromonema is cut *crosswise* at more or less regular intervals by fission of the thread as a whole. How the continuous anaphase- or telophase-chromonema is formed from their products remains undetermined and the whole hypothesis is thereby materially weakened. As will presently be seen, however, Vejdovský's conclusions on this particular point have to a certain extent received support from the recent work of Martens (p. 898). Bonnevie ('13), on the other hand, was unable to find either spiral or rings in the metaphase-chromosomes.

The chromonema-hypothesis involves the three main postulates, each of which has been called in question by other observers. These postulates are: (1) The presence of a definite spiral or zigzag thread in the anaphase or telophase-chromosomes from which is formed the framework of the interphase-nucleus; (2) the identity of the prophase-threads, individually considered, with those of the preceding telophase; (3) the longitudinal splitting of the thread during the prophase or an earlier period. We may briefly consider these in order:

(1) Definite anaphasic or telophasic spiral formations have been described by a few other observers; [1] but some of them describe the spirals as longitudinally double, consisting of two interlacing threads (Brunelli, Schneider) while another finds the spiral single, temporary, and not in the form of a separate thread but rather a transitory ridge on the surface of a chromatic axis (Lee). A considerable group of careful observers have, however, concluded that the appearance of a coiled thread is but an optical illusion due to the vacuolization of the anaphase and telophase-chromosomes, leaving the partition-walls so disposed as to offer the appearance of a contorted, zigzag or coiled thread (Fig. 55).[2] Martens, however, in one of the most recent studies of the subject gives a very circumstantial account of the formation of a true telophasic chromonema (Fig. 420), irregularly zigzag or convoluted, and arising by a differentiation of the chromosome into an "achromatic" core and a single basichromatic peripheral thread.

---

[1] Brunelli ('10) in the grasshopper *Tryxalis*, Schneider ('11) in Amphibia; and Bolles Lee in the plant *Paris* ('13), and more recently ('20) in urodeles, insects and other cases.

[2] Among these may be named especially Sharp ('13, '20), and Litardière ('21), whose conclusions concerning the telophasic vacuolization are closely akin to those of Grégoire and other observers referred to above. See also Kuwada ('21), Overton ('22).

In this respect his account is close to that of Bonnevie and Vejdovský save for the irregularity of the thread; but otherwise it is wholly different.

(2) The proof that the prophase-threads are identical with the telophasic chromonema involves the same difficulties encountered under any hypoth-

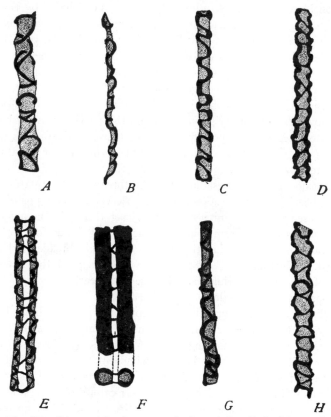

Fig. 420.—Scheme of the chromonema in the seed-plant *Paris* (MARTENS).

A, portion of the early prophase-thread; *B*, its elongation; *C*, *D*, bilateral accumulation of the chromonema-substance; *E*, *F*, longitudinal division; *G*, early telophase; *H*, later telophase, semblance of longitudinal duality.

esis of genetic continuity. Bonnevie's belief that the spirals might often be distinguished as such even in the vegetative nucleus still lacks confirmation, and even if correct the fact may be explicable because in rapidly dividing meristem-cells the nuclei often do not return completely to the "resting" state (p. 890). The substantial evidence on this point is thus practically limited to the fact, that the prophasic spiral threads in *Ascaris* reappear with their free ends in the nuclear lobes which represent the free ends of the preceding telophase-chromosomes, as described by Boveri.

There are, however, many other facts to be taken into account. No doubt can now exist that the early prophasic spireme-threads often show a fine, contorted, zigzag or even spiral appearance, later uncoiling or straightening out as they shorten and thicken (Figs. 55, 422). It is also certain that in many cases the fine contorted threads arise by uncoiling or unravelling from larger or massive bodies (p. 902);[1] and that in some cases the prophasic spiral formations are formed in the interior of the vesicles or karyomeres resulting from enlargement of the telophase-chromosomes. Such cases differ only in degree from those earlier mentioned (p. 121) in which the spireme-threads disentangle themselves from localized areas of

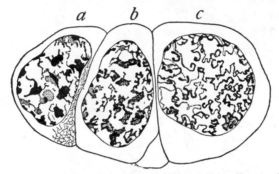

a   *b*   *c*

Fig. 421.—Spermatogonial prophases in the newt *Triton* (JANSSENS).

a, early stage with chromatin-blocks (chromatin-nuclei or prochromosomes); *b*, resolution into convoluted threads, which in *c* have uncoiled to form the early spireme.

the nuclear framework which become marked off in the earliest prophases[2] and, as several recent observers have especially emphasized, are closely similar to the alveolized telophase-chromosomes.[3] A step beyond brings us to cases where the threads arise by a spinning out or internal regrouping of the substance of more or less massive chromatin blocks or bodies (chromocenters or prochromosomes) as described for instance by Janssens ('01) in the spermatogonial prophases of *Triton* (Fig. 421) and more particularly by Davis ('08) and many later observers in the presynaptic nuclei of Orthoptera, by Wilson ('12) in those of Hemiptera, or by Nonidez ('10) in those of Coleoptera (Figs. 266–288).

All points to the conclusion that in these various cases, whether chromosome-vesicles, localized nuclear areas or massive prochromosomes, we are dealing with chromosomes, variously modified, derived severally from the

[1] *Cf.*, Wilson ('12, '13, '14).   [2] Mano ('04), Grégoire ('06).
[3] See especially the above cited works of Sharp, Litardière and Martens.

telophase-chromosomes and destined to give rise each to one of the prophase threads. All this, evidently, harmonizes with the chromonema-hypothesis; its present weak point, evidently, is the telophasic chromonema.

(3) Concerning the third postulate, all observers, with two exceptions, have found that the prophase-threads split lengthwise, in preparation for the ensuing metaphase. The first exception is offered by Bolles Lee's account ('20), of the phenomena in the seed-plant *Paris*, where these threads are said to be longitudinally double in consequence of a *transverse* division of the preceding V-shaped anaphase-chromosomes at the apices of the V's. This result, contradictory of those of so many other good observers, and

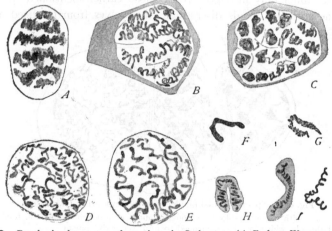

Fig. 422.—Prophasic chromonema-formations in Orthoptera (*A–E*, from WILSON; *F–I*, from MOHR).

A, early spermatogonial prophase of *Phrynotettix*, side-view, polarized massive bodies, which in *B* and *C* (polar view) are seen uncoiling in the form of spiral threads; *D*, *E*, later stages; *F*, the X-chromosome of *Locusta*, last spermatogonial telophase; *G–I*, successive stages in its transformation into a vesicle containing a coiled thread.

evidently inapplicable to rod-shaped anaphase-chromosomes, is specifically denied by Martens ('22), after a reëxamination of the facts in the same species. This observer, however, in his turn, contradicts his predecessors by denying that the zigzag chromonema within the original prophase-spireme *is set free or straightens out to form a single fine thread*. On the contrary, the whole spireme is said to shorten and thicken, while the chromonema retains its spiral or zigzag disposition. Its substance now concentrates on opposite sides, until the chromosome gives an appearance of longitudinal duality, and finally splits lengthwise, the cleft cutting across the delicate turns of the spiral, by which the two halves are at first connected (Fig. 420). According to this account, similar in principle to that of Vejdovský (p. 897), there is no longitudinal division of the chromonema at any period. Martens describes an appearance in the anaphase- and telophase-chromosomes that is closely similar except that the concentration of the chromonema on opposite sides does not in this case lead to actual longitudinal division.

How to harmonize these results with the chromonema-hypothesis, does not yet clearly appear; but in the judgment of the writer it seems impossible to doubt that the finely coiled or convoluted prophase-threads do in many cases actually uncoil and split lengthwise.[1]   Until these doubts and discrepancies have been cleared up, however, the chromonema-theory of genetic continuity must await further critical study.

3. The Prochromosomes

In the foregoing section the prochromosomes have been treated somewhat incidentally as an interesting but inconstant element in the mitotic process.

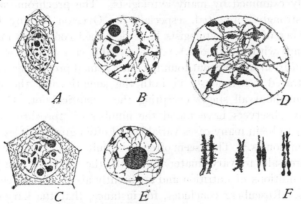

Fig. 423.—Prochromosomes in the early meiotic stages of seed-plants (OVERTON).

A–D, Thalictrum; E, F, Calycanthus.
  A, somatic nucleus from anther-wall; *B, C, E*, young pollen mother-cells; *D*, early synizesis (more enlarged); *F*, paired prochromosomes before and during synizesis.

Attempts to give them a more general significance have been made by observers who were struck by the fact that the nuclei of the vegetative cells in higher plants in some cases contain numerous karyosomes which are approximately the same in number as the chromosomes.[2]   A study of the behavior or these bodies in various plants led Overton to the conclusion that under favorable conditions of growth the nuclei may contain an

---

[1] See the figures and photographs in partial illustration of this in the early prophase of the spermatogonia of grasshoppers (Wilson, '12) and also the figures of earlier observers there cited.

[2] Rosenberg ('04, '09) in *Drosera;* Overton ('05, '09, '11) in *Thalictrum, Helleborus, Podophyllum,* etc.; Laibach ('07) in *Cruciferæ;* Tischler ('10) in *Musa;* and others.

excess of chromatin, a part of which remains aggregated about definite centers without passing out into the framework formed by the chromo-somes. Around these centers the remaining chromatin collects to form the definitive chromosomes as the cell prepares for division (Fig. 423). Over-ton found the prochromosomes both in the vegetative somatic nuclei of various plants and in the presynaptic nuclei, where they conjugate two by two as they pass into synapsis. He also found the prochromosomes arranged in pairs in the somatic nuclei (in *Calycanthus* and *Podophyllum*); so that the synaptic mates are already associated in pairs when they enter the reconstruction-stages of the germ-nuclei ('09, p. 52). Overton de-scribes the prochromosomes of the early prophases as local accumulations of chromatin in the spireme-thread, as first often more or less elongated, but later shortening and thickening to form the chromosomes while the intervening strands of "linin" disappear.

The phenomena on which this interpretation was based have therefore been closely examined by many cytologists. The prochromosome theory has been strongly supported, especially by Overton and by Rosenberg, and a number of other cytologists have described conditions more or less in accordance with the theory.[1] A remarkable case is that of the sedge, *Carex aquatilis*, in which Stout found about 74 small prochromosomes which could be traced continuously in both the somatic and the meiotic di-visions throughout all stages excepting the synaptic knot. On the other hand, many observers have found the number of "prochromosomes" or karyosomes to be in many cases variable and often greater or less than that of the chromosomes.[2] They seem often to be quite absent; and their number and size are said to vary materially with the mode of fixation under different conditions of nutrition and apparently also with the length of the interkinesis. Rosenberg concludes, for instance, that the karyosomes are more distinct and more constant in number in the stages of "complete rest."

For these reasons the prochromosome-theory has thus far failed to pro-vide an adequate basis for a general theory of chromosome-continuity; but the observed facts nevertheless are of much cytological interest. It is probable that prochromosomes are related on the one hand to chroma-tin-nucleoli or karyosomes, on the other to the chromatin-blocks, massive bodies, or nuclear areas from which the spireme-threads so often arise (pp. 122, 539). In all these cases we are dealing with localized reservoirs of

[1] *Cf.* Yamanouchi ('06), Davis ('07), Malte ('08), Tahara ('10), Frisendahl ('12), Stout ('13), and Lundegårdh ('13).

[2] *E. g.* Allen ('06), Miyake ('06), Laibach ('07), Grégoire ('07), Sykes ('08), Mottier ('07), Lewis ('08), Lundegårdh ('08, '12,' 13), Gates ('08, '10, '11), Geerts ('09), Strasberger ('05, '09), Digby ('10. '14), De Smet ('14), Litadière ('21).

basichromatin which (as was recognized by Flemming) is destined ultimately to enter into the formation of chromosomes. In the case of chromosome-nucleoli (sex-chromosomes, etc.) or of karyospheres it is evident that these chromatin-nucleoli represent chromosomes or groups of chromosomes. It is equally clear that the prochromosomes of the presynaptic stages of insects likewise represent chromosomes. There is, therefore, no reason to doubt that in some cases the prochromosomes described in the vegetative nuclei of plant-cells really are such, and that some of the observed variations in number may be due to the fact that they may often represent only portions of chromosomes, or several chromosomes united (as is certainly the case with karyospheres, p. 93).[1]

It is important to bear in mind the fact that very often, both in the presynaptic stages and in somatic prophases, no trace of prochromosomes can be discovered; and even when such bodies are unquestionably present (as in the presynaptic stages of insects), they very rarely if ever arise directly from the telophase-chromosomes [2] but from a net-like stage in which the telophase-chromosomes are for a short time at least lost to view (p. 536).

VIII. ORGANIZATION OF THE CHROMOSOMES

There are many grounds for the conclusion that the chromosomes possess a complex and definite internal organization, and one that varies not only from species to species but also from one chromosome to another in the same species. The most cogent of this evidence is perhaps that offered by genetic experiment (p. 949); but although the direct cytological evidence still lags behind, it points unmistakably to the same conclusion.

1. The Chromosomes as Compound Bodies

The metaphase-chromosomes often show no visible structure, appearing as nearly or quite homogenous bodies. That they are nevertheless to be regarded as compound bodies at this time is proved both by their earlier history and by comparative studies. The fact is obvious in cases of linkage; and equally convincing is the evidence offered by the multiple X-element in various species of insects, and nematodes, such as *Ascaris incurva* or *lumbricoides*, *Gelastocoris*, *Acholla multispinosa*, etc. (pp. 772–779). All the evidence indicates that this is not due to linkage in the ordinary sense, and that the group as a whole corresponds to the single X-chromosome

---

[1] *Cf*. Rosenberg ('09), Lundegårdh ('09, '13).

[2] Such a mode of origin is described by Janssens ('05) for the " chromoplast" or karyosome of the early spermatocytes of *Batracoseps*, by B. M. Davis for the "chromatin bodies" of the premeotic nuclei of *Œnothera* and by Lundegårdh ('13) in *Cucurbita*. The same was believed to be the case by Montgomery and some other observers for the presynaptic prochromosomes in insects.

of other forms. We might consider its multiple character as a simple fragmentation; but this leaves unexplained the remarkable fact that *the X-
components are constant not only in number but in size-relations,* the latter
often extremely marked and characteristic. No other explanation of this
is apparent save that these components are qualitatively different. The
force of these facts is evident when we consider, for example, the remarkable
X-chromosome of *Notonecta indica,* in which X likewise consists of several
components during the late prophases, metaphase and anaphases of the
heterotypic division, but in the spermatogonia appears as a single and
simple chromosome (Fig. 424). A slight increase of independence on the
part of these components would cause them to appear as separate chro-

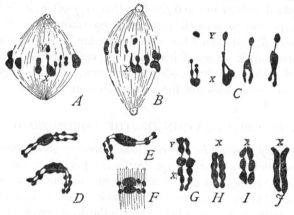

Fig. 424.—Structure of the sex-chromosomes in Hemiptera (*A–F* from BROWNE).

A, B, second spermatocyte-metaphases in *Notonecta indica; C,* four examples of the *XY*-pair from
same; *D–E,* the *X*-chromosomes in the prophases; *F,* same in metaphase of first division; *G–J,* the
sex-chromosomes in the growth-period of *Lygæus bicrucis; H, I,* and *J* show the *X*-chromosome
only, *G* probably the *X*- and *Y*-chromosomes united end to end.

mosomes. Further evidence in the same direction is afforded by the earlier
mentioned cross-sutures or constrictions (p. 889) which, as many observers
have noted, often appear in certain chromosomes and *at particular points.*
The classical case of this is the median cross-suture ("Querkerbe") described
by Haecker ('95, '02, etc.) in the bivalents of copepods (Fig. 425). This
suture was regarded by Haecker as representing the point of telosynaptic
union of the two synaptic mates; but later researches [1] showed this interpretation to be untenable. The suture does not mark a plane of division,
either in meiosis or mitosis; and it is found in the univalent chromosomes
of the somatic divisions as well as in the bivalents. All points to the conclusion that it marks the point of juncture of two closely united components

[1] Lerat ('05), Schiller ('09), Braun ('09, '10), Matschek ('10), Krimmel ('10), Kornhauser ('15).

that have not, as yet, the value of separate chromosomes but might easily become such.[1]   Similar transverse sutures or constrictions have been described by many other observers both in plants and animals.[2]

These sutures or constrictions may be median or at any other point; but in some cases at least are constant in position for each particular chromosome, as has been emphasized by all the observers named.   In *Vicia*, for example, Sakamura found that several of the chromosomes show a subterminal constriction and that those of one pair of these characteristically

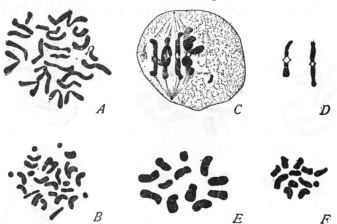

Fig. 425.—Chromosome-sutures in the copepod *Hersilia* (KORNHAUSER).

A, metaphase of cleavage-stage *B*, of spermatagonium, in each case a cross-suture in certain chromosomes; *C*, 1st spermatocyte-division in side-view, cross-sutures in two tetrads; *D*, similar tetrads; *E*, first oöcyte-division in polar view, *F*, second spermatocyte-division.

show also a median constriction in addition (Fig. 426).   Agar found further, in *Lepidosiren* that these sutures (varying in position in different chromosomes) *correspond with the points of attachment to the spindle*[3] and that their position in the chromosomes of the meiotic divisions corresponds with that in the spermatogonial groups, just as does the point of attachment in case of the Orthoptera, as shown by McClung, Carothers and other observers (p. 511).

Some of the so-called "tetrads" described by various authors in the somatic divisions[4] particularly after treatment by narcotics or when in a

[1] Wilson ('11).   *Cf.* Vejdovský, ('11–'12).

[2] See Janssens, '01 (*Triton*); Grégoire and Wygærts, '04 (*Trillium*); Lundegårdh, '10 (*Allium*), Fraser and Snell, '11, Sharp, '14 (*Vicia*); Kowalsky, '04, Della Valle, '07 (urodeles); Rosenberg, '09; Digby, '14 (*Crepis*); Sakamura, '20 (*Triticum, Lathyrus, Pisum*, etc.); Hance, '18, Gates, '20 (*Œnothera*); Agar, '12 (*Lepidosiren*), Nawaschin, '14, '15 (*Fritillaria*); Litardière, '21 (ferns).

[3] It is important to note that the sutures or constrictions are visible in the prophases before the spindle has been formed, and hence are not caused by the attachment.

[4] See Della Valle ('08), Popoff ('07), Nemec ('04, '10), Schiller ('09), Kemp ('10), Nawaschin ('14) etc

pathological condition, are no doubt due to the presence of such constrictions or sutures. Schiller has in fact demonstrated that upon treatment of developing *Cyclops* eggs by chloroform or ether the cross-suture is exaggerated so that a perfect tetrad appearance is given by the univalent chromosomes during the process of cleavage and in other somatic divisions (Fig. 426).

Such facts [1] indicate that each chromosome possesses a constant serial differentiation, and that the nature and order of the components are constant in each particular chromosome; and this is borne out by direct observations on the actual structure of the spireme-threads. They make

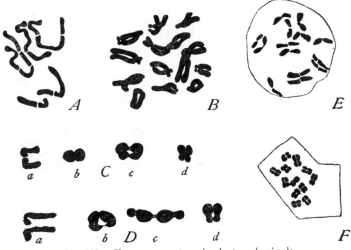

Fig. 426.—Chromosome-sutures in plants and animals.

A, spermatogonial chromosomes of *Triton* (JANSSENS); *B*, from root-tips of *Vicia*, with sub-terminal constrictions (SAKAMURA); *E*, *F*, from blastomere-divisions of *Cyclops*, slightly etherized (SCHILLER); *C*, *D*, from *Lepidosiren* (AGAR). In the latter two *a* shows a pair of somatic chromosomes with sub-terminal constriction and attachment, *b* and *c* the corresponding bivalents and *d*, late anaphase-forms of same.

easy the assumption that single chromosomes may readily break apart into separate components which thenceforth behave as independent chromosomes. A partial explanation is here offered of the origin of supernumerary chromosomes, of fluctuations of chromosome-number in the individual, and of permanent changes of chromosome-number (p. 868).

2. The Chromosomes as Linear Aggregates. The Chromomeres

We are thus brought, finally, to one of the most fundamental conceptions of cytology and genetics, namely, that the spireme-threads are linear aggregates of much smaller self-perpetuating bodies, aligned in single series, and

[1] See Wilson ('11), Agar ('12).

in definite order. The importance of the spireme-formation in mitosis was early perceived by Strasburger and Flemming (hence Flemming's term *mitosis*); but its fundamental significance was first fully grasped by Roux ('83) with whom arose the conception of a differentiation of the thread along its longitudinal axis, so that it represents a linear series of smaller components ("qualities") that are to be distributed to the daughter-cells in a particular manner. To this conclusion the whole course of later discovery, in both cytology and genetics, has continually added weight.

In *Ascaris megalocephala* it is certain that the long chromosomes of the early cleavage-stages (and of the later germ-line) are each the equivalent of a much larger number of smaller chromosomes in linear series, as is proved by the fact that in all the somatic cells it actually breaks up into such smaller independent chromosomes which approximate in number to those observed in other species of this genus in which no linkage occurs, *e. g.*, in *Ascaris lumbricoides* or *A. incurva* (p. 855). It is therefore highly probable that in *A. megalocephla* the long chromosomes of the early cells and of the germ-track are plurivalent as compared with the small chromosomes of the somatic cells or of other species.

Somewhat similar to this in type is the case of the sedge *Carex*, as described by Stout ('12). In the prophases of mitosis appear about 74 small, rounded chromosomes which become aligned in a single linear series, like beads upon a string. The continuous spireme thus formed seems to persist even during cell-division, and splits lengthwise in the metaphase. Only in the synaptic and leptotene stages do the small chromosomes spin out into thin threads and disappear from view. A similar case is offered by *Amœba glebæ*, in which Dobell ('14) describes 16 small globular "chromosomes," which seem to arise by the coalescence of a much larger number of smaller granules derived from the large "karyosome" of the vegetative nucleus. As in *Carex* these chromosomes become aligned in a single linear series to form a continuous spireme, which in this case forms a closed ring and as such splits lengthwise and divides at the equator of the spindle.

The foregoing three cases show how conventional and artificial is our common conception of "univalence," "bivalence" or "plurivalence." In *Amœba glebæ*, for example, we might equally well describe the facts by saying that division takes place with a single, ring-shaped chromosome composed of a linear series of chromomeres. In *Ascaris megalocephala* such a description seems inadmissible because the smaller bodies may become wholly independent, to divide as separate chromosomes.

The Chromomeres. We are thus brought to the fact that even the so-called single or univalent chromosomes (spireme-threads) often give a beaded appearance, as if consisting of a linear series of smaller basichromatic bodies suspended in a more lightly staining or oxychromatic sub-stance. It was long since suggested that these bodies might have a persist-ent identity (Balbiani, '76, '81) and that *longitudinal splitting of the threads might be due to their fission.* (Pfitzner, '82). This was supported by Van Beneden who showed (in *Ascaris*) that the granules are of different sizes, emphasizing especially the fact that after splitting of the thread the granules of the daughter-threads exactly correspond to one another.[1] These bodies (Fig. 8) first known as "Pfitzner's granules" and later as *chromomeres*, were later found in many plants and animals. Their existence has been disputed by a considerable group of observers, including especially Grégoire and his followers, who have either failed to find the chromomeres or have considered them as due to accidents of coagulation, local differences of density, or the like without further significance.[2] Such scepticism, however, cannot be maintained in view of the positive results of recent careful studies. Chambers has shown that chromomeres can be seen as paired swellings in the diplotene stages of the spermatocytes of grasshoppers exam-ined *in vivo* and that they are not destroyed but only moved further apart by stretching the double threads under the microscope by means of the micro-dissection-apparatus (Fig. 429). The evidence from sections, though less direct, is hardly less convincing.

The chromomeres have been described as spheroidal bodies (Pfitzner, Van Beneden), or discs (Strasburger, Carnoy, etc.); sometimes as rings surrounding a central "achromatic" core (Van Beneden, '83, Merriman, '04, Vejdovský, '11–'12) and by some observers as irregular both in shape and in size (Allen, '04, '05; Sands, '22, '23). Many observers, beginning with Eisen ('99, '00) have considered them to be compound bodies or aggregates of smaller granules or "chromioles." This lacks confirmation but we should not take too sceptical an attitude towards the principle here involved.

The chromomeres are most readily seen in the spireme-threads during the earlier stages of mitosis or meiosis before the condensation of the chro-mosomes has proceeded very far. As the threads shorten and thicken the chromomeres undergo various changes, often becoming less evident and in many cases disappearing from view so that many observers have been unable to find them in the metaphase-chromosomes. During this process, the chromomeres often seem to diminish in number and also to increase in size, so that we may infer that they become closely associated, per-

[1] "What strikes us is the perfect symmetry of the two filaments; they are identical with each other. Each chromatin-granule of the one has its counterpart in the other; and there is not the least peculiarity of one that is not found exactly duplicated in its fellow" ('83, '84, p. 541).

[2] See Grégoire and Wygærts ('03), Bonnevie ('08), Grégoire ('05, '06, '07, '10), Mano ('04), Maré-chal ('04, '07), Berghs ('09), Stomps ('10), Sharp ('13, '20), Lundegårdh ('12), Litardière ('21), etc.

haps even fuse, to form larger bodies. Certainly the original disposition of these bodies must be greatly altered during the condensation that takes place in course of the prophases; and perhaps it is partly owing to these changes that some observers have described the chromomeres as having a quite irregular grouping. In spite of these complications some of the most careful recent studies in this field have confirmed Van Beneden's results on the size-differences of the chromomeres, and have made it nearly certain that in some cases at least these differences are constant and that *the chromomeres display a definite serial order in the spireme-threads.* A simple example is seen in the hemipter *Lygæus bicrucis* (Fig. 424), where

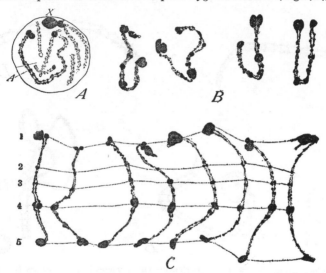

Fig. 427.—Organization of certain chromosomes in the spermatogenesis of the grasshopper *Phrynotettix* (WENRICH).

A, diplotene, showing chromosomes "A" and *X; B,* four examples of chromosome "B," showing chromomeres of different sizes; *C,* eight examples of the same chromosome, similarly placed to show constancy of serial order of the principal chromomeres.

the rod-shaped X-chromosome during the growth-period characteristically shows three (sometimes four) large chromomeres, each longitudinally double, (Wilson, '12). Still more definite and striking is the X-chromosome of *Notonecta indica* (Browne, '16) which in the diakinesis consists of six chromomeres, a large central one with two small ones at one end and three at the other, all longitudinally split and connected by thin threads (Fig. 424). These components are still clearly distinguishable at the time the chromosomes pass upon the spindle and even, in a measure, during the anaphases.

Still more remarkable conditions have been found in the autosomes of Orthoptera by Pinney ('08), Carothers ('16), and especially by Wenrich

('16). The latter observer found in the spermatocytes of *Phrynotettix* that certain of the autosome bivalents are individually distinguishable in the early diplotene stage by the characteristics of their chromomeres. In the most striking of these cases ("Chromosome B") the constancy of the size-differences and of the serial order is strikingly demonstrated (Fig. 427); and this bivalent is also characterized during the heterotypic division by a peculiar roughened or brush-like contour at one end.[1] Wenrich was able to distinguish at least one other bivalent in *Phrynotettix* ("chromosome A") which differs from "chromosome B" both in the size relations of the chromomeres and their serial order; and he gives reason to conclude that other

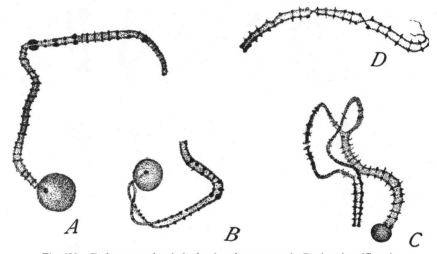

Fig. 428.—Early stages of meiosis showing chromomeres in *Dendrocœlum* (GELEI).

C, bivalent from amphitene, with parasynapsis in progress; B, early diplotene thread seen in the conjugation-plane; D, early diplotene to show twisting (?chiasmatype); A, somewhat later stage, viewed from the side, to show the first indications of the secondary (equatorial) longitudinal cleft, the conjugation-plane being that of the paper. Size-differences of the chromomeres.

autosome-bivalents likewise show constant differences in this regard. More recently Gelei ('21, '22) shows with great clearness that the post-synaptic chromosomes of the platode *Dendrocœlum* consist of regular series of chromomeres, showing marked size-differences, accurately paired in the diplotene stage, and quadipartite after the appearance of the secondary or equational cleft (Fig. 428).

Closely connected with the foregoing, are the "polar granules" as first described by Pinney ('08) in *Phrynotettix*. These are very distinct, deeply staining and often enlarged granules, typically found at the proximal or

[1] See also McClung, '14.

attached end   but said also to occur at the distal end.   In the spermatogonia these granules are single and persist in a compact form in
the vesicular stage of these chromosomes (Fig. 361).   In the leptotene-
nuclei, when the threads form polarized loops, the polar granules are crowded
together at the pole and often unite to form large composite granules;
but Wenrich ('16) believes that their identity is not lost at this time, the
granules separating again in the pachytene-stage, and retaining their original
connections.   The studies of Carothers and of Wenrich make it probable
that these bodies are derived from terminal chromomeres, serially homologous with those of the central region; and they also raise interesting questions concerning their relations to the plasmosomes.   Wenrich found that
in certain cases the polar granules become enlarged, more or less vesicular
in appearance and stain less deeply, thus assuming somewhat the character
of a plasmosome, and is thus led to suggest a relationship between these
granules (enlarged chromomeres) and plasmosomes.   Carothers ('13, '16)
had observed such vesicular chromomeres in the central region of the thread
(Fig. 438) and has produced evidence that they are constant both in number
and position (p. 142).

Such observations, made by cautious observers, are not to be explained
away by the supposition that the chromomeres are coagulation-products
of no significance.   Coagulations they undoubtedly are as observed in sections; but the significant fact is the *constancy of the result*, which demonstrates
the existence of a definite longitudinal differentiation in the spireme-thread,
the expression of a serial organization in the living object.   As a working
hypothesis, therefore, we need not hesitate to accept the cytological evidence
at its face value so far as concerns the essential point at issue.

If, as the foregoing facts indicate, smaller chromomeres may aggregate
or fuse to form larger ones, we once more reach the conception that in many
cases they may themselves be compound bodies having perhaps a definite
internal architecture.   In point of fact it seems clear that at least the larger
chromomeres, as seen in sections, are aggregates of still smaller granules;
and in case of *Batrachoseps* Eisen went so far as to maintain that the number
of granules is constant.   This conclusion, certainly a rash one in view of the
fact that proteins generally so often coagulate in the form of minute granules, has not been confirmed by later observers; and the problems here
arising lead us into a region beyond the present reach of our technique.
Nevertheless the cytological evidence points unmistakably to the conclusion that the chromosomes arise from spireme-threads which in some sense
or other are serial aggregates which have a perfectly definite organization,
and one that differs specifically from chromosome to chromosome and from
species to species.   This is a surprising conclusion, but it involves further

consequences more astonishing still. The serial organization of the chromosomes, as displayed by the chromomeres is not only duplicated in the daughter-threads produced by fission in the somatic divisions, but also in the bivalent chromosomes of the meiotic period, where the longitudinal duality arises (if the theory of parasynapsis be correct) by the side-by-side conjugation of previously separate threads. We thus come in view of the possibility that the chromomeres, whatever be their ultimate significance,

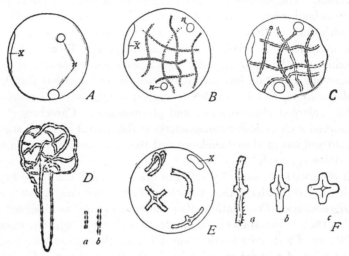

Fig. 429.—Nuclear structures in the spermatocytes of the grasshopper *Dissosteira* studied *in vivo* with the micro-dissection needle (CHAMBERS).

A, nucleus of intact living cell, showing only the chromosome-nucleolus (*X*) and plasmosomes (*n*); *B*, appearance of double threads on puncture of the cytosome; *C*, four minutes later; *D*, diplotene loop pulled out by needle (chromomeres); *a*, portion of the thread before stretching, *b* upon stretching; *E*, late diakinesis, tetrads and *X*-chromosomes; *F*, *a–c*, successive changes in a tetrad removed from the nucleus, in the body-fluid.

are capable not only of growth, definite alignment and division, but also of conjugating two by two and like with like (p. 952).

To some minds, perhaps to many, this result may seem too staggering for serious consideration. If so we may with advantage reflect on the fact that precisely the same result concerning the relations of the Mendelian unit-factors or genes of heredity has been independently reached by the exact experimental methods of modern genetic analysis. That these two lines of research are but dealing with different sides of the same problem is demonstrated by evidence now to be outlined in the following chapter.

LITERATURE XI

(See also II, VI, VII, X, XII. For abbreviations, see General Literature List.)

Artom, C., '12. Analisi comparata della sostanza cromatica etc. dell' uova dell' *Artemia: A. Zf.*, VII.

Baumgartner, W. J., '04. Some new Evidence for the Individuality of the Chromosomes: *B. B.*, VIII.

Bonnevie, Chr., '08. Chromosomen von *Ascaris, Allium* und *Amphiuma*, etc.: *A. Zf.*, I.

'13. Ueber Struktur und Genese der Askaris Chromosomen: *Ibid.*, IX.

Boveri, Th., '03. Ueber die Konstitution der chromatischen Kernsubstanz: *Vortrag Deutsch. Zool. Ges.*

'04. Ergebnisse über die Konstitution der chromatischen Substanz des Zellkerns: *Jena.*

'09. Die Blastomerenkerne von *Ascaris megalocephala* und die Theorie der Chromosomen-individualität: *A. Zf.*, III, 1, 2.

Braun, H., '09. Die specifische Chromosomenzahlen der einheimischen Arten der Gattung *Cyclops: A. Zf.*, III.

Browne, Ethel N., '13. (See also Harvey.) A Study of the male Germ Cells in *Notonecta: J. E. Z.*, XIV.

Carothers, E. E., '13 (XII).

Della Valle, P., '09. L'organizzazione della chromatina studiata mediante il numero dei cromosomi: *A. I. B.*, 4.

'11. La continuità delle forme in divisione nucleare ed il valore morfologico dei cromosomi: *Ibid.*, V.

'12. La morfologia della cromatina dal punto di vista fisico: *Ibid.*, VI.

Digby, L., '12. The Cytology of *Primula kewensis* and of other related *Primula* Hybrids: *A. Bot.*, XXVI.

Fick, R., '05. Betrachtungen über die Chromosomen, etc.: *A. A. P.*, Suppl.

Gates, R. R., '09. The Stature and Chromosomes of *Œnothera gigas*, DeVries: *A. Zf.*, 3.

'13. Tetraploid Mutants and Chromosome Mechanisms: *B. C.*, XXXIII.

'20. Mutation and Evolution: *N. P.*, XIX.

'24. Polyploidy: *Brit. Journ. Exp. Biol.*, I.—

Grégoire, V., '06. La structure de l'élément chromosomique au repos et en division dans les cellules végétales: *L. C.*, XXIII.

Hance, R. V., '17c. The diploid Chromosomes of the Pig (*Sus scrofa*): *J. M.*, XXX.

'18a. Variations in somatic Chromosomes: *B. B.*, XXIV.

'18b. Variations in the Number of Somatic Chromosomes in *Œnothera scintillans: Genetics*, III.

Harrison, J. W. H., and Doncaster, L., '14. On Hybrids between Moths of the Geometrid Sub-family Bistoninæ, etc.: *J. G.*, III.

Harvey (Browne), E. B., '16, '20. A Review of the Chromosome numbers in Metazoa, I, II: *J. M.*, XXVIII, XXXIV.

Ishikawa, Mitsuharu, '16. A List of the Number of Chromosomes: *Bot. Mag.*, Tokyo, XXX.

Kihara, H., '24. Cytologische und genetische Studien bei wichtigen Getreide-arten, etc.: *Mem. Coll. Sci. Kyoto Imp. Univ.*, B., 1.

Lutz, A. M., '12. Triploid Mutants in *Œnothera: B. C.*, XXXII.

'16. *Œnothera* Mutants with Diminutive Chromosomes: *A. J. B.*, III.

'17. Fifteen- and Sixteen-Chromosome *Œnothera* Mutants: *A. J. B.*, IV.

Marchal, Él., et Ém., '12. Recherches cytologiques sur le genre *Amblystegium: Bull. Acad. Roy. Belg.*, LI.

Marchal, E., '20. Recherches sur les variations numériques des chromosomes dans la série végétale: *Mém. Acad. Roy. Belg.*, IV, 2.

Maréchal, J., '04. Ueber die morphologische Entwicklung der Chromosomen im Keimbläschen des Selachiereies: *A. A.*, XXV.

McClung, C. E., '05. The Chromosome Complex of orthopteran Spermatocytes: *B. B.*, IX.

'08a. Cytology and Taxonomy: *Kansas Univ. Sci. Bull.*, IV.

'14. (VI).

'17. The multiple Chromosomes of *Hesperotettix* and *Mermiria: J. M.*, XXIX.

'24. (See XII.)

Metz, C. W., '14. Chromosome Studies on the Diptera, I: *J. E. Z.*, XVII.

'16a. Studies II. The Paired Association of Chromosomes in the Diptera, and its Significance: *Ibid.*, XXI.

'16b. Studies III. Additional Types of Chromosome Groups in the Droso-philidæ: *A. N.*, L.

Moenkaus, '04. The Development of Hybrids between *Fundulus* and *Menidia*, etc., *A. J. A.*, III.

'10. Cross Fertilization among Fishes: *Proc. Ind. Acad. Sci.*

Montgomery, T. H., '01. A Study of the Chromosomes of Metazoa: *Trans. Am. Phil. Soc.*, N. S., XX.

'06a. Chromosomes in the Spermatogenesis of the Hermiptera-heteroptera: *Ibid.*, XXI, 3.

Overton, J. B., '09. On the Organization of the Nuclei in Pollen Mother-cells, etc.: *A. B.*, XXIII.

Rabl, C., '89. Ueber Zellteilung: *M. J.*, X.

Raffaele, F., '21. Ancora poche parole intorno ai cromosomi: *Rass d. Sci. Biol.*, III.

Richards, A., '17. The History of the Chromosonal Vesicles in *Fundulus*, etc.: *B. B.*, XXXII.

Robertson, W. R. B., '08. The Chromosome Complex of *Syrbula: Kansas Univ. Bull.*, IV, 13.

'15. Inequalities and Deficiences in homologous Chromosomes, etc.: *J. M.*, XXVI.

'16. Taxonomic Relations shown in Chromosomes, etc.: *Ibid.*, XXVII.

'17. A deficient supernumerary Chromosome, etc.: *Kans. Univ. Bull.*, X, 14.

Rosenberg, O., '04. Ueber die Individualität der Chromosomen in Pflan-zenreich: *Flora*, XCIII.

'07. Cytological Studies on Apogamy in *Hieracium: Bot. Tidskr.*, XXVIII.

'09. Cytologische und Morphologische Studien an *Drosera longifolia* x *rotundifolia: Kungl. Svenska Vetenskaps, Hand.*, XLIV.

'17. Die Reductionsteilung und ihre Degeneration in *Hieracium: Svensk. Bot. Tidskr.*, XI.

Roux, W., '83. Die Bedeutung der Kerntheilungsfiguren: *Engelmann, Leipzig.*

Rückert, J., '92. Zur Entwicklungsgeschichte des Ovariales bei Selachiern: *A. A.*, VII.

Sands, H. C., '23. The Structure of the Chromosomes in *Tradescantia: A. J. B.*, X.

Sax, K., '22. Chromosome-Behavior in partially sterile Hybrids: *G.*, VII.

Stevens, N. M., '08. A Study of the Germ-cells of certain Diptera, etc.: *J. E. Z.*, V.' 12b. Further Observations on Supernumerary Chromosomes and Sex-ratios in *Diabrotica: B. B.*, XXII.

Stomps, T. J., '19. Gigas-mutationen mit und ohne Verdoppelung der Chromosomenzahl: *Z. A. V.*, XXI.

Stout, A. B., '12. The Individuality of the Chromosomes and their serial Arrangement in *Carex: A. Zf.*, IX.

Strasburger, E., '07. Ueber die Individualität der Chromosomen und die Propfhybriden-Frage; *J. W. B.*, XLIX.
'08. Chromosomenzahlen, Plasmastrukturen, Vererbungsträger, etc.: *J. W. B.*, XLV, 4.
'09. The Minute Structure of Cells in Relation to Heredity: In *Darwin and Modern Science:* Cambridge.
'10. Chromosomenzahl: *Flora*, V.

Täckholm, G., '22. Zytologische Studien über die Gattung *Rosa: Acta Bergiani*, VII, 3.

Tischler, G., '10. Untersuchungen über die Entwicklung des Bananen-Pollens, I: *A. Zf.*, V.
'15. Chromosomenzahl-, Form und Individualität im Pflanzenreiche: *P. R. B.*, V, 5.

Vejdovský, F., '11-'12. Zum Problem der Vererbungsträger: *Böhm. Ges. Wiss.*, Prag.

Wenrich, D. H., '17. (See VI.)

Wilson, E. B., '09. Studies on Chromosomes, V. The Chromosomes of *Metapodius.* A Contribution to the Hypothesis of the Genetic Continuity of Chromosomes: *J. E. Z.*, VI. 2.
'10b (X).

Winge, O., '17. The Chromosomes, their Numbers and general Importance: *Comptes-rendus des travaux du Laboratoire de Carlsberg*, XIII, 2.

Winkler, H., '09. Ueber die Nachkommenschaft der *Solanum* propfbastarde und die Chromosomenzahlen ihrer Keimzellen: *Z. B.*, II. Rev. in *Z. A. V.*, III.
'16. Ueber die exp. Erzeugung von Pflanzen mit abweichenden Chromosomenzahlen: *Z. B.*, VIII.

CHAPTER XII

HEREDITY AND THE CHROMOSOMES

"Normal development is dependent upon a particular combination of chromosomes; and this can only mean that *the individual chromosomes must possess different qualities*." Boveri.[1]

The important part played by the nucleus in heredity has been indicated in a general way in Chapter VIII, and more specifically demonstrated in Chapter X in considering the heredity of sex and of sex-linked characters. We have now to examine this subject more broadly. A continually growing body of data demonstrates irresistibly that the phenomena of Mendelian heredity generally result from combinations, segregations and recombinations of the chromosomes in successive generations. Even were the chromosome-theory of heredity based on evidence less demonstrative, it would still be indispensable as a practical means for the analysis of genetic phenomena. Opposition to it has largely arisen through a failure to grasp the mechanism of development as conceived by students of cytology, embryology, and genetics. No one familiar with these subjects now conceives the chromosomes as exclusive agents of heredity. They may be considered as modifiers in a reaction-system (p. 637), the specific products of their activity being determined not alone by the chromosomes but by the whole system of which they form a part. Chromosomes are to be regarded as *differential factors of heredity*, rather than central governing elements; nevertheless it is often convenient to speak of them as "determiners," taking the rest for granted.

I. QUALITATIVE DIFFERENCES OF THE CHROMOSOMES. THE EVIDENCE FROM MULTIPOLAR MITOSIS

By earlier writers it was generally assumed that in any given species all the chromosomes are essentially alike, both morphologically and physiologically; and Weismann held that every chromosome contains an idioplasm or germ-plasm in which are embodied all the hereditary qualities of the individual, and even of large groups of individuals.[2] This view was over-

---

[1] *Verh. d phys. med. Ges. zu Würzburg*, XXXIII, p. 75, 1902.

[2] Weissmann assumed that each chromosome consists of many slightly differing germ-plasms ("ids"), which correspond to individual variations in the species. To this extent the chromosomes were regarded as qualitatively different; but this conception is fundamentally different from that of Boveri.

thrown by Boveri ('02, '07), in his remarkable experimental researches on multipolar mitosis in dispermic sea-urchin eggs.

It was made known by O. Hertwig and Fol, that when this egg is fertilized by two sperms, the first cleavage-figure is multipolar with four poles (less commonly three), such eggs dividing at once into four or three blastomeres (Fig. 430).[1] After the initial multipolar division, cleavage proceeds by regular bipolar division and a blastula of normal appearance and activity is often produced. Such blastulas occasionally produce normal larvæ (Fig. 431), but only in a small percentage of cases. As a rule, as was first noted by Fol ('79), their development leads to the production of a variety of monstrous forms (Fig. 431). In the least modified forms the larvæ differ from the normal only in their somewhat asymmetrical form. Others may still

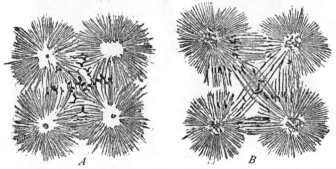

Fig. 430.—Multipolar mitosis in the first cleavage of dispermic sea-urchin eggs (*B* from BALTZER).
A, Toxopneustes, in metaphase; *B, Paracentrotus,* in anaphase.

be called plutei, but exhibit local defects or abnormalities, such as absence of pigment, abnormalities in the mesenchyme and skeleton, alimentary canal, etc.; such larvæ are not uncommonly normal on one side, or in one-third or one quadrant, but abnormal in the remaining regions. In more extreme cases monsters are produced, some of which may differentiate small patches of normal structure (pigment, skeleton) while others are purely nondescript. A common form is the "stereoblastula," actively swimming but unable to gastrulate and ultimately becoming filled with a solid mass of mesenchyme-like cells. The most abnormal forms are amorphous and finally disintegrate without any visible attempt to form an embryo. Many of these monsters are similar to those which often result from multipolar mitosis in artificial parthenogenesis.

[1] Dispermic eggs may often be obtained by adding a large excess of sperm. The tetrasters arise by the formation of two centers in connection with each sperm. Boveri found that triasters are readily produced by shaking the dispermic eggs, which often prevents the division of one center.

Driesch ('92), iso'ated more than 80 dispermic tetraster-eggs without obtaining a single gastrula and observed that when the tetraster is symmetrical, *i. e.*, when the four centers lie in a plane passing at right angles to the egg-axis, the later cleavage of the egg is in some respects double, eight instead of four micromeres being formed at the lower pole; but he succeeded no

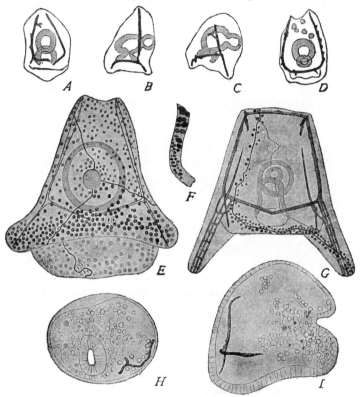

Fig. 431.—Dispermic and dwarf larvæ of sea-urchins (BOVERI).

A–D, four dwarf plutei from isolated blastomeres of a single normally fertilized egg in the 4-cell stage (*Paracentrotus*); *E*, normally formed pluteus from dispermic egg which divided by tripolar mitosis; the three areas developed from the three cells (as indicated by size of the nuclei) indicated by black outlines; *F*, portion of ciliated belt at junction of small and large nuclei; *G*, normally formed dispermic larva of similar origin and type (*Sphærechinus*), showing junction of small-nucleate and larger-nucleate thirds; *H*, highly pathological dispermic larva of *Paracentrotus*; *I*, monstrous dispermic, anenteric larva of *Echinus*.

better than Fol in explaining the abnormal development. Boveri's solution of the riddle, a masterpiece of experimental-analytical research, proved that the *disturbance of development results from an irremediable derangement in the distribution of the chromosomes, produced by the initial multipolar mitosis.*

That an asymmetrical distribution of the chromosomes to the daughter-cells occurs in most cases of dispermy is readily seen in sections of the tripolar or tetrapolar anaphases. Is such cases the nuclei rarely receive the same number of chromosomes, the distribution taking place in a quite irregular and apparently random manner (Fig. 430). The results are plainly apparent to the eye in the cells of the resulting larvæ, which always show conspicuous variations in the size of the nuclei. Nuclei of different sizes

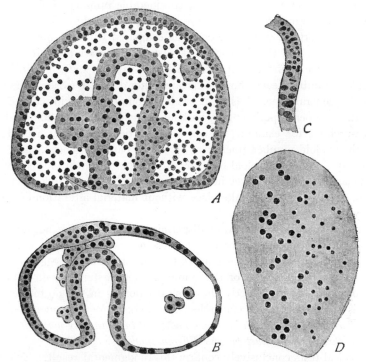

Fig. 432.—Nuclear size in sea-urchin larvæ from dispermic eggs (BOVERI).

A, dispermic sea-urchin larva (*Echinus*), showing large nuclei on one side and small on the other, the latter presumably of haploid constitution, the former of diploid; *B*, gastrula of *Paracentrotus* (in section) resulting from partial fertilization, having haploid on the left side and diploid on the right; *C*, portion of the ciliated belt of dispermic pluteus showing junction of regions of large and small nuclei; *D*, from wall of dispermic pluteus, junction of diploid and haploid regions.

are not in general intermingled haphazard but *are grouped in definite areas* which in some cases may be seen to occupy approximately the same position as the original three or four cells resulting from the multipolar mitosis (Figs. 431, *E*, *G*).

It is essential to bear in mind the fact that the mere number of chromosomes, though it may have a considerable effect on the developing organism does not *per se* determine its characters as a whole. Among Hymenoptera, for example, the males are haploid, the females diploid, yet apart from the sexual characters they are of the same specific type. In plants having an antithetic alternation of generations the sporophyte, normally diploid, may exceptionally possess only the haploid number of chromosomes, being produced by vegetative apogamy (p. 469) from the gametophyte; [1] while conversely diploid gametophytes occasionally rise by apospory, e. g., by budding from the sporophyte.[2]   Again, in a considerable number of cases certain individuals or races of a species are tetraploid, yet show few or no corresponding morphological differences as compared with the normal diploid forms (p. 870). In the jimson weed, *Datura*, Blakeslee and his colleagues ('22, etc.) have found sporophytes with the haploid, diploid, triploid and tetraploid numbers, each showing certain minor distinctive characters yet all of similar general type.   Lastly, it has been found possible in many cases to alter the number experimentally without changing the morphological type. In sea-urchins, for example, an egg (or a portion of an egg) may develop with the haploid number (merogony, artificial parthenogensis), the triploid (dispermy), or the tetraploid number (after doubling of the normal number by monaster formation); yet in all these cases, as Boveri and others have shown, development may take place without material alteration of the normal type (p. 729).

The abnormal development of dispermic eggs is therefore not due to variations in the mere number of chromosomes or quantity of chromatin. Neither is it due to a derangement of the cytoplasm of the egg, as is made clear by the development of the symmetrical tetraster-eggs, in which the first four cells occupy exactly the same position as in the normal embryo. All this shows, as Boveri concluded, that *normal development is dependent on the normal combination of chromosomes; and this can only mean that the individual chromosomes must possess different qualities.*

Statistical tests conclusively confirm this fundamental result. Evidently, in a random distribution, the chances of obtaining the normal chromosome-combination in all of the cells are much greater in tripolar mitosis than in quadripolar. The actual results accord with this expectation. Thus, 1500 tetraster-eggs produced only two normal plutei, and one of these was of doubtful origin; while 719 triaster-eggs gave rise to 58 perfect plutei, or 8.0%. These figures approximate fairly well to the theoretic expectation according to the theory of probabilities (*op. cit.*, p. 80). The same result is reached from the study of the development of single blastomeres isolated immediately after the multipolar mitosis. Obviously, the chance of obtaining

---

[1] In ferns (Farmer and Digby, '07, Yamanouchi, '08, Steil, '19).

[2] In pteridophytes (Farmer, '07, Strasburger, '07) and various seed-plants (Murbeck, Juel, Rosenberg, etc.).   Literature in Sharp ('21).

the normal combination in any single one of these cells is much greater than in all three, and is also greater in the isolated one-third than in the one-fourth. Figs. 433, 434. Further, larvæ derived from isolated blastomeres of triaster-eggs should show a much higher percentage of normal development than those from tetraster-eggs (since their chances of obtaining the normal chromosome-combination are greater). These expectations also are realized, though for various reasons the figures are less adequate than in case of the whole eggs. Driesch had previously shown ('oo) that by the use of Herbst's calcium-free sea-water (p. 1046) ¼-blastomeres of normal (monospermic) eggs may be isolated and

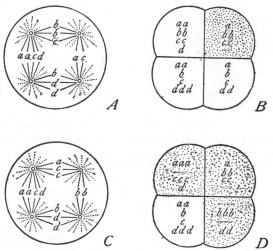

Fig. 433.—First cleavage of dispermic eggs (BOVERI). In each case the gametic groups are assumed to contain four chromosomes, a, b, c, d.
A, B, first cleavage, with chromosomes so disposed as to show defective combination in one quadrant (stippled); C, D, the same, showing three defective quadrants.

may produce normally formed dwarf plutei. Boveri demonstrated that by this method all four blastomeres from the 4-cell stage of a normal single egg may thus be isolated and that in the greater number of cases each of the four gastrulates and produces a dwarf pluteus, the four being in general of similar type (Fig. 431). When the same experiment is performed with the 4-cell stage of a dispermic egg, the four products are often abnormal, and rarely of similar type. Further, the larvæ from $^1/_4$-blastomeres (from a quadripolar cleavage) are in general more diverse than those from $^1/_3$-blastomeres (from a tripolar cleavage), as is illustrated by the following data. Out of 57 dispermic eggs 34 divided by tripolar mitosis and 23 by quadripolar. In each of these cases all of the blastomeres from each egg were isolated and separately reared. From 102 such $^1/_3$-blastomeres (from 34 tripolar eggs) were produced 44 nearly or quite normal gastrulas, or 47%, while 92 $^1/_4$-blastomeres (from 23 quadripolar eggs) produced only 17 nor-

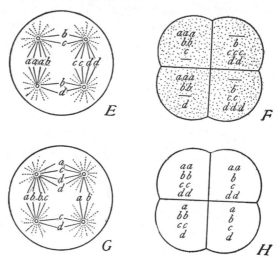

Fig. 434.—First cleavage of dispermic eggs (BOVERI). (Continuation of Fig. 433.)
E, F, first cleavage producing defective combinations in all of the quadrants; *G, H,* first cleavage giving complete combination (*a, b, d, c*), in all the quadrants.

mal gastrulas, or 18%. The distribution of these gastrulas with reference to the individual eggs was as follows:

A. 34 Tripolar Eggs		B. 23 Quadripolar Eggs	
No. of gastrulas from a single egg	% of whole number of blastomeres	No. of gastrulas from a single egg	% of whole number of blastomeres
3.	14.4%	4.	0.0%
2.	22.8	3.	4.5
1.	40.0	2.	4.5
0.	22.8	1.	54.5
		0.	36.5
	100.00		100.00

Allowing for a large error, the foregoing data strikingly demonstrate (1) the far smaller probability of normal development in blastomeres from dispermic eggs as compared with those from monospermic; and (2) the greater probability of normal development in $^1/_3$-blastomeres from dispermic eggs as compared with $^1/_4$-blastomeres.

It is clear (1) that in normal or monospermic fertilization the normal chromosome-combination established by fertilization is automatically maintained by mitosis; (2) that in dispermic eggs the normal combination is most commonly deranged by the initial multipolar cleavage; (3) that although the normal combination *may* accidentally be established in one or more of the cells the probability of this is relatively small after a tripolar mitosis, and still smaller after a quadripolar; and (4) that the chance of all the blastomeres receiving the normal combination is still smaller in the tripolar eggs and almost *nil* in the quadripolar.   (*Cf.* Figs. 433, 434.)   The conclusion is irresistible that normal development, whether in a whole larva or in any of its component cells, depends upon a normal combination of chromosomes.   And since heredity is the product of development it follows that each chromosome must play a particular part in its determination. This conclusion, more specifically demonstrated by the relation of the chromosomes to sex, is established by a multitude of additional facts.   We now proceed to its more specific development as applied to the phenomena of Mendelian heredity generally.

II. CYTOLOGICAL BASIS OF THE MENDELIAN PHENOMENA. THE SUTTON–BOVERI THEORY

1. General Outline

When the long-forgotten phenomena of Mendelian heredity were re-discovered in 1900 by Correns, DeVries and Tschermak it quickly became evident that in a general way they run parallel to the history of the chromosomes.   Van Beneden and his successors had demonstrated that in the zygote and its products the chromosome-group is double, or diploid, while in the gametes it is single or haploid.   The same was now seen to be true in respect to the unit-factors of heredity.   The conclusion was obvious that the Mendelian disjunction and segregation of unit-factors might be caused by the reduction of the diploid chromosome-groups to haploid ones in the course of the reduction-division.   The cytological parallel soon became evident in respect to the relative independence or free assortment of the Mendelian units as displayed in their power to combine, dissociate and recombine.   They are like cards in a pack, which may be shuffled and re-distributed in continually new combinations, without in the least degree losing their individual character.   All this, evidently, suggests that the units of heredity are dependent upon separate material bodies or substances that undergo corresponding combinations, dissociations and recombinations. Almost from the start it was seen that the material entities in question might be the chromosomes, or their components, and that in their behavior during the period of meiosis might be found an adequate mechanical explanation of the Mendelian phenomena. That such is really the case was soon decisively demonstrated.

The way to this demonstration was but gradually cleared. Independently of the rediscovery of Mendel's fundamental law of genetic segregation, cytological observation and experiment were almost at the same moment bringing to light the most essential of the cell-phenomena by which it is explained. A first step had been taken by Henking ('91) with the sug-

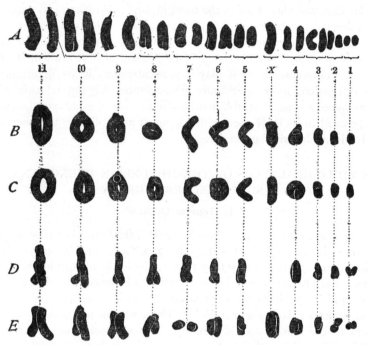

Fig. 435.—The chromosomes of the grasshopper *Syrbula* (ROBERTSON).

A, the 23 spermatogonial chromosomes artificially arranged in pairs according to their size (*cf.* Fig. 356); *X* is the unpaired *X*-chromosome; *B*, the corresponding bivalents (tetrads) of the first spermatocyte-mitosis; *C*, similar series from another cell; *D, E*, chromosomes of the secondary spermatocytes, showing two types, according to the absence of *X* (*D*) or its presence (*E*).

gestion that the process of reduction is initiated by a conjugation of chromosomes two by two and completed by a subsequent disjunction of the two members of each pair in the reduction-division; and this was early accepted by Boveri ('92) as offering the first intelligible explanation of the reduction-process. Rückert also, in two noteworthy short papers ('92a, '92b) on the oögenesis of elasmobranchs, accepted the conjugation of chromosomes, suggesting the possibility that the conjugants may be of different parental descent, and that an exchange of chromatic material from the two parental lines (an "amphimixis of the chromosomes") may thus take place producing new hereditary combinations. Here is the germ of the later conclusions of Montgomery ('01) and Sutton ('02, '03) of which the most fundamental one was that the *synaptic mates, or conjugating chromosomes of each pair, are respectively of maternal and paternal ancestry.* This result, first reached by Montgomery without knowledge of Mendel's law, was based on the size-relations of the chromosomes in insects. Montgomery urged the constancy of the size differences among the chromosomes; the occurrence in the diploid groups of symmetrical pairs of chromosomes (Fig. 435) and the existence in the meiotic divisions of size differences among the bivalents exactly corresponding to those previously existing between different chromosome-pairs. From these observed facts he concluded:

(1) That the members of each chromosome-pair are homologous, and are respectively of maternal and paternal derivation; (2) that in each case these two members play the part of synaptic mates, conjugating in synapsis to form a bivalent of corresponding size; (3) that this process may be regarded as "the final step in the process of conjugation of the germ-cells"; and (4) that in the reduction-division the maternal and paternal homologues are disjoined.

These conclusions provide all the essential data for an explanation of Mendel's law of segregation; but Montgomery did not attempt to bring them into any relation with genetic phenomena, concluding only that the synaptic conjugation is a means of effecting a "rejuvenation of the chromosomes." [1] From a purely cytological point of view, however, his conclusions displayed a remarkable insight into the essentials of the phenomena. They were soon afterwards confirmed and extended by the studies of Sutton ('02) on the chromosomes of a particularly favorable object, the great "lubber" grasshopper *Brachystola magna*, in which the double nature of the somatic chromosome-groups (especially in the spermatogonia) is clearly visible. Here the diploid number of the male is 23, among which may be distinguished eleven pairs of chromosomes of graded sizes in addition to the unpaired "accessory" or "X-chromosome." Subsequent to synapsis eleven bivalents of correspondingly graded sizes are distinguishable besides the univalent or unpaired X-chromosome (Fig. 436). Similar facts have since been determined in many other cases and throughout a wide range of species; and in some forms the chromosomes of the diploid groups are actually paired, homologous chromosomes lying side-by-side throughout the diploid cycle (p. 837), a fact conspicuously displayed in the Diptera (Figs. 395, 396).

[1] Like Rückert, Montgomery accepted the probability of an interchange of material between the conjugation chromosomes and compared this to the interchange of nuclear substances between conjugating Infusoria.

Meanwhile Boveri's experimental demonstration of the qualitative differences of the chromosomes (p. 920) supplied additional data necessary for a complete cytological interpretation of the Mendelian phenomena as then known, as first clearly formulated by Sutton ('02, '03) and in certain directions further developed by DeVries ('03).[1] In these papers we find

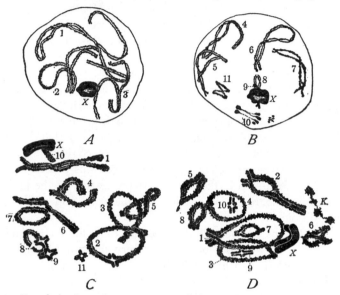

Fig. 436.—Tetrads in the early spermatocytes of the grasshopper *Brachystola*, from smear-preparations (SUTTON).

A, B, from the same nucleus, early diplotene; *C, D,* two separate nuclei each showing all the tetrads. Each nucleus shows ten tetrads and the condensed *X*-chromosome (*X*); the tetrads numbered in the order of their size from 1 to 11. These figures show some of the most characteristic heterotype-figures—rings, double crosses, double V's and their mode of origin; parasynapsis clearly indicated, *e. g.,* by *B,* 7; *C,* 1; *D,* 2.

an almost completely reasoned analysis in which are foreshadowed both the modern theory of linkage and also that of recombination or "crossing-over" between homologous linkage-groups.

In brief summary Sutton's conclusions were as follows:

(1) The somatic or diploid chromosome-groups are made up of two

[1] See p. 952. A possible connection between the Mendelian disjunction and the reduction-division was suggested by Strasburger ('00, '01) and Correns ('01). Slightly later the last-named writer ('02) offered a more detailed cytological interpretation which, though incomplete, included both the Mendelian disjunction and the recombination of factors by random assortment. Guyer also was led by his studies on the spermatogenesis of hybrid pigeons ('00, '02, '03), made without knowledge of Mendel's law, to the suggestion that both in hybrids and in "ordinary crosses," there is a separation of the paternal and the maternal chromosomes which had fused during synapsis" ('00, p. 47). Cannon ('02, '03) was led to a similar conclusion by studies on the spermatogenesis of hybrid cotton, and brought his results into definite relation with Mendel's law; but his interpretation, though correct in principle, remained inadequate in certain important respects.

equivalent chromosome-groups or series, one of maternal derivation and one of paternal (Van Beneden, Boveri, Montgomery).

(2) The chromosomes retain their morphological individuality and are genetically continuous throughout the life-cycle (Van Beneden, Rabl, Boveri).

(3) The process of synapsis consists in the union or conjugation of corresponding or homologous maternal and paternal chromosomes which in the reduction-division disjoin, pass to opposite poles of the spindle, and thus always into different germ-cells (Montgomery, Sutton).

(4) Each chromosome plays a definite part in the determination of development (Boveri).

To the foregoing Sutton added the following theoretic postulates:

(5) A given size-relation is characteristic of the physical basis of a definite set of genetic units. Each chromosome of any haploid series in the species has a homologue in any other series, and these homologous members of each pair "cover the same field" in development. This means, in more modern terminology, that the synaptic mates contain the physical units (factors or genes) that correspond to the Mendelian allelomorphs.

(6) "In the reduction-division the position of the chromosome-pairs or bivalent chromosomes in the equatorial plate is purely a matter of chance— that is, any chromosome-pair may lie with maternal or paternal chromatid toward either pole irrespective of the positions of other pairs—and hence a large number of different combinations of maternal and paternal chromosomes are possible in the mature gametes of an individual."

Sutton clearly showed that the formulas of Mendelian heredity generally (as then known) could be applied without alteration alike to the hypothetical "factors" or "genes" and to the chromosomes; and that the combinations, segregations and recombinations of the former are paralleled by those of the latter. Sutton also foreshadowed the modern theory of linkage, pointing out the necessity for the assumption that "some chromosomes at least are related to a number of different allelomorphs"; that "all the allelomorphs represented by any one chromosome must be inherited together"; and further, that "the same chromosome may contain allelomorphs that may be dominant or recessive independently" ('03, p. 240). This, as far as it goes, is in all essentials identical with the results afterwards worked out by Morgan and his co-workers in genetics which demonstrate that in case of *Drosophila* at least *the number of linkage-groups is the same as the haploid number of chromosomes* (p. 938).

DeVries's interesting discussion was in considerable measure based on Sutton's, and followed the same general lines but went beyond them in regard to the recombination-phenomena in the treatment of which De-

Vries may be said to have foreshadowed the modern theory of "crossing over," as Sutton did the modern theory of linkage.   Like Correns ('02), however, DeVries ('03), emphasized throughout the individual units rather than the chromosomes, and seems not to have had in mind the theory of linkage suggested by Sutton.   His discussion of the recombination-phenomena thus deals almost wholly with the exchange of *units* rather than the recombination of the linkage-*groups* (chromosomes).

In the meantime Boveri himself had reached conclusions in all essentials identical with Sutton's, though with the exception of a brief reference in his paper of 1902 they were not published until 1904.   Boveri had provided two of the fundamental postulates of Sutton's theory, namely, the individuality or genetic continuity of the chromosomes (which he had done more than any other to establish) and especially their qualitative differences in respect to development, for which he alone was responsible.   The names of Sutton, Boveri and DeVries will therefore always be closely associated with the cytological interpretation of Mendelism.   That this interpretation is fundamentally correct now seems to be placed beyond doubt by its numerous successful applications to more specific and detailed problems. Conspicuous among these is the cytologic-genetic analysis of sex, where the parallelism between the cytological and the genetic phenomena leaves nothing to be desired in point of schematic clearness.   The similar analysis of such phenomena as linkage, reduplication, non-disjunction, deficiencies, and the like is hardly less striking.   The most essential addition that has been made to the chromosome-interpretation by later observers is the chiasmatype-theory of Janssens and Morgan, a sketch of which will be offered in a later section (p. 954).

It does not lie within the scope of this work to consider the genetic phenomena *in extenso*.[1]   We offer here only a few illustrations of their connection with the cytological facts, for the most part in cases where the latter have been actually observed.

2. Mendelian Segregation and the Reduction-division

The most obvious, and perhaps the most decisive proof that the Mendelian segregation or disjunction is accomplished by the reduction-division is derived from the heredity of sex and of sex-linked characters.   Here the cytological and genetic evidence coincide in proving that the sex-factors are borne by the chromosomes, and that the composition of the gametes in respect to them is determined during meiosis in the reduction-division (p. 751).   A remarkable example of this demonstration is offered by the case

[1] See especially Morgan ('13, '19, '24), Morgan, Sturtevant, Bridges and Muller ('23) and works there cited.

of the liverwort *Sphærocarpus*, as earlier described, where Douin and Strasburger were able to show that of the four spores of the spore-quartet formed during sporogenesis two are male-producing and two female-producing, while Allen later demonstrated the sex-chromosomes by which this disjunction is effected (p. 812). The experimental researches of the Marchals on mosses, though less complete, point unmistakably in the same direction (p. 746). The later discoveries of Bridges ('14) on non-disjunction of the sex-chromosomes, and of L. V. Morgan ('22) on X-linkage likewise afford conclusive proof of the same general conclusion as applied to sex-linked characters (p. 946). In harmony with this is the whole body of evidence derived from hybrids or mutants having uneven chromosome-numbers (p. 944) and from triploid or tetraploid forms (p. 943); in general also that from the genetic behavior of individuals showing other departures from the typical or normal chromosome-constitution. A remarkable example of this is offered by Federley's moth-hybrids. In the spermatogenesis of these, as earlier stated (p. 853), synapsis and disjunction nearly or quite fail, so that the sperms receive nearly or quite the diploid number (Fig. 406). In correspondence with this, when such hybrids are back-crossed with one of the original parents almost no segregation is observed, the progeny (unlike the usual result of such a back-cross) being in nearly all respects the same in appearance as the first hybrid.

Less direct but convincing evidence is drawn from many other sources. Plough's experiments ('17) proved that crossing-over must take place near the synaptic period of the auxocytes, and hence that disjunction is effected between this period and the final production of the gametes. Genetically a pretty piece of evidence is offered by hybrid Hymenoptera. As shown by Newell ('15) in reciprocal crosses between pure bred Italian bees (*Apis ligustica*) and the Carniolan (*A. carnica*) the hybrid females (queens, workers) in both cases show the dominant yellow color of *ligustica*, while the males are strictly matriclinous. This gives, of course, fresh proof of the origin of the males from unfertilized eggs (Dzierzon theory). But, secondly, if the hybrid females be fertilized by drones of *ligustica* all the female offspring again show only the dominant *ligustica* yellow, but half the male offspring are of the *ligustica* type and half of the recessive *carnica*. Parallel results were obtained by Whiting ('18, '21) in crosses between an orange-eyed recessive mutation of the parasitic wasp *Hadrobracon* with the normal black-eyed form. The natural interpretation of these results, evidently, is that disjunction of the factors for the two parental types takes place in the maturation of the eggs of the hybrid queen, and that the mature eggs are as likely to receive one type as the other.

These cases, quite analogous to an ordinary Mendelian back-cross, give an especially clear result because the males are of haploid constitution and have chromosomes of purely maternal origin. Still more conclusive in type, but based on less complete evidence, are the results of Pascher ('16) on the flagellate *Chlamydomonas*, a unicellular organism, believed to be of haploid constitution, and to have 10 chromosomes. Meiosis is here zygotic, the zygotic dividing into four swarm-spores all of which alike are functional (as in *Œdogonium* or *Bulbochæta*, p. 604). This organism could be reared in large numbers on agar by special culture-methods which readily make possible isolation-experiments and the study of pure lines. Two species or races of this organism (A and B) differing markedly in external form and in several definite structural characters, were found to hybridize readily. The hybrid zygote is intermediate in type between the zygotes of the pure parental lines. Isolation-cultures of these zygotes and of their products, showed them to be of three kinds, two being of the pure parental types and two of mixed type (Fig. 437); further, by isolating all four zoöspores from

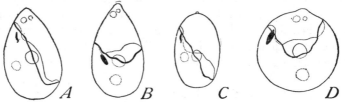

Fig. 437.—Three types of *Chlamydomonas* from the germination of a heterozygote (PASCHER).

A is nearly like Form *A*, *D* nearly like Form *B*, while *B* and *C* are hybrids showing different recombinations of the original gametic type, as shown by the general shape, the chromatophore, stigma, pyrenoid and other characters.

a single zygote one was found to give offspring of only the A-type, one of only the B-type, while two were of mixed type. A Mendelian segregation has therefore taken place during the germination of the zygote, *i. e.*, its division into four zoöspores; these divisions, therefore, are almost certainly meiotic, and the ordinary vegetative individuals are haploid, as in *Spirogyra* or the desmids. If this is substantiated we shall have a complete proof of Mendelian disjunction in the meiotic divisions, exactly analogous to that demonstrated in *Sphærocarpus* in respect to the sex-characters (p. 748).

The foregoing facts are only examples of a great and continually growing body of evidence that sustains the same conclusions. It is indeed probable that non-disjunction or other chromosome-dislocations taking place at any period of the life-history may to a limited extent produce genetic results of related type, for instance in the production of gynandromorphs (p. 811). Such phenomena do not, however, belong to the normal life-cycle; and the whole body of evidence now indicates the extreme improbability of true Mendelian segregation taking place outside the period of meiosis.[1]

3. Random Assortment of the Synaptic Mates.   Heteromorphic Chromosome-pairs

Sutton expressed the opinion that the distribution of the chromosomes during the reduction-division produces a free or random assortment (p. 927) such that the gametes receive all combinations of the original paternal and maternal elements possible within the limits of a complete haploid group, in accordance with the laws of probability (Fig. 105).

This (linkage being for the moment disregarded) is in accordance with Mendel's so-called second law, *i. e.*, that of the independent assortment (or recombination) of different pairs of unit factors or allelomorphs; but Sutton had no adequate cytological proof of his conclusion.   The conclusive evidence in its favor was first found in the meiotic behavior of *heteromorphic* chromosome-pairs, in which the synaptic mates differ visibly in size or shape and thus offer conspicuous landmarks by which the relative positions of the bivalents in the reduction-division may be determined.   In such cases the gametic recombinations to which they give rise may readily be recognized.   It has thus been possible to set aside every doubt concerning the independent segregation or assortment of the synaptic mates as maintained by Sutton.

Heteromorphism of the synaptic mates may appear in not less than five different ways, all of which are exemplified both in the XY-type of sex-chromosomes and in the autosomes.   These are: (1) inequality in size, of which many degrees exist; (2) a difference in mode of attachment to the spindle-fibers, one member being telomitic (terminal attachment) the other atelomitic (non-terminal attachment) in various degrees, or (3) both members being atelomitic in different degrees; (4) a difference in structure, one member showing a transverse suture or constriction that is absent in the other; and (5) a difference of shape without other visible differences.   Of these, the first four have been clearly recognized in the autosomes of Orthoptera.

a. Inequality in the Synaptic Mates.   Inequality of the autosomal mates reported by several observers in Orthoptera was first carefully examined in *Brachystola*, *Arphia*, and *Dissosteira*, by Carothers ('13) whose results were borne out by those of Voïnov ('14) on *Gryllotalpa*, of Wenrich ('14, '16) on *Phrynotettix*, and of Robertson ('16) on *Tettigidea* and *Acridium* (Fig. 438). Such chromosome-pairs bear a very close resemblance to an XY-pair of sex-chromosomes and have in fact been confused with them.   The origin of

---

[1] *Cf.*, however, Bateson, '20.

these unequal pairs is doubtful.   The problem here offered is the same as in
case of the XY-pair, in which the inequality is almost certainly due to a reduction or progressive loss of substance on the part of the smaller member,
perhaps accompanied by a corresponding loss of genetic factors (p. 748).
A similar explanation is adopted by Robertson and by Wenrich in case of
certain heteromorphic pairs; but as Robertson ('15) especially has shown,
it is probable that other modes of origin may have taken place.   One is a
simple fragmentation by cross-division of one synaptic mate, producing a
"deficient" smaller chromosome which still may serve as the smaller synaptic mate of the intact normal member of the pair (in *Tettigidea*).   Another

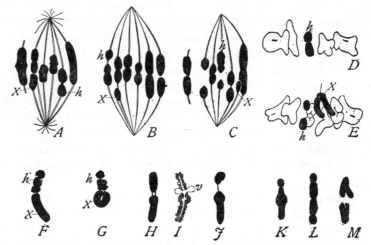

Fig. 438.—Heteromorphic bivalents in Orthoptera (*A–C*, Robertson; *D–M*, Carothers).
h, heteromorphic bivalent, *X*, *x*-chromosome.
A, first spermatocyte-division in *Tettigidea; B, C*, the same in *Acridium; D, E*, the same in
Arphia; F, H, heteromorphic bivalent attached to *X* during the growth-period; *H*, heteromorphic
bivalent in *Trimerotropis; I, J*, in *Circotettix, I* in the growth-period, showing vesicles (*v*); *K, L, M*,
different conditions of the same tetrad in three different individuals of *Trimerotropis, K*, heteromorphic, *L* and *M*, homomorphic of two types.

is by a similar fragmentation of one synaptic mate (a) in a tetrad so as to
form a sesquivalent element $(A + \frac{a}{2})$ and a semivalent element, $\frac{a}{2}$, which
may later disappear or to give rise to a supernumerary (p. 877).   On the other
hand, the sesquivalent element, may pair with a single, normal chromosome
of the next generation to form the unequal pair $A\frac{a}{2} + a$.   Such a mode of
origin is suggested both by the shape and size-relations of the unequal pair,
in *Acridium;* and the subsequent observations of Carothers on *Trimeropteris*
('17) gave direct evidence of such a mode of origin (Fig. 438), the fragmentation taking place at a point marked by two large chromosome-vesicles which
mark the point of spindle-attachment.   Robertson points out the explana-

tion that such phenomena may give of the dropping out or loss of unit-factors; and the subsequent researches of Bridges on the genetic phenomena of "deficiency" have rendered this interpretation extremely probable (p. 948).

Carothers ('13) demonstrated, especially in *Brachystola*, using the X-chromosome as a standard of comparison, that the unequal mates of such a pair are distributed at random to the sperms, *i. e.*, equally to the female-producing or X-class and the no-X or male-producing, thus giving rise to four

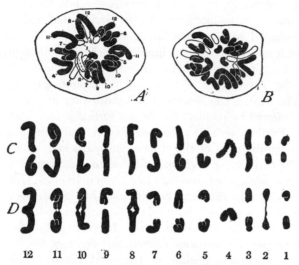

Fig. 439.—Chromosomes of the grasshopper *Trimerotropis* (CAROTHERS).

A, spermatogonial group from an individual with 15 atelomitic chromosomes (black) and 8 telomitic (white); *B*, similar group from individual with 17 atelomitic and 6 telomitic; *C*, the chromosomes of *A* arranged according to size, with 7 homomorphic and 4 heteromorphic; *D* the corresponding bivalents.

approximately equal classes of sperm.[1] With respect to these chromosomes, we should therefore expect to find not only individuals with the unequal pair (which may be designated as Aa) but also some with a small equal pair (aa) and others with a large pair (AA). Robertson established in *Tettigidia* the existence, in different individuals, of classes Aa and AA, and in *Acridium* of classes Aa and aa, and in spite of the absence of one expected class in each case concluded that we have here "the basis for a Mendelian ratio" ('15, p. 117). In *Phrynotettix* Wenrich ('16) found all of the ex-

---

[1] Out of 300 first spermatocytes in *Brachystola* the large member of this pair was seen passing to the X-pole in 154 cases or 51.3% of the whole number, to the no-X pole in 146 cases, or 48.6%. Similar results were obtained, in *Arphia* and *Dissosteira*, but the data were less extensive. The results obtained by the study of the second division bear out the result since X may be accompanied by either the large or the small member.

pected classes in case of a particular heteromorphic chromosome-pair ("B"). We have here the first complete demonstration of the free or random assortment of chromosomes in the meiotic process, and it is obvious that very strong support is thus lent also to the theory of the genetic continuity of the chromosomes.

b. Differences of the Synaptic Mates in respect to Attachment and Shape. The foregoing results are confirmed and largely extended by the later remarkable studies of Carothers ('17, '21) on the chromosomes of *Trimerotropis* and *Circotettix* (p. 835). In these cases certain of the chromosome-pairs are markedly heteromorphic owing to the fact that while one synaptic mate is rod-shaped with terminal attachment its fellow is hook-shaped or V-shaped with non-terminal attachment, which varies in degree in different cases but again is constant in the individual. These pairs are represented in the heterotypic division by correspondingly heteromorphic bivalents (Fig. 439). The heteromorphic pairs vary in number from one to eight in different individuals but *in any particular individual the number is constant.* Further, owing to the size-relations and other characters it is possible to recognize most of the chromosome-pairs individually, especially as seen in the heterotypic division, and thus to demonstrate the fact that the character of each pair is constant in a given individual, though differing from one individual to another. For example, in Fig. 441, B, F, are shown all the chromosomes of the heterotypic division spread out in a series, from five different cells of the same individual. It is seen here that in each case three heteromorphic bivalents are present, namely, 1, 7, and 8 (No. 4 is the univalent X-chromosome), while of the eight homomorphic ones, four (2, 3, 5, 6) are telomitic and four atelomitic. In Fig. 440, D, from another individual, two bivalents (6 and 7) are heteromorphic; in a second (E) three are heteromorphic (3, 6 and 7); in a third (F) all are homomorphic. These figures also show the variation in the total number of atelomitic chromosomes in different individuals; in D this number is 15, in E it is 11, in F 17. In every case, comparison of the spermatogonial groups with those of the first spermatocytes shows that these fiber-attachments remain constant throughout. This will be seen from a comparison of Fig. 441, A with 441, B–F; the former showing the spermatogonial group, the latter five groups from the heterotypic division of the same individual. In each case twelve of the chromosomes are atelomitic, all being free in the spermatogonia while in the spermatocytes 8 are united to form 4 homomorphic bivalents (12, 11, 10, 9), 3 are found in heteromorphic association (8, 7, 1), while the twelfth is the unpaired X-chromosome or accessory (4), always recognizable by its rough contour. In like manner, Fig. 439 is a spermatogonial group showing 15 atelomitic chromosomes, which are shown arranged

in pairs in Fig. C.   D shows the corresponding tetrads of the first spermatocyte-division of the same individual, with 5 homomorphic atelomitic bivalents (12, 11, 10, 7, 5), 4 heteromorphic ones (9, 8, 6, 1), and the X-chromosome, in exact correspondence with the spermatogonial condition shown
in B.

By means of these characters it may readily be demonstrated that in respect to position the heteromorphic bivalents in the heterotypic division are
wholly independent of one another and also of the pole to which the un-

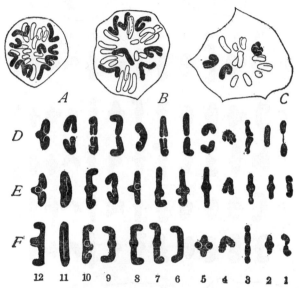

Fig. 440.—Chromosomes of the grasshopper *Trimerotropis* (CAROTHERS).
  A, diploid female group, with 10 atelomitic chromosomes (black) and 14 atelomitic (white);
B, spermatogonial group of another individual (male) with seven atelomitic chromosomes (the
minimum number observed) and 14 atelomitic; *C*, second spermatocyte group, from an individual
with 7 atelomitic chromosomes; note here 3 such attachments only; *D*, the tetrads of an individual
having one heteromorphic pair (7); *E*, the tetrads of another individual having three heteromorphic
pairs (3, 6, 7); *F*, from another individual having only homomorphic tetrads.

paired X-chromosome passes.   Their relative position varies from cell to
cell *in the same individual*, as may be seen for instance in Fig. 441 by comparison of the relative positions of Nos. 1, 4, 7 and 8, which demonstrate
clearly that independent assortment (free segregation) takes place for
these four chromosomes, thus producing 16 different gamete-combinations.
That this conclusion applies to the chromosomes generally in these forms is
demonstrated in several ways.

First, in the second spermatocyte division the chromosome-attachments
(and shapes) persist unchanged, but the relative number of terminal and

non-terminal attachments is no longer constant (as it is in the first division)
but varies from cell to cell, owing to the varying relative positions of the
bivalents in the first division.

Secondly, statistical studies show that the various combinations of telo-

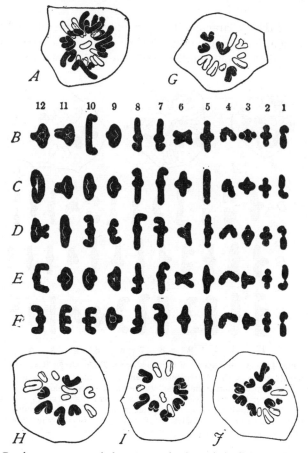

Fig. 441.—Random assortment of chromosomes in the meiotic divisions of the grasshopper
Trimerotropis. The chromosomes arranged in the order of their size; the *X*-chromosome is No.
4 (CAROTHERS).

A, spermatogonial group, from an individual with twelve atelomitic chromosomes (black, j-
shaped or v-shaped) and 11 telomitic (white, rod-shaped); *B–F*, lateral view of the tetrads of the
heterotypic division of same individual from 5 different spermatocytes; note especially variation
in relative positions of Nos. 7 and 8; *G–J*, second spermatocyte metaphases from same individual;
H, with 5 V's and 7 rods; *I*, 7 V's and 5 rods; *J*, 8 V's and 4 rods (the appearance of V-shape in
certain of the white rods is produced by the longitudinal split seen obliquely).

mitic and atelomitic chromosomes found in different individuals correspond
closely to the expected Mendelian ratios. Taking, for example, the smallest

of the chromosomes (No. 1), which is one of the most easily recognized, out of 62 individuals this pair is homomorphic and telomitic in 18, homomorphic and atelomitic in 13, and heteromorphic in 31—a close approximation to the Mendelian ratio 1:2:1 to be expected under the assumption of random assortment. Certain individuals also show one or two supernumerary chromosomes which likewise segregate in the heterotypic division without relation to the accessory or to each other.

Thirdly, in *Circotettix* Carothers ('21) has succeeded in crossing certain individuals of known chromosome-character and subsequently determining the resulting combinations in the offspring (Fig. 442). Twenty-eight male offspring have thus been examined from five matings with especial reference

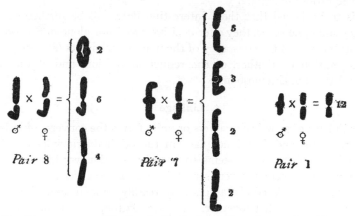

Fig. 442.—Chromosome-recombinations in F₁ offspring of *Circotettix verruculatus* (CAROTHERS).
Three selected bivalents from the heterotypic mitosis are shown, numbered (according to size) 8, 7 and 1. In each case the parental types are at the left, those of the F₁ offspring at the right, with the numbers of each observed in 12 male offspring.

to three chromosome-pairs (Nos. 1, 7 and 8) which may be either heteromorphic or homomorphic. The data thus obtained, though not very extended, offer a result that seems to be decisive. They demonstrate, in case of these three pairs, that when a particular pair is homomorphic (whether telomitic or atelomitic) in both parents, the corresponding chromosomes of the offspring are likewise homomorphic, and of the same type. When one parental pair is homomorphic and one heteromorphic both parental types appear among the offspring. When both parental pairs are heteromorphic and of the same type this type appears in some of the offspring, while in others two new *homomorphic* types appear, one telomitic and one atelomitic. All this, of course, exactly parallels the Mendelian phenomena. The numbers are as yet too small to be demonstrative but as far as they go conform to expectation. Fig. 442 shows the history of the three pairs in the best of the observed matings, which produced 12 male offspring. Pair 1, homomorphic and telomitic in both sexes, appeared in the same form in all of the 12 female offspring. Pairs 7 and 8 were heteromorphic in both parents, in 7 the same condition was present in the mother, while in the father both were atelomitic but in different degrees. In F_1 appeared three types, one heteromorphic like the parent forms (6), one homomorphic-telomitic (4) and one homomorphic-atelomitic (4). This ratio (2:6:4) is a close approximation to the Mendelian expectation (3:6:3). In case of pair 7 all the male F_1 offspring show this pair heteromorphic; but it is of four types (AB × ab = Aa + Ab + aB + ab) which should theoretically appear in equal numbers; the observed ratios are 2:3:5:2.

It is to be hoped that these interesting data will be further extended. As they stand, however, they offer decisive proof not alone of Sutton's conclusions but also of the constancy of the fiber-attachments (and shape) from one generation to another, of the reduction-division, and of the genetic continuity of the chromosomes.

4. Linkage

The linkage of genetic characters or units forms the converse of independent assortment and found no place in the original principles of Mendel, to whom the phenomenon seems to have been unknown; but some of the early students of heredity were struck by the fact that in crossing different races certain associated characters may readily be split apart while others tend to be transmitted together. To cite Galton, one of the first to emphasize the fact of "particulate inheritance" (*i. e.*, the independence of heredity-units): "We appear, then, to be severally built up of a vast host of minute particles, of whose nature we know nothing, any one of which may be derived from any one progenitor but which usually transmitted in aggregates, considerable groups being derived from the same progenitor" (*Natural Inheritance*, 1889). The phenomena were at the time too imperfectly known to affect the later development of the subject. The true explanation was first found with the development of the hypothesis that each chromosome represents a group of associated hereditary units ("factors," "genes") which tend to cohere in a linkage-group; if they enter a hybrid together they tend to issue together from it and to hold together in its descendants. This conclusion was in a measure foreseen by Sutton but in the absence of sufficient data was treated by him as a difficulty in the way of the chromosome-theory of heredity as it also was by Lock ('06) and some later writers. Sutton could not himself meet this supposed difficulty; but it disappeared when subsequent genetic research demonstrated that the unit-factors are in fact linked together in groups precisely as the chromosome-theory demands.

   a. The Linkage-groups in General.   Linkage in the modern sense of the term was first recognized by Bateson and Punnett in 1906 in certain characters of sweet peas which show a tendency to be coupled in heredity ("gametic coupling"); *i. e.*, if they enter an F_1 hybrid together they tend to make their exit together in the gamete-formation, so as still to remain in association in the F_2 offspring.   This fact, since widely observed, evidently calls for an important modification in the law of independent assortment as originally formulated by Mendel; for if the free assortment of Mendelian units be compared (as has often been done) to the random shuffling of cards in a pack we must add the qualifying assumption that certain of the cards tend to stick together in certain groups which may reappear as such in successive deals.   The reality of this and its explanation were first fully placed in evidence by the remarkable analysis of linkage made by Morgan, Sturtevant, Bridges, Muller and their co-workers in the case of *Drosophila melanogaster*.

   In this fly, bred under standardized artificial conditions, a large number of definite heritable mutations have arisen since 1910, affecting most of the external characters of the animal and in some instances (wing structure) of extreme type.   The study of innumerable crosses, of many kinds, proves that these mutations fall into four definite linkage-groups; and thus far every new mutation (more than four hundred are now known) has fallen at once into one of these groups.   The units of each group are quite independent of those of other groups.   The especial cytological interest of this discovery lies in the fact that in this animal *the gametic number of chromosomes is also four* (Fig. 396), which creates a very strong presumption that each linkage-group is represented by a chromosome.   This presumption has been tested in many ways, of which the most important are the relations of the linkage-groups to sex and to abnormal chromosome-combinations. Both tests afford a conclusive confirmation of the hypothesis.

   b. Sex-linked Heredity.   If each chromosome forms the basis of a linkage-group, one of the latter obviously should show a specific relation to sex, as is the case with the X-chromosome; and such is the fact.   One of the four groups, and one only, shows sex-linked or sex-limited heredity. This form of linkage, long known in the heredity of color-blindness, hæmophilia, and a few other characters in man, has more recently been studied in case of the color-patterns of moths and of birds, and of numerous characters in flies (*Drosophila*) and various other cases.   The behavior of these characters may be summed up in the statement that they follow precisely the course to be expected if their determining or differential factors be borne by the X-chromosome; and the key to this behavior lies in the fact that when the male is digametic the X-chromosome of the male (single in this sex) is always derived in fertilization from the egg, while the two X-chromosomes of the female are derived one from the sperm and one from the egg (p. 752). In other words, in fertilization the chromosome of the male normally passes from father to daughter, while those of the female pass, one from mother to son and one from mother to daughter. In these facts lies the explanation of "criss-cross heredity"; and of its exceptions in "non-disjunction" (p. 947); of the fact that the sex-linked characters are always heterozygous or singly represented in the male but in the female may be either heterozygous or homozygous.[1]

In Fig. 443, for instance, the homozygous recessive female xx, crossed with the dominant male XY, gives criss-cross heredity, the heterozygous

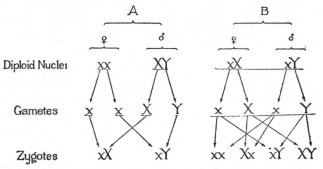

Fig. 443.—Diagrams of sex-linked heredity and the X-chromosome; X is assumed to bear the factor for a dominant and x that for its recessive allelomorph.

A, criss-cross heredity. The homozygous recessive female $xx \times$ the dominant male XY, gives F[1] daughters xX, showing the dominant paternal character and sons xY showing the maternal recessive. B, the F[1] offspring crossed together give the grandparental and the F[1] forms in equal numbers.

daughters Xx showing the dominant character of the father (X), while the sons show the recessive character of the mother since they contain only a recessive x-chromosome received from the mother. When these are paired together the F_2 offspring show the grandparental conditions in equal numbers. This is graphically shown in Fig. 444 (from Morgan), showing reciprocal crosses between the normal (dominant) red-eyed *Drosophila* and the recessive white-eyed form, both sex-linked or X-borne characters; the course of the X-chromosomes shown by the connecting lines. In the first case (A) the F_1 offspring are all red-eyed, while the F_2 generation shows the typical 3:1 Mendelian ratio, including one pure female dominant, two female heterozygotes and one recessive, *which is always a male*. In the reverse

---

[1] In cases where the male is homogametic (Lepidoptera, birds) these conditions are reversed.

cross (B) the F_1 sons are like the mother and the daughters like the father (criss-cross heredity), in each case owing to the crossing-over of the X-chromosomes from one sex to the other. The F_2 forms show red-eyed and white-eyed individuals in equal numbers, for a similar and evident reason. These are but particular examples of a large class of cases in which the behavior of the sex-linked characters, formerly offering so enigmatical an aspect, at once becomes clear when their connection with the X-chromosome is

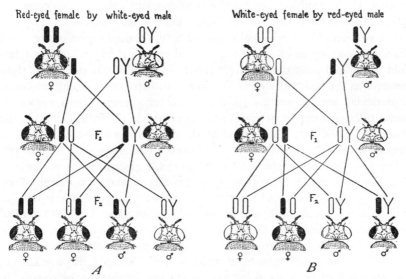

Fig. 444.—Sex-linked and criss-cross heredity of a pair of sex-linked allelomorphic characters, dominant red-eye and recessive white eye, in *Drosophila*, showing the history of the sex-chromosomes X and Y. In each case the black X-chromosome stands for red-eye and the white for white-eye (MORGAN).

 A, the result of crossing female red-eye with male white-eye. By crossing white-eyed males with heterozygous females may be obtained homozygous white-eyed females (shown in B).

 B, the reverse cross, showing criss-cross heredity, the F_1 daughters like the father (red-eyed) and the sons like the mother white-eyed.

recognized. For the problem of linkage the decisive fact is that female homogamety is associated with the presence of two homologous sex-linked genetic groups in the female and but one in the male, in exact correspondence with the constitutions of the respective sexes as XX and XO or XY. Precisely the same correspondence, *mutatis mutandis*, is found in cases of female digamety (p. 783).

5. The Chromosomes of Certain Mutants. Tetraploids and Triploids. Genetic Instability of Uneven Chromosome-numbers [1]

Many observed mutations have involved no visible changes in the chromosomes, a fact illustrated by many of the mutants of Œnothera and Drosophila. There are other cases in which definite visible changes have occurred in the chromosome-groups; and some of these offer important evidence concerning the determinative action of the chromosomes in development. The subject can here be considered in only a cursory manner by indication of a few illustrative cases.[2] The chromosome-changes in question have been of two principal types, namely: (1) duplication of the entire chromosome-group or of one of the haploid groups, thus producing a tetraploid or triploid condition, and (2) the duplication of one or several chromosomes as the result of a preceding irregular distribution of chromosomes, in particular non-disjunction (p. 872), or other causes.[3] Both modes are known to have occurred in the evening-primrose, in the fruit-fly, and in the jimson weed, Datura. The second of these types has afforded demonstrative evidence of the causal connection between chromosomes and heredity.

The first type is exemplified by the so-called gigas or giant mutants of Œnothera, where the cytological facts have been carefully examined especially by Gates, Lutz and Stomps. The fundamental or gametic number in this genus is 7 and the diploid 14, as in Œ. lamarckiana (DeVries's original parent-form), grandiflora, biennis, etc.; and the same number appears in certain of the mutants from these forms, e. g., rubrinervis, nanella, or brevistylis. The gigas mutants, of which several distinct forms are known, are characterized by marked increase in stature, in the size of organs, in the size of cells and nuclei, and by certain structural differences in the leaves, flowers, seed-capsules, pollen-grains and other characters. In many respects they are closely paralleled by certain giant races of the Chinese primrose. In most of these cases the chromosome number is tetraploid instead of diploid—namely, in Œnothera gigas 28 (sometimes 27 or 29) instead of the original 14 (Lutz, '07, Gates, '08, etc.), and in Primula 48 instead of 24 (Gregory, '12, '14). In both cases the giants are fertile, and produce gametes that are diploid as compared with the original type.

---

[1] The term "mutant" will here be employed in the older sense to designate sudden heritable deviations from the usual specific type, without raising the more modern question whether they are due to a qualitative change in the units of the germ-plasm or merely to a recombination of previously existing units.

[2] See Gates ('15), Stomps ('12), Lutz ('17), Morgan, Sturtevant, Müller and Bridges ('15, '23), Morgan ('19), Blakeslee ('21), Täckholm ('22).

[3] By Blakeslee ('21) mutants of the latter type are called trisomic, tetrasomic, etc., according to the number of synaptic mates in a set of duplicates; the number of such sets is indicated by the terms simple, double, triple, etc. The most frequent condition is the simple triosomic (i. e., with one set of three).

Tetraploids of this type having even chromosome-numbers breed true, and in their genetic behavior offer a remarkable confirmation of the chromosome-theory in the fact that in back-crosses or in the F_2 generation they show modified ratios such as are to be expected if the normal number of linkage-groups have been doubled.[1]

Whether the doubling of the chromosome-groups is itself the cause of these giant forms is not positively known; but there is reason to conclude that other factors have been involved, for it is certain that *gigas* mutants have arisen in several groups of plants without any increase in the number of chromosomes.[2] Conversely a number of cases have earlier been cited (p. 870) in which related species, or even different individuals or races within the same species, have twice the number of chromosomes found in others without increase in size or other change so far as known.

How the doubling has been effected is likewise unknown, though many interesting possibilities have been discussed. It may have been caused by a "suspended mitosis" or splitting of the chromosomes of a zygote without division of the nucleus (Gates, '09, Strasburger, '10) such as occurs in the monocentric mitosis of the animal egg. It may, however, have occurred at an earlier period, the gametic nuclei having been already diploid (Stomps, '10, '12, '16); and this is made plausible by the existence of triploid mutants or *semi-gigas* forms which, as Stomps has urged, may have followed the union of a diploid and a haploid gamete.[3] Such triploid mutants, evidently, are closely analogous to hybrids between tetraploid and diploid forms and perhaps may in some cases have arisen as such.

Geerts ('07) observed in *Œ. lamarckiana* a tetraploid primary megasporocyte with 28 chromosomes. From such a cell might arise a tetraploid race directly by apospory (Gates); or it might give rise to a diploid egg, fertilization of which by a similarly produced diploid pollen-nucleus would produce a tetraploid zygote (Stomps). Nevertheless the suggestion of Gates and Strasburger seems at least equally probable in view of the doubling of the zygotic number by monocentric mitosis in animal eggs (p. 729), a process which may occur spontaneously as well as under experimental conditions.

The evidence from tetraploid mutants leaves us somewhat in doubt concerning the relation of the chromosomes to mutation, though it is interesting as indicating a change of nuclear organization. That derived from triploids and from non-disjunction, on the other hand, has given a complete

---

[1] See Gregory ('14), Müller ('14), Blakeslee, Belling and Farnham ('20), etc.

[2] Thus in *Primula* (Gregory, '09, '14), in *Narcissus* and *Œnothera* (Stomps, '14, '19) and in *Phragmites* (Tischler, '18). See also Gates '13. *Cf.* p. 101.

[3] Triploid mutants were discovered in *Œnothera* by Lutz ('12) and Stomps ('12), and later found in *Drosophila* (Bridges, '21), *Datura* (Blakeslee, '22) and some other forms.

demonstration of the determinative action of the chromosomes and also is important from a cytological point of view. In *Œnothera* the 21-chromosome triploids ("*semi-gigas*" mutants) are intermediate in character (as in number of chromosomes) between *gigas* and the parent form, *lamarckiana;* and DeVries has shown that they are closely similar to, if not identical with, actual hybrids between these two forms, which of course likewise have 21 chromosomes. The *semi-gigas* mutants are not, however, hybrids in the usual sense; for they have arisen in pure cultures both of *lamarckiana* and of *lata* as well as in crosses between *lata* and *lamarckiana* (Lutz, '12, Stomps, '12). They produce highly variable offspring (Lutz, '12), in this respect differing from *gigas* and agreeing with the 15-chromosome *lata*-types, presently to be described. In this case the chromosome-distribution seems not to have been worked out; but in the closely similar 21-chromosome hybrids it has been found to vary widely. In the hybrid *gigas* × *lata*, Gates ('09) found the distribution usually to be 10 and 11, occasionally 9 and 12. Geerts ('11) found in the same hybrids, on the other hand, that only seven of the chromosomes reach each pole, the remaining seven lagging on the spindle and degenerating—a difference possibly due, as Gates indicates, to a difference of season. The cytological facts are much clearer in a *triploid Canna* (Belling, '21) and in *Datura* (Belling and Blakeslee, '22) in both of which the homologous chromosomes regularly conjugate to form trivalents of the haploid number (9 in the former case, 12 in the latter). These regularly disjoin in the first division, passing two and one to opposite poles, quite like the *m*-trivalent of *Metapodius* (p. 876). Since there is no correlation between the position of different trivalents with respect to the poles, various combinations are thus produced by the heterotypic division; *e. g.*, in *Canna* 18 + 9, 17 + 10, etc., up to 14 + 13; and in *Datura* 24 + 12, 23 + 13, etc., to 18 + 18. A remarkable demonstration is here offered of the free or random assortment of chromosomes; and the same is equally true of the pollen-formation in the triploid and tetraploid Daturas as recently described by the same observers.[1]

A large and growing body of evidence of the same general type is derived from mutants which show one or more supernumerary chromosomes as compared with the parent forms. Among the most widely known of these cases are the so-called "*lata*-types," so called from De Vries's 15-chromosome mutant *Œnothera lata*, known to have arisen from a 14-chromosome form, probably by non-disjunction. Such forms, of which a considerable number are now known,[2] are of course cytologically unbalanced (like the analogous forms among hybrids) and in meiosis show a corresponding

[1] See p. 567.
[2] Literature in Gates, '12, '20, Lutz, '17, etc.)

asymmetry of chromosome-distribution. Though the phenomena are still incompletely known (owing to difficulties that may here be disregarded), the work of Gates and Thomas ('14) and others seems to leave no doubt that the segregation tends towards an 8+7 distribution, though it may be 9+6 (perhaps other numbers). Self-fertilization of such 15-chromosome forms should therefore give inconstant offspring, with three main classes having 14, 15, or 16 chromosomes; and this is borne out by the facts.

The striking genetic instability of these mutants was emphasized by De-Vries and confirmed by all later observers; and this has been shown by several observers to be correlated with differences of chromosome-number in the offspring. When self-fertilized the *lata*-form (derived from *lamarckiana*) produces not only many *lata* offspring (8 + 7 chromosomes) but also a large proportion of *lamarckiana* (7 + 7 chromosomes) and smaller numbers of other mutants of several types.[1] It is evident that the *lamarckiana* forms result from the union of two 7-chromosome gametes, the *lata* from the union of 7- and 8-chromosome gametes. The fact that self-fertilized *latas* produce many *lamarckianas* seems clearly to indicate that the *lata*-form is produced directly by the new equilibrium induced by presence of the odd or extra chromosome, *i. e.*, by the trisomic condition of this chromosome in conjunction with the disomic condition of the others; since the *lata* characters disappear on restoration of the normal number.

Since any chromosome-pair (presumably) might undergo non-disjunction we should expect to find 15-chromosome forms of several different genetic types, and such is actually the case. Lutz found 7 such types in addition to typical *lata*. A remarkable example of the same thing is offered by mutants of the Jimson weed (*Datura stramonium*) in which the normal diploid number of chromosomes is 24. Blakeslee ('20) has found twelve distinct 25-chromosome mutants of this species which produce pollen-grains having either 12 or 13 chromosomes. It seems almost certain that each of the twelve mutations has been associated with the triplication of a different chromosome (presumably due to non-disjunction) and that a way may here be opened for the identification of the particular chromosomes concerned in each case.

The foregoing facts indicate that disturbances of the normal equilibrium by changes in the number of the chromosomes may be *per se* a cause of mutation; and further, that whenever such changes produce an odd number one may look for genetic instability in the offspring.

6. The Genetic Phenomena in Chromosome-linkage and Non-disjunction

A crucial demonstration of the determinative action of the chromosomes is given by the heredity of sex and of sex-linked X-borne characters of

---

[1] See especially Bartlett ('15), Gates ('08, '15), Gates and Thomas ('14), Lutz ('17).

Drosophila in cases of non-disjunction and XX-linkage. Both these cases offer definite exceptions to the so-called "criss-cross" type of sex-linked heredity, in which the sons are like their mothers and the daughters like their fathers. To recall this type of heredity, if a female homozygous for a recessive sex-linked character,[1] such as white eye or yellow body-color, be fertilized by a normal or "wild" male, XY, having the corresponding dominant, all the daughters (xX) will show the dominant color of the father (red-eye or yellow body) and all the sons (xY) the recessive color of the mother. This is because the single x-chromosome of the sons is in fertilization derived from the mother (Fig. 443) while the daughters (xX) receive one X from each parent, the recessive one (x) being dominated by the normal paternal (X). In the two exceptional cases under consideration this rule is reversed—regularly in XX-linkage, in a certain small percentage in non-disjunction—the sons being like their fathers and the daughters like their mothers. Both cases find a very simple explanation in the behavior of the sex-chromosomes, as was first made evident by Bridges' brilliant studies on non-disjunction (p. 877).

The subject may be most conveniently approached by considering the somewhat simpler phenomena in XX-linkage (p. 880) more recently discovered by L. V. Morgan ('22) in a certain strain of *Drosophila* showing the recessive sex-linked character yellow body-color. This strain shows a constant and complete reversal of the expected criss-cross heredity, homozygous yellow females (xx) mated to normal gray males (XY) giving regularly yellow daughters and gray sons. Cytological examination proved that the diploid chromosome group of every female shows, in place of a normal pair of separate rod-shaped x-chromosomes, a single v. Most females show also a supernumerary Y-chromosome (recognizable by its non-terminal attachment), as in Fig. 415, and a very few show one normal X in addition to the v. All this at once becomes clear under the assumption that the v represents two rod-shaped x's, attached at one end, which do not disjoin in the reduction-division. For, evidently, in the usual case the meiosis of such yellow females [v (=xx) Y] produces mature eggs having either v (xx) or Y; and when fertilized by the sperm of a normal fly (XY) bearing the dominant gray body-color, the result should be as actually observed:

(1) Egg v (=xx) + sperm Y = v (=xx) Y, (yellow ♀)
(2) Egg Y   + sperm X =   XY   (normal, gray ♂).

[1] In the following formulas x denotes the sex-chromosome bearing a recessive and X that bearing the corresponding dominant.

There should be two additional classes, namely:

(3) Egg v (=xx) + sperm X = v (= xx) X   (trisomic gray ♀).
(4) Egg Y   + sperm Y = YY   ?

Of these, class 3 is of low viability and rarely survives; but its existence is proved by the occasional presence of one free x besides the v. Class 4 appears to be completely non-viable, as Bridges showed to be the case in non-disjunction.

The demonstration here is complete that it is not the sperm or egg as a whole that determines sex but the X-chromosome. The Y-class of sperm, normally "male-producing," becomes female-producing if it fertilizes an

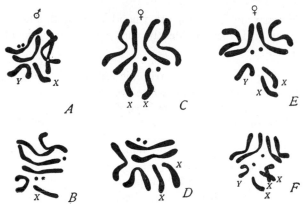

Fig. 445.—Supernumerary chromosomes due to non-disjunction in *Drosophila melanogaster* (BRIDGES).

A, B, normal diploid groups (spermatogonia) of ♂ composition *XY; C, D,* normal diploid groups of ♀, composition *XX; E,* female diploid groups of the composition *XXY; F,* female diploid group of the compostion *XXXY.*

egg which contains two X's. Conversely, the X-class of sperm, normally "female-producing," becomes male-producing if it enters an egg of the Y-class. *Sex, therefore, is not predetermined in the gametes as such, but is determined by the chromosome-combination established at the time of karyogamy.*

Precisely the same demonstration is offered by the facts in non-disjunction. Bridges discovered a certain definite strain which regularly throws about 4% of exceptions to criss-cross heredity; and he demonstrated that these exceptions are due to a non-disjunction of the two X-chromosomes of the female that is itself due to the presence of a suprenumerary Y-chromosome in the diploid groups (Fig. 445). A female homozygous for a sex-linked recessive character (*e. g.*, white-eye or vermilion-eye) has therefore the constitution xxY (p. 946); and in meiosis should produce four types of mature eggs, according to varying groupings of the triad-components and to varying positions on the spindle, as follows:

Polocyte	$\dfrac{xY}{x}$	$\dfrac{x}{xY}$	$\dfrac{Y}{xx}$	$\dfrac{xx}{Y}$
Egg				

Of these classes, the first two, x and xY, are produced by a normal disjunction of the xx-pair, and should give normal criss-cross heredity, thus:

(1) Egg   x + sperm X = xX   red-eye ♀
(2) Egg   x + sperm Y = xY   white-eye ♂
(3) Egg xY + sperm X = xXY red-eye ♀
(4) Egg xY + sperm Y = xYY white-eye ♂

The egg-classes xx and Y, on the other hand, result from a non-disjunction of the xx-pair; and it is these, evidently, that give the exceptional non-criss-cross cases, thus:

(5) Egg xx + sperm X = xxX trisomic red-eye ♀   (missing)
(6) Egg xx + sperm Y = xxY white-eye ♀
(7) Egg Y + sperm X = XY red-eye ♂
(8) Egg Y + sperm Y = YY   ?   (missing)

The two missing classes are probably non-viable. The sixth and seventh show white-eyed daughters and red-eyed sons, or non criss-cross heredity.

Here again it is clear that the Y-bearing sperm, normally male-producing, becomes female-producing if it enter an egg containing two X-chromosomes (as in case 6) and in like manner that the x-bearing sperm, normally female-producing, becomes male-producing if it enter an egg containing no x-chromosome (case 7). The result therefore *depends on the chromosome-combination*, however it be established, since the remainder of the cell-system, so far as can be determined, is the same in both cases.

7. Deficiency. Duplication

We mention finally two other correlated types of mutation discovered by Bridges which strikingly illustrate the correlation between the genetic and the cytological phenomena. In neither case has the cytological basis of the phenomena been sufficiently worked out; but cytological conditions of similar type are well-known in other cases (p. 932).

In deficiency the genetic phenomena (Bridges '17, '19) show a failure to transmit a certain group of genes or characters which points to the inactivation or complete loss of a measurable section of a chromosome. This condition is usually if not always lethal, and in the case of sex-linked characters (*e. g.*, in the neighborhood of the mutant "bar" in *Drosophila*), can only be preserved through heterozygous females, in which the lethal effect is counteracted by the presence of a second, normal X-chromosome. The reality of the interpretation in this case is shown by the fact that *no crossing-over takes place in the region of the deficiency* and also by the fact that recessive characters (such as "forked") whose loci lie opposite to the deficient region show themselves in heterozygous females. So far as its active components are concerned, therefore, the chromosome concerned is shortened by the length of the deficient region. Though this has not actually been seen in *Drosophila* the correctness of the interpretation can hardly be questioned when we consider such observations as those of Hance on the fragmentation of chromosomes by cross division (pp. 878, 879) and especially the conclusions of Robertson and of Carothers concerning the origin of heteromorphic bivalents (p. 932).

Duplication offers a condition that is the converse of deficiency and is probably correlated with it. Bridges ('17) found, for example, that certain individuals of *Drosophila* behaved genetically as though a piece of one X-chromosome, normally lying near the middle of the chromosome, had become detached (thus producing a deficiency) and then attached to *one end* of the other X-chromosome, duplicating the normal corresponding region near the middle of that chromosome. In another case the facts seem to show that a piece taken from the second chromosome has become interpolated in the middle of the third chromosome.[1] In these cases the complementary character of deficiency and duplication is clearly seen, and is closely analogous to the relation between supernumerary and missing whole chromosomes due to non-disjunction (p. 872). It is also clear that duplication is only a form of chromosome-linkage (p. 879), though one of the linked components is only part of a chromosome. Both deficiency and duplication illustrate remarkably the practical value of the chromosome-interpretation in the analysis of genetic phenomena which under any other interpretation seem unintelligible.

III. RECOMBINATION PHENOMENA. CROSSING–OVER AND THE CHIASMATYPE THEORY

Introduction

The recombination of factors displayed in the offspring is of two types which differ widely in their mechanism. In a mixed population, heterozygous in respect to a certain number of units, new combinations of these units are continually arising both by random assortment and by crossing, which bring together chromosomes differing in respect to one or more units.

---

[1] Reported in Morgan ('19).

Sutton had in mind only recombinations of this type, which may be called *chromosomal;* but we now see that the results thus produced are no more than recombinations of *linkage-groups*. Of widely different type are recombinations which involve a partial dissolution and re-formation of the linkage-groups themselves—a process now believed to take place during the side-by-side association of homologous chromosomes or synaptic mates during their conjugation in meiosis. This may be called *chromomeric* in contradistinction to the chromosomal type of recombination. Its recognition has largely been due to the work of Morgan and his co-workers, by whom this form of recombination has been called "crossing-over"; but Correns, De-Vries and Strasburger had earlier offered a general interpretation of somewhat similar nature.

It is essential to keep clearly in mind the fact that recombinations of the second type take place *only between homologous linkage groups* or, in cytological terms, between homologous chromosomes or synaptic mates; and from the standpoint of the chromosome-theory this can only mean that it involves *an exchange of material between these chromosomes*. If, for instance, AB be two dominant sex-linked units derived from one parent and *ab* the corresponding recessive units from the other parent, the hybrid offspring will have the composition ABab. The gametes of these hybrids (as proved by the characters of the grandchildren) are for the most part the same as those of their parents, *i. e., AB* and *ab;* but along with these may appear also a certain number of the new combinations *Ab* and *aB*. The original linkage-groups *AB* and *ab* must therefore in some cases have been split apart and re-combined by an exchange of corresponding factors. The phenomenon becomes more striking when a larger number of units is concerned. When, for instance, one parent contributes the linkage-group *ABCD*, and the other the allelomorphic group *abcd*, the diploid group of the hybrid offspring will be $\dfrac{ABCD}{abcd}$. When inbred these hybrids produce offspring which may show not only this combination, but also in a certain percentage of cases $\dfrac{abCD}{ABcd}, \dfrac{AbcD}{aBCd}, \dfrac{abCD}{ABcd}$, etc. Here it is plain that new groups of unit-factors have been formed equivalent to the original ones but differing from them in the replacement of certain units by corresponding ones derived from the allelomorphic group. Such a result, obviously, must be due to some definite and orderly process of give and take between the linkage-groups (chromosomes), in which a *quid pro quo* is always rendered. Evidently this process leaves the original *unit*-pairs unchanged, so that considered individually each such pair will conjugate and disjoin in accordance with Mendel's first law, and irrespective of the behavior of other units.

That the exchanges are actually of this type is fully established by genetic evidence, especially in the case of *Drosophila*, but their cytological mechanism is not yet certainly known. DeVries ('03) clearly indicated that the exchange of units probably takes place between homologous maternal and paternal chromosomes or spireme-threads when lying side by side in synapsis. Such an hypothesis, evidently, involves the four following assumptions or postulates (Figs. 447–450).

(1) The synaptic mates (homologous spireme-threads or chromosomes) must lie side-by-side, in parasynaptic association.

(2) The unit-factors must lie in serial order in the threads.

(3) Homologous or allelomorphic units, maternal and paternal respectively, must lie opposite one another; consequently,

(4) In both synaptic mates the individual units must lie *in the same serial order and at corresponding distances.*

The second of these assumptions is identical with that which formed the basis of Roux's general interpretation of mitosis (1883). The third was first advocated by Correns ('02) in his attempt to explain the recombination-phenomena generally. Assuming the allelomorphic units ("Anlagen") to lie in pairs and in serial alignment, as in the diagram (Fig. 446), crossing over then becomes readily explicable by the assumption that one or more of the unit-pairs may rotate on the longitudinal axis so as to reverse their original position. Through such a process, evidently, any recombination of maternal and paternal units might arise.

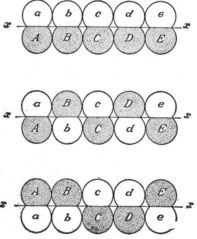

Fig. 446.—Correns' diagram of crossing-over by rotation. The unmodified synaptic mates above, with different types of exchange below.

This simple construction falls in line with cytological observations which show that parasynapsis is often followed by so close a union of the synaptic mates that they appear externally as a single thread (p. 569). Correns failed, however, to take account of the chromosomes as such (and hence to explain the linkage-groups) and also failed to recognize the necessity of assuming a constant serial order of units in the threads, without which many of the most important of the data as now known are inexplicable. DeVries, on the other hand, clearly recognized all of the essential postulates

without attempting to explain the precise mechanism. In his own words: [1]
"Shortly before their separation the chromosomes lie together in pairs,
always one in the paternal pronucleus (*i. e.*, of paternal origin) united with
the corresponding thread of the maternal pronucleus. . . . We consider
that the structure of the nuclear threads is such that it not only makes
possible, but regulates and dominates the relations of the two pronuclei. . . .
We assume that the individual units in the stretched threads lie in the
same numerical order; then, when the threads are closely appressed lengthwise, in pairs, we can imagine that all the like units of the two pronuclei lie

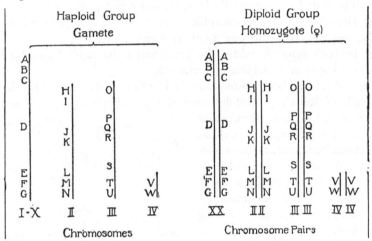

Fig. 447.—Diagram of serial alignment of unit-factors or genes in the chromosomes of the haploid
and diploid groups.

opposite each other. . . . If the two like units lie opposite each other at any
given moment, we may assume a simple exchange of them." [2] (Figs. 447, 448.)
The distribution of these exchanges along the thread DeVries considered to
be a matter of chance, so that "all kinds of new combinations of paternal
and maternal units may occur in the two pronuclei, and when these separate
at the formation of the sexual cells each of them will harbor in part paternal, in part maternal units. These combinations must be governed by the
laws of probability, and from these calculations may be derived which lead
to the explanation of the relations of affinity between the children and
their parents, the grandchildren and their grandparents."

Finally, however: "Every unit can be exchanged only for a like one—

[1] Quoted from Gager's translation ('10) of the Haarlem address. The passage is here considerably
abbreviated.

[2] Throughout his discussion DeVries employs the word "pronucleus" to designate a haploid nucleus, or one of the two haploid chromosome-groups that are mingled to form a diploid nucleus.
This is to be regretted, since it obscures his otherwise clear statements. (*Cf.* p. 928).

which means for one which, in the other pronucleus, represents the same hereditary character. . . . For the children must inherit all specific characters from their parents, and they must also transmit all of them to their own progeny. The exchange must hence be accomplished in such a way that every pronucleus (*i. e.*, haploid group) retains the entire series of units of all the specific characters, and this result can evidently be obtained only when the interchange is limited to like units." [1] DeVries, like Weismann, considered the "essential purpose" of sexual reproduction to be the increase of variability and the power of individual adaptation; and this may be effected, in his view, by the exchange of individual units "and thus cause the creation of those countless combinations of characters of which nature is in need in order to make species as plastic as possible and to enable

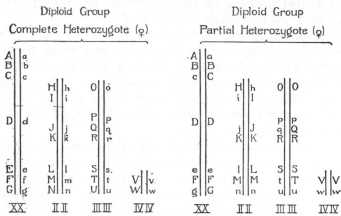

Fig. 448.—Diagram of serial alignment of unit-pairs (allelomorphs) in the chromosomes of a heterozygous form with four pairs of chromosomes, including *XX*.

them to adapt themselves in the highest degree to their ever changing environment." Here, DeVries, in teleological language, seeks to bring his recombination-theory into relation with the theory of natural selection, adaptation and evolution.

A little later Strasburger emphasized especially the importance of the spinning out of the nuclear substance into spireme-threads as a process which not alone aligns the nuclear units in linear series in the spireme-threads for meristic division but also adjusts them for orderly exchanges during the association of maternal and paternal elements in synapsis.[2] "I assume that these units (pangens) succeed one another in *fixed order* in the separate chromosomes and that they there divide by the products passing into the longitudinal halves of the chromosomes." [3] When ho-

[1] *Op. cit.*, pp. 241--244.   [2] '05, '08, '09.   [3] '09, p. 114.

mologous maternal and paternal threads place themselves side-by-side in synapsis they undergo the same degree of elongation. "As a result of equal elongation of the two members a pair of homologous ids (units) take up corresponding positions in them; they lie opposite one another. . . . The juxtaposition of homologous ids thus brought about is adapted to facilitate the interaction and thus seems to me to offer an especially desirable basis for an insight into the processes that are here theoretically to be expected." [1] The principal advance beyond these earlier results was the discovery, due to Morgan and his collaborators,[2] that the exchange of allelomorphic units rarely if ever affects a single pair alone, but *groups of factors,*—whole pieces, as it were, of the original linkage-groups—in which the units *retain their serial order.* The only explanation thus far offered of this fact is that provided by the *chiasmatype* theory of Janssens and Morgan, which will now briefly be considered.

The Chiasmatype Theory. The basis for a more adequate cytological interpretation of crossing-over was first provided by Janssens' theory of the *chiasmatype* ('09) as elaborated by Morgan and his co-workers. Unfortunately this ingenious theory, though it may be correct in principle, still rests upon an inadequate cytological basis; it was, indeed, founded originally upon what now seems to have been a misinterpretation of certain cytological appearances.[3]

In its simplest form the chiasmatype-theory assumes that crossing-over results from three events: (1) a spiral twisting about each other of the synaptic mates, lying side-by-side, during the strepsinema stage (Fig. 273); (2) a fusion (chiasma) of the two threads at certain points where they cross each other as a result of the twisting; (3) a subsequent *straight* longitudinal splitting apart of the threads at these points. The result of such a process, evidently (as will appear from the diagrams, Figs. 449, 450), would be an exchange of corresponding pieces or regions, longer or shorter according to the character of the torsion and the distance between the points of fusion. Obviously such a process would leave unimpaired the integrity of the threads as such, since the loss of any particular region is simultaneously made good by the substitution of an homologous region. Janssens offered only a very general statement of the genetic bearings of his theory which were later worked out in a most remarkable manner by the investigators of *Drosophila.*

Janssens' conclusions were based wholly on cytological studies, originally ('09) on the bivalent chromosomes of Amphibia and later ('19) on those

---

[1] '08, p. 564.
[2] See Morgan, Sturtevant, Muller and Bridges ('23), Morgan ('19), etc.
[3] Cf. footnote, p. 960.

of Orthoptera, which led him to indicate two types of chiasma-formation as follows:

The first or "two strand chiasma," will readily be understood from Janssens' diagrams, here reproduced with slight modification (Figs. 451, 452). The tetrad is here assumed to have arisen from two originally parallel threads, each longitudinally split, and twisted or bent upon each other, so as to form an X-shaped figure. Two of the four threads, or strands, were assumed to fuse at the point of crossing to form an anastomosis or "chiasma," followed by a straight split across this point, in such a manner as to leave a piece from each side connected with one from the opposite side

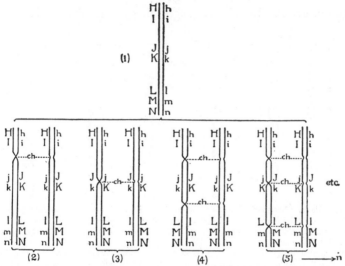

Fig. 449.—Diagram of a single heterozygous chromosome-pair showing various forms of crossing over according to the chiasmatype-theory.

1, the primary parasynaptic pairing, allelomorphs indicated by letters; 2 and 3, single crossovers at different levels; 4, double and 5 triple cross-overs.

(Fig. 451, D–F). Such a process, evidently, would lead to an exchange of equal and corresponding regions of two of the four threads (chromatids), so that two of the resulting threads would be "cross-overs" or recombinations while two would be unmodified. This type was considered by Janssens as the most frequent, but he also recognized the possibility of a second one, the "four-strand chiasma," in which all four of the threads might undergo this process, so as to give cross-overs in all four of the spermatids (Figs. 451, A–C, 452).

The foregoing two types were based on facts observed in the urodeles (*Triton, Batrachoseps*); but the existence of a third type was there indicated which in Janssens' latest papers (19a, 19b), based on a study of the Orthoptera, is given an important place. In this case it was assumed that the chiasmatype occurred in a tetrad of the double or multiple ring-type as described in the works of many students of the Orthoptera (Sutton, Granata, McClung, and others), of which an account has earlier been given (p. 527). Here (as may more readily be understood from the diagrams, Fig. 453, than from a description) the plane of cleavage is assumed, as before, to cut longitudinally through the tetrad in a single plane; and owing to the alternations of successive rings in planes at right angles to one another (*cf.* p. 959), this cleavage passes in every other ring through the equational split, and in the alternate rings through the plane which separates the synaptic mates. In this case, accordingly, the division is equational

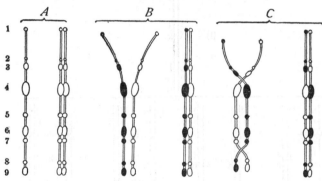

Fig. 450.—Diagram comparing mitosis, synapsis and crossing-over. The figures symbolize spireme-threads containing serially arranged components which may stand for either chromomeres, chromioles, or Mendelian units (genes, etc.) These components are assumed to be qualitatively different and to be placed in definite serial order.

A, simple longitudinal fission (mitosis); *B*, side-by-side conjugation of homologous pairs (parasynapsis) without crossing-over; *C*, the same with two cross-overs.

in some regions, reductional in others; and is followed by a second division of the same mixed type. Were this result correct, two maturation-divisions, obviously would be necessary to effect complete disjunction of all the synaptic mates or allelomorphs.

The principle involved in Janssens' ingenious interpretations has been applied on a grand scale by Morgan and his associates to the Mendelian analysis;[1] and in their hands the chiasmatype-theory has proved itself a powerful instrument of genetic research. We can here only touch on one or two of the most interesting features of the development that it has undergone. The most important, perhaps, relates to variations in the so-called "strength of linkage" between different units of the same group. A "cross-

[1] References at p. 928.

over" (or chiasma), obviously leads to a breakage of linkage within the linear group (spireme). Accepting the chiasmatype-theory, it is obvious that the number of cross-overs between the two members of any pair of associated chromosomes will depend on the nature of the twisting, and the

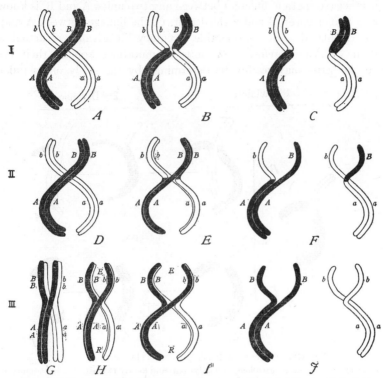

Fig. 451.—Diagrams illustrating the chiasmatype-theory (I and II, after JANSSENS).

I. The "four-strand" chiasma; two double threads (synaptic mates), twisted about each other (A) come into contact, fuse and split apart straight through the fusion-point (B), giving four cross-over chromatids (C).

II. The "two-strand" cross-over, fusion and splitting apart of only two of the four threads (D, E), giving two cross-over chromatids (F).

III. Corresponding figures, showing their origin and mode of division without torsion or chiasma-formation.

points at which fusions take place. It was pointed out especially by Sturtevant ('13) that, other things equal, the chance of chiasma-formation between any two given points in the thread would increase with the distance by which they are separated. The number of cross-overs between such points may thus, with certain qualifications,[1] be used as *a measure of the dis-*

---

[1] Crossing over has been found to be affected by temperature (Plough, '17), age (Bridges, '15, Plough *op. cit.*), and the action of X-rays (Mavor and Svenson, '23).

tance between them; or, to state the matter differently, variations in the strength of linkage between different units may be interpreted in terms of their relative distances and positions in the linear series of the spireme-thread. The practical value of this is demonstrated by the fact that when the distance (strength of linkage) between any two units, A and B, is known, and also that between B and a third unit, C, the linkage between A and C may be calculated with considerable accuracy in advance of actual ob-servation. When, therefore, new units or mutations appear, their posi-tion in the series may readily be determined by the study of its linkage

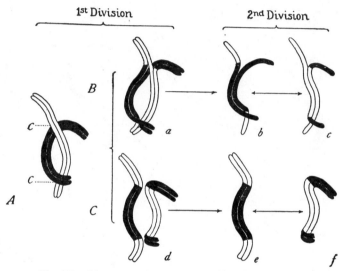

Fig. 452.—Diagrams of double cross-overs (JANSSENS).

A, a pair of synaptic mates, each longitudinally split, and loosely twisted; *B*, a two-strand cross-over at each point of contact, giving *b* and *c; C*, corresponding figures of four-strand cross-over.

with other units of known position. By this ingenious method it has been found possible, in case of *Drosophila*, to construct chromosome-diagrams or maps in which the serial alignment and relative distances of more than 150 unit-factors have been determined.[1] These maps are in principle akin to the structural diagrams of the organic chemist and fulfill a similar function. Whether they are to be taken literally at their face value is a question of method rather than of fact. The important thing is that the conceptions which they embody have made clear a vast number of genetic phenomena otherwise mysterious: and the genetic working method which they provide has proved superior to all others in respect to simplicity, efficiency and wide-

[1] See the frontispiece of *The Mechanism of Mendelian Heredity*, by Morgan, Sturtevant, Müller, and Bridges ('23) in which 50 of these units are plotted.

ness of range. Unfortunately the same cannot yet be said of its cytological basis; for the cytological facts at present seem more in accordance with a much simpler interpretation based on the observations of many investigators of meiosis, including especially the Schreiners ('06) and many students of meiosis in the insects.[1]

These observations prove conclusively that the apparent crossing-over of two of the four threads in such cases as Figs. 451, 452 involves in itself no chiasma and secondary splitting, but results simply from the separation of the four-strand thread or rod, from one end along one plane, and from the other end along the other plane, as has earlier been explained (Figs. 254,

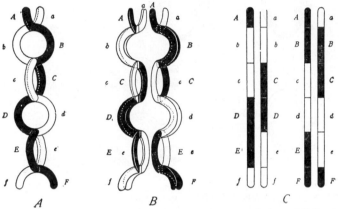

Fig. 453.—Diagram of Janssens' interpretation of the compound rings of Orthoptera (after Janssens).

A, the ring-series in perspective, synaptic mates in black and white; B, its first division, the second following in the plane of the paper; C, the four classes of mixed spermatids resulting from such a division.

257). In later stages such figures do not break apart at the point of crossing; on the contrary the four threads draw apart and separate without loss of their identity. A similar explanation applies to the various other figures of this type, including the double crosses, the double rings, etc. (Fig. 454). Robertson even goes so far as to suggest that the twisted appearance of the strepsinema so often described may in some cases be an illusion produced by successive alternating regions of separation along the two respective planes of cleavage; but this almost certainly goes too far. In any case it is clear that the original basis on which Janssens founded his theory is still insufficiently based. So remarkably, nevertheless, does the hypothesis fit the genetic facts that we are almost compelled to accept the correctness

---

[1] See especially Robertson ('16), Wenrich ('16), Mohr ('16), Wilson and Morgan ('20).

of the principle involved, and to seek an explanation in some process of torsion and splitting at an earlier stage of maturation.[1]

We are led to look for this in the synaptic period of meiosis by both genetic and cytological results. The experimental researches of Plough ('17) on the effect of temperature on crossing-over give strong ground to conclude that the process does in fact take place in the early stages, near the time of meiosis. As earlier indicated (p. 555), a considerable number of observers (Janssens included) have described or figured the leptotene-threads as twisting together during synapsis to form the pachytene; and

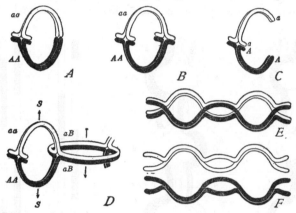

Fig. 454.—Diagrams of single rings (A, B), of their relations to double crosses (C), and to double (D) and multiple (E) rings; F, mode of division of multiple ring.

the latter, often apparently undivided for a time, afterwards undergoes a nearly straight longitudinal split. The evidence for the synaptic twisting is, however, still dubious, while the assumption that the cleft that produces the diplotene cuts straight through a synaptic spiral in the manner demanded by Janssens' theory is almost wholly unsupported by well-determined cytological facts. The same may be said for the later changes which follow the strepsinema, nearly all observers having found that the spiral simply untwists during the later stages (diakinesis, metaphase) without any visible process of fusion and secondary splitting.[2]

To the author, all seems to point to the conclusion that the mechanism

[1] I much regret that Professor Janssens' new extended memoir "*La chiasmatypie dans les insectes*" (*La Cellule* XXXIV), is received too late for more than a very brief mention. In this important work its author reiterates and extends his earlier conclusions, emphasizing particularly his interpretation of the double crosses and double rings in accordance with the chiasmatype theory. If the work does not set aside the doubts expressed above and in an earlier critique (Wilson and Morgan, '20), it makes known a great number of interesting observations which demand the most attentive study.

[2] Gates, in a very recent work ('21) on *Lactuca*, seems inclined to accept a chiasmatypy at this time, but gets no further than a hypothetical statement, admitting that no "demonstrable evidence" of it exists.

of crossing-over must be sought in the pachytene stage during the period following synapsis when the two synaptic mates are so closely associated as often to give the appearance of a single, undivided thread. The possibility has earlier been indicated (p. 555) that the two conjugants may in fact fuse into one without destroying the identity of the two linear series of smaller units originally contained within them. The genetic evidence— above all the orderly exchange of *groups* of unit-factors between the linkage-groups, and the phenomena of "interference"—leads almost irresistibly to the conclusion that crossing-over must involve some process of torsion and subsequent splitting apart of the two series. It does not seem too much to hope that it may be found practicable to observe directly some such process in the pachytene and early diplotene stages; but we must admit that on its cytological side the problem still remains unsolved.[1]

The difficulties here encountered by the chiasmatype-theory have led to certain attempts to explain crossing-over in a different way. Here belong the reduplication-theory of Bateson and Punnett (Bateson, '09) and the hypothesis of variable force of Goldschmidt ('17); both of which are purely theoretical constructions.[2] Seiler[3] has discussed the possibility of a partial explanation based on the phenomena of linkage, disjunction and recombination already referred to in the case of *Lymantria monacha* and *Solenobia pineti* (p. 883). In the first of these cases four of the chromosome-pairs become linked during the maturation-process, to form a compound element.

In a hybrid heterozygous for such a group, *e. g.*, $\frac{ABCD}{abcd}$, the grouping might take place in various ways, $\frac{AbcD}{ABCd}$, etc., thus giving corresponding recombinations *in the linkage group*, similar to those produced by chiasmatypy. In *Solenobia pineti* different races or strains differ in respect to the linkage, which is absent in the 32-chromosome race, partial in the 31-race and complete in the 30-race (p. 883), the random assortment of these pairs varying accordingly. In a mixed hybrid population of the three races would appear corresponding variations of the linkage groups somewhat analogous to those due to chiasmatypy. Goldschmidt ('23) has tried to carry this further in a study of *Lymantria dispar*, showing that the 31 bivalents of this species are in the prophases associated to form 9 or 10 linear aggregates which persist as such more or less distinctly up to the heterotypic division, when the tetrads are again separate. Since the chromosomes in general are themselves linear aggregates (p. 906) the possibility is thus suggested of recombination-phenomena due to varying modes in the assembling of the chromosomes of

---

[1] *Cf*. Morgan and Wilson ('20).
[2] For critiques of these conceptions, see Morgan ('19), Bridges ('17).
[3] '23, Seiler and Hanel, '21.

hybrids by linear aggregation of smaller components. All this is too vague and hypothetical to be of much present value, though the temporary linear aggregation of chromosomes in the heterotypic prophases is a highly interesting fact (p. 566).

It is a singular fact that in some cases "crossing-over" takes place only in the homozygous or homogametic sex; e. g., in the females of *Drosophila* (Morgan) or in the males of Lepidoptera (Tanaka).[1] The explanation of this is not known; but a clue may possibly be found in the different behavior of the sex-chromosomes in the auxocytes of the digametic sex (p. 758). Thus far, however, this fact goes no further than to show that sex, when once established, may react in a specific manner upon the chromosomes. The question is made more puzzling by the fact that in some forms crossing-over seems to take place in both sexes.[2] Another interesting fact, discovered by Nabours in *A potettix* is that crossing-over takes place as freely in *parthenogenetic* heterozygous females as in those resulting from fertilization. This must mean that synapsis and a reduction division occur; and Nabours found that after such segregation the F_2 parthenogenetic generation was homozygous for the characters concerned. Unfortunately the cytological conditions are not yet known, and it is even doubtful whether the offspring are haploid or diploid. In either case the case offers no special difficulty. This is obvious if parthenogenesis be of the haploid type, since the egg has undergone complete meiosis. If, as is more likely, it be diploid, the most probable conjecture is that after complete reduction a secondary doubling takes place, by an additional equation-division, or by a reunion of the second polar nucleus with the egg-nucleus such as has been observed in the parthenogenesis of several other forms (pp. 477, 962).

Leaving these particular cases it may be said finally that for the present the chiasmatype-theory can hardly be regarded as more than a working method, one that is in the highest degree fruitful if it be not indispensable, but nevertheless on its cytological side insecurely based. Apart from all questions of the particular mechanism of "crossing-over" the evidence is irresistible that somehow during the process of meiosis orderly exchanges of material between the synaptic mates take place. The facts indicate, further, that this process occurs at only a single point in the life-cycle, the integrity of the chromosomes being strictly preserved at other times. To whatever extent this process may go the post-synaptic chromosomes are not precisely the same individuals as before. Once more, therefore, we may cite Boveri's comparison of the conjugation of chromosomes to the conju-

---

[1] See Sturtevant, '15.

[2] *E. g.*, in rats (Castle and Wright, Sturtevant, '15); in the grasshoppers *A potettix* (Nabours, '19); and in the sporogenesis of *Primula* (Gregory, '11).

gation of ciliate Infusoria (p. 925), and emphasize the conclusion that the chromosome is not an absolutely unchanging structure. It is an assemblage of smaller units or genes which vary in tactical formation not alone from species to species but also more narrowly from individual to individual within the species.

It is clear, finally, that as applied to the chromosomes considered as wholes the old distinction between the "reduction-division" and the "equation-division" breaks down in so far as the process of crossing-over takes place. As applied to the smaller units aligned within the spireme-threads the distinction retains its full force. In this respect our modern views on the subject, different as they otherwise are, approach those of Weismann (p. 502); but all this, in the writer's view, serves to render the doctrine of the individuality or genetic continuity of chromosomes more acceptable rather than less.

IV. ADDITIONAL EVIDENCE

We here append certain additional data of importance for the chromosome-theory.

1. Evidence from Certain Reciprocal Crosses

An interesting demonstration of the determinative action of the chromosomes in development is afforded by certain cases of reciprocal crosses, in which the result differs according to which parental form is taken as the male or the female. The best known of these are the crosses between different species (and even genera) of sea-urchins already considered (p. 842).[1]

The pluteus larvæ of *Sphærechinus granularis* and *Paracentrotus* (*Strongylocentrotus*) *lividus* differ markedly both in form and in the structure of the skeleton (Fig. 456). The hybrid from *Sph.* ♀ × *Par.* ♂ develops into a normal pluteus, somewhat variable in type, but showing distinctly the influence of both parents (456, C). The reverse cross, *Par.* ♀ × *Sph.* ♂, is often more or less abnormal, but is always distinctly matriclinous in type and often purely maternal in appearance. An explanation of these facts, noticed more or less definitely by earlier observers (Vernon, Fischel, Doncaster, Herbst, etc.) was found by Baltzer ('09, '10) in the different behavior of the chromosomes in the two cases, which has been described at p. 843. In the first cross all the chromosomes from both parents take part equally in the development; hence the approximately equal effect of both parents on

---

[1] In considering these it is necessary to bear in mind the fact that the dominance of paternal or maternal characters in sea-urchin-larvæ varies considerably with external conditions, including seasonal changes possibly due to relative maturity of eggs and sperms (Vernon, '98, '00), temperature (Doncaster, '04, Vernon, '95, Herbst, '06, '07, etc., Tennent, '10) concentration of the sea-water (Vernon) or in its relative alkalinity, which may itself be dependent on season and temperature (Tennent ('10), and apparently to some extent also individual differences among the parental individuals. Such sources of error are not, however, here in question.

the hybrid larva. In the second cross all but 3 or 4 of the paternal (*Sphœ-rechinus*) chromosomes are eliminated during the first two cleavages (Fig. 455) while the full complement of maternal chromosomes (18) is preserved.

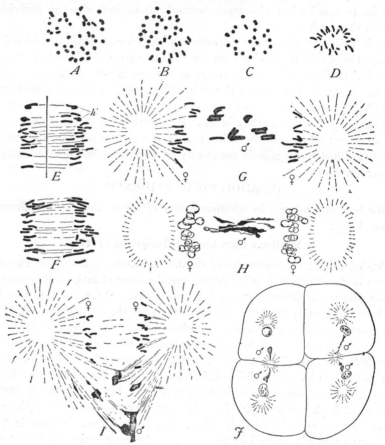

Fig. 455.—The chromosomes in reciprocal crosses of sea-urchins (Baltzer).

A, diploid group of *Sphœrechinus*, 40 chromosomes; *B*, diploid group from hybrid *Sphœrechinus* ♀ ✕ *Paracentrotus* ♂, 38 chromosomes (20 + 18); *C*, corresponding group from the reverse cross second cleavage, 22 chromosomes (18 + 4); *D*, diploid group from a blastula-cell of a similar hybrid, *Paracentrotus* ♀ ✕ *Sphœrechinus* ♂, 24 chromosomes (18 + 6); *E, F*, anaphase chromosomes of the first cross from two sections showing 38 chromosomes including two hook-shaped chromosomes *h* characteristic of *Paracentrotus; G, H*, anaphase and early telophase of the cross *Paracentrotus* ♀ ✕ *Sphaer.* ♂, showing eliminated chromosomes of latter (♂♂); *I*, similar view of *Arbacia* ♀ ✕ *Sphœrechinus* ♂; *J*, 4-cells stage of *Paracent.* ♀ ✕ *Sphaer.* ♂, eliminated chromatin at ♂♂.

The result is clearly evident in the size of the larval nuclei which, as is to be expected, are materially smaller in the second cross.[1]

[1] Tennent ('12) has observed a somewhat similar case in the cross *Toxopneustes* ✕ *Hipponöe*.

That the eliminated chromosomes are derived from the sperm-nucleus is proved by the following facts: (1) One pair of especially long chromosomes characteristic of *Sphærechinus* always appear when this form is taken as the ♀, but never in the reverse case; while in the latter two long hook-shaped chromosomes characteristic of *Paracentrotus* are always present. (2) In monospermic hybrid eggs the total number of normal daughter-chromosomes, counted in anaphase of the first (bipolar) cleavage is 42 44 (18 plus (3 or 4) × 2). In dispermic eggs of the same cross the number, counted in anaphases of the tetraster, is 52 or 53. The difference, which Baltzer reckons at 8, must be ascribed to the second sperm-nucleus (18 plus 8) × 2 = 52; hence each sperm-nucleus of *Sphærechinus* contributes at most but 4 of its 20 chromosomes. (3) The elimination may be observed in enucleated fragments of *Paracentrotus* eggs fertilized by *Sphærechinus* sperm, which proves conclusively that it is due to a lack of adjustment between most of the *Sphærechinus* chromosomes and the *Paracentrotus* cytoplasm. In the reverse cross all the *Paracentrotus* chromosomes are able to survive and perform their normal functions in the foreign cytoplasm.

Baltzer has studied a number of other reciprocal crosses among sea-urchins, most of which give results similar in principle, though the period of elimination varies considerably, in some cases taking place in the course of the first two cleavages, in others not until the blastula stage. Up to this time the blastulas appear quite normal and possess nuclei of normal size. They now undergo a period of temporary physiological disturbance after recovery from which the nuclei are much reduced in size and divide with a much smaller number of chromosomes. There is here no definite proof of the source of the eliminated chromosomes, but in view of the results already demonstrated, it may be concluded that in these cases, likewise, it is the paternal chromosomes that are cast out.

Taken as a whole these results afford fresh evidence of the qualitative difference of the chromosomes; for the fact that in several cases a nearly constant number of chromosomes are eliminated strongly indicates that these particular ones differ qualitatively from the others in their reaction to the foreign protoplasm. Still more important is the weight added by these facts to the conclusion that the chromosomes are a determinative factor in the development of the larvæ. The eliminated chromosomes, evidently, must include those which are necessary to the development of the distinctive paternal characters of the skeleton. Could these hybrids be reared to sexual maturity and reproduce themselves, the lost paternal characters should not reappear in the offspring, owing to complete loss of the eliminated chromosomes. In this respect, as Baltzer points out, these hybrids resemble the so-called "false hybrids" of Millardet, which show only the character of one parent, and breed true.[1]

2. The Combined Effects of Parthenogenetic Activation and Crossing

Results of the same type have been obtained by a preliminary activation of the egg by a parthenogenetic agent followed by its fertilization with sperm. This experiment was first performed by Loeb ('06, '07) and by Tennent (Tennent and Hogue, '06). Tennent treated the eggs of starfish (*Asterias*) by Delage's CO_2 method and then fertilized them with their own sperm. The results varied with the length of exposure to the parthenogenetic agent. With a relatively short exposure normal union of the germ-nuclei and cleavage ensues. If fertilization be delayed to a later period, various abnormalities appear in respect to the sperm-nucleus, the paternal chromosomes entering the first mitosis irregularly and often being in part cast out. Similar experiments were later performed by Herbst ('06, '07, '09, '12), Godlewski ('11) and Hinderer ('14), all of whom fertilized the egg, subsequent to chemical treatment, by the sperm of a different species. Among the most interesting of these cases is Baltzer's cross of *Sphærechinus* ♀ × *Paracentrotus* ♂, the eggs of the former being first treated with one of the fatty acids (p. 475) and then fertilized by the foreign sperm. Under normal conditions, as stated above, this cross produces hybrids intermediate in type between the two parental forms (Fig. 456, C), and no elimination of chromosomes takes place. Under the conditions of the experiment hybrids are produced, as shown by Herbst, that still show both parental characters, but as a rule show a definite matroclinous tendency both in shape and in the structure of the skeleton.

Such larvæ often show a mosaic-like mingling of the *Sphærechinus* and *Paracentrotus* characters, certain areas being of intermediate type, others purely or mainly maternal. Interesting examples of such mosaic types are offered by larvæ which show maternal characters on one side and hybrid characters on the other. A striking feature of these larvæ is the fact that the size of the nuclei varies in these various areas, *those of the maternal areas being in general much smaller than those of mixed type*—a condition conspicuously shown in the lateral mosaics (Figs. 456, F, 457, G). Cytological examination (Herbst, '09) yielded a partial explanation of these conditions similar in principle to that found by Baltzer in the cross *Paracentrotus* ♀ × *Sphærechinus* ♂. Before the sperm enters, the parthenogenetic agent initiates a mitotic transformation of the egg-nucleus, the latter thus

---

[1] Millardet himself ('94) suggested as an explanation of such hybrids in the process of fertilization "certain important parts of the male and female cell have been neutralized, perhaps destroyed, by the adverse cell." A somewhat similar suggestion is made by Sutton ('03, p. 244).

gaining a lead which the sperm-nucleus is often unable to overcome—a fact quite analogous to that determined by Tennent in the starfish, as mentioned above. Hence, although the germ-nuclei conjugate as usual, the *Paracentrotus* chromosomes show a marked tendency to fall behind, lagging on the spindle and undergoing many abnormalities of distribution; some of them

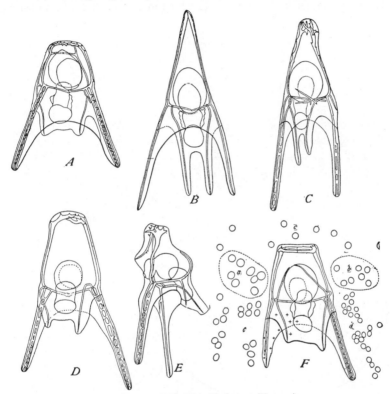

Fig. **456.**—Hybrid sea-urchin larvæ (HERBST).

A, normal pure-bred pluteus (parthenogenetic) of *Sphærechinus granularis; B*, normal pure-bred pluteus of *Paracentrotus (Strongylocentrotus) purpuratus; C*, normal hybrid form *Sphær.* ♀ × *Par.* ♂; *D, E, F*, hybrids from the same cross after preliminary treatment of eggs with butyric acid; *F*. showing size of nuclei from adjoining regions; *E, F*, show predominantly maternal characters on one side (skeleton) and hybrid characters on the other. In *F, a* and *b* are respectively diploid and haploid nuclei from corresponding regions of the right and left oral fields; *c* and *d*, nuclei of the ciliated belt of the two sides.

pass to one pole only, others fail to reach either pole, while in some cases (Fig. 457, A, C) the whole paternal group passes to one pole (somewhat as in Boveri's "partial fertilization," p. 458). While all the nuclei thus receive the normal complement of *Sphærechinus* chromosomes they often receive only a defective set of *Paracentrotus* chromosomes, or even none.

Here, obviously, lies a partial explanation of the mosaic-like patchwork of maternal and hybrid characters shown by these larvæ; of the variations in the size of their nuclei; and of larvæ which show maternal characters on one side, hybrid on the other.

Further work along the same lines by Herbst ('12) and by Hinderer ('13) showed that another factor may be involved in the results. Both observers

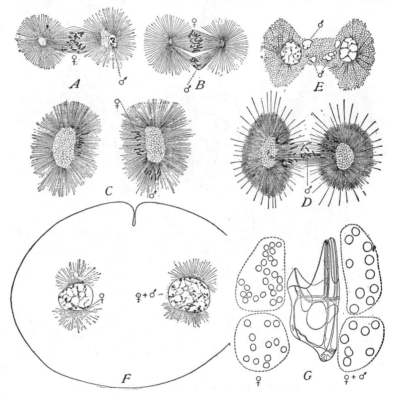

Fig. 457.—Development of eggs of *Sphærechinus* first treated with valerianic acid and then fertilized with sperm of *Paracentrotus* (HERBST).

A, late prophase, with sperm-nucleus at ♂; *B*, similar stage, sperm-nucleus at ♂; *C*, anaphase with lagging sperm-chromosomes; *D*, anaphase, with sperm-chromosomes at ♂; *E*, later stage like last, sperm-karyomerites at ♂; *F*, 2-cell stage (cleavage suppressed); following form like *C*, with one maternal and one hybrid nucleus; *G*, lateral mosaic-larvæ, hybrid (diploid) on one side, maternal (haploid) on the other. At right and left enlarged nuclei from the two sides.

found that after treatment of these eggs by certain parthenogenetic agents (valerianic acid, ammonia, CO_2), many of them give rise to monasters which may pass through one or several mitotic cycles and may then be fertilized by the sperm of *Paracentrotus*. Since the number of chromosomes is doubled at each such cycle (p. 168) such eggs contain a diploid or polyploid set of maternal chromosomes, the size of the nuclei being thus increased correspondingly at each step. Upon fertilization by a sperm such eggs receive only a haploid group of paternal chromosomes, a large excess of maternal chromosomes being present. Such eggs, having nuclei of double the normal size following a monocentric mitosis, and fertilized by the sperm of *Paracentrotus*, give rise to larvæ with abnormally large nuclei and showing a matriclinous tendency even more marked than in the preceding case.[1] Herbst at first attributed this likewise to a partial elimination of the sperm-chromosomes; and Hinderer's observations on the same material indicate that the chromosome-numbers in these crosses are in fact often somewhat below the expected number 58 (*Sph.* 20 + 20 + *Paracentr.* 18). How the deficiency is caused was not determined; but Hinderer showed that no elimination takes place during cleavage, and careful measurements of the larval nuclei leaves no doubt that a large excess of maternal chromosomes is present.

The later studies of Landauer ('22) on the same hybrids, first activated by ammonia and then fertilized, confirm this, showing that no chromosomes are eliminated during cleavage, and also giving reason to conclude that the deficiency of chromosome-number below the expected one is due to a failure of certain chromosomes to divide during the monaster-formation or to a reunion of their halves after division. Apart from this, however, the conclusion was fully established by the studies of both Herbst and Boveri of giant eggs presently to be considered (p. 972).

Godlewski's experiments ('11) form the converse of Herbst's, sea-urchin eggs (*Sphærechinus*) being first fertilized by the sperm of an annelid, *Chœtopterus*, and then treated with hypertonic sea-water. Neither of these processes alone will lead to complete development; the first of them is followed by the formation of a fertilization-membrane, by conjugation of the germ-nuclei, and by the appearance of a monaster which never divides; while the hypertonic sea-water by itself has no visible effect. When the two processes are combined, complete development may ensue, the product being a typical *Sphærechinus* larvæ of purely maternal type. The study of sections proves that conjugation of the germ-nuclei is followed by an elimination of chromatin that takes place before the formation of the astral figure and causes a marked reduction in the size of the nucleus. The chromosomes of the dividing eggs are of the *Sphærechinus* type, in respect both to shape and size differences. Their number was not accurately determined; but the nuclei of the "hybrid" plutei are conspicuously smaller than in the pure-bred forms, indicating that they are at least approximately haploid. From all this Godlewski concludes that before cleavage takes

[1] Cf. Boveri ('14. p. 124).

place the *Chætopterus* chromosomes are eliminated and degenerate, so that the larval nuclei contain only maternal or *Sphærechinus* chromosomes.[1]

3. Heterogeneous Crosses

The work of Godlewski introduces us to a third type of experiment that leads to the same general result. It has long been known that under normal conditions crossing rarely takes place save between nearly related species; though Giard ('oo) succeeded in fertilizing the eggs of a sea-urchin, *Psammechinus*, with the sperm of a starfish, *Asterias*.   Loeb ('o3, 'o4) demonstrated that such "heterogeneous crossing" may be greatly facilitated by slightly altering the chemical nature of the surrounding medium, *e. g.*, by rendering the sea-water slightly alkaline,[2] or by altering its concentration.   In his first successful attempt, sea-urchin eggs(*Paracentrotus*) were fertilized by the sperm of a starfish (*Asterias*), the result being normal young plutei, of purely maternal type, showing no influence whatever of the foreign sperm.   He subsequently showed that the eggs of sea-urchins could be fertilized by the sperms of various starfish, of an ophiuran and even of a mollusk, *Chlorostoma*, always with the same result; the larvæ were of purely maternal type.   A partial explanation of this was discovered by Kupelwieser ('o6, 'o9, '12), in sea-urchin eggs (*Parechinus*), fertilized by the sperm of the mollusk *Mytilus* or the annelid *Adouinia*, both of which crosses again give rise to characteristic sea-urchin plutei of purely maternal type.   In both these cases the germ-nuclei approach each other in the egg, a typical sperm-aster and amphiaster are formed, and the egg-nucleus divides as usual (Fig. 458), but the sperm-chromatin degenerates.   In the cross *Parechinus* ♀ × *Mytilus* ♂ the sperm-nucleus fails to fuse with that of the egg, usually undergoes no mitotic transformation, lags upon the spindle, and usually passes into one of the daughter-cells, where it degenerates.   In the cross *Parechinus* ♀ × *Adouinia* ♂ the nuclei unite and may even fuse; but in the ensuing prophases the paternal nucleus fails to produce chromosomes and breaks up into formless clumps which also finally degenerate.   In both cases the functional chromosomes are of the sea-urchin type and form a haploid group of nine, as in a parthenogenetic or merogonic larva.   From all this it is *clear that these eggs develop with only the maternal chromosomes, as if they were parthenogenetic.*

Up to this point all the facts are in harmony. Godlewski's results ('o6, 'o9) on the heterogeneous cross between the sea-urchin egg *Parechinus*

---

[1] See, however, p. 971. Godlewski finds that an elimination of the sperm-chromatin takes place also when the eggs of sea-urchins are fertilized with the sperm of the mollusc *Dentalium;* but such eggs do not develop into larvæ even after treatment by hypertonic sea-water.

[2] The writer found in 1903 that the eggs of *Dentalium* and *Patella* are more readily fertilized if a small amount of NaHO be added to the water.

and the crinoid sperm (*Antedon*) seems to offer a contradiction. In this cross, too, the larvæ are purely of the sea-urchin type; nevertheless Godlewski (whose results have been confirmed by Baltzer), shows that *no elimination of the paternal chromosomes takes place* and that in all probability the larvæ develop with the full complement of both *Parechinus* and *Antedon* chromosomes. This result was regarded by Godlewski as giving demonstrative evidence that the oöplasm, as well as the chromosomes, plays a definite rôle in determination; and this was especially supported

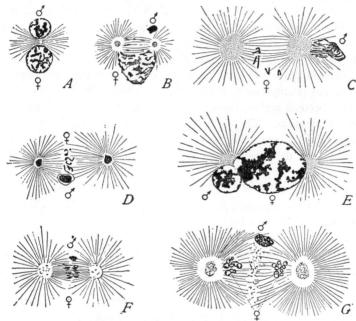

Fig. 458.—Heterogeneous fertilization (KUPELWIESER).

A, conjugation of the gamete-nuclei, sea-urchin (*Echinus*) ♀ × annelid (*Adouinia*) ♂; *B, C, D*, sea-urchin (*Echinus*) ♀ × pelecypod (*Mytilus*) ♂; *E, F, G*, sea-urchin (*Echinus*) ♀ × gastropod (*Patella* ♂).

by the further observation that supposedly *enucleated egg-fragments of Parechinus fertilized by Antedon sperm likewise produce merogonic embryos of maternal type.*

We possess in fact demonstrative evidence, derived from other sources, which demonstrates the reality of such determinative action by the oöplasm, as will later be shown (p. 1062). Such a conclusion would in no way contradict those already reached in respect to the sperm-chromosomes. The evidence from the *Parechinus-Antedon* cross, is, however, inconclusive in several respects. So far as the entire eggs are concerned, the case might be one of simple Mendelian dominance, as already suggested in the case of Tennent's *Toxopneustes-Hipponoë* crosses. Again, it is possible, as both Boveri and Baltzer pointed out, that although the *Antedon* chromosomes are able to maintain themselves in the *Parechinus* egg they are unable to play any effective part in the special phenomena of differentiation in the foreign protoplasm. As already indicated, Baltzer found in many of his heterogeneous crosses that the embryos pass through a period of physiological disturbance (in the blastula stage) in the course of which many of them perish; and it is at this time in several of these cases (*e. g.*, in *Arbacia* ♀ × *Paracentrotus* ♂, or *Parechinus* ♀ × *Arbacia* ♂) that the elimination of paternal chromatin takes place. Baltzer has observed at this time a similar disturbance, and the accompanying high mortality, in the *Parechinus-Antedon* cross and ascribes it to a lack of normal adjustment between the egg-protoplasm and the paternal chromosomes at the time the latter first become active, though it does not go so far in this case as to produce elimination. The problems here involved will, however, appear in a clearer light after further consideration of the relative rôles of nucleus or cytoplasm in development (p. 1172).

4. Evidence from Hybrids Produced by Giant Eggs

The occasional occurrence in several groups of animals of giant eggs of double the usual size has long been known.[1] They are known to arise in some cases by the fusion of two originally separate eggs into one, either spontaneously or as a result of experimental conditions;[2] but it is probable that they may arise in other ways; *e. g.*, by the failure of protoplasmic cleavage in the final oögonial division (Sala), or by the formation of a monaster accompanied by the doubling of the chromosome-number and the subsequent growth of the egg to twice its normal size (Boveri). Such giant eggs may contain two separate nuclei or only one of double the normal size. In either case, it is evident that they are bivalent in respect to both nuclear and cytoplasmic content. When fertilized, they often produce double monsters of various types; but they may give rise to single larvæ, normally formed, but of twice the normal size (Fig. 520) as was shown by Zur Strassen in the case of *Ascaris*, and later by Driesch and Bierens de Haan in the sea-urchin. The last-named observer found, as was to be expected, that when fertilized with their own sperm, *these eggs divide with the triploid number of*

---

[1] For review, see Bierens de Haan ('13a).

[2] Spontaneously, *e. g.*, in the gasteropod *Philine* (Lacaze-Duthiers, '75), in the annelid *Ophryotrocha* (Korschelt, '95), in *Ascaris* (Zur Strassen, '96, '98). Induced by cold in *Ascaris* (Sala, '96); by shaking the eggs, or treatment by alkaline sea-water in sea-urchins (Driesch, '00, '10); by adding salts to the sea-water in sea-urchins (Herbst, '93) and in annelids (Loeb, '01, Lillie, '06); or by centrifuging the eggs in gasteropods (Conklin, '17).

chromosomes (in *Sphærechinus* 60 in place of the usual 40), and the nuclei of the resulting larvæ are correspondingly larger, as was also found by Herbst, Hinderer and Boveri.

Herbst ('14) and Boveri ('14) have shown, independently, that when such giant eggs of *Sphærechinus* are fertilized by the sperm of *Paracentrotus* or *Parechinus* the resulting larvæ are markedly matriclinous (as compared with the same hybrids from eggs of normal size) and have demonstrated that in this case, too, the result must be ascribed to the preponderance of maternal chromosomes. Herbst's conclusion was based on a comparison of these hybrids with those from eggs of normal size in which the nuclei had been doubled by a preceding monaster-formation. In the giant hybrid the quantity of maternal cytoplasm is double that in the latter, yet the matriclinous tendency is no greater. The result, therefore, cannot be ascribed to the maternal cytoplasm but must be due in both cases, to the preponderance of maternal chromosomes.

Boveri reached the same result by a stricter proof, comparing (1) hybrids from entire *Sphærechinus* eggs (× *Paracentrotus* sperm) with (2), those from isolated blastomeres of the 2-cell stage of the same eggs, and (3) those from nucleated egg-fragments of the same size fertilized by the same sperm. All of these gave substantially the same result. A possible influence of the cytoplasm is thus excluded; for were the maternal cytoplasm concerned the hybrids from whole eggs should be more matriclinous than those from egg-fragments of half size; and were the sperm-cytoplasm concerned the larvæ from ½-blastomeres should be less matriclinous than those from egg-fragments of the same size, since the latter have relatively twice as much sperm-cytoplasm as the former. Since, however, no such differences appear in the results the decisive factor must be the nucleus, *i. e.*, the chromosomes.

5. The Evidence from Merogonic Hybrids

Boveri ('89, '96) ingeniously attempted to demonstrate the determinative action of the nucleus by fertilizing enucleated egg-fragments of one species (*Sphærechinus granularis*) by the sperm of a different species (*Parechinus microtuberculatus*) having markedly different larval characters.[1] It might be expected that merogonic dwarf Plutei derived from such egg-fragments would show only paternal characters (since the maternal chromosomes are missing); and in point of fact Boveri obtained a few such larvæ identical in form and in the structure of the skeleton with the paternal (*Parechinus*) type (Fig. 459). These larvæ had smaller nuclei than those of the normal hybrids; and this was taken by Boveri as a proof that the nuclei were of haploid

[1] These sea-urchins belong to different genera and even, according to Mortensen, to different families.

constitution and derived solely from the sperm; later observers showed, however, that this result is inconclusive.

In the first place, even normal crosses (*i. e.*, from whole nucleated eggs) between these and other species of sea-urchins often produce larvæ which

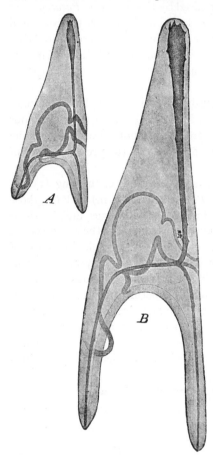

show only the paternal characters, or predominately these characters.[1] This is no doubt a case of individual dominance. Boveri himself, in a recent posthumous paper of great interest ('18), has brought forward still more weighty reasons to question the validity of his earlier conclusions. One of these is the fact that it is not possible to make sure of the absence of a nucleus by simple inspection of the living egg-fragment; for the operation of shaking the eggs to pieces often causes a breaking down of the nuclear wall, leaving the nuclear substance as an irregular clump of granules and fibrillæ that is invisible in the living egg or egg-fragment, though clearly seen in sections. This operation does not kill the nucleus; for if the egg or egg-fragment be allowed to stand unfertilized in sea-water the nuclear clump gives rise to a group of typical chromosomes near which appears an astral radiation, as so often happens in artificial parthenogenesis (p. 484). Boveri found nearly demonstrative evidence that such chromosomes, or some of them, may take part in the development when the supposedly non-nucleated eggs or fragments are subsequently fertilized. Thus, on repeating his earlier experiments with "non-nucleated" egg-fragments of *Sphærechinus*, fertilized with the sperm of *Paracentrotus* or *Parechinus* and isolated, they were found in many cases

Fig. 459.—Normal larva and dwarf merogonic larva of the sea-urchin. (Boveri).
A, dwarf pluteus arising from an enucleated egg-fragment of *Sphærechinus granularis*, fertilized with sperm of *Parechinus microtuberculatus*, and showing purely paternal characters; *B*, normal pluteus of *Parechinus microtuberculatus*.

---

[1] See Seeliger ('95, '96), Morgan ('94, '95), Vernon ('00).

to produce dwarf Plutei having all the characteristics of hybrids, being of intermediate form and structure and having nuclei of the typical diploid size. These facts indicate that the larvæ in question must have arisen from fragments in which the broken-down nucleus still was present and took part in the development.

Boveri demonstrated also that the development of merogonic larvæ from enucleated egg-fragments differs according to the species employed. When such fragments are fertilized by sperm of the same species, perfect dwarf Plutei may be produced, having nuclei of the correct haploid size (Boveri, '89, '02, '05); and the same result was obtained with egg-fragments of *Parechinus* fertilized with *Paracentrotus* sperm (Boveri, '96). This cross, however, is not available for the purposes of the experiment owing to the close similarity of the larvæ of the two species. The case is different with the hybrids originally studied by Boveri (egg-fragments of *Sphærechinus* fertilized by sperm of *Parechinus*). In this cross, as is demonstrated in Boveri's final work ('18) a really non-nucleated fragment (as judged by exact study of the size of the nuclei) *never produces a perfect dwarf Pluteus*. Dwarf larvæ with nuclei of the typical haploid size are indeed frequently produced, but only in very rare cases do they develop beyond the beginning of gastrulation and at most never beyond the "prism" or initial pluteus stage. It seems probable, therefore, that the few perfect dwarf hybrids obtained from this cross in Boveri's earlier work were in reality derived from nucleated fragments and contained some chromosomes of maternal origin, though the paternal characters dominated. To this day, therefore, the case remains inconclusive, so far as the sea-urchins are concerned, and can only be decided by renewed experiments.

As Boveri has indicated ('18, p. 461, ff.), the facts observed in the merogonic hybrids of sea-urchins greatly weaken the force of Godlewsky's conclusions. In his experiments the egg-fragments were likewise obtained by shaking the eggs to pieces, and there is nothing to show whether they were really non-nucleated or not; furthermore, none of the four cases observed developed to a sufficiently late stage to show the influence of the sperm-chromosomes. The question is here at once raised as to the respective parts played by the nucleus and the cytoplasm in determination. To this subject we shall return in the final chapter (p. 1106).

V. CONCLUSION. CHROMOSOMES AND DETERMINATION

In what sense can the chromosomes be considered as agents of determination? By many writers they have been treated as the actual and even as the exclusive "bearers of heredity"; numerous citations from the literature of the subject might be offered to show how often they have been treated as central, governing factors of heredity and development, to which all else is subsidiary. The most complete example of this conception, perhaps, is embodied in the theory of the germ-plasm as developed by Weismann; but in one form or another it has persisted almost to the present day.[1] Many writers, while avoiding this particular usage, have referred to the chromosomes, or their components as "determiners" of corresponding characters; but this term, too, is becoming obsolete save as a convenient descriptive device. The whole tendency of modern investigation has been towards a different and more rational conception which recognizes the fact that the egg is a reaction-system (p. 635) and that (to cite an earlier statement) "the whole germinal complex is directly or indirectly involved in the production of every character." [2] Genetic research is constantly bringing to light new cases of the coöperation of several or many factors in the production of single characters (e. g., in that of sex, p. 815); and it is possible that all the chromosomes, or even all of the units which they contain, may be concerned in the production of every character. Beyond this it is evident that every character is produced during development by an activity in which the cytoplasm, and what we call the "organism as a whole" plays a most important part. When, for example, we speak of the X-chromosome as a "determiner" of sex, we mean only that it is a differential factor or modifier (p. 635) the relative quantity of which in relation to the autosomal material (p. 817) conditions a particular reaction by the developing germ. The value of the chromosome-theory of heredity does not lie in our identification of this or that "determiner" or "bearer of heredity," but in its practical importance as a means of experimental analysis. In this respect, in the writer's opinion, the theory has the same kind of value as the molecular and atomic constructions of physico-chemical science; and the "mystical" and "unscientific" character ascribed to it by some writers is purely imaginary.

LITERATURE XII

(See also II, V, VI, X, XI. For abbreviations, see General Literature List.)

Agar W. E., '20 (I).
Baltzer, F., '10. Ueber die Beziehung zwischen dem Chromatin und der Entwicklung und Vererbungsrichtung bei Echinodermenbastarden: *A. Zf.*, V.
　'17. Ueber Entwicklung und Vererbung bei Bastarden: *Verh. Schweiz. Nat. Ges., Zürich.*
Bateson, W., '13. Mendel's Principles of Heredity: *Cambridge (Eng.) and New York.*

---

[1] *Cf.* the title of Vejdovský's important work *Die Vererbungsträger*, 1912.
[2] Wilson, ('12a, p. 60, etc.).

Baur, E., '14. Einführung in die experimentelle Vererbunglsehre.

Blakeslee, A. F. '21. Types of Mutations and their possible Significance in Evolution: *A. N.*, LV.

'22. Variations in *Datura* due to changes in Chromosome-number: *Ibid.*, LVI.

Blakeslee, Belling and **Farnham, '20.** Chromosomal Duplication and Mendelian Phenomena in *Datura* mutants: *Sci., N. S.*, LII, 1347.

Boveri, Th., '02. Ueber mehrpolige Mitosen als Mittel zur Analyse des Zellkerns: *V. P. M. G.*, XXXV.

'04a. Ueber die Entwicklung dispermer Ascariseier: *Z. A.*, XXVII.

'07. Zellen-Studien, VI: *Jena*.

'14. Zur Frage der Entstehung maligner Tumoren: *Fischer, Jena*.

Brachet, A., '08. L'hérédité dans l'œuf: *Revue des Idées*.

Bridges, C. B., '13. Non-disjunction of the Sex-chromosomes of *Drosophila*: *J. E. Z.*, XV.

'14. The Chromosome Hypothesis of Linkage Applied to Cases in Sweet Peas and *Primula: A. N.*, XLVIII.

'16. Non-disjunction as a Proof of the Chromosome Theory of Heredity: *Genetics*, I.

'17. Deficiency: *Ibid.*, II.

Bridges and **Morgan, '19.** The Second-chromosome Group of Mutant Characters: *P. C. I.*, 278.

'23. The Third-chromosome Group of Mutant Characters of *Drosophila: Ibid.*, 327.

Carothers, E. E., '13. The Mendelian Ratio in Relation to certain orthopteran Chromosomes: *J. M.*, XXIV.

'17. The Segregation and Recombination of homologous Chromosomes, etc.: *J. M.*, XXVIII.

'21. Genetical Behavior of Heteromorphic Homologous Chromosomes of *Circotettix: J. M.*, XXXV, 2.

Correns, C., '02. Ueber den Modus und den Zeitpunkt der Spaltung, etc.: *B. Z.*, LX.

Doncaster, L., '14. Chromosomes, Heredity, and Sex: *Q. J.*

'20 (I).

East, E. M., '15. The Chromosome View of Heredity and Its Meaning to Plant Breeders: *A. N.*, XLIX.

Fick, R., '06. Vererbungsfragen, Reduktions- und Chromosomenhypothesen, Bastardregeln: *E. A. E.*, XVI.

Gates, R. R., '10. The Material Basis of Mendelian Phenomena: *A. N.*, XLIV.

'13. Tetraploid Mutants and Chromosome Mechanisms: *B. C.*, XXXIII.

'15. The Mutation Factor in Evolution, with Particular Reference to *Œnothera: London*.

'23. The trisomic Mutations of *Œnothera: A. Bot.*, XXXVII.

Gates, R. R., and **Thomas, N., '14.** A Cytological Study of *Œnothera lata* and *O. semilata* in Relation to Mutation: *Q. J.*, LIX.

Godlewski, Emil, Jun., '06. Untersuchungen über die Bastardierung der Echiniden- und Crinoidenfamilie: *A. Entwm.*, XX.

Goldschmidt, R., '13. Einführung in die Vererbungswissenchaft: 2 Aufl. *Leipzig.*

Gregory, R. P., '14. On the Genetics of tetraploid Plants in *Primula: P. R. S.,* LXXXVII.

Haecker, V., '04. Bastardirung und Geschlechtszellenbildung: *Z. J., Suppl.,* VII.

'07. Die Chromosomen als angenommene Vererbungsträger: *Ergeb. Fortschritt. Zool.,* I.

'10. Ergebnisse und Ausblicke in der Keimzellforschung: *Z. A. V.,* III.

Herbst, '06–'14. Vererbungstudien: '06, I–III (Introductory): *A. Entwm.,* XXI; '06, '07, '09, '12, IV–VII (Hybrids): *Ibid.,* XXII, XXIV, XXVII, XXXIV; '13, VIII–IX (Hybrids): *Sitzber. Heidelb. Ak. Wiss.,* Math-Nab. Klasse; '14, X (Hybrids): *A. Emtwm.,* XXXIX.

Janssens, F., '09. La théorie de la chiasmatypie: *L. C.,* XXV.

'19. (a) À propos de la chiasmatypie et la théorie de Morgan, etc.: *Soc. Biol. Belg.*

'24. La chiasmatypie dans les insectes: *L. C.,* XXXIV, 1.

McClung, C. E., '24. The Chromosome Theory of Heredity: in *General Cytology, Chicago.*

Morgan, T. H., '10. Chromosomes and Heredity: *A. N.,* XLIV.

'10b. Sex-limited Inheritance in *Drosophila: Sci.,* XXXII.

'11a. Random Segregation versus Coupling in Mendelian Inheritance: *Ibid.,* XXXIV.

'11b. The Origin of nine Wing-mutations in *Drosophila: Ibid.,* XXXII.

'11c. An Attempt to analyze the Constitution of the Chromosomes, etc.: *J. E. Z.,* XI.

'14a. The Mechanism of Heredity as indicated by the Inheritance of linked Characters: *P. S. M.*

'15. Localization of the hereditary Material in the Germ-cells: *P. N. A.,* I.

'17. The Theory of the Gene: *A. N.,* LI.

'19. The Physical Basis of Heredity: *Philadelphia.*

'22. On the Mechanism of Heredity. Croonian Lecture: *P. R. S.,* XCIV.

Morgan, T. H., and **Bridges, C. B.,** '16. Sex-linked Inheritance in *Drosophila: P. C. I.,* 237.

Morgan, Bridges and **Sturtevant,** '19. Contributions to the Genetics of *Drosophila melanogaster: P. C. I.,* 278.

Morgan and **Lynch,** '12. The Linkage of two Factors in *Drosophila* that are not sex-linked: *B. B.,* XXIII.

Morgan, Sturtevant, Bridges and **Muller,** '23. The Mechanism of Mendelian Heredity: Rev. Ed., *New York.*

Muller, H. J., '14. A new Mode of Segregation in Gregory's tetraploid Mutants: *A. N.,* XLVIII.

'16. The Mechanism of Crossing Over: *A. N.,* L.

'18. Genetic Variability, twin Hybrids and constant Hybrids, etc.: *G.,* III.

'20. Are the Factors of Heredity arranged in a line?: *A. N.:* LIV.

Nachtsheim, H., '19. Die Analyse der Erbfaktoren bei *Drosophila* und deren cytologische Grundlage. Sammelreferat: *Z. A. V.*, XX.

Plough, H. H., '17. The Effect of Temperature on Crossing Over: *J. E. Z.*, XXIV.

Prenant, A., '11. La substance héréditaire et la base cellulaire de l'hérédité: *J. A. P.*, XLVII.

Rückert, J., '92a, '92b (VI).

Stomps, T. J., '16. Ueber den Zusammenhang zwischen Statur und Chromosomenzahl bei den Œnotheren: *B. C.*, XXXVI.

Strasburger, E., '08a. Die Stofflichen Grundlagen der Vererbung im Organischen Reiche, etc.: *Fischer, Jena.*
'08b. Chromosomenzahlen, Plasmastrukturen, Vererbungsträger und Reduktionsteilung: *J. W. B.*, XLV.
'10. The Minute Structure of Cells in Relation to Inheritance: In *Darwin and Modern Science* (Seward Edition).

Sturtevant, A. H., '13. The linear Arrangement of six sex-linked Factors in *Drosophila*, as shown by their Mode of Association: *J. E. Z.*, XIV.
'14. The Reduplication Hypothesis as Applied to *Drosophila*: *A. N.*, XLVIII.
'15. The Behavior of the Chromosomes as Studied through Linkage: *Z. A. V.*, XIII.
'21. Linkage, Variation and Chromosome-maps: *P. N. A.*, VII.

Sutton, W. S., '03. The Chromosomes in Heredity: *B. B.*, IV.

De Vries, Hugo, '03. Fertilization and Hybridization: In Die Mutationslehre, II, *Leipzig;* Eng. Trans. by Gager in Intracellular Pangenesis (see IX), *Open Court Pub. Co., Chicago,* 1910.

Wilson, E. B., '02. Mendel's Principles of Heredity and the Maturation of the Germ-cells: *Sci.*, XVI.
'05-'12. Studies on Chromosomes I–VIII (see Lit. X).
'12a. Some Aspects of Cytology in Relation to the Study of Genetics: *A. N.*, Feb.
'14. The Bearing of Cytological Research on Heredity (The Croonian Lecture): *P. R. S.*, B, LXXXVIII.

Wilson, E. B., and **Morgan, T. H.,** '20. Chiasmatype and Crossing-over: *A. N.*, LIV.

Winiwarter, H., '21. Chiasmatypie et réduction: *C. R. Soc. Biol.*, LXXXV.

CHAPTER XIII

GROWTH, CELL–DIVISION, AND DEVELOPMENT

"Finally, therefore, we may state the conclusion that all the cells or their equivalents in the fully developed organism have arisen by a progressive segmentation of the egg-cell into morphologically similar elements; and that the cells which form the early basis of any part or organ of the embryo, however small their number, form the exclusive source of all the formed elements (*i. e.*, cells) of which the developed organ consists." REMAK. [1]

The point of departure for every approach to the problem of inheritance and development is given by the fact that the germ is originally a single cell, equivalent in all of its essential features to any one of the tissue-cells of which the body is composed. The development of this cell involves four characteristic series of operations, as follows:

(1) *Cell-division or Cleavage*, a process in which, as was first clearly recognized by Kölliker and Remak, the egg undergoes a series of rapidly succeeding mitotic divisions, thus splitting up into blastomeres or embryonic cells from which, by further continued division, are produced all the cells of the new individual.

(2) *Growth and Morphallaxis*. By growth as here employed is meant not merely increase in size but also growth into a particular form. In this latter respect growth merges insensibly into morphallaxis (to use the useful term of Morgan) by which may conveniently be designated the plastic moulding of the body into a particular form by a process in which mere enlargement and cell-division are not directly involved. If, for instance, a *Hydra* or a *Planaria* be cut into rather small pieces each piece may soon be converted into a dwarf whole by a process involving little or no increase in size or cell-multiplication. It is, in the phrase of Driesch, as if a plan or mould of a new little *Hydra* or worm were first prepared and the old material poured into it.

(3) *Localization*, or the appearance of the parts of the embryo, in a typical order of space and time. This process is often foreshadowed before cleavage begins, and often before it is fertilized, by the appearance in the egg of prelocalized areas or *germ-forming regions;* but at a sufficiently early period even such prelocalization seems to be absent. Localization includes the most difficult and obscure problems of development.

(4) *Differentiation*, the actual transformation of the embryonic struc-

---

[1] Untersuchungen, 1855, p. 140.

tures, whether cells or groups of cells, into the particular parts to which they are destined to give rise.

These four processes are closely correlated but not necessarily connected. Localization and differentiation, for instance, take place in many *Protista* without cell-division, and to a certain extent may occur in eggs in which cleavage has been experimentally suppressed (p. 1083). Growth and morphallaxis may likewise take place without cell-division, as we see in the cœnophytes or non-cellular plants (*e. g. Caulerpa*), in the apical regions of certain algæ (p. 1030), or in regenerating fragments of Protista (p. 658). In higher plants and animals generally the four processes are so closely associated as to offer a complex problem, as yet only partially solved. At this point we will direct attention especially to certain aspects of cleavage that will serve to define more clearly the nature of this problem.

During the growth-period the egg leads a vegetative and almost parasitic existence within the maternal body. A spectacular contrast to this is offered by the sudden resumption of intense mitotic activity with the onset of cleavage; but this involves no real breach of continuity. Cleavage is but a continuation, after a brief interval, of that series of cell-divisions which, as was emphasized especially by Virchow, has been going on uninterruptedly, though with periodic pauses, since the most remote antiquity (p. 11). The divisions of the egg during cleavage are in all essentials of the same type as those of the adult tissue-cells; such differences as may appear— *e. g.*, the prominence of the asters, the frequent asymmetry of the amphiaster, and the consequent inequality of cleavage—are of minor importance, though often interesting for analyzing the mechanism of mitosis. The cleavage of the ovum possesses, however, a fundamental significance of its own because of the phenomena of localization and differentiation with which it is so closely accompanied. Even in its earliest stages we may often trace definite relations between the planes of cleavage and the structural axes of the adult body; in the ascidian or the cephalopod, for example, and often in the frog, the first cleavage-plane coincides almost exactly with the median plane. In slightly later stages we often find whole systems, organs, or definite parts of them hewn from the egg, as it were, by a single stroke. Cleavage, therefore, is not merely a vegetative repetition of similar cells, as was formerly assumed by many writers, but is closely bound up with the formative activity. This connection is too intimate to be analyzed adequately by observation alone. By means of experiment, however, the phenomena may in some measure be disentangled, so that we are enabled to identify certain features of cleavage as due to simpler mechanical factors and primarily an expression of certain general rules or laws of cell-division, and others as a definite expression of the formative process. It is often convenient, accordingly, to distinguish between the merely *geometrical* relations of cleavage on the one hand, and on the other the so-called *promorphological* relations which foreshadow the morphological value of the individual blastomeres or cleavage-planes in the building of the body. The distinction has only a provisional value; but is useful for a first approach to the problems of cleavage. The brief discussion of these topics here offered is a prelude to a consideration of the more general aspects of development in the light especially of experimental embryology.

I. GEOMETRICAL RELATIONS OF CLEAVAGE–FORMS

A. Some General Rules of Cell-division

The geometrical relations of the cleavage-planes, and the consequent relative sizes and positions of the cells, show endless variations of detail, many of them plainly due to comparatively simple mechanical conditions, such as the amount and distribution of specific cytoplasmic materials (yolk, etc.), the shape of the egg as a whole, or the effect of mutual pressure of the cells, others to more complex conditions. All, however, may conveniently be treated as variants of a single fundamental type which has been moulded this way or that by special conditions and which is itself an expression of certain general rules of cell-division, first formulated by Hofmeister and Sachs in the case of the cells of growing plants.[1] Hofmeister ('63, '67) pointed out that in the division of plant-cells the new partition-wall tends as a rule to stand at right angles to the principal direction of growth of the cell, *i. e.*, perpendicular to the long axis. Sachs ('77, '87, etc.) developed this into two general principles or rules, as follows:

(1) Cells typically tend to divide into equal parts.

(2) Each new plane of division tends to intersect the preceding one at right angles.

Disregarding for the moment the frequent exceptions to these rules, the actual patterns formed by cell-aggregates *are conditioned by the general form of the dividing mass;* for, as Sachs showed, the division-planes tend to be either vertical to the surface (anticlines) or parallel to it (periclines). Ideal schemes of division may thus be constructed for various geometrical figures. In a flat circular disc, for example, the anticlinal planes pass through the radii, while the periclines are circles concentric with the periphery. If the disc be elongated to form an ellipse the periclines also become ellipses, while the anticlines are converted into hyperbolas confocal with the periclines. If it have the form of a parabola, the periclines and an-

---

[1] For an interesting fuller description of this subject see D'Arcy Thompson's work, *Growth and Form*, '17.

ticlines form two systems of confocal parabolas intersecting at right angles. All these schemes are *mutatis mutandis*, directly convertible into the corresponding solid forms in three dimensions.

Sachs showed further, in a beautiful manner, that all the above ideal types are closely approximated in nature, and Rauber ('82) early applied the

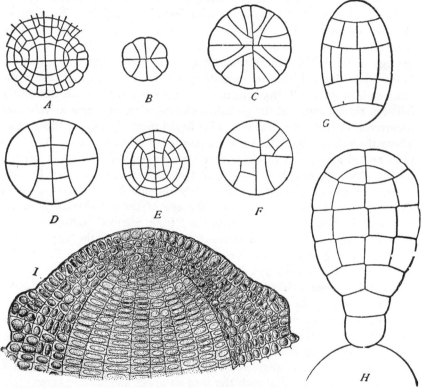

Fig. 460.—Geometrical relations of cleavage-planes in growing plant-tissues (from SACHS, after various authors).

A, flat ellipsoidal germ-disc of *Melobesia* (Rosanoff); nearly typical relation of elliptic periclines and hyperbolic anticlines; *B*, *C*, apical view of terminal knob on epidermal hair of *Pinguicola;* *B*, shows the ellipsoid type, *C*, the circular (spheroid type), somewhat modified (only anticlines present); *D*, growing point of *Salvinia* (Pringsheim); typical ellipsoid type, the single pericline is however incomplete; *E*, growing point of *Azolla* (Strasburger); circular or spheroid type transitional to ellipsoidal; *F*, root-cap of *Equisetum* (Nägeli and Leitgeb), modified circular type; *G*, cross-section of leaf-vein, *Trichomanes* (Prantl); ellipsoidal type with incomplete periclines; *H*, embryo of *Alisma;* typical ellipsoid type, pericline incomplete only at lower side; *I*, growing point of bud of the pine (*Abies*); typical paraboloid type, both anticlines and periclines having the form of parabolas (SACHS).

same principle to the cleavage of animal cells. The discoidal, spheroidal and ellipsoidal forms are more or less nearly realized in the thalloid growths of various lower plants, and in the embryos of flowering plants. The paraboloid form is according to Sachs characteristic of the growing points of many higher plants, which offer cell-patterns that are sometimes remarkably similar to the ideal scheme (Fig. 460).

For the study of animal development the most important form is the spheroid, since most forms of cleavage may be related to the typical division of a sphere in accordance with Sachs' rules. The ideal form of cleavage would here be a succession of rectangular cleavages in the three dimensions of space, the anticlines passing through the center so as to split the egg in the initial stages successively into halves, quadrants, and octants, while the periclines are parallel to the surface so as to separate the inner ends of these cells from the outer. In no case is this order accurately followed throughout, and the periclinal cleavages are of comparatively rare occurrence in the early cleavage, being found regularly only in those cases where the primary germ-layers are separated by delamination. The simplest and clearest form of cleavage occurs in eggs like those of echinoderms, which are of spherical form, and in which the deutoplasm is small in amount and distributed nearly equally through its substance. Such a cleavage is beautifully displayed in the egg of the holothurian *Synapta*, as shown in Fig. 4, slightly schematized from Selenka's drawings. The first cleavage is vertical, or *meridional*, passing through the egg-axis and dividing the egg into equal halves. The second, also meridional, cuts the first plane at right angles and divides the egg into quadrants. The third is horizontal, or *equatorial*, dividing the egg into equal octants. The order of division is thus far exactly that demanded by Sachs' rule, but the later ones depart from the ideal type in the absence at first of periclinal divisions, the embryo becoming hollow, and its walls consisting of a single layer of cells in which anticlinal cleavages continue in regular succession. The fourth cleavage is again meridional, giving two tiers of eight cells each; the fifth is horizontal, dividing each tier into an upper and a lower layer. The regular alternation is continued up to the ninth division (giving 512 cells), when the divisions pause while the gastrulation begins. In later stages the regularity is disturbed and finally lost. The eggs of few animals or plants display so regular a cleavage as this; nevertheless, many of them conform to it in the first three cleavages and often in several later ones, and even when the cleavage has become highly modified, traces of the same plan may usually be discerned.

Sachs' rules were supplemented by O. Hertwig ('84) in the following statements, which are of especial interest as applied to the analysis of the cleavage of the egg.

(1) *The typical position of the nucleus (and hence of the mitotic figure) tends*

towards the center of its sphere of influence, i. e., of the protoplasmic mass in which it lies.

(2) *The axis of the spindle typically lies in the longest axis of the proto-plasmic mass, and division therefore tends to cut this axis transversely.*

In the early cleavage of a homogeneous spheroidal egg, for instance, the first division is followed by a second one at right angles to it, since each hemisphere is twice as long in the plane of division as in any plane vertical to it. The spindle of the second division lies therefore parallel to the first plane, which forms the base of the hemisphere, and the ensuing division is vertical to it. The same applies to the third division, since each quadrant is as long as the entire egg while at most only half its diameter. Division is therefore transverse to the long axis and vertical to the first two planes. The later stages of cleavage offer a more complicated problem; but in general it may be said that prior to and during each cleavage the cell tends to elon-gate in an axis perpendicular to that of the preceding spindle—a condition which may often be observed up to a late stage, though there are many ex-ceptions due to a great variety of modifying conditions.

The mechanical basis of Hertwig's second rule is still unknown. It would seem obvious that in many cases the position of least mechanical resist-ance for the spindle is in the long axis of the cell; and the pressure-experi-ments described beyond (p. 1059) prove that the spindle may be forced to take up such a position by mechanical deformation of the cell. Undoubt-edly, however, this explanation is too simple; for there are numerous excep-tions to the rule,[1] traceable to many causes, some simple, such as the dis-tribution of formed bodies in the cell; others less obvious, such as localized changes of surface-tension (p. 194), conditions of radial tension in the astral systems (p. 180), protoplasmic currents (p. 195), or the nature of preceding telokinetic movements (p. 139), and still others of more compli-cated nature involved in the fundamental organization of the egg (p. 1006).

B. The Geometrical Forms of Cleavage

The rules of Sachs and Hertwig must not be pushed too far. They are no more than a rough approximation, yet they offer a convenient basis of comparison for the study of cleavage-forms in general. Departures from them may appear in the rhythm of division, in the direction of the cleav-age-planes (including displacements of the cells), or in inequalities of cell-division of various degree. Any of these, as will be seen, may be due either to relatively simple mechanical conditions or to more complex causes. Dis-regarding at this point the latter aspect of cleavage, and passing over the conventional embryological classifications (meroblastic, holoblastic, etc.)

[1] See Wilson ('92, '96), Jennings ('96) Zur Strassen ('96), Conklin ('97), Lillie ('95), etc.

based on the amount and distribution of the yolk, we may in a descriptive sense recognize three main geometrical forms or types of cleavage, namely: (1), the *radial* (or *orthoradial*), (2), the *spiral* (*oblique* or *alternating*) and (3) the *bilateral*.   To these might be added (4) *mixed* forms that combine certain features of the others (the annelid egg, for instance, divides at first spirally but later to some extent bilaterally), and (5) *indefinite* and *irregular* forms, which either show no constant form (as in some cœlenterates) or do not conform to any of the preceding three (*e. g.*, in the nematodes)

1. The Orthoradial Type

This type, well illustrated by the cleavage of *Synapta* (Fig. 4) or the sea-urchins (Figs. 512, 513), most nearly conforms to the rules of Sachs and Hertwig, successive cleavages cutting straight through the egg, at right angles to one another and symmetrically disposed around the egg-axis, so that when the egg is viewed from one pole the blastomeres lie in simple radial symmetry.   In all these cases, as above indicated in the case of *Synapta*, meridional and horizontal cleavages following in more or less regular alternation, sometimes up to a late stage.   In the sea-urchin egg the regular alternation between vertical and horizontal cleavages is disturbed already in the fourth cleavage, the four upper cells dividing meridionally while the lower divide horizontally and unequally, budding forth four small micromeres surrounding the lower pole (Fig. 513).

Orthoradial symmetry in cleavage is rarely as perfect as in these cases and in all cases it does not long persist, sooner or later giving way to irregularities due to shiftings of the cells, or to non-radial processes of growth.

2. The Spiral Type

This type, characteristic of platodes, annelids, and molluscs (cephalopods excepted), admirably illustrates many of the problems of cleavage, both mechanical and promorphological, and has been the subject of many investigations.   Different as it is from the orthoradial type, the two are closely related and have no doubt had a common origin.   It may most readily be thought of as arising by a bending or twisting of the radii, so that the cleavages instead of cutting straight through the egg (as in *Synapta*) become oblique with respect to both the egg-axis and the equator.   This apparently simple cause leads to a profound modification in the grouping of the blastomeres and in the relation of the cleavage planes to the egg-axis; for both the vertical (meridional) and horizontal (equatorial or parallel) planes are converted into spirals, or segments of spirals; and in consequence the blastomeres do not lie in regular tiers, as in the orthoradial type but interlock or alternate with one another after the fashion of soap-bubbles in a mass.

The most convenient approach to a study of this type is offered by cases in which the first two cleavages are equal and only slightly oblique, and in which the later cleavages are unequal in various degrees. In such cases, more or less nearly approached by the gasteropods *Trochus* (Fig. 464), *Patella* (Fig. 478), or *Crepidula* (Fig. 477) or the leech *Clepsine* (Fig. 471), we may distinguish four basal quadrants, or *macromeres* (A, B, C, D), typically larger, from which smaller *micromeres* are cut off towards the upper pole in successive quartets a^1, b^1, c^1, d^1; $a^2 - d^2$; $a^3 - d^3$; etc). Owing to the obliquity of the cleavages these quartets do not lie exactly above the basals (as in the orthoradial type) but are displaced towards one side or the other so as to alternate with them in regular order (hence the term "alternating" cleav-

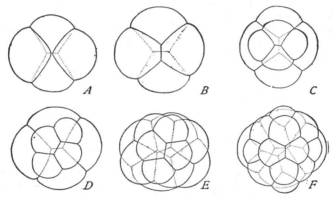

Fig. 461.—Soap-bubble models of cleavage-figures in *Trochus*. Compare Fig. 464 (ROBERT). *A* and *B*, models of 4-cell stages; *C*, *D*, 8-cell models; *E*, 12-cell model; *F*, 16-cell model.

age). The first quartet is displaced towards the left as seen from the side, or rotated clockwise as seen from the upper pole (Fig. 464, etc.), the second in the opposite direction, so as to alternate with the first, the third again towards the left, like the first, and so on, the resulting blastomeres being fitted together more or less like the cells of a honeycomb. As a rule not more than four or five regular quartets are formed; and often the quartet-formation becomes disturbed or irregular after the third or fourth. As new quartets form, the cells of the earlier ones divide, so that the boundaries of the quartets are often lost to view soon after their formation; but by sufficiently careful study they may usually be made out.

The regular alternating displacement of the quartets is a noteworthy phenomena; and still more remarkable is its constancy of direction. Throughout the platodes, nemertines, annelids, and molluscs (excluding the cephalopods), with a single significant exception (p. 994), the odd-numbered quartets (3, 5, etc.) are rotated in a clockwise direction, the even-numbered (2, 4, etc.) in an anticlockwise.   Close study of the whole process has shown that this effect is not due primarily to an actual movement of the quartets (though this may contribute to the result) but to *the direction of the successive*

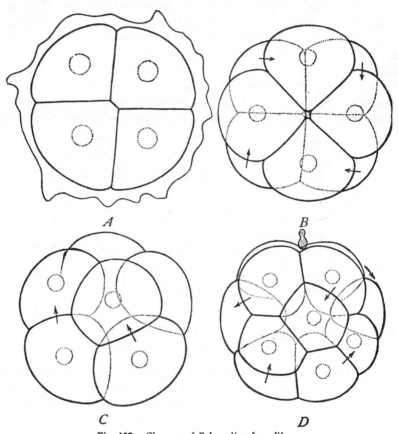

A   *B*

C   *D*

Fig. **462.**—Cleavage of *Polygordius,* from life.

A, four-cell stage, from above; B, corresponding view of eight-cell stage; C, side-view of the same; D, sixteen-cell stage from the side.

cleavage-planes, which are themselves often more or less clearly foreshadowed by the direction of the spindles before cleavage begins.   These planes follow a more or less spiral course, the spirals being alternately right-handed or *dexiotropic (i. e.,* with the hands of a clock, or clockwise) and left-handed or *leiotropic* (anti-clockwise).   These spirals cut across each other (*i. e.,* tend to follow Sachs' rule); but owing to the interlocking of the blastomeres the resulting angles of intersection tend to increase towards 120°, as will be plain from the figures.

The relation of the cleavage-planes may therefore be summed up in the statement that from the third cleavage onwards *the odd-numbered planes tend to follow dexiotropic spirals, the even-numbered leiotropic.*[1]

The same rule of alternation is followed also in the subsequent divisions of the quartet-cells. In typical cases, up to a certain period, every cleavage throughout the egg follows the same general direction, *i. e.*, a dexiotropic spiral in the odd cleavages and a leiotropic in the even. This will be made clear by the purely diagrammatic Fig. 463, which shows only the general direction of the successive cleavage-planes in a single quadrant, disregarding the ensuing displacements. Owing to this rule the cleavage-pattern is in

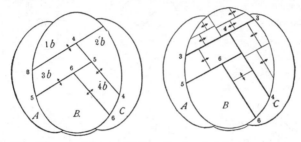

Fig. 463.—Diagram of the quartet-formation in spiral cleavage.

A, the four primary quadrants, showing the plan of formation of the first four quartets, 1^b, 2^b. 3^b, 4^b, in the *B*-quadrant. Successive cleavages from the third to the sixth indicated by numerals,

B, scheme showing the subdivisions of the quartets up to the 64-cell stage. Displacements of the cells not shown.

many cases of such remarkable regularity that when the egg is viewed exactly from one pole, even at a comparatively late stage, every cell in view falls exactly into place (Fig. 479) and may readily be identified. The symmetry of the cleavage-pattern is thus at once seen to be radial in type; hence the view of some cellular embryologists that the orthoradial and spiral types should be regarded as modifications of a single fundamental radial type.[2]

The rule of alternation of the spirals is in large measure independent of the relative sizes of the cells. It occurs in typical form when the quartet-cells are nearly or quite as large as the basals (*e. g.*, in *Polygordius*, Fig. 462); when they are extremely small, as in certain leeches and gasteropods (Fig. 477); or when they are even larger than the basals (a very rare condition) seen in the first quartet of nemertines (Fig. 527). It is seriously disturbed

---

[1] Among the numerous observers who contributed to the demonstration of this law or rule may be mentioned Rabl ('76), Whitman ('78), Blochmann ('82, '83), Selenka ('81), Lang ('84), Wilson ('92), Heymons ('93), Conklin ('91, '97), Kofoid ('95), Mead ('97), Child ('00). A full review of the literature in Robert ('03).

[2] Conklin, '97.

or wholly lost only in certain highly modified forms of development, especially fœtal types, such as occur in certain platodes, earthworms, leeches, and in cephalopods.

In some cases the spiral character of the cleavage first clearly appears at the third division, the first two planes being almost exactly vertical (meridional) dividing the egg into symmetrical and orthoradial quadrants; an example of this is seen in the nemertine egg (Fig. 527), and is approximated in that of *Patella* or *Polygordius* (Figs. 462, 478). More commonly the spiral character clearly appears in the second cleavage and may even be foreshadowed in the first. In such cases the four resulting quadrants no longer meet at the poles (as they do in the nemertine), but are so disposed that

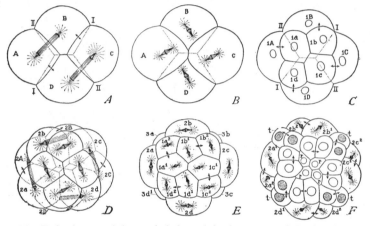

Fig. 464.—Early cleavage of the egg (spiral type) in the gasteropod *Trochus* (ROBERT).

A, B, 4-cell stages from upper pole; *C*, 8-cell stage, first micromere-quartet; *D*, 12-cell stage, transitional to 16-cell, second quartet just formed; *E*, 20-cell stage (transitional to 32-cell), from upper pole, third quartet formed; *F*, 36-cell stage from upper pole; showing apical rosette (*r*), trochoblasts (*t*) and all the blastomeres of the first two quartets (28 cells).

two of them (typically A and C) meet along a "cross-furrow" or "polar furrow" which passes through the upper pole while the other two (B and D) meet along a corresponding furrow passing through the lower pole but at right angles to the upper one (Fig. 464). This is due to the fact that the spindles of the second cleavage are both inclined to a horizontal plane, but in opposite directions, which causes two diagonal opposites (A and C) to lie higher in the egg and two (B and D) lower, the cells thus interlocking from the start. As the figures show, this particular disposition results from the fact that the second cleavage (like the fourth) is left-handed or leiotropic. Conklin ('97) has even shown that the position of the nuclei and central bodies in the early 2-cell stage is such as would result from a slightly dexiotropic first cleavage, thus agreeing with the third cleavage. The rule of the regular alternation of the spirals is thus extended to the series of early cleavages from the beginning.

It is obvious that the effect of the spiral cleavage is to cause the blastomeres to dovetail or interlock from the beginning, so as to form polyhedral bodies of the same general type seen in later stages of development and commonly also in tissue-cells when aggregated in solid masses (*e. g.*, in parenchyma). This form approximates to that of massed plastic spheres (such as soap-bubbles or balls of clay) when flattened together by pressure or capillary attraction, and also to that seen in a honeycomb. The position of stable equilibrium assumed under these conditions is that which gives the greatest economy of space; and it has been shown by Plateau, Lameere, Kelvin, and other physicists that this position is attained when *the area of surface-contact between such bodies is a minimum* (law of minimal contact- or partition-area). When, for instance, such bodies are grouped in a single layer on an extended surface, as is often the case with cells, they tend to assume the form of hexagonal prisms with three faces or planes meeting along a line and forming angles of 120° with one another. When they are massed in three dimensions they tend towards the form of tetrakaidecahedrons having 14 faces, of which certain ones are slightly curved. We need not enter here into the rather complicated problems here involved further than to point out that in the actual tissues these forms vary widely, being affected by many modifying conditions, such as the direction of growth, the effect of recent cell-divisions and the like.[1] Broadly speaking, nevertheless, it is evident that massed cells in many forms of tissues tend towards polyhedral forms that approximate to those demanded by the theory, as was early pointed out by Berthold ('86), Errera ('86, '87), and Chabry ('87), and the conclusion is irresistible that this grouping of cells conforms to the same general physical law as that of non-living bodies.

It seems certain that the spiral form of cleavage is an expression of the same tendency, and in a general way has been determined by mechanical conditions. This conclusion is supported by the fact that many of its stages may be accurately imitated by physical models. Robert ('03) in particular has published a series of photographs of soap-bubble models imitating with remarkable exactness the cleavage of *Trochus* up to the 16-cell stage (Fig. 461), showing the characteristic size-relations of the blastomeres and even the cross-furrows of the 4- and 8-cell stages. When crowded in solid masses (*i. e.*, in three dimensions), they assume a more complicated poly-

---

[1] The forms of vegetable parenchymena have recently been carefully studied by F. T. Lewis ('23), who gives an interesting discussion of the subject. See also the remarkable work of D'Arcy Thompson on *Growth and Form* ('17).

hedral form, interlocking in such a manner that four lines, each formed by the intersection of three planes 120° apart, meet at one point, there forming with one another angles that approximate to those of a tetrakaidecahedron (109° 28′ 16″).[1]

In an interesting earlier work by Roux (’97) it was shown that oil-drops suspended between alcohol and water in a cylindrical vessel may be divided

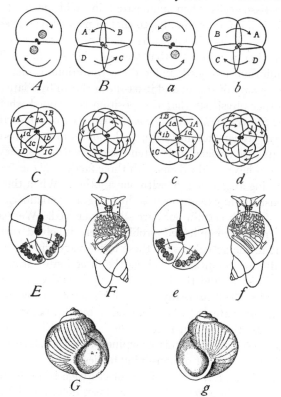

Fig. 465.—Diagram comparing the development of dextral and sinistral gasteropods (CONKLIN).

A–F, dextral forms (modelled on *Lymnæa*) showing 2-cell stage; *A*, 4-cell, *B*, 8-cell, *C*, 16-cell; *D*, the gastrula and mesoblast-bands (*E*) and asymmetry of adult (*F*); *a–f*, corresponding sinistral type (modelled on *Physa*) *G, H*, dextral and sinistral shells.

by a glass rod in various ways so as to imitate certain of the early forms of cleavage, including even the bilateral. Many of these groupings are, how- ever, unstable and tend to take up ultimately the position of minimal con- tact-areas according to Plateau’s law. A pretty illustration of this is that

---

[1] This is the same relation shown by the interlocking bases of the two tiers of cells of the honey- comb, and may readily be imitated by clay models. These will make clear the fact that under these conditions six planes meet at one such point.

four equal drops may be divided crosswise so as to produce an orthoradial 8-drop group like that of the 8-cell of *Synapta;* but any slight disturbance will cause a regrouping such that the upper quartet comes to alternate with the lower, as in the spiral type of cleavage. It is, however, important to bear in mind that the spiral type of cleavage is not directly caused by the displacement of plastic spheres in some degree free to shift their position, though to a certain extent such movements may occur. The study of cell-lineage has shown that the direction of the cleavage is often clearly foreshadowed by the position of the spindles before the cell divides.[1] Plateau's law fails to account for the regular alternation of the spiral cleavages; and above all it fails to give any clue to the remarkable reversal of the spiral type that occurs in the sinistral gasteropods,[2] a fact very strikingly shown by the comparison of closely related forms (Fig. 465) that are respectively sinistral (*e. g.*, *Physa*) and dextral (*Lymnæa*). The explanation of this fact is unknown, though Conklin ('03) has offered some interesting speculations on the subject. This is but one of many facts showing that spiral cleavage has a significance beyond that suggested by simple and obvious mechanical conditions, and one which clearly belongs among the promorphological relations of cleavage (p. 1006).

3. The Bilateral Type

In this form the spindles, and hence the cleavage-planes, are bilaterally disposed with reference to a plane of symmetry which coincides with the median plane of the resulting embryo. This type of cleavage is therefore essentially promorphological, and might more appropriately be considered under a later heading. The most perfect examples of it appear in the tunicates and the cephalopods, where the first cleavage-plane passes through the plane of symmetry and all later cleavages up to a late stage are symmetrical with respect to it.[3] The cleavage of these eggs offers most striking pictures in which violations to the simple mechanical rules of cleavage may everywhere be seen, particularly in the early stages; for instance, four planes instead of three meeting along a line, or cells dividing along their shorter instead of their longer axis (Figs. 466, 467, 468).

In other cases, bilateral cleavage, though often recognizable, is less constant. In the frog, for example, the early cleavages often show striking indications of bilaterality—it was indeed in this case that Newport ('54) first discovered the coincidence of the first cleavage-plane with the median

---

[1] Wilson, '92, Conklin, '97, etc.

[2] This was first clearly recognized by Crampton ('94), later confirmed by Holmes ('oo), and others; but Kofoid ('94) also independently gave reasons for accepting it, based on the earlier observations of Rabl ('79) on *Planorbis* and of Haddon ('82), on *Janthina.*

[3] See especially Van Beneden and Julin ('84), Vialleton ('88), Watase ('91), Castle ('96), Conklin ('05).

plane of the embryo—but it is here subject to many variations (p. 1069) and in any case is soon lost to view. On the other hand, in the annelids and molluscs (the cephalopods excepted), bilateral cleavages only appear at a relatively later stage of development, all the early cleavages being typically spiral in type (p. 998). In the annelid *Nereis* the writer found the first bilateral cleavage appearing suddenly in the 38-cell stage in certain ectoblastic

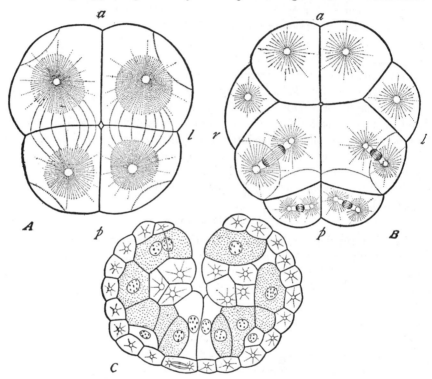

Fig. 466.—Bilateral cleavage of the tunicate egg.

A, four-celled stage of *Clavelina*, viewed from the ventral side; *B*, sixteen-cell stage (VAN BENE-DEN and JULIN); *C*, cross-section through the gastrula stage (CASTLE); *a*, anterior; *p*, posterior end; *l*, left, *r*, right side (orientation according to CASTLE).

cells of the upper hemisphere [1] while nearly at the same moment the first bilateral division of the lower hemisphere takes place in the primary mesoblast cell or teloblast ("4D"). Thus is initiated (Fig. 469) the formation in the upper hemisphere of a bilateral cross-shaped structure which forms the main foundation of the cerebral ganglia, while the symmetrical division of 4D leads the way in the formation of the cœlomesoblast bands which form

[1] Mead ('97) found the first bilateral cleavage in *Amphitrite* and *Clymenella* taking place after the 64-cell stage.

the foundation of the segmented trunk-region and incloses the cœlom (Fig. 473). The facts in the gasteropod or pelecypod are similar in principle. In these cases, the cleavage is of mixed type, being at first strictly spiral, later both spiral and bilateral. This again illustrates the fact that in all cases the original form of the early cleavage is gradually obliterated

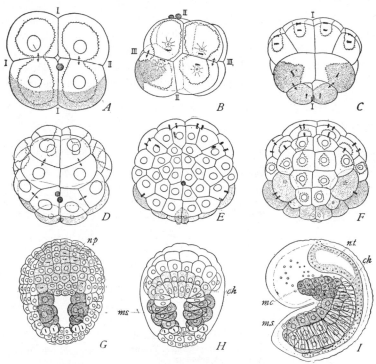

Fig. 467.—Normal cleavage of the ovum in the tunicate *Styela* (*Cynthia*) *partita* (Conklin). *A*, 4-cell stage, from animal pole, yellow crescent, showing through from below; *B*, early 8-cell stage, from the right side; *C*, 20-cell stage, from the vegetal (dorsal) pole; *D*, 20-cell stage, from animal (ventral) pole; *E*, corresponding view of 64-cell stage; *F*, the same egg seen from the vegetal (dorsal) pole; *G*, *H*, two views of the same gastrula (180 cells), *G*, showing the superficial cells, *H*, those at a deeper focus; *np*, the neural plate; *ms*, muscle-cells; *ch*, the chorda-cells; *I*, young tadpole, from left side; *nt*, neural tube; *mc*, mesenchyme; *ch*, notochord.

by displacements of the cells, irregularities of division, or specific forms of growth as development proceeds.

4. Special Modifications.

The preceding cleavage-forms are not dependent upon the amount and distribution of yolk or similar conditions—the bilateral form, for example, is equally marked in the small holoblastic egg of the ascidian (Fig. 467) and in the large meroblastic one of the cephalopod (Fig. 468) but each of them may be modified in its detail by definite changes in the rhythm of division or in its size-relations. Attempts have been made to reduce both these to simple mechanical rules but thus far with little success.

In the least modified forms division is equal and synchronous throughout the embryo, the number of cells increasing in regular geometrical progression to 2, 4, 8, 16, etc.; this rhythm is nearly approached by the cleavage of *Synapta* up to the 512-cell stage, as mentioned above. Nothing, however, is more common than departures from such regularity, some of them slight and inconstant, others marked and definite. To take but a single example, in the annelid *Nereis* (Fig. 470) the typical succession in the number of

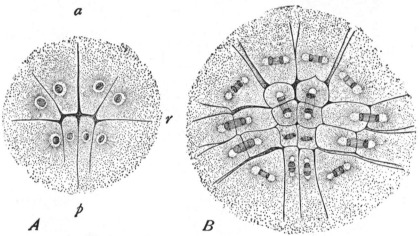

Fig. 468.—Bilateral cleavage of the squid's egg (WATASÉ).

A, eight-cell stage; *B*, the fifth cleavage in progress. The first cleavage (*a–p*) coincides with the future median plane; the second (*l–r*) is transverse.

blastomeres is with considerable constancy 2, 4, 8, 16, 20, 23, 29, 32, 37, 38, 41, 42, after which the order is more or less variable. The factors that determine such special rhythms were at first referred to very simple mechanical conditions—Balfour, for example ('75, '80), held that the rate of division in any particular blastomere or region of the embryo is inversely proportional to the amount of deutoplasm that it contains; and in a rough way this seems to be true of many forms of cleavage. In telolecithal ova such as those of the frog or the ganoid, for example, the slower rate of division of the blastomeres of the lower hemisphere is correlated with the greater relative amount of passive yolk in this region. Numerous accurate studies in cell-lineage have, however, shown the entire inadequacy of such an explanation, demonstrating that remarkable differences of rhythm are often displayed by blastomeres that show no perceptible differences of deutoplasmic content.[1] Among annelids and mollusks, for example, the two upper sister-cells in each quadrant of the 16-cell stage differ wholly in division-potential. The upper one continues to divide rapidly and gives rise to numerous small cells of many kinds in the pre-trochal region, while the lower one divides but twice more, producing four large cells which develop cilia, differentiate into primary trochoblasts, and never divide again (Fig. 478). This striking difference between sister-cells, of the same size and nearly in the same region of the embryo is not visibly correlated with differences of deutoplasmic content. It has obviously a promorphological significance arising from a different prospective relation to the development of the embryo. Analysis of the cell-lineage of annelids and mollusks led F. R. Lillie to the conclusion that in many cases the rate of cleavage obviously shows a direct relation to the period at which the products become functional and the number of cells required at this time. In *Unio*, for example, a certain large cell of the second quartet ("d, 2") formed at the fourth cleavage shows individually an accelerated division-rate that is correlated with the early formation of the shell-gland to which it gives rise, and with the large number of its component cells; conversely, the relatively slow division-rate of the first quartet of ectomeres is correlated with the reduced condition and small number of cells of the pre-trochal region formed from it. The prospective character of cleavage, here clearly evident, applies to many other of the blastomeres.

The study of unequal division in cleavage clearly reveals the same principle. Such divisions sooner or later appear in all forms of cleavage, the long maintenance of perfect equality, as in *Synapta*, being rarely seen. The period at which inequalities first appear differs greatly in different forms. In *Polygordius* (Fig. 462) it first clearly appears at the fifth cleavage; in sea-urchins at the fourth (Fig. 512); in *Amphioxus* at the third (Fig. 471); in the tunicate *Clavelina* at the second (Fig. 466); in *Nereis* at the first division (Fig. 470). The extent of the inequality varies in like manner. Taking the third cleavage as a type, we may trace every transition from an equal division (echinoderms, *Polygordius*) through forms in which it is but slightly marked (*Amphioxus*, frog), those in which it is conspicuous (*Nereis, Limnæa*, polyclades, *Petromyzon*, etc.), to forms such as *Clepsine* or *Fulgur*, where the cells of the upper quartet are so minute as to appear like mere buds from the four large lower cells (Fig. 477). At the extreme of the series we reach the partial or meroblastic type of cleavage, such as occurs in the cephalopods, in elasmobranchs, teleosts, birds and reptiles. Here the lower hemisphere of

---

[1] See Wilson ('92), Kofoid ('94), Lillie ('95, '99), Zur Strassen ('95), Ziegler ('95), Jennings ('97), Mead ('97), Child ('oo), and later observers.

the egg does not divide at all, or only at a late period, cleavage being confined to a disc-like blastodisc or blastoderm at one pole of the egg (Fig. 472).

Among the most interesting of these various cases is that of the teloblasts or pole-cells characteristic of the development of many annelids and
mollusks and found in some arthropods.   These remarkable cells are
large blastomeres, set aside early in the development, which bud forth
smaller cells in regular succession at a fixed point, thus giving rise to
long cords of cells while form the most important part of the segmented
trunk-region.   Teloblasts are especially characteristic of apical growth
such as occurs in the elongation of the body in annelids, and they

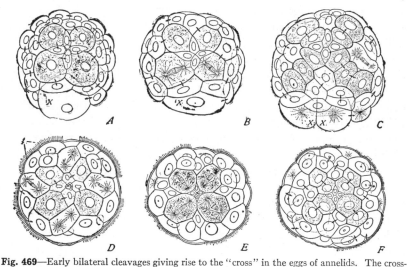

Fig. 469—Early bilateral cleavages giving rise to the "cross" in the eggs of annelids. The cross-
cells shaded in each case. *A–C*, from *Nereis* (WILSON); *D–F* from *Amphitrite* (MEAD).

A (36 cells) and *D* are almost exactly at the same stage; *E* is slightly later than *B* (38 cells); *C*,
somewhat later than *F*.   Note the close correspondence between the two species in cleavage-pattern
in spite of different size-relations of the cells.

are closely analogous to the apical cells situated at the growing point in
many plants such as the ferns and stoneworts.   The most familiar of them
are the primary mesoblasts (Fig. 473) discovered by Kowalewsky ('71) in
the oligochætes (*Lumbricus*, etc.) and later found in a large number of other
animals.[1]   Equally interesting are the ectoblastic teloblasts discovered by
Whitman ('78) in leeches, and subsequently by other observers in a number
of annelids (Wilson, Bergh, Vejdovský) and a few Crustacea (Bergh,
McMurrich).   In the annelids one pair of these are *neuroblasts*, from which
arise the ventral nerve-cord, while two or three additional pairs, the so-

[1] See the works for instance of C. O. Whitman, Hatschek, Vejdovský, Wilson, Bergh, Meyer,
Heymons. Kofoid. Mead, Conklin, Holmes, Heath, Torrey. Robert.

called "myoblasts" (Fig. 473) give rise to circular muscles and possibly also to a part of the nephridia.

Of general interest, likewise, is the formation of rudimentary cells (Fig. 474) arising as minute buds from the larger blastomeres, and taking only an insignificant part, or even no part, in the formation of the embryo Precise studies in cell-lineage have shown that some at least of these cells are constant both in origin and in number; and there is reason to be-

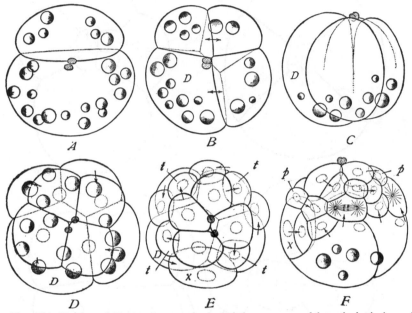

Fig. 470.—Cleavage of *Nereis*. An example of spiral cleavage, unequal from the beginning and of markedly determinate character.

A, two-cell stage (the circles are oil-drops); *B*, four-cell stage; the second cleavage-plane passes approximately through the future median plane; *C*, the same from the right side; *D*, eight-cell stage; *E*, sixteen cells; from the cells marked *t* arises the primary prototroch or larval ciliated belt, from *X*, the ventral nerve-cord and other structures, from *D* the mesoblast-bands, the germ-cells, and a part of the alimentary canal; *F*, twenty-nine-cell stage, from the right side; *p*, girdle of prototrochal cells which give rise to the ciliated belt.

lieve that they are probably to be regarded as vestigial structures that no longer play an active part in the building of the body but still persist as part of a definitely ordered mechanism of development.[1]

In all these various cases analysis quickly shows that cleavage-patterns are due in part to simpler mechanical causes, in part to more complex and obscure ones belonging to the formative process. The size-relations of cleavage, like its rhythm, are often correlated with the distribution of

[1] See Wilson ('92, '98, '99b), Lillie ('95), Torrey ('03), Robert ('03), etc.

yolk (deutoplasm) in the egg, a result generalized by Balfour ('80) in the statement that the size of the cells varies inversely with the relative amount of protoplasm in the region of the egg from which they arise. Thus, in telolecithal ova, where the deutoplasm is mainly stored in the lower or vegetative hemisphere (worms, mollusks, vertebrates), the cells of the

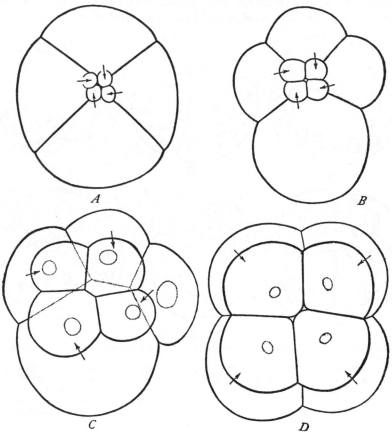

Fig. 471.—The eight-cell stage of four different animals showing gradations in the inequality of the third cleavage.

A, The leech *Clepsine* (Whitman); B, the chætopod *Rhynchelmis* (Vejdovský); C, the lamellibranch *Unio* (Lillie); D, *Amphioxus*.

upper or protoplasmic hemisphere are smaller than those of the lower, and may be distinguished as *micromeres* from the larger *macromeres*. The size-ratio between micromeres and macromeres is often directly proportional to the ratio between protoplasm and deutoplasm. Partial or discoidal cleavage occurs when the mass of deutoplasm is so great as entirely to prevent cleavage in the lower hemisphere. This relation was experimentally established by O. Hertwig ('98) who, by placing frogs' eggs in a centrifugal machine, has caused them to undergo a meroblastic cleavage through the artificial accumulation of yolk at the lower pole, due to the centrifugal force.

That inequalities of yolk-distribution often lead to inequality in cleavage is beyond doubt; but the most cursory survey of the known facts at once shows its hopeless inadequacy considered as a general interpretation. Every student of cell-lineage has been impressed by the characteristic behavior of individual blastomeres in respect to both the rhythm and the size-relations of division without discoverable relation to the amount and distribution of the yolk. In *Nereis*, for example, a large cell of the second quartet known as the first somatoblast, formed at the fourth cleavage (X, Fig.

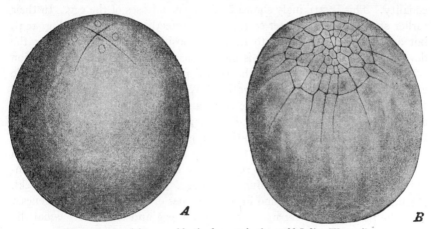

A   *B*

Fig. 472.—Partial or meroblastic cleavage in the squid *Loligo* (WATASÉ).

470), undergoes three very unequal divisions followed by an equal one, then by three other unequal divisions and again by an equal. This cell contains little or no deutoplasm and shows no other visible correlation of the form of division with the distribution of the cytoplasmic substances. Analogous phenomena (not always quite the same in detail) have been observed in case of this particular cell in various other annelids and molluscs.[1] The teloblasts, large protoplasmic cells commonly containing little or no deutoplasm, divide always unequally and in the same plane. The collapse of Balfour's second rule is most complete in the case of rudimentary or vestigial cells, as above mentioned. Such phenomena again demonstrate that the causes which determine the form of cell-division are not confined to simple and obvious mechanical conditions but are determined less im-

[1] See Conklin ('97), Mead ('97), Child ('00), Treadwell ('01), Lillie ('98, '99b), etc.

mediately by that intricate complex of factors which we call the specific organization of the germ.

It is none the less an interesting question what are the immediate conditions by which the form of cleavage is determined. The fact was early recognized (Conklin, '94 '97) that the immediate cause of unequal division seems not to lie either in the nucleus or in the amphiaster; for the chromosomes always divide equally; and although during division the asters are usually unequal in direct ratio to the inequality of cell-division, they often seem to be equal in the early prophases of these same divisions. The inequality is in this case obviously correlated with (perhaps a result of) the position of the amphiaster, which is central in equal division, eccentric in unequal division; and the greater the eccentricity the greater the inequality. This is strikingly shown in the polar mitoses of the egg. In their earlier stages the amphiaster seems to be perfectly symmetrical (Fig. 103), but as the spindle moves into its radial position near the periphery the development of the outer aster is more or less suppressed. The conclusion is here indicated that the size of the aster depends on that of the cytoplasmic area that forms its sphere of operation. We should therefore expect to find that artificial displacement of the polar amphiaster would correspondingly affect the inequality of the polar divisions; and such appears actually to be the case. The occasional formation of giant polocytes has earlier been mentioned (p. 494), and Conklin has shown that this result may be produced experimentally in the eggs of *Crepidula* by displacement of the polar amphiasters as a result of centrifuging the egg. Again, Lefevre, Kostanecki, Buchner and others have found in certain types of artificial parthenogenesis that the polar amphiaster may sink into the egg and lead to its equal division as the first step in cleavage (p. 477).

These conclusions, however, do not reach the root of the matter. Lillie's important observations on *Nereis* ('12) show that the inequality of the first cleavage is foreshadowed already in the early prophases by a marked inequality of both the asters and *the central bodies* that is already present in the sperm-amphiaster before the gamete-nuclei have united, and long before the cleavage-figure has taken up its definitive position (Fig. 475). Here, therefore, the inequality of the centers and asters seems to be due to a more deeply lying cause somehow involved in the organization of the egg. A similar conclusion seems to be forced upon us by studies on the direction of cleavage in later stages, where simple mechanical factors undoubtedly play an important rôle yet often fail to explain all the facts. Experiments by Pflüger ('84), Roux ('85), Driesch ('92) Ziegler ('94) and later investigators have proved that the direction of cleavage may be determined, or at least modified, by mechanical pressure which changes

the form of the dividing mass. Driesch and his successors, for example, demonstrated that when the eggs of sea-urchins are flattened

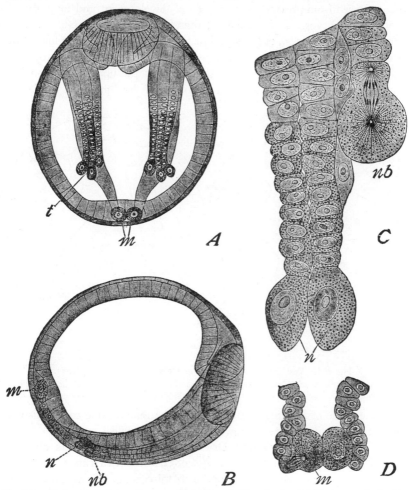

Fig. 473.—Embryos of the earthworm *Allobophora fœtida*, showing teloblasts or apical cells.

A, gastrula from the ventral side; B, the same from the right side; m, the terminal teloblasts or *primary mesoblasts*, which bid forth the mesoblast-bands, cell by cell; t, lateral teloblasts, comprising a *neuroblast, nb*, from which the ventral nerve-cord arises, and two nephro-myoblasts from which arise a portion of the circular muscles and possibly of the nephridia; C, lateral group of teloblasts, more enlarged, the neuroblast, nb, in division; n, the nephro-myoblasts; D, the primary mesoblasts enlarged; one in division.

by pressure the amphiasters as they are successively formed assume
the position of least resistance, *i. e.*, parallel to the flattened sides,
so that the cleavages are all vertical. The egg therefore segments as a

flat plate of eight, sixteen or thirty two or even sixty-four cells (Fig. 505). This is totally different from the normal form of cleavage; yet such eggs, when released from pressure, are capable of development and may give rise to normal embryos. It is probable, therefore, that the disc-like cleavage of meroblastic eggs (*e. g.*, of the squid or bird) is in some degree a mechanical result of the accumulation of yolk by which the formative protoplasmic region of the ovum is reduced to a thin layer at the upper pole; and it indicates, further, that the unequal cleavage of less modified telolecithal

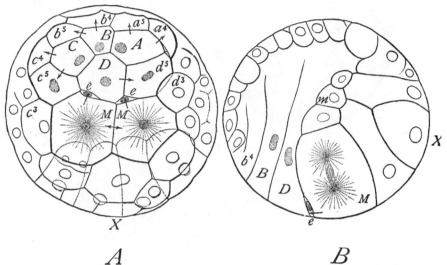

A   *B*

Fig. 474.—Vestigial blastomeres in the embryo of an annelid, *Aricia*.

A, from lower pole; vestigial cells at *e, e;* the heavy outline is the lip of the blastopore; *B*, the same in sagital optical section, showing vestigial cell (*e*), primary mesoblast (*M*), and mesoblast-band (*m*).

eggs, like those of the frog or snail, are in like manner due to the displacement of the mitotic figures toward the upper pole.

The results of Pflüger's and Driesch's pressure-experiments obviously harmonize with Hertwig's second rule (p. 985), and with Drüner's hypothesis of the active elongation of the spindle in mitosis (p. 182). Nevertheless numerous facts prove that neither the form of the protoplasmic mass nor the distribution of metaplasmic materials is sufficient to explain the position of the spindle, whether with reference to the direction or the inequality of the cleavage. Berthold ('86) long since clearly pointed out that prismatic or cylindrical vegetable-cells, for instance, those of the cambium, often divide lengthwise; and numerous contradictions of Hertwig's "law" have since been observed by students of cell-lineage (Fig. 476).[1]   In some of

[1] *Cf.* Watasé ('91), Mead ('94, '97, '02), Heidenhain ('95), Wheeler ('95), Castle ('96), Jennings ('97).

these cases the position of the spindle seems to be not that of least but of greatest resistance,[1] the spindle actually pushing away the adjoining cell to make way for itself. Similar difficulties stand in the way of the attempt to explain the eccentricity of the spindle in unequal division. All these considerations drive us to the view that the simpler mechanical factors, such as pressure, form and the like, are subordinate to more subtle and complex operations involved in the general development of the organism. This conclusion is strikingly illustrated by the phenomena of teloblastic division (p. 1001). The constant succession of unequal divisions, always in the same plane, is here correlated with the apical growth of the embryo,

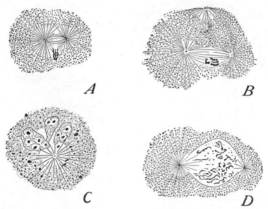

Fig. 475.—Sperm-centers and cleavage-centers in the fertilization of *Nereis* (F. R. LILLIE).

A, young sperm-amphiaster (heteropolar) and sperm-nucleus; B, later stage, secondarily connected above with inner pole of polar amphiaster; C, following karyogamy, only larger center visible; D, later phase, with heteropolar figure.

and this expresses a deeply lying law of growth in animals of this type. This is quite analogous to the definite forms of division in the apical cells of plants. In all such cases we cannot comprehend the specific forms of cleavage without reference to the end-result of the formative process; and the problems here encountered cannot be separated from those of development in the larger sense. The teleological aspect of cleavage thus suggested has been recognized more or less clearly, by many observers;[2] most adequately perhaps by Lillie, who has urged that with this principle in mind "one can thus go over every detail of the cleavage, and knowing the fate of the cells, can explain all the irregularities and peculiarities displayed." The egg is not merely a cell dividing as best it may, under the stress of simple

[1] See especially the case observed by Mead ('94, '97, '02), in the egg of *Amphitrite*.
[2] See Wilson ('92), Roux ('94), Bræm ('94), Lillie ('95, '99), Jennings ('97), etc.

and obviously mechanical conditions. It is "a builder which lays one stone here, another there, each of which is placed with reference to future development."[1] Of the truth of this anyone must, I think, be convinced who has critically studied these phenomena. Such a conclusion need involve no mystical doctrine of teleology or of final causes. It means only that the factors by which cleavage is determined are in greater or less degree bound up with an underlying organization of the egg that precedes cleavage and is responsible for the general morphogenic process. The nature of this organization is almost unknown; but we can proceed with its in-

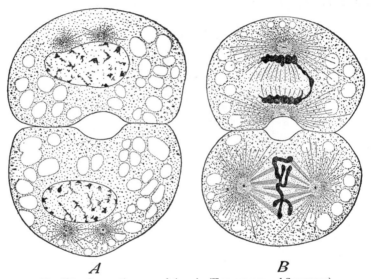

A   *B*

Fig. 476.—Segmenting eggs of *Ascaris* (Kostanecki and Siedlecki).

A, early prophase of second division, showing double central bodies; *B*, second cleavage in progress; upper blastomere dividing parallel to long axis of the cell.

vestigation only on the mechanistic assumption that it involves some kind of material configuration in the substance of the egg (p. 1035).

We are thus brought to the second or promorphological aspect of cleavage in which are involved the most fundamental problems of development.

II. PROMORPHOLOGICAL RELATIONS OF CLEAVAGE

By many of the earlier writers cleavage was regarded primarily as a problem merely of cell-division; the eminent physiologist Pflüger, for example, considered it as no more than a process by which the egg splits up into equivalent or indifferent cells, which, in his words, have no more def-

[1] Lillie ('95), p. 46.

inite or predetermined relation to the adult body than have snowflakes to the avalanch to which they contribute.[1] Many later writers adopted a view similar in principle, the egg being considered as "isotropous" and the blastomeres into which it segments as "equipotent" (p. 1056); but the hopeless inadequacy of such a conception was long since demonstrated. In a very large number of cases a precise relation exists between the cleavage-products and the adult parts to which they give rise—one which in some cases may be traced back to the beginning of development, so that from the first division onward we are able to predict the exact future of every individual cell. In this regard the cleavage of the ovum often goes forward with a wonderful clock-like precision, giving the impression of a strictly ordered series in which every division plays a definite rôle and has a fixed relation to all that precedes and follows it. Beyond all this, the predestination of the embryonic areas may often be recognized in the undivided ovum, even before it has been fertilized. The egg itself, therefore, may exhibit a distinct promorphology which underlies that of the cleavage-process and certain features of which may sometimes be identified even in early ovarian life.

1. Special Promorphology of Cleavage

This subject may be illustrated by further consideration of the spiral type which offers some of the most striking known cases of cellular pre-destination and mosaic development. Comparative studies on cell-lineage of this type have demonstrated that the successive quartets of cells have definite promorphological values which, with only minor variations, hold constant throughout a large series of platodes, annelids and molluscs. These values are independent of the size of the egg or the amount and distribution of the yolk: Conklin ('07), for instance, has shown that in gasteropods the quartets are not only formed in the same way but also have the same value in the large yolk-laden and very unequally dividing eggs of the snail *Fulgur* as in the small, yolk-poor, and almost equally dividing eggs of *Lymnæa* (Fig. 477). Similar examples might be given from the annelids; and it is noteworthy that the values of the quartets seem to be uninfluenced by the character of the first two cleavages, i. e., whether equal (as in *Patella* or *Crepidula*) or unequal (as in *Nereis* or *Spio*), and whether these are nearly or quite radial (as in *Patella* or *Cerebratulus*) or markedly spiral (as in *Nereis* or *Fulgur*). These values are in brief as follows (Figs. 463, 469, 477, 481):

(a) From the first, second and third quartets is formed the entire ecto-blast of the larva, which is thus completely segregated from the entoblast

[1] ('83), p. 64.

by three successive divisions in each quadrant.   In the trochophore larva of annelids and molluscs the first quartet gives rise to the entire pretrochal ectoblast (including the preoral ganglia and the main part of the prototroch), its posterior limit being marked in a general way by the prototroch or ciliated belt (Figs. 478–480).   The principal part of the latter arises from a group of "primary trochoblasts," typically four in number, to the products of which are

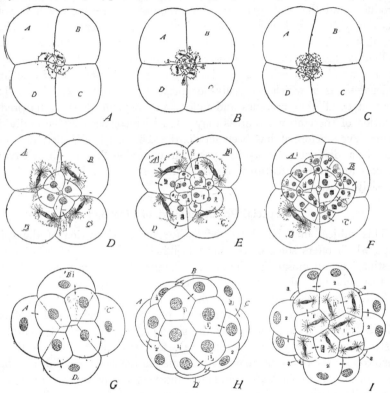

Fig. 477.—A comparison of the early stages of spiral cleavage in three gasteropods.

A, B, C, 8-cell, 16-cell and 24-cell stages in *Fulgur* (Conklin); *D, E, F,* corresponding stages in *Crepidula* (Conklin); *G, H, I,* corresponding stages in *Trochus* (Robert).

In all three cases, in spite of the wide differences in the size-relations, the cells correspond exactly in origin, position and promorphological value.

usually added certain additional cells ("secondary trochoblasts") from the first or second quartet, or from both.   From the second and third quartets arises the post-trochal ectoblast.   From the left posterior member of the second quartet, called the "first somatoblast" (2d) often distinguished by its large size (X in Fig. 470), arises the ectoblast of the ventral plate, giving rise to the ectoblastic teloblasts (when such are present, above referred to, p. 998), including the neuroblasts, nephroblasts and myoblasts which bud forth the material for the ventral nerve-cord, and circular muscles.[1]

An interesting detail is the origin, in many cases, from certain blastomeres of the ectoblastic quartets of certain cells (ectomesoblast) which contribute to the mesoblast, their number and origin varying somewhat in different types.[2] These cells show a series of conditions that seem clearly to indicate a phylogenetic series culminating in rudimentary or vestigial cells

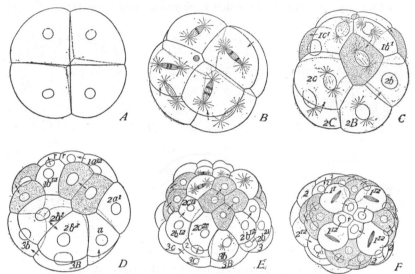

Fig. 478.—Earlier stages of typical spiral cleavage in the limpet *Patella*.

A, 4-cell stage; *B*, 4th cleavage; *C*, 16-cell stage, from the side, primary trochoblasts stipped; *D*, 32 cells; *E*, 48 cells; *F*, same, from upper pole.

otherwise inexplicable. In some of the Turbellaria they are formed in all four quadrants, are of relatively large size, and give rise to a considerable part of the mesoblast (Fig. 481). In the annelids and gasteropods mesoblastic cells are in many cases produced by certain cells of these quartets, but only in certain quadrants; and they are often very small, and in some cases seem to produce only transitory larval structures, hence the terms "larval mesoblast" (Lillie) or "pædomesoblast" (Eisig). In the polyclade the ectomesoblast seems to be formed only from the second quartet.[3] In the gasteropod *Crepidula* Conklin ('97) found mesoblast forming from three cells of the same quartet; in *Unio* Lillie ('95) found it in only one. Further

---

[1] See Whitman ('78, '87), Wilson ('98), Bergh ('90), Vejdovský ('88, '92).

[2] Review in Wilson ('98), Torrey ('03), Robert ('03).

[3] Lang ('84) believed the whole of the second and third quartets produced mesoblast alone; but both the writer ('98, *Leptoplana*) and Surface ('07, *Planocera*) found the facts as above stated.

studies showed that in some cases the ectomesoblast is formed mainly or wholly by two or three small cells from the *third* quartet;[1] and finally it was found by Torrey ('03) in the annelid *Thalassema* that a considerable number of such cells were produced by all three quartets. Of these, only two (from the third quartet) are functional, the others being vestigial and degenerating like polar bodies. All this, evidently, suggests that ectomesoblast or larval mesoblast of annelids and mollusks is a more or less reduced formation derived from an ancestral one in which it played a more important rôle, as is

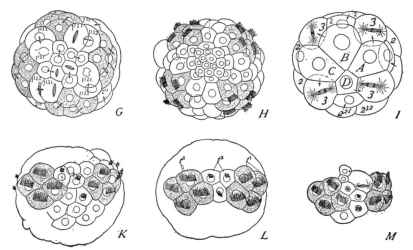

Fig. 479.—Continuation of Fig. 478. Spiral cleavage in *Patella*.

G, 58 cells, upper pole; H, later "ctenophore stage," ciliation of primary trochoblasts; I, 52 cells, lower pole; K–M, side-views, appearance of secondary trochoblasts.

still the case in the platodes. As will presently be seen, a similar result is indicated with equal clearness in case of the fourth quartet.

(b) The formation of the fourth quartet marks an abrupt transition, the ectoblast and ectomesoblast having completely split off. Three members of this quartet, 4A, 4B, and 4C are purely entoblastic. The fourth or posterior member, 4D, is the "second somatoblast" or "primary mesoblast" which divides into two equal teloblasts (Fig. 474, A); and from these are budded forth the main mesoblastic bands (cœlomesoblast) which form the walls of the cœlom, including the cœlomic epithelium, the gonads and an important part of the muscular system (longitudinal muscles of annelids).

The history of this cell again brings prominently to attention the occurrence of rudimentary cells which seem explicable only as reminiscences of bygone conditions. In some cases, possibly in all, 4D is not purely mesoblas-

[1] E. g., in *Physa*, Wierzejksi ('97), *Planorbis*, Holmes ('97), *Thalassema*, Torrey ('03).

tic but makes a small contribution to the entoblast, in some cases so much reduced in amount as to include but two minute and rudimentary cells no larger than polocytes and probably to be regarded as true vestigial structures.[1] These cells are formed immediately after the first equal division of 4D prior to the production of the mesoblast-bands. In some cases (*Aricia*) they lie superficially and are quite rudimentary (Fig. 474); in others they are represented by larger cells which enter into the formation of the end-portion of the enteron (*Nereis, Crepidula, Clymenella*).[2] It is difficult in

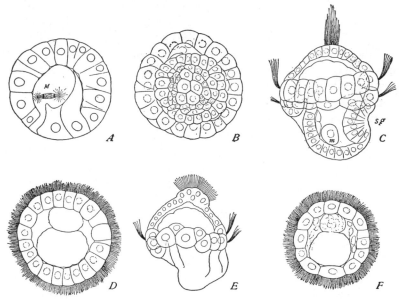

Fig. 480.—Continuation of Fig. 478. Early larvæ of *Patella* (WILSON).

A, larva of 9 hours in sagittal optical section, showing primary meso-teloblasts, *M; B*, 20 hours, from upper pole; *C*, trochophore 30 hours; *D*, optical horizontal section of same through ciliated belt; *E*, dwarf trochophore from fertilized egg-fragment; *F*, optical horizontal section of same.

the former case not to consider the rudimentary cells as reminiscent of earlier conditions in which they were larger and contributed to the functional entoblast, as they still seem to do in *Crepidula* and *Clymenella*.

(c) Beyond this point the residual substance of the basal quadrants, so far as known, is purely entoblastic and the quartet-formation is not long continued. When a fifth or sixth quartet is formed (*e. g.*, in *Aricia*,

---

[1] See especially Wilson ('92, '98), Heymons ('93), Mead ('94, '97), Lillie ('95), Holmes ('97), Conklin ('97), Robert ('02).

[2] In some of the molluscs they seem not to be connected with the enteron but are carried into the interior, lying near the front end of the mesoblast-band on each side. See Wierzejski ('97). General review in Robert ('02).

Fig. 474) the cells are always entoblastic like the basal quadrants from which they arise.

In some cases there seem to be certain minor exceptions to the foregoing account; and there are some forms (e. g., in the fœtal types of development in the oligochætes and some of the leeches) in which the regular quartet-formation is obscured and perhaps lost. Nevertheless, the striking fact is the constancy shown by the history and values of the quartets in so extended and varied a series of animals. Equally impressive are the promorphological relations seen in the bilateral type of cleavage, which has been studied with great exactness of detail in the ascidians by a long series of observers from the time of Van Beneden and Julin ('84) down to that of Conklin ('05). In all these cases cleavage offers the appearance of a mosaic-work in which every cell has its definite value and which is built up by a precisely ordered series of events. That such is actually the fact has been shown by numerous experimental researches which demonstrate that the cleavage-pattern is a true mosaic of potencies. This mosaic owes its character to an antecedent segregation of cytoplasmic materials the main features of which preëxist in the unsegmented egg; but the problems here involved belong to a later stage of our discussion (Chapter XIV).

2. Axial Relations of the Primary Cleavage-planes

Attention was early drawn by Newport ('54), to the fact that in the frog's egg the first cleavage furrow often corresponds with the median (sagittal) plane of the larva and adult, the first two blastomeres giving rise respectively to the right and left sides of the body. This discovery was confirmed long afterwards by Pflüger ('85) and especially by Roux,[1] who found, however, that this relation is not here wholly constant, the first cleavage-plane being in a few cases more or less oblique to the plane of symmetry, or even at right angles to it. The latter condition he ascribed to an "anachronism" in cleavage, the former to errors of observation. Later and more precise studies by many observers [2] proved, however, that in the frog the relation really is somewhat variable, though coincidence is the rule. On the other hand, in the eggs of ascidians (Clavelina, Ciona, Cynthia, etc.) all observers from the time of Van Beneden and Julin ('84) have found a very precise correspondence, without noticeable exception, between the plane of first cleavage and the future median plane,[3] and also have shown that all the later stages of cleavage display a most striking bilateral symmetry with respect to the first cleavage-plane. This symmetry can be traced up to so late a

---

[1] See especially Roux ('83, '85, '88), also Gesammelte Abhandlungen, 1894.

[2] See especially O. Hertwig ('93), Morgan and Boring ('93), Kopfsch ('95), 'oo, O. Schultze ('oo), Brachet ('04, '06), Jenkinson ('06).

[3] See Chabry ('86), Castle ('96), Conklin ('02, '05), with full reviews of the literature.

stage that the coincidence of the first cleavage-plane with the median plane of the larva is placed beyond all doubt (Fig. 467).[1] In the eggs of cephalopods the same relation occurs, the early cleavages being strictly bilateral with respect to the plane of first cleavage (Fig. 468), and the latter in its turn coinciding with the plane of symmetry of the unsegmented egg (Fig. 485) and of the bilateral larva to which it gives rise. In both the foregoing cases, accordingly, we can from the beginning clearly distinguish the right and left halves of the future larva, its anterior and posterior regions, and its dorsal and ventral aspects, even in the unsegmented egg (*cf.* p. 1019). In the ctenophore, likewise, the first cleavage-plane corresponds accurately with the sagittal or gastral plane, while the second is at right angles to it (Fol, '69).

Van Beneden ('84, p. 64) surmised that the development of animals generally would be found to show the same relation, but this proved to be untenable. In a second class of cases, the first cleavage, though constant in direction, is nearly transverse to the future sagittal plane; well-determined examples of this are offered in the annelids (*Nereis, Chætopterus*) gasteropods (*Crepidula, Umbrella*), and pelecypods (*Teredo*).[2] In the newt *Diemyctilus* Jordan found the first cleavage-plane to be often transverse to the larval plane of symmetry, though varying more or less from it. In a third class, commonly found in polyclades, annelids and molluscs, both the first and second cleavages cut the sagittal plane at a considerable angle, sometimes nearly at 45°. Examples of this among the polyclades are offered by *Thysanozoön* or *Leptoplana;* among the annelids by *Clepsine, Rhynchelmis, Amphitrite, Arenicola* or *Thalassema;* and among the molluscs by *Planorbis, Aplysia, Unio,* or *Trochus*.[3]

In a fourth class may be placed the nematodes, in which, almost alone among animals, the first cleavage-plane is equatorial, cutting the egg-axis horizontally and corresponding roughly to the horizontal plane of the larva (Boveri, '99). In a fifth class, lastly, the relation is more or less variable (as in the frog or newt), and sometimes wholly inconstant, as has been proved by careful study, especially on the eggs of fishes and urodeles. Examples of this are offered by the toad-fish *Batrachus*, the teleosts *Ctenolabrus* and *Serranus*, and the salamander *Amblystoma*.[4]

[1] See Ussow ('81), Vialleton ('88), Watasé ('91).

[2] See Hatschek, '80 (*Teredo*); Wilson, '92 (*Nereis*); Heymons, '93 (*Umbrella*); Conklin, '97 (*Crepidula*), Lillie, '06 (*Chætopterus*).

[3] See Lang, '84 (*Polyclades*); Whitman, '78 (*Clepsine*); Lillie, '95 (*Unio*); Mead, '97 (*Amphitrite*); Child, '00 (*Arenicola*); Torrey, '03 (*Thalassema*); Rabl, '79 (*Planorbis*); Blochmann, '83 (*Aplysia*); Robert, '03 (*Trochus*). All of these eggs belong to the spiral type, and as cleavage proceeds the direction of the original cleavage-planes becomes more or less twisted, distorted or interrupted, though in a general way their relation to the adult symmetry can still be determined. The same is true of the conditions seen in *Nereis, Crepidula* or *Umbrella* and the spiral type generally.

[4] Clapp, '91 (*Batrachus*); Morgan, '93 (teleosts); Jordan and Eycleshymer, '94 (*Amblystoma*).

From all this it is plain that no fixed rule can be laid down concerning the promorphological relations of the early cleavages—not even the rule that the first two cleavages pass through the egg-axis—and that we cannot ascribe to them any fundamental significance. This is borne out by the fact (p. 1059), that the normal pattern of cleavage, even in a highly determinate type, such as *Nereis* (Wilson, '96) may be very widely modified by means of mechanical pressure and other agents, with comparatively little disturbance of the development. Nevertheless it is of the utmost interest that definite promorphological relations are so often seen in the early normal cleavage; and the very fact that the adjustment between the pattern of cleavage and that of the process of localization varies from group to group, and even in the individual, and may in some measure be experimentally modified in the laboratory, opens the way to a fruitful experimental analysis of the whole problem.

III. PROMORPHOLOGY OF THE OVUM

Reference has already been made to the fact that the ovum itself, before cleavage begins and even before its maturation and fertilization, often shows certain structural features that foreshadow corresponding features of the future embryo and adult. The most fundamental of these is the polarity of the egg, which is probably characteristic of all eggs, even when not visible to the eye.

1. Polarity and the Egg-Axis

This subject, briefly treated at p. 275, may here be somewhat further considered. It was long ago recognized by von Baer ('34) that the unsegmented egg of the frog shows two hemispheres, visibly differentiated by the distribution of pigment and further distinguished by the constant position of the two hemispheres of the floating egg with respect to gravity, the egg being deeply pigmented on that hemisphere that is ordinarily turned upwards, while pigment is nearly or quite absent in a considerable area surrounding the lowest point. This position of the egg is determined by the greater abundance of yolk—(which in this case is relatively heavy) in the lower hemisphere. In the frog's egg, accordingly, the egg may be thought of as having two poles connected by an ideal egg-axis. Von Baer pointed out, further, that the early cleavage-planes are definitely related to the axis, the first two passing through it in two meridians intersecting each other at a right angle, while the third is transverse to it, and hence horizontal. He also observed that the later cleavages are somewhat unequal, in such a manner that the cells of the upper hemisphere are smaller than those of the lower; and Remak afterward proved that the larger cells of the lower hemisphere represent, broadly speaking, the "vegetative layer' of von Baer, *i. e.*, the inner germ-layer or entoblast, from which arise the enteron and its appendages; while the smaller cells of the upper hemisphere represent the "animal layer," outer germ layer or ectoblast which gives rise to the epidermis, the

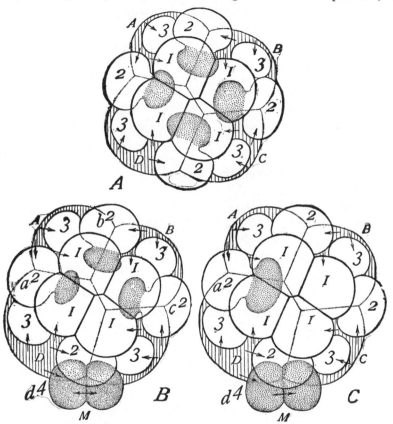

Fig. 481.—Diagrams illustrating the value of the ectoblast quartets in a polyclade (*Leptoplana*), a lamellibranch (*Unio*), and a gasteropod (*Crepidula*).

A, Leptoplana, showing ectomesoblast-formation in the second quartet; *B, Crepidula*, showing source of ectomesoblast (from a^2, b^2, c^2) and entomesoblast (from quadrant *D*); *C, Unio*, ectomesoblast formed only from a^2.

In all the figures the successive quartets are numbered with Arabic figures; ectoblast unshaded, mesoblast dotted, entoblast vertically lined.

nervous system, and the sense-organs. This fact led to the designation of the two poles (and hemispheres) respectively as *animal* and *vegetative, formative* and *nutritive*, or *protoplasmic* and *deutoplasmic*. Von Baer spoke of these poles or hemispheres (in case of the frog's egg) as the "upper" and the "lower" because of the position assumed by the floating egg; and these terms have persisted in common usage down to the present day, though often wholly inappropriate. In some cases it is the vegetative or "lower" hemisphere that is turned upwards owing to the presence of fat-drops in this part of the egg (*e. g.*, in the pelagic eggs of certain teleosts and annelids, such as *Nereis*, Figs. 199, 470), while in very many cases the telolecithal egg floats indifferently in any position.

The polarity thus clearly recognized in the frog's egg by Von Baer and Remak (p. 1014)[1] was subsequently found to be expressed in one way or another in the eggs of all other animals and probably always shows fundamentally similar relations to the formation of the embryo. The tendency of the yolk or deutoplasm to accumulate in the lower hemisphere is of widespread occurrence ("telolecithal" type of Balfour) though even in eggs of

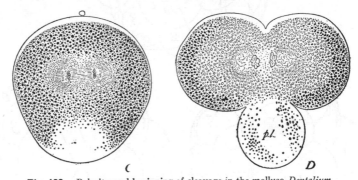

Fig. 482.—Polarity and beginning of cleavage in the mollusc *Dentalium*.

C, beginning of the first cleavage; *D*, first cleavage in progress, formation of the polar lobe (*p. l.*). "trefoil"-stage.

this type certain exceptions occur. In some cases, *e. g.*, in the eggs of certain annelids (*Myzostoma*, Fig. 524), molluscs (*Dentalium*, Fig. 107) and (after fertilization) tunicates (*Styela*, Fig. 523), the lower pole is surrounded by a definite protoplasmic *polar area* nearly devoid of yolk (*cf.* p. 1064). In others a small special protoplasmic area is also found at the upper pole (Fig. 107). Certain other cases agree with the frog in showing a distribution of pigment that is symmetrical with respect to the egg-axis. In the sea-urchin *Paracentrotus lividus* the unsegmented egg is encircled after its maturation by a rather broad band of superficial red pigment just below the equator and exactly at right angles to the egg-axis (Fig. 512). In the mollusc *Dentalium* the egg, even before its maturation, is surrounded by a somewhat similar but much broader band of pigment (reddish or olivaceos) leaving only two white polar areas surrounding the upper and the lower poles

---

[1] Among others who early laid stress on the importance of the egg-polarity may be mentioned Auerbach ('74), Hatschek ('77), Whitman ('78), Mark ('81) and Van Beneden ('83-'84).

(Figs. 483, 509). Sections show that in this egg the lower colorless polar area corresponds with a mass of clear protoplasm into which the yolk does not extend; while the upper pole is occupied by a similar but a very much smaller protoplasmic disc at the center of the upper colorless area (Fig. 107). In *Myzostoma* (Fig. 525) the lower pole of the unfertilized egg is surrounded by a green substance, while the remaining portion of the egg is colored red by a superficial layer of pigment (Driesch, Carazzi). In the tunicate *Styela partita* the egg contains orange-yellow pigment-granules at first scattered

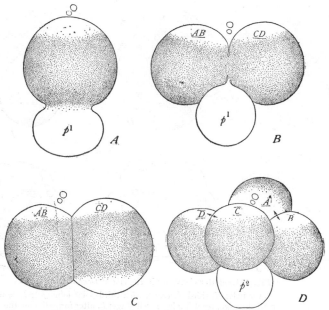

Fig. 483.—Early cleavage in the mollusc *Dentalium*.

A, beginning of the first cleavage by formation of the polar lobe (p^1); *B*, later (trefoil) stage of the same cleavage; *C*, resulting 2-cell stage; *D*, second cleavage in progress, with second polar lobe (p^2).

in the cortical layer but soon after fertilization collecting to form a very definite disc that lies at first exactly at the lower pole and later moves to the posterior side of the egg (Fig. 524).

To the foregoing more obvious manifestations of polarity may be added the position of the micropyle or micropyles (when such structures are present) which are usually either at one of the poles, or symmetrically placed with reference to it. In some cases the micropyle is exactly at the upper pole, as in sea-urchins (Fig. 512), cephalopods (Fig. 113), or fishes (Fig. 114). In others it lies at the lower pole, as in gasteropods or pelecypods (Fig. 488).

In many insects a group of micropyles is found at or near the upper (anterior) pole.

The polarity of the egg is manifested by other phenomena which, though less conspicuous, are of great significance.   In very many cases the original egg-nucleus (germinal vesicle) is eccentric, usually towards the animal pole; and in all cases *it is at or very near to this pole that the polar bodies or polocytes are extruded from the egg.*[1]

These facts make it evident that polarity is present even in eggs in which it is not made evident by the distribution of yolk or pigment (*e. g.*, in the

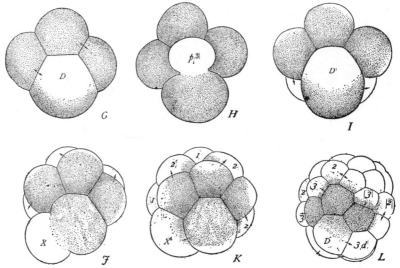

Fig. 484.—Later cleavages in the egg of *Dentalium.*

G, 4-cell stage, from lower pole; *H*, third cleavage, with third polar lobe (p^3); *I*, resulting 8-cell stage, lower pole; *J*, fourth cleavage, resulting in 16-cell stage; *L*, after formation of the 3d quartet.

centrolecithal eggs of cœlenterates or the "alecithal" eggs of many echinoderms).   All the evidence thus converges to the conclusion that the polarity of the egg is of universal occurrence among animals.   Its fundamental promorphological significance lies in the fact that the axis of the egg shows a definite relation to that of the gastrula of the later embryo, and of the adult body; and this relation, broadly considered, appears to be constant

---

[1] A single seeming exception to this is offered by the eggs of ctenophores (Ziegler, '98, Yatsu, '11, '12a, Komai '22) where the polocytes lie near what appears to be the vegetative pole.   Ziegler's observations indicate that this is due to a special peculiarity of the fourth (micromere-producing) cleavage which seem to involve a flow of yolk towards the original animal pole while the ectoblast-forming cortical oöplasm is carried down into the lower hemisphere where the micromeres finally are cut off.   An apparent reversal of polarity is thus caused which almost suggests that occurring in the inverted frog's egg (p. 1076).   This account does not, however, seem to be supported by the later studies of Yatsu ('12).

throughout the Bilateralia, though it is often disguised in later stages through processes of asymmetrical growth such as are strikingly seen in the metamorphosis of echinoderms or, in a simpler form in the platodes, annelids or molluscs. The questions here involved would lead us far into the more special problems of embryology.

The nature of the polarity of the egg is wholly unknown; but there can be little doubt that it is fundamentally of the same nature as the polarity of the tissue-cells. At this point we emphasize the fact that the polarity of the egg cannot be regarded as merely the expression of a polarized grouping of its visible materials (such as yolk or pigment) or even such an arrangement of its structural components (such as the position of nucleus and central apparatus). Experimental evidence hereafter reviewed (p. 1087) makes it probable that polarity is inherent in the protoplasmic substance itself; and both Boveri and Driesch were thus led to refer it to a polarization of ultimate structural particles of which the oöplasm is built (p. 1090).[1]

2. Bilateral Symmetry of the Ovum

Second in interest only to the polarity of the ovum is the bilateral symmetry shown in the shape of the egg and sometimes also in the grouping of its structural components, a condition so clearly marked in some cases that the position of the future embryo may be exactly predicted in the egg before it has been laid or fertilized. The classical case of this is offered by the eggs of insects, where it was originally pointed out by Leuckart and Metschnikoff and later studied by many observers,[2] and a bilateral structure was also inferred by Van Beneden and Julin ('84) in case of the unsegmented egg of ascidians which display so marked a bilaterality in the form of cleavage. Watasé ('91) observed the same fact in the egg of the cephalopod (*Loligo*), and demonstrated that the plane of symmetry during cleavage coincides with that of the ovum before cleavage begins. The form of the new-laid egg, prior to cleavage, is somewhat like that of a hen's egg, but is distinctly flattened on one side which Watasé proved to be the future posterior region, while the more convex side is anterior, the more pointed end dorsal and the larger end ventral (Fig. 485). The first cleavage-furrow here may be seen to lie in the plane of symmetry, the second in the transverse plane, while all the later ones, up to a late stage, are symmetrically disposed with reference to the median plane (Fig. 468).[3] It is probable from this that the egg of the

---

[1] For further remarks on polarity, see pp. 1023, 1087.

[2] See Hallez ('86), Blochmann ('87), Wheeler ('87, '93).

[3] Watasé observed, however, the remarkable fact that the blastodisc, *cleaving bilaterally* as usual, may sometimes lie on the side of the egg instead of in its normal position on the dorsal aspect. The bilaterality of cleavage is therefore not a mechanical result of the bilateral shape of the egg but inheres in the protoplasmic substance.

ascidian is also bilateral before cleavage (as inferred by Van Beneden and Julin) though not sufficiently marked to be visible to the eye.

The great variety of shapes offered by the eggs of insects has long been familiar; but many of them are known to be bilateral in shape, and this may be true of all. Most commonly the egg is more or less elongated, often angular in shape, and shows a very distinct plane of symmetry, together with antero-posterio and dorso-ventral differentiation which coincide with those of the future embryo; while Blochmann and Wheeler have observed a corresponding bilateral distribution of yolk. Hallez found, in a study of the cockroach (*Periplaneta*), the water-beetle (*Hydrophilus*) and the locust

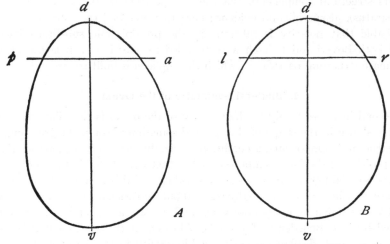

Fig. 485.—Outline of unsegmented squid's egg, to show bilaterality (Watasé).
A, from right side. B, from posterior aspect.
a–p, antero-posterior axis; *d-v*, dorso-ventral axis; *l*, left side; *r*, right side.

(*Locusta*) that "the egg-cell possesses the same orientation as the maternal organism that produces it; it has a cephalic pole and a caudal pole, a right side and a left, a dorsal aspect and a ventral; and these different aspects of the egg-cell coincide with the corresponding aspects of the embryo." Wheeler ('93) reached the same result after a study of over thirty species of insects and concluded that even in insect eggs that approach the spherical form the symmetry still exists, though not obvious. Hallez ('86) also determined the remarkable fact, confirmed by a number of later observers, that the egg always lies in the same position in the oviduct, with its anterior or cephalic end towards the upper end of the oviduct and hence towards the head-end of the mother. When, therefore, the eggs are laid in regular series or are massed in flat plates (a frequent condition) all occupy the same position. The writer has observed a good case of this in the beautiful eggs of the hemipter *Metapodius*, which are large, of a pearl-like luster, and markedly bilateral in form (Fig. 486). These eggs are often deposited one after another in regular series on the surface of plant-stems or leaves. When, therefore, the embryos become visible through the semi-transparent envel-

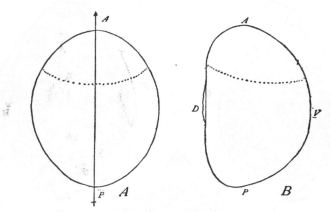

Fig. 486.—Bilateral egg of the hemipter *Metapodius femoratus*.
A, viewed from the ventral aspect; B, from the right side.
A, P, the anterior and posterior poles; D, V, dorsal and ventral aspects. The egg is always attached in the mid-dorsal surface (at D). Actual length 2.6 mm.

opes they are seen to be perfectly aligned as if marching forward in single file.

3. General Interpretations

The interpretation to be placed on the promorphology of the ovum and of cleavage offers a series of questions that belong to the more general problem of development, hereafter to be considered; nevertheless it may briefly be considered at this point Should polarity and bilaterality be regarded as primary or preformed characters of the egg-cell, or are they a secondary condition established in the egg by a process of epigenetic development? The first alternative was adopted, or at least implied, by Van Beneden, Flemming, Whitman and other of the earlier writers. More modern studies have tended to support the second alternative, which was early adopted by Mark, Pflüger, O. Hertwig, Driesch and Watasé, and later sustained by Boveri and many others. That the polarity of the egg involves no fixed and immutable organization was proved by the experiments of Pflüger ('84), Born ('85), Schultze ('94), Morgan ('95) on the frog's egg, which showed that if the egg be kept in an inverted position the cytoplasmic materials undergo a rearrangement under the influence of gravity which involves a more or less marked displacement of the old axis.[1]

Many other observations point to the conclusion that polarity, bilaterality

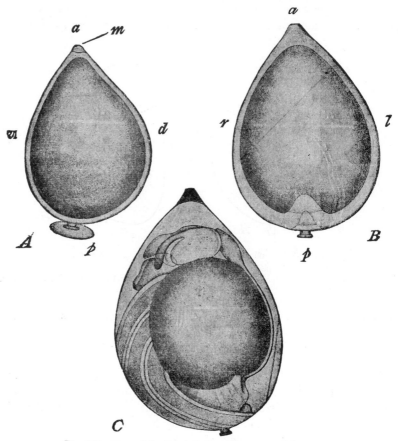

Fig. 487.—Eggs of the insect *Corixa* (METSCHNIKOFF).

A, early stage before formation of the embryo, from one side; *B*, the same viewed in the plane of symmetry; *C*, the embryo in its final position.

a, anterior end; *p*, posterior; *l*, left side, *r*, right; *v*, ventral, *d*, dorsal aspect. (These letters refer to the *final* position of the embryo, which is nearly diametrically opposite to that in which it first develops); *m*, micropyle; near *p* is the pedicle by which the egg is attached.

and other promorphological features of the egg are as truly a result of epigenetic development as are the characters which first become visible at later stages. They are gradually established during the preëmbryonic

[1] In this process the cortical, pigment-containing plasma remains fixed, thus giving a very definite landmark for identification of the original axis. Whether the original polarity is actually lost or merely shifted to a new direction is a rather delicate question. Born's studies showed that the inter-

stages, and the egg when ready for fertilization, has already accomplished part of its task by laying the basis for what is to come. Mark ('81), who was one of the first to examine the subject carefully, concluded that the ovum is at first an indifferent, homaxial, or isotropic cell which afterwards *acquires* polarity and other promorphological features; and essentially the same view was clearly formulated by Watasé, who urged that the ovum "which may start out without any definite axis at first, may acquire it later and at the moment ready for its cleavage the distribution of its protoplasmic sub-stances may be such as to exhibit a perfect symmetry, and the furrows of cleavage may have a certain definite relation to the inherent arrangement of the protoplasmic substances."[1] This is a remarkably close approach to the conclusions developed in later years by experimental studies (p. 1093).

In considering the questions here involved we must hold fast to the fact that the egg is a cell, similar in its essential features to other cells. There are many reasons to conclude, accordingly, that the cytoplasmic differen-tiations that the egg undergoes must arise in essentially the same way as in other cells. In the latter case such differentiations, whether in form or in internal structure, often show a definite relation to the environment of the cell—to its fellows, to the source of food, and the like; and we may expect the same to be true of the egg-cell. Mark made the pregnant suggestion that the primary polarity of the egg might be determined by "*the topographical relation of the egg* (when still in an indifferent state) *to the remaining cells of the maternal tissue from which it is differentiated,*" and added that this rela-tion might operate through the nutrition of the ovum. "It would certainly be interesting to know if that phase of polar differentiation which is manifest in the position of the nutritive substance and of the germinal vesicle bears a constant relation to the free surface of the epithelium from which the egg takes its origin. If in cases where the egg is directly developed from epithe-lial cells this relationship were demonstrable, it would be fair to infer the existence of corresponding, though obscured, relations in those cases where (as, for example, in mammals) the origin of the ovum is less directly traceable to an epithelial surface."[2] In this case the polarity of the egg would therefore be comparable to the polarity of epithelial gland-cells, where, as the nucleus usually lies toward the base of the cell near the source of food, while the central bodies, and often also characteristic cytoplasmic products, such as zymogen-granules, typically appear in the peripheral portion.[3]

nal oöplasmic substances undergo a kind of rotation, the more coarsely granular or yolk-bearing portion moving downward on one side while the more finely granular moves upward on the other; but the exact meaning of this is not yet clear.

[1] Watasé, '91, p. 280.

[2] '81, p. 515.

[3] See also Hatschek, *Zoölogie*, p. 112.

This conception has received strong support from numerous observations which demonstrate the existence of definite relations between the oöcyte and the maternal tissues. The germinal vesicle, as Korschelt ('89) especially pointed out, usually lies eccentrically towards the point of attachment or of food-supply; and this point has been proved in many cases to coincide with one of the poles of the egg, as is demonstrated by the position of the micropyle, of the polocytes, often also by the distribution of pigment or yolk. That the micropyle is formed at one pole of the oöcyte is made certain in some cases by the fact, first established by Jhering in the pelecypod *Scrobicularia* and later in other forms [1] that the egg is in some cases drawn out from the point of attachment to form a more or less attenuated pedicel, which persists until the egg-envelopes are formed, thus causing an interruption which becomes the micropyle (Fig. 488). The latter is sometimes actually traversed by the pedicel until the time when the egg breaks loose, when the pedicel is withdrawn, sometimes leaving a temporary papilla which (in the nemertine) may be identified with certainty as lying at the lower pole (Wilson, '03). In other cases [2] the micropyle is marked, and at first partially filled, by a special cell, derived from the ovarian epithelium.

The fact now seems well established that the micropyle (when present) may be situated either at or near the upper pole (echinoderms, insects, fishes) or the lower pole (nemertines, many molluscs). In the maturation of eggs of the latter type the central bodies first appear near the upper (originally free) pole, as is the case with epithelial cells generally (p. 108). This comparison seems to fail in cases where the micropyle lies at the upper pole; but the relations in this case call for further study. In the sea-urchin Boveri (02) believed that the micropyle, undoubtedly situated at the upper pole, marks the point of attachment in the ovary. Jenkinson ('11) has tried to show that (in *Paracentrotus*) the oöcyte is originally attached at the vegetative pole; and that the micropyle is here a new formation. The evidence of this, however, leaves much to be desired and the question as to whether a uniform relations exists among animals generally between the point of attachment and the pole therefore remains open.

Less is known of the bilaterality of the egg; but the presumption is the same as in the case of polarity. The constant position of the bilateral egg in the ovary of insects (p. 1020) is hard to explain under the hypothesis that the egg is bilateral from the beginning; and it seems more probable that bilaterality arises epigenetically in correlation with the intra-ovarian environment of the egg. In any case the experimental evidence (p. 1087) shows that the basis of bilaterality, like that of polarity, is not to be sought

---

[1] See Jhering ('77), Stauffacher ('94), C. B. Wilson ('99), E. B. Wilson ('03, '04), etc.
[2] See Eigenmann, '90 (teleosts), Mark '90 (*Lepidosteus*), Buchner, '10 (*Sagitta*).

merely in the shape of the egg or in the topographical distribution of its
materials. As in the case of polarity, therefore, Driesch and Boveri were
led to the conclusion that the fundamental basis of bilaterality must lie in
a bilateral orientation of ultimate protoplasmic particles of the oöplasm.

IV. GROWTH, CELL–FORMATION AND MORPHOGENESIS

1. The Limits of Growth and Cell-division

A distinction is often conveniently drawn between determinate and indeterminate growth and division, the former being strictly limited by inherent

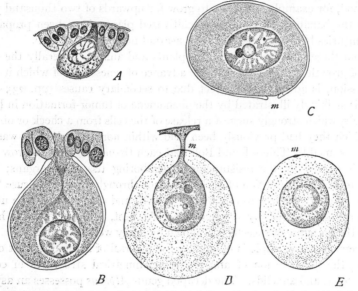

Fig. 488.—Attachment of the oöcyte and micropyle-formation in pelecypods. (*A–C,* in *Cyclas*
from STAUFFACHER; *D, E* in *Scrobicularia* from JHERING).
   A, B, earlier and later oöcytes, stalk of attachment to epithelial wall of ovary; *C,* oöcyte after
detachment, with amphi-nucleolus and micropyle (*m*); *D,* oöcyte, still attached to ovarian wall,
surrounded by "albuminous envelope" traversed by stalk of attachment; *E,* egg free in ovarian
cavity, with envelope and micropyle (*m*).

conditions (as in higher animals) the latter having no definitely assignable
limit, as is seen in many perennial plants. Even in the determinate type
it is probable that the cessation of growth and division is due to secondary
causes. In any case it is certain that different cells and tissues differ
widely in this respect. In the course of individual development growth
and division are in general most active and general in the embryonic
tissues and become more restricted as differentiation proceeds. Sooner or
later an approximate condition of equilibrium is established. Some of the

somatic cells, such as the nerve-cells, appear to lose the power of division altogether; others, such as the muscle-cells, connective tissue-cells and various forms of gland-cells, may divide under special conditions; still others continue to divide throughout life, thus replacing the worn out or dead cells of the same tissue (e. g., in the Malpighian cells of the epidermis). In all higher animals, where growth is limited, a nearly balanced state is finally reached in which replacement only suffices to make good the losses. In higher plants, on the other hand, progressive growth and division may continue for very long periods of time in the apical regions and in the cambium, thus leading to indeterminate growth with no assignable limit; the giant redwood, for example, is known to grow for upwards of two thousand years, while the banana and some other cultivated plants, have been propagated for centuries by purely vegetative or asexual processes (p. 235).

From these facts we infer that in plants and animals generally the cessation of growth and division, like the advance of senescence of which it is one expression, is an inhibitory effect due to secondary causes (pp. 235–237). This is strikingly illustrated by the phenomena of tumor-formation in higher animals, which strongly suggest a release of the cells from a check or obstacle by which they had previously been held within normal limits. It was long since assumed by Thiersch and Boll that each tissue continues to grow up to a limit offered by the resistance of neighboring tissues or organs; hence the removal or diminution of such resistance through injury or disuse leaves the remaining cells free to renew their growth and division until the normal barriers are restored by regeneration. At best, however, this is hardly more than a figure of speech, as is shown by many well-known facts.

A remarkable example is offered by the reversal of symmetry that occurs during the regeneration of amputated asymmetrical structures in certain crustaceans and annelids. The decapod genus *Alpheus* possesses an asymetrical pair of chelæ, one a small and simple structure with cutting edges, the other a very large and complicated crushing chela (Fig. 489). Individuals of the species as found in nature are indifferently right handed or left handed in this respect and either chela is readily regenerated after amputation.[1] Przibram discovered that if both chelæ be removed the original condition is restored; and the same result follows if only the small one be removed. When, however, the large chela is amputated a small cutting chela is regenerated in its place, while *the original cutting chela enlarges and is transformed into a large crushing chela*, thus reversing the original asymmetry. Zeleny obtained a closely similar result in the serpulid annelids (*Hydroides*, etc.) which originally possess two opercula, one large and functional and one very small and non-functional. Amputation of the

[1] Przibram ('o1, 'o2), Wilson ('o3), Zeleny ('o5).

large operculum causes a new small one to grow forth in its place, while the former small one quickly grows forth into a large functional one, of typical form and size.

In these curious cases it is evident that the smaller structure possesses a power of growth, cell-division and differentiation that is held in check,—we

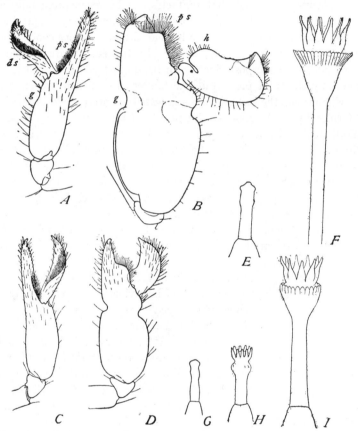

Fig. 489.—Reversal of asymmetry in crustaceans and annelids (*A–D*, Wilson; *E–I*, Zeleny).

A, B, normal left and right chelæ (the latter widely opened to show the "hammer," *h*) of *Alpheus heterochelis; C,* cast skin of right small chela after the first moult of an individual following amputation of left large chela *D,* the right chela withdrawn from *C* at the first moult, already showing character of a large chela; *E, F,* normal left rudimentary and right functional operculum of *Hydroides dianthus; G, H, I,* stages in transformation of a left rudimentary operculum into a large functional one after removal of original right functional one.

know not how, but conceivably through the action of hormones—by the presence of the larger chela. This check, obviously, is not a direct mechanical barrier but is somehow involved in the normal equilibrium of the organism; and this is a character of the species. Many illustrations of the same principle might be offered. The adult salamander, for example, is able to regenerate an amputated limb, whereas the adult frog only heals the wound without further regeneration (Fraisse).[1] Again, among cœlenterates, as was long since shown by Loeb, certain forms such as the polyp *Cerianthus*, show a polarity so marked that tentacles can be regenerated only at the distal end of a section; but in the hydroids tentacles may be produced at both ends of a cut stem if the piece be placed under proper conditions, and this is the case also in certain polyps.[2] In the earthworm (to take still another example) if the posterior region be amputated a new tail is readily developed by the front piece, but the hinder piece usually regenerates no head. If, however, the section be made near the anterior end a new head is often formed by the larger posterior piece. If the trans-section be made in the middle region the posterior piece sometimes regenerates a head but more usually a tail.[3] All this shows the futility of attempting to treat the compensatory changes that may follow upon removal, atrophy or displacement of particular parts as direct mechanical effects of the disturbance. They are complex specific physiological responses which belong in the general category of regulative phenomena.

Both the limitations of growth and cell-division and their release may be affected by a great variety of agents, many of which may in themselves be simple enough, such as the amount of available food-stuffs, or the presence or absence of particular hormones or the like in the blood. Fundamentally, however, the various types of behavior are determined by heredity, *i. e.*, they are an outcome of the specific organization of the germ-cells. This is at once obvious from the familiar fact that the specific mean size of organisms generally is hereditary. Size, however, is in general determined by the number of cells produced by the egg rather than by their size (p. 99)—the mouse, for example, differs in size from the elephant mainly because of the smaller number of its cells. The modern Mendelian analysis, beginning with Mendel's own experiments on tall and short races of peas, has shown that within the same species racial differences in size (and hence in the number of cells) may segregate in typical fashion; hence we conclude that, in some cases at least, the limits of growth and cell-division are determined by the chromosomes. We thus see that a valid general basis exists for the hypothesis of Boveri ('14) that the release of growth and cell-division from their normal restraints which so impresses us in the formation

---

[1] In salamanders regeneration only takes place if the bone is cut across, failing to occur if the limb be exarticulated at the joint. In frogs, the tadpole is able to regenerate an amputated limb, but not the adult.

[2] *Renilla*, Wilson ('03).

[3] See Morgan ('99).

of tumors, may be traceable to a definite disturbance that has taken place in the chromosome-group.

2. Cell-division and Morphogenesis

The problem takes on a broader aspect when we consider the phenomena of apical or teloblastic growth and cell-division in relation to the formative process to which reference has earlier been made.   In the *Characeæ* for example, we see a characteristic kind of metamerism produced by successive divisions of the apical cell, the single cells thus cut off, giving rise in regular alternation to the nodes and internodes of the mature stem.   In annelids and some arthropods we find a quite analogous though more complex process, in which successive divisions of the apical cells or teloblasts (Fig. 473) form the fundamental basis of the adult metamerism, including that of the mesoblast-bands and cœlomic cavities, the nervous system, nephridia and many other structures.[1]   In particular Vejdovský's observations on the annelid *Dendrobœna* give strong ground to believe that the number of metamerically repeated parts of this animal, and probably of other annelids, corresponds in like manner with that of the number of cells segmented off from the teloblasts.   A remarkable case is offered by the isopod crustacea, where the number of somites is limited and constant.   In the embryos of these animals as shown by McMurrich ('95), and by Bergh ('00) there are two groups of teloblasts near the hinder end of the embryo, an inner group of mesoblasts from which arise the mesoblast-bands, and an outer group of ectoblasts, from which arise the neural plates and the ventral ectoblast. The mesoblasts divide sixteen times, the ectoblasts thirty-two (or thirty-three) times, before relinquishing their teloblastic mode of division and breaking up into smaller cells, and the sixteen groups of cells thus formed give rise to the sixteen respective somites of the post-naupliar region of the embryo (*i. e.*, from the second maxilla backward).   Each single division of the mesoblasts, and each two succeeding divisions of the ectoblasts, thus splits off the material for a single somite.   The number of these divisions, and hence of the resulting somites, is a fixed inheritance of the species.   Such cases bring prominently into view the long debated question as to whether the character of growth and morphogenesis is a cause or a result of the corresponding activities on the part of the component cells individually considered.   This question was first raised in case of the apical growth of plants by Hofmeister, DeBary and Sachs.   All of these reached essentially the same result, namely (in the words of Hofmeister), that "the growth of the individual cells of a growing point is controlled and conditioned by the growth

---

[1] See Whitman's observations on leeches ('78), and those of Wilson ('87) and of Vejdovský ('88–'02), on earthworms and other oligochætes.

of the entire vegetative point, whether it be striving towards increased size alone or towards the development of a particular shape."[1]   This conclusion was based largely on the fact that the characteristic form of growth is often shown by the growing mass before it splits up into cells, and the form of cell-division adapts itself to that of the mass.   Herein lies the explanation of Sachs's rule that the direction of both anticlines and periclines is definitely adjusted to the form of the growing mass (p. 982); and here is the basis for the oft-quoted aphorism of DeBary: "The cells do not form the plant: the plant forms cells."

The same conclusion, evidently, is strongly suggested by the growth and division of teloblasts, and also by the fact that in many cases the form of cleavage may be altered experimentally (*e. g.*, by mechanical pressure) without materially affecting the end-result of development (p. 1059).   A presumption is thus created that the primary factor lies in the development of the embryo as a whole; and that the adjustment of the cleavage-pattern to it, however accurate, is of secondary significance.   Among earlier writers who urged this view may be mentioned Rauber, Hertwig, Adam Sedgwick and especially Whitman, in his striking essay *The Inadequacy of the Cell-theory of Development* ('93).   The same general conclusion is indicated by experiments on regeneration, which show that definitely formed material, in some cases even the adult tissues, may be *directly moulded into new structures* by morphallaxis with little or no accompanying cell-division.   Driesch showed ('95, 2, '99) that if gastrulas of *Sphærechinus* be bisected through the axis so that each half contains both ectoderm and entoderm, the wounds heal, each half forming a typical gastrula, in which the enteron differentiates itself into three typical regions (fore, middle, and hind gut) correctly proportioned, though the whole structure is but half the normal size.   Here, therefore, the formative process is in the main independent of cell-division or increase in size.   Bickford ('94) found that in the regeneration of decapitated hydranths of tubularian hydroids the new hydranth is primarily formed, not by new-cell formation and cell-formation and growth from the cut end, but largely by direct transformation of the distal portion of the stem.   Morgan's interesting observations on *Hydra* and *Planaria* showed that here also, when the animal is cut into pieces, complete animals are produced from these pieces, but only in small degree through the formation of new tissue, and mainly by direct remolding of the old material into a new body having the correct proportions of the species.

All this, evidently, is on the side of the original contention of Hofmeister and Sachs and (so far as growth, cell-division and development are con-

[1] Cited by Harper ('08, p. 281).

cerned) seems opposed to Schwann's conception of the multicellular organism as a composite or mosaic (p. 101).   On the other hand, it is certain that this result represents only one side of the truth; for it has been conclusively shown that multicellular aggregates having very definite and constant structural characters may be built up by the aggregation of cells originally separate.   Notable examples of this are offered by certain simple plants, including *Hydrodictyon*, *Pediastrum* and others, in which new colonies are formed by endogenous division within the old cells.   The cells thus produced become separate motile zoöspores or swarm-spores, in *Hydrodictyon* numbered by thousands, which after swimming freely for a short time within the mother-cell, become aggregated and build up new colonies, each within a mother-cell, having all the characteristic features of the species.[1]   These aggregates undoubtedly owe their characters to the interaction of cells originally separate.

Even more remarkable are the observations of H. V. Wilson ('07, '10, '11) and his successors on sponges and hydroids more or less completely dissociated into their component cells by being rubbed through fine bolting cloth.   In the resulting débris of the sponge, the cells reassemble in small groups each of which may produce a perfect little sponge of characteristic type; and Galtsoff ('23, '24) has shown that this is effected by amœboid movements of the cells, which creep together and coalesce to form small aggregates from which the new sponges arise.   Even in hydroids (*Eudendrium*, *Pennaria*) Wilson obtained a similar result, characteristic small hydranths being formed by the aggregation, coalescence, growth and differentiation of separate cells or very small cell-aggregates.   Wilson at first considered that in sponges this was effected by the amœbocytes (archæocytes), assumed to be totipotent cells of embryonic type; but later concluded (in case of the hydroids, and by inference also in sponges) that the differentiated tissue-cells become dedifferentiated to form masses of "totipotent regenerative tissue."   This conclusion was, however, not supported by the subsequent work of Huxley ('20) and of Galtsoff, which shows that while certain of the dissociated cells may become somewhat simplified—the collar-cells, for example, often lose their flagella and collars—this does not involve a true dedifferentiation or a return to the embryonic state.   For the most part the dissociated cells retain their histological character and reaggregate without (at first) the occurrence of mitosis.   In Huxley's phrase: "The development of a restitution body is primarily a sorting-out of different kinds of cells, followed by a redifferentiation of the individual types of cells." . . . "The fate of the cells is not a function of their position (as in substance was assumed by Wilson), but their essential

[1] See Harper ('08, '14, '18).

position is a function of their constitutional differences." Galtsoff's conclusion is in principle similar.

To the foregoing may be added the fact that in many cases cells possess so high a degree of independence that profound modifications may occur in special regions through injury or disease, without affecting the general equilibrium of the body. The most striking proof of this lies in the fact that grafts or transplanted structures may perfectly retain their specific character, though transferred to a different region of the body, or even to another species; and equally demonstrative is the fact that in many cases single blastomeres of the segmenting egg, on removal from their fellows, continue to develop as if still forming part of a complete embryo. It is evident, therefore, that further analysis will be required to show what is the true relation between the cells, individually considered, and the body which they form. Such an analysis will be offered in the following chapter.

LITERATURE XIII

(See also II, IV, V, X, XI. For abbreviations, see General Literature List).

Berthold, G., '86. Studien über Protoplasma-mechanik: *Leipzig.*

Blochmann, F., '82. Ueber die Entwicklung der *Neritina fluviatilis: Z. W. Z.,* XXXVI.

    '83. Zur Entwicklung von *Aplysia,* etc.: *Z. W. Z.,* XXXVIII.

Boveri, Th., 'o1a. 'o1b (XIV).

    '10. Die Potenzen der *Ascaris-Blastomeren: Festschr. f. R. Hertwig,* III.

Cerfontaine, P., '06–'07. Recherches sur le dévelopment de L'Amphioxus: *A. B.,* XXII.

Child, C. M., '00. The Early Development of *Arenicola* and *Sternaspis: A. Entwm.* IX, 4.

Conklin, E. G., '96. Cleavage and differentiation: *W. H. L.*

    '97. The Embryology of *Crepidula: J. M.,* XIII.

    '99. Protoplasmic Movements as a Factor in Differentiation: *W. H. L.*

    '02. Karyokinesis and Cytokinesis, etc., in *Crepidula* and other Gasteropoda: *Jour. Acad. N. S.,* Phil., XII.

    '05a. The Organization and Cell-Lineage of the Ascidian Egg: *Ibid.,* XIII.

    '05b. Organ-Forming Substances in the Eggs of Ascidians: *B. B.,* VIII.

    '07. Embryology of *Fulgur*—A Study of the Influence of Yolk on Development: *P. N. A., Philadelphia.*

Crampton, H. E., '94. Reversal of Cleavage in a sinistral Gasteropod: *Ann. N. Y. Acad. Sci.,* VIII.

Delsman, H. C., '12. Entwicklungsgeschichte von *Littorina obtusata: Tijd. Ned. Dierk. Vereen.,* XIII, 3–4.

    '13. Eifurchung und Gastrulation bei *Emplectonema: Ibid.,* XIV, 2.

Dimpker, A. M., '17. Die Eifurchung von *Herpobdella: Z. J., Anat. Oni.,* XL. 2.

Eisig, H., '99. Zur Entwicklungsgeschichte der Capitellidæ: *M. Z. S.,* XIII.

Errera, L., '87. Ueber Zellenformen und Seifenblasen: *Tagbl. Deutsch. Naturf. u. Aertze, Wiesbaden.*

Gerould, J. H. '06. The Development of *Phascolosoma: Z. J., Anat. Ont.,* XXXIII, 1.

Hallez, P., '96. Sur la loi de l'orientation de l'embryon chez les insectes: *C. R.,* CIII.

    '87. Embryogénie des Dendrocœles d'eau douce: *Paris.*

Harper, R. A., '18a. Organization, Reproduction and Inheritance in *Pediastrum: Proc. Am. Phil. Soc.,* LVII.

    '18b. The Evolution of Cell Types and Contact and Pressure Responses in *Pediastrum: Mem. Torr. Bot. Club,* XVII.

Heath, H., '99. The Development of *Ischnochiton: Z. J., Anat. Ont.,* XII.

Heymons, R., 93. Zur Entwicklungsgeschichte von *Umbrella: Z. W. Z.,* LVI.

Holmes, S. J., '99. Reversal of Cleavage in *Ancylus: A. N.,* XXXIII.

    'oo. The Early Development of *Planorbis: J. M.,* XVI.

Jennings, H. S., '96. The Early Development of *Asplanchna: B. M. Z.,* XX.

Kofoid, C. A., '95. On the early Development of *Limax: B. M. Z.,* XXVII.

Kowalevsky, A., '71. Embryologische Studien an Würmern und Arthropoden: *Mém. Acad. Imp. Sci. de St. Petersburg,* VII, 16.

Kühn, A., '12. Die Sonderung der Keimbezirke in *Polyphemus: Z. J., Anat. Onto.,* XXXV, 2.

Lang, A., '81. Die Polycladen: *Fauna v. Flora d. Golfes von Neapel,* XI.

Lewis, F. T., '23. The typical shape of Polyhedral Cells, etc.: *Proc. Am. Acad. Arts and Sci.,* LVIII.

Lillie, F. R., '95. The Embryology of the Unionidæ: *J. M.,* X.

    '99. Adaptation in Cleavage: *W. H. L.*

    'o1. The Organization of the Egg of *Unio: J. M.,* XVII.

Lillie, R. S., '22. Growth in living and non-living Systems: *S. M.,* Febr.

MacDougal, D. T., '20. Hydration and Growth: *P. C. I.,* 297.

Mead, A. D., '97. The Early Development of marine Annelids: *J. M.,* XIII.

Meisenheimer, J., 'oo. Entwicklungsgeschichte von *Dreissensia: Z. W. Z.,* LXIX, 1.

McMurrich, J. P., '95. Embryology of the Isopod Crustacea: *J. M.,* XI, 1.

Nelson, J. A., '04. The early Development of *Dinophilus: Proc. Acad. N. S., Phil.,* Oct.

Newport, G., '54. On the Impregnation of the Ovum in the Amphibia: *Phil. Trans.,* CXLI, CXLIV.

Rabl, C., '79. Ueber die Entwicklung der Tellerschnecke: *M. J.,* V.

    '06. Ueber "Organbildende Substanzen," etc.: *Engelmann, Leipzig.*

Robert, '02. Recherches sur la développement des Troques: *A. Z. E.,* 3e sér., X.

Roux, W., '85. Ueber die Bestimmung der Hauptrichtungen des Froschembryo im Ei, etc.: *Breslau Aertzl. Zeit.*

    '87. Die Bestimmung der Median-ebene des Froschembryo, etc.: *A. M. A.,* XXIX.

Sachs, J., '82. Vorlesungen über Pflanzenphysiologie: *Leipzig.* Würzburg.

    Ueber die Anordung der Zellen in jüngsten Pflanzentheile: *Arb. Bot., Inst. Würzburg,* II.

Schultze, 'oo. Ueber das erste Auftreten der bilateralen Symmetrie, etc.: *A. M. A.,* LV.

Surface, F. M., '07. The early Development of a Polyclad: *Proc. Acad. N. S., Phil.*

Thompson, D'Arcy W., '17. On Growth and Form. *Cambridge.*

Torrey, J. C., '03. The Early Embryology of *Thalassema: Ann. N. Y. Acad. Sci.,* XIV, 3.

Treadwell, A. L., '01. The Cytogeny of *Podarke: J. M.,* XVII.

Van Beneden et Julin, '84. La segmentation chez les ascidiens dans ses rapports avec l'organization de la larve: *A. B.,* V.

Vejdovský, F., '88–'92. Entwicklungsgeschichtliche Untersuchungen: *Prag.*

Vialleton, L., 88. Recherches sur les premiéres phases du développement de la Seiche (*Sepia*): *Ann. Sci. Nat., Zoöl.,* VI.

Watasé, S., '90. Studies on Cephalopods. I, Cleavage of the Ovum: *J. M.,* IV.

Whitman, C. O., '78. The Embryology of *Clepsine: Q. J.,* XVIII.

'87. Germ Layers in *Clepsine: J. M.,* I.

Whitman and **Eycleshymer, '97.** Egg of *Amia* and its Cleavage: *J. M.,* XII.

Wierzejski A., '05. Embryologie von *Physa: Z. W. Z.,* LXXXIII.

Wilson, E. B., '92. The Cell-lineage of *Nereis: J. M.,* VI.

'98. Considerations on Cell-lineage and Ancestral Reminiscence, etc.: *Ann. N. Y. Acad. Sci.,* XI.

Wilson, H. V., '07. On some Phenomena of Coalescence and Regeneration in Sponges: *J. E. Z.,* 5.

Woltereck, R., '04. Beiträge zur praktischen Analyse der *Polygordius*-Entwicklung: *A. Entwm.,* XVIII, 3.

Zur Strassen, O. L., '98. Ueber die Riesenbildung der Ascaris-Eiern: *A. Entwm.* VII.

'06. Die Geschichte der T-Riesen von *Ascaris: Z.,* XL.

CHAPTER XIV

DEVELOPMENT AND HEREDITY

"It is certain that the germ is not merely a body in which life is dormant or potential, but that it is itself simply a detached portion of the substance of a preëxisting living body." HUXLEY.[1]

"Inheritance must be looked at as merely a form of growth." DARWIN.[2]

"I would like, therefore, to make an attempt, by giving an account of the observed facts, to lead you to a deeper insight into the reproduction and development of organized bodies, and to show that these are neither preformed nor, as is commonly supposed, do they come forth suddenly, at a particular moment, out of a formless mass." VON BAER.[3]

I. INTRODUCTORY

From a merely physico-chemical point of view the germ appears as a magazine of matter and of energy which undergoes a series of specific transformations during development to produce a typical result. From a cytological and embryological point of view the germ is a single cell built upon the same plan as other cells. That a single cell can carry the total heritage of the complex adult, that it can in the course of a few days or weeks give rise to a mollusc or a man, is one of the great marvels of nature. In attempting to attack the problems here involved we must from the outset hold fast to the fact that the specific formative energy of the germ is not impressed upon it from without, but is somehow determined by an internal organization, inherent in the egg and handed on intact from one generation to another by cell-division. Precisely what this organization is we do not know. We do know that it is a heritage from the past somehow perpetuated by cell-division, and that development is only a further extension of processes that have been going on since life began. The dramatic aspect of development is due to the apparent simplicity of its starting-point, the suddenness of its onset, the prodigious speed with which it goes forwards, and the complexity of the results achieved within a span so brief.

But when we have grasped this fundamental fact we have only focussed our instruments for a study of the problem. In what form are the potencies of the adult borne by the germ-cell, and how do they become visible realities as development proceeds? We can answer only imperfectly; but we are at least able to formulate many of its problems in terms of cell-activities. The

---

[1] *Evolution, Science and Culture*, p. 291.   [2] *Variation of Animals and Plants*, II, p. 398.
[3] Entwick. der Thiere, II, 1837, p. 8.

gross errors of the early preformationists were long since dispelled. We know that the germ-cell contains no pre-delineated embryo; that the parts of the embryo are gradually formed in a typical order by a process which, externally at least, is one of epigenesis as understood by Aristotle, Harvey and Wolff. The fact has been made clear that the operations of development do not differ in any essential way from those which take place in the adult organism. The cleavage of the egg is a series of rapidly succeeding cell-divisions by mitosis. The moulding of the cells to form tissues and organs in characteristic groupings, as many eminent naturalists have perceived, is essentially a phenomenon of growth. Differentiation involves specific transformations of the cell-substance which, like other cell-phenomena, have their root in the processes of metabolism. The problems of development and heredity are therefore inseparable from the more specific phenomena of cell-structure and cell-activity that have formed the subject of the foregoing chapters.

1. Statement of the Problem

The course of development is conditioned by both external and internal factors. The egg, like the adult organism, is a *reaction-system* attuned or adapted to a particular set of external conditions, and it responds to changes in these conditions by corresponding changes in its mode of development. For example, the eggs of most marine invertebrates undergo normal development only in sea-water; and even a slight change in the chemical composition of this medium may lead to profound changes in the normal mode of development. If, for instance, sea-water be deprived of calcium chloride (of which less than 1% is normally present) the cells of the segmenting egg are unable to maintain their normal association (Herbst, '00) [1] and the embryo develops and differentiates up to a certain point as a mass of dissociated living cells instead of forming a single multicellular body. Typical development is dependent upon the adjustment of the germ in a thousand ways to the typical or normal external conditions. For the purposes of our analysis, however, we shall treat the external factors as conditions of development rather than primary or determining causes. This is justified by the fact that the eggs of widely different animals give rise each to its own typical product under identical external conditions;—the eggs of a sea-urchin, a snail, a worm and a fish undergo their characteristic transformations, each after its own kind, side by side in the same vessel of sea-water. The specific differences of development shown by these various animals must be determined primarily by internal factors inherent in the egg-organization. It is

[1] *Cf.* p. 1046.

these factors which we shall henceforward treat as the primary causes of development and as offering us its major problems.

We may define heredity as an innate capacity of the organism to develop ancestral traits.[1] Heredity as thus defined depends, in Weismann's phrase, upon the continuity of the "germ-plasm," *i. e.*, upon a physical continuity of cell-substance from one generation to another by means of growth and cell-division, through the medium of the germ-cells or (in somatogenic reproduction) of reproductive groups of cells. Development may be defined as the sum total of the operations by which the germ gives rise to its typical product. Its particular course is determined (given the normal conditions) by the specific "organization" of the germ-cells which form its starting-point. As yet we have no adequate conception of this organization, though we know that a very important part of it is represented by the nucleus. Its nature constitutes one of the major unsolved problems of nature; and by some leading investigators, such as Driesch, is regarded as insoluble from the mechanistic standpoint (p. 1115). Nevertheless the only available path towards its exploration lies in the mechanistic assumption that somehow the organization of the germ-cell must be traceable to the physico-chemical properties of its component substances and the specific configurations which they may assume. The fundamental problem, therefore, which includes all others, is that of *determination*.

From a cytological point of view this problem first began to take definite form with the *idioplasm theory* of Nägeli (1884) and its more specific development by O. Hertwig, Strasburger and Weismann. That part of the problem that relates to the mechanism of development centers in the phenomena of *localization* and *differentiation* (p. 1083). How do the various parts of the developing organism take on their specific characteristics in the course of development? How do they come to form an orderly system in space and time? The first of these questions was first taken up to a certain extent from the cytological side by Beale (1861) in his conception of "germinal" and "formed" matter in the cell. The second was first clearly formulated in the modern form by the discussions of His (1874) on germinal localization, and the mosaic theory of Roux ('83, '88) and Weismann ('85, '92).

2. The Idioplasm Theory

Nägeli's celebrated theory was a purely speculative attempt to conceive heredity as determined by the transmission of a particular substance or *idioplasm* carried by the germ-cells and constituting the essential physical

[1] It must be borne in mind that such traits are often latent or recessive, and may be inherited through many generations without actually coming into view; also that no single individual bears in itself the entire heritage of the species.

basis of heredity.[1] This substance was assumed to be quite distinct from the other components of the cell, which were regarded as forming a "nutritive plasma" or trophoplasm which plays no direct part in inheritance.

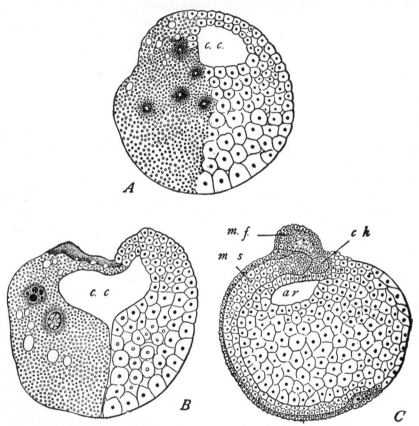

Fig. 490.—Half-embryos of the frog (in transverse section) arising from a blastomere of the two-cell stage after killing the other blastomere (ROUX).

A, half-blastula (dead blastomere on the left); *B*, later stage; *C*, half-tadpole with one medullary fold and one mesoblast plate; post-generation of the missing (right) half in process.

ar, archenteric cavity; *c. c.*, cleavage-cavity; *ch*, notochord; *m. f.*, medullary fold; *m. s.*, mesoblast-plate.

Hereditary traits were assumed to depend upon a definite molecular organization of the idioplasm. The hen's egg differs from the frog's because it contains a different idioplasm. The species is as completely contained in the one as in the other, and the hen's egg differs from the frog's as widely as a

[1] Views more or less similar to this had earlier been suggested by Buffon in his theory of organic molecules, by Darwin in his provisional hypothesis of pangenesis, by Herbert Spencer in his theory of physiological units, and by Haeckel and Elssberg in the theory of plastidules and perigenesis.

hen from a frog. The idioplasm was conceived as an extremely complex substance consisting of elementary complexes of molecules or "micellæ"; and these were assumed to be variously grouped to form units of higher orders, which, as development proceeds, determine the development of the adult cells, tissues, and organs.

Nägeli made no attempt to identify the idioplasm with any particular morphological component of the cell. It was somewhat vaguely conceived as a network extending through both nucleus and cytoplasm and from cell to cell throughout the organism. Meanwhile, however, cytological researches were pointing more clearly towards the nucleus as a leading factor in heredity. Soon after the publication of Nägeli's theory, the conclusion was drawn by O. Hertwig, Strasburger, and later by Kölliker, Weissmann, and other prominent leaders of biological research, that Nägeli's idioplasm is nothing other than the so-called "chromatin" (=basichromatin) of the nucleus; and this view was brought into especial prominence through its ingenious speculative development by Weismann, whose term *germ-plasm* as a substitute for "idioplasm" is still in common use.

The far-reaching influence of the idioplasm theory upon later studies in heredity is evident; but it is now plain that the theory can be accepted only in greatly modified form. Nägeli seems to have conceived the idioplasm as a single substance that is chemically homogeneous; and a similar view concerning the chromatin appears to have been held at first by many other early investigators. Roux's speculations on the significance of mitosis (p. 500) pointed from the beginning towards a more complicated conception; and this was fully borne out by Boveri's epoch-making discoveries concerning the genetic continuity of the chromosomes and their qualitative differences (pp. 829, 916). In the light of these discoveries and their later developments it became evident that the nucleus cannot be thought of as composed of a single, homogeneous idioplasm or germ-plasm. It is a biological *system*, built up from a specifically organized group of different chromosomes which are themselves highly complex bodies; and it is only one part of a larger protoplasmic system, represented by the germ-cell as a whole. The term idioplasm or germ-plasm thus lost much of its original meaning; nevertheless it is often convenient as a collective name for all those components of the cell-system, whether nuclear or cytoplasmic, that are transmitted unchanged from generation to generation and which embody the primary and essential factors of determination.

II. THE LOCALIZATION PROBLEM

A. Theories of Germinal Prelocalization

To Bonnet and other preformationists the localization problem offered no difficulties. The Gordian knot was cut by the assumption that the embryo is from the first preformed in the egg. The final overthrow of this doctrine

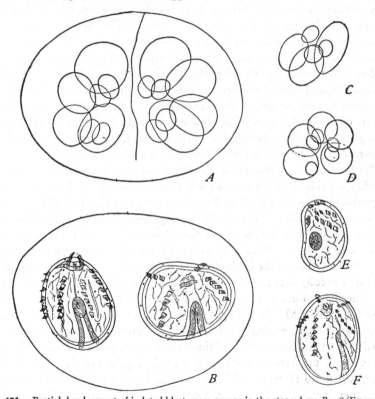

Fig. 491.—Partial development of isolated blastomere-groups in the ctenophore *Beroë* (FISCHEL).

A, 16-cell stage divided along the line of first cleavage, each with 4 micromeres and 4 macromeres; *B*, the resulting larvæ, each with 4 rows of paddles; *C, D*, asymmetrical fragments from an egg like *A*, with 3 and 5 micro-macromeres respectively; *E, F*, the resulting larvæ, with 3 and 5 rows of paddles, correspondingly.

by Wolff and his successors excluded this easy solution, but the possibility still remained that the egg may contain prelocalized regions that are inevitably predestined for the parts to which they give rise—to a certain extent such predestination is indeed a matter of observation in the case of eggs that visibly display polarity and bilaterality. The questions here raised were discussed by Wilhelm His ('74) in his interesting work *Unsere Körperform*. "It is clear, on the one hand," he says, "that every point in the embryonic region of the blastoderm (of the chick) must represent a later organ or part of an organ, and, on the other hand, that every organ developed from the blastoderm has its preformed germ (*vorgebildete Anlage*) in a definitely located region of the germ-disc. . . . The material of the germ is already present in the flat germ-disc (in the chick), but is not yet morphologically marked off and hence not directly recognizable. But by following the development backwards we may determine the location of every such germ, even at a period when the morphological differentiation is incomplete or before it occurs; logically, indeed, we must extend this process back to the fertilized or even the unfertilized egg. According to this principle, the germ-disc contains the organ-germs spread out in a flat plate, and, conversely, every point of the germ-disc reappears in a later organ; I call this the

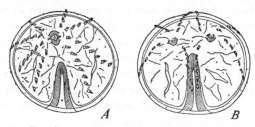

Fig. 492.—Experiment on the egg of the ctenophore *Beroë* (FISCHEL).

A, normal larva, with eight rows of paddles; *B*, larva from 8-cell stage partially separated along the line of first cleavage into two groups of four cells, showing paddles in two groups of four each and two apical organs.

principle of organ-forming germ-regions." Ray Lankester ('77) developed this conception as follows: " Though the substance of a cell may appear homogeneous under the most powerful microscope, it is quite possible, indeed certain, that it may contain, *already formed and individualized*, various kinds of physiological molecules. The visible process of segregation is only the sequel of a differentiation already established and not visible." [1] The egg-cytoplasm has a definite molecular organization directly handed down from the parent; cleavage sunders the various "physiological molecules" and isolates them in particular cells Whitman expresses a similar thought in his classical work on *Clepsine:* "While we cannot say that the embryo is predelineated, we can say that it is predetermined. The 'histogenetic sundering' of embryonic elements begins with the cleavage, and every step in the process bears a definite and invariable relation to antecedent and subsequent steps." [2] . . . The conclusion of Rabl ('79) was similar: "In spite of our-

[1] '77, p. 14.

[2] '78, p. 49.

selves the question is forced upon us whether we must not assume the existence, even in the unsegmented egg, of a quite definite and orderly grouping and distribution of the protoplasmic particles and molecules." [1] Van Beneden ('84) pointed out the close kinship of this conception to that of a theory of preformation: "If this were the case (*i. e.*, if the egg-axis coincided with the principal axis of the adult body), the old theory of evolution would not be as baseless as we think to-day. The fact that in the ascidians, and probably in other bilateral animals, the median plane of the body of the future animal is marked out from the beginning of cleavage, fully justifies the hypothesis that the materials destined to form the right side of the body are situated in one of the lateral hemispheres of the egg, while the left hemisphere gives rise to all of the organs of the left half."

Later researches, both comparative and experimental, have brought forward a complete demonstration of the essential correctness of these conclusions.   Many cases have now been made known in which the egg-substance is more or less definitely marked out—by the presence of pigment, specific types of granules and the like—into visibly different areas which give rise to particular parts of the embryo; and artificial destruction or removal of these areas is followed by the formation of an embryo from which the corresponding parts are absent or defective.[2]   Before considering these facts more critically (p. 1062) it is desirable to examine the so-called mosaic theory of development as applied to cleavage.

B. The Mosaic Theory of Cleavage and Development

1. Foundation and Early History of the Theory

The earlier observers considered cleavage to be no more than a multiplication of indifferent and essentially similar cells; but after the development of studies on cell-lineage by Whitman, Rabl, Van Beneden and their successors all close students of cleavage and cell-lineage were increasingly impressed with the mosaic-like character of the cleavage-pattern.   Rabl and Whitman, for example (following Kowalewsky's earlier work) traced the mesoblastic germ-bands to a single cell (pole-cell or teloblast), while Rabl demonstrated the origin of the entire ectoblast (in *Planorbis*) from twelve cells formed in three successive quartets (p. 1007).   Whitman discovered the fact, at that time received with incredulity by some of the foremost embryologists, that the central nerve-cord (in *Clepsine*) could be traced to a single pair of sister-cells (neuroblasts, p. 998).   Facts of this type, afterwards made known on a far more extended scale, strongly suggested that the cleavage-pattern should be regarded as a composite or mosaic-

---

[1] See also Flemming, '82.

[2] For instance in the eggs of gasteropods, scaphopods, ctenophores, and ascidians, *cf.* p. 1062.

work of specifically different, self-differentiating cells. This view seemed at first to be placed on an assured basis by the independent experimental work of Chabry ('87) on the ascidian egg and of Roux ('88) on that of the frog. Both operators worked by destroying one or more of the blastomeres of the early cleavage-stages by a fine glass stylet (Chabry) or a heated needle (Roux). Save in one important respect their results were closely similar. Chabry found (1) that after destruction of one or more of the blastomeres of the 2-cell or 4-cell stage the remaining cell (or cells) con-

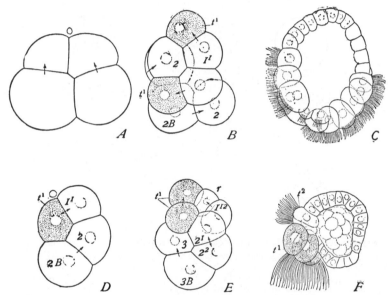

Fig. 493.—Development of isolated ½-blastomere (*A–C*) and ¼-blastomere (*D–F*) in *Patella*.

A, 4/8 stage, from the side; *B*, 8/16 stage, trochoblasts stippled; *C*, resulting larva, with ½ proto-troch; *D*, 4/16-stage; *E*, 8/32-stage; *F*, resulting larva, with primary trochoblasts (*t¹*) below and secondary ones (*t²*) above.

tinued to segment as if forming part of a whole embryo; (2) that although the products of their development gave rise to a gastrula and in some cases to tadpole-like larvæ, the latter always displayed certain defects corresponding to the region of the destroyed cells. The anterior or posterior 2/4 embryo differs markedly from the right or left 2/4; the 1/4 larva is less complete than the 1/2 or 2/4. Chabry therefore concluded, that: "Every blastomere contains the potentiality of certain parts, its death involves irremediable loss, and the different parts of the animal are preformed in the different parts of the egg." These results were later confirmed and much extended by Conklin in a beautiful experimental study (p. 1049).

The real founder of the mosaic theory was Roux, by reason both of his experimental work and his subsequent theoretical interpretation of the facts. On killing one of the blastomeres of the 2-cell stage of the frog the uninjured half developed in some cases into a well-formed half-larva (Fig. 490) representing approximately the right or left half of the body, containing one medullary fold, one auditory pit, etc.[1] Analogous though less complete results were obtained by operating with the 4-cell stage. Roux was thus led to the conclusion that "the development of the frog-gastrula and of the embryo

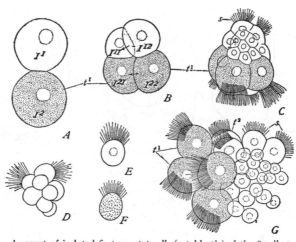

Fig. 494.—Development of isolated first quartet-cells (ectoblastic) of the 8-cell stage in *Patella*.

A, its first division; B, its second (4/32–stage); C, the product, 24 hours, actively swimming, with 4 primary trochoblasts (t^1), two secondary ones (shown in G) and two sensory cells; D, group from apical region with two sensory cells; E, F, isolated sensory cells (flagella non-motile); G, entire group resulting from continued development in calcium-free sea-water.

formed from it is from the second cleavage onward a mosaic-work, consisting of at least four vertical independently developing pieces."

Roux observed, however, that in the end the half-larva restores the missing structures by a kind of regeneration which he called *post-generation*. Even in the tunicate, as found by Chabry and later by Conklin, the half or quarter embryo does not remain an exact half or quarter but closes the wound and in the case of the half-embryo assumes a form so much resembling a complete dwarf tadpole that it was actually mistaken for such by some later observers. The mosaic theory, evidently, must not be taken in too rigid a

[1] The accuracy of this result was disputed by Oscar Hertwig ('93,) and others; but later observers, especially Schultze, Endres and Morgan, showed that both Hertwig and Roux were right, proving that the uninjured blastomere may give rise to a true half-larva, to a larva with irregular defects, or to a whole larva of half-size, according to circumstances. The explanation of this fact (p. 1069) has been given by the more recent work of Brachet ('11).

sense, for the partial embryo or larva still retains, in some degree at least, the power to approach a whole development.[1] Roux tried to meet this fact by the assumption that differentiation is of two types, namely, *self-differentiation*, or self-determination, due to intrinsic factors within the cells, and *correlative differentiation* depending upon the relation of the individual cell or group of cells to the embryo considered as a whole.[2] Primarily the cleavage-mosaic is an expression of self-differentiation, each blastomere being, as it were, set for the production of a particular structure or group of struc-

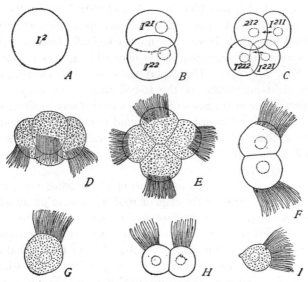

Fig. 495.—Isolated living trochoblasts in *Patella*.

A–D, isolated primary trochoblast and its later development up to 24 hours; *E*, similar result; *F*, pair of trochoblasts, from isolated half of primary trochoblast after its first division; *G*, single primary trochoblast; *H, I*, secondary trochoblasts, all actively free-swimming.

tures by virtue of its internal organization. Secondarily the predestination of any particular blastomere is capable of modification by regulative processes, akin to those of regeneration, that are thrown into action by disturbance of the normal development. This conclusion has not been shaken by later investigation, though the nature of "correlative differentiation" remains almost wholly unknown. It has been vaguely ascribed to "interaction" of the cells (O. Hertwig), to the "development of the organism as a whole" and the like; but such phrases are only restatements of a fact which in its essential nature still remains unexplained.

[1] *Cf.* McClendon p. 1054.   [2] *Cf.* p. 1076.

2. Later Development of the Mosaic Theory

The mosaic theory was sustained by a long series of later experimental studies which can here be reviewed only in brief outline. Its first confirmation came from experiments on the eggs of ctenophores and gasteropods which proved conclusively that blastomeres completely isolated from their fellows continue to segment as if still forming part of a whole embryo and give rise to corresponding partial structures. In the ctenophore *Beröe* the work of Driesch and Morgan ('95), amplified by that of Fischel ('98), Ziegler ('98), and of Yatsu ('11–'12) showed that isolated blastomeres of the 2-cell, 4-cell or 8-cell stages give rise correspondingly to larvæ which, though closed like whole larvæ, are morphologically fractions, showing in particular a number of swimming plates reduced to 4, 2, or 1, in place of the normal 8 (Figs. 491, 492). The experiments of Fischel clearly proved that each of the eight micromeres of the 16-cell stage is definitely specified for the formation of one of the rows of plates, and this was confirmed by Yatsu ('12). In like manner Crampton ('96) found in case of the marine gasteropod *Ilyanassa* that isolated blastomeres of 2-cell or 4-cell stages segment exactly as if forming part of an entire embryo, and give rise to larvæ correspondingly defective.

More extensive and detailed experiments of the same type, carried out by the writer ('04a, '04b) on the eggs of molluscs and of an annelid *Lanice*, and by Conklin ('05, '12) on those of tunicates and gasteropods, confirmed and much extended the foregoing conclusions and placed the mosaic theory on a firm basis.[1] It was thus demonstrated that in *Patella* and *Dentalium* blastomeres isolated at any period up to the 32-cell stage, continue to segment as if forming part of a whole embryo; that, if of sufficient size, they may close and gastrulate; but that they nevertheless always give rise to defective structures that correspond more or less accurately to those to which they would have produced in the normal embryo. For example, the primary "trochoblasts" of the 16-cell stage of *Patella*, upon isolation, divide twice equally to form four equal cells (as in a whole embryo), and at the proper time each develops a row of powerful cilia and the group swims actively about (Figs. 495, 497). The isolated sister-cell ($a^{1.1}$, $b^{1.1}$, etc.) of the primary trochoblast, though identical in appearance with the latter, has a wholly different fate, giving rise to two "secondary trochoblasts," to a portion of the apical sense-organ, and to a group of smaller ectoblast-cells,—*i. e.*, to the same structures that it would have produced if still part of a whole embryo. The entire upper (ectoblastic) quartette from the 8-cell stage produces a structure comparable with the upper hemisphere of the trocho-

[1] This work was greatly aided by Herbst's discovery that the blastomeres of segmenting eggs may be readily and completely separated by placing them temporarily in calcium-free sea-water (*cf.* p. 1036).

phore larva, *i. e.*, a mass of ectoblast-cells bearing an apical organ and a ciliated belt but devoid of alimentary canal (Fig. 494). A 1/8 cell from the upper quartet fails to gastrulate but produces an apical organ, and the four typical primary trochoblasts (Fig. 494 C). The corresponding 1/8 cell from the lower quartet gastrulates but produces no apical organ, and no primary trochoblasts. In *Dentalium* the results are not less striking. The 1/2 or

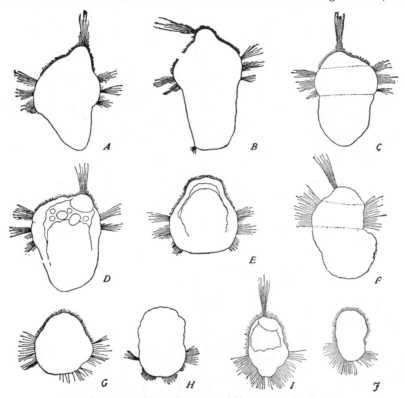

Fig. 496.—Defective larvæ from isolated blastomeres of *Dentalium*.

A, B, C, ½-larvæ from *CD*; half of 2-cell stage; *D, E,* twin ½-larvæ from same egg; *D,* from *CD*-half, *E* from *AB*-half; *F,* ¼-larva from *D*-quadrant; *G,* ¼-larva from *C*-quadrant of same egg; *H,* similar ¼-larva; *I,* 1/8-larva from posterior (*d*) micromere of 8-cell stage; *J,* 1/8-larva from *c*-micromere of same egg.

1/4 blastomeres segment as if still forming part of a whole embryo, and only the CD (posterior) half or the D quadrant forms a polar lobe. (Fig. 496).

These and many similar experiments demonstrate that in these embryos the cells possess individually an inherent power of self-differentiation that cannot be ascribed merely to the interaction of blastomeres as such. Whether in union or separated, they run through with their preordained course of development and even perform their normal functions (*e. g.*, in case of the trochoblasts) when completely isolated. The early cleavage-stages of these animals therefore represent as a whole and in detail a mosaic-work of self-differentiating cells among which the developmental potencies are definitely distributed; and while correlative action is no doubt in some

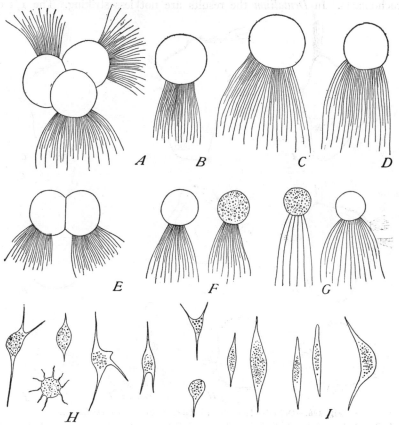

Fig. 497.—Isolated living cells from *Dentalium* eggs developing for 24 hours in calcium-free sea-water.

A–G, ciliated free-swimming trochoblasts of *Dentalium; H–I*, cells resembling mesenchyme and muscle-cells of *Patella.*

measure also concerned, its main part seems to be played at an earlier stage of the ontogeny (p. 1094).

This is borne out by observations on the annelid *Lanice* (Wilson, '05) though the experiments were here less detailed. As in *Dentalium* the first two cells are unequal in size, the larger one (as in annelids generally) pro-ducing the greater part of the metameric trunk and of the cœlomesoblast in which the segmentation of the body takes its origin. If the smaller cell be destroyed the larger one produces an embryo having a segmented trunk, while if the larger cell be destroyed the smaller one produces no trunk-region and remains unsegmented. Both embryos produce a ciliated belt,

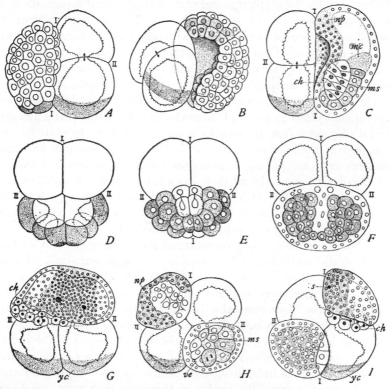

Fig. 498.—Development of partial embryos in the tunicate *Styela* (*Cynthia*) *partita* (CONKLIN).

A, 2/4-embryo, in about 180-cell stage, right half-embryo; *B*, corresponding 2/4 half-gastrula, about 220-cell stage; *C*, right 2/4 half-tadpole; *D*, posterior 2/4-embryo, half 32-cell stage; *E*, later stage (half 76-cell stage) of similar half-embryo; *F*, later 2/4-embryo, posterior half-embryo showing muscle-and mesenchyme-cells (shaded); *G*, somewhat earlier anterior half-embryo, showing sensory spots, chorda-cells (*ch*), absence of tail or muscle-cells, yellow crescent still evident in injured cells (*y, c*); *H*, from 4-cell stage, left anterior and right posterior ¼-embryos, the former with neural plate-cells, the latter with muscle-cells, and ventral entoderm; *I*, similar embryo, right anterior ¼ (sensory spot) and left posterior (with yellow cells).

a small pre-trochal region and an apical organ, their normal products when forming parts of a whole embryo. Conklin's experiments ('05) on ascidian blastomeres (*Styela*) have given results quite similar in principle.[1] If at any period a blastomere or group of blastomeres be destroyed cleavage con-

[1] Conklin employed mainly the method of spurting the segmenting eggs in and out of a pipette, selecting such as showed the mechanical destruction of one or more blastomeres.

tinues with little or no modification. The 1/2, 2/4, and 3/4 embryos close and gastrulate, but in a defective manner. The 1/8-embryos fail to gastrulate. The 1/2 larva from a 2-cell stage, or from the lateral half of a 4-cell stage, produces a head and tail; a notochord composed of half the normal number of cells; an atypical neural plate, a single atrial invagination, and the muscle-cells of one side only (Fig. 498). The anterior 2/4-larva (Fig. 498, G) never forms a tail or muscle-cells, possesses the normal number of chorda-cells (though the chorda is rarely if ever formed), and of neural-plate cells, and may form the sense-spots. The posterior 2/4 larva forms no chorda-cells, neural-plate or sense-spots but produces a mass of muscle and mesenchyme-cells and a double row of caudal entoderm-cells. The 1/4 embryos (Fig. 498, H, I) form chorda-cells, neural plates and sense-spots if they come from the anterior quadrants; if from the posterior quadrants none of these structures appear; but muscle, mesenchyne and caudal entoderm cells are present. Analogous results were obtained from 1/8 and 1/16 blastomeres. In all these cases the isolated cell produces essentially the structures for which it is predestined, the result being only modified by the more or less complete closure of the embryo and the overgrowth of the region of injury by cells from the uninjured side.

The foregoing observations demonstrate the validity of Roux's conception of self-differentiation, and specification of the cleavage-cells. The only question that can be raised is how it arises, and in what measure it may be overcome by subsequent regulative processes such as have earlier been referred to in the "post-generation" of the frog (p. 1044). The specification of the blastomeres is undoubtedly of the same general nature as that of the tissue-cells in later stages, which is so strikingly displayed in the independence of grafted tissues, or in the long-continued culture, without loss of their specific type, of living tissue-cells isolated *in vitro*, which has received so much attention from the works of Harrison, Burroughs, the Lewises and many others (p. 102).[1]

The questions raised by the foregoing results thus apply to all stages of the ontogeny and open the broader problem of the mechanism of development generally.

3. The Development of Totipotent or Equipotent Blastomeres

We now encounter an apparent contradiction which, however, will disappear upon critical analysis (p. 1106). Driesch discovered in 1891 that in the sea-urchin an isolated blastomere of the 2-cell, the 4-cell, *or* even (with certain restrictions) of the 8-cell stage, *may give rise to a perfect larva.*

---

[1] See especially Harrison ('07, '10), Burroughs ('11), Lewis and Lewis ('15), and literature there cited.

of correspondingly diminished size but of normal proportions. In one respect only do these blastomeres suggest a mosaic development, namely, in the fact that *they segment as if still forming part of a normal larva* and often give rise to a small blastula that is at first more or less widely open on one side (Fig. 499). These blastulas soon close and gastrulate in normal fash-

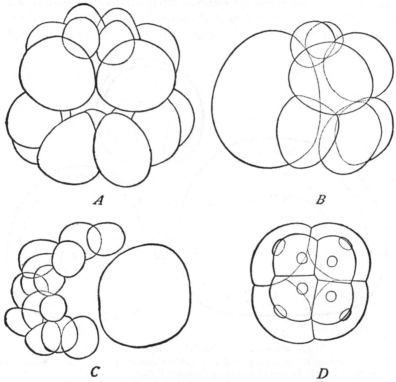

A   *B*

C   *D*

Fig. **499.**—Half and whole cleavage in the eggs of sea-urchins.

A, normal sixteen-cell stage, showing the four micromeres, above at the vegetative pole (from Driesch, after Selenka); *B*, half sixteen-cell stage developed from one blastomere of the two-cell stage after killing the other by shaking (Driesch); *C*, half blastula resulting, the dead blastomere at the right (Driesch); *D*, half-sized sixteen-cell stage of *Toxopneustes*, viewed from the micromere-pole (the eight upper not shown). This embryo was probably from an egg-fragment.

ion and in many cases give rise to normally formed dwarf plutei. In this way it is easy to produce two or even four quadruple embryos from a single egg; or, if the blastomeres be incompletely separated, double or multiple embryos, united in various ways.[1] In this case the blastomeres have been

---

[1] Driesch's original method ('92) was to shake the blastomeres apart in a small glass tube. Later ('00) he made use of Herbst's calcium-free sea-water (see p. 1036) and was thus able to make a very accurate study of the phenomena.

called *totipotent* (Roux) or *equipotential* (Driesch) since each, though normally producing only one-half or quarter of an embryo, nevertheless possesses the capacity to produce a whole one.

Driesch's remarkable discovery has repeatedly been confirmed and extended to other animals. In *Amphioxus* (Wilson, '93) the facts are similar (Figs. 500, 501) though the 1/8 embryos rarely attained the gastrula-stage. In the hydromedusa *Clytia* Zoja ('95) obtained perfect dwarf embryos even from isolated cells of the 16-cell stage. Morgan ('95) obtained complete

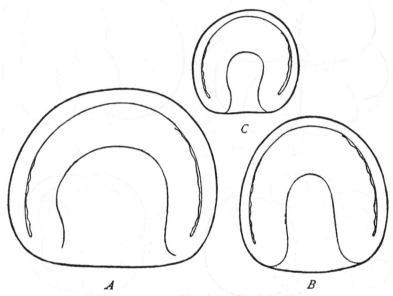

Fig. 500.—Normal and dwarf gastrulas of *Amphioxus*.

A, normal gastrula; *B*, half-sized dwarf, from an isolated blastomere of the two-cell stage; *C*, quarter-sized dwarf, from an isolated blastomere of the four-cell stage.

embryos from the egg of the teleost *Fundulus* after total destruction of one of the first two blastomeres. In the salamander *Molge* Herlitzka ('95, '97) succeeded in completely separating the first two blastomeres by means of constriction with a fine loop of hair, and in rearing from the two separated blastomeres two perfectly formed dwarf tadpoles. In this case each isolated blastomere seems to develop like an entire egg without giving rise first to a 1/2 embryo, as in Roux's experiments on frogs. In a beautiful series of later studies by this method Spemann ('01, '02, '03) showed that in *Triton* double monsters or "Siamese twins" of various types may be produced according to the degree of constriction of the egg while in the 2-cell stage by a loop of hair. A very deep constriction may lead to the production of a monster having two perfect heads, two pairs of fore-legs (Fig. 502) and longitudinally divided nearly as far back as the root of the tail. A less degree of constriction produces a head slightly constricted in the middle, with two pairs of eyes, a brain double as far back as the medulla, but with

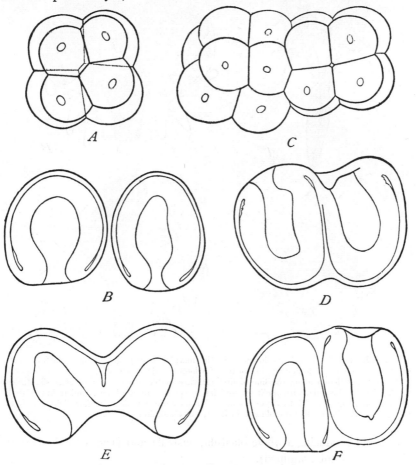

Fig. 501.—Dwarf and double embryos of *Amphioxus*.

A, isolated blastomere of the two-cell stage apparently segmenting like an entire egg (*cf*. Fig. 499, *D*); twin gastrulas from a single egg; *C*, double cleavage resulting from the partial separation, by shaking, of the blastomeres of the two-cell stage; *D*, *E*, *F*, double gastrulas arising from such forms as the last.

a single body. Still slighter constriction may produce a head that is single in form but possesses a median double eye, and two pairs of cerebral hemispheres. In these eggs, accordingly, all degrees of duplicity may readily be induced at will in the product of a single egg.

In harmony with this was the discovery of McClendon ('10c) that even in the Anura (*Chorophilus*) if one blastomere be destroyed and *completely removed*, the remaining one develops in the main as a whole, becoming sphe-

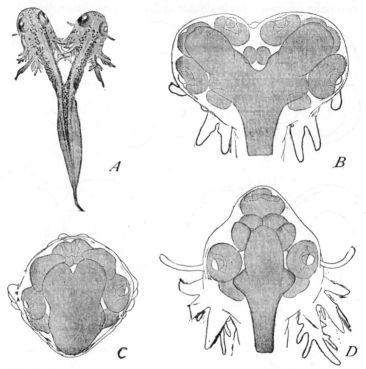

Fig. 502.—Double-headed development in the newt (*Triton*) produced by various degrees of constriction of the developing egg by means of a loop of hair (SPEMANN).

A, after constriction along the line of first cleavage in the 2-cell stage; *B*, after slighter constriction in the blastula, with auditory vesicles in contact anteriorly; *C*, similar but with less constriction, anteriorly with two eyes in contact but no auditory vesicle; *D*, after slight constriction in 2-cell stage, with median double eye in front, but no auditory vesicles.

roidal and producing a whole blastula, gastrula and larva of half size (the cleavage was not examined).

The nemertine *Cerebratulus* (Wilson, '03) [1] agrees closely with the sea-urchin; the isolated 1/2 or 1/4 blastomere segments as though still forming part of a complete embryo and usually gives rise to a blastula that is open on one side (Fig. 503) though it completely closes before gastrulation begins and gives rise to a perfect gastrula and pilidium larva (Fig. 504). The partial cleavage of isolated blastomeres is indeed the general rule; and such apparent exceptions as have been noted (*e. g.*, in *Amphioxus* or the hydro-

[1] See also Zeleny, '04, Yatsu, '10.

medusa) require further examination. The partial character of the cleavage
is shown by the size-relations, by the direction of cleavage, and by its
rhythm. In the sea-urchin, for example, the normal embryo forms four
micromeres at the lower pole during the fourth cleavage, the 1/2 embryo two,
and the 1/4-embryo but one. In *Cerebratulus* the regular alternation of
clockwise and anti-clockwise spirals is accurately followed in the partial
development. During the fifth normal cleavage of this egg the four cells
of the second quartet are always last to divide (Fig. 527). The same is
true of the partial embryos, the 1/2 embryos, therefore, passing characteris-

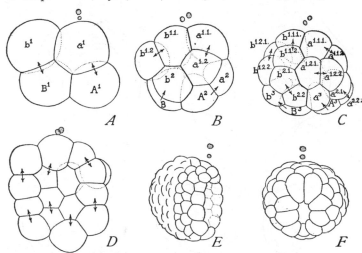

Fig. 503.—Cleavage of isolated ½-blastomere in the nemertine *Cerebratulus*.
A, 4/8-stage; B, 8/16; D, 16/32, half-blastula seen from inner side; E, F, later half-blastulas,
closing.

tically through a 14-cell stage (28/2) and the 1/4 correspondingly through a
7-cell (28/4) stage.

It is an interesting fact that the closure of the open blastula to form a
whole structure differs in different species. For example, among sea-urchins, as shown by Driesch, the open type is typical in *Echinus* as in *Cerebratulus;* but in both these cases the cells may shift at an early period so as
to produce a "compact" or closed bastula from the beginning. In *Sphærechinus*, on the other hand, the compact or closed type is the rule, though as
in the open type of *Echinus* the form of the cleavage is strictly partial.
Similar differences are seen in the partial development of *Patella* and *Dentalium* (p. 1046) some individuals following the closed and others the open
type. In *Cerebratulus* the open type is sometimes exaggerated, the blastomere producing a curved or almost flat plate of cells; yet even these forms

may ultimately close and produce normal dwarf larva. In the hydromedusa, as shown by Maas ('01), the isolated blastomere often segments in
still more loose and open fashion, giving rise to very irregular plates or even
cords of cells, which nevertheless are often able to close and develop.

Facts of this kind at first sight seemed fatal to the theory of mosaic development and self-differentiation and led some leading investigators in
this field, notably Driesch, to abandon the hope of arriving at a mechanistic
interpretation of development (p. 1115). Driesch held, in opposition to Roux,

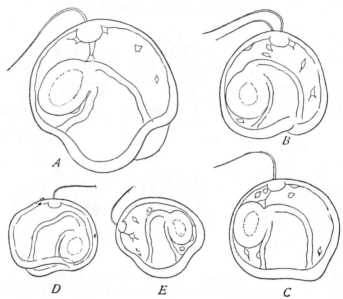

Fig. 504.—Pilidium larvæ of the nemertine *Cerebratulus lacteus*.
A, normal larva of 72 hours, from whole egg; *B*, *C*, twin dwarf larvæ from blastomeres of one
egg isolated at 2-cell stage; dwarf 1/4-larvæ from isolated 1/4 blastomeres.

that "the fragments (*i. e.*, cells) produced by cleavage are completely equivalent or indifferent." "The blastomeres of the sea-urchin are to be regarded
as forming a uniform material, and they may be thrown about, like balls in a
pile, without in the least degree impairing thereby the normal power of development." [1] "*The relative position of a blastomere in the whole determines
in general what develops from it; if its position be changed, it gives rise to
something different;* in other words, *its prospective value is a function of its
position.*" [2] Hertwig ('92, etc.) in like manner insisted that the organism

---

[1] Studien IV, p. 25.
[2] Studien IV, p. 39. *Cf.* His, "Es muss die Wachstumserregbarkeit des Eies eine Function des
Raumes sein" ('74, p. 153).

develops as a whole as the result of a physiological interaction of equivalent blastomeres. The transformation and differentiation of the embryonic cells was ascribed by him not to an inherent specific power of self-differentiation, as in Roux's mosaic theory, but to the action upon them of the whole system of which they are a part. Cell-lineage is therefore devoid of causal significance and is merely an incidental result of the continuity of development, since every group of cells is derived from an earlier group and hence at a sufficiently early period from a single cell. Kindred views were expressed by Whitman and a number of other observers; but these conclusions were premature, as was demonstrated by subsequent experimental researches.

Some of the earlier writers sought a reconciliation between these two divergent interpretations by assuming two different types of cleavage, one of definite and mosaic-like character, the other indefinite and, in its earlier stages at least, without fixed specification of the cells. Conklin ('97) thus distinguished between the "determinate" cleavage of such forms as annelids or gastropods and the "indeterminate" cleavage of sea-urchins or medusæ, in which a single blastomere may produce a perfect embryo. Heider ('oo) spoke correspondingly of "mosaic-eggs" and "regulative eggs." Later observations demonstrated that these distinctions are misleading, yet they have a certain utility for our discussion. Turning aside for a moment from this question, we return to the earlier attempts to find a specific interpretation of mosaic development and self-differentiation, which began with a theory especially associated with the names of Roux and of Weismann.

4. The Theory of Qualitative Nuclear Division and Its Experimental Disproof

The theory of qualitative division, due to Roux ('83 and later papers) was most highly elaborated by Weismann ('85, '92, etc.). Both these authors, like O. Hertwig and Strasburger, considered the primary determination of development to be effected by the nucleus and held that "chromatin" is identical with the germ-plasm or "idioplasm" of Nägeli. Both assumed, however, that the original chromatin of the egg-nucleus is a highly complex substance consisting of numerous different components; and further, that cleavage involves divisions that are either *quantitative* only or *qualitative*, the former involving merely an exact halving of all the nuclear components (as in ordinary mitosis of the tissue-cells), the latter a sifting apart of different components which are then allotted to different cells. Division of these two types were assumed to take place in a fixed and predetermined order, the original idioplasm thus being progressively split up during ontogeny. "Ontogeny depends on a gradual process of disintegration of the germ-plasm, which splits into smaller and smaller groups of determinants in the development of each individual. . . . Finally, if we neglect possible complications, only *one* kind of determinant remains in each cell, viz., that which has to control that particular cell or group of cells. . . . In this cell it breaks up into its constituent biophores, and gives the cell its inherited specific character." [1] Development as thus conceived is essentially evolutionary and not epigenetic;[2] its point of departure is a substance in which all of the adult characters are represented by preformed, prearranged germs;

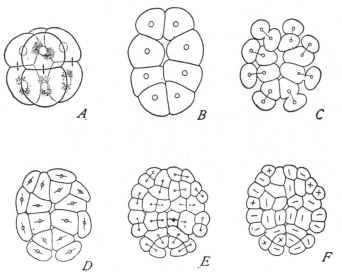

Fig. 505.—Normal and modified cleavage in sea-urchin eggs.

A, normal 8-cell stage of *Toxopneustes* (WILSON); *B–F,* successive stages of a single egg of *Parechinus* (ZIEGLER) compressed vertically between two glass plates, and continuously observed. The 8-cell, 16-cell, 32-cell and transition to the 64-cell stages figured. All the spindles are horizontal and the cleavages are in the line of pressure.

its course, the result of a predetermined harmony in the succession of the qualitative divisions by which the hereditary substance is progressively disintegrated.

In order to account for heredity Roux and Weismann were obliged to assume that, by means of quantitative or equational division, a certain part of the original germ-plasm is carried on unchanged, and is finally delivered, with its original architecture unaltered, to the germ-nuclei; the power of regeneration is explained, in like manner, as the result of a transmission of unmodified or slightly modified germ-plasm.

This theory of development has met with decisive experimental dis-

[1] *Germ-plasm,* pp. 76, 77.   [2] *l. l.,* p. 15.

proof, as was fully recognized by Roux himself and in substance by Weismann. The evidence in question came from two sources One of these consisted in experiments on the unsegmented eggs of various animals (ctenophores, nemertines, molluscs) which proved that the removal of particular regions of the oöplasm of unsegmented eggs *without injury or disturbance of the nucleus* is followed by corresponding defects in the resulting embryos and larvæ. Since the work of Driesch and his followers had proved that a complete embryo might arise from a single blastomere representing only 1/2, 1/4 or even 1/8 of the original egg, the defective development in question cannot be ascribed to a quantitative defect of oöplasm. It must be due to some other condition, such as the lack of a particular *kind* of oöplasm or a lack of regulative capacity. A presumption was thus created that the *immediate* (as distinguished from the *primary*) causes of self-differentiation and mosaic development are to be sought in the oöplasm (cytoplasm) rather than in the nucleus.

Still more decisive evidence was drawn from the pressure-experiments of Driesch and his followers, which directly contradicted the theory of qualitative nuclear division. Pflüger ('84) and Roux ('85) had shown that if frog's eggs be flattened between two glass plates (or otherwise) they divide parallel to the direction of pressure (vertically to the protoplasmic elongation).[1] Extending these experiments Driesch demonstrated that the eggs of sea-urchins, if sufficiently flattened, may be caused to segment in the form of flat plates of 8, 16, 32 or even a larger number of cells (Fig. 505). If this process be not carried too far, such plates, when released from the pressure, quickly divide horizontally (parallel to the direction of elongation) thus forming a more or less flattened blastula which finally rounds out, gastrulates and *may produce a normal larva*. These experiments have often been repeated since with the same result.[2] In such eggs the cytosome has been artificially deformed, without regrouping of its materials. The nuclei, on the other hand, have been forced into a new position, wholly different from the normal; yet normal development results. Specification of the blastomeres *cannot, therefore, be due to specific nuclear differences produced by a fixed order of qualitative nuclear divisions but must be sought in conditions of the oöplasm.* In Fig. 505, for example, the normal 8-cell stage of a sea-urchin is shown at A, an 8-cell plate under pressure at B. These nuclei are obviously the same in both cases, but their distribution in the oöplasm is totally different; yet the result is the same (*cf.* the schematic Fig. 507). The case will become still clearer if we consider the corresponding experiment with the eggs of an annelid (*Nereis*) [3] which give a demonstrative result since their development is of pronouncedly mosaic type from the beginning. In the

---

[1] *Cf.* p. 982.   [2] See Ziegler ('94), Yatsu ('10) etc.   [3] Wilson ('96).

normal development of this animal (Fig. 506, A-C) the archenteron arises from four large cells or macromeres (entomeres), which are distinguishable as such as late as the young swimming trochophore; their substance always retaining a characteristic appearance that differs from that of the other

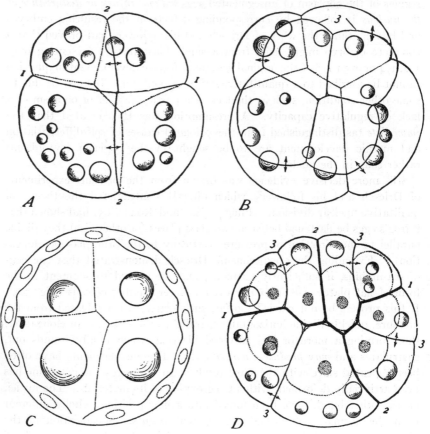

Fig. 506.—Modifications of cleavage by pressure in *Nereis*.

A, B, normal four- and eight-cell stages; *C,* normal young trochophore larva with four macromeres; *D,* eight-cell stage arising from an egg flattened by pressure; such eggs may give rise to nearly normal trochophores with eight instead of four entoderm-cells. Numerals designate the successive cleavages.

blastomeres in its pale non-granular character and in the presence of large oil-drops. If unsegmented eggs be subjected to pressure in the direction of the egg-axis, they segment in a flat plate, all of the cleavages being vertical. In this way are formed 8-cell plates in which all of the cells contain oil-drops (Fig. 506, D). When released from the pressure they show many irregularities, but often divide in a plane approximately horizontal, a smaller granular micromere being formed above, leaving below a larger clear macromere in which the oil-drops remain. Such eggs produce a sixteen-cell stage, therefore, consisting of eight deutoplasm-laden macromeres and eight protoplasmic micromeres (instead of four macromeres and twelve micromeres). Some of these embryos develop into free-swimming trochophores nearly normally formed but having eight instead of four entomeres.

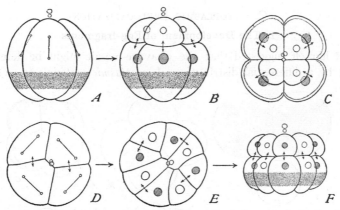

Fig. 507.—Diagrams of cleavage, normal and under mechanical pressure in the direction of the egg-axis. Cleavage is assumed to be of the orthoradial type. The dotted area represents the entoblast-zone, the upper clear area the ectoblast-zone, and the lower the mesoblast-zone (as in the sea-urchin).
A, normal 4-cell stage, from the side, spindles for third cleavage; B, normal 8-cell stage, from the side; C, the same from upper pole; D, 4-cell stage flattened by vertical pressure from above, showing position of spindle for third cleavage; E, resulting 8-cell stage, in a flat plate; F, cleavage ensuing on release from pressure, from the side.
In the normal development nuclei left white are destined for the ectoblast, those shaded for both ectoblast and entoblast. In Figs. E and F they are drawn to correspond with those in the normal, but their distribution and fate are widely different.

In this case four of the ectoblastic nuclei were normally destined for the first quartet of micromeres (Fig. 506, B), from which arise the apical ganglia and the prototroch. Under the conditions of the experiment, however, they have given rise to the nuclei of perfectly characteristic entoblast cells.[1]

Even in a highly differentiated type of cleavage, therefore, the nuclei of the segmenting egg are not specifically different but contain the same materials in cells that undergo the most diverse subsequent fate. How

[1] Morgan ('10) in repeating these experiments likewise found that some of the larvæ closely approached the normal form, but emphasized the fact that they were always abnormal in some respects. This result, to be expected in view of the changed relations of the cleavage-pattern and consequent displacement of the germ-regions, does not seem to invalidate the main result as above stated. Yatsu also ('10b) found that eggs of Cerebratulus segmenting under pressure produced flat plates of 8–16 cells, which likewise produced Pilidium larvæ, but always showed some abnormal features.

long this identity of the nuclei persists we do not know; but since it is maintained during some of the most fundamental of the early specifications of the blastomeres, a presumption is created that it may persist throughout the whole ontogeny. In any case the Roux-Weismann theory of qualitative nuclear division as an explanation of differentiation and mosaic development has become untenable. That it offered any explanation of localization was never maintained by its authors.

C. Cytoplasmic Prelocalization

1. The Development of Egg-fragments

Roux himself suggested that the cleavage-mosaic might be determined in part by a differential distribution of *cytoplasmic materials* as well as of

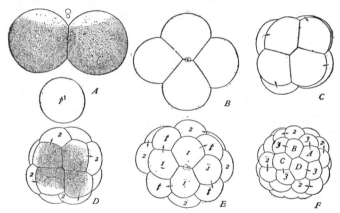

Fig. 508.—Symmetrical cleavage of egg of *Dentalium* after removal of first polar lobe (Wilson). *A*, 2-cell stage and the separated polar lobe (p^1); *B–F*, later stages of cleavage up to the 32-cell stage.

nuclear; and it was here that the solution of the problem ultimately was found. Evidence gradually accumulated to show that definite prelocalization exists in the cytoplasm of the unsegmented egg and that His, Lankester and Whitman had come close to the truth when they spoke of cleavage as a process of "histogenetic sundering" or segregation of preëxisting "physiological molecules," or the like (p. 1041). This evidence was derived especially from the development of egg-fragments or of eggs from which particular cytoplasmic regions had artificially been removed; but many other observations converged to the same conclusion.

Among the earliest experiments of this type were those of Driesch and Morgan ('95) who showed that if part of the oöplasm of unsegmented ctenophore eggs (*Beroë*) were removed the remainder gave rise to a larva lacking certain particular parts.   The later and more detailed work of Fischel [1] on the same object proved very clearly that at the time the first cleavage begins the material which gives rise to the eight rows of swimming plates is prelocalized in the egg in a rather definite peripheral zone encircling the egg in the animal hemisphere; for if a part of this zone is cut away the resulting

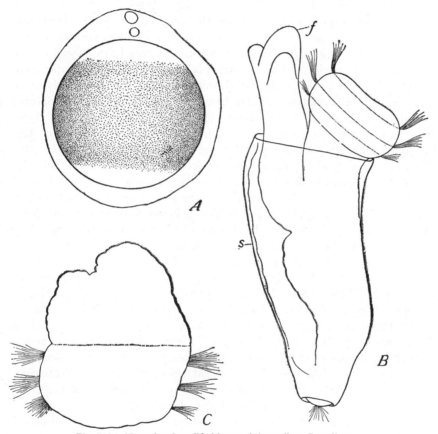

Fig. 509.—Normal and modified larvæ of the mollusc *Dentalium*.

A, egg showing three horizontal zones; *B*, normal trochophore of 72 hours, metamorphosing, with foot (*f*), and shell (*s*); *C*, corresponding larva of 72 hours produced by egg after removal of the polar lobe (lower polar area).

larva lacks one or more of these rows of plates in a region corresponding to the injury.   Again in the gasteropod *Ilyanassa* the egg passes during the first cleavage through a "trefoil" stage (*cf*. Fig. 483) in which a large cytoplasmic "yolk-lobe" or "polar lobe" is formed at the lower pole.

[1] '97, '98, '03.

Crampton ('96) found that this lobe may readily be removed without altering the power of the egg to segment and produce an active larva. Such larvæ lack, however, the mesoblast-bands of the normal larva—a result of striking significance in view of the fact that from this region of the normal egg arises the cell "4D" (p. 1010) from which the mesoblast-bands are formed.

Subsequent experimental work on the scaphopod mollusc *Dentalium* (Wilson, '03, '04) confirmed and considerably extended Crampton's results. The egg of this animal produces a typical trochophore larva closely similar to that of an annelid and is an extremely favorable object for experimentation—it seems, indeed, as Lacaze-Duthiers long ago said, "expressly made for the study of development." The broad horizontal pigment-band (p. 1016) affords a ready means of orientation (Fig. 509). During the first cleavage the egg forms a large polar lobe from the region of the lower white polar area (Fig. 483) and the later cleavage is of typical spiral form (Fig. 484). From the lower (white) polar area are derived the two large "somatoblasts," 2d and 4d, which together give rise to nearly the whole of the post-trochal region of the embryo. After removal of the polar lobe in the trefoil stage the egg segments in typical spiral fashion as before but the first two cleavages are now equal owing to the absence of the material of the polar lobe from the posterior or CD half (Figs. 508–510). It produces an actively free-swimming larva which in favorable cases lives as long as a normal larva but differs from the latter in the following three very important particulars (Fig. 509): (1) the post-trochal region is wholly lacking or represented only by a small group of cells by which the larva is closed in behind; (2) sections show that the mesoblast-bands are lacking (as in *Ilyanassa*); (3) these larvæ uniformly lack an apical organ. These differences become accentuated as development proceeds; for, while the normal larva elongates, forms its foot from the ventral post-trochal region, and also its delicate conical shell, the lobeless larva produces neither of these structures, makes no visible attempt to regenerate the missing structures, and finally perishes.

This result is particularly striking when compared with that of the isolated anterior (AB) or posterior (CD) 1/2-blastomere, since it is always the latter that receives the substance of the polar lobe. The AB half undergoes a development in all respects similar to that of the lobeless egg (Fig. 496). The CD half, though no larger than the lobeless egg, produces a trochophore with well-developed post-trochal region and apical organ (Fig. 496) though it is always more or less distorted and out of normal proportions. This proves that the lobeless larva does not owe its defects to lack of sufficient materials but to lack of a *particular kind* of material that is prelocalized in the polar lobe. This result may readily be extended to the egg before cleavage begins.

If the egg be bisected (with a fine scalpel) exactly through the vertical axis two complete though often deformed larvæ may be obtained from the same egg. If, however, the egg be cut in such a plane that one fragment contains and the other lacks the lower white area and both fragments be fertilized, the upper one produces a larva like that from a lobeless egg or from the AB half (Fig. 511) while the lower one produces a more or less nearly normal larva of diminished size. The conclusion is irresistible that prelocalization of the structures in question exists in the *oöplasm* of the unsegmented

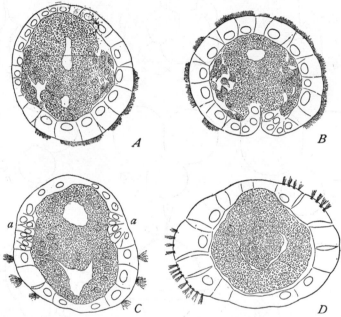

Fig. 510.—Cross-sections through normal trochophore of *Dentalium*, and through larva from egg after removal of polar lobe.

egg, and that to this extent at least, *the specification of the blastomeres is due to the nature of the specific cytoplasmic materials which they receive during cleavage.* These materials we may conveniently designate as *organ-forming substances or formative stuffs.* It is further evident that in this egg *qualitative division is an observed fact;* in the first division it is only the posterior or CD half that receives the substance of the polar lobe; hence its specification for the production of the apical organ and the post-trochal complex, and the corresponding limiting specifications of the AB-half.

An equally striking demonstration of these conclusions is offered by the ascidian *Styela partita*, where Conklin ('05, '12) distinguished no less than five visibly different oöplasmic substances that undergo a quite definite mode of distribution to the blastomeres during cleavage, and give rise each to its own specific product. These substances are (1) a yellow *myoplasm,* which produces the muscles of the larval tail; (2) a light-yellow *chymoplasm,* producing mesenchyme; (3) a light gray substance that gives rise to the chorda and the neural plate; (4) a slate-gray *endoplasm* producing the endo-

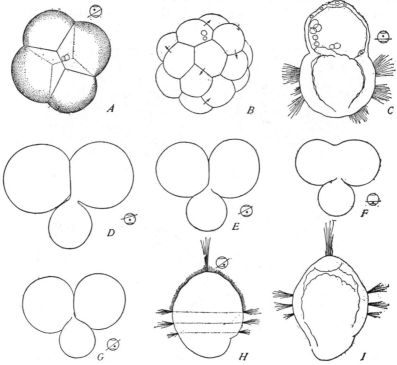

Fig. 511.—Development of egg-fragments of *Dentalium* with and without presence of the lower polar area. Plane of section indicated by key-figures at right (WILSON).

A–C, from large fragment without lower area, 4-cell stage, 16-cell stage and larva of 24 hours; *D–I,* from fragments of different sizes containing lower polar area; *D–G,* trefoil stages of various sizes, with nearly correct proportions; *H,* dwarf trochophore (24 hours) from *G; I,* similar but slightly larger trochophore, of similar origin.

derm; and (5) a transparent ectoderm-producing *ectoplasm.* These substances are distinguishable by the eye owing to the presence in them of specific forms of granules or pigment; and may thus be readily followed during cleavage. The yellow myoplasm forms in the unsegmented egg a crescent on the posterior side of the egg, and in the tadpole larva is symmetrically divided by the first cleavage; but in the second cleavage it passes wholly into the two posterior blastomeres (Fig. 467). Thus, evidently, is explained the fact that the larva from either of the first two blastomeres (though defective in some other respects) develops tail-muscles, while it is only the posterior or CD half of the 4-cell stage which possesses this power (Fig. 498). In this particular respect, therefore, the first cleavage in this egg is merely quantitative, while the second is qualitative. Similar visible differences between the germ-forming regions of the egg, before or during cleavage have been described by many other embryologists.[1] It is, however, important to note at this point that centrifuging experiments have demonstrated that these granules or other formed bodies are not in themselves the true organ-forming substances or formative stuffs. They are secondary products of the oöplasmic activity which can at most be regarded as only external signs or indices of a more deeply-lying organization of the clear ground-substance or hyaloplasm of the egg. This point is more fully considered beyond (p. 1090).

2. " Mosaic " Eggs and " Regulative " Eggs

The apparent contradiction between the totipotent blastomeres of the so-called "regulative eggs" and those of limited potency as shown in the so-called "mosaic eggs" will now disappear. The key to its resolution was provided by the important investigations of Boveri ('02) on the egg of the sea-urchin *Paracentrotus lividus*. This egg, as earlier mentioned (p. 263), is encircled by a clearly marked horizontal pigment-band (Fig. 512) lying below the equator and at right angles to the egg-axis. It therefore shows a condition not unlike that of *Dentalium;* and Boveri found that its three visible strata have similar promorphological value. In both cases the upper white area gives rise to ectoblast, the lower one to mesoblast (mesenchyme in the sea-urchin) while the middle pigmented zone contains the material for formation of the archenteron (Fig. 513). That this prelocalization is not a mere coincidence is proved by the fact that when the eggs are shaken to pieces and fertilized it is *only those fragments that contain at least a portion of the pigment-band* that are able to gastrulate, and thus to produce an embryo. The pigmented zone roughly represents, therefore, the entoblast zone; and we may infer that a similar zone exists in the unpigmented eggs of other sea-urchins even when not made visible by the presence of pigment.[2]

These facts demonstrate that the sea-urchin egg is no more isotropic than that of the mollusk or annelid. In principle the two cases differ only in respect to the mode in which the oöplasmic materials (*i. e.*, the formative stuff) are distributed by the cleavage. For, in the sea-urchin egg, the first

---

[1] Duesberg ('13) has shown that many of the granules in the ascidian egg show the cytological characters of mitochondria.

[2] The pigment itself is not to be regarded as the entoblast-forming stuff but only accompanies the latter. See p. 1087.

two cleavages cut the three strata of the egg symmetrically (both passing
through the egg-axis and at right angles to each other); both, therefore, are
purely quantitative.   The first two or four cells thus receive identical
portions of each of the three zones, and are consequently equipotential and
totipotent.   In the mollusc or annelid, on the other hand, at the first cleav-

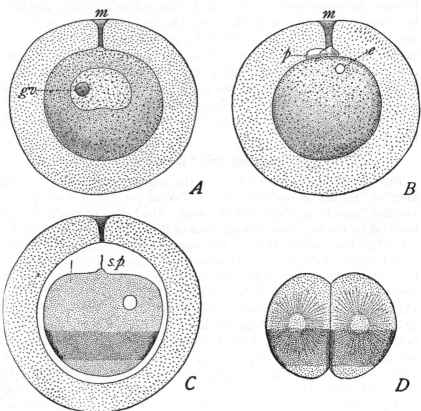

Fig. 512.—Polarity and prelocalization in the egg of the sea-urchin *Paracentrotus (Strongylocen
trotus) lividus* (BOVERI).

A, egg before maturation, surrounded by thick jelly perforated by micropyle (*m*) at the upper
pole, with pigment uniformly distributed in cortical layer; *B*, after extrusion of the polocytes (*p*);
e, egg-nucleus; *C*, later stage, after localization of the pigment-band; *sp.*, entrance-cone immediately
after entrance of sperm; *D*, 2-cell stage.

age the lower stratum (lower polar area) passes bodily into one of the two
cells.   This division, therefore, is qualitative, allotting different combinations of oöplasmic materials to the first two blastomeres; hence the mosaic-
like character of cleavage from the beginning.   We may therefore conclude
that *one important difference between the so-called "mosaic eggs" and the*

"regulative eggs" lies merely in a different relation of the cleavage-pattern to the oöplasmic materials. The primary factor in both cases is, clearly, the localization-pattern in the unsegmented egg, and the character of the cell-mosaic is determined by the relation of the cleavage-planes to it.

This conclusion is placed in a very clear light by experimental studies on the frog's egg. In this case (p. 1012), the first cleavage-plane often coincides nearly with the median or sagittal plane of the future embryo; but Roux and his successors (O. Hertwig, Kopsch, O. Schultze, Morgan, Jenkinson, Brachet) found many exceptions to this. The contradiction at first led to doubts concerning the accuracy of Roux's conclusions; but the whole subject was cleared up by the discovery that the egg possesses a very distinct bilateral symmetry before cleavage begins, and that *the relation of the first cleavage-plane to the plane of symmetry is somewhat variable.* Before fertilization the egg seems to be radially symmetrical (Fig. 514) showing only a large upper pigmented area and a smaller unpigmented one surrounding the vegetative pole. After fertilization, as has long been known (O. Schultze, '00) the egg becomes visibly bilateral owing to the appearance of a gray crescent (apparently caused by a retreat of pigment into the interior) at one side of the white area (Fig. 514, B, C). This side is opposite to the point at which the sperm has entered the egg; and all observers are agreed that in this region arises the dorsal lip of the blastopore. The observations of Schultze and later observers [1] demonstrated that the first cleavage-plane commonly bisects the crescent at or near its central point; but not infrequently deviates more or less widely from this plane and sometimes is even transverse to it.[2]

An elegant demonstration of this is offered by Brachet ('11) who employed Roux's puncture method (p. 1044), and compared the development of 1/2-blastomeres from eggs showing varying angles between the first cleavage-plane and the median plane of the gray crescent. As is to be expected,

---

[1] Morgan and Boring ('03) Brachet ('04), Jenkinson ('06).

[2] The data for different species vary considerably. In *Rana palustris*, for example, the variation is much greater than in *R. temporaria* (Morgan and Boring, '03). All observers have found, however, a marked tendency towards coincidence. In *R. fusca* Brachet ('04) found that 100 eggs, taken at haphazard, showed the following conditions:

Divergence	%
0°	48
10° or less	20
10–45°	10–13
45°	10
45–90°	5
90°	8–10

Jenkinson's ('06) figures from a more extended study of *R. temporaria* agree fairly well with this, though the number showing close coincidence is considerably smaller. His frequency charts clearly show a much greater correlation between the plane of egg-symmetry and the sagittal plane of the embryo than between the latter and the plane of first cleavage.

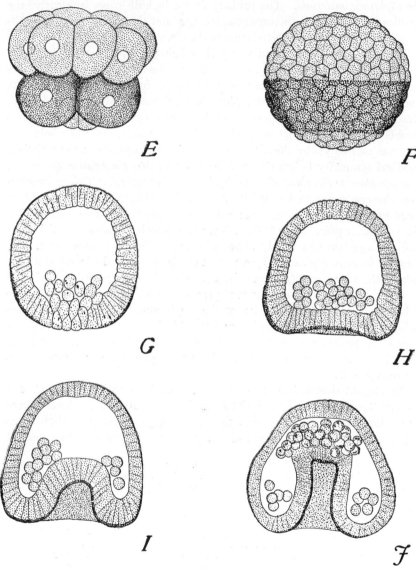

Fig. 513.—Continuation of Fig. 512, showing later history of the three zones (BOVERI) *E*, 16-cell stage; *F*, blastula; *G*, *H*, formation of the mesenchyme; *I*, *J*, gastrulation.

such operations give rise to many abnormal forms; nevertheless the results bear out the expectation created by study of the normal eggs. When the first cleavage-plane passes vertically through the center of the crescent the resulting 1/2-embryo corresponds nearly to a longitudinal vertical half of a normal embryo like those figured by Roux (Fig. 514, D, G,).

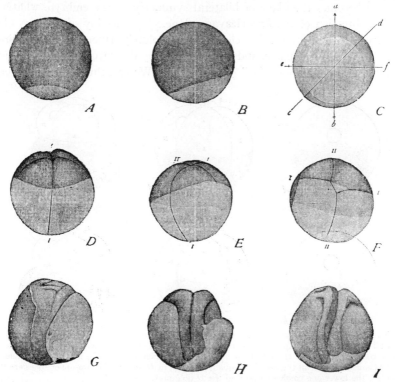

Fig. 514.—Promorphological relations of the early cleavage-planes in the frog (*A–C* somewhat schematized after JENKINSON; *D–F*, MORGAN and BORING; *G–I*, BRACHET).

A, before appearance of the crescent; *B*, side-view of crescent (*c*); *C*, same from lower pole, *a–b*, the plane of symmetry; *D*, 2–4-cell stage, first cleavage-plane (*I*) passing through middle of crescent; *E*, 2–4-cell stage, first plane passing obliquely through crescent; *F*, 4–8-cell stage, second plane (*II*) passing through middle of crescent; *G*, left half-embryo, after killing of one blastomere of 2-cell stage with furrow through the line *a–b* (Fig. C); *H*, defective embryo after similar operation with first furrow through line *c–d* (Fig. *C*); *I*, after similar operation with first furrow through line *e–f* (*C*).

When the first cleavage-plane is transverse to the plane of symmetry, destruction of the posterior blastomere is followed by the production of a symmetrical embryo normally formed anteriorly, but defective posteriorly (Fig. 514, F, I). Finally, when the angle between the two planes is approximately 45° and the posterior oblique half is destroyed the remaining blastomere shows an oblique defect posteriorly, on the right or left side according to the direction of the first cleavage-plane (Fig. 514, E, H). These results, obviously, show that *the primary factor in localization is not the pattern of cleavage but that of the distribution of oöplasmic substances in the egg.* In the words of Brachet: "The plane of bilateral symmetry in the fertilized egg always becomes the plane of bilateral symmetry in the embryo, whatever be the direction of the first cleavage-plane. The destiny of the two blastomeres produced by the first cleavage is absolutely dependent on the direction of the cleavage-plane, and is determined by the nature of the oöplasmic materials that they contain " ('04, p. 113). We can thus understand how

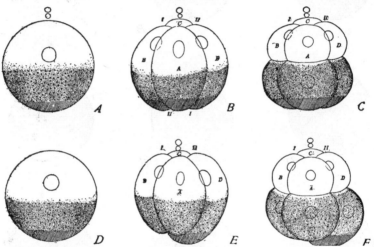

Fig. 515.—Diagrams of the primary stratification in the eggs of the sea-urchin (*A–C*) and the annelid or gastropod (*D–F*). The first two cleavage-planes designated as I or II. The upper or white zone is ectoblastic, the middle or granular one the entoblastic, the lower or lined one the mesoblastic. In *A–C* all the zones are equally divided; in *D–F* only the two upper zones are thus divided, the lower one passing entire into the *D* quadrant.

it is that in the toad-fish, for example, the direction of the first cleavage is quite variable and shows no constant relation to the plane of symmetry, without thereby affecting in any manner the outcome of development (Clapp, '91). In the frog's egg the plane of first cleavage is somewhat variable, though tending towards a constant condition. In the annelid, the ascidian or the mollusc the relation appears to have become nearly or quite fixed under natural conditions, though even here it may readily be altered experimentally by pressure or other agents.[1]

The foregoing conclusions opened the way for a rational interpretation of "mosaic development," that runs closely parallel to the general theory of Roux and Weismann but is now transferred from the nucleus to the cyto-

[1] In connection with these subjects see the important later papers of Spemann on *Triton* in *Arch. Entwin.*, XLIII (1918), XLV (1919), XLVIII (1921), LII (1922), and *Naturwiss.*, XXXII (1919)

some. For it is now clear that, in respect to the distribution of the *cyto-plasmic* materials, cleavage may indeed be either quantitative or qualitative and that the latter at once differentiates the resulting blastomeres from each other in respect to their prospective value in the development. How this conception works out will be made clearer by a return to particular cases.

Totipotence on the part of the early blastomeres is dependent primarily on a symmetrical or merely quantitative distribution of the protoplasmic stuffs by the cleavage. In the hydromedusa (Fig. 516, J–L), the original grouping of these materials is, broadly speaking, concentric about the center of the egg; and all of the radial cleavages ac-

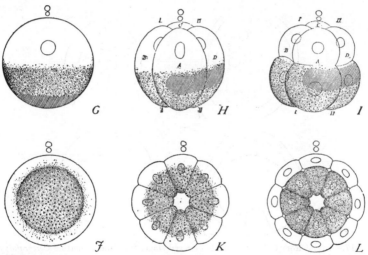

Fig. 516.—Continuation of Fig. 515. Diagram of the primary stratification in the ascidian (*G–I*) and the hydromedusa (*J–L*). Strata indicated as in Fig. 516. In the ascidian the lower (mesoplasmic) stratum is equally divided between the *A* and *D* quadrants. In the hydromedusæ this stratum is absent and the remaining two are equally distributed up to the time of delamination (*L*).

cordingly are quantitative (Maas, '01). Since the first five cleavages are of this type, complete dwarfs may be produced from any of the blastomeres up to the 16-cell stage (Zoja) when the first qualitative divisions begin by the delamination-cleavages parallel to the surface. In the nemertine or sea-urchin the oöplasmic stuffs are polarized, displaying a symmetrical horizontal stratification at right angles to the axis of the egg. Since the first two cleavages pass exactly through the axis and cut all the strata symmetrically (515, A–C) the first two or four blastomeres receive equal allotments of these strata in their normal proportions and hence remain totipotent, though retaining the same polarity as that of the original egg. Here therefore we should expect the third cleavage (which is the first horizontal one) to be qualitative; this is borne out both by observation and experiment. In the normal development the upper quartet produced by this cleavage always gives rise to ectoblast and most commonly to ectoblast only, while the lower quartet always produces all or nearly all of the ento-blast, also to the main mass of the mesoblast and to some ectoblast. It is instructive to compare these facts with those derived from an experimental separation of the upper and lower quartets or of their component cells.

The simplest case is offered by the nemertine or mollusc. In both cases a sharply marked contrast appears between the upper and the lower quartets,

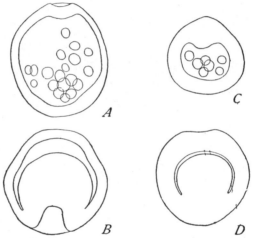

Fig. 517.—Larvæ from isolated quartets of 8-cell stage, from the nemertine *Cerebratulus marginatus* (ZELENY).
A, 4/8-larva, from entire upper (ectoblastic) quartet, with apical organ and no enteron; *B*, 4/8-larva from lower quartet, with enteron and no apical organ; *C* and *D* a similar pair, showing the same characters, at a slightly earlier stage.

the former giving rise to purely ectoblastic structures (as earlier described for *Dentalium*) while the latter are able to gastrulate. A pretty demonstration of this was given in *Cerebratulus*. Zeleny ('04) was able to separate the 8-cell embryo into halves either vertically or horizontally, and to compare the development of the isolated 4/8 embryos thus obtained After horizontal section (*i. e.*, along the plane of the third cleavage) either the upper or the lower quartet readily develops into a ciliated larva; but the upper 4/8 larva develops an apical organ but never gastrulates, while conversely the lower one gastrulates characteristically but never produces an apical organ (Fig. 517). This result, confirmed by Yatsu ('10a), is especially convincing because in the nemertine (contrary to the general rule) the upper quartet-cells are larger than the lower. The failure to gastrulate must therefore be due not to a lack of sufficient protoplasmic material but of a particular kind of material. The demonstration is made complete by the control experiment of separating the 8-cell stage into two 4/8 embryos by forcing the blastomeres apart along the vertical line of the first or second cleavage. Such half (4/8) embryos develop characteristically into larvæ that are normal except in size. It is thus clearly demonstrated that while both the first two cleavages are quantitative the third is qualitative, *i. e.*, separates materials of different promorphological value in the specification of the blastomeres.

A particular interest attached to the case of the sea-urchin—the "regulative egg " *par excellence*—where Driesch ('oo) was able to obtain gastrulas from isolated cells of either the upper or the lower quartet of the 8-cell stage. At first sight this seems quite subversive of all the foregoing results. Driesch himself demonstrated, however, that such is not the case, for certain constant and significant differences exist between the development of upper and lower 1/8ths. The former are more transparent, more active and more tenacious of life; they gastrulate in much smaller numbers and frequently show abnormalities in the archenteron. The lower 1/8ths show the opposite qualities; they are more granular, less active and more perishable; but a much larger number gastrulate and with fewer abnormalities. This can only mean that the upper and lower cells differ in respect to their oöplasm,—*i. e.*, the third cleavage is in some degree qualitative but not strictly so. The facts therefore become readily explicable if we assume that the entoblast-zone extends higher in this egg than in the nemertine or mollusc so that a small portion of it may be included in the upper 1/8 blastomeres. Driesch tested this by subjecting the eggs to slightly diluted sea-water which frequently causes displacement of the third cleavage plane towards the lower pole. Isolated upper 1/8 blastomeres from such eggs showed a large increase in the number of gastrulations. All the facts therefore fall into line under the assumption that the relation between the third cleavage-plane and the upper limit of the entoblast-zone is not completely fixed in this egg, and also that this zone graduates insensibly into the ectoblast-zone. We thus explain, further, how it is that in the nemertine or the mollusc the lower quartet still retains the power to produce ectoblast after total removal of the first quartet.

Quite analogous conclusions apply to the mesoblast, though the facts are less completely known. In the sea-urchin, ascidian, mollusc (*Dentalium*) and annelid alike, the principal part of the mesoplasm, appears to lie near the lower or vegetative pole (Fig. 515, D–F). In the sea-urchin it remains at this point and is symmetrically divided by the first two cleavages so that the first four cells contribute equally to the mesenchyme (possibly also to the archenteric pouches, though this is not known). In the ascidian this material moves to the posterior side of the egg before cleavage, is equally divided by the first cleavage but is isolated by the second cleavage in the two posterior cells (516, G—I) which alone contribute to the formation of the mesenchyme (p. 995). In *Dentalium* or the annelid the main mass of meso-plasm passes into the posterior blastomere (CD) which therefore alone retains the power of producing mesoblast-bands and the post-trochal region. In the sea-urchin the first qualitative division takes place at the third cleavage, in the ascidian at the second, and in the mollusc or annelid at the first. All these eggs alike conform to the mosaic principle, but it is more conspicuous in the ascidian or the mollusc because qualitative division takes place earlier.

3. Mosaic Cleavage and Totipotence

It is thus made plain that the principle of mosaic development and self-differentiation applies as much to "regulative eggs" as to "mosaic eggs." Their differences of behavior are due in part to a different relation of the cleavage-pattern to the original pattern of localization, in part to differences in regulative capacity. An instructive example is offered by the develop-ment of the fresh water annelid *Tubifex*. This egg undergoes a highly de-terminate spiral cleavage and gives rise to teloblasts, ectoblastic (2d) and mesoblastic (4d), from which grow forth germ-bands closely similar to those of leeches and earthworms (pp. 998, 1003). Penners [1] showed experimen-tally that this cleavage is in many respects a true mosaic-work. If, for in-stance, both teloblasts be destroyed the resulting embryo is closely similar to the lobeless larva of *Dentalium* (p. 1064) and is likewise devoid of germ-bands. If only one of the teloblasts is killed the germ-bands are formed but correspondingly lack completely either the ectoblastic or the meso-blastic components. These and other experiments fully establish the mosaic-character of the cleavage; nevertheless a complete dwarf embryo may be produced from either the CD-half or the D-quadrant alone, while the AB-half or the A-, B- or C-quadrants lack such a capacity. This means, obviously, that only those cells are totipotent which receive the material of 2d and 4d in addition to the general ectoblast and entoblast shared by all the quadrants.

Even more remarkable is the fact that twins or double embryos may arise from a single egg; but this is possible only in those abnormal cases where the first cleavage is equal instead of unequal. Cytological examina-

[1] References at p. 1120.

tion proves that in such cases the material from which the teloblasts arise (*i. e.*, the polar rings) is divided between the first two blastomeres instead of passing into one of them as in normal cleavage. Both cells are thus rendered totipotent.

In all these various cases, obviously, the totipotence (*i. e.*, the power to produce a whole) of any particular blastomere depends upon its possession,

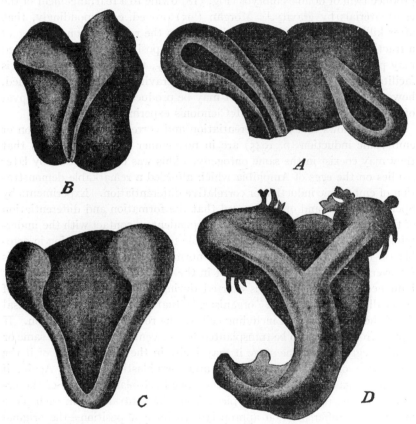

Fig. 518.—Double embryos of frog developed from eggs inverted when in the two-cell stage (O. Schultze).

A, twins with heads turned in opposite directions; *B*, twins united back to back; *C*, twins united by their ventral sides; *D*, double-headed tadpole.

first of the necessary materials, and second of sufficient plasticity or regulative capacity to build from them a whole though smaller body. This capacity is no doubt of the same nature as in the so-called regulative eggs, *e. g.*, of the nemertine or sea-urchin. Even in the latter cases the isolated blastomere usually segments as a part and is only gradually moulded into a whole as development proceeds. Such fractional cleavage may depend, as Driesch long ago suggested, upon simple conditions like protoplasmic rigidity or the deformation of the living blastomere by the dead; and this is supported by various experiments on frogs' eggs. O. Schultze ('94) showed that if these eggs be kept inverted during the 2-cell stage they often produce twin or double embryos (Fig. 518) owing to a rearrangement of the egg-materials by gravity.[1] Morgan ('95) proved, correspondingly, that after killing one of the first two blastomeres the remaining one undergoes a fractional development if kept in its normal position, but if kept inverted may produce a whole dwarf. Here, evidently, the remodelling process is facilitated by the rearrangement caused by gravity. As earlier mentioned, however (p. 1954), the same result may be produced by complete removal of the dead blastomere, as in McClendon's experiment.

All this shows that self-differentiation and correlative differentiation or embryonic induction (p. 1045) are in no manner incompatible, and that they may coexist in the same ontogeny. This was clearly shown by later studies on the eggs of Amphibia which afforded a remarkable demonstration of embryonic induction or correlative differentiation. Experiments by Spemann, Lewis and others proved that the formation and differentiation of the lens from the outer ectoblast is dependent on contact with the underlying optic cup, and that the latter is able to incite lens-formation in ectoblastic regions far removed from the normal position. Spemann and his followers subsequently proved [2] that in the urodeles (*Triton*) an important influence on differentiation is exerted during gastrulation by a group of cells called by Spemann the "organiser," situated just in front of the dorsal lip of the blastopore and including cells of the roof of the archenteron. If a piece from this region be transplanted to the ventral region of the same or another egg at the same stage it may incite in the cells in front of it the production of neural folds, chorda and mesoblastic somites. Again, if during the gastrulation a piece of the dorsal ectoblast in front of the organiser be interchanged with a piece from the ventral region, each piece undergoes a differentiation appropriate to its new position—the original dorsal piece now produces undifferentiated ectoblast, the original ventral piece neural folds and their products. Correlative differentiation is here conspicuously shown; nevertheless, experiments by Spemann and by Ruud on the 2-cell and 4-cell stages of *Triton* proved that even at this early period the blastomeres are not all alike equipotent. The first cleavage may here be either vertical (median) or transverse (horizontal). In the former case

---

[1] *Cf.* Born, '85.   [2] References at p. 1120.

either ½-blastomere may produce a perfect dwarf, in the latter case only the dorsal one has such a capacity. This result, evidently, is akin in principle to that obtained in the case of *Tubifex*.

Lastly, one of the most important results in this field is the proof that the germ-regions can be thought of neither as sharply delineated nor as absolutely fixed areas. The egg is not a fixed mechanical structure; it is a plastic protoplasmic system comprising substances that tend towards a certain grouping in the egg. The predestination of the germ-regions is primarily qualitative; though a quantitative factor is also present it is in considerable degree subject to regulatory control. In the spiral type of cleavage, for example, the larger size of the left posterior or D-macromere is evidently correlated with storage in it of the main mass of material for formation of the post-trochal region (p. 1010). In *Dentalium* this material is already to some extent recognizable in the unsegmented egg as the lower white polar area, from which arises the polar lobe. As earlier stated, complete removal of this area involves the absence of a polar lobe and of the main post-trochal region derived from it (p. 1064). It is, however, very noteworthy that when the egg is cut in two horizontally the upper half develops like a whole egg from which the polar lobe has been removed; while the lower half, though it contains the whole of the polar area, develops like a whole egg of diminished size, *forming a polar lobe of correspondingly diminished size and in some cases producing a correctly proportioned dwarf larva* (Fig. 511).[1] In this respect the lower half differs remarkably from an isolated CD-half or D-quadrant, in which the polar lobe and the post-trochal region are in each case nearly or quite as large as in a complete embryo or larva.

Again, in the ctenophore egg, Yatsu ('10) has shown that when even a large portion of the lower region of the egg has been removed during the first cleavage the micromeres (produced at the 4th cleavage) are of correspondingly reduced size, having the correct proportions. Similar results were reached in *Cerebratulus* (Yatsu, '10a). If a portion of the vegetal hemisphere be cut off during the first cleavage, or in the 2-cell stage, the upper and lower quartets of the 8-cell stage show the correct proportions, the upper cells being reduced to a size in proper ratio to that of the embryo as a whole. All this again shows clearly that prelocalization of the cytoplasmic regions, while definite in respect to quality, is subject quantitatively to regulative control.

4. The Formation of Single Embryos from Double Eggs or Blastulas

Among the most remarkable examples of regulative phenomena in development is the production of a single normally formed giant larva from

---

[1] Wilson, '04.

a double egg and the converse phenomena of the formation of a normally formed dwarf larva from a fragment of a single egg (merogony, p. 465). Of similar type is the production of a giant larva from two blastulas fused into one of double the normal size.[1] A careful study of such cases in sea-urchins,

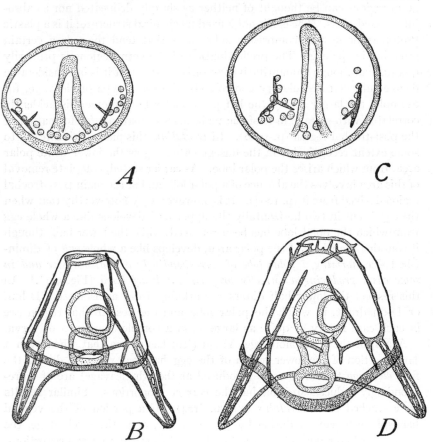

Fig. 519.—Normal and giant larvæ of the sea-urchin *Sphærechinus* (BIERENS DE HAAN). *A, B*, gastrula and pluteus larva from normal egg; *C, D*, corresponding stages from giant egg

especially by Driesch and Bierens de Haan, showed that although fusion of the two blastulas is often complete, the later development often is more or less definitely double, two archentera commonly being formed while the later larva is often double in various degrees in respect to other structures. In many cases, however, the product of such fusion is a single giant larva,

---

[1] Metschnikoff in *Mitrocoma* ('86), Morgan (95), and especially Driesch ('00, '10) and Bierens de Haan ('13a, 13b), in sea-urchins.

normally formed but of double the normal size. The latter case, obviously, offers a remarkable case of regulation, and at first sight seems to offer a flat contradiction of the mosaic theory of development, as was in fact originally urged by Driesch. As pointed out by Boveri, however ('01), whether a single larva or a double one is produced by such embryos may depend on the relation of the original axes to one another; and this is strongly supported by the work of Bierens de Haan, which makes it probable that in the double larvæ the axes form all possible angles with each other, and that a single development "occurs only when two germs are from the first united in the same way as two blastulas, i. e., only when from the beginning their axes and planes of symmetry lie side by side." Even so, the single development offers a remarkable example of regulation, and shows that the specification of the embryonic regions in the blastula stage is not an absolutely fixed prelocalization. In these facts we see another proof of the conclusion that the localizing process is a progressive one, which in its earlier stages marks out only the more general features of the future larva.

The analysis of giant larvæ formed from giant or double eggs is more difficult than in the preceding cases owing to the fact that the double (giant) eggs often fail to develop beyond an early stage and also are often polyspermic. In the case of *Ascaris* Zur Strassen ('96, '98) found that the development of the giant eggs is typically normal, and that the abnormal forms observed were due entirely to polyspermy; and essentially the same conclusion was reached by Bierens de Haan in the case of sea-urchins (Fig. 519). The evidence thus far available seems to show that if the egg develops at all it develops as a single whole, in this respect contrasting remarkably with the double larvæ from fused blastulæ.[1] The explanation of this is still conjectural; but it seems probable that fusion takes place at a time when the localizing operations so often occurring at the time of maturation and fertilization (p. 1094) have not yet taken place. This is supported by the work of *Geinitz* ('13) which indicates that in *Ascaris* fusion takes place near the time of fertilization before or shortly after the fertilization membrane has been formed, and hence before the localizing operations which in many eggs occur at this time.

5. Summary on Mosaic Development and Protoplasmic Prelocalization

From the foregoing analysis it may be concluded that the development of all eggs conforms to the mosaic principle in greater or less degree. The difference between the so-called "mosaic eggs" and "regulative eggs"

---

[1] Conklin states that in *Crepidula*, following centrifuging, all double eggs, whether fused before or during cleavage, retain their respective polarities and develop as more or less double structures ('17, p. 353); but the proof is not apparent that any of these double embryos arose from fused *unsegmented* eggs.

depends on two leading factors, namely, the nature of cytoplasmic division and regulative capacity. The cleavage mosaic in general, and the power of self-differentiation displayed by its component blastomeres, is the result, broadly speaking, of a distribution or segregation of different protoplasmic materials among the blastomeres and their isolation in the latter by cell-division. In this respect the individual cleavages may be either quantitative or qualitative in precisely the same sense as originally maintained by Roux and Weismann in case of nuclear division. The totipotence of a particular blastomere is due first to the allotment to it by a merely quantitative division of all the essential protoplasmic components of the original egg, as in the first one or two cleavages of the sea-urchin, nemertine, *Amphioxus* or frog. But, secondly, the totipotence of an isolated blastomere depends also upon the possession of a sufficient degree of plasticity to enable the regulative process to restore the normal form and structure of a whole embryo. What determines this capacity is as little known as that which determines the form of growth in a whole structure or the process of morphallaxis in a fragment of an adult *Hydra* or *Planaria* (p. 980).

Partial development is dependent on the same two factors. "Mosaic eggs" differ from "regulative eggs" either in respect to the relation between cleavage and the original pattern of localization in the unsegmented egg (*e. g.*, *Dentalium* as contrasted with the nemertine or sea-urchin) or in the degree of regulative limitation in the isolated blastomere (*e. g.*, the ascidian or ctenophore as compared with *Amphioxus* or the frog); or both types of difference may exist. In this respect we may trace a nearly continuous series between widely separated extremes. In the mollusc or annelid qualitative division begins with the first cleavage and the regulative capacity of the isolated blastomeres is limited. At the opposite extreme are such eggs as those of hydromedusæ, where qualitative division is deferred at least to the fifth cleavage or later, and the regulative capacity of the isolated blastomere is highly developed. Intermediate conditions are offered by the ascidian or ctenophore. In the ascidian the first qualitative division is the second, in the ctenophore the fourth, but apart from this the regulative capacity is in both cases decidedly limited. Lastly it may be pointed out that the regulative power on the part of an isolated blastomere is akin to Roux's "correlative differentiation," to the development of the organism as a whole, and to Morgan's "morphallaxis"—a group of phenomena (or of different names for the same phenomenon)—which for the present escape further analysis.

III. LOCALIZATION AND DIFFERENTIATION

1. The Relation of Cleavage to Localization and Differentiation

Cleavage was formerly often thought of as a direct cause of differentiation; but the facts show that it is only indirectly such a cause. Cleavage only marks off and stabilizes areas or germ-forming regions that to a certain extent preëxist as such and are often in a general way recognizable in the undivided egg. Cell-division is, however, not even a necessary condition of differentiation, as is obvious in the case of unicellular organisms, some of which (the ciliates in particular) display a differentiation almost comparable in degree with that of many of the simpler Metazoa. Even in animals as high as annelids, as has earlier been indicated (p. 474) cleavage may be entirely suppressed by artificial means, yet the unsegmented egg may undergo to a certain extent differentiations similar in type to those occurring in the normal embryo, and may even give rise to actively swimming ciliated structures that have some resemblance to normal trochophore larvæ. In the case of *Chætopterus* Lillie obtained this result by treatment of the eggs, fertilized or unfertilized, by the addition to the sea-water of a certain percentage of potassium chloride. In some cases the egg becomes multinucleated, either by complete cleavage followed by fusion of the blastomeres or by division of the nucleus without cytoplasmic cleavage. In others the nucleus seems never to divide but becomes greatly enlarged, while the number of chromosomes correspondingly increases, a condition probably resulting from successive cycles of monocentric mitosis.

Meanwhile the cytoplasmic materials of these eggs undergo a process of segregation comparable in some respects with those which precede and accompany cleavage in the normal development. A part of the ectoplasm containing characteristic granules flows towards the animal pole, and there aggregates; a part remains at the vegetative pole, where the polar lobe normally forms (p. 1063), while the entoplasm remains in the equatorial region (Fig. 520). This is followed by a rapid overgrowth, partial or complete, of the entoplasm by the upper ectoplasm, so as to produce a "unicellular gastrula." The egg then develops cilia, typically over the whole ectoplasmic surface, and actively swims about. At the same time it often elongates so as to approach the form of a young trochophore larva, while a series of vacuoles are developed in or just beneath the ectoplasm, especially in the equatorial region, which evidently correspond to those which appear in the prototrochal cells of the normal larva (Fig. 520). All these changes recall those seen in the normal larva; and the unsegmented ciliated larvæ are so similar in external appearance to trochophores as to have actually been mistaken for such. These larvæ, however, never form an apical organ,

mouth, anus, mesoblast-bands or cœlome, and never become segmented.
The main results reached in the case of *Chætopterus* were confirmed by Treadwell ('02) in *Podarke*, and by Scott ('06) in *Amphitrite;* in both these cases
it was found that the cilia may be arranged in a definite band which shows a

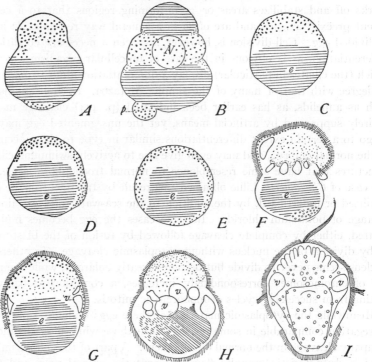

Fig. 520.—Differentiation without cleavage in eggs of the annelid *Chætopterus* after treatment
with salt-solution.   From living eggs (F. R. LILLIE).

In each case the clear ectoplasm is indicated by small circles, the yellow entoplasm by horizontal
lines.

A, B, stages in the segregation of the egg-materials, polar ectoplasm at *p,* nucleus shown at *N;*
C, D, E, overgrowth of entoplasm by ectoplasm to form the "unicellular gastrula"; *F, G, H,* ciliated
embryos with vacuoles (*v*) in position corresponding with those seen in the prototroch of the normal
trochophore (*I*).

considerable resemblance to normal prototroch (Fig. 520).   Phenomena of
similar type were also observed by Lefevre ('07) in *Thalassema.*

These facts demonstrate that even in the multicellular animals cytoplasmic cleavage, and even nuclear division, is not a necessary condition of either
localization or differentiation.   Normal cleavage plays, however, an essential part in the normal development of higher organisms by isolation of the
cytoplasmic materials in cells separated by definite and apparently impass-

able barriers. The pattern of localization is thus given form and stability, providing a definite fundamental plan for later processes of differentiation and no doubt also for further and more detailed processes of segregation. The question is here raised as to whether new cytoplasmic materials or organ-forming substances are continually and progressively formed by the embryonic cells as development advances or whether all such materials already preëxist in the unsegmented egg. So far as external appearances go the cytoplasmic diversity steadily increases as cleavage proceeds, and many observers have described definite localizing movements of the cytoplasmic substance in the individual blastomeres, even up to comparatively late stages.[1] It seems probable, therefore, that only the more general features of localization and differentiation have been accomplished at the time cleavage begins, and that as the process proceeds the individual blastomeres themselves continue the formation and segregation of cytoplasmic materials in ever increasing detail by operations similar to those that took place in the original egg. On this subject, however, great uncertainty still prevails.[2]

2. The Immediate Causes of Differentiation

The purely speculative side of this question need not long detain us. DeVries, in his remarkable work *Intracellular Pangenesis* (1889) considered differentiation to result from the activities of invisible, organized "pangens" (analogous in some respects to Darwin's "gemmules") which migrate from the nucleus into the cytosome and in large measure build up the active cytoplasmic substance. A view similar in all its essentials was subsequently adopted by Weismann, O. Hertwig and other writers. More accessible to investigation are hypotheses which assume differentiation to be effected by the transformation of visible cytoplasmic granules or other definite bodies, arising either by migration from the nucleus or independently in the cytosome; and these views are based to some extent on direct cytological observations. The questions that here arise (p. 720) evidently apply alike to the ovum before its cleavage begins, to the early blastomeres and the embryonic cells derived from them, and to the tissue-cells in so far as they may be capable of further differentiation (by dedifferentiation, redifferentiation and the like).

Existing knowledge of this subject is still too fragmentary and discordant to offer a sufficient basis for adequate discussion. At one extreme are authors who have ascribed cytoplasmic differentiations to the activities of chromidia, extruded from the nucleus of the egg. This view remains to say the least very doubtful, though there is a certain amount of evidence that certain of the formed cell-components may arise from extruded nucleolar fragments (p. 705). At the opposite extreme is the view of Altmann, Benda

[1] See Wilson ('92, '03), Driesch ('96), Conklin ('97), Lillie ('06). [2] See footnote, p. 1072.

and Meves that the leading rôle in differentiation is played by granules (in particular mitochondria and other forms of chondriosomes) that are of purely cytoplasmic origin, and which possibly may arise by the growth and division of preëxisting bodies of the same kind (p. 706).

An intermediate position between these opposite extremes is taken by Schaxel in an interesting series of studies on the development of cœlenterates, echinoderms and annelids.[1] This observer accepts up to a certain point the conclusions of both sides, recognizing the existence of both chromidia and chondriosomes in the egg and the tissue-cells and ascribing to both an important rôle in differentiation. Schaxel admits that the chondriosomes or "plastosomes" may become directly transformed into differentiated components of the tissue-cells but considers the main rôle to be played by extruded nuclear material in the form of chromidia.

This process, according to Schaxel, takes place either at an early period of the ovarian egg (Fig. 344) or in the blastomeres or their products immediately preceding the conversion of these cells into the differentiated tissue-cells; and the latter process is carefully described by Schaxel in the mesenchyme-cells of annelids, and other objects. Development thus falls into two well-marked periods, an earlier one in which the general framework of development is established in the egg, and a later one in which more specific differentiations are initiated. Schaxel does not, however, believe that the chromidia are directly transformed into the formed elements of the cytoplasm. They disappear as such, having accomplished the initiation of differentiation and localization. The nucleus, therefore, initiates differentiation, while the cytoplasmic elements (chondriosomes and others) are the more immediate agents of the process.[2]

One would like to accept this conception of development and differentiation, which offers so simple a view of the mechanism of the process. Unfortunately evidence concerning the extrusion of chromidia from the nucleus in the manner described by Schaxel is still too conflicting to be accepted without much further inquiry (p. 703); and the same must be said concerning the direct origin of formed cytoplasmic elements from extruded fragments of nucleoli. On the other hand, it is certain that a large amount of nuclear material, both liquid and formed, is given off from the germinal vesicle in the prophases of the polar mitoses (p. 356), and to a less extent in the prophases of other mitoses. Experiment has shown that the material thus set free has a most important physiological effect upon the cytoplasm of the egg (p. 405); and there is evidence that the escaped material or "residual substance" of the germinal vesicle may contribute directly to the formative

---

[1] See Schaxel ('09, '10, '11, '12, '13), and especially ('15), with complete literature.
[2] See '15, p. 250, etc

material of the egg. In the case of pulmonate gasteropods, for instance, Conklin ('03, '10) has shown that the residual material spreads out over the upper hemisphere of the egg and constitutes in large part the upper stratum from which the ectoblast in these animals takes it origin; and he has found reason for a similar conclusion in the ascidian ('05). F. R. Lillie ('06) has reached a similar result in case of the annelid *Chætopterus*, in which the residual substance is more specifically described as constituted of fine granules or microsomes visible in life both before and after their discharge from the germinal vesicle (p. 356).

3. Organ-forming Substances.   Experiments with the Centrifuge

These conclusions fit with the conclusion, derived from experiment, that while the cytoplasmic substance plays a direct part in the immediate processes of differentiation and development it is one that is influenced in an important manner by the nucleus; and this remains true even though we are not yet in a position to state the respective parts played by formed elements and by unformed (such as soluble enzymes or hormones) of nuclear origin. Important light is thrown on this question, by subjecting eggs to the action of centrifugal force which seems to demonstrate that the so-called formative stuffs, or organ-forming materials, cannot be identified with any of the larger visible granules or other cytoplasmic "inclusions" in the egg (pigment-granules, yolk, etc.), by which the strata or other regions of the egg are marked off. Boveri ('01) as earlier indicated (p. 1067), pointed out that the red pigment-granules which mark the entoblast zone in *Strongylocentrotus* do not in themselves constitute the specific entoblast-producing stuff, but are only an accompanying "symptom"—a conclusion based on the fact that the intensity of the color varies considerably in different individuals of this sea-urchin, and in some localities the eggs show no pigment, yet develop normally; while in other species the pigment ring never appears. Later experiments initiated by Gurwitsch ('04) and Lyon ('07) gave an important confirmation and extension of this conclusion.[1] Lyon and his successors found that when the eggs of various animals are subjected to a powerful centrifugal force the granules of yolk, pigment, and the like may readily be dislocated becoming grouped in parallel strata, at right angles to the direction of the force. The number, and relative bulk of these strata vary considerably with the nature of the cytoplasmic components—most commonly there are three or four, their order of succession being of course determined by their specific gravity. In general yolk-granules

[1] See especially F. R. Lillie ('06, '09) on the annelids *Chætopterus* and *Nereis;* Morgan ('07, '09, '10) on the sea-urchin *Arbacia*, the pelecypod *Cumingia*, the nemertine *Cerebratulus*, the rotifer *Hydatina*, and on the fish and the frog; Boveri ('10) and Hogue ('10) on *Ascaris;* Conklin ('10, '12, '17) on various molluscs; Konopacki ('11) and Jenkinson ('14) on the frog.

(usually the heaviest of the inclusions) collect at the outer or centrifugal pole, fatty substances (apparently including many of the mitochondria) at the centripetal pole, while the main bulk of clear substance (largely hyaloplasm) forms a central zone in which lies the nucleus (Fig. 521). In case the first polar spindle is formed before the experiment (*e. g.*, in *Chætop-*

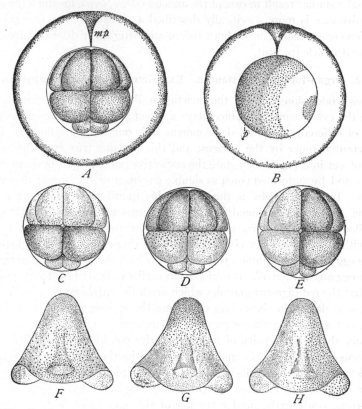

Fig. 521.—Development of centrifuged eggs of the sea-urchin *Arbacia* (MORGAN and SPOONER).

A, 16-cell stage surrounded by the thick jelly-envelope perforated by the micropyle (*mp*) at the animal pole; *B*, unsegmented egg after centrifuging, showing stratification at right angles to the egg-axis (*p*, pigment-layer); *C*, 16-cell stage with pigment in vegetative (micromere) hemisphere; *D*, pigment in animal hemisphere; *E*, pigment on one side; *F*, *G*, *H*, three types of larvæ resulting from the three corresponding types of 16-cell stages (*C*, *D*, and *E*).

terus) it may become detached from its peripheral position and comes to rest in the clear band (Lillie). The position of the pigment varies in different cases; in *Arbacia* (Fig. 521) it is found in the distal hemisphere of the egg.

All observers, beginning with Lillie ('06, '09) have found that these dislocations of material exert little or no effect on the polarity of the egg. Since the eggs may in most cases lie in any position with reference to the direction of the centrifugal force it follows that the strata form all possible angles with the original axis, as determined by the point at which the polycytes are extruded from the egg and also by certain relations during cleavage. The cleavage-planes nevertheless maintain their normal relation to the original egg-axis and seem for the most part to remain unchanged by the redistribution of the coarser visible cytoplasmic materials. It thus comes to pass in some cases that the polocytes may be extruded at the center of the yolk-containing stratum or at any other point with reference to the plane of stratification. Such eggs may not only segment normally but often produce larvæ which up to a certain point are normally formed.

This is strikingly demonstrated by the work of Lyon ('95–'06); confirmed and extended by that of Morgan and Spooner ('09), on *Arbacia*. The normal egg contains red pigment-granules nearly uniformly distributed. Lyon showed that when centrifuged this egg shows four zones or strata, viz. (1) a deep red one containing most of the pigment, (2) a yellowish equatorial band, (3), a rather broad white zone, and (4) a small grayish cap opposite the red zone. These strata are parallel, and thus define a "secondary axis" at right angles to them as was proved by Morgan and Spooner; but this axis may form any angle with the primary or true axis of the egg, as marked by the position of the micropyle, near which the polocytes always are extruded (*cf.* Figs. 512, 521). Cleavage proceeds normally, and has the normal relation to the true or primary axis, having therefore no constant relation to the direction of the strata, save in one respect, namely, that the first cleavage usually is *vertical to the stratification* (Lyon). The micromeres, formed at the third cleavage, always appear at the crossing point of two cleavage-planes, but *also approximately opposite the original upper pole* (marked by the position of the micropyle) as in a normal egg—*i. e.*, at the lower pole, as usual. This point (Fig. 521) may lie in the center of the red zone, of the white (gray) zone, or at one side where the red and white zones join and at this point gastrulation takes place. The resulting larvæ, accordingly, may show the red zone either in the posterior, anterior or lateral region—a striking proof of the non-significance of the pigment (and presumably of other visible zone-materials) for the formative and localizing process.

In this case the direction of the strata seems to have a slight effect on the direction of the cleavage-planes; but in others no such effect has been detected; for instance in *Chætopterus* (Lillie '06, '09) cleavage follows its normal course and retains its usual relation to the original egg-axis, but shows no discernible constant relation to the stratification. Morgan's observations on *Cumingia* seem to bear this out, as do also Conklin's more recent studies on *Crepidula* ('17).

All observers are substantially in agreement, therefore, that neither the polarity of the egg, nor the pattern of cleavage, nor the localization of morphogenic factors can be ascribed to the distribution in the oöplasm of the larger visible inclusions; and it seems probable that the same may apply to the smaller granules that are less readily displaced by the centrifuge.

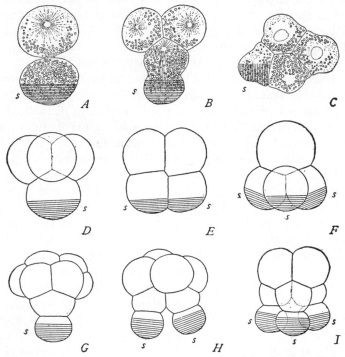

Fig. 522.—Three observed types of cleavage in dispermic eggs of *Ascaris megalocephala* compared with the normal (BOVERI).

A–C, normal cleavage; *D–I*, dispermic eggs; *D, G*, 4-cell and 8-cell stages of dispermic egg, Type I; *E, H*, Type II; *F, I*, Type III. In each case the cytoplasmic region of the future stem-cells (*s*) is indicated by parallel lines.

The topographical grouping of these components in the egg is therefore not the cause but a result of polarity, bilaterality and other prelocalizations in the egg-substance; and this must mean, as was urged especially by Lillie ('06, '09) that the "formative stuffs" or organ-forming substances of the oöplasm are not its visible inclusions, but belong to the apparently structureless fundamental ground-substance or hyaloplasm. Perhaps, therefore, what we call "organ-forming substances or "formative stuffs" may be localized physico-chemical modifications of this substance, perhaps hormones or the like localized within it.

An interesting confirmation of these conclusions is offered by the work of Boveri [1] on the formation of the primordial germ-cells in dispermic eggs of *Ascaris* or in monospermic eggs after centrifuging.   In the normal eggs,

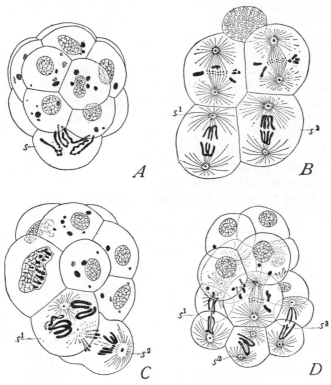

Fig. 523.—Abnormally segmenting eggs of *Ascaris megalocephala*, to show variations in number of stem-cells (BOVERI).

A, dispermic egg, Type I (Fig. 522, D, G); B, centrifuged egg, Type II (Fig. 511, E, H); C, dispermic egg, Type II; D, dispermic egg, Type III (Fig. 511, F, H), one stem-cell in A, two in B and C, and three in D.

as earlier described (p. 323), the stem-cells from which the primordial germ-cells ultimately arise, take their origin from a particular cell of the 4-cell stage (Fig. 144) which divides into two; and one of these undergoes diminution, giving rise to somatic cells, while the other repeats the process in each of the two succeeding mitoses (Fig. 145). In the normal egg, there fore, each step in cleavage up to the 16-cell stage always shows one stem-

[1] Boveri ('09, '10), Boveri and Hogue ('10).

cell, at once distinguishable during its division by its large undiminished chromosomes (Fig. 145, A, D, F, G). In both dispermic and centrifuged eggs the early embryo often shows two or three such stem-cells, owing in the first case to the fact that the dispermic egg typically divides into four blastomeres variously grouped (Fig. 523). A study of these various groupings shows that the varying number of stem-cells is due to varying relations of the cleavage-planes to the cytoplasmic regions of the egg. Thus, if in the diagrams the region of the future stem-cells be indicated by the shaded areas in Fig. 522, it is evident that this area may remain undivided or divided into two or three such areas, according to the position of the spindles in the first cleavage. Every cell that fails to receive a portion of this area undergoes diminution; and diminution finally ceases when this area has been finally isolated in the primordial germ-cells. This can only mean that the behavior of the nuclei in these eggs *is determined by the cytoplasm in which they lie;* the whole nuclear content being retained only in the particular cytoplasmic region predestined to form the germ-cells. The explanation of the similar facts in centrifuged eggs is of similar type, the result being due to dislocation of the normal adjustment between the cleavage-planes and the cytoplasmic regions.

The difficulty of conceiving how the prelocalized organization of the egg can be bound up in a liquid or semi-liquid substance, such as the hyaloplasm often seems to be, is obvious. Lillie and Conklin have accordingly argued in favor of a relatively firm condition of aggregation in the hyaloplasm, yet one of such a nature that the cytoplasmic inclusions can still move through it. " Flowing movements," accordingly, whether in the normal egg or produced by the centrifuge, are regarded as no more than granule-movements within this semi-solid framework of the oöplasm.[1] Conklin has produced considerable specific evidence that such a persistent framework of more viscid protoplasm (hyaloplasm) exists in the clear substance of the *Crepidula* egg, and that it forms the basis of the true localizing activities. Its substance is assumed by Conklin to be elastic and contractile, and thus to produce the so-called flowing movements of living protoplasm and its contained granules which make visible to the eye the localizing activities of the oöplasm. He emphasizes the fact, also noted by earlier observers, that if the centrifuging acts at a sufficiently early period and is not too long continued the dislocated egg-components tend to return more or less completely to their original position; and this too is ascribed to the action of the contractile framework which has maintained unchanged its original polarity.

This conception is closely akin physiologically to the original contractility

---

[1] Lillie ('09), Conklin ('17).

theory of Van Beneden ('87) and of Boveri ('87), but morphologically it is widely different; for Conklin does not consider the framework as a reticulum but identifies it with the "interalveolar or continuous substance." [1] To this he applies Leydig's old term *spongioplasm*, designating the clear alveolar material or enchylema as *hyaloplasm*.[2] Conklin's observations on the topographical relations and movements of materials in the centrifuged eggs, seem to show that the spongioplasmic framework holds the nuclei, centrospheres and mitotic figures more or less firmly to a peripheral or cortical layer; that its material is more abundant towards the animal pole; and that it differs in physical consistency in different regions of the egg and at different stages of development. How all this can be reconciled with the evidence of flowing movements in the hyaloplasm itself—such as its centripetal flow towards the astral centers (p. 192)—is not easy to see, nor is it easy to grasp the conception of an interalveolar substance that is firm enough to maintain its typical configuration, yet plastic enough to permit extensive movements of granules and other inclusions through it. It must be admitted, therefore, that the mechanics of localization still present an unsolved problem.

IV. THE ORGANIZATION OF THE EGG AND ITS GENESIS

We now enter upon the last stage of our analysis with the inquiry whether cytoplasmic germinal prelocalization exists from the beginning or is itself a product of antecedent development. In the first case prelocalization would closely approach preformation, in substance if not in form; in the second it would fall into line with an essentially epigenetic interpretation.[3] In the writer's view the results alike of observation and experiment point to the second alternative as the correct one, so far at least as some of the more obvious features of prelocalization are concerned.

Our analysis has shown that some of the most obvious of the oöplasmic prelocalizations are expressed by the presence of a number of zones, either concentric (various coelenterates) or vertical to the egg-axis (echinoderms, nemertines, etc.) which mark the primary germ-regions, irrespective of the direction of the cleavage-planes that later intersect them. Do these zones

---

[1] '17' p. 369.

[2] This usage is the reverse of that employed by Rhumbler ('96), and other students of protoplasm, who have applied the term hyaloplasm to the continuous or interalveolar substance (Wilson, '01a, p. 540, etc.). Since the latter usage accords more nearly with Hanstein's original use of the word and has become widely current among those who accept the alveolar theory of protoplasm it seems unfortunate to introduce new confusion by resuscitating the word "spongioplasm," which is so closely associated with the reticular theory of protoplasm.

[3] We shall find it convenient, here and later, to distinguish between "preformed" and "epigenetic," characters or qualities in the egg. This usage (Boveri's) is purely provisional, and must not be taken to imply any fundamental distinction between the two sets of characters (*cf.* p. 1107).

preëxist in the egg from the beginning or are they the product of a secondary localizing process? This question has been attacked both by simple observation and by experiment. Both methods seem to give conclusive evidence in favor of the second alternative, demonstrating the occurrence of a localizing process that takes place prior to cleavage, and often as an immediate consequence of maturation, fertilization or both. It is in any case certain that some features of the prelocalization existing at the time cleavage begins are the result of an antecedent process of epigenesis.

1. Observations on Localizing Activities Prior to Cleavage

Observations on movements of the oöplasm are made possible by the presence of suspended granules of various kinds and are particularly facilitated by the presence of pigment-granules; but it may again be emphasized that these are only the external signs of underlying processes in the hyaloplasm that for the most part escape direct observation (p. 1090). Localizing activities thus made visible have been studied by many observers, prominent among them Driesch, Boveri, Lillie and Conklin. The simplest and clearest of these cases show a progressive localization of ectoplasm, entoplasm and mesoplasm prior to cleavage. In *Paracentrotus (Strongylocentrotus) lividus*, for example, Boveri ('01) showed that prior to the maturation of the egg the three characteristic strata (p. 1067) do not appear, the pigment-granules being uniformly distributed around the periphery of the egg (Fig. 512). Only after both polar divisions have been completed does the pigment collect to form the sub-equatorial red zone; and the experimental evidence, as will be seen (p. 1100), indicates further that only at this time does the localization of the three zones take place. Boveri's observations, together with those of Selenka ('78), prove however that this process is preceded, and no doubt conditioned, *by a preëxisting polarity* to which the stratification precisely conforms, as is demonstrated by the position of the micropyle.

Similar to this in principle are the cases of the ascidian *Styela partita* (Conklin, '05) or of the fresh-water pulmonates *Physa, Lymnæa* and *Planorbis* (Conklin, '10). In *Styela* the unmatured egg shows no visible polarized stratification, consisting of a central, gray, yolk-containing substance surrounded by a thin cortical layer filled with yellow pigment-granules. After the egg is set free the germinal vesicle breaks down, liberating a clear residual substance, and the first polar spindle forms; but no visible localizing action occurs until entrance of the sperm near the lower pole of the egg. This event is immediately followed by a down-rush of the peripheral yellow protoplasm to the lower pole to form the mesoplasm, while the clear residual substance of the germinal vesicle moves to a position just above it and enters the middle stratum.   The gray yolk-bearing material remains at first in the upper hemisphere (Fig. 524).

During and subsequent to the extrusion of the polocytes remarkable further localizing movements of the oöplasm take place.   The yellow meso-plasm, accompanied by the clear stratum derived from the germinal vesicle (ectoplasm) moves to the posterior side of the egg, and as cleavage ap- proaches the clear protoplasm moves into the upper hemisphere, while the gray substance (endoplasm) moves forwards and downwards, finally

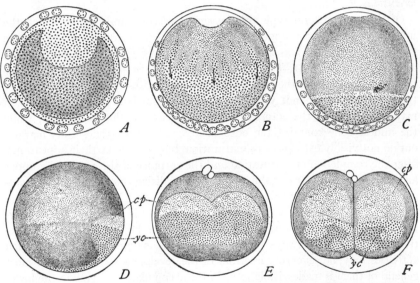

Fig. 524.—Localizing activities following maturation and fertilization in the egg of the tunicate *Styela* (*Cynthia*) *partita* (CONKLIN).

A, unfertilized egg, germinal vesicle above, gray yolk in center and periphera layer of yellow mesoplasm; *B*, five minutes after insemination, downrush of the yellow peripheral mesoplasm; *C*, resulting yellow cap at lower pole; *D*, posterior movement of mesoplasm to form the posterior crescent, with clear oöplasm above it; *E*, posterior view of the crescent as division begins; *F*, resulting 2-cell stage, in the same view.

lying in the lower hemisphere (Fig. 524).   The final result of these proc-esses is a grouping of materials somewhat similar to that seen in the *Para-centrotus* egg, save that the mesoplasm has moved away from the lower pole.   From the upper (clear) zone arises the ectoblast; from the lower gray zone the entoblast together with the chorda and the neural plate (chorda-neuroplasm); while the yellow mesoplasm gives rise to the mesen-chyme and the muscle-cells of the tail-region.   By the completion of the first cleavage no less than six different kinds of cytoplasmic substances are distinguishable by the eye, namely (according to the structures which they produce), ectoplasm, entoplasm, myoplasm, chymoplasm, caudal chymo‧plasm and chorda-neuroplasm.

In the pulmonates the clear material set free by the breaking down of the germinal vesicle spreads over the upper hemisphere to form an upper stratum from which the ectoblast is largely derived, while the remaining portion, yellow in color and containing the yolk, gives rise to the entoplasm and mesoplasm. Only two definite zones here are visible; but it is wholly probable that the same three zones exist as in *Dentalium*, *Styela* or *Strongylocentrotus*.

Of the same general type are the eggs of certain annelids, in which the upper and lower strata appear to be represented, broadly speaking, by the "polar rings" (p. 415), as described by Whitman ('78) in the leech *Clepsine* and by Vejdovský ('81, '88) in the oligochæte *Rhynchelmis*. In these cases the rings have at first the form of protoplasmic disks lying at either pole of the egg; their fate is not yet precisely known but it is probable that both may contribute to the ectoplasm, the lower one to the mesoplasm, while the middle zone contains the entoplasm.[1] The three zones thus marked out do not visibly exist prior to maturation, but first make their appearance after the completion of maturation and the entrance of the sperm, the upper and lower strata (polar rings) appearing as localizing thickenings of the ecto‧plasmic layer of the egg.

In all the foregoing cases the localizing activity is first actually in prog‧ress *during maturation and fertilization*, and it is highly probable that ac‧tivities of this type always take place to some extent at this time. Such activities may, however, occur earlier in the development. One of the most general of them is made visible to us in the accumulation of yolk in the lower or vegetative hemisphere in eggs of the telolecithal type, though this process may be deferred, or may be accentuated at the time of maturation. In some cases the same is shown in the localization of pigment, a pretty case of which is seen in the parasitic annelid *Myzostoma* (Fig. 525).[2] Here the egg before its maturation already shows two pigment zones at right angles to the axis, an upper red one and a lower green; but during maturation the upper one segregates into an upper red zone and an equatorial colorless one. The egg thus acquires three horizontal strata, which have the same general morphological value as in *Strongylocentrotus*, *Styela* or *Dentalium*, *i. e.*, the red zone is composed mainly of ectoplasm, the clear equatorial one of entoplasm, while the green one has a fate quite similar to the lower white area in *Dentalium* (p. 1064). Here, however, the segregation begins already before maturation, and is not completed until afterwards. An analogous case seems to be offered by the frog's egg, in which an upper dark area and a

[1] *Cf.* Vejdovský and Mrázek ('03).　　　　[2] See Driesch ('96), Carazzi ('04).

lower white one are already evident before the egg is fertilized, while the gray crescent (p. 1069) first appears after the sperm has entered, somewhat as does the yellow crescent of the *Styela* egg.

Finally we have such cases as that of *Dentalium*, where the same three zones are established long before maturation, and even before the egg has completed its full growth in the ovary. The morphogenic value of these zones, seems to be essentially the same as in the other cases reviewed (p. 1074). The important point, here readily determined, is that *the egg is*

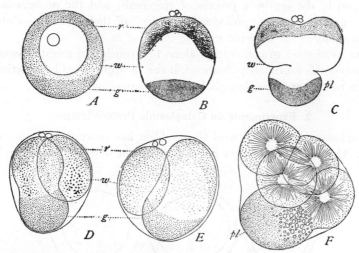

Fig. 525.—Localizing activities in the early development of the annelid *Myzostoma* (*B, C*, from DRIESCH, *A, D–F* from CARAZZI).

A, the egg before maturation and fertilization, *r*, red zone, *w*, white zone, *g*, green zone; *B*, after fertilization and extrusion of the polocytes, concentration of the red and green zones; *C*, trefoil stage of first cleavage; *D* and *E*, 2-cell stage, green zone in larger cell; *F*, second cleavage with second polar lobe (*p. l.*) and green zone passing into large posterior cell (*cf. Dentalium*, Fig. 480).

attached to the ovary by the lower or vegetative pole, the lower polar area being drawn out at this time into a stalk-like prominence that is withdrawn into the egg after its severance from the ovarian wall. We are thus enabled to observe directly the important fact that the strata make their appearance quite independently of maturation or fertilization, in a position and order definitely correlated with the preëxisting polarity of the egg; we observe also the fact that the axis of polarity is in its turn correlated with the position of the egg with reference to the maternal tissues. And this points clearly to the conclusion that the polarity itself is determined by an epigenetic process during the early history of the egg (p. 1023).[1]

---

[1] Vejdovský ('81, '88) has found that three strata that seem comparable to those of *Dentalium* are also found at an early period in the egg of the annelid *Sternaspis*.

A comparison of the facts indicates that the various cases reviewed—in particular the eggs of *Strongylocentrotus*, *Rhynchelmis*, *Styela* (*Cynthia*), *Myzostoma*, *Dentalium* and *Sternaspis*—offer a common general type of prelocalization *that is attained at different periods in the ontogeny*, the process occurring late in the sea-urchin or ascidian, very early in *Dentalium*, and at an intermediate period in *Myzostoma*. If this be admitted, the pre-localization in question, obviously, cannot be considered as a primary character or "preformed quality" of the egg. It is a secondary condition developed in the egg by a process of epigenesis; and the presumption is thus created that other "preformed qualities" of the oöplasmic substance are essentially of the same nature.

Were we limited to observation alone this conclusion might reasonably be questioned. Fortunately, however, it can be approached by experiment, and the results, as far as they go, lead to the same conclusion.

2. Experiments on Cytoplasmic Prelocalization

Experimental investigation of the problem has proceeded along several paths. One of the most direct is the study of the development of egg-frag-

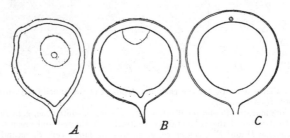

Fig. 526.—Polarity of the unsegmented egg of the nemertine *Cerebratulus lacteus*, from life.

A, unfertilized egg immediately after liberation, surrounded by membrane, showing stalk at point of attachment and eccentric germinal vesicle; *B*, the same egg, still unfertilized, one hour later, disappearance of germinal vesicle leaving clear polar area in which lies the first polar spindle in metaphase (*cf.* Fig. 189); *C*, an egg 40 minutes after fertilization, first polocyte.

ments. In such cases as *Dentalium* we should expect to find the development of egg-fragments to differ according to the region of the egg from which they come; and such is actually the case (p. 1064). The case is different with eggs in which the stratification first appears after maturation and fertiliza-tion; for here we should expect the development of egg-fragments to differ according to the period of the operation; and again such is actually the case. The most fully known of these cases is offered by the egg of *Cerebratulus*, in which, as Yatsu's observations proved ('04), a marked redistribution of the oöplasmic materials takes place when the germinal vesicle breaks down, the yolk accumulating especially in the lower hemisphere and the protoplasm in the upper.[1]

This object is a highly favorable one because of the facility with which the egg may be cut in two under the lens, the ease with which the plane of section may be determined, and the tolerance of the egg to mechanical injury. The newly laid egg is somewhat pear-shaped, but soon after discharge into the sea-water (before fertilization) becomes nearly spheroidal. At its narrower end is a distinct protuberance which marks the point at which the egg was attached to the ovarian wall and is diametrically opposite the point at which the polycytes are extruded (Fig. 526).[2] This protuberance therefore is situated at the lower pole of the egg and there persists until the first polocyte is formed at the upper pole.

After discharge into the water the germinal vesicle breaks down and the first polar spindle advances as far as the metaphase but proceeds no further until entrance of the sperm when maturation proceeds (Coe). The egg may therefore readily be cut in any desired plane at any period and both fragments from a single egg may be fertilized, isolated, and reared. If the operation be performed before the germinal vesicle breaks down only the nucleated fragment develops, first forming polar bodies like a whole egg. If the operation be deferred until after breaking down of the germinal vesicle both fragments may develop (*cf.* p. 405). The fact should be recalled that the nemertine egg has a very characteristic form of spiral cleavage differing from all other known cases in that the first quartet of ectomeres are larger than the basal cells (Fig. 527), also that an isolated blastomere of the 2- or 4-cell stage segments as if still forming part of a whole embryo (p. 1055).

If the egg be cut in two at any period before maturation and fertilization the egg-fragment, *whatever be the plane of section, may segment in every detail like a whole egg of diminished size* (Fig. 527) and if of sufficient size may produce a perfectly formed dwarf larva (Fig. 528).[3] In the latter respect the egg-fragment is like an isolated 1/2- or 1/4-blastomere but in the former respect is widely different. It is nearly certain that the egg-fragments at this time retain their original polarity; for in nucleated fragments, the cleavage pattern shows the normal relation to the point at which the polocytes are extruded. Nevertheless, the results show that neither the factors determining cleavage nor those involved in the morphogenic process have assumed a fixed localization up to the time the germinal vesicle breaks down.

A very different result is obtained when the eggs are cut in the stages following the entrance of the sperm and the completion of maturation. The in-

[1] It is probable that sufficiently close observation would show the presence of the usual three strata in these eggs prior to cleavage.
[2] C. B. Wilson ('99), E. B. Wilson ('03), Zeleny ('04), Yatsu ('04, '08, '09, '10a, '10b).
[3] Wilson ('03), Yatsu ('04), Zeleny ('04).

dependent experiments of Yatsu ('04) and of Zeleny ('04), on the development
of egg-fragments obtained at different periods, carried out on a considerable
scale, bring out several very interesting points. Yatsu found that the percent-

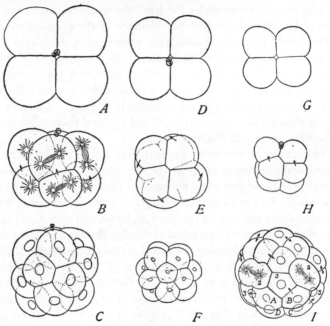

Fig. 527.—Segmentation-stages of entire eggs and of egg-fragments of different sizes from *Cere-bratulus*.

A, B, C, typical 4-, 8- and 16-cell stages from entire egg; D, E, 4- and 8-cell stages from rather
large fragment cut from upper hemisphere (E is seen from the lower pole); F, typical 16-cell stage
from smaller fragment; G, H, 4- and 8-cell stages from smaller fragment; I, normal 28-cell stage,
entire egg, to show delayed cleavage of second quartet.

age of normally formed dwarf larvæ produced from egg-fragments steadily
decreases from the time the germinal vesicle disappears up to the time of the
first cleavage, but suddenly increases in case of the development of isolated
blastomeres at the 2-cell-stage. This is shown in the following table:

TIME OF OPERATION	TOTAL NO. OF DWARF LARVÆ	PERCENTAGE OF NORMAL LARVÆ
Before disappearance of germinal vesicle	35	85.7%
Metaphase of first polar spindle	65	52.3%
Period of conjugation of gamete-nuclei	26	24.0%
Before completion of first cleavage	4	one case
Isolated blastomeres of 2-cell stage	8	100%

The decrease in percentage of normal larvæ in the period following maturation clearly points to a progressive regrouping or localization of materials that is in progress at this time. In a later confirmatory study ('10) Yatsu found that prior to fertilization the germinal localization does not advance noticeably for as long as five hours after formation of the first polar spindle (in metaphase); but proceeds as soon as the sperm enters. The facts do not, however, show whether the effect is direct (as would seem

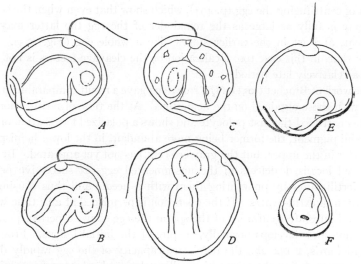

Fig. 528.—Dwarf larvæ of the nemertine *Cerebratulus* from egg-fragments before and after maturation (*E*, *F*, from YATSU).

A, *B*, twin larvæ, nearly normal, from horizontal section of an egg before the completion of maturation; *C*, similar larva, from upper hemisphere; *D*, abnormal larva from later stage, after removal of upper polar region; *E*, *F*, twin larvæ from egg-fragments; *E*, from upper hemisphere; *F*, from lower.

to be in case of the ascidian egg, p. 1103) or is indirectly caused by release of the maturation-divisions.[1] Yatsu believed that most of the egg-fragments segmented like whole eggs; and essentially similar results were obtained by him in a later work ('11) on the ctenophores. Fragments of *Beroë* eggs obtained by cutting in any plane before formation of the polocytes typically segment like whole eggs and often give rise to nearly normal larvæ. If the operation is deferred until after the completion of maturation the fragments

---

[1] Theoretically the observed facts might be interpreted as due merely to a decrease of regulative capacity at the maturation and fertilization period. Such a decrease manifestly takes place; but it is clearly a consequence of the new conditions created by the segregation going on in the egg. That such is the correct conclusion is indicated by the sudden increase in percentage of normal larvæ in the ½ blastomere; for this obviously is due to a normal quantitative distribution of the egg-materials by normal cleavage, such as is only rarely possible by means of the rude operation of artificial section.

still segment like a whole egg; but the resulting larvæ most commonly show marked defects, as described by Fischel (p. 1046). From this Yatsu concluded, as before, that there is a decided advance in the specification of the germ-regions after formation of the polocytes; but that the factors determining the form of cleavage are not necessarily identical with those of the localization-pattern—a conclusion also indicated by many other facts (p. 1072).

These results have been supplemented by the more recent experiments of Conklin ('17) on the production of giant polocytes in *Crepidula* as a result of centrifuging the egg (p. 494), which show that even when the second polocyte is fully as large as the remainder of the egg the latter may still segment, at least in the earlier stages, like a whole egg (Fig. 235). This shows that, in this case too, localization of the cleavage-factors is not fixed until a relatively late period.

The work of Brachet ('05) on the frog's egg gave a result comparable in principle with those obtained on the nemertine. At the time of fertilization this egg has extruded the first polocyte and shows a polarized localization of both yolk and pigment, the former being more abundant in the lower hemisphere, the latter in the upper; but the gray crescent has not yet appeared. Brachet produced localized defects in the unsegmented eggs at successive periods after fertilization by puncturing them with a needle and thus causing the formation of extra-ovates. If the operation is performed at any time within 45–50 minutes after entrance of the sperm the egg shows a perfect power of regulation and develops normally in spite of the initial lesions. From this time forwards, 1 1/4–2h., the regulative capacity of the egg rapidly diminishes, the egg losing the power of expelling the dead substance remaining in the wound and producing embryos that are correspondingly asymmetrical or show localized defects comparable with those resulting from destruction of one of the blastomeres of the 2-cell or 4-cell stage. This progressive limitation of regulative capacity is ascribed by Brachet to the progressive segregation of the egg-materials at this time, an external sign of which is given by the appearance of the gray crescent about two hours after entrance of the sperm (p. 1069).

3. The Rôle of the Sperm in Localization

It is evident from the foregoing that in some species important localizing activities may take place independently of the sperm, and prior to its entrance. In parthenogenesis, obviously, the action of the sperm is wholly excluded, yet the same localizing activities take place as in the fertilized egg.[1]

---

[1] This is shown specifically by Bataillon in the parthenogenetic eggs of the frog when activated by puncture with a needle (p. 474). In these eggs the gray crescent and the bilateral symmetry of the egg make their appearance as usual; and it is an interesting fact that the gray crescent, which in the

Nevertheless it is an important question whether the sperm may not play a part in the localizing activities of the fertilized egg. It is not an easy one to answer because of the close association between maturation and fertilization in many animals. In *Styela*, for example, the movement of the sperm-nucleus seems to determine the posterior region and the bilaterality of the egg and embryo; but the reverse interpretation is also possible and Conklin gives reasons in favor of such a conclusion.[1] There is, however, apparently conclusive evidence that in some cases the sperm may have an important direct influence on the localizing activities.

One of the most important questions here involved is how the first plane of cleavage is determined, particularly in mosaic-like types in which all the earlier cleavages have a definite promorphological significance. Roux ('85 and subsequently) demonstrated that the first cleavage of the frog's egg *passes nearly through the point at which the sperm enters*, and that this point is later found on the ventral side near the posterior end of the larva. He therefore concluded that it is the entrance-point that determines the plane of first cleavage, and thus indirectly the median plane of the embryo. The first of these conclusions has received confirmation from various sources. The second is open to discussion, owing to the fact that while the plane of symmetry of the egg before cleavage becomes that of the larva, the plane of first cleavage often forms a considerable angle with it, even up to 90° (p. 1069).[2] Roux examined the question experimentally by fertilizing the egg locally (with a silk thread or a fine pipette) in a selected meridian. The results proved that fertilization may be effected in any meridian, that the first cleavage-plane most frequently passed through or near this meridian, and that the point of entry is afterwards found in the median ventro-posterior region of the embryo.

Approximate coincidence between the entrance-point and the first cleavage-plane has also been demonstrated in several other animals. Such coincidence is a matter of course when the sperm enters at either the upper or the lower pole of the egg, as in the ascidian egg (p. 1094) and a common condition in many other animals (p. 409). The significant cases are those

fertilized egg is formed on the side of the egg opposite to the entrance-point of the sperm, shows no constant relation to the point of puncture in the parthenogenetic egg.

[1] '05, p. 91.

[2] Roux showed that the entering sperm carries in with it some of the pigment from the cortical layer, thus leaving behind it a trail which persists during the first two cleavages or even later. The plane of first cleavage always passes through or parallel to this trail and hence through or near the point of entrance, as may readily be observed in sections. This has received repeated confirmation by later observers, but is modified by the curved path of the sperm, since the "copulation-path" (p. 424) may form a considerable angle with the "penetration path," and it is the former that influences the direction of the first cleavage in accordance with Van Beneden's law. This is because division of the sperm-center produces a spindle at right angles to the copulation-path and copulation of the gamete-nuclei takes place in a plane parallel to this axis. The first cleavage-plane of course cuts this at right angles and hence passes through the copulation-path.

in which the entrance-point may be outside the polar region. The best known of these are the sea-urchin (*Toxopneustes*) and the annelid (*Nereis*), which, taken together, seem to give conclusive evidence. In the sea-urchin [1] the sperm may enter the egg anywhere, and the entrance-cone at the periphery of the egg (p. 410) persists long enough to give a landmark for some time after the sperm enters. The plane of first cleavage passes through or near this point (Fig. 190). Since the first cleavage also always passes through the original egg-axis (as conclusively proved by Boveri, '01) the particular meridian of this cleavage must be approximately fixed by the entrance-point of the sperm. Whether the first cleavage-plane also has a fixed relation to the symmetry of the larva in this case is not certainly known. Driesch concluded from certain experimental evidence that the first cleavage-plane is transverse to the larval plane of symmetry; but Boveri, whose results are supported by those of Herbst, has made it more probable that this result reverses the actual condition. In either case, evidently, the entrance-point of the sperm could be a determining factor in the establishment of the symmetry of the larva.

The most decisive evidence seems to be offered by Just's observations ('12) on the egg of *Nereis*, a particularly valuable object because of the highly determinate constant character of the cleavage. In this egg the sperm remains attached for a long time to the periphery before its entrance (p. 414); so that, when the egg throws off its gelatinous envelope the sperm lies in a somewhat funnel-shaped canal, communicating with the surrounding sea-water. If insemination be effected in sea-water containing a fine suspension of India ink the black mixture is left within the sperm-canal and thus forms a very definite mark pointing exactly to the entrance-point (Fig. 529).[2] In all cases the first cleavage-plane passes very nearly through the point of entrance as thus indicated, and is approximately transverse, separating a smaller anterior cell (AB) from a larger posterior one (CD) which contains the mesoplasm and the main foundation of the post-trochal region, precisely as in *Dentalium* or *Myzostoma*. Since this relation is perfectly constant it seems at least extremely probable that in this case the direction of the first cleavage-plane, and of the plane of symmetry (with all that this implies) is not prelocalized in the egg or determined by the changes accompanying maturation, but depends upon the entrance-point of the sperm.

This does not mean that the sperm is the sole determining cause of this localization. It is highly probable that if this egg, like those of other annelids

---

[1] Wilson, in Wilson and Mathews, '95, Boveri, '95.

[2] A similar method was originally employed by Boveri ('01) to demonstrate the micropyle in the sea-urchin egg.

having a similar type of cleavage (*Amphitrite, Thalassema*), could be caused to undergo a normal parthenogenetic development, the first cleavage would take place in the same way and show the same relation to localization. In such cases the plane of symmetry would be determined by the egg alone; and the same may be said of the appearance in some eggs of a perfect bilateral symmetry in the ovarian egg, long before either maturation or fertilization, as we see in the egg of the insect or the cephalopod (p. 1019). From all this we must conclude that the sperm merely acts as a selective or limiting factor, serving as it were as a *point d'appui* about which the localizing action is centered, and thus fixes the actual cleavage-meridian out of many possible ones. And here again we must conclude that bilaterality, like the

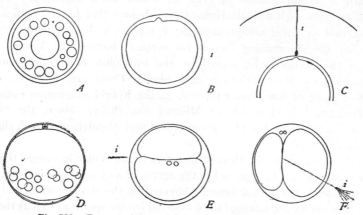

Fig. 529.—Entrance-point and first cleavage-plane in *Nereis* (Just).

A, the egg at the time of insemination with equatorial girdle of oil-drops; *B*, extrusion of first polar body (*p. b.*), indicator at right; *C*, entrance-cone, indicator forming behind the sperm-head (*h*), the outer line is the boundary of the jelly; *D*, egg with two polar bodies, oil drops have sunk into lower hemisphere; *E*, *F*, 2-cell stages with indicator.

stratification of the egg, may be developed epigenetically in the egg at different periods in different cases, and may be conditioned by different factors— in some cases, perhaps, by the relation of the ovarian egg to the maternal tissues (insects), in others by cytoplasmic changes occurring at the time of maturation, in still others by the entrance-point of the sperm. It may be difficult to distinguish with certainty between these various cases, owing to the overlapping of the different stages; but in any case the establishment of bilaterality and other fundamental promorphological characters in the egg appears to us as an epigenetic process. This conclusion at once brings into view broader horizons of inquiry that are still in large measure unexplored.

V. The Mechanism of Development

The fact that specification of the blastomeres of the segmenting egg is determined by their specific cytoplasmic materials seems at first sight to offer a contradiction when we recall the equally demonstrative proof of the important part played by the nucleus and the chromosomes in determination and heredity. The contradiction cannot, however, be real, for both sides rest upon experimentally demonstrated facts, and both must be included in any adequate general interpretation.

Some writers have sought such an interpretation in the assumption that heredity is essentially a dual process, including both "nuclear" and "cytoplasmic" heredity; and both cytology and genetics have in fact brought forward a certain amount of evidence which when superficially viewed seems to favor such a distinction. It is obvious that formed bodies such as plastids or other self-propagating cytoplasmic bodies may in some cases be the determining factors for certain characters. A very clear case of this seems to be offered by the leaf-colors of certain plants as determined by Bauer, Correns and Shull. There are, however, other cases of more or less similar type (e. g., the hybrid silk-worms examined by Toyama, '12) in which, as Morgan has clearly shown, the "cytoplasmic" inheritance is really chromosomal and Mendelian, though slightly disguised in type.[1]

On the cytological side Meves ('08, etc.) in particular has urged that the chondriosomes may be regarded as the agents of a cytoplasmic heredity that runs parallel to the nuclear heredity effected by the chromosomes; and both forms of heredity are assumed to be effected by the sperm as well as the egg. This view is still unsupported by definite genetic evidence, but a means of testing its validity should be offered by such evidence; for it is only in case of the chromosomes that we have thus far been able to identify a mechanism for the orderly segregation of unit-factors, while the distribution of the chondriosomes in the maturation-divisions appears in most cases to be a haphazard process. The possibilities of discovery in this direction have still been too little explored to warrant extended discussion. There are, however, certain more general questions that must here be examined.

A number of observers have suggested an interpretation of heredity which assumes that the larger group-characters are transmitted by the cytoplasm; while those of the species, variety or individual (which alone display Mendelian behavior), are transmitted by the nucleus. In the picturesque phrase of Loeb, the cytoplasm of the egg is "the embryo in the rough," carrying the genus- or even the species-heredity, while Mendelian

---

[1] See Morgan ('19), Bauer ('14).

heredity adds only the finer details to the rough block ('19, p. 152). This singular notion originally grew out of the study of hybrids, more particularly those produced by heterogeneous crosses between different genera or even more widely separated groups. Boveri ('92, '03) found that in crosses between different species of sea-urchins (*Sphærechinus* ♀ × *Parechinus* ♂) the cleavage of the ovum is purely of maternal type though the resulting larvæ show the characters of both parents. From this fact, and others, he concluded that the form and rate of cleavage is determined wholly by the organization of the cytoplasm of the egg, and is uninfluenced by the nucleus of the sperm.[1] This was confirmed and extended in a more extended series of experiments (Driesch, '96, '98)[2] which seemed to show that the general type of the blastula, the number of primary mesenchyme-cells, the pattern of pigmentation, and even the form of the young pluteus larva in the crosses examined by him showed only maternal characters, the influence of the sperm first being shown in the character of the skeleton. Boveri showed ('03) that in several of these characters the influence of the sperm may be seen at a somewhat earlier period; but like Driesch he concluded that up to a certain point the character of the development is wholly determined by the cytoplasm of the egg.[3] Boveri suggested a provisional distinction between "preformed" and "epigenetic" ontogenetic characters, the former being to a certain extent blocked out or prelocalized in the cytoplasm of the egg independently of the sperm. These include certain very general characters of the embryo, including obviously the promorphological characters of the egg (polarity, symmetry and the like) the plasma-structure of the early blastomeres, the form of cleavage and that of the resulting blastula, the *tempo* of the early development,[4] initial size of the embryo, and the primary axial relations. The epigenetic characters were assumed by Boveri to be determined directly by the nucleus, being gradually superimposed, as it were, on the "preformed" cytoplasmic characters; as development proceeds the latter characters, accordingly, may thus become obscured by the nuclear

---

[1] '92, p. 469.

[2] See also Peter ('06), and Tennent ('12).

[3] The important part in determination played by the cytoplasmic structures had been clearly recognized by Driesch in his interesting earlier work *Analytische Theorie der Organischen Entwicklung* (1894); but he there treats that cytoplasmic structure as only a limiting condition, the nucleus being the original source of all determination. This is nearly the position adopted in the first edition of this work (1896).

"In so far as it possesses a nucleus every cell during the ontogeny is the bearer of the totality of all the factors of heredity (Anlagen); but in so far as it possesses a specific protoplasmic cell-body it is only capable of responding to certain causes. . . . The specific potency of the cells of every elementary organ is founded in the specific nature of their cytoplasm by which it is limited, and becomes always more limited in the course of the (developmental) process." Wilson, *op. cit.*, pp. 81, 82.

[4] Newman ('10) has found, on the other hand, that in fish-hybrids the rate of cleavage is distinctly affected by the sperm.

(epigenetic) or even in greater or less degree lost to view.[1] Boveri included in the epigenetic characters "all the essential characteristics of the individual and of the species,"[2] and, by implication at least, placed among the "preformed" qualities those that are common to different species and hence are characteristic of higher groups.

Out of this grew Loeb's conception of the "embryo in the rough" as determined by the cytoplasm alone, and of the nucleus as merely adding the finer details to the rough model.[3] Jenkinson ('17) adopted a similar view, holding that the larger characters are transmitted by the cytoplasm, the smaller by the nucleus. Conklin is more specific. "We are vertebrates because our mothers were vertebrates and produced eggs of the vertebrate pattern; but the color of our skin and hair and eyes, our sex, stature and mental peculiarities were determined by the sperm as well as by the egg from which we came." These statements are rhetorically effective, but will not stand the test of critical analysis; and they do not represent the conclusions at which Boveri himself finally arrived. They fail to reckon with the fact that the cytoplasmic organization of the egg by which Boveri's "preformed qualities" are determined *is itself the product of an antecedent process of epigenetic development* in the course of which, as we have every reason to believe, the chromosomes have played their part. Boveri's distinction between "preformed" (cytoplasmic) and epigenetic (chromosomal) characters was drawn in a purely provisional sense; and in later works he emphasized the probability that "preformed" characters, even such fundamental ones as polarity and bilaterality, are established by an epigenetic process at an early period in the history of the egg.[4] If this be correct, the whole force of the evidence drives us to the conclusion *that the chromosomes are as much concerned in the determination of the so-called "preformed" or cytoplasmic characters as in any others.* It would therefore be highly misleading to state that the "embryo in the rough" is determined solely by the cytoplasm. The cytoplasmic characters of the ovum are themselves the product of biparental heredity, even though they may be determined before the sperm enters.

Conklin points out that a real difference of *modus operandi* nevertheless exists between the two kinds of characters. Obviously those promorphological characters of the embryo that are foreshadowed in the egg-cytoplasm before fertilization make their appearance unaffected by the sperm that

---

[1] "When we consider the differences that we can actually perceive between the cytoplasm of an *Echinus*-egg and that of a *Sphærechinus*-egg, it is astonishing to see in the hybrid larvæ how in the course of a few days these preformed cytoplasmic qualities are completely overcome" ('03, p. 254).

[2] '03, p. 362.

[3] '16, p. 151.

[4] '10. p. 207, '18, p. 466, etc.

subsequently enters the egg. So far as they have been affected by the chromosomes, it must have been by those of the egg, which have been derived from both grandparents.[1] Conklin has rightly maintained, therefore, that to this extent the parental egg and sperm do not play identical parts in determination, the former contributing more to the heredity of the offspring than does the latter.

A pretty example of this fact is offered by the heredity of dextral and sinistral coiling in the gasteropods as shown by Sturtevant ('23) in an analysis of the work of Boycott and Diver ('23). With rare exceptions a particular individual, whether dextral or sinistral, produces only dextral or only sinistral offspring in a brood; e. g., a dextral individual produces either dextral or sinistral young, but not both types at once. This is made intelligible by the assumptions (1) that genetically the dextral type is dominant over the sinistral, but (2) that the character of a particular brood is due to the genetic constitution of the egg before maturation and fertilization. The reversal of symmetry is apparent at least as early as the second cleavage (perhaps at the first) and is almost certainly due to conditions in the maternal cytoplasm that are established before the sperm has acted on the egg. The eggs of a sinistral individual therefore produce sinistral offspring *even if fertilized by sperm carrying the dextral* (dominant) factor. The eggs of heterozygotes thus produced, if self-fertilized, should produce three genetic types of offspring, DD, Ds and ss; but all of these, *even including the ss individuals, will be dextral in somatic appearance*, because of the constitution of the egg from which they arose. The offspring of the first two types will obviously all be dextral; but those of the ss dextral class will all be sinistral, since the mother carries no D. These curious relations, at first sight so mysterious, at once become perfectly plain when we perceive that the effect of the sperm-chromosomes is delayed for one generation, producing no effect upon the F_1 soma (already predetermined before fertilization) but so affecting the cytoplasm of its eggs as to determine the direction of coiling in F_2. It is, however, obvious that when the whole life-cycle is taken into account both the "epigenetic" and the "preformed" characters are alike determined by an activity in which the chromosomes have played an essential part, and that both alike may be forms of Mendelian heredity.

The possibility may finally be indicated that cytoplasmic predetermination (in the foregoing sense) may have played some part in the matriclinous tendency of hybrids from heterogeneous crosses (p. 971), even in cases where the paternal chromosomes have been in part or wholly eliminated; but such a fact would be hard to prove, and if established would not weaken the conclusions based on the history of the sperm-chromosomes. The only

[1] *Cf.* Conklin, '20, p. 197.

case which points directly to such a conclusion is that of Godlewsky's *Parechinus-Antedon* crosses; yet even here, for the reasons already pointed out (p. 972) the results are inconclusive.

VI. PREFORMATION AND EPIGENESIS. HEREDITY

We have now arrived at the furthest outposts of investigation in this field and may more clearly perceive the modern aspect of the old controversies that grew up about the problem of preformation and epigenesis. Perhaps this problem is scientifically insoluble; at any rate no general agreement has yet been reached in regard to it. The modern biologist must be permitted to treat the problem in pragmatic fashion, employing the terms of one hypothesis or the other according to the procedure that he finds most useful in practice. The physiologist and experimentalist have for the most part instinctively turned towards an epigenetic interpretation of development, the morphologist towards a preformistic or evolutionary one; but many conspicuous exceptions might be named. Weismann and Driesch, for example, though standing in many respects at opposite poles of thought in respect to their treatment of this problem, alike express the opinion that fundamentally epigenesis is inconceivable.[1] This does not, of course, mean the acceptance of preformation in the older and cruder sense. It means (to paraphrase the expression of Driesch) that we are unable to conceive how a self-determining system can increase its own initial complexity by interaction of its chemical and physical components. In so far as such a system is independent of external causes it can only transform and redistribute components that are inherent in the system from the beginning. Huxley, with characteristic acuteness, had long before approximated to a similar conclusion. Writing in 1878, he says: "It is not impossible that when the analysis of the process of development is carried still further . . . the theory of development will approach more nearly to metamorphosis than to epigenesis. . . . From this point of view the process which in its superficial aspects is epigenesis appears in essence to be evolution in the modified sense adopted in Bonnet's later writings; and development is merely the expansion of a potential organism or 'original preformation' according to fixed laws." [2]

In their purely logical aspects the questions here raised belong perhaps rather to metaphysics than to science. Nevertheless we cannot fail to perceive that in certain respects the conclusion expressed by Huxley approaches the results of modern experimental research. We have seen that many features of this so-called "initial structure" of the cytoplasm are

[1] See Weismann, *The Germ Plasm*, p. 14.
[2] Evolution, in *Encyclopedia Britannica*, VIII, 1878. Also in *Science and Culture*, 1882, pp. 295-6

products of an epigenetic process; and grounds have been given for the conclusion that the same is probably true even of such fundamental features as polarity and symmetry. What determines the pattern of these initial localizations is still almost completely unknown; but there are certain indications that it may be regarded as a product of the response of the egg to conditions external to itself. This seems to be true of both the polarity and the symmetry of the egg; for polarity is known to be correlated in many cases with the position of the egg in the ovary, and bilaterality with the position of the egg in the oviduct, or with the entrance-point of the sperm (pp. 1020, 1103). Directly or indirectly, therefore, formative stimuli from without may play a part in all localizing processes in the egg. It seems clear, however, that external formative stimuli are but limiting conditions to which the egg adjusts itself. This we see, for instance, in the determination of the direction of the first cleavage-plane, in one case by the entrance-point of the sperm, in another by the egg itself developing after parthenogenetic activation. In spite, therefore, of numerous well-established cases of determinative formative stimuli in development, the general problem of localization in the egg still remains in large measure unsolved. The outstanding result that emerges from our study of the problem is that the localizing process appears essentially as one of cytoplasmic epigenesis, and that its superficial likeness to preformation disappears when all the phenomena are taken into account.

When we turn to the nucleus the problem offers a different aspect. All the available evidence indicates that the nucleus is indeed a kind of "original preformation" in which are contained great numbers of self-perpetuating, definite entities grouped in a definite though shifting pattern. Their nature is unknown. They are conceivably single molecules of nucleoproteins, in which the protein component may perhaps be the determining element to which the different genes owe their several specific characters (p. 652). Heredity may thus be determined fundamentally by the chemical constitution of the various proteins, as so many biochemists have held (p. 641).[1] If such be the case the root of heredity may lie in the processes by which these proteins are built up or perpetuate themselves (p. 199).[2] On the whole, however, it seems for the present more convenient to think of the nuclear units as molecular aggregates, analogous to the plastids or centrioles of the cytosome and capable of division, but lying for the most part beyond the reach of direct microscopical vision. The essential fact, from which the genetic evidence seems to leave no escape, is that they are self-perpetuat-

[1] Cf. R. S. Lillie's interesting work ('18); also D'Arcy Thompson ('17).

[2] The analogy between growth and heredity, recognized by Darwin and many other earlier writers, has been accepted by many later writers, such as Loeb, Robertson, Ostwald, R. S. Lillie and others, who have also emphasized the resemblance of growth to an autocatalytic process.

ing, and must, in some fashion or other, preserve their identity from one generation of cells to another.

Genetic and cytological evidence unite in the demonstration that the primary units are aggregated in linear series and in definite order to form more complex linkage-groups which appear to the eye as spireme-threads or chromosomes; which persist without loss of their specific character throughout the individual life-cycle; but which may also, within certain well-defined limits, undergo reconstruction at the time of meiosis (p. 950). In this result, there is much that calls for further elucidation. We must reckon with the possibility, worked out with so much ingenuity by Weismann (p. 500) that there may be in the nucleus aggregates intermediate in order of magnitude between the gene and the chromosome; and there is much to suggest that the "chromomeres" may represent such aggregates. We do not know with certainty how the identity of the linkage-groups (*i. e.,* the genetic continuity of chromosomes) is preserved in the diffused vegetative state of the nucleus or interkinesis. But these are questions of detail. The large fact is that both the genetic and the cytological facts find their most natural interpretation in the conception, first clearly formulated by Roux, DeVries and Weismann, that the nucleus possesses a definite architecture of which the most fundamental feature is the presence of a vast number of self-perpetuating and independent elementary units which correspond severally to genes or unit-factors of heredity. The evidence indicates that it is only these units that pass on unchanged from generation to generation. In other respects the nuclear organization is periodically reconstructed in greater or less degree by the phenomena of crossing-over in meiosis and by the replacement of chromosomes that takes place as a result of meiosis and syngamy. Fundamentally, however, we reach the conclusion that in respect to a great number of characters *heredity is effected by the transmission of a nuclear preformation which in the course o, development finds expression in a process of cytoplasmic epigenesis.*

Whether all hereditary traits are represented in the nuclear organization is an open question. At least a partial exception seems to be offered by plastid-inheritance; and should a similar conclusion apply to the chondriosomes, Golgi-bodies and other formed elements of the cytoplasm, the conception of a cytoplasmic preformation (in the sense that has been indicated) might be greatly enlarged. Even were this established, however, we should still have to reckon with the possibility that such self-perpetuating cytoplasmic bodies might take their first origin in the nucleus or be influenced by its activity.

The foregoing conclusions, evidently, have somewhat in common with DeVries' hypothesis of intra-cellular pangenesis and with its development by Weismann, O. Hertwig and other writers though different in many important details. Hypotheses of this type have met with small favor in the eyes of most modern writers. They have been characterized as crude and artificial devices, which ignore the problem of individuality in the organism as a whole, are beyond the reach of verification, and carry anthropomorphic and teleological implications that are in conflict with scientific principles. No one, however, has pretended that such corpuscular theories of the cell-substance offer a complete solution of the problems of life; and it is not easy to see in what respect they are more anthropomorphic or teleological than the cell-theory itself or than the molecular and atomic theories of non-living matter. The same may be said of the use by geneticists of the chromosome-hypothesis of linkage, of the serial alignments of genes in the spireme-threads, and of "crossing-over" by chiasmatypy. "It is, I suppose, theoretically possible to consider such hypotheses as nothing more than a convenient fiction or algebraic symbolism, a kind of ideal mental model by means of which the genetic facts may conveniently be grouped. Those, however, who prefer to take their point of departure in the observed cytological facts will be more likely to make use of the actual model which every dividing cell displays to us in visible reality—a model that is not less impressive because at present the cytologist sees it only in broad outline, with no more than dim indications of the finer complications inferred from the results of genetic research. At any rate it was this actual model that gave the point of departure for the foregoing conceptions concerning the nuclear organization and thus made possible some of the most fundamental of modern experimental researches on heredity. Considered only as working instruments, therefore, these conceptions have a practical value almost comparable to that of the atomic theory as employed in chemistry and physics;"[1] and "as biologists we are interested in heredity not primarily as a mathematical formulation but rather as a problem concerning the cell, the egg and the sperm."[2]

How genes or chromosomes operate is unknown; but we may suspect that they, like plastids and other cytoplasmic bodies, are centers of specific chemical action, and possibly may serve for the production of soluble enzymes or hormones. Without speculating on this question we here again emphasize the conception that the cell is a reaction-system and that the whole cell-system may be concerned in the production of every hereditary trait (p. 976). In practice all the purposes of experimental analysis are sufficiently met if the hereditary "units," "genes" or "pangens" be thought of merely as modifiers which call forth responses, this way or that, according to their specific nature. To speak of them as "determiners" is to make

[1] Wilson, '23.   [2] Morgan, '15.

use of a convenient figure of speech; but this need imply no more than that they are differentials by the use of which we are enabled accurately to analyze the observed results. Such a procedure makes no pretense of solving all the problems of development and heredity; but its value as a practical working hypothesis was long since made plain to all.

VII. CONCLUDING REMARKS. MECHANISTIC AND VITALISTIC INTERPRETATIONS OF DEVELOPMENT

A retrospect on the ground traversed in the foregoing pages impresses us alike by the great advances that have been made by cytological and genetic research and by the limitations of our present knowledge. Viewed from the standpoint of fifty or even twenty years ago these advances astonish us, by reason of the clearness which which the general mechanism of heredity has been revealed and of the precision with which its *modus operandi* may now be examined. The convergence of cytological and genetic research that has made this possible marks one of the most noteworthy advances in modern biology.

Two outstanding results above all others claim our attention, namely, that the mechanism of heredity is intimately bound up on the one hand with the phenomena of constructive metabolism and on the other with those of mitotic cell-division. In one of its primary aspects, therefore, heredity has become a problem of biochemistry; for the evidence has steadily accumulated that fundamentally the specific type of each organism is an expression of the chemical nature of its component substances. The production of these substances, obviously, is a problem of metabolism. Their maintenance (or of that which determines them) in successive generations is primarily a problem of cytology; for it is the apparatus of mitosis by means of which the factors of heredity are handed on unchanged from cell to cell and are also enabled to undergo those dissociations and recombinations the results of which are made visible to us in the Mendelian phenomena. The operation of this mechanism is most clearly displayed to us in the distribution of the nuclear substance; but it is the same mechanism that we see at work also in the distribution of the cytoplasmic components of the cell-system during cleavage and differentiation.

On the other hand, the new horizons of investigation that are continually being opened in this field of work impress us with the present limitations of our knowledge. We are still without adequate understanding of the physiological relations between nucleus and cytoplasm and of the manner in which the nucleus is concerned in the operations of constructive metabolism, of growth and repair, and in the determination of hereditary traits. The same may be said of our present knowledge of development, above all in respect to the problem of localization, which has been so puzzling a crux of experimental embryology and cytology and has even formed the rallying point for a modern revival of vitalism. What determines the appearance of hereditary traits in regular order of space and time? How are the operations of development so coördinated as to give rise to a definitely ordered system?

It is our scientific habit of thought to regard the operation of any specific system as determined primarily by its specific physico-chemical composition. We continually refer the particular mode of development of an organism to its so-called "organization"; but we are unable to define precisely the meaning of this vague term. The mechanistic assumption implies some kind of specific structure or material configuration in the system; and since the organization of the egg is hereditary the structure or configuration must somehow be preserved by cell-division without loss of its specific character. This treatment of the problem has, however, not been permitted to go unchallenged by modern investigators. It has been seriously questioned by Driesch, an accomplished master of experimental embryology. His earlier work was guided largely by mechanistic principles, as may be seen from the serious and carefully elaborated attempt to formulate a mechanistic theory of development contained in his *Analytical Theory of Organic Development* (1894). With the progress of his experimental work, however, Driesch became convinced of the hopelessness of this attempt. His argument was based primarily on the phenomena of localization in the light of his discovery that a single blastomere of the sea-urchin egg may produce a perfect dwarf larva (p. 1050), and on Boveri's discovery that the same is true of a fertilized fragment of an unsegmented egg (p. 465). Driesch considered this egg (and the so-called regulative eggs generally) to be an "equipotential system," *i. e.*, one in which any part contains the potentiality of the whole, and may give rise to the whole, subject only to the limitations imposed by the primary symmetry and bilaterality of the egg, which he considered to be inherent in the component particles of the egg-substance. The development of such fractional parts of the egg, like the whole egg, displays a "harmony" or definite order and sequence of localization (hence the term "harmonic equipotential system") originally referred to the initial structure of the egg and the environmental conditions under which it develops. In the end, however, Driesch became convinced that the harmony of development cannot thus be explained. For (to give only the most essential of his arguments) the action of a mechanism or machine depends upon the maintenance of its structural integrity, *i. e.*, of its component parts in their normal relations. We can not conceive a mechanism that can be subdivided without being destroyed. But the egg can be thus subdivided, deprived of this part or that, or suffer displacement of its parts, without impairing its power to produce a perfect embryo of normal proportions and structure. The direction or control of its development cannot, therefore, be sought in an original machine-like structure or material configuration. A similar argument is based upon the phenomena of regeneration, functional adaptation and the so-called "purposive" or regulative processes generally. Driesch argues, therefore, that we can only find a sufficient explanation of these phenomena in the vitalistic assumption of an immaterial entity or guiding principle of development, neither energy nor matter nor a configuration of matter; and to this he gives the name of *entelechy* (a word borrowed from Aristotle) or (in some later discussions) that of "psychoid."

Driesch's interesting development of this conception has failed of wide acceptance partly because it is contrary to the spirit of modern scientific inquiry, and involves a practical abandonment of the problem; but even more because of new discoveries that struck at the very foundations of his argument. The most important of these was Boveri's experimental demonstration of the qualitative differences of the chromosomes (p. 916), which proves that *normal development is strictly dependent upon the integrity of the nuclear organization, i. e.*, on the maintenance of the normal combination of chromosomes (p. 920). This applies alike to the entire egg, to the cells into which it may split up and to fragments of the unsegmented egg. In its original form, therefore, Driesch's main argument is thus materially weakened; for the *nucleus* is seen to conform with his own definition of a mechanism or machine-like structure, a fact of course unknown to him when his general interpretation was formulated. The removal from the egg of any portion of its protoplasm, or the destruction of one or more blastomeres of the early cleavages, leaves the nucleus intact. On the other hand, removal of any of the chromosomes of the normal combination is irremediable. In Boveri's words: "We may take away from the young sea-urchin germ any of the *nuclei* we like, but can take away nothing from the *nucleus*." So long as the nucleus remains intact the power of reproducing the whole remains, except in so far as it may be held in check by secondary obstacles that result from differentiation. Here again, obviously, we find reason for considering the nucleus as an "original preformation" (in the sense that has been indicated) which plays a leading part in determination. A second, though less serious, objection to Driesch's conclusions lies in Boveri's demonstration that the sea-urchin egg agrees closely with the so-called "mosaic" eggs in type of prelocalization before cleavage, and that only in a much restricted sense is it an equipotential system at this time. For all we know, therefore, localization may be determined by the nucleus, or at least by a process in which the nucleus is concerned.

There is good reason to hope for further light on the problem from the study of the relation of the developing germ to external conditions. Undoubtedly a multitude of localizing activities are called forth in the developing organism as responses to localized external "formative stimuli";[1] the developing embryo appears indeed not merely as a complicated piece of mechanism but as a response of the inherited organization to the external conditions of its development. The production of roots and other structures on plants as a result of localized stimuli is familiar to all. In hydroids Loeb's interesting experiments ('91, etc.) showed that the production of new hydranths or roots at particular points is determined in the same manner by localized conditions of light, exposure to the sea-water, contact with the substratum and the like.

That such localized conditions of the environment may be concerned in the localizing activities of the egg seems to be clearly established by the fact that both the polarity of the egg and its bilateral symmetry are often correlated with the mode of attachment of the egg to the ovary, or its position in the oviduct (p. 1021). In the same category, perhaps, may be placed the effect of the entrance of the sperm on the plane of symmetry and the direction of the first cleavage (p. 1114), and perhaps also on the determination of the antero-posterior differentiation of the embryo (e. g., in the ascidian egg, p. 1103). Since all subsequent localizations show definite orientation to the initial ones thus established, we can in some fashion imagine how, by subsequent "interaction of the parts," or the influence of the "organism as a whole" on the development of its component parts, all localizations may originally be conditioned by the external environment; and certainly the possibilities of an analysis of this problem by observation and experiment seem by no means to have been exhausted.

Modern experiment has emphasized the long familiar fact that polarity involves an underlying "axial metabolic gradient" in the direction of the axis (cf. p. 107), and has thus added new weight to the early view that the polarity of the ovum may thus be determined as a reaction to its ovarian environment (p. 1023). Even if this view could be accepted, however, the problem is only thrown further back; for the inescapable fact remains that the specific reactions of the developing egg *depend upon its organization.* Concerning the fundamental nature of this organization we are still ignorant; but we have nothing to gain by the vitalistic assumption that the guiding principle in development is not only unknown but unknowable. Existing mechanistic interpretations of vital phenomena, evidently, are inadequate; but it is equally clear, as someone has said, that they are a "necessary fiction." Knowledge will be

---

[1] See Herbst's work ('01), *Formative Reize in der tierischen Ontogenese,* and those of Loeb ('16) and Child ('13, '15, etc)

advanced most surely by assuming that the problems of the cell can be solved by converging upon them all our forces of observation and experiment. If we are confronted still with a formidable array of problems not yet solved, we may take courage from the certainty that we shall solve a great number of them in the future, as so many have been in the past. If Mendelian heredity, at first sight so inscrutable, is effected by so simple a mechanism, we may hope to find equally simple explanations for many other puzzles of the cell that lie beyond our present ken.

LITERATURE XIV

Baer, C. E., v., '28, '37. Ueber Entwicklungsgeschichte der Thiere. Beobachtung und Reflexion: I. *Königsberg,* '28; II, '37.

Barfurth, D., '91, '13. Regeneration and Involution: *E. A. E.,* I–XVIII.
'13. Transplantation: *H. Nw.* X. *Fischer, Jena.*

Bateson,W., '14. Address: *British Assoc. Adv. Sci.,* Part I. Ref. 1, Part II, Ref. 66.

Bonnet, C., 1762. Considérations sur les Corps organisés: *Amsterdam.*

Born, G., '85. Ueber den Einfluss der Schwere auf das Froschei: *A. M. A.,* XXIV.

Boveri, Th., '89. Ein geschlechtlich erzeugter Organismus ohne mütterliche Eigenschaften: *Situngsb. d. phys.-med. Ges. Würzburg.*
'01a. Ueber die Polarität des Seeigeleies: *V. P. M. G.,* Würzburg. (N. F.) XXXIV.
'01b. Die Polarität von Oöcyte, Ei und Larve des *Strongylocentrotus lividus: Z. J., Anat. Ont.,* XIV, 4.
'03. Ueber den Einfluss der Samenzelle auf die Larven-charaktere der Echiniden: *A. Entwm.,* XVI.
'09. (See XI.)
'18. Zwei Fehlerquellen bei Merogonie-versuchen, etc.: *A. Entwm.,* XLIV.

Brachet, A., '05. Recherches expérimentales sur l'œuf de *Rana fusca: A. B.,* XXI.
'11. Étude sur les localisations germinales, etc.; *Rana fusca: Ibid.,* XXVI.
'17. L'œuf et les facteurs de l'ontogénèse: *Doin et Fils, Paris.*

Chabry, L., '87. Contribution à l'embryologie normale et tératologique des Ascidies simples: *J. A. P.,* XXIII.

Child, C. M., '15b. Individuality in Organisms: *Chicago.*

Conklin, E. G., '03. The Cause of inverse Symmetry: *A. A.,* XXIII.
'05. Mosaic Development in Ascidian Eggs: *J. E. Z.,* II.
'05a. (See XIII.)
'17. Effects of centrifugal Force on the Structure and Development of *Crepidula: J. E. Z.,* XXII.

Correns, C., '09. Zur Kenntniss der Rolle von Kern und Plasma bei Vererbung: *Z. A. V.,* II.

Crampton and **Wilson,** '96. Experimental Studies on Gasteropod Development (H. E. Crampton). Appendix on Cleavage and Mosaic-Work (E. B. Wilson): *A. Entwm.,* III.

Delage, Yves, '99. Études sur la mérogonie: *A. Z. E.* (Sér. III), VII.

Driesch, H., '92. Der Werth der beiden ersten Furchungszellen in der Echinodermenentwicklung: *Z. W. Z.,* LIII.

'94. Analytische Theorie der Organischen Entwicklung: *Leipzig*.

'96. Betrachtungen über die Organisation des Eies und ihre Genese: *A. Entwm.*, IV.

'99a. Resultate und Probleme der Entwicklungs-physiologie der Thiere: *E. A. E.*, VIII.

'99b. Die Localisation morphogenetischer Vorgänge: *A. Entwm.*, VIII.

'oo. Die isolierten Blastomeren des Echinodenkeimes: *A. Entwm.*, X.

'o6a. Studien zur Entwicklungsphysiologie der Bilateralität: *A. Entwm.*, XXI.

'o6b. Die Entwicklungsphysiologie von 1902–1905: *E. A. E.*, XIV.

'o8a. Die Entwicklungsphysiologie von 1906–1908: *E. A. E.*, XVII.

'o8b. The Science and Philosophy of the Organism. 2 Vols.: *London*.

Erdmann, R., '09. Experimentelle Untersuchungen der Massenverhältnisse von Plasma, Kern und Chromosomen, etc.: *A. Zf.*, II.

Fischel, A., '97. Experimentelle Untersuchungen am Ctenophorenei. I: *A. Entwm.*, VI.

'98. Id., II–IV: *Ibid.*, VII.

'03. Entwicklung und Organ-Differinzierung: *Ibid.*, XV.

Godlewski, E., 'o6. Untersuchungen über die Bastardierung der Echiniden- und, Crinoidenfamilie: *A. Entwm.*, XX.

'o8. Plasma und Kernsubstanz in der normalen und der durch äussere Faktoren veränderten Entwicklung der Echiniden: *A. Entwm.*, XXVI.

'o9. Das Vererbungsproblem im Lichte der Entwicklungsmechanik betrachtet: *Leipzig, Engelmann*.

'13. Physiologie der Zeugung: Handbuch der vergleichenden Physiologie, H. Winterstein, III, II.

Goldschmidt, R., '13. Einführung in die Vererbungswissenschaft 2nd Ed.: *Leipzig*.

Guyer, M. F., '11. Nucleus and Cytoplasm in Heredity: *A. N.*, XLV.

Heider, K., 'oo. Das Determinationsproblem: *V. D. Z. G.*

Herbst, Curt., 'o1. Formative Reize in der tierischen Ontogenese: *Leipzig, Engelmann*.

'o6-'14. (See XII.)

Herbst, C. '12. Entwicklungsmechanik, etc.: *H. Nw.*, III.

Hertwig, O., '92. Ältere und neuere Entwicklungstheorieen: *Berlin*.

His, W., '74. Unsere Körperform und das physiologische Problem ihrer Entstehung: *Leipzig*.

Huxley, T. H., '78. Evolution in Biology: *Enc. Brit.*, 9th Ed. '78, *Science and Culture*, N. Y., '82.

Jenkinson, J. W., '07. On the Relationship between the Symmetry of the Egg and Symmetry of the Embryo, etc.: *B.*, V.

'o9. Experimental Embryology: *Oxford*.

'14. The Relation between the Structure and the Development of Centrifuged Eggs of the Frog: *Q. J.*, April.

'17. Three Lectures on Experimental Embryology: *Clarendon Press, Oxford*.

Just, E. E., '12. The Relation of the first Cleavage-Plane to the Entrance-Point of the Sperm: *B. B.*, XXII, 4.

Lillie, F. R., 'o6. Observations and Experiments concerning the elementary Phenomena of Development in *Chætopterus: J. E. Z.*, III.

Loeb, J., '16. The Organism as a Whole: *New York*.

Lyon, E. P., '07. Results of centrifugalizing eggs: *A. Entwm.*, XXIII.

Maas, O., '03. Einführung in die experimentelle Entwickelungsgeschichte: *Wiesbaden.*

Marx, A., '25. Experimentelle Untersuchungen zur Frage der Determination der Medullarplatte: *A. Entwm.*, CV.

Morgan, T. H., '99, '00. Half Embryos and whole Embryos from one of the first two Blastomeres of the Frog's Egg: *A. A.*, X.

'95a. Half Embryos and whole Embryos, etc. (Frog): *A. A.*, X.

'08. The Effect of Centrifuging the Egg of the Mollusc *Cumingia: Sci.*, N. S., XXVII.

'09. The Effects Produced by Centrifuging Eggs before and during Development: *A. R.*, III.

'10a. Cytological Studies of Centrifuged Eggs: *J. E. Z.*, IX.

'17. The Theory of the Gene: *A. N.*, LI.

'23b. The Modern Theory of Genetics and the Problem of embryonic Development: *Phys. Rev.*, III.

Morgan and **Spooner,** '09. The Polarity of the Centrifuged Egg: *A. Entwm.*, XXVIII.

Müller, E., '96. Ueber die Regeneration der Augenlinse nach Exstirpation derselben bei *Triton: A. M. A.*, XLVII, 1.

Newmann, H. H., '10. Further Studies of the Process of Heredity in *Fundulus* Hybrids: *J. E. Z.*, VIII.

Penners, A., '22. Die Furchung von *Tubifex: Z. J. Anat. Ont.*, XLIII.

'24. Die Duplicitas cruciata und organbildende Keimbezirke: *A. M. A.*, CII.

'26. Experimentelle Untersuchungen zum Determinations-problem am Keim von *Tubifex: Z. W. Z.*, CXXVII, 1.

Przibram, H., '08. Experimental Zoölogy. Pt. I, Embryogeny: *Cambridge.*

Rabl, C., '06. Ueber Organbildende Substanzen, etc., *Engelmann. Leipzig.*

Ritter, W. E., '19. The Unity of the Organism: *Boston.*

Roux, W., '92–'93. Ueber Mosaikarbeit und neuere Entwicklungshypothesen: *An. Hf.*, 1, *Abt.*, II.

'95. Gesammelte Abhandlungen, II, 33, Nachwort.

'03. Ueber die Ursachen der Bestimmung der Hauptrichtungen des Embryo im Froschei: *A. A.*, XXIII.

'05. Die Entwicklungsmechanik, ein neuerer Zweig der biologischen Wissenschaft. Vorträge und Aufsätze über Entwicklungsmechanik der Tiere: *Leipzig, Engelmann.*

Ruud, G., '25. Die Entwicklung isolierter Keimfragmente frühester Stadien von *Triton: A. Entwm.*, CI, 2.

Schaxel, J., '12. Versuch einer cytologischen Analyse der Entwicklungsvorgänge, I: *Z. J., Anat. Ont.*, XXXIV.

Schultze, Oskar, '94. Die küntsliche Erzeugung von Doppelbildungene bei Froschlarven, mit Hilfe abnormer Graviationsrichtung: *A. Entwm.*, I.

'00. Ueber das erste Auftreten der bilateralen Symmetrie, etc.: *A. M. A.*, LV.

Spemann, H., '01–'03. Entwicklungsphysiologische Studien am Tritonei: *A. Entwm.*, XII, XV, XVI.

'18. Ueber die Determination der ersten Organanlagen des Amphibienembryo, I–VI: *A. Entwm.*, XLIII.

'19. Experimentelle Forschungen zum Determinations- und Individualitäts-Problem: *Die Naturwiss.*, VII, 32.

'25. Ueber Organizatoren in der Tierischen Entwicklung: *Ibid.*, XII.

Spemann und **Mangold**, '24. Ueber Induktion von Embryonalanlagen durch Implantation, etc.: *A. M. A.*, C.

Weismann, A., '85. Die Continuität des Keimplasmas als Grundlage einer Theorie der Vererbung: *Jena.*

'93. The Germ-plasm: Eng. Tr. by W. N. Parker and Harriet Ronnfeldt, *New York.*

Whitman, C. O., '88. The Seat of Formative and Regenerative Energy: *J. M.*, II.

'94. Evolution and Epigenesis: *W. H. L.*

Wilson, E. B., '96. On Cleavage and Mosaic-work: *A. Entwm.*, III.

'03. Experiments on Cleavage and Localization in the Nemertine Egg: *A. Entwm.*, XVI.

'04a. Experimental Studies on Germinal Localization. I and II: *J. E. Z.*, I.

'04b. Mosaic Development in the Annelid Egg: *Sci.*, XX.

Yatsu, N., '04. Experiments on the Development of Egg Fragments in *Cerebratulus: B. B.*, VI.

'10a. Experiments on Cleavage in the Egg of *Cerebratulus: J. C. S.*, Tokyo, XXVII.

'10b. Experiments on Germinal Localization in the Egg of *Cerebratulus: Ibid.*, XXVII.

'11, '12. Observations and Experiments on the Ctenophore Egg: I ('12), *J. S. C.*, Tokyo, XXXII; II ('11), *Ann. Zoöl. Jap.*, VII; III ('12), *Ibid.*, VIII, I.

Zeleny, C., '04. Experiments on the Localization of Developmental Factors in the Nemertine Egg: *J. E. Z.*, I.

GLOSSARY

The following list includes for the most part only terms actually employed in the text. Many obsolete terms included in former editions have been omitted; those still mentioned are enclosed in brackets. Wherever convenient the derivation of each term, with its author and date of first use, are given; but no attempt at completeness in this respect has been made. Most of the derivations are from the Greek.

Achromatin (see **Chromatin**), (*a*, without; *chroma*, color), originally applied to the non-staining or oxyphilic components of the nucleus, including especially the linin or plastin and nucleolar substance, but sometimes applied also to the enchylema or the membrane. (FLEMMING, 1879.)

Acidic (originally " acid "), applied by Ehrlich to dyes (in particular coal-tar colors) in which the color-determining radical plays the part of an acid. They are in general " plasma-dyes " (eosin, light-green, orange G, etc.).

Acroblast (*akros*, tip; *blastos*, bud, germ), a body or group of bodies in the spermatid, derived from the substance of the idiozome and Golgi-bodies, from which arises the acrosome. Variously called " idiosome," " sphere," " archoplasm," etc. (KING, '07–'08.)

Acrosome (*akros*, tip; *soma*, body), the apical body or " perforatorium," situated at the anterior tip of the sperm. Originally applied to a granule within the acroblast from which the acrosome arises. (LENHOSSÉK, 1897.)

Alecithal (*a*, without; *lekithos*, yolk), applied to eggs having little or no yolk. (BALFOUR, 1880.)

Allelomorph (*allelon*, one another; *morphe*, form), one of a pair of alternative hereditary units or characters. (BATESON and SAUNDERS, 1902.)

Alloplasmatic or **alloplasmic formations** (alloplasm), specially differentiated elements of the cell such as the neurofibrils and myofibrils, not forming autonomous organs, but arising as special transformations of the cell-substance for the performance of special functions; contrasted with " protoplasmatic formations " (plastids, chromosomes, centrosomes) which form autonomous organs capable of division. (MEYER, 1896.)

Allosomes (*allos*, other; *soma*, body) = **Heterochromosomes**, *q. v.*, special kinds of chromosomes distinguished from the ordinary chromosomes or *autosomes* by certain peculiarities of behavior. (MONTGOMERY, 1906.)

[Allotypical] (*allos*, other), applied to the special types of mitosis (heterotypical or homeotypical) concerned in meiosis. (STRASBURGER, '1905.)

Amitosis (*a*, without); (in contradistinction to **Mitosis,** *q. v.*), direct or amitotic nuclear division; mass-division of the nucleus without the formation of spireme, chromosomes or spindle-figure. (FLEMMING, 1882.)

Amphiaster (*amphi*, both; *aster*, a star), the achromatic figure in mitosis, comprising two asters connected by a spindle. (FOL, 1887.)

Amphikaryon (*amphi*, both; *karyon*, nut, nucleus) (*cf.* **Hemikaryon**)**,** a diploid nucleus containing two haploid groups of chromosomes or their descendants. (BOVERI, 1905.)

Amphimixis (*amphi*, both; *mixis*, mingling), the union or association of paternal and maternal elements by syngamy. (WEISMANN.)

Amphinucleolus (*amphi*, both), a double nucleolus consisting typically of a basophilic and an oxyphilic component in close association.

[Amphipyrenin (*amphi*, both), see **Pyrenin**], the substance of the nuclear membrane. (SCHWARZ, 1887.)

Amphitene (= **Zygotene, Synaptene,** *q. v.*) (*amphi*, both; *tænia*, band, ribbon), the synaptic stage of meiosis in which the nucleus contains thin spireme-threads (*leptotene*) uniting two by two to form thick threads (*pachytene*). (JANNSSENS, 1905.)

Amyloplasts (*amylum*, starch; *plastos*, formed), the colorless starch-forming plastids of plant-cells. (ERRERA, 1882.)

Anachromasis (see **Katachromasis**) (*ana*, up, up along), the sum total of the prophasic transformations of the nucleus by which arise the spireme-threads and chromosomes. (VEJDOVSKÝ, 1907.)

Anaphase (*ana*, up, up along; *phasis*, appearance), the period of mitosis following the metaphase, during which the daughter-chromosomes are passing towards the poles. (STRASBURGER, 1884.)

Anaschistic (*ana*, as in anaphase; *schistein*, to cleave) (= *Eumitotic*), applied to bivalents or tetrads that undergo two longitudinal divisions in meiosis and are typically split longitudinally in the anaphases of the heterotypic division. Correlative, *Diaschistic*. (FARMER and MOORE, 1905.)

Androcytes (*aner*, man; *kytos*, hollow, cell), the equivalent of *spermatid* in the case of the sperm-producing cells of plants. (ALLEN, 1912.)

Androgenesis (*aner*, man), development of the egg with only chromosomes and nuclei of paternal origin. Correlative to *Gynogenesis*.

Androgonia (*aner*, man; *gonos*, offspring), the earlier cell-generation from which arise the androcytes and sperm-cells of plants. (ALLEN, 1912.)

Anisogamy (see **Isogamy**) (*a*, not; *isos*, equal; *gamos*, union), in general, the condition in which the gametes are unlike. More specifically, a condition characterized by a size-difference between gametes which are otherwise of similar type.

Anisotropy (see **Isotropy**) (*a*, not; *isos*, equal; *trepein*, to turn), having a pre-determined axis or axes (as applied to the egg). (PFLÜGER, 1883.)

Antherozoids (see **Spermatozoid, Sperm**) (*anthos*, flower; *zoön*, animal; *eidos*, resemblance), the microgametes (usually motile) in heterogamous plants, *e. g.*, in algae, bryophytes or pteridophytes.

Antipodal cone, the cone of astral rays opposite the spindle. (VAN BENEDEN, 1883.)

Antithetic (as applied to alternation of generations), alternation between haploid (gametophyte) and diploid (sporophyte) generations, which are usually of different structural type; opposed to *homologous* alternation.

Apogamy (*apo*, away; *gamos*, marriage, union), the production of a sporophyte from the gametophyte by a vegetative process, without the formation or union of gametes (DE BARY, 1878.)

Apospory (*apo*, away; *sporos*, seed, spore), the production of a gametophyte from the sporophyte by a vegetative process (budding or the like) without spore-formation or meiosis. (BOWER, 1887.)

Apparato reticolare = the *Golgi-apparatus* or the *Golgi-bodies* collectively, specific formed components of the cytosome, distinct from the chondriosomes. (GOLGI.) See p. 48.

Apyrene (*a*, without; *pyren*, fruit-stone, nucleus), pathological sperms occurring in certain animals (Lepidoptera) and characterized by the absence of a nucleus, contrasted with *eupyrene, oligopyrene, q. v.* (MEVES, 1903.)

Archiplasm or **Archoplasm** (*archi*, first; *archon*, ruler; *plasma*, a thing formed), the substance of which consist, or from which arise, the spindle-fibers and astral rays; believed by Boveri to constitute a specific material; nearly equivalent to **Kinoplasm** (*q. v.*). Originally written *archoplasm* (1888), later changed to *archiplasm* (1901). (BOVERI, 1888.)

[Arrhenokaryon (Arrhenokaryotic)] (*arrenos*, male; *karyon*, hollow, nucleus), the sperm-nucleus. The arrhenokaryotic organism arises from an egg (or egg fragment) having only paternal nuclei. (BOVERI, 1905.)

Aster (*aster*, a star). 1. The radiating, star-like structure surrounding the central body, during mitosis or in the vegetative condition of the cell. (Fol, 1877.) [2. A star-shaped group of chromosomes seen in mitosis (see **Karyaster,** both terms in this sense obsolete). (FLEMMING, 1892.)]

[Astrocenter], the central body. (FOL, 1891.)

Astrosphere (see **Centrosphere**). 1. The central mass of the aster exclusive of the rays, equivalent to the attraction-sphere of Van Beneden, the centrosphere of Strasburger, or the centrosome of Boveri. (FOL, 1891.) [2. The entire aster exclusive of the centrosome, equivalent to the "astral sphere" of Mark. (BOVERI, 1895)].

[Attraction-sphere] (see **Sphere, Centrosphere, Centrosome**), the central mass of the aster from which the rays proceed; also the mass of " archiplasm," supposed to be derived from the aster, by which the central bodies are surrounded in the " resting " cell. In this sense often equivalent to *idiozome.* (VAN BENEDEN, 1883.)

Atelomitic (*a*, not; *telos*, end; *mitos*, thread), non-terminal, as applied to the attachment of chromosomes to the spindle, in contradistinction to *telomitic* or terminal. (CAROTHERS, 1917.)

[Autoblast] (*autos*, self; *blastos*, bud, germ), applied to bacteria and other minute organisms conceived as independent solitary " bioblasts." (ALTMANN, 1890.)

Axial filament, the central filament, probably contractile, of the sperm-flagellum. (EIMER, 1874.)

Autogamy (*gametes*, spouse), originally, self-fertilization; more recently often used to denote the conjugation of closely related cells or (in Protista) karyogamy within a single cell.

Autosomes (*autos*, self; *soma*, body), the typical or ordinary chromosomes as distinguished from the specially modified heterochromosomes or allosomes. Synonymous with *euchromosomes.* (MONTGOMERY, 1906.)

Auxocyte (*auxein*, to grow or increase; *kytos*, hollow, cell), the cyte (spermatocyte, oöcyte, or sporocyte) during the growth-period. (BOLLES LEE, 1897.)

Auxospireme (*auxein*, to grow; *spireme*), a term somewhat vaguely applied to the spireme of the auxocytes. (JANSSENS, 1905.)

Basic (dyes), a term applied primarily to the coal-tar colors, in which the color-determining radical plays the part of a base (used in contradistinction to *acidic dyes, q. v.*), *e. g.*, safranin, methyl green, or Bismarck brown. Basic dyes are in general " nuclear " as distinguished from " plasma " staining agents. (EHRLICH.)

Basichromatin (see **Chromatin**) (*L. basis*, base; *chroma*, color), equivalent to " chromatin " in the older sense. The basophilic part of the nuclear substance which is deeply stained by basic dyes (*q. v.*), in contradistinction to *Oxychromatin.* (HEIDENHAIN, 1894.)

Basophilic (**Basiphilic, Basophilous**) (*philein*, to love), having a special affinity for basic dyes. Used in contradistinction to *Oxyphilic* (*q. v.*).

[Bioblasts] (*bios*, life; *blastos*, bud, germ), hypothetical, ultimate vital units (equivalent to *plasomes, biophores, pangens*, etc.) and identified as granules, visible or invisible, having the power of growth and division. (ALTMANN, 1890.)

Biogens (**Biogenes**) (*bios*, life; *-gen*, producing), hypothetical large molecules or molecule-complexes, of which " living matter " is composed, and in the properties of which lies the source of the protoplasmic or " vital " activities. (VERWORN, 1895).

Biophores (*bios*, life; *pherein*, to carry), hypothetical, ultramiscroscopical, supramolecular vital units (equivalent to *pangens* of De Vries, *plasomes* of Wiesner, etc.). (WEISMANN, 1893.)

Bioplasm (*bios*, life; *plasma*, a thing formed), nearly equivalent to *protoplasm* in the wider sense. The active, " living," " formative " or "germinal " part of the cell-substance; perhaps equivalent to *hyaloplasm* (*q. v.*). (BEALE, 1870.)

Bioplast (*bios*, life; *plastos*, formed) (see **Protoplast, Energid**), nearly equivalent to *cell*, applied especially to the sum-total of the active " bioplasm." (BEALE, 1870.)

Bivalent (see **Univalent**) (*bis*, twice; *valere*, to be worth), having a double value. Applied to double chromosomes or " gemini " formed by the coupling of two chromosomes, especially in the process of synapsis. (HAECKER, 1892.)

Blepharoplast (*blepharis*, an eye-lash; *plastos*, formed), the basal body from which a cilium or flagellum grows forth. In many cases identical with a centriole. (WEBBER, 1897.)

Bouquet, the polarized stage of synapsis in which the spireme-threads, commonly loop-shaped, are polarized towards one pole of the nucleus near which the central bodies lie. (EISEN, 1900.)

Canalicular apparatus, a term employed by those who consider the Golgi-apparatus to be essentially a system of intra-cellular canals. (HOLMGREN.)

Caryotin (see **Karyotin**), the substance of the nuclear reticulum, including both " chromatin " (basichromatin) and " linin " (oxychromatin) in the ordinary sense. (LUNDEGÅRDH, 1910.)

Cell-plate (see **Phragmoplast, Mid-body**), a protoplasmic lamella arising as a series of thickenings of the spindle-fibers in the equatorial plane which fuse to form a continuous plate. This splits into two layers between which the new partition-wall is formed. (STRASBURGER.)

Cell-sap = **Enchylema, Cytochylema,** *etc.*

Central Bodies, a vague term designating the structures at the center of the aster, during mitosis. They include the minute *centriole* at the focus of the aster, and a larger *centrosome* by which it is surrounded. It is often difficult to determine whether a central body represents one or the other or both of these structures.

Central spindle, the primary spindle by which the central bodies are connected, as opposed to the " contractile mantle-fibers " by which it is surrounded. (HERMANN, 1891.)

Centriole (see **Central Body**), (diminutive of *centrum*, center), a minute body, commonly surrounded by the centrosome (*q. v.*), lying at the center of the aster. It is often regarded as an autonomous cell-organ arising only by the growth and division of a preëxisting centriole. (BOVERI, 1895.)

Centrodesmus, Centrodesmose, Centrodesm (*kentron*, center; *desmos*, band), the primary connection between the centrioles from which the central spindle has been assumed to arise. See **Paradesmose.** (HEIDENHAIN, 1894.)

Centrolecithal (*kentron*, center; *lekithos*, yolk), applied to that type of ova in which the yolk is mainly accumulated in the central region. (BALFOUR, 1880.)

[Centromere] (*kentron*, center; *meros*, part), that part of the sperm containing the central bodies; especially the neck-region. See **Karyomere, Cytomere.** (WALDEYER, 1903.)

[Centronucleus], a nucleus that contains a central body or which itself plays the part of a division-center. (BOVERI, 1901).

Centrophormium (*kentron*, center; *phormis*, a basket), a form of the Golgi-apparatus which appears in the membrane of Descemet as a basket-like hollow sphere. (BALLOWITZ, 1900.)

Centroplasm (*kentron*, center; *plasma*, as in protoplasm), the substance of the centrosome. (ERLANGER, 1897, more precisely defined by BOVERI, 1901.)

Centrosome (*kentron*, center; *soma*, body). 1. Originally, the central body lying at the astral center, and constituting an autonomous cell-organ; the division-center or dynamic center of the cell. (BOVERI, 1888.) 2. Subsequently, in a more specific sense, the larger central body, composed of *centroplasm*, within which lies the much smaller *centriole*. (BOVERI, 1895, 1901.)

Centrosphere (see **Sphere**, etc.), a relatively large central body lying at the center of the aster during mitosis, but assumed to persist in many cases in the vegetative state of the cell; equivalent to the " attraction sphere " of Van Beneden, and in many cases to the centrosome of Boveri. (STRASBURGER, 1893.)

Centrotheca (Idiozome or **Idiosome,** *q. v.*) (*kentron*, center; *theke*, a case or box). (MEVES, 1902.)

Centrum (see **Central Body, Centrosome, Centrosphere**), often used as equivalent to *central body* (*q. v.*). A term of somewhat vague meaning applied to the division-center of the cell.

Chiasmatype (Chiasmatypy) (*chiasma*, two crossed lines, like an X-figure), the supposed cytological process of " crossing over " by torsion of the synaptic mates, fusion at certain points, and recombination. (JANSSENS, 1909.)

Chloroplastids (*chloros*, green) green plastids which possess chlorophyll and have the power of forming starch by photosynthesis. (SCHIMPER, 1883.)

Chondriocont (*cf.* **Chondriomites**) (*chondrion*, granule), chondriosomes (*q. v.*) in the form of homogeneous rods or fibrillae. (MEVES, 1907.)

Chondrioma (*chondrion*, granule), a collective term for the entire chondriosome-system of the cell. (MEVES, 1908.)

Chondriomere = Plastomere (*q. v.*) (MEVES, 1918), (*chondrion*, granule; *meros* part).

Chondriomite (*cf.* **Chondriocont**) (*chondrion*, granule; *mitos*, thread), chondriosomes (*q. v.*) having the form of linear series of granules (mitochondria), in contradistinction to homogeneous **chondrioconts.** (MEVES, 1900.)

Chondriosomes (*chondrion*, granule; *soma*, body), a generic term including all forms of mitochondria, chondrioconts, chondriomites and other cytoplasmic bodies of the same nature. (BENDA, 1904.)

Chondriosphere, a chondriosome having the form of a sphere. (BENDA.)

Chromatid, each of the four parts (univalent chromosomes) of which a meiotic tetrad is composed. (McCLUNG, 1900.)

Chromatin (*chroma*, color), equivalent to *basichromatin* in the modern sense. Originally applied to the basophilic part of the nuclear substance which forms the most conspicuous part of the nuclear network and the chromosomes, and stains deeply with the "nuclear" or basic dyes. (FLEMMING, 1879.)

Chromatoid bodies (chromatin, *eidos*, form), intensely staining cytoplasmic bodies of unknown function found in the spermatocytes and passed on to certain of the spermatids. They are probably always cast out of the sperm.

Chromatophore (*chroma*, color; *pherein*, to bear), a general term applied to color-producing plastids, including chloroplasts and chromoplasts. (SCHAARSCHMIDT, 1880, SCHMITZ, 1882.)

Chromidia (*chroma*, color), minute granules of chromatin supposed to be derived from the nucleus or constituting a scattered chromidial system lying in the cytoplasm, appearing in the form of separate granules or forming a chromidial network. (R. HERTWIG, 1902.)

Chromiole, the smallest visible organized parts of the chromosomes, grouped to form chromomeres (*q. v.*) (EISEN, 1900.)

Chromomeres (*chroma*, color; *meros*, part). 1. First employed as equivalent to *chromosomes* but in this sense obsolete. (FOL, 1891.) 2. The serially aligned granules of the spireme-threads of chromosomes; equivalent to "Pfitzner's granules" or Weismann's "ids," believed in many cases to be composed of smaller *chromioles.* (WILSON, 1896.)

Chromonema (*chroma*, color; *nema*, thread), a fine basichromatic thread from which arises the spireme-thread. (VEJDOVSKÝ, 1912.)

Chromoplasts (*chroma*, color; *plastos*, formed) 1. Pigment-producing plastids, other than the chloroplasts (originally written **Chromoplastids**). (SCHIMPER, 1883.) 2. The large, basichromatic nucleolus or nucleoli of the pre-synaptic nuclei. (EISEN, 1900).

Chromosomes (*chroma*, color; *soma*, body; in allusion to their intense staining-capacity), separate, deeply staining basophilic bodies, commonly rod-shaped or loop-shaped, into which the substance of the nuclear network resolves itself during mitosis, and which split lengthwise in the course of this process. (WALDEYER, 1888.)

Cleavage-nucleus, the primary nucleus of the egg which gives rise by division to all the nuclei of the embryo. In the fertilized egg it is the zygote-nucleus, in the parthenogenetic egg, the egg-nucleus.

Cœnocyte (*koinos*, common; *kytos*, hollow, cell), a syncytial plant-body, as in various algæ and fungi.

Cœnogamete (*koinos*, common) a multinucleate gamete. (DAVIS, 1900.)

Crossing over, the recombination of genes or Mendelian units by interchange between homologous linkage-groups or synaptic mates. (STURTEVANT, 1912.)

Cyanophilous (*kyanos*, blue; *philein*, to love), having an especial affinity for certain blue or green dyes as opposed to red. See **Erythophilous**. (AUERBACH.)

Cytaster (*kytos*, as in cytoplasm; *aster*, a star). 1. The same as *aster* (*q. v.*), in contradistinction to *karyaster*. (FLEMMING, 1882.) 2. An aster not associated with chromosomes; commonly employed as equivalent to " accessory aster " or supernumerary aster. (*Cytoaster*, MOTTIER, 1897, *Cytaster*, WILSON, 1901.)

[**Cytoblast**] (*kytos*, as in *cytoplasm; blastos*, bud, germ). 1. The cell-nucleus. (SCHLEIDEN, 1838.) 2. One of the hypothetical vital units (bioblasts or " granula ") of which the cell was assumed to be built up. (ALTMANN, 1890.)

[**Cytoblastema**] (*kytos*, as in *cytoplasm: blastema*, bud), the formative material from which cells were supposed to arise by " free cell-formation." (SCHLEIDEN, 1838).

Cyte = Auxocyte (*kytos*, hollow, *i. e.*, cell.)

Cytocentrum = Centrum, *q. v.*

Cytochylema = Enchylema (*kytos*, as in *cytoplasm; chylos*, juice). (STRASBURGER, 1882.)

[**Cytode**] (*kytos*, as in *cytoplasm; eidos*, form), a supposedly non-nucleated cell. (HAECKEL, 1866.)

Cytodieresis = Mitosis (*kytos*, as in *cytoplasm; diairesis*, division). (CARNOY, 1885.)

Cytohyloplasm (see **Hyaloplasm**). (STRASBURGER, 1882.)

Cytolysis, Cytolitic (*kytos*, as in *cyte* = cell; *lysis*, loosening), cell-disintegration or disorganization.

Cytolymph (*kytos*, as in *cytoplasm; lympha*, water), cell-sap, the cytoplasmic enchylema, or ground-substance. (HAECKEL, 1891.)

Cytokinesis (*kytos*, as in *cytoplasm; kinesis*, change, movement), the changes of the cytoplasm during mitosis, meiosis and fertilization. Opposed to *karyokinesis* = the nuclear changes. (WHITMAN, 1891.)

Cytomere (composed of cytoplasmic and *meros*, part) = **Plastomere** or **Chondriomere,** that part of the sperm formed of cytoplasm only; especially the flagellum. (WALDEYER, 1903.)

Cytomicrosomes (see **Microsomes**), cytoplasmic microsomes in contradistinction to those of nuclear origin. (STRASBURGER, 1882.)

Cytomitome (*kytos*, as in *cytoplasm; mitos*, thread), the cytoplasmic threadwork in contradistinction to the nuclear threadwork. (FLEMMING, 1882.)

Cytomorphosis (*kytos*, as in *cytoplasm; morphosis*, shaping), the transformation of the cell-substance during development, especially that involved in differentiation and regarded as a cause of senescence. (MINOT.)

Cytoplasm (*kytos*, hollow, cell; *plasma* = protoplasm). 1. The protoplasm or substance of the cytosome (cell-body) in contradistinction to the substance of the nucleus (*karyoplasm* or *nucleoplasm*). (STRASBURGER, 1882.) 2. By earlier writers sometimes employed as equivalent to *hyaloplasm*. (KÖLLIKER), or to *protoplasm* as used by MOHL, REMAK, SCHULTZE or DE BARY.

Cytoreticulum = Cytomitome (*q. v.*).

Cytosome (*kytos*, as in *cytoplasm; soma*, body), the cell-body or cytoplasmic mass, in contradistinction to the nucleus. (HAECKEL, 1891.)

[Determinants], hypothetical units of the germ-plasm formed by the aggregation of " biophores " and determining the development of a single cell or independently variable group of cells. (WEISMANN, 1891.)

Deutobroch (*deuteros*, second; *brochos*, mesh of a network, see **Protobroch**). The second stage (b) of the presynaptic auxocyte-nuclei as they begin to prepare for the leptotene-formation.

Deutoplasm (*deuteros*, second; *plasma*, as in *protoplasm*), a general term applied to passive or " lifeless " protoplasmic components in contradistinction to those which are active or "living." Equivalent to *metaplasmic* or *paraplastic*, but applied especially to reserve food-stuffs such as yolk. (VAN BENEDEN, 1870.)

Diakinesis (*dia*, through; *kinesis*, change, or movement), stage *j* of meiosis, including the later prophases in the auxocytes. During this stage the bivalents gradually assume their definitive forms and commonly lie on or near the nuclear membrane. (HAECKER, 1897.)

Diarch (*dis*, twice; *arche*, beginning), a type of anastral spindle in higher plants that is bipolar from the beginning. See **Polyarch**. (STRASBURGER, 1900.)

Diaschistic (*dia*, through; *schistein*, to cleave), undergoing one transverse and one longitudinal division in meiosis. Correlative, *Anachistic, q. v.* (FARMER and MOORE, 1905.)

Diastema, Diastem (*diastema*, severance), a structural modification of the cytoplasm in the equatorial plane through which the cytosome divides.

Digametic (*dis*, twice; *gametes*), (=**Heterogametic**), having gametes of two classes, in particular a male-producing and a female-producing class. (WILSON, 1911).

Diploid (*diploos*, double), applied to the zygotic or fundamental somatic number of chromosomes (double the *haploid* or gametic number). (STRASBURGER, 1907.)

[Diplokaryon] (*diploos*, double; *karyon*, as in *karyokinesis*), a tetraploid nucleus; i. e., one with twice the normal diploid number of chromosomes; used in contra-distinction to *Amphikaryon* (*q. v.*). (BOVERI, 1905.)

Diminution (not to be confused with *Reduction*), the elimination of a portion of the nuclear substance in the formation of the primordial germ-cells or at a later point in the germ-line.

Diplosome (*diploos*, double; *soma*, body). 1. Any small double body in the cell, *e. g.*, a pair of centrioles. [2. Applied by MONTGOMERY (1904), to the paired " chromatin-nucleoli " (m-chromosomes and XY-pair), in contradistinction to the unpaired X-chromosome or *monosome* (*q. v.*).]

Diplotene (*diploos*, double; *tænia*, band, ribbon), adjective form of *diplonema* (*q. v.*). Applied to Stage *h* of meiosis in which the auxocyte-spireme is longitudinally double. WINIWARTER, 1900.)

Diplonema (*diploos*, double; *nema*, thread), substantive form of *diplotene*.

Diplophase (see **Haplophase**) (*diploos*, double), that phase of the life-history, particularly in the antithetic alternation of generations, in which the nuclei are haploid, as in the sporophyte. (GOEBEL.)

[Directive bodies] = *Polocytes*, the English equivalent of *Richtungskörper;* now obsolete. (F. MÜLLER, 1848.)

Dispermy (see **Polyspermy**) (*dis*, twice), the entrance of two sperms into the egg.

Dyad (*dyas*, two), a double chromosome; especially used in contradistinction to a quadripartite *tetrad*, particularly in the meiotic divisions.

[Dyadocyte = Homeocyte], (*dyas*, two; *kytos*, as in *cytoplasm*) a second spermatocyte or auxocyte containing dyads. Correlative *tetradocyte*. (GRÉGOIRE, 1905.)

[Dyaster] (*dyas*, two; *aster*, a star). 1. The double group formed by the anaphase chromosomes in mitosis. (FLEMMING, 1882.) 2. Sometimes used as equivalent to *amphiaster* (*q. v.*).

Ectoplasm (Exoplasm) (*ektos*, outside; *plasma*, as in *protoplasm*), in general, the cortical or peripheral protoplasmic layer of the cytosome in contradistinction to *endoplasm;* often used in more specific senses. Originally applied to Protozoa. (HAECKEL, 1873.)

Ectosomes (*ektos*, outside; *soma*, body), specific cytoplasmic granules characteristic of the primordial germ-cells and stem-cells in copepods. A form of " germ-cell determinant." (HAECKER, 1897.)

Elaioplast (*elaion*, oil; *plastos*, formed), a fat-producing plastid. (WAKKER, 1888.)

Electosomes (*eklegein*, pick out or select, *soma*, body), a general term applied to chondriosomes (mitochondria) considered as centers of specific chemical action. (REGAUD.)

Enchylema (*en*, in; *chylos*, juice). 1. Originally applied to the cell-sap or cytolymph. (HANSTEIN, 1880.) 2. The inter-filar substance, cytolymph or ground-substance, of protoplasm as opposed to the reticulum. (CARNOY, 1884.) 3. The alveolar substance of protoplasm. (RHUMBLER, 1896.)

Endoplasm or **Entoplasm** (*endos*, within; *plasma*, as in *protoplasm*), the inner or medullary substance of the cytosome as opposed to ectoplasm. Originally applied to Protozoa. (HAECKEL, 1873.)

[Endoplast] (*endos*, within; *plastos*, formed), the cell-nucleus. (HUXLEY, 1853.)

Energid (*en*, in; *ergon*, work), nearly equivalent to **Protoplast,** (*q. v.*), the cell-nucleus together with the cytoplasm lying within its sphere of influence. (SACHS, 1892.)

Equatorial Plate, the plate formed by the metaphase-chromosomes lying at the equator of the spindle. (VAN BENEDEN, 1875.)

Ergastic (*ergazomai*, to work), applied to relatively passive formed products of protoplasmic activity such as starch or cellulose. Nearly equivalent to *metaplasmic* or *paraplastic*. *Cf. alloplasmatic.* (A. MEYER, 1896.)

Ergastoplasm (see **Ergastic**), a supposed specific protoplasmic material from which arise various fibrillar formations, *e. g.*, in gland-cells. Related to the *kinoplasm* of Strasburger. Later writers have greatly extended the meaning of the term. (GARNIER, 1897.)

Erythrophilous (*erythros*, red; *philein*, to love), having an especial affinity for red dyes as opposed to blue or green. *Cf.* **Cyanophilous.** (AUERBACH.)

Erythroblasts (*erythros*, red; *blastos*, bud, germ), the cells from which arise the *erythrocytes* or red corpuscles.

Euchromosome = Autosome (*eu*, well, good), a chromosome of the ordinary or typical kind, in contradistinction to *heterochromosome* or *allosome*. (McCLUNG, 1914.)

[Eumitotic] (*eu*, well, good; *mitosis*) = *Anaschistic;* applied to bivalents or tetrads which undergo two longitudinal cleavages in the course of the meiotic divisions. Correlative, *pseudomitotic*, *q. v.* (KORSCHELT and HEIDER, 1903.)

Eupyrene (*eu*, well, good; *pyren*, fruit-stone, nucleus), the normal type of sperms (*e. g.*, in gastropods or Lepidoptera) in contradistinction to the *oligopyrene* or *apyrene* (*q. v.*). (WALDEYER, 1903.)

Fertilizin, a soluble substance produced by the egg and assumed to play an essential part in fertilization as a chemical link between egg and sperm. (F. R. LILLIE, 1913.)

Gametes (*gametes*, spouse), the germ-cells that unite by syngamy in the processes of conjugation and fertilization.

Gametocyte (*gamete* plus *kytos*, cell), a cell by the division of which are produced gametes, *e. g.*, the spermatocyte or oöcyte.

Gametophyte (*gametes*, as in gamete; *phyton*, plant), the haplont or haploid, gamete-producing plant in the antithetic alternation of generations, *q. v.* Correlative, *sporophyte*.

[Gemmule] (*gemma*, a bud), hypothetical germs assumed to be thrown off by the somatic cells, and stored in the germ-cells, and to determine the development of particular characters. (DARWIN, 1868.)

Gene (-*gen*, produce or producing), the unit of Mendelian heredity; an hypothetical elementary entity that is essential to, or determines the development of, a particular character. (JOHANSSEN.)

[Genoblasts] (=*gen*, producing; *blastos*, bud, germ), the mature germ-cells. (MINOT, 1877.)

Germ Plasm, equivalent to idioplasm, *q. v.* (WEISMANN.)

Germinal Spot, the nucleolus of the egg-nucleus. (PURKINJE, 1825.)

Germinal Vesicle, the egg-nucleus before formation of the polocytes. Often restricted to the later stages in which this nucleus is much enlarged, and often in a net-like condition. (PURKINJE, 1825.)

Gonad (*gone*, seed), the gamete-producing gland; ovary, testis or an equivalent structure.

Gonia, a general term for *spermatogonia* or *oögonia* (*q. v.*).

Gonocyte (*gone*, as in gonad; *kytos*, cell), a gamete-producing cell.

Gonomery (*gone* as in gonad; *meros*, part). The condition in which paternal and maternal chromosomes remain in two separate groups in the products of the zygote (see p. 431.)

Gonotokont (*gone*, as in *gonad; tokos*, bringing forth), equivalent to *auxocyte* (*q. v.*). (LOTSY, 1904.)

Gynogenesis (*gyne*, woman, female), development of an egg activated by the sperm but lacking the paternal chromosomes.

Haploid (*haploos*, single), applied to the reduced or gametic number of chromosomes (*i. e.*, of a single group), in contradistinction to *diploid*. (STRASBURGER, 1907.)

Haplophase (*haploos*, as in *haploid*), that phase of the life-history, particularly in the antithetic alternation of generations in plants, in which the nuclei are *haploid*. Used in contradistinction to *Diplophase*. (GOEBEL.)

Hemikaryon (*hemi*, half; *karyon*, nucleus), a nucleus containing the haploid number of chromosomes. (BOVERI, 1905.)

Heterochromosomes (=**Allosomes**) (*heteros*, other), chromosomes distinguished by special peculiarities of behavior, form or size, in contradistinction to *autosomes* or *euchromosomes*. Often used (erroneously) as synonymous with sex-chromosomes. (MONTGOMERY, 1904.)

Heterogametic (=**Digametic**) (*heteros*, different; *gam-*, as in *gamete*), having gametes of more than one kind, especially as applied to sex-production. Correlative, *Homogametic*. (WILSON, 1910.)

Heterogamy (*heteros*, other; *gamos*, as in gamete), a condition in which the gametes are unlike, commonly used to designate differences of both size and structure.

Heterokinesis (*heteros*, other), that meiotic division in the course of which the sex-producing gametes become separated by differential distribution of the sex-chromosomes. (GUTHERZ, 1906.)

Heterolecithal (*heteros*, different; *lekithos*, yolk), having unequally distributed deutoplasm (applied to both centrolecithal and telolecithal eggs). (MARK, 1892.)

Heteromorphic (*heteros*, other, different; *morphe*, form), applied to synaptic mates, whether separate or united to form bivalents or tetrads, that differ in size, form or structure; in contradistinction to **Homomorphic,** *q. v.* (CAROTHERS, 1917.)

Heteromorphosis (*heteros*, different; *morphe*, shape) the production, by regeneration or otherwise, of a structure not normal to the place in which it arises, as in case of a head in place of a tail, etc. (LOEB.)

Heteropycnosis (*heteros*, as in *heterochromosome; pyknos*, dense), condensation of a chromosome (in general a heterochromosome) to form a chromosome-nucleolus during the " resting-stage " or interphase, especially in the gonia or cytes. (GUTHERZ, 1906.)

Heterotypic (**Heterotypical**) (*heteros*, different; *typus*, type), applied to the first meiotic division, in contradistinction to the second or *homeotypic;* in the former the chromosomes, and sometimes also the achromatic figure, differ in certain characteristic ways from those of the somatic divisions. (FLEMMING, 1887.)

Hologamy (=**Macrogamy**) (*holos*, whole; *gam*, as in *gamete*), a condition in which the gametes are of same size and structural type as the vegetative cells.

Homeotypic (or **Homeotypical**) (*homoios*, same; *typus*, type), applied to the second meiotic division (in contradistinction to the first or *heterotypic*), which approaches more nearly to the ordinary somatic type. (FLEMMING, 1887.)

Homogametic (*homos*, alike; *gam-*, as in *gamete*), having gametes of but one class in respect to sex-production, in contradistinction to *digametic* or *heterogametic*. (WILSON, 1910.)

Homolecithal = *alecithal* (*homos*, alike; *lekithos*, yolk), having equally distributed and often little or no deutoplasm. (MARK, 1892.)

Homomorphic (*homos*, like; *morphe*, form), applied to synaptic mates of similar size and form. Correlative, *Heteromorphic*. (CAROTHERS, 1917.)

Hyaloplasm (*hyalos*, glass; *plasma*, as in *protoplasm*). 1. The clear ground-substance of protoplasm as distinguished from the granules or microsomes (HANSTEIN, 1880) or from the *spongioplasm* or *reticulum*. (LEYDIG, 1885.) 2. The exoplasm or peripheral layer of the cytoplasm in plant cells. (PFEFFER). 3. The clear, homogeneous substance of the protoplasmic framework (whether cytoplasmic or nuclear and whether alveolar or reticular) in which are suspended *cytomicrosomes* or *karyomicrosomes*, while the interstices of the framework are occupied by the *enchylema* or *cell-sap* (*cytochylema* or *karyochylema*). In harmony with this, as applied to the cytoplasm, is the more recent usage of Rhumbler, Wilson and many others. (STRASBURGER, (1882.)

Idiochromatin (*idios*, as in *id*), chromatin concerned especially with the reproductive functions (chromosome-formation, etc.) as distinguished from the nutritive or " somatic " *trophochromatin*. (LUBOSCH, 1902.)

Idiochromidia (*idios*, as in *id*), chromidia derived from *Idiochromatin* (*q. v.*), which are of predominantly generative functions, and may enter into the formation of gamete-nuclei. (MESNIL, 1905).

Idiochromosome = **Sex-chromosome,** *q. v.* (*idios*, peculiar), originally applied to sex-chromosomes of the XY-type, later to sex-chromosomes in general. (WILSON, 1905.)

Idioplasm (*idion*, the characteristic of a species; *plasma*, as in *protoplasm*), equivalent to *germ-plasm*, identified by many writers with " chromatin." That which constitutes the physical basis of heredity. (NÄGELEI, 1884.)

Idiosome (*idios*, as in *id; soma*, body) [1. The same as *idioblast, plasome, pangen*, etc. (WHITMAN, 1893.) 2. The same as *idiozome*. (REGAUD, 1910.)

Idiozome (**Idiosome**) (*idios*, as in *id; zoma*, a girdle) =*Centrotheca*, a spheroidal cytoplasmic body in the early auxocytes, particularly in the spermatocytes, variously called by earlier writers the " attraction-sphere," " archoplasm-sphere," "sphere," etc. It surrounds the centrioles and is itself surrounded by the Golgi-apparatus (of which it may form a part) and often also by chondriosomes. (MEVES, 1896.)

[Ids] (*idios*, distinct or peculiar; *idion*, the characteristic property of a species), hypothetical structural units of the nucleus resulting from the successive aggregation of biophores and determinants, and assumed to be represented by the *chromomeres*. (WEISMANN, 1891.)

Interfilar substance (*inter*, between; *filum*, thread), the ground-substance or *enchylema* as opposed to the fibrillar substance or *mitome*. The *paramitome*. (FLEMMING, 1882.)

Interkinesis (*inter*, between), originally the stage between the first and second meiotic divisions, now often applied to the " resting " or " vegetative " stage of nuclei generally. (GRÉGOIRE, 1905.) (*Interphase* of LUNDEGÅRDH, 1912.)

Interzonal fibers (*filaments réunissants*), the connecting fibers of the mitotic spindle that extend between the two daughter-groups of chromosomes during the anaphases and telophases. (MARK, 1881.)

Isogamy (*isos*, equal; *gam-*, as in *gamete*), similarity of the gametes in size and structure.

Isotropy (*isos*, equal; *trepein*, to turn), without predetermined axes, especially as applied to the egg.

Interphase = **Interkinesis.**

Karenchyma (*karyon*, as in *karyokinesis; enchyma*, infusion), the nuclear sap or *karyochylema*. (FLEMMING, 1882.)

Karyochylema (**Nucleochylema, Karyenchyma**) (*karyon*, as in *karyokinesis; chylos*, juice), the nuclear sap or ground-substance. (FLEMMING, 1882.)

Karyogamy (*karyon*, as in *karyokinesis; gamos*, union), the conjugation of nuclei in contradistinction to *plastogamy*.

Karyokinesis (*karyon*, nut, nucleus; *kinesis*, change, movement) (=**Mitosis**), indirect nuclear division, involving the formation and longitudinal splitting of spireme-threads and chromosomes, and of an achromatic spindle (see **Cyto-kinesis**); often applied to indirect division of the cell as a whole. (SCHLEI-CHER, 1878.)

Karyolymph (*karyon*, as in *karyokinesis; lympha*, water), =karyochylema or "nuclear sap." (HAECKEL, 1891.)

[**Karyolysis**] (*karyon*, as in *karyokinesis; lysis*, loosing), the apparent disappear-ance of the nucleus during mitosis. Karyokinesis in the modern sense. (AUERBACH, 1874.)

Karyomere (*karyon*, as in *karyokinesis; meros*, part). 1. Originally used as nearly equivalent to chromomere (*q. v.*). (FOL, 1896.) 2. By most later writers applied to the chromosomal vesicles formed in the telophases of certain types of mitosis. 3. The anterior region or head of the sperm containing the nucleus. See **Centromere, Cytomere**. (WALDEYER, 1903.)

Karyomerites (*karyon*, as in *karyokinesis; meros*, part), by some writers used as equivalent to *karyomeres* (see GRÉGOIRE and WYGAERTS, 1904); by others to designate partial nuclei, whether formed from one or several chromosomes. (See GOLDSCHMIDT, 1902.)

[**Karyomicrosome**=**Nucleomicrosome**] (*karyon*, as in *karyokinesis*), nuclear microsome (see **Microsome**). (STRASBURGER, 1882.)

[**Karyomitome**] (*karyon*, as in *karyokinesis*, the nuclear as opposed to the cytoplasmic fibrillar formations. See **Mitome**. (FLEMMING, 1882.)

Karyomitosis (=**Karyokinesis**). (FLEMMING, 1882.)

[**Karyon**] (*karyon*, nut, nucleus), the cell-nucleus. (HAECKEL, 1891.)

Karyoplasm (Nucleoplasm) (*karyon*, as in *karyokinesis; plasma*, a thing formed or moulded), the nuclear substance in contradistinction to the cytoplasmic. (FLEMMING, 1882.)

[**Karyoplast**] (*karyon*, as in *karyokinesis; plastos*, formed), the cell-nucleus as opposed to *protoplast* =*cytosome*. (STRASBURGER, 1905.)

Karyosome (*karyon*, as in *karyokinesis; soma*, body). 1. A chromatin-nucleolus or net-knot, in contradistinction to plasmosome. (OGATA, 1883.) 2. Com-monly applied to the large karyosphere of Protista from which may arise many or all of the chromosomes. 3. The same as chromosome. (PLATNER, 1886.) 4. The cell-nucleus. (WATASÉ, 1894.)

Karyotin (Caryotin) (*karyon*, nucleus), the substance of the nuclear framework whether basichromatic or oxychromatic. (LUNDEGÅRDH, 1910.)

Katachromasis (*kata*, down; *chroma*, color), the sum total of the telophasic trans-formations by which the daughter-chromosomes reconstruct the daughter-nuclei. See **Anachromasis**. (VEJDOVSKÝ, 1907.)

Kinetonucleus (*kinein*, to move), a body found in flagellates in connection with the basal apparatus of the flagellum, and by some earlier observers called the *blepharoplast*, by others *kinetonucleus* in the belief that it represents a second nucleus especially concerned with the kinetic functions (movement, division). Probably identical with the cytoplasmic *parabasal body* (*q. v.*). (WOODCOCK, 1906.)

Kinetosome (*kinein*, to move; *soma*, body), granular or rod-like bodies often aggregated to form plate-like bodies, which occupy the spindle-poles in the sporogenetic mitoses of mosses. (ALLEN, 1912.)

Kinoplasm (*kinein*, to move; *plasma*, a thing formed), a supposedly specific type of cytoplasmic substance, from which arise fibrillar and other structures (mitotic fibrillæ, etc.); nearly equivalent to *archiplasm*. See **Trophoplasm**. (STRASBURGER, 1892.)

[**Kinosphere**] (*kinein*, to move), the astral system surrounding the central bodies. Nearly equivalent to *aster*. (BOVERI, 1901.)

Leptonema (*leptos*, slender; *nema*, thread), substantive form of *Leptotene* (*q. v.*). (GRÉGOIRE, 1907.)

Leptotene (*leptos*, fine or thin; *tænia*, ribbon, band), applied to the fine spireme-threads of Stage *e* of meiosis just before their union in synapsis. (WINIWARTER, 1900.)

Leucoplasts (Leucoplastids, see **Plastids)** (*leukos*, white; *plastos*, formed), colorless plastids from which may arise the more specialized forms such as *chloroplasts*, *chromoplasts*, etc. (SCHIMPER, 1883.)

Limosphere, a rounded cytoplasmic body formed in the androcytes (spermatids) of bryophytes, apparently comparable to the *acroblast* in animals, from which arises an " apical body." (M. WILSON, 1911.)

Linin (*linum*, flax, thread). 1. The oxyphilic (formerly called " achromatic") portion of the nuclear framework. (SCHWARZ, 1887.) 2. The structureless clear substance in which are suspended granules of basichromatin and oxychromatin. (HEIDENHAIN, 1894.)

Macrosome (Megasome) (*makros*, *megas*, large; *soma*, body), applied to the larger bodies or alveolar spheres in alveolar protoplasm, in contradistinction to the small *microsomes*. (CHAMBERS, 1917.)

Matriclinous, Matroclinous (*mater*, mother), inclined in heredity towards the maternal side. Correlative **patriclinous.**

Maturation, the " ripening " or final stages in the formation of the germ-cells. Though often applied only to the nuclear changes (meiosis, reduction) it properly includes also the cytoplasmic.

Megaspore, Macrospore (*megas*, large), a spore of the large type in the heterosporous higher plants. In the seed-plants gives rise to the embryo-sac. Correlative to *microspore*.

Meiosis (Maiosis) (*meiosis*, reduction), the process by which is effected the reduction of the chromosome-number from diploid to haploid. (FARMER and MOORE, 1905.)

Meristic (*meros*, a part), relating to the component parts of a larger structure or aggregate.

Merocytes (Merocyte-nuclei) (*meros*, part; *kytos*, as in *cyte*), the nuclei derived from supernumerary sperm-nuclei which have failed to conjugate with the egg-nucleus in cases of physiological polyspermy. (RÜCKERT, 1899.)

Merogamy (=**Microgamy)** (*meros*, part; *gamos*, union), a condition in which the gametes are smaller than the vegetative cells, often of different structure, arising by division from the *gametocytes*.

Merogony (*meros*, part; *gone*, generation), the development of a non-nucleated egg-fragment upon its fertilization by a sperm. (DELAGE, 1899.)

[**Metakinesis**] (=**Metaphase)** (*meta*, after; *kinesis*, change, movement). (FLEMMING, 1892.)

Metaphase (*meta*, beyond, *i. e.*, further), the middle stage of mitosis, when the chromosomes are grouped in the equatorial plate. (STRASBURGER, 1884.)

Metaplasm (*meta*, after, beyond; *plasma*, as in *protoplasm*), a term collectively applied to the so-called lifeless inclusions (deutoplasm, starch, etc.) in protoplasm as opposed to the living substance. (HANSTEIN, 1868.)

Metasyndesis (*meta*, after; *syndesis*, binding together) [=**Telosynapsis**] end-to-end union in synapsis. Correlative, *Parasyndesis*. (HAECKER, 1907.)

Micellæ (dim. of *mica*, morsel), hypothetical ultimate supra-molecular units of the cell. (NÄGELI, 1884.)

Microcentrum, the centrioles or group of centrioles, united by a " primary centrodesmus," and forming the center of the astral system. (HEIDENHAIN, 1894.)

Micropyle (*mikros*, small; *pyle*, gate), the aperture in the egg-membrane through which the sperm in many cases enters. (First applied by Turpin, in 1806, to the opening through which the pollen-tube enters the ovule.)

Microsome (*mikros*, small; *soma*, body), originally the granules as opposed to the ground-substance of protoplasm; now used in a more specific sense for certain types of small granules (p. 32). (HANSTEIN, 1880.)

Microchromosomes (=*m*-chromosomes) (*micros*, small), originally, a pair of very small chromosomes in coreid Hemiptera characterized by long delayed synapsis. (WILSON, 1905.) Later often applied to any chromosomes of unusually small size irrespective of their behavior.

[**Microsphere**] = **Centrosome,** the central region of the aster (centrosphere) at the center of which lie the centrioles. (KOSTANECKI and SIEDLECKI, 1896.)

Microspore (see **Megaspore**). A spore of the small type in the heterosporous plants. In seed-plants = the pollen-grains.

Mid-body (" Zwischenkörper "), a body or group of granules, probably comparable with the cell-plate in plants, formed in the equatorial region of the spindle during the anaphases of mitosis. (FLEMMING, 1890.)

Middle-piece (= **Connecting-piece**), a term of vague meaning applied to the middle region of the sperm, lying between the head and the main part of the flagellum. (SCHWEIGGER-SEIDEL, 1865.)

Mitochondria (= **Plastochondria**) (*mitos*, a thread; *chondrion*, grain, granule), a specific form of granule, belonging to the general class of *chondriosomes*, *q. v.* (BENDA, 1897.)

[**Mitokinetism**] (*mitoma*, thread; *kinesis*), a supposed special form of energy involved in the formation and action of the mitotic figure. (HARTOG, 1914.)

Mitome (*mitoma* from *mitos*, a thread), the reticulum or thread-work as opposed to the ground-substance of protoplasm. (FLEMMING, 1882.)

Mitosis (*mitos*, thread), indirect nuclear division involving the formation of a spindle, conversion of the chromatin into threads (spireme), and longitudinal splitting of the threads. (FLEMMING, 1882.)

Mitosome (*mitos*, a thread; *soma*, body), a cytoplasmic body supposed to be derived from the spindle-fibers of the preceding mitosis = Spindle-remnant. (PLATNER, 1889.)

Mixochromosome (*mixis*, mingling), the chromosomes (pachytene-threads) formed by a supposedly complete fusion of the synaptic mates (leptotene-threads) in parasynapsis. (WINIWARTER and SAINTMONT, 1909.)

Monaster (*monos*, alone; *aster*, star), a single aster, formed in monocentric mitosis, which does not ordinarily give rise to an amphiaster. (WILSON, 1901.)

Monosome (*monos*, alone; *soma*, body), the X-chromosome when unpaired (in the digametic sex) particularly when in the condition of a chromosome-nucleolus during the growth-period of the spermatocytes. (MONTGOMERY, 1904.)

[Morphoplasm] (*morphe*, form; *plasma*, as in *protoplasm*), the substance of the protoplasmic framework (reticulum), in contradistinction to the ground-substance (**enchylema**). (HIS, 1899.)

Mycetocytes (see **Mycetoma**) (*mykes*, fungus; *kytos*, cell).

Mycetoma (= **Pseudo-vitellus** of HUXLEY), a group of follicle-cells (mycetocytes) by which the oöcyte, in aphids, is infected with intracellular symbiotic organisms. (BUCHNER, 1912.)

Myofibrillæ (*mys*, muscle), the intra-cellular fibrils of the muscle-cell.

Myonemes (*mys*, muscle; *nema*, thread), minute, supposedly contractile fibrillæ in Protista.

Nebenkern (German *neben*, beside; *kern*, nucleus) (*Paranucleus*), the chondriosome-body or chondriosome-sphere of the animal spermatid formed by the aggregation of mitochondria or chondrioconts, and ultimately drawn out to form the envelope of the axial filament in the flagellum. The word has been incorrectly used in many other senses. (BÜTSCHLI, 1871.)

Net-knot, a chromatin-nucleolus formed as a local aggregation of basichromatin and often irregular in shape. (FLEMMING, 1882.)

Neurofibrillæ (*neurou*, nerve), the elementary intracellular fibrillæ of the nerve-cell. (APÁTHY, 1897.)

Nuclear sap, the ground-substance or *enchylema* of the nucleus. *Karyochylema.*

Nucleolo-centrosome, an intra-nuclear division center simulating a nucleolus, especially in Protista.

Nucleochylema (= **Karyochylema**) (*chylos*, juice), the nuclear sap or ground-substance of the nucleus as opposed to that of the cytoplasm. (STRASBURGER, 1882.)

Nucleohyaloplasm (see **Hyaloplasm**), the achromatic substance (linin) in which the chromatin-granules are suspended. (STRASBURGER, 1882.)

Nucleolinus, a minute deeply staining granule contained in the nucleolus, and said in some cases to divide regularly in the course of mitosis. (HAECKEL.)

Nucleomicrosomes (see **Microsome**), the nuclear (chromatin) granules as opposed to those of the cytoplasm. (STRASBURGER, 1882.)

Nucleoplasm (see **Karyoplasm**). (STRASBURGER, 1882.)

Nucleoplasmic or **Karyoplasmic Ratio** (**Kernplasmarelation**). The ratio of nuclear to cytoplasmic volume. (R. HERTWIG, 1903.)

Oligopyrene (*oligos*, few; *pyren*, stone of a fruit, *i. e.*, relating to the nucleus) applied to abnormal forms of sperms, in which only a part of the normal chromosome group enters the nucleus. See **Apyrene, Eupyrene.** (MEVES, 1902.)

Oöcyte (Ovocyte) (*oön*, egg), the egg-cell prior to completion of the maturation-process (BOVERI, 1891.)

Oögenesis (Ovogenesis) (*oön*, egg), genesis of the egg (oöcyte) after its origin by division from the mother-cell (*oögonium*). Often used more specifically to denote meiosis in the female.

Oögonium (*oön*, egg; *gonos*, offspring), cells which by their continued division give rise to the oöcytes or egg-cells. (BOVERI, 1891.)

Oökinesis (*oön*, egg; *kinesis*, change, movement), the mitotic phenomena in the egg-cell during maturation and fertilization. (WHITMAN, 1887.)

Oöplasm (*oön*, egg; *plasma*, as in *protoplasm*), the cytoplasm of the egg or oöcyte.

Oötid (Ovotid) (*oön*, *ovum*, egg), the egg or polocyte subsequent to meiosis; one of the four products of the meiotic divisions in the female. Correlative, *Spermatid*, *q. v.*

Oösome (*oön*, egg; *soma*, body), the so-called " germ-cell determinant "; a cytoplasmic body or group of bodies in the mature ovum that passes into the primordial germ-cells or stem-cells. (SYLVESTRI, 1914.)

Oöcenter (Ovocenter), the division-center of the egg. (FOL, 1891.)

Oxychromatin (*oxys*, sharp, acid; *chroma*, color), that portion of the nuclear framework that stains with acidic dyes; correlative, *Basichromatin*. Equivalent to *linin* in the older sense, *q. v.* (HEIDENHAIN, 1894.)

Oxyphilic (*oxys*, sharp, acid; *philein*, to love) having a special affinity for acidic dyes, *e. g., oxychromatin.*

Pachynema (*pachys*, thick; *nema*, thread), the post-synaptic spireme, consisting of thick threads, often longitudinally double (*diplonema*). (GRÉGOIRE, 1907.)

Pachytene (*pachys*, thick; *tænia*, band, ribbon), adjective form of *pachynema*. (WINIWARTER, 1900).

Pangen (*pan*, all; *gen*, producing, as in *gene*), hypothetical, ultimate unit of the cell, originally intra-nuclear, ultimately cytoplasmic. See **Biophore, Idiosome, Plasome,** etc. (DE VRIES, 1889.)

Pangenesis (*pan*, all; =*gen*, producing), the theory of "gemmules " (pangens) conceived as germs or determiners of hereditary characters. (DARWIN, 1868.)

Panmeristic (*pan*, all; *meros*, part), applied to the conception of protoplasm and the cell as aggregates of more elementary bodies.

Parabasal Body (*para*, beside) (probably = **Kinetonucleus**, *q. v.*), a cytoplasmic body connected with the basal apparatus of the flagellum in many flagellates, supposed to be an accessory part or " kinetic reservoir " of the motor apparatus. (JANICKI, 1910.)

[Parachromatin] (*para*, beside), the achromatic nuclear substance (linin of SCHWARZ) from which the spindle-fibers arise. (PFITZNER, 1883.)

Paradesmose (Paradesmus) (*para*, beside; *desmos*, band), an extra-nuclear filament connecting the division-centers in the mitosis of flagellates. (KOFOID and SWEZY, 1915.)

[Paramitome] (see **Mitome**), the ground-substance or interfilar substance of protoplasm, opposed to mitome. (FLEMMING, 1892.)

Paranuclein, see **Nuclein**, the substance of true nucleoli or plasmosomes. Pyrenin of SCHWARZ. (O. HERTWIG, 1878.) Applied by Kossel to " nucleins " derived from the cytoplasm. These are components of protein bases with " paranucleic " acid which yields no xanthin-bodies.

Paranucleus, see **Nebenkern.**

Paraplasm, Paraplastic (*para*, beside; *plasma*, as in *protoplasm; plastos*, formed), the less active portion of the cell-substance. Originally applied to the cortical region of the cell (exoplasm). In its adjective form now commonly used as equivalent to *metaplasmic* or *ergastic*, *q. v.* (KUPFFER, 1896.)

Parasynapsis (=**Parasyndesis**) (*para*, beside), side-by-side union of the chromosomes in synapsis. (WILSON, 1912.)

Parasyndesis (=**Parasynapsis**, *q. v.*) (*para*, beside). (HAECKER, 1907).

Parthenogenesis (*parthenos*, virgin), the development of an egg without activation by a sperm. Correlative, *Fertilization*. (OWEN, 1849.)

Patriclinous, Patroclinous (*pater*, father), inclined in heredity towards the paternal side.

Pellicula (**Pellicle**), often applied to the surface-film of " naked " cells or protoplasmic masses; the plasma-membrane.

Percnosome, a small granule in the androcytes (spermatids) of bryophytes, possibly comparable either to a chromatoid body or an acrosome-granule (M. WILSON, 1911.)

Perforatorium, the acrosome. (WALDEYER, 1906.)

[**Periplast**] (*peri*, around; *plastos*, formed or moulded). 1. The peripheral part of the cell, including those parts outside the nucleus or " endoplast." (HUXLEY, 1853). 2. A term somewhat vaguely applied to the attraction-sphere or the centrosome (VEJDOVSKÝ, 1888.)

[**Perisphere**] (*peri*, around), a term applied to the outer region of the attraction-sphere in nerve-cells, in contradistinction to an inner " centrosphere." (LENHOSSÉK, 1895.)

Phragmoplast (*phragma*, a fence; *plastos*, formed or moulded), the enlarged connecting spindle, barrel-shaped or greatly broadened, in the later phases of anastral plant-mitoses, within which is formed the cell-plate.

Plasma (*plasma*, a thing formed, as in *protoplasm*), often used as the equivalent of *Protoplasm*, or *Cytoplasm*. (HAECKEL, KÖLLIKER, 1866.)

Plasmodesms (**Plasmodesmus**) (*plasma*, as in *protoplasm; desmos*, band), the cytoplasmic filaments or bridges by which in many tissues adjoining cells are connected.

Plasmodium (*plasma*, as in *protoplasm; eidos*, form), a syncytium, especially in the case of Protista.

[**Plasmosphere**,] the same as **Perisphere**.

Plasmolysis (*plasma*, as in *protoplasm; lysis*, dissolution), the withdrawal of water from the cell by altered osmotic pressure.

Plasmosome (*plasma*, as in *protoplasm; soma*, body). 1. the true nucleolus, typically staining with acidic or " plasma " dyes. (OGATA, 1883.) 2. Minute cytoplasmic granules or microsomes, in general connected by fibrillæ and supposed to be fundamental units of protoplasmic structure. (ARNOLD, 1898.)

Plasmogamy (*plasma*, as in *protoplasm*; *gamos*, as in *gamete*), cytoplasmic as distinguished from nuclear fusion. See **Karogamy**.

[**Plasome**] (*plasma*, as in *protoplasm; soma*, body) hypothetical, ultimate supramolecular vital units. See **Biophore, Pangen,** etc. (WIESNER, 1890.)

Plastid (*plastos*, formed or moulded). 1. A cell or cytode. (HAECKEL, 1866.) 2. Cytoplasmic bodies, multiplying by growth and division, the seat of specific chemical activities, and believed to be persistent structures arising by division. See **Chloroplast, Leucoplast, Amyloplast,** etc. (SCHIMPER, 1883.)

Plastidome (*plastos*, as in *plastid*), the sum-total of plastid-content in the cell. Parallel to *chondriome*, etc. (DANGEARD, 1919–20.)

Plastin (*plastos*, formed or moulded), often used as equivalent to *linin*, but originally applied also to the substance of the cytoplasmic framework. (REINKE and RODEWALD, 1881, CARNOY, 1885.)

Plastochondria (*plastos*, as in *plastid; chondria*, grains, granules) = *Mitochondria*. (MEVES, 1910.)

Plastocont = **Chondriocont** (*plastos*, formed). (MEVES, 1910.)

Plastogamy (**Plasmogamy**) (*plastos*, formed; *gamos*, union), cytoplasmic fusion as opposed to nuclear (*karyogamy*).

Plastosome (*plastos*, formed; *soma*, body) = Chondriosome. (MEVES, 1910.)

Plastomere (*plastos*, formed; *meros*, a part), that part of the sperm containing the chondriosomes (plastosomes). See **Cytomere**. (MEVES, 1918.)

[Plastidule,] the ultimate supra-molecular vital unit of protoplasm. (ELSSBERG, 1874; HÄCKEL, 1876.)

Plurivalent (*plus*, more; *valere*, to be worth), applied to chromosomes that are multiples, *i. e.*, have the value of more than one univalent chromosome. (HÄCKER, 1892.)

Polar Bodies (**Polar Globules**) = **polocytes,** two minute cells segmented off from the ovum before union of the pronuclei. (Disc. by CARUS, 1824; named by ROBIN, 1862.)

Polar Rays, a term sometimes applied to all of the astral rays as opposed to the spindle-fibers, sometimes to the group of astral rays opposite to the spindle-fibers (= antipodal cone).

Pole-plates (**Polar-plates**), condensed plate-like bodies at the ends of the spindle in certain forms of mitosis. (R. HERTWIG, 1877.)

Polocyte = **Polar Body** (*polos*, axis; *kytos*, cell). (WALDEYER, 1898.)

Polyarch (*polys*, many; *arche*, beginning), a type of anastral spindle in higher plants that is multipolar from the beginning. (STRASBURGER, 1900.)

Polyspermy (*polys*, many), the entrance into the ovum of more than one sperm, whether normally or pathologically.

Post-heterokinesis (*post*, after; *heteros*, other; *kinesis*, change, movement), differential distribution of the sex-chromosomes in the second meiotic division. Correlative, *Pre-heterokinesis*. (GUTHERZ.)

Post-reduction, chromosome-reduction in the second meiotic division. Correlative, *Pre-reduction*. (KORSCHELT and HEIDER, 1903.)

Precession, passage of the undivided X-chromosome in the heterokinesis to one pole in advance of the other chromosomes. (WILSON.)

Pre-heterokinesis (see **Post-heterokinesis**), segregation of the sex-chromosomes in the first meiotic division. (GUTHERZ.)

Pre-reduction, chromosome-reduction in the first instead of the second meiotic division. See **Post-reduction**. (KORSCHELT and HEIDER, 1903.)

[Prochromatin = **Paranuclein** of O. HERTWIG, or **Pyrenin** of SCHWARZ] (*pro*, before), the substance of true nucleoli or plasmosomes. Later " pseudochromatin." (PFITZNER, 1883, 1886.)

Prochromosomes (*pro*, before), separate masses of basichromatin in the " resting " nuclei, or in the presynaptic stages, supposed to be forerunners of the definitive chromosomes or centers for their formation. (OVERTON, 1909.)

Promitosis (*pro*, before), a primitive type of mitosis in Protista in which the whole process is intranuclear, asters are absent, and a large " karyosome " is present. (NÄGLER, 1909.)

Pronucleus (*pro*, before), a gamete-nucleus (egg-nucleus or sperm-nucleus) during fertilization = *germ-nucleus* of O. HERTWIG. (VAN BENEDEN, 1875.)

Protoblast (*protos*, first; *blastos*, bud or germ), a blastomere of specific promorphological significance to which is traceable the origin of a particular organ or group of structures. (WILSON, 1892.)

Protobroch (*protos*, first; *brochos*, mesh of a network). Stage *b* of meiosis, in which the auxocyte-nucleus is net-like; the " resting-stage." (WINIWARTER, 1900.)

Protoplasm (= **Bioplasm** of BEALE) (*protos*, first; *plasma*, a thing formed), " living matter," the " physical basis of life." Specifically: 1. The active or " living " substance of the cytosome exclusive of the nucleus. (PURKINJE, 1840; VON MOHL, 1846.) 2. The active or living substance of the cell as a whole, comprising *cytoplasm* and *karyoplasm*. (STRASBURGER, 1882.)

Protoplast (*protos*, first; *plastos*, formed), the protoplasmic portion of the cell, including nucleus and cytoplasm, regarded as a unit. Nearly equivalent to the *energid* of SACHS. (HANSTEIN, 1880.)

[Pseudochromosomes = Archoplasmic loops of HERMANN], an early name for the " batonettes " or rod-like Golgi-bodies of the spermatocytes. (HEIDENHAIN, 1900.)

[Pseudomitotic] (= **Diaschistic** of FARMER), a type of meiosis showing one longitudinal and one apparently transverse division of the bivalents or tetrads. Correlative, *Eumitotic*, *q. v.* (KORSCHELT and HEIDER, 1903.)

[Pseudonucleolus] (*pseudos*, false) = **Karyosome, Net-knot, Chromatin-nucleoli.** (ROSEN, 1894.)

Pseudoreduction, the apparent halving of the chromosome-number by synapsis. (RÜCKERT, 1894.)

Pyrenoid (*pyren*, the stone of a fruit; like a nucleus), rounded bodies, formed within the chromatophores (chloroplasts) of algæ, and acting as centers of starch-formation. (SCHMITZ, 1883.)

Quartet, the group of four cells, whether spores, spermatids or egg+polocytes, produced by the two maturation-divisions; contrast *Tetrad*.

Reduction = Meiosis, the change of chromosome-number from diploid to haploid (halving of the number) during maturation or meiosis.

Sarcode (*sarx*, flesh) the protoplasm of Protista. (DUJARDIN.)

Sertoli cells, supporting and nutritive cells of the testis to which the sperms are attached by their heads at an early period. (v. EBNER, 1871.)

Sex-chromosome (see **Idiochromosome**), a particular pair or group of chromosomes having a special relation to sex-determination. They are commonly designated as X- and Y-chromosomes (WILSON, 1906.)

Skein = Spireme.

Sperm (Spermium) (*sperma*, seed). The *spermatozoön, spermatosome* or sperm-cell of the male.

Spermatid (*sperma*, seed), one of the final generation of cells which, without further division, is metamorphosed into a sperm. (LA VALETTE ST. GEORGF, 1886.)

Spermatocyte (*sperma*, as in sperm; *kytos*, cell), one of the cells to which the spermatogonia give rise and which divide twice to produce the spermatids; they are distinguished as *primary* (before their division) and *secondary* (after their first division). (LA VALETTE ST. GEORGE, 1876.)

Spermatogenesis (*sperma*, seed; *genesis*, origin), the phenomena involved in the production of the sperms. Often used more especially to denote the process of reduction or meiosis in the male.

Spermatogonium (" **Ursamenzelle** ") (*sperma*, seed; *gone*, generation), one of the descendants of the primordial germ-cells in the male. Each ultimate spermatogonium becomes a primary spermatocyte (auxocyte) and typically gives rise to four sperms. (LA VALETTE ST. GEORGE, 1876.)

Spermatozoïd = **Antherozoid** (see **Sperm**), the ciliated paternal gamete in plants. The word was first used by VON SIEBOLD as synonymous with sperm.

Spermioteleosis, Spermateleosis = **Spermiogenesis** (*sperm*, as in sperm; *teleios*, finished), the metamorphosis of the spermatid into the sperm. (GATENBY, 1918.)

Spermiogenesis 1. = **Spermioteleosis**, metamorphosis of the spermatid into the sperm. (WALDEYER, 1903.) 2. = **Spermatogenesis**. (BENDA and LENHOSSÉK, 1905.)

Spermatozoön = **Sperm** (*sperma*, seed; *zoön*, animal), the male gamete of animals. (LEEUWENHOEK, 1677.)

Sperm-nucleus, the nucleus of the sperm especially applied to it after entrance into the egg before its union with the egg-nucleus. In this sense equivalent to the " male pronucleus " of VAN BENEDEN. (O. HERTWIG, 1875.)

[Sphærosome] (*sphaira*, globe; *soma*, body), the envelope of the " statosphere " or idiozome, formed by the Golgi-bodies. (KUSCHAKEWITSCH, 1913.)

Spireme (*speirema*, a thing wound or coiled; a skein), the skein or " Knäuel " stage of the nucleus in mitosis, during which the chromatin appears in the form of a thread, continuous or segmented. (FLEMMING, 1882.)

Spongioplasm (*spongia*, sponge; *plasma*, as in *protoplasm*), the cytoplasmic framework. (LEYDIG, 1885.)

Sporophyte (*sporos*, spore; *kytos*, cell), the asexual, spore-producing diplont or diploid generation of plants in the antithetic alternation of generations. See **Gametophyte** (=the haplont).

[Statosphere] (=**Idiozome** or **Centrotheca**). (KUSCHEKEWITSCH, 1913.)

Strepsinema (*streptos*, pliant, easily twisted; *nema*, a thread), substantive form of *strepsitene*. (GRÉGOIRE, 1907.)

Strepsitene (*streptos*, pliant, easily twisted; *tænia*, band, ribbon), the twisted form of diplotene during meiosis. (DIXON, 1900.)

Synaptene (= **Zygotene** or **Amphitene**) (*synapsis* and *tænia*, band), the synaptic stage in meiosis while the chromosomes (leptotene-threads) are conjugating two by two. (WINIWARTER, 1900.)

Syncytium (*syn*, together; *kytos*, cell), a multinucleate mass of protoplasm. See **Plasmodium**. (HAECKEL.)

Synapsis (*synapto*, to fuse together), the conjugation or union in pairs of homologous chromosomes (synaptic mates), respectively of maternal and paternal origin, to form bivalents; the primary step in reduction or meiosis. Often erroneously applied to the contraction-figure or synizesis that is its frequent accompaniment. (MOORE, 1895.)

Syndesis = **Synapsis** (*syndesis*, a binding). See **Metasyndesis, Parasyndesis**. (HAECKER, 1907.)

Syngamy (*syn*, with; *gamos*, marriage, union), union of the gametes in fertilization or conjugation.

Synizesis (*synizesis*, a collapse), the contraction-figure often seen at the time of synapsis, with the chromatin massed towards the center or one side of the nucleus. Often called " *synapsis* " *q. v.* (McCLUNG, 1905.)

Synkaryon (*syn*, with; *karyon*, nucleus), a nucleus resulting from the union of two nuclei; in general, the zygote-nucleus.

[Synmixis, Synmixia] (*syn*, with; *mixis*, mingling), a supposed exchange of chromosome-parts during the second meiotic division in copepods. (HAECKER, 1904.)

Teloblast (*telos*, end; *blastos*, bud or germ), large cells situated at the growing end of the embryo (in annelids, etc.), which bud forth rows of smaller cells. (WHITMAN, WILSON, 1887.)

Telokinesis (*telos*, end; *kinesis*, change or movement), certain movements of the central bodies, nuclei and spindle accompanying or following the telophases of mitosis. (HEIDENHAIN, 1894.)

Telolecithal (*telos*, end; *lekithos*, yolk), that type of ovum in which the yolk is mainly accumulated in one hemisphere. (BALFOUR, 1880.)

Telomitic (*telos*, end; *mitos*, thread), terminal attachment of the chromosomes to the spindle-fibers. Correlative, *Atelomitic*. (CAROTHERS, 1917.)

Telophases (*telos*, end), the closing phases of mitosis, during which the daughter-nuclei are re-formed and the cytosome divides. (HEIDENHAIN, 1894.)

Telosynapsis = Metasyndesis (*telos*, end; *synapsis*, union), end-to-end union of the chromosomes (synaptic mates) in synapsis. (WILSON, 1912.)

Tetrad (*tetras*, four), the quadruple group of chromosomes (chromatids) formed by the bivalent chromosomes in the later stages of meiosis.

Tetraploid, Polyploid (*tetras*, four; *polys*, many), having the value of four or many gametic or haploid chromosome-groups; often applied to the organism having chromosomes of double (or a higher multiple of) the typical number.

[Thelykaryon] (*thelys*, female; *karyon*, nucleus), a maternal gamete-nucleus or its descendant. Correlative, *Arrhenokaryon*. See *Hemikaryon*. (BOVERI 1905.)

Tonoplasts (*tonos*, tension; *plastos*, as in plastid), plastids which are supposed to produce vacuoles in plant-cells. (DE VRIES, 1885).

Trophochromatin (*trophe*, food), chromatin assumed to be concerned especially with the vegetative or nutritive functions of the cell. Correlative, *Idiochromatin*, *q. v.* (LUBOSCH, 1902.)

Trophochromidia (*trophe*, food), chromidia arising from *trophochromatin* (*q. v.*) and of predominantly vegetative or nutritive functions. See **Chromidia, Idiochromidia.** (MESNIL, 1905.)

Trophoplasm (*trophe*, food; *plasma*, as in *protoplasm*). 1. The nutritive or vegetative substance of the cell, as distinguished from the *idioplasm*. (NÄGELI, 1884.) 2. The active substance of the cytoplasm other than the "kinoplasm" or archiplasm. (STRASBURGER, 1892.)

Trophoplast (*trophe*, food; *plastos*, formed) = **Plastid.** (A. MEYER, 1882–83.)

Trophospongium (*trophe*, food; *spongia*, sponge), a system of intracellular canals identified by some observers with the Golgi-apparatus, by others with ingrowths of surrounding cells. (HOLMGREN.)

Yolk-nucleus = Vitelline Body, a cytoplasmic body in the young oöcyte, which serves as a center for the yolk-formation in many forms. In many cases it is traceable to the idiozome and its associated structures. (CARUS, 1850.)

Zygote (*zygotes*, yoked), the cell formed by union of the gametes; the fertilized egg, zygospore, etc.

Zygotene (= **Synapteno, Amphitene**) (*zygon*, yoke; *tænia*, band, ribbon), the synaptic stage during which occurs the side-by-side conjugation of spireme-threads. (GRÉGOIRE, 1907.)

GENERAL LITERATURE LIST

The following list makes no approach to completeness. It includes for the most part titles of works referred to in the text and certain others which for one reason or another it has seemed desirable to refer to. For more complete bibliography the reader is referred to the literature-lists in the special works cited, among others the following. For reviews of the early history of the cell-theory see Remak's *Untersuchungen* ('50–'55), Huxley on the *Cell-theory* ('53), Sach's *History of Botany* and Tyson's *Cell-doctrine* ('78). An exhaustive review of the earlier literature on protoplasm, nucleus, and cell-division will be found in Fleming's *Zellsubstanz* ('82), and a later review of theories of protoplasmic structure in Bütschli's *Protoplasma* ('92) and in Fischer's *Fixierung, etc., des Protoplasmas* ('99). The earlier work on mitosis and fertilization is thoroughly reviewed in Whitman's *Clepsine* ('78), Fol's *Hénogénie* ('79), and Mark's *Limax* ('81). For more recent reviews see among others the following works cited in the chapter-lists, as indicated. Delage, '03 (Intr.), Haecker, '99 (Intr.), Heidenhain, '07 (Intr.), Henneguy, '03 (Intr.), O. Hertwig, '06, '10, '12, '20, '23 (Intr.); Lillie, '19, Strasburger, '07, Agar, '20, Buchner, '15, Doncaster, '20, Prenant, Bouin, Maillard, '04, Sharp, '21 (I); Brachet, '11, '17 (XIV); Jenkinson, '09 (XIV); Morgan, '19, Morgan, Sturtevant, Bridges and Muller, '23 (XII); Korschelt-Heider, '03 (V), Gelei, '22; Waldeyer, '06 (IV), etc.

The titles are arranged in alphabetical order, according to the system originally adopted in Minot's *Human Embryology*. Each author's name is followed by the date of publication (the first two digits being omitted, except in case of works published before the nineteenth century), and this by a letter to designate the paper, in case two or more works were published in the same year. For example, **Boveri, Th.**, '87b, denotes the second paper published by Boveri in 1887. In order to avoid repetition titles that have already been given in the special lists are here referred to only by name and date with the number of the chapter-list in which they will be found in full indicated by Roman numerals in brackets; for example, **Boveri, Th.,** '04 (IX). In many cases titles have been more or less shortened by the omission of certain words, as indicated in general by " etc." or a series of dots; and titles of purely preliminary papers have often been omitted unless for special reasons. For the sake of further economy of space titles of journals and other publications most often referred to have been abbreviated as much as possible, in accordance with the following list.

ABBREVIATIONS

A. A., Anatomischer Anzeiger. (*Jena*).
A. A. M., Archives de l'anatomie microscopique (*Paris*).
A. A. P., Archiv für Anatomie und Physiologie (*Leipzig*).
A. B., Archives de Biologie (*Liège and Paris*).

A. Bot., Annals of Botany (*London*).
A. Entwm., Archiv für Entwicklungsmechanik (*Berlin*).
A. I. B., Archives Italiennes de Biologie (*Pisa*).
A. Z. I., Archivio Zoologico Italiano.
A. J. A., American Journal of Anatomy (*Philadelphia*).
A. J. B., American Journal of Botany (*Brooklyn*).
A. J. P., American Journal of Physiology (*Baltimore*).
A. M. A., Archiv für Mikroscopische Anatomie (*Bonn*).
A. N., American Naturalist (*Garrison's, New York*).
An. B., L'Année Biologique (*Paris*).
An. Hf., Anatomische Hefte (*Munich and Wiesbaden*).
Ark. B., Arkiv för Botanik (*Stockholm*).
A. P., Archiv für Protistenkunde (*Jena*).
A. Ph., Archiv für die gesammte Physiologie (*Berlin*).
A. R., Anatomical Record (*Philadelphia*).
A. S. N., Annales des Sciences Naturelles (*Paris*).
A. Z. E., Archives de Zoologie Expérimentale (*Paris*).
A. Z., Acta Zoologica (*Stuttgart*).
A. Zf., Archiv für Zellforschung (*Leipzig*).

B., Biometrika (*Cambridge, Univ. Press*).
B. A. B., Bulletin de l'Académie Royale de Belgique (*Brussels*).
B. B., Biological Bulletin (*Woods Hole, Mass.*).
B. B. F. B. (see *B. S. F. B.*)
B. C., or *B. Z.*, Biologisches Centralblatt (or Zentralblatt) (*Leipzig*).
B. G., Botanical Gazette (*Chicago*).
B. D. B. G., Berichte der Deutschen Botanischen Gesellschaft (*Berlin*).
B. M. Z., Bulletin of the Museum of Comparative Zoölogy, Harvard (*Cambridge, Mass.*).
B. S. F. B., Bulletin Scientifique (later Biologique) de la France et de la Belgique (*Paris*).
B. S. Z., Bulletin de la Societé Zoologique de France (*Paris*).
B. Z., Botanische Zeitung (*Berlin*).

C. R., Comptes Rendus de l'Académie des Sciences (*Paris*).
C. R. S. B., Comptes Rendus des Seances de la Societé de Biologie (*Paris*).

E. A. E., Ergebnisse der Anatomie und Entwicklungsgeschichte (Merkel and Bonnet, Anatomische Hefte, 2te Abtheilung) (*Wiesbaden*).
E. P., Ergebnisse der Physiologie (*Wiesbaden*).

G., Genetics. *Menaska, Wisconsin (Brooklyn Bot. Garden)*.

H. Nw., Handwörterbuch der Naturwissenschaften (*Fischer, Jena*).

J. A. P., Journal de l'Anatomie et de la Physiologie (*Paris*).
J. C. S., Journal of the College of Science, Imperial Univ. (*Tokyo*).
J. E. Z., Journal of Experimental Zoölogy (*Philadelphia*).
J. G., Journal of Genetics (*Cambridge, England*).

J. G. P., Journal of General Physiology (*New York*).
J. H., Journal of Heredity (*Washington, D. C.*).
J. M., Journal of Morphology (*Philadelphia*).
J. P., Journal of Physiology (*London, Cambridge Univ. Press*).
J. R. M., Journal of the Royal Microscopical Society (*London*).
J. W. B., Jahrbuch für Wissenschaftliche Botanik (*Leipzig*).
J. Z., Jenaische Zeitschrift für Medicin und Naturwissenschaft (*Jena*).

L. C., La Cellule (*Louvain*).

M. J., Morphologisches Jahrbuch (*Leipzig*).
M. Z. S., Mittheilung aus der Zoologischen Station zu Neapel (*Naples*).

N. P., The New Phytologist (*London*).
N. S., Natural Science (*London*).

P. A. A. A. S., Proceedings of the American Academy of Arts and Sciences (*Boston*).
P. C. I., Publications of the Carnegie Institution of Washington (*Washington*).
P. N. A., Proceedings of the National Academy of Sciences (*Philadelphia*).
P. R. B., Progressus Rei Botanicae (*Jena*).
P. R. S., Proceedings Royal Society (*London*).
P. S. B. M., Proceedings of the Society for Experimental Biology and Medicine (*New York*).
P. T., Philosophical Transactions of the Royal Society (*London*).
P. S. M., Popular Science Monthly. *New York* (see *S. M.*).

Q. J., Quarterly Journal of Microscopical Science (*London*).

R. B., Revue Biologique du Nord de la France (*Lille*).

S. B. G. M. P., Sitzungs-Berichte der Gesellschaft für Morphologic und Physiologie (*München.*)
S. B. P. M. G., Sitzungs-Berichte der Physikalisch-Medicinisch Gesellschaft zu Würzburg (*Würzburg*).
S. M., Scientific Monthly (formerly Popular Science Monthly). *New York.*
S. P., Science Progress (*London*).
Sci., Science (*New York and Garrison*).

V. A. G., Verhandlungen der Anatomischen Gesellschaft (*Jena*).
V. D. Z. G., Verhandlungen der Deutschen Zoölogischen Gesellschaft (*Berlin*).
V. P. M. G., Verhandlungen der Physikalische-medizinischen Gesellschaft zu Würzburg (*Würzburg*).

W. H. L., Woods Hole Biological Lectures (*Woods Hole, Mass.*).

Z., Zoologica (*Stuttgart*).
Z. A., Zoölogischer Anzeiger (*Leipzig*).
Z. A. V., Zeitschrift für Induktive Abstammungs-und Vererbungslehre (*Leipzig*).
Z. B., Zeitschrift für Botanik (*Jena*).

Z. C., Zoölogisches Centralblatt (*Leipzig*).
Z. J., Zoölogische Jahrbücher (*Jena*).
Z. W. M., Zeitschrift für Wissenschaftliche Mikroscopie (*Leipzig*).
Z. W. Z., Zeitschrift für Wissenschaftliche Zoölogie (*Leipzig*).

ABDERHALDEN, EMIL, '09, '14. (VIII). — **Acton, E.,** '14. Observations on the Cytology of the Chroöcoccaceae: *A. Bot.*, XXVIII. — **Adami, J. G.,** '08. (VIII). — '18. Medical Contributions to the Study of Evolution: *London.* — **Adler, Leo,** '16. Untersuchungen über Entstehung der Amphibienneotenie: *A. Ph.*, 164. — '17. Metamorphosentudien an Batrachierlarven: *A. Entwm.*, XLIII. — **Agar, W. E.,** '11. (VI). — '12. Transverse Segmentation and Internal Differentiation of Chromosomes: *Q. J.*, LVIII. — '14. Parthenogenetic and Sexual Reproduction in *Simocephalus*, etc.: *J. G.*, III. — '20. (I). — **Agassiz and Whitman,** '84. On the Development of some Pelagic Fish Eggs: *P. A. A. A. S.*, XX. — **Albrecht, E.,** '98. Untersuchungen zur Structur des Seeigeleies: *S.-Ges. Morph. Phys. München*, III. — **Alexeieff, A.,** '16a. Mitochondries chez quelques protistes, etc.: *C. R., Soc. Biol.*, LXXX. — '17a. Sur les mitochondries à fonction glycoplastique: *Ibid.* — '17b. Nature mitochondriale du corps parabasal des Flagellés: *Ibid.* — '17b. Mitochondries et rôle morphogène du noyau: *Ibid.* — **Allen, B. M.,** '06. The Origin of the Sex-cells of *Chrysemys*: *A. A.*, XXIX. — '07. An important Period in the History of the Sex-cells of *Rana pipiens*: *Ibid.*, XXXI. — '09. The Origin of the Sex-cells of *Amia* and *Lepidosteus*: *A. R.*, III. — **Allen, C. E.,** '01. On the Origin and Nature of the Middle Lamella: *B. G.*, XXXII. — '04. Chromosome Reduction in *Lilium*: *B. G.*, XXXVII. — '05a. Nuclear Division in the Pollen Mother Cells of *Lilium*: *A. Bot.*, XIX. — '05b. Das Verhalten der Kernsubstanz der Synapsis in den Pollenmutterzellen von *Lilium*: *J. W. B.*, XLII. — '05. Die Keimung der Zygote bei *Coleochaete*: *B. D. B. G.*, XXIII. — '12. Cell Structure Growth, and Division in the Antheridia of *Polytricum*: *A. Zf.*, VIII. — '17. (IV). — '19. The Basis of Sex Inheritance in *Sphaerocarpos*: *Proc. Am. Phil. Soc.*, LVIII. — **Allen, Edgar** '23 (IV). **Allen, Ezra,** '16. Studies on Cell-Division in the Albino Rat: *A. R.*, X. — '16. Experiments in Technique: *A. R.*, X. — '18. Spermatogenesis in the Albino Rat: *J. M.*, XXXI. — '19. A Technique which preserves the normal cytological Conditions, etc.: *A. R.*, XVI. — **Allen, R. F.,** '11. Studies on Spermatogenesis and Apogamy in Ferns: *Trans. Wis. Acad. Sci.*, XVII. — **Altmann, R.,** '86, '90, '94. (I). — '92. Ueber Kernstuktur und Netzstrukturen: *A. A. P.* — '93. Die Granulatheorie und ihre Kritik: *A. A. P.* — **Alverdes, F.,** '12. Die Kerne in den Speicheldrüsen der *Chironomus*-Larve: *A. Zf.*, IX. — **Amelung, E.,** '93. Ueber mittlere Zellengrössen: *Flora*, LXXVII. — **Amici, G. B.,** '30. Note sur le mode l'action du pollen sur le stigmate: *A. S. N.*, I, XXI. — **Amma, K.,** '11. (IV). — **Ancel, P.,** '03. Histogénèse et structure de la gland hermaphrodite d'Helix: *A. B.*, XIX. — **Andrews, E. A.,** '98. Filose Activities in Metazoan Eggs: *Zool. Bull.*, II, 1. — '98. Activities of Polar Bodies of *Cerebratulus*: *A. Entwm.*, VI, 2. — **Andrews G. F.,** '97. The Living Substance as Such and as Organism: *J. M.*, XII, 2, Suppl. — **Apáthy, S.,** '97. Das leitende Element des Nervensystems, etc., *M. Z. S.*, XII. — '08. Fixierbarkeit und Färbbarkeit, etc.: *Akad. Wiss. Budapest*, XIX. — '12. Neuere Beiträge zur Schneidetechnik: *Z. W. M.*, XXIV. — **Arber, A.,** '14. On Root Development in *Stratiotes aloides L.*, etc.: *Proc. Camb. Phil. Soc.*, XVII. — **Armbruster, L.,** '13. Chromosomenverhältnisse bei der Spermatogenese solitärer Apiden: *A. Zf.*, XI. — **Armbruster, Nachtsheim** and **Roemer**, '17. Die Hymenoptera als Studienobjecte, etc.: *Z. A. V.*, XVII. — **Arnold, G. A.**, '08. The Nucleolus and Microchomosomes in the Spermatogenesis of *Hydrophilus: A. Zf.*, II. — '09. The Prophase in the Ovigenesis and Spermatogenesis of *Planaria: Ibid.*, III. — '12. The Rôle of the Chondriosomes in the Cells of the Guinea-pig Pancreas: *A. Zf.*, VIII. — **Arnold, J.**, '79. Ueber feinere Struktur der Zellen, etc.: *Virchow's Arch.* — '07. Plasmosomen, Granula, Mitochondrien, Chondriomiten und Netzfiguren: *A. A.*, XXXI. — '08. Supravitale Färbung Mitochondrien und ähnlicher Granula, etc.: *A. A.*, XXXII. — '13. (I). — '14. (IX). — **Artom, C.**, '12a. (XI). — '12b. Le basi cytologiche de una nuova sisematica del genere Artemia, etc.: *A. Zf.*, IX, 1. — '21. Il significato delle razze e delle specie tetraploidi, etc.: *Revista de Biologia*, III. — **Asvadourova, Nina**, '13. Recherches sur la formation de quelques cellules pigmentaires et des pigments: *A. A. M.*, XV. — **Auerbach, L.**, '74. (Int.). — '91. Uber einen sexuellen Gegensatz in der Chromatophilie der Keimsubstanzen: *Sitzb. der Königl. preuss. Akad. d. Wiss Berlin*, XXXV.

BABCOCK AND CLAUSEN, '18. (XII). — **Bachhuber, L. J.**, '16. The Spermatogenesis of the Rabbit: *B. B.*, XXX. — **Baehr, W. de**, '09, '20 (X). — '12. Contribution a l'étude de la caryocinèse somatique, de la pseudoreduction et de la reduction (*Aphis saliceti*): *L. C.*, XXVII. — **Baer, C. E. von**, '28, '37. (XIV). — '34. Die Metamorphose des Eies der Batrachier: *M. A.* — **Bailey, I. W.**, '19. Phenomena of Cell-Division in the Cambium of Arborescent Gymnosperms, etc.: *P. N. A.*, V. — '20a. Size Variations of Cambial Initials in Gymnosperms and Angiosperms: *A. J. B.*, VII. — '20b. The Cambium and its Derivative Tissues, III. A Reconnaissance of Cytological Phenomena in the Cambium: *A. J. B.*, VII. — **Baitsell, G. A.**, '14. A Study of the so-called Life-cycle in *Oxytricha*, etc.: *J. E. Z.*, XVI. — **Balbiani, E. G.**, '61. Recherches sur les phénomènes sexuels des Infusoires: *Journ. de la Phys.*, IV. — '81. Sur la structure du noyau des cellules salivaires chez les larves de *Chironomus: Z. A.*, — '89. Recherches expérimentales sur la mérotomie des Infusoires ciliés: *Recueil Zoöl. Suisse.* — '93. Centrosome et Dotterkern: *J. A. P.*, XXIX. — **Balfour, F. M.**, '80. Comparative Embryology: I. — **Ballowitz, E.**, '08. Fibrilläre Struktur und Contractilität: *A. Ph.*, XLVI. — Untersuchungen uber die Struktur der Spermatozoen, etc.: *Vögel: A. M. A.*, XXXII. — '90. Insekten: *Z. W. Z.*, L. 3. — '90. Fische, Amphibien, Reptilien: *A. M. A.*, XXXVI. — '95. Die Doppelspermatozoa der Dytisciden: *Z. W. Z.*, XLV, 3. — '98. Zur Kenntniss der Zellsphäre: *A. A. P.*, II, III. — '00. Eine Bemerkung zu dem . . . "Apparato reticolare," etc.: *A. A.*, XVIII. — '05. Die Spermien des Batrachiers *Pelodytes punctatus: A. A.*, XXVII. — '06. Uber das regelmässige Vorkommen heteromorph Spermien im reifen Sperma des Grasfrosches: *Z. A.*, XXX. — '07. Zur Kenntniss der Spermien der Cetaceen: *A. M. A.*, LXX. — '13. (IV). — **Baltzer, F.**, '08. Ueber mehrpolige Mitosen bei Seeigeleiern: *Inaug. Diss.* — '09. Ueber die Entwicklung der Echiniden-bastarde, etc.: *Z. A.*, V. — '09. Die Chromosomen von *Strongylocentrotus lividus* und *Echinus microtuberculatus: A. Zf.*, II. — '10, '17. (XII). — '13. Ueber die Herkunft der Idiochromosomen bei Seeigeln: *S. B. P. M. G.* — '14. (X). — '14. Die Bestimmung und der Dimorphismus des Geschlechts bei *Bonellia: S. B. P. M. G.*, *Würzburg.* — '20. Ueber die experimentelle Erzeugung, etc., vom Triton-Bastarden ohne mütterliches Kernmaterial: *Verh. Schweiz. Naturforsch. Ges.*

Neuenberg. — **Bancroft, W. D.**, '14. The Theory of Colloid Chemistry: *Jour. Phys. Chem.*, XVIII. — **Banta, A. M.**, '19. The Extent of the Occurrence of Sex Intergrades in Cladocera: *A. R.*, XV. — **Baranecki, J.**, '80. Die Kernteilung in den Pollen-mutterzellen einiger Tradescantien: B. Z. — **Barber, M. A.**, '11a. A Technic for the Inoculation of Bacteria and other Substances into living Cells: *Jour. Infect. Diseases*, VIII. — '11. The Effect on the Protoplasm of *Nitella* of various chemical Substances, etc.: *Ibid.* IX. — '14. The Pipette Method in the Isolation of Single Microorganisms, etc.: *Philip. Journ. Sci.*, IX. — **Barber, H. G.**, '11. The Resurrection of *Thyanta calceata* from Synonomy: *J. N. Y., Ent. Soc.*, XIX. — **Barfurth, D.**, '91–'93, '13. (XIV). — **Barnard, J. E.**, '19. The Limitations of Microscopy: *J. R. M.*, March. — **Barratt, J. O.**, '13. Changes in Chondriosomes occurring in Pathological Conditions: *Q. J.*, LVIII. — **Barry, M.**, '38–'41. Embryological Memoirs in *P. T.*, 128–131. — '43. Spermatozoa observed within the Mammiferous ovum: *Ibid.* — **Bary, H. A. de**, '58. Untersuchungen uber die Familien der Conjugaten: *Leipzig.* — '62. Ueber den Bau und das Wesen der Zelle: *Flora.* — '64. Die Mycetozoa: 2nd. Ed., *Leipzig.* — **Bataillon, E.**, '00. La pression osmotique et les grands problèmes de la biologie générale: *A. Entwm.*, XI. — '01. Études expérimentales sur l'évolution des Amphibiens. *Ibid.*, XII. — '04. Nouveaux essais de parthenogénèse expérimentale chez les Vertébrés inférieurs: *Ibid.*, XVIII. — '06. Imprégnation et técondation: *C. R.*, '09. L'imprégnation hétérogène sans amphimixie nucleaire chez les Amphibiens et les Echinodermes: *A. Entwm.*, XXVIII. — '10. L'embryogénèse complète provoquées chez les amphibiens par piqure de l'œuf vièrge: *C. R.*, 150. — '10, '12. (V). — '10a. Contribution a l'analyse expérimentale des phénomènes karyocinétiques chez *Ascaris megalocephala*: *A. Entwm.*, XXX. — '16. Nouvelle contribution a l'analyse expérimentale de la fécondation par la parthénogénèse: *Ann. Inst. Pasteur*, 1916. — '19. Analyse de l'activation par la technique des œufs nus et la polyspermie expérimentale chez les Batraciens: *Ann. Sc. Nat. Zool.* — **Bateson, W.**, '09, '13. (XII). — '18. Problems of Genetics: *Yale Univ. Press.* — '14. (XIV). — **Bateson** and **Punnett**, '08. The Heredity of Sex: *Sci.*, XXVII. — '11a. On the Inter-relation of genetic Factors: *P. R. S.*, LXXXIV. — '11b. On Gametic Series involving Reduplication of certain Terms: *J. G.*, I. — **Bateson, Saunders,** and **Punnett**, '06. *Reports to Evolution Committee of the Royal Society*, III. — **Baumgärtel, O.**, '18. Chromatische Fixierung: *B. D. B. G.* — '20. (IX). — **Baumgartner, W. J.**, '02. Spermatid Transformations in *Gryllus*, etc.: *Kansas Univ. Sci. Bull.*, I. — '04. (XI). **Baur, E.**, '14. (XII). — **Bayliss, W. M.**, '11, '18, '21, '23. (VIII). — **Bayliss** and **Starling**, '06. — **Beale, Lionel S.**, '61. — (Int.). — '70. Bioplasm and its Degradation: *Q. J.*, XVIII. — **Beard, J.**, '02. (X). — **Béchamp and Estor**, '82. De la constitution élémentaire des tissues: *Montpellier.* — **Bechold, H.**, '12. (VIII). — **Beckwith, C. J.**, '08. Early History of the Egg and Embryo of certain Hydroids: *B. B.*, XVI. — '14. (IV). — **Beer, R.**, '04. (I). — '05. On the Development of the Pollen Grain and Anther of some Onagraceae: *Beih. Bot. Centr.*, XIX. — '09. On Elaioplasts: *Ibid.*, XXIII. — '09. The Development of the Spores of *Equisetum*: *N. P.*, VIII. — '11, '12, '13. Studies in Spore Development: *A. Bot.*, XXV, XXVI, XXVII. — '21. Notes on the Cytology and Genetics of the genus *Fuchsia*: *J. G.*, V, 11. — **Beer** and **Arber**, '19. On the occurrence of Multinucleate Cells in Vegetative Tissues: *P. R. S.*, XCI. — **Belajeff, W.**, '88, '89. Mittheilung uber Bau und Entwicklung der Spermatozoiden: *B. D. B. G.*, — '92a. Uber den Bau und die

Entwicklung der Antherozoiden, I., Characeen. — '92b. Ueber die Karyokinesis in den Pollenmutterzellen bei *Larix* und *Fritillaria: Sitzb. Warsch. Naturf. Ges.* — '94. (IV). — '94. Zur Kenntniss der Karyokinese bei den Pflanzen: *Flora*, LXXIX, Erg. Heft. 3. — '97a. Ueber den Nebenkern in Spermatogenen Zellen und die Spermatogenese bei den Farnkräuten: *B. D. B. G.*, XV. — '97b. Ueber die Spermatogenese bei den Schachtelhalmen: *B. D. B. G.*, XV. — '97c. Ueber die Aehnlichkeit einiger Erscheinungen in der Spermatogenese bei Thieren und Pflanzen: *Ibid.* — '97d. Einige Streitfragen in den Untersuchungen über die Karyokinese: *Ibid.* — '98. Uber die Cilienbildner in den spermatogenen Zellen: *B. D. B. G.*, XVI. — '98a. Ueber die Reductionstheilung des Pflanzenkerns: *B. D. B. G.*, XVI. — '99. Ueber die Centrosomen in den spermatogenen Zellen: *B. D. B. G.*, XVII. — **Bĕlař, K.**, '21. Untersuchungen über Formwechsel von *Actinophrys: B. C.*, XLI. — '23. (VII). — **Belling, J.**, '21. The Behavior of homologous Chromosomes in a triploid Canna. *P. N. A.*, VII. — '21a. The Behavior of Homologous Chromosomes in Pollen-mother-cells: *A. N.*, LV. — '21b. On counting Chromosomes in Pollen-mother-cells: *Ibid.* — **Belling** and **Blakeslee**, '22, '24. (XII). — **Benda, C.**, '97. Untersuchungen über den Bau des funktionirenden Samenkanälchens einiger Säugetheire: *A. M. A.*, XXX. — '97. Neuere Mitteilungen über die Histogenese des Säugetierspermatozoon: *Verh. d. Phys. Gesell. Berlin.* — '98. (IV). — '98. Zellstructuren und Zellteilungen des Salamanderhodens: *V. A. G.*, — '99a. Weitere Mittheilungen uber die Mitochondria: *Verh. d. Physiol. Ges.* — '99b. Weitere Beobachtungen uber die Mitochondria und ihre Verhältniss zu Secretgranulationen, etc.: *V. P. G.* — '01. Die Mitochondriafärbung, etc.: '03, '14 (I). — **Bensaude, M.**, '18. (VII). — **Bensley, R. R.**, '10. On the Nature of the Canalicular Apparatus of Animal Cells: *B. B.*, XIX. — '11. Studies on the Pancreas of the Guinea-pig: *A. J. A.*, XII. — **Berenberg-Gossler, H. v.**, '14. (IV). — **Berezowski, A.**, '10, '11. Studien uber die Zellgrösse: *A. Zf.*, V, VII. — **Bergen, F. v.**, '04. Zur Kenntnis gewisser Strukturbilder, etc.: *A. M. A.*, LXIV. — **Berghs, J. B.**, '04. La formation des chromosmes héterotypiques. II.: *L. C.*, XXI, 2. — '05. La formation des chromosmes hétérotypiques dans la sporogénèse végétale, IV: *L. C.*, XXII. — '06. Le noyau et la cinèse chez le *Spirogyra: L. C.*, XXIII. — '09. Les cinèses somatiques dans le *Marsilia: L. C.*, XXV. — **Bergh, R. S.**, — '94. (I). — '95. Ueber die relativen Theilungspotenzen einiger Embryonalzellen: *A. Entwm.*, I, 2. — **Berliner, E.**, '09. Flagellaten-Studien: *A. P.*, XV. — **Bernard, Claude**, '78, '85. (VIII). — **Berthold, G.**, '86. (XIII). — **Bickford, E. E.**, '94. Notes on Regeneration and Heteromorphosis of Tubularian Hydroids: *J. M.*, IX, III. — **Bigelow, H. B.**, '07. Studies in the nuclear Cycle of *Gonionemus: B. M. Z.*, XLVIII. — **Binford, Raymond**, '13. The Germ-cells and the Process of Fertilization in *Menippe mercenaria: J. M.*, XXIV. — **Blackburn, J. W. H.**, '21. The Status of the British Rose Forms as determined by their cytological Behavior: *A. Bot.*, XXXV. — **Blackburn** and **Harrison**, '21. The Status of the British Rose Forms, etc.: *A. Bot.*, XXXV. — **Blackman, F. F.**, '12. (I). — **Blackman, M. W.**, '01. The Spermatogenesis of the Myriapods, I: *Kans. Univ. Quart.*, X. — '03. On the Chromatin in the Spermatocytes of *Scolopendra heros: B. B.*, V. — '05. The Spermatogenesis of *Scolopendra heros: B. M. Z.*, XLVIII. — '06. On the Spermatocytes of the Myriapods: *Proc. Am. Ac. Arts and Sci.*, XLII. — **Blackman, V. H.**, '98. On the Cytological Features of Fertilization and Related Phenomena in *Pinus: P. T.*, CXC. — '04. (VII). — '04a. (V). — '06. On the

Sexuality and Development of the Ascocarp of *Humaria: P. R. S.*, LXXVII. — **Blackman** and **Fraser**, '06. Further Studies on the Sexuality of the Uredineae: *A. Bot.*, XX. — **Blakeslee, A. F.**, '04, '06a, '15, '20. (VII). — '06, Zygospore Germinations in the Mucorineae: *Ann. Mycol.*, IV, 1. — '13. Conjugation in the heterogamic Genus *Zygorhyncus: Mycol. Centralbl.*, II. — '21, '22. (XII). — **Blakeslee, Belling** and **Farnham**, '20. (XII). — **Blakeslee, Belling, Farnham,** and **Bergner**, '22. A Haploid Mutant in the Jimson Weed, *Datura stramonium: Sci.*, LV, 1433. — *A. N.*, LV, LVI. — **Blakeslee** and **Farnham**, '23. Trisomic Inheritance in the *Poinsettia* Mutant. of *Datura: A. N.*, LVII. — **Blochman, F.,** '82, '83. (XIII). — '86. Ueber die Eireifung bei Insekten: *B. C.*, VI. — '87. Ueber die Richtungs-Körper bei den Eiern Insekten: *M. J.*, XII. — '00. Ueber das Vorkommen von bakterialähnlichen Gebilden in den Geweben und Eiern verschiedener Insekten: *Centralbl. Bakteriol.*, XI. — '88. Ueber die Richtungskörper bei Insekteneiern: *M. J.*, XII. — '88. Ueber die Richtungskörper bei unbefruchtet sich entwickelnden Insekteneiern: *Verh. Naturh. Med. Ver. Heidelberg*, N. F., IV, 2. — '89. Ueber die Zahl der Richtungskörper bei befruchteten und unbefruchteten Bieneneiern: *M. J.* — **Böhm, A.,** '88. Uber Reifung und Befruchtung des Eies von *Petromyzon: A. M. A.*, XXXII. — '91. Die Befruchtung des Forelleneies: *S. B. G. M.*, VII. — **Boll, Fr.,** '76. Das Princip des Wachsthums: *Berlin.* — **Bolsius, H.,** '11. Sur la structure spirale ou discoid d'élément chromatique dans *Chironomus: L. C.*, XXVII. — Bonnet, C., 1762. (XIV). — **Bonnet, J.,** '11a. Sur le groupement par paires, etc.: *A. Zf.*, VII. — '12. Recherches sur l'évolution des cellules-nourricières du pollen, etc.: *A. Zf.*, VII. — '14. (VII). — **Bonnevie, K.,** '02. Ueber Chromatin-diminution bei Nematoden: *J. Z.*, XXXVI. — '08. (XI). — '04. Zur Kenntniss der Spermiogenese bei den Gastropoden: *B. C.*, XXIV. — '06. Beobachtungen an den Keimzellen von *Enteroxenos: J. Z.*, XLI. — '07. Physiologische Polyspermie bei Bryozoen: *J. Z.*, XLII. — '07. "Heterotypical" mitosis in *Nereis: B. B.*, XIII. — '08. Heterotypische Mitose als Reifungscharacter: *A. Zf.*, II. — '10. Ueber die Rolle der Centralspindel etc.: *A. Zf.*, V. — '11. Chromatinreifung in *Allium: A. Zf.*, I. — '13. (XI). — **Bordás, M.,** '12. Contribution a l'étude de la spermatogénèse dans le *Sagitta: L. C.*, XXVIII. — '21. La profase de reduccion en . . . *Dendrocoelum: Trab. Mus. Nac. Cienc. Nat.*, XLIV. — **Borgert, A.,** '01. Untersuchungen uber die Fortpflanzung der tripyleen Radiolarien, etc.: *A. P.*, XIV, also *Z. J.*, XIV. — **Boring, A. M.,** '07. A Study of the Spermatogenesis of twenty-two Species of the Membracidae, Jassidae, Cercopidae, and Fulgoridae: *J. E. Z.*, IV. — '09. A Small Chromosome in *Ascaris megalocephala: A.Zf.*, IV. — **Boring** and **Pearl**, '14. (X). — **Boring** and **Morgan**, '18. Lutear Cells and Henfeathering: *J. G. P.*, I. — **Born, G.,** '83. Bastardierung zwischen Anurenarten: *A. Ph.*, XXXII. — '85. (XIV). — '94. Die Struktur des Keimbläschens, etc.: *A. M. A.*, XLIII. — '97. Ueber Verwachsungsversuche mit Amphibienlarven: *A. Entwm.*, IV. — **Bourne, G. C.,** '95. A Criticism of the Cell-Theory, etc.: *Q. J.*, XXXVIII. — **Bourquin, H.,** '17. Starch Formation in *Zygnema: B.G.*, LXIV. — **Boveri, M.,** '03. Ueber Mitosen bei einseitiger Chromosomenbindung: *J. Z.*, XXXVII. — **Boveri, Th.,** '86. Ueber die Bedeutung der Richtungskörper: *S. B. G. M. P., München.* II. — '87. Ueber den Anteil der Spermatozoen an der Teilung des Eies: *Ibid.*, III. — '87b. Ueber die Befruchtung der Eier von *Ascaris megalocephala: Ibid.*, III. — '87. Die Bildung der Richtungskörper bei *Ascaris: Jena.* — '87c. Ueber Differenzierung der Zellkerne während der Furchung des Eies von *Ascaris: A. A.*

— '88. Die Befruchtung und Teilung des Eies von *Ascaris: J. Z.*, XXII. — '88. Ueber partielle Befruchtung: *S. B. G. M. P. München.*, IV. — '89, 'o1a, 'o1b, '18. (XIV). — '90. Zellenstudien, Heft III: *J. Z.*, XXIV. — '92a, '95. (V). — '92. Die Entstehung des Gegensatzes zwischen den Geschlechtszellen und den somati- schen Zellen bei *Ascaris: S. B. G. M. P. München*, VIII. — '95. Ueber die Befruch- tungs- und Entwicklungsfähigkeit kernloser Seeigel-eier, etc.: *A. Entwm.*, II, 3. '96. Zur Physiologie der Kern-und Zelltheilung: *S. B. P. M. G., Würzburg.* — '97. Zur Physiologie der Kern- und Zelltheilung: *Ibid.*, IX. — '99. (IV). — 'oo, 'o4, 'o5. (IX). — 'o2. (XII). — 'o2. Das Problem der Befruchtung: *Jena, G. Fischer.* — 'o3. (XIV, XI). — 'o4a, 'o7, '14. (XII). — 'o4b. Protoplasmadifferenzierung als auslösender Faktor für Kernverschiedenheit: *S. B. P. M. G.* — 'o8. Ueber die Beziehung des Chromatins zur Geschlechtsbestimmung: *S. B. P. M. G.* — 'o9. (XI). — 'o9. Ueber " Geschlechtschromosomen " bei Nematoden: *A. Zf.*, IV. — '10. (IV, XIII). — '11. Ueber das Verhalten der Geschlechtschromosomen bei Hermaphroditismus: *V. P. M. G., Würzburg.* — '11. Ueber die Charaktere von Echiniden-Bastardlarven bei Hermaphroditismus: *Ibid.*, XLI. — '14. Ueber die Charaktere von Echiniden-Bastardlarven bei verschiedenem Mengenver- hältnis mütterlicher und väterlicher Substanzen: *Ibid.*, XLIII. — **Boveri** and **Stevens,** '04. Ueber die Entwicklung dispermer Ascariseier: *Z. A.*, XXVII. — **Boveri** and **Hogue,** '09. Ueber die Möglichkeit, Ascariseier zur Teilung in Zwei gleichwertige Blastomeren zu veranlassen: *V. P. M. G., Wirzburg.* — **Bowen, R. H.,** '19. New methods for the Analysis of cytoplasmic Structures: *P. S. B. M.*, XVII. — '19. (II, IV). — '20, '22a, '22b, '22c, '22d, '24. (IV), — '22e. Abnormal Mitoses in Spermatogenesis: *B. B.*, XLIII. — '22f. On certain Features of Sper- matogenesis in Amphibia, etc.: *A. J. A.*, XXX. — '22g. On the Idiosome, Golgi Apparatus, and Acrosome, etc.: *A. R.*, XXIV. — '23a. The Origin of Secretory Granules: *P. N. A.*, IX. — '23b. On the Nature of Mitochondria: *A. R.*, XXVI. — **Bower, F. O.,** '89–'91, '19. (VII). — '94. A Theory of the Strobilus in Archegoniate Plants: *A. B.*, VIII. — **Brachet, A.,** '05, '11, '17, (XIV). — '06. Recherches expérimentales sur l'œuf non segmenté de *Rana fusca: A. Entwm.*. XXII. — '07. Les idées actuelles sur la potentialité des blastomères: *Bull. Soc, Royale Zool. et Malacologique de Belg.*, LXIII. — '08. (XII). — '12. La poly- spermie expérimentale dans l'œuf de *Rana fusca: A. M. A.*, LXXIX. — '15. Sur l'évolution cyclique du cytoplasme de l'œuf activé: *C. R.* — '22. Recherches sur la fécondation prématurée de l'œuf de *Paracentrotus: A. B.*, XXXII. — **Braem, F.,** '10. Die Ungeschlechtliche Fortpflanzung als Vorläufer der Geschlechtlichen: *B. G.*, II. — **Brauer, A.,** '92. Das Ei von *Branchipus* von der Bildung bis zur Ablage: *Abh. Preusse. Akad. Wiss.* — '93. Zur Kenntniss der Spermatogenese von *Ascaris: A. M. A.*, XLII. — '93. (V). — '94. Ueber die Encystierung von *Actinosphaerium: Z. W. Z.*, LVIII. — **Braun, Alex.,** '50. Betrachtung über die Erscheinung der Verjüngung in der Natur, etc.: *Eng. Trans., Ray Soc.*, '66. — **Bridges, C. B.,** '14. Direct Proof through Non-disjunction that the sex-linked Genes of *Drosophila* are borne by the X-chromosome: *Sci.*, n. s., XL. — '13, '14, '16, '17, '22. (XII). — '17. Duplication: *A. R.*, XV. — '21. Triploid Intersexes in *Drosophila: Sci.*, n. s., LIV. — '22a. The Origin of Variations in Sexual and Sex-limited Characters: *A. N.*, LVI. — '22b. Variations due to Changes in Chromosomal Materials: *Proc. Cong. Genet.* — **Bridges** and **Morgan, T. H.,** '19. The Second Chromosome Group of Mutant Characters: *P. C. I.*, 278, Part II. — **Broman,** 'ooa. Ueber Riesenspermatiden bei *Bombinator: A. A.*, XVII. — 'oob.

Ueber Bau und Entwickelung der Spermien von *Bombinator: Ibid.*, XVII. — '02.
Ueber atypische Spermien, etc.: *A. A.*, XXII. — '02. Ueber gesetzmässige
Bewegungs-und Wachsthumserscheinungen (Taxis- und Tropismenformen) der
Spermatiden, etc.: *A. M. A.*, LIX. — '07. Ueber Bau und Entwicklung der
Spermien von *Rana: Ibid.*, LXX. — **Brooks, W. K.**, '83. The Law of Heredity:
Baltimore. — **Brown, E. D. W.**, '19. Apogamy in *Camptosorus rhizophyllus:
Bull. Torr. Bot. Club*, XLVI. — **Brown, H. H.**, '85. On Spermatogenesis in
the Rat: *Q. J.*, XXV. — **Brown, Robert**, '33. Observations on the Organs
and Mode of Fecundation in Orchidae and Asclepiadeae: *Trans. Linn. Soc.* — '66.
A brief Account of microscopical Observations on the Particles contained in the
Pollen of Plants, etc.: *Misc. Bot. Works, Ray Soc.* — **Brown, W. H.**, '08. The
Nature of the Embryo Sac of *Peperomia:* B. G., XLVI. — '09. Nuclear Phenom-
ena in *Pyronema: J. H. U. Circ.*, VI. — '10. The Exchange of material between
Nucleus and Cytoplasm in *Peperomia: B. G.*, XLIX. — **Browne, Ethel N.** (see
also E. B. Harvey), '10. The Relation between Chromosome-number and Species:
B. B., XX. — '13. (XI). '16a. A comparative Study of the Chromosomes of
six Species of *Notonecta: J. M.*, XXVII. — '16a, '20. (See E. B. Harvey). **Brücke,
E.**, '61. Die Elementarorganismen: *Wiener Sitzber.*, XLIV. — **Bruel, L.**, '13.
(I). — **Brunelli, G.**, '09. La spermatogenesi del *Gryllus desertus* Pall.: *Mem
Accad. dei Lincei.*, V, VII. — '10. La spermatogenesi della *Tryxalis*, I.: *Mem.
Soc. Ital. del Sci.*, ser. 33, XVI. — '11. La spermatogenesi della *Tryxalis*, II.
Mem. Acc. d. Lincei, ser. 5a, VIII. — **Brunn, M. v.**, '89. Beitrage sur Kennt-
niss der Samenkörper und ihrer Entwicklung bei Vögeln und Säugethieren: *A. M.
A.*, XXXIII. — **Bryce, T. H.**, '02. Maturation of the Ovum in *Echinus esculen-
tus: Q. J.*, XLVI. — **Bruyne, C. de**, '95. La sphère attractive dans les cellules
fixes du tissu conjonctif: *Bull. Acad. Sc. de Belg.*, XXX. — **Buchner, P.**, '09.
Das accessorische Chromosom in Spermatogenese und Ovogenese der Orthop-
teren: *A. Zf.*, III. — '10, '18. (IV). — '10. Ueber die Beziehungen zwischen
Centriol und Bukettstadium: *A. Zf.*, V. — '11. Die Reifung des Seesterneies bei
experimenteller Parthenogenese: *A. Zf.*, VI. — '15. (I). — **Buchtien, O.**, '87.
Entwicklungsgeschichte des Prothalliums von *Equisetum: Casse..* — **Buder, J.**,
'16. Zur Frage des Generationswechsel im Pflanzenreiche: *B. D. B. G.*, XXXIV.
Bugnion, E., '10. Les cellules sexuelles, etc.: *Bull. Soc. Vaud. Sc. Nat.*, LXVI. —
Buller, A. H., '02. (V). — **Buresch, J.**, '12. Untersuchungen uber die Zwit-
terdrüse der Pulmonaten: *A. Zf.*, VII. — **Burgeff, H.**, '14-'15. (VII). — **Burrows, M. T.**, '11. Growth of Tissues of the Chick Embryo, etc.: *J. E. Z.*, X. —
Burian, R., '06. (VIII). — **Bury, Janina**, '13. Experimentelle Untersuchungen uber die Einwirkung der Temperatur auf die Entwicklung Echinideneier:
A. Entwm., XXXVI. — **Bütschli, O.**, '71a. Vorläufige Mittheilung uber Bau
und Entwicklung der Samenfäden bei Insecten und Crustaceen: *Z. W. Z.*, XXI. —
'71b. Nähere Mittheilungen über die Entwicklung und der Bau der Samenfäden
der Insecten: *Z. W. Z.*, XXI. — '73. Beiträge zur Kenntniss der Freilebenden
Nematoden: *Nova Acta Acad. Car. Leopold*, XXXVI. — '75. Vorl. Mitteilung
einiger Resultate von Studien uber Conjugation der Infusorien und die Zelltheilung: *Z. W. Z.*, XXV. — '75. Vorläufige Mitteilungen über . . . die ersten
Entwicklungsvorgänge im befruchteten Ei von Nematoden und Schnecken:
Z. W. Z., XXV. — '76. (III). — '82. Gedanken über Leben und Tod: *Z. A.*, V. —
'85. Gedanken uber die Morphologische Bedeutung der sogenannten Richtungskörperchen: *B. C..* IV. — '87-'89. Protozoa III: Bronn's Klassen und Ordnungen

des Tierreichs. — '90. Ueber den Bau der Bakterien und verwandter Organismen: *Leipzig.* — '91. Ueber die sogenannten Centralkörper der Zellen und ihre Bedeutung: *Verh. Naturhist. Med. Ver. Heidelberg.* — '92. Ueber die künstliche Nachahmung der Karyokinetischen Figuren: *Ibid.*, n. s., V. — '92, '94, '08. (I). — '96. Weitere Ausführungen über den Bau der Cyanophyzeen und Bakterien: *Leipzig.* — '01. Meine Ansicht uber die Struktur des Protoplasmas und einige ihrer Kritiker: *A. Entwm.*, XI. — '02. Bemerkungen uber Cyanophyzeen und Bakteria: *A. P.*

CAJAL, S. R., '08. Les conduits de Golgi-Holmgren du protoplasm nerveux, etc.: *Trab. Lab. Invest. Biol. Univ. Madrid*, VI. — '15. (I). — **Calkins, G. N.,** '98. Mitosis in *Noctiluca: J. M.*, XV. — '01, '09. (VII). — '02, '16, '19, '20, '23. (III). — **Calkins and Cull,** '07. The Conjugation of *Paramoecium aurelia (caudatum): A. P.*, X. — **Calkins** and **Gregory.** Variations in the Progeny of a single Ex-conjugant of *Paramoecium: J. E. Z.*, XV. — **Campbell, D. H.,** '88–'89. On the Development of *Pilularia: A. Bot.*, II. — '01. The Embryo Sac of *Peperomia: A. Bot.*, XV. — '03, '05. Studies on the Araceae: *A. B.*, XVII, XIX. — '05. (VII). — '11a. The Endosperm of Angiosperms: *B. G.*, LII. — '11b. The Embryo Sac of *Pandanus: A. B.*, XXV. — **Cannon, W. A.,** '03. Studies in Plant Hybrids. The Spermatogenesis of Hybrid Cotton: *Bull. Torrey Bot. Club*, XXX. — **Carazzi, D.,** '04. Ricerche . . . sull' uovo di *Myzostoma: Mon. Zool. Ital.*, XV. — **Carleton, H. M.,** '20. Observations on the Intranuclear Body in Columnar Epithelium Cells of the Intestine: *Q. J.*, LXIV. — '23. Tissue Culture: *Brit. Journ. Exp. Biol.*, I, 1. — **Carnoy, J. B.,** '84. (Int.). — '85. La cytodiérèse des Arthropodes: *L. C.*, I. — '86. La vésicule germinative et les globules polaires chez quelques Nematodes: *L. C.*, III. — '86. La cytodiérèse de l'œuf: *Ibid.*, III. — '86. La ségmentation de l'œuf chez les Nematodes: *Ibid.*, III. — '97. La fécondation chez *l'Ascaris megalocephala: Ibid.*, XIII. — **Carnoy et Lebrun,** '97, '98, '99. La vésicule germinative et les globules polaires chez les batraciens; I, II, III: *Ibid*,. XII, XIII, XIV, XVII. — **Carothers, E. E.,** '13, '17. (XII). — **Carrol, M.,** '20. An extra Dyad and an extra Tetrad in *Cammula: J. M.*, XXXIV. — **Carruthers, D.,** '11. Contributions to the Cytology of *Helvella crispa: A. B.*, XXV. — **Carter, N.,** '19, '20. Studies on the Chloroplasts of Desmids: *A. Bot.*, XXXIII, XXXIV. **Casteel, D. B.,** '04. (XIII). — '17. Cytoplasmic Inclusions in male Germ-cells of the Fowl-tick, etc.: *J. M.*, XXVIII. — **Castle, W. E.,** '96. The early Embryology of *Ciona: B. M. Z.*, XXVII. — '03, '09. (X). — '11. Heredity in Relation to Evolution and Animal Breeding. — '14. Nabour's Grasshoppers, Multiple Allelomorphism, etc.: *A. N.*, XLVIII. — '19. Is the Arrangement of the Genes in the Chromosome Linear?: *P. N. A.*, V. — '21. A New Type of Inheritance: *Sci ,. n. s.*, LIII. — '22. The Y-Chromosome Type of Sex-linked Inheritance in Man: *Sci.*, LV, 1435. — **Caullery, Maurice,** '06. L'œuf et la génèse des organes: *Revue du mois*, I. — '10. Variation et l'hérédité. Tendances et problèmes actuels: *Ibid.*, X. — '13. (X). — **Cavers, F.,** '14. (IX). — **Cerfontaine, P.,** '06—'07. (XIII). — **Chabry, L.,** '86, '87. (XIV). — **Chamberlain, C. J.,** '99. Oögenesis in *Pinus: B. G.*, XXVII. — '05. Alternation of Generations in Animals from a Botanical Standpoint: *B. G.*, XXXIX. — '09. Spermatogenesis in *Dioön edule: Ibid.*, XLVII. — '10. Fertilization and Embryogeny in *Dioön edule: Ibid.*, L. — '16. *Stangeria paradoxa: Ibid.*, LXI. — **Chambers, R.,** '14. Some Physical Properties of the Cell Nucleus: *Sci.*, XL. — '17a. The visible Structure of the Cell Protoplasm and Death Changes: *A. J. P.*, XLIII. — '17b. (IX). — '18.

The Microdissection Method: *B. B.*, XXXIV. — '19. (II). — '17, '21. (I). — '19. Studies on the Surface-Layer in the living Egg-cell: *P. S. B. M.*, XVII. — '21a. The Formation of the Aster in Artificial Parthenogenesis: *J. G. P.*, IV. — '21b. Studies on the Organization of the Starfish Egg: *J. G. P.*, IV. — '23. The Mechanism of the Entrance of the Sperm into the Starfish Egg: *J. G. P.*, V. — '24. (I). — **Chambers, Conklin, Cowdry** and **others,** '24. (I). — **Champy, C.,** '11. (IX). — '13. (IV). — '13b. La différenciation des tissus cultivés en dehors de l'organisme: *Bibl. Anat.*, XXIII. — **Champy** and **Carleton,** '21. Observation on the Shape of the Nucleus, etc.: *Q. J.*, LXV. — **Charlton, H. H.,** '21. The Spermatogenesis of *Lepisma domestica: B. B.*, XXXV. — **Child, C. M.,** '00. (XIII). — '04. Amitosis in *Moniezia: A. A.*, XXV. — '07. Studies on the Relation between Amitosis and Mitosis, I–III: *B. B.*, XII, XIII; *A. A.*, XXX. — '11a. The Method of Cell Division in *Moniezia: B. B.*, '21. — '11b. A Study of Senescence and Rejuvenescence based on Experiments with *Planaria: A. Entwm.*, XXXI. — '11c. Die physiologische Isolation von Teilen des Organismus, etc.: *Vortr. und Aufs. Entwicklungsm. der Organismen,* XI. *Leipzig, Engelmann.* — '11d. The axial Gradient in *Planaria,* etc.: *J. E. Z.*, X. — '12. Certain dynamic Factors in the regulatory Morphogenesis of *Planaria* in Relation to the axial Gradient: *J. E. Z.*, XIII. — '13. The Nature of the axial Gradients in *Planaria,* etc.: *A. Entwm.*, XXXVII. — '13. The Relation between Resistance to depressing Agents and Rate of Metabolism in *Planaria,* etc.: *J. E. Z.*, XIV. — '14. Starvation, Rejuvenescence and Acclimation in *Planaria: A. Entwm.*, XXXVIII. — '15. (III). — '15a. A Dynamic Conception of the Organic Individual: *Proc. Nat. Acad. Sci.*, I. — '15b. (XIV). — '16. Axial Susceptibility Gradients in Algae: *B. G.*, LXII. — **Christman, A. H.,** '05. Sexual Reproduction in the Rusts: *B. G.*, XXXIX. — '07. (VII). — **Chubb,** '06. The Growth of the Oöcyte in *Antedon: P. T.*, 198. — **Clapp, C. M.,** '91. Some Points in the Development of the Toad-Fish: *J. M.*, V. — **Claussen, P.,** '07. Zur Kenntniss der Kernverhältnisse von *Pyronema: B. D. B. G.*, XXV. — '08. Ueber die Entwicklung und Befruchtung bei *Saprolegnia: B. D. B. G.*, XXVI. — '12. Zur Entwicklungsgeschichte der Ascomyceten: *Bot. L.*, IV. — **Cleland, R. E.,** '19. The Cytology and the Life History of *Nemalion* Ag.: *A. Bot.*, XXXIII. — '22. The Reduction Divisions in the Pollen-mother-cells of *Oenothera: A. J. B.*, IX. — **Clowes, G. H. A.,** '16. (VIII). — **Coe, W. R.,** '99. The Maturation and Fertilization of the Egg of *Cerebratulus: Z. J.*, XII. — **Cohn, Ferd.,** '51. Nachträge zur Naturgeschichte des *Protococcus: Nova Acta,* XXII. — **Cohnheim, O.,** '11. (VIII). — **Coker, W. C.,** '03. On the Gametophytes and Embryo of *Taxodium: B. G.*, XXXVI. — '07. Fertilization and Embryogeny in *Cephalotaxus: B. G.*, XLIII. — **Collin, R.,** '13a. Les mitochondries de la cellule nevroglique, etc.: *C. R. Soc. Anat.*, '13b. Les mitochondries du cylindraxe, etc.: *C. R. S. B.*, LXXIV. — **Collins, E. J.,** '19. Sex Segregation in the Bryophyta: *J. G.*, VIII. — **Conklin, E. G.,** '96, '97, '99, '02, '05a, '05b, '07. (XIII). — '97c. Nuclei and Cytoplasm in the Intestinal Cells of Land Isopods: *A. N.*, Jan. — '99. Protoplasmic Movements as a Factor in Differentiation: *W. H. L.*, '98. — '01. Centrosomes and Spheres in the Maturation, Fertilization and Cleavage of *Crepidula: A. A.*, XIX. — '01. The Individuality of the Germ-nuclei during the Cleavage of the Egg of *Crepidula: B. B.*, II. — '02, '12, '17. (II). — '03a, '05, '17. (XIV). — '03b. The earliest Differentiations in the Egg: *Sci.*, XVII. — '04. (V). — '06. Does Half of an Ascidian Egg give rise to a whole Larva?: *A. Entwm.,* XXI. — '10. The

Effects of centrifugal Force on the Organization and Development of the Eggs of fresh Water Pulmonates: *J. E. Z.*, IX. — '12a, '12b. (I, IX). — '15. Heredity and Environment: *Princeton Univ. Press.* — '15. Why polar Bodies do not develop: *P. N. A.*, I. — '17. The Share of the Egg and the Sperm in Heredity: *P. N. A.*, '19–'20. The Mechanism of Evolution in the Light of Heredity and Development: *Sci. Mo.*, IX, X. — '24. (XIV). — **Cook, M. H.**, '10. Spermatogenesis in Lepidoptera: *P. N. A.*, LXII. — **Cook** and **Swingle**, '05. Evolution of Cellular Structures: *U. S., Dept. Agric. Bur. Plant Ind. Bull.*, '81. — **Correns, C.**, '02. (XII). — '06, '13. (X). — '08. Die Rolle der männlichen Keimzellen bei der Geschlechtsbestimmung der gynodiözischen Pflanzen: *B. D. B. G.*, XXVIa. — '08. Zur Kenntnis der Geschlechtsformen polygamer Blütenpflanzen und ihre Beeinflussbarkeit: *Ibid.*, XLV. — '09. (XIV). — '16. Ueber den Unterschied von tierischen und pflänzlichen Zwittertum: *B. C.*, XXXVI. — '17–'18. Ein Fall von experimenteller Verschiebung des Geschlechtsverhältnisses, etc.: *Sitzb. d. preuss. Akad. d. Wissensch.* — **Correns** and **Goldschmidt**, '13. (X). — **Coulter, J. M.**, '08. Relation of Megaspores to Embryo Sacs in Angiosperms: *B. G.*, XLV. — '11. The Endosperm of Angiosperms: *B. G.*, LII. — '14. (VI). — **Coulter, J. M.**, and **Chamberlain, C. J.**, '03. Morphology of Angiosperms: Chicago. — '10. Morphology of Gymnosperms: *Ibid.* — **Cowdry, E. V.** — '13a. The Relation of Mitochondria and Other Cytoplasmic Constituents in Spinal Ganglion Cells of the Pigeons *Internat. Monatschr. f. Anat. u. Phys.*, XXIX. — '14a. The Vital Staining of Mitochondria with Janus green and Diethylsafranin in Human Blood Cells: *Ibid.*, XXXI. — '14b. The Comparative Distribution of Mitochondria in Spinal Ganglion Cells of Vertebrates: *A. J. A.*, XVII. — '14c. Mitochondria and Neurofibrils: *A. J. A.*, XV. — '16, '18. (I). — '22. The reticular Material as an Indicator of physiologic Reversal, etc.: *A. J. A.*, XXX. — '23. The Independence of Mitochondria and the *Bacillus radicola: A. J. A.*, XXXI. — '24. (IX). — **Cowdry, N. H.**, '17. (I, IX). — '18. The Cytology of the Myxomycetes with special reference to Mitochondria: *B. B.*, XXXV. — '20. Experimental Studies on Mitochondria in Plant Cells: *B. B.*, XXXIX. — **Crampton, H. E.**, '94. (XIII). — '97. The Ascidian Half-Embryo: *Ann. N. Y. Acad. Sci.*, X. — '99. The Ovarian History of the Egg of *Molgula: J. M.*, XV. Suppl. — **Crampton, H. E.** and **Wilson**, '96. (XIV). — **Cuénot**, '99. (X). — **Cunningham, B.**, '17. (VII). — **Cutler, D. Ward**, '17–'18. Natural and Artificial Parthenogenesis in Animals: *Proc. Manch. Lit. and Phil. Soc.*, LXII, 1. — **Czapek, F.**, '11. (VIII). — **Czermak, N.**, '99. Ueber die Desintegration und die Reintegration des Kernkörperchens, etc.: *A. A.*, XV, 22.

DA FANO, C., '21. On Golgi Apparatus of transplantable Tumor Cells: *Rep. Imp. Cancer Res. Fund*, VII. — '22. On Golgi's Internal Apparatus in . . . the mammary Gland: *J. P.*, LVI. — **Dahlgren, K. V. O.**, '15. Der Embryosack von *Plumbagella: A. B.*, XIV. — **Dahlgren** and **Kepner**, '08. (I). — **Dakin, H. D.**, '12. (VIII). — **Dalc, A.**, '21. (VI). — **Danchakoff, V.**, '16. Studies on Cell-division and Cell-differentiation: *J. M.*, XXVII. — **Dangeard, P. A.**, '94, '95. La reproduction sexuelle des Ascomycetes: *Le Botaniste*, IV, V. — '95. Mémoire sur les Chlamydomonadinées, etc.: *Ibid.*, VI. — '01. Étude comparative de la zoöspore et du spermatozoide: *Ibid.*, VII, 6. — '01. Étude sur la structure de la cellule et ses fonctions. *Polytoma: Ibid.*, VIII. — '19. Sur la distinction du chondriome des auteurs en vacuome, plastidome, et sphèrome: *C. R.*, CLXIX. —

'20. Sur l'évolution du système vacuolaire chez les gymnospermes: *C. R.*, CLXX. — '20b. La structure de la cellule végétale et son metabolisme: *Ibid.*, CLXX. — **Davenport, C. B., '12.** Sex-limited Inheritance in Poultry: *J. E. Z.*, XIII. — **Davenport, C. B., '17.** Inheritance of Stature: *G.*, II. — **Davis, B. M., '96.** *A. Bot.*, X. — '98. Kerntheilung in der Tetrasporenmutterzelle bei *Corallina: B. D. B. G.*, XVI. — '99. The Spore-mother-cell of *Anthoceros: B. G.*, XXVIII. — '00. The Fertilization of *Albugo: B. G.*, XXIX. — '01, '03. (VII). — '04–'05. (I). — '05. Fertilization in the Saprolegniales: *B. G.*, XXXIX. — '09. Pollen Development of *Oenothera grandiflora: A. Bot.*, XXIII. — '09–'11. Cytological Studies on *Oenothera: Ibid.*, XXIII, XXIV, XXV. — '10. (VII). — '10. The Reduction Divisions of *Oenothera biennis: B. G.*, XXIV. — '11. A Comparison of the Reduction Divisions of *Oenothera lamarckiana* and *O. gigas: A. B.*, XXV. — **Davis, H. S., '08.** (VI). — **Debaisieux, P., '09.** Les débuts de l'ovogénèse dans le *Dytiscus: L. C.*, XXV. — **Dederer, P. H., '07.** Spermatogenesis in *Philosamia: B. B.*, XIII. — '15. Oögenesis in *Philosamia: J. M.*, XXVI. — '10. Pressure Experiments on the Egg of *Cerebratulus: A. Entwm.*, XXIX. — **Dehorne, A., '11.** Le duplicisme constant du chromosome somatique chez *Salamandra*, etc.: *A. Zf.*, VI. — '14. Sur les Chromosomes de *Corethra: Ass. Fr. Avanc. Sci.*, *C. R.*, XLIII. — '21. Le méchanism de la metaphase, etc., chez *Corethra: C. R.*, CLXXII. — **Deineka, D., '12.** (II). — '12b. Die Morphologie des Zellkerns und die Physik der Kolloide: *Z. f. Chemie u. Indus. d. Kolloide*, XII. — **Delage, Yves, '99.** Sur l'interprétation de la fécondation mérogonique, etc.: *A. Z. E.*, III, VII. — '99. (XIV). — '01. (V). — '01. L'acide carbonique comme agent de choix de la parthénogénèse expérimentale chez les Astéries: *C. R.*, CXXXV. — '03. (Int.). — '08. Élévage de larves parthénogénétiques, etc.: *A. Z. E.*, IV, VII. — **Delage** and **Goldsmith, '13.** (V). — '14. Les facteurs méchaniques de la division cellulaire: *Mercure de France*, CX. — **Della Valle, P., '07.** Osservazione de tetradi in cellule somatiche, etc.: *Atti. Acc. Napoli*, XIII. — '09, '11, '12. (XI). — '11. Le analogie fisico-chimiche della formazione e della dissoluzione dei cromosomi: *Monitore Zool. Ital.*, XX. — **Dellinger, O. P., '09.** The Cilium as a Key to the Structure of Contractile Protoplasm: *J. M.*, XX. — **Delsman, H. C., '12.** (XIII). — **Demoll, R., '13.** Ueber Geschlechtsbestimmung, etc.: *Z. J.*, *Allg. Zool.*, XXXIII. — **Demoor, J., '95.** Contribution à l'étude de la physiologie de la cellule: *A. B.*, XIII. — **Dendy, A., '88.** Studies on the Comparative Anatomy of Sponges: *Q. J.*, Dec. — '14–'15. The Gametogenesis of *Grantia: Ibid.*, LX. — **Derschau, M. V., '08.** Beiträge zur pflänzlichen Mitose: *J. W. B.*, XLVI. — '11. Ueber Kernbrücken und Kernsubstanz in pflänzlichen Zellen: *A. Zf.*, VIII, 3. — '14. (IX). — **Deton, W., '08.** " l'Étape synaptique " dans le *Thysanozoön: L. C.*, XXV. — **Devisé, R., '21.** (II). — **Digby, L., '05.** On the Cytology of Apogamy and Apospory, II: *P. R. S.*, LXXVI. — '09. Observations on " Chromatin Bodies " and their Relation to the Nucleolus in *Galtonia: A. B.*, XXIII. — '10. (VI). — '12. (XI). — '14. A critical Study of the Cytology of *Crepis virens: A. Zf.*, XII. — '19. The Archesporial and Meiotic Mitoses in *Osmunda: A. Bot.*, CXXX. — **Dimpker, A. M., '17.** (XIII). — **Divaz, N., '14.** Die Spermatogenese von *Naucoris cimicoides: Z. A.*, XLV. — **Dixon, H. H., '94.** Fertilization of *Pinus: A. Bot.*, VIII. — '96. On the Chromosomes of *Lilium longiflorum: Proc. R. Ir. Ac.*, III. — **Dobell, C., '08.** The Structure and Life-History of *Copromonas: Q. J.*, LII, 205. — '09. (IX). — '11. Contributions to the Cytology of the Bacteria: *Q. J.*, LVI. — '13. Observations on the Life History of . . . *Arach-*

nula: A. P., XXXI. — '14a. (III). — '14b. Cytological Studies on three Species of *Amoeba: A. P.*, XXIV. — **Dodds, G. S.**, '10. (IV). — **Dodel, A.**, '76. *Ulothrix zonata: J. W. B.*, X. — **Doflein, F. J.**, '13. (III). — '16. (VII). — '16. *Polytomella agilis: Z. A.*, XLVII. — **Dogiel, A. S.**, '90. Zur Frage über das Epithel der Harnblase: *A. M. A.*, XXXV. — **Dogiel, V.**, '23. The Transformation of the male Pronucleus into a Spermatozoön: *Zootom. Lab. Univ. Petrograd.* — **Doncaster, L.**, '06. On the Maturation of the Unfertilized Eggs and the Fate of the Polar Bodies in the Tenthredinidae: *Q. J.*, XLIX. — '07. Gametogenesis and Fertilization in *Nematus: Q. J.*, LI. — Correction of the above: *Nature*, LXXXII, and *Sci.*, XXXI. — '08. On Sex Inheritance in the Moth, *Abraxas grossulariata: 4th Rep. Evol. Comm., R. Soc. Lond.* — '08. Animal Parthenogenesis: *Science Progress.* — '10, '11, '16. Gametogenesis of the Gall-fly, *Neuroterus lenticularis:* I, II, III: *P. R. S.*, XXXII–XXXIV. — '11. Some Stages in the Spermatogenesis of *Abraxas grossulariata,* etc.: '11. The Chromosomes in the Oögenesis and Spermatogenesis of *Pieris brassicae* and the Oögenesis of *Abraxas grossulariata: J. G.*, II, 3. — '14. (X). — '14b. (XII). — '14c. On the Relation between Chromosomes, Sex-limited Transmission and Sex-determination in *Abraxas grossulariata: J. G.*, IV. — '20. (I). — **Doncaster** and **Cannon**, '20. On the Spermatogenesis of the Louse, etc.: *Q. J.*, LXIV. — **Doncaster** and **Gray**, '11. Cytological Observations on Cross-fertilized Echinoderm Eggs: *Proc. Camb. Phil. Soc.*, XVI. — '13. Cytological Observations on the Early Stages of Segmentation of *Echinus* Hybrids: *Q. J.*, LVIII. — **Doncaster** and **Raynor**, '06. Breeding Experiments with Lepidoptera: *Proc. Zool. Soc. Lond.* — **Douin, C.**, '09. Nouvelles observations sur *Sphaerocarpos: Rev. Bryol.*, XXXVI. — **Driesch, H.**, '92. Entwicklungsmechanisches: *A. A.*, VII, '18. — '92. Entwicklungsmechanische Studien, I, II: *Z. W. Z.*, LIII. — '93. III–VI, *Ibid.*, LV. — '93. VII–X, *M. Z. S.*, XI. — '92a, '94, '96, '99a, '99b, '00, '06a, '06b, '07, '08a, '08b. (XIV). — '92b. 2. Ueber einige allgemeine Fragen der theoretischen Morphologie: *Ibid.*, LV. — '93. Ueber einige allgemeine entwicklungsmechanische Ergebnisse: *M. Z. S.*, XI, 2. — '93. Entwicklungsmechanische Studien: *Z. W. Z.*, LV. — '95. Zur Analysis der Potenzen embryonaler Organzellen: *A. Entwm.*, II. — '95. Entwicklungsmechanische Studien, IX: *M. Z. S.*, XI. — '96. (XIV). — '98. Ueber rein-mütterliche Charaktere and Bastardlarven von Echiniden: *A. Entwm.*, VII. — '98. Von der Beendigung morphogener Elementarprozesse: *A. Entwm.*, VI. — '00. Die Verschmelzung der Individualität, etc.: *A. Entwm.*, X. — '01a. Vorbereitungen zu einer Theorie des Lebens: *Leipzig.* — '01b. Die organische Regulationen: *Leipzig, Engelmann.* — '02. Neue Antworten und neue Fragen: *Erg., Merkel u. Bonnet.* XI. — '02. Neue Ergänzungen zur Entwickelungsphysiologie des Echinidenkeimes: *A. Entwm.*, XIV, 3, 4. — '02. Die restitutionem der *Clavellina: A. Entwm.*, XIV. — '03. Drei Aphorismen zur Entwicklungsphysiologie jüngster Studien: *A. Entwm.*, XVII, 1. — '03. Ueber Seeigelbastarde: *A. Entwm.*, XVI, 4. — '03. Ueber Aenderung der Regulationsfähigkeiten im Verlauf der Entwicklung bei Ascidien: *Ibid.*, XVII. — '05. Zur Cytologie parthenogenetischer Larven von *Strongylocentrotus: A. Entwm.*, XIX. — '05. Der Vitalismus: *Leipzig.* — '06. Die Physiologie der tierischen Form: *E. P.*, V, 1, 2. — '07. Die Entwicklungsphysiologie, '05–'08: *E. A. E.*, XVII. — '08. Zur Theorie der organischen Symmetrie: *A. Entwm.*, XXVI. — '10. Neue Versuche uber die Entwicklung verschmolzener Echinidenkeime: *A. Entwm.*, XXX. — **Driesch** and **Morgan, T. H.**, '95. Zur Analyse der ersten Entwicklungsstadien des Ctenophoreneies·

A. Entwm., II. — **Drüner, L.,** '94. Zur Morphologie der Centralspindel: *J. Z.*, XXVIII. — '95. Studien über den Mechanismus der Zelltheilung: *J. Z.*, XXIX. — **Dubreuil, G.,** '13. Le chondriome de le dispositif de l'activité sécrétaire: *A. A. M.*, XV. — **Duesberg, J.,** '07. Der Mitochondrialapparat in den Zellen der Wirbeltiere und Wirbellosen: *A. M. A.*, LXXI. — '08. Sur l'existence de mitochondries dans l'œuf et l'embryon d'*Apis mellifica: A. A.*, XXXII. — '09. Ueber Chondriosomen und ihre Verwendung zu Myofibrillen beim Hühnerembryo: *V. A. G.*, XXXIV. — '09. Note complémentaire sur la spermatogénèse du rat: *A. Zf.*, III. — '09. Les chondriosomes der cellules embryonnaires du poulet, etc.: *A. Zf.*, IV. — '09. La spermatogénèse chez le rat: *Ibid.*, II. — '10. (IV). — '11, '13, '15. (IX). — '12, '14. (I). — '17. Chondriosomes in the Cells of Fish Embryos: *A. J. A.*, XXI. — '18. Chondriosomes in the Testicle-cells of *Fundulus. A. J. A.*, XXIII. — '19. On the Present Status of the Chondriosome-problem: *B. B.*, XXXVI. — '20. (IV). — **Duesberg** et **Hoven,** '10. Observations sur la structure du protoplasme des cellules végétales: *A. A.*, XXXVI. — **Dujardin, F.,** '35. Sur les prétendus estomacs des animalcules infusories et sur une substance appelée sarcode: *A. S. N., Zool.*, II, 4. — **Dupler, A. W.,** '17. The Gametophytes of *Taxus canadensis Marsh.: B. G.*, LXIV. — **Düsing, C.,** '86. Die Regulierung des Geschlechtsverhältnisses, etc.: *J. Z.*, XIX. — **Dutrochet, H. J.,** '37. Mémoires pour servir à l'histoire anatomique et physiologique des végétaux et des animaux:

    EAST, E. M., '13. Xenia and the Endosperm of Angiosperms: *B. G.*, LVI. — '15. (XII). — **East** and **Hayes,** '12. (III). — **Ebeling, A. H.,** '22. A ten-year old Strain of Fibroblasts: *J. Exp. Med.*, XXV, 6. — **Ebner, V. v.,** '71. Untersuchungen über den Bau der Samencanälchen, etc.: *Inst. Phys. u. Hist. Graz.* (*Leipzig*). — '88. Zur Spermatogenese bei den Säugethieren: *A. M. A.*, XXXI. — **Edwards, C. L.,** '10. The Idiochromosomes in *Ascaris*, etc.: *A. Zf.*, V, 3. — '11. The Sex-chromosomes in *Ascaris felis: A. Zf.*, VII. — **Ehrlich, P.,** '79. Ueber die specifischen Granulationen des Blutes: *A. A. P.* (*Phys.*). — **Ehrlich, Krause, Mosse, Rosin,** '10. Enzyklopädie der Mikroscopischen Technique: *Berlin, Wien.* Article on Färbungen by L. Michaelis. — **Eigenmann, C. H.,** '90. On the Egg-membranes and Micropyle, etc.: *B. M. Z.*, XIX. — **Eisen, G.,** '99. The Chromoplasts and the Chromioles: *B. C.*, XIX, 4. — '00. The Spermatogenesis of *Batrachoseps: J. M.*, XVII. — **Eisig, H.,** '99. (XIII). — **Eklof, H.,** '14. Chondriosomenstudien an den Epithel- und Drüsenzellen des Magen-Darmkanals, etc.: *A. Hf.*, I, *Abt.*, LI. — **Elpatiewsky, W.,** '09. Die Urgeschlechtzellenbildung bei *Sagitta: A. A* ., XXXV. — '10. Entwicklungsgeschichte der Genitalprodukte bei *Sagitta: Biol. Zeitschr.* (*Moscow*), I. — **Emberger, L.,** '20a. Évolution du chondriome chez les cryptogames vasculaires: *C. R.*, CLXX. — '20b. Évolution du chondriome dans la formation du sporange chez les fougères: *Ibid.*, CLXX. — **Engelmann, T. W.,** '80. Zur Anatomie und Physiologie der Flimmerzellen: *A. Ph.*, XXIII. — **Enriques, P.,** '07, '09, '16. (VII). — '11. La Teoria Cellulare: *Bologna:* — **Entz, G.,** '18. (IX). — **Erdmann, R.,** '09, '13. (IX). — '10. Depression und fakultative Apogamy bei *Amoeba diploidea: Festschr. R. Hertwig*, I. — '15. Endomixis und ihre Bedeutung für die Infusorienzelle: *S. B. d. Ges. naturf. Freunde Berlin.* — **Erhard, H.,** '11. (IX). — **Erlanger, R. v.,** '96. Die neuesten Ansichten über die Zelltheilung und ihre Mechanik: *Z. C.*, III, 2. — '96. Die Entwicklung der männlichen Geschlechtszellen: *Z. C.*, III, 12. — '96.

Neuere Ansichten uber die Struktur des Protoplasmas: *Z. C.*, III, 8, 9. — '97. Beobachtungen über die Befruchtung und ersten Teilungen an den lebenden Eiern kleiner Nematoden *B. C.*, XVII. — '97. Ueber die Spindelbildung in den Zellen der Cephalopoden Keimscheibe: *B. C.*, XVII. — '97. Beiträge zur Kenntniss des Protoplasmas, etc.: *A. M. A.*, XLIX. — '98. Zur Befruchtung des Ascariseies, etc.: *Z. A.*, XIX. — **Ernst, A.**, '02. Chromosomenreduction, etc.: *Flora*, XCI. — '18. Bastardierung als Ursache der Apogamie in Pflanzenreich: *Jena.* — **Errera,** '86. Eine fundamentale Gleichgewichtsbedingung organischen Zellen: *B. D. B. G.* — '87. Zellformen und Seifenblasen: 60 *Versamml. Naturf. und Aerzte Wiesbaden.* — **Escoyez, E.,** '07. Le noyau et la caryocinèse chez le *Zygnema: L. C.*, XXIV. — '07. (IX). — '09. Caryocinèse, centrosome et kinoplasme dans le *Stypocaulon: L. C.*, XXIV. — **Esmarch, G. v.,** '02. *Centralbl. f. Bakteriol.*, XXXII. — **Ewart, A. J.,** '03. On the Physics and Physiology of Protoplasmic Streaming in Plants: *Oxford.* — **Ewing, H. E.,** '16. Eighty-seven Generations in a Parthogenetic Pure Line of *Aphis: B. B.*, XXXI. — **Eycleshymer, A.,** '04. The Cytoplasmic and nuclear Changes in the striated Muscle Cell of *Necturus: A. J. A.*, III.

FAIRCHILD, D. G., '97. Ueber Kerntheilung und Befruchtung bei *Basidiobolus: J. W. B.*, XXX. — **Farmer, J. B.,** '94. Studies in Hepaticae: *A. Bot.*, VIII, 29. — '95b. On Spore-formation and Nuclear Division in the Hepaticae: *A. Bot.*, IX. — '07. On the Structural Constituents of the Nucleus, etc.: *P. R. S.*, LXXIX. — '12. Telosynapsis and Parasynapsis: *A. Bot.*, XXVI. — **Farmer** and **Digby,** '07. (V). — '10. On the Somatic and Heterotype Mitoses in *Galtonia candicans: Rep. Brit. Assn.* Sheffield. — '10. On the Cytological Features exhibited by certain Varietal and Hybrid Ferns: *A. Bot.*, XXIV. — '14. On Dimensions of Chromosomes, etc.: *P. T.*, 205. — **Farmer** and **Moore,** '95. On the Essential Similarities existing Between the Heterotype Nuclear Divisions in Animals and Plants: *A. A.*, XI, 3. — '03. New Investigations in the Reduction Phenomena of Animals and Plants: *P. T.*, LXXII. — '05. (VI). — **Farmer, Moore,** and **Digby,** '03. On the Cytology of Apogamy and Apospory; I: *P. R. S.*, LXXI. — **Farmer** and **Shove,** '05. On the Structure and Development of the Somatic and Heterotype Chromosomes of *Tradescantia: Q. J.*, XLVIII. — **Farmer** and **Williams,** '96. On Fertilization, etc., in *Fucus: A. Bot.*, X. — '98. (VII). — **Farr, C. H.,** '18. Cell-Division by Furrowing in Magnolia: *A. J. B.*, V. — **Fasten, N.,** '14. Spermatogenesis of the American crayfish, etc.: *J. M.*, XXV. — '18. Spermatogenesis of the Pacific Coast edible Crab, *Cancer magister: B. B.*, XXXIV. — **Fauré-Fremiet, E.,** '07. Mitochondries et sphèroplastes chez les Infusoires ciliés: *C. R. S. B.*, LXII. — '08. Évolution de l'appareil mitochondrial dans l'œuf de *Julus: C. R. S. B.*, LXIV. — '10. (I, IV). — '10a. Mitochondries et liposomes; *C. R. S. B.*, LXII. — '10b. La continuité des mitochondries a travers des générations cellulaires et le rôle de ces éléments: *A. A.*, XXXVI. — '13. Le cycle germinatif chez l'*Ascaris megalocephala: A. A. M.*, XV. — '21. Constitution de l'œuf de *Sabellaria: C. R.*, CLXXIII. — **Fauré-Fremiet** et **du Vivier de Streel,** '21. Composition chémique de l'œuf et du têtard de *R. temporaria: C. R.*, CLXXIII. — **Faust, E. C.,** '13. Size Dimorphism in Adult Spermatozoa of *Anasa: B. B.*, XXV. — '15. Size Dimorphism in the Spermatozoa for single testes: *J. E. Z.*, XVIII, 2. — **Federley, H.,** '12. Das Verhalten der Chromosomen bei der Spermatogenese der Schmetterlinge, etc.: *Z. A. V.*, IX. — '14. Ein Beitrag zur Kenntniss der Spermatogenese bei Mischlingen, etc.: *Finska Vetenskaps-Soc. Forhandl.*, LVI. — **Ferguson, M. C.,** '01a. The Development of the Egg and Fertilization in *Pinus A. Bot.*, XV. — '01b. The Development of the Pollen Tube and the Division of the generative Nucleus in certain Species of *Pinus: Ibid.*, XV. — '04. Contributions to the Life History of *Pinus: Proc. Washington Acad. Sci.*, VI. — '13. Included Cytoplasm in Fertilization: *B. G.*, LVI. — **Fick, R.,** '93. Ueber die Reifung und Befruchtung des Axolotl: *Z. W. Z.*, LVI. — '05. (XI). — '06. (VI, XII. — '08. Zur Konjugation der Chromosomen: *A. Zf.*, I. — '09. Bemerkungen zu Boveris Aufsatz über die Blastomerenkerne von *Ascaris* und die Theorie der Chromosomen: *A. Zf.*, III. — **Firket, J.,** '11. Recherches sur la génèse des fibrilles épidermiques chez le poulet: *A. A.*, XXXVIII. — '14. Recherches sur l'organogénèse des glandes sexuelles: *A. B.*, XXIX. — **Fischel,** '97, '98, '03. (XIV). — '99. *A. Entwm.*, XXII. — '06. Zur Entwicklungsgeschichte der Echinodermen: *A. Entwm.*, XXII. — '06. Ueber Bastardierungsversuche bei Echinodermen: *A. Entwm.*, XXII. — **Fischer, A.,** '94. Untersuchungen über Bakterien: *J. W. B.*, XXVII. — '94a. Zur Kritik der Fixierungsmethoden der Granula: *A. A.*, IX. — '94b. Ueber die Geisseln einiger Flagellaten: *J. W. B.*, XXVII. — '95. Neue Beiträge sur Kritik der Fixierungsmethoden: *A. A.*, X. — '99. (I). — '03. Vorlesungen über Bakterien. 2 Aufl.: *Jena.* — '05. (IX). **Flemming, W.,** '75. Studien an der Entwicklungsgeschichte der Najaden: *Sitzb. d. k. k. Akad. Wiss. Wien.*, LXXI, 3. — '76. Beobachtungen über die Beschaffenheit des Zellkerns: *A. M. A.*, XIII. — '79a, '80, '81. (Int., II). — '79b. Ueber das Verhalten des Kernes bei der Zelltheilung, etc.: *Virchow's Arch.*, LXXVII. — '82. (Int.). — '87. Neue Beiträge zur Kenntniss der Zelle, II: *A. M. A.*, XXXVII. — '92. Ueber Unsichbarkeit lebender Kernstrukturen: *A. A.*, VII. — '95. Zur Mechanik der Zelltheilung: *A. M. A.*, XLVI. — '96. Ueber Intercellularlücken des Epithels, etc.: *An. Hf.*, VI, 17. — '97. Ueber den Bau der Bindegesgewebezellen, etc.: *Z. B.*, XXXIV. — **Floderus, M.,** '96. Ueber die Bildung der Follikelbilden bei den Ascidien: *Z. W. Z.*, LXI, 2. — **Fol, H.,** '73. Die erste Entwickelung des Geryonideies: *J. Z.*, VII. — '75. Sur le développement des Ptéropodes: *A. de Zool.*, IV. — '75. Études sur le développement des Mollusques: '76. Sur les phénomènes de la division cellulaire: *C. R.*, LXXXIII. — '77. Sur le commencement de l'hénogénie chez divers animaux: *Arch. Sci. Nat. et Phys. Genève*, LVIII. See also *A. Z. E.*, VI. — '79. (Int.). — '91. Die "Centrenquadrille," ein neue Episode aus der Befruchtungsgeschichte: *A. A.*, VI; also in *Arch. des Sci. Phys. et Nat.*, 15 Avril, '91. — **Fontana,** '81. Sur la structure primitive du corps animal: In *Traité sur le venin de la vipère, Florence.* — **Foot** and **Strobell, E. C.,** '05. Prophases and Metaphase of the first Maturation Spindle of *Allolobophora: A. J. A.*, IV. — '10. Pseudoreduction in the Oögenesis of *Allolobophora: A. Zf.*, V. — '11. Amitosis in the Ovary of *Protenor belfragi*, etc.: *A. Zf.*, VII. — '12. A Study of Chromosomes and Chromatin Nucleoli in *Euschistus: A. Zf.*, IX. — '13. Preliminary Note on the Results of Crossing Two Hemipterous Species, etc.: *B. B.*, XXIV. — **Forenbacher, A.,** '11. Die Chondriosomen als Chromatophorenbildner: *B. D. B. G.*, XXIX. — *Fortpflanzung der Gewächse.* (VII). — **Francotte, P.,** '97. Recherches sur la maturation, etc., chez les Polyclades: *A. Z. E.*, VI. Also *Mém. Cour. Acad. Belg.*, LV. — **Fraser, H. C. I.,** '07. On the Sexuality and Development of the Ascocarp of *Lachnea: A. Bot.*, XXI. — '08. Contributions to the Cytology of *Humaria: A. Bot.*, XXII. — '12. The Pairing of the Chromosomes: *N. P.*, XI. — '14. The Behavior of the Chromatin in the

Meiotic Divisions of *Vicia: A. Bot.*, XXVIII. — **Fraser** and **Snell,** '11. The vegetative Divisions in *Vicia: A. Bot.*, XXV, VI. — **Fraser, H. C. I.**, and **Welsford, E. J.**, '08. Further Contributions to the Cytology of the Ascomycetes: *A. A.*, XXII. — **Frederikse, A. M.**, '22. Études sur l'Ovogénèse des Dytiscides: *A. B.*, XXXII. — **Fries, W.**, '10. Die Entwicklung der Chromosomen im Ei von *Branchipus,* etc.: *A. Zf.*, IV. — **Frisendahl, A.**, '12. Cytologische und entwicklungsgeschichtliche Studien an *Myricaria: Kgl. Svensk. Vet. Handl.*, XLVIII. — **Fritsch, F. E.**, '05, '07. (IX). — **Frolowa, S.**, '13. Idiochromosomen bei *Ascaris megalocephala: A. Zf.*, IX. — **Fromman, C.**, '65. Ueber die Struktur der Bindesubstanzzellen des Rückenmarks: *Centrl. f. med. Wiss.*, III, 6. — '75. Zur Lehre von der Struktur der Zellen: *J. Z.*, IX. — '84. Untersuchungen über Struktur, Lebenserscheinungen und Reactionen thierischer und pflänzlicher Zellen: *J. Z.*, XVII. — **Fulton, John F.**, '22. Animal Chlorophyll, etc.: *Q. J.*, LXVI, 2. (Lit.). — **Furth, O. v.**, '12. (VIII).

GAJEWSKA, H., '17. Ueber die morphologischen Veränderungen des Kern- und Plasmasubstanzen im Verlaufe des Wachstums der Oöcyten: *A. Zf.*, XIV, 4. — **Gaidukov, N.**, '10. Dunkelfeldbeleuchtung und Ultramikroscopie: *Jena.* — **Gallardo, A.**, '96. Essai d'interprétation des figures karyokinétiques: *Ann. Mus. Nac. de Buenos Aires*, V. — '06. L'interprétation bipolaire de la division karyocinétique: *Ibid.*, VI. — '09. (II). — '09. Bipolaridad de la division celular: *Rev. del Mus. de La Plata* (2), III. — **Galtsoff, P. S.**, '23. The amoeboid Movement of dissociated Sponge Cells: *B. B.*, XLV. — '24. Regeneration after Dissociation (*In press*). — **Gardiner, E. G.**, '98. The Growth of the Ovum, etc., in *Polychaerus: J. M.*, XV. — **Gardiner, W.**, '83. Continuity of Protoplasm in Vegetable Cells: *Phil. Trans.*, CLXXIV. — '84. On the Continuity of the Protoplasm through the Walls of Vegetable Cells: *Arb. Bot. Inst. Würzburg*, III. — '97. The Histology of the Cell Wall, etc.: *P. R. S.*, LXII. — '00. The Genesis and Development of the Wall and connecting Threads of the Plant Cell: *Ibid.*, LXVI. — **Gardner, N. L.**, '06. Cytological Studies in Cyanophyceae: *Univ. Calif. Publ. Bot.* — **Gardiner** and **Hill**, '01. The Histology of the Cell Wall with special Reference to the Mode of Connexion of Cells: *P. T.*, CXCIV. — **Gatenby, J. B.**, '17a, '17b, '18, '19a, '19b, '20a, '20b, '20c, '21, '22. (IV). — '17. The Degenerate (apyrene) Sperm-formation of Moths, etc.: *Q. J.*, LXII. — '17. The Embryonic Development of *Trichogramma,* etc.: *Ibid.* — '18a. The Segregation of the Germ-Cells in *Trichogramma: Ibid.*, LXIII. — '18b. Polyembryony in Parasitic Hymenoptera: *Ibid.* — '19. (I). — '20a. Further Notes on the Oögenesis and Fertilization of *Grantia: J. R. M.*, III. — '20b. *Grantia compressa: J. Linn. Soc.* — '22b. Gametogenesis of *Ornithorhyncus: Q. J.*, LXVI. — **Gatenby** and **Woodger**, '20. (IV). — **Gates, R. R.**, '07. Pollen Development in Hybrids of *Oenothera: B. G.*, XLIII. — '08. (VI). — '09. The Behavior of the Chromosomes in *Oenothera lata x O. gigas: Ibid.*, XLVIII. — '09, '13, '20, '24. (XI). — '10, '15, '23. (XII). — '11. The Mode of Chromosome Reduction: *Ibid.*, LI. — '11. Pollen Formation in *Oenothera gigas: A. Bot.*, XXV. — '12. Somatic Mitoses in *Oenothera: A. Bot.* — '24. (XI). — **Gates** and **Rees**, '21. (VI). — **Gates** and **Thomas**, '14. (XII). — **Gaudissart, P.**, '13. Réseau protoplasmique et chondriosomes dans la génèse des myofibrilles: *L. C.*, XXX. — **Geddes** and **Thompson**, '99. (X). — **Geerts, J. M.**, '09. Beiträge zur Kenntniss der Cytologie und der partiellen Sterilität in *Oenothera lamarckiana: Rec. Trav. Bot.*

Néerland., V. — '11. Cytologische Untersuchungen einiger Bastarde von *Oenothera gigas: B. D. B. G.*, XXIX, 3. — **Gegenbaur, C.**, '54. Beiträge zur näheren Kenntniss der Schwimmpolypen: *Z. W. Z.*, V.—**Geinitz, B.**, '15. Ueber Abweichungen bei der Eireifung von *Ascaris: A. Zf.*, XIII. —**Gelei, J.**, '13. Ueber die Ovogenese von *Dendrocoelum lacteum: A. Zf.*, XI. — '21, '22. (VI). — **Georgevitch, P.**, '08. Zur Nukleolusfrage, etc.: *Beih. Bot. Centr.*, XXIII. — '10a. Preliminary Note on Apospory and Apogamy in *Trichomanes: A. Bot.*, XXIV: *J. W. B.*, XLVIII. — **Gérard, '09.** Recherches sur la spermatogénèse chez *Stenobothrus: A. B.*, XXIV. — **Gerassimoff, J.**, '00. Ueber die Lage und die Function des Zellkerns: *Bull. Soc. Imp. Natur., Moscow.* — '01. Ueber den Einfluss des Kerns auf das Wachstums der Zelle: *Ibid.* — '02. Die Abhängigkeit der Grösse der Zelle von Menge ihrer Kernmasse: *Zeitsch. f. allgem. Physiol.*, I. — **Gerould, J. H.**, '06. (XIII). — '11. The Inheritance of Polymorphism and Sex in *Colias philodice: A. N.*, XLV. — '22. (Int.). — **Giard, A.**, '77. Sur la signification morphologique des globules polaires, etc.: *B. S. F. B.*, XXII. — **Giardina, '01.** (IV). — **Gierke, H.**, '85. Färberei zu mikroskopischen Zwecken: *Z. W. M.*, II. — **Giglio-Tos** and **Granata, '08.** I mitocondri nelle cellule seminali maschili di *Pamphagus: Biologica*, II. — **Girgolaff, S. S.**, '11. Kompressionsversuche am befruchteten Ei der *Ascaris: A. M. A.*, LXXVI. — **Gille, K.**, '14. Untersuchungen uber die Eireifung, Befruchtung, und Zellteilung von *Gyrodactylus: A. Zf.*, XII. — **Gläser, H.**, '12. Ueber die Teilung einiger Amöben, etc.: *A. P.*, XXV. — **Glaser, O. C.**, '05. Ueber den Kannibalismus bei *Fasciolaria*, etc.: *Z. W. Z.*, LXXX. — '08. A Statistical Study of Mitosis and Amitosis in the Entoderm of *Fasciolaria: B. B.*, XIV. — '14a. The Change in Volume of *Arbacia* and *Asterias* Eggs in Fertilization: *B. B.*, XXVI. — '14b. On inducing Development in the Sea-urchin, etc.: *Sci.*, XXXVIII. — **Godlewsky, E.**, '97a. Ueber mehrfache bipolar Mitose bei der Spermatogenese von *Helix: Anz. Akas. Wiss. Krakau.* — '97b. Weitere Untersuchungen über die Umwandlung der Spermatiden, etc.: *Ibid.* — '06, '08, '09, '13. (XIV). — '10, Plasma und Kernsubstanz bei der Regeneration der Amphibien: *A. Entwm.* XXX. — '11. Kombination der heterogenen Befruchtung mit der künstlichen Parthenogenese: *Ibid.*, XXXIII, 1, 2. — '18. (VI). — **Goebel, U.** Ueber sexuellen Dimorphismus bei Pflanzen: *B. C.*, XXX. — **Goette, A.**, '07. (IV). — **Goldschmidt, R.**, '02. Untersuchungen über die Eireifung, Befruchtung, etc.: *Z. W. Z.*, LXXI. — '05. Eireifung, Befruchtung und Embryonalentwicklung des *Zoogonus mirus: Z. J., Abt. f. Anat. u. Ont.*, XXI. — '08a. Ueber das Verhalten des Chromatins bei der Eireifung, u. s. w., des *Dicrocoelium: A. Zf.*, I. — '08b. Die Chromatinreifung des Geschlechtzellen des *Zoögonus* und die Primärtypus der Reduktion: *A. Zf.*, II. — '11-'14. Erblichkeitstudien an Schmetterlingen: I u. II, *Z. A. V.*, VII and XI. — '12. Bemerkungen zur Vererbung des Geschlechtspolymorphismus: *Ibid.*, VIII. — '13. (XII, XIV). — '15. Some Experiments on Spermatogenesis *in vitro: P. N. A., Washington*, I. — '16. Experimental Intersexuality and the Sex-Problem: *A. N.*, L. — '16. Genetic Factors and Enzyme Reaction: *Sci.*, XLIII. — '16. A Preliminary Report on Further Experiments in Inheritance and Determination of Sex: *P. N. A.*, II. — '16. Theodor Boveri: *Sci.*, XLIII. — '17. Crossing Over ohne Chiasmatypie: G, II. — '17. On a Case of Facultative Parthenogenesis in the Gypsy-moth, *Lymantria*, etc.: *B. B.*, XXXII. — '17. A Further Contribution to the Theory of Sex: *J. E. Z.*, XXII. — Intersexualität und Geschlechtsbestimmung: *B. Z.*, XXXIX. — '20a, '20b. (X). — '20c. Die Spermatogenese eines parthenogenetischen Frosches: *A. Zf.*, XV. — '20d. Die Bedeutung der atypischen Spermatozoen: *Ibid.*, XV. — '20. Kleine Beobachtungen u. Ideen zur Zellenlehre, II: *A. Zf.*, XV. — '23a. Die Sammelchromosomen der Schmetterlinge: *Ibid.*, XVII. — '23. Untersuchungen über Intersexualität, III: *Z. J.*, *Abst. Vererb.*, XXI. — **Goldschmidt** and **Popoff**, '07. Die Caryokinese der Protozoa und der Chromidialapparat der Protozoen- und Metazoenzelle: *A. P.*, VIII. — **Goldsmith, W. M.**, '19. A comparative Study of the Chromosomes of the Tiger Beetles: *J. M.*, XXXII. — **Golgi, C.**, '98. Sur la structure des cellules nerveuses: *A. I. B.*, XXX. — '09. Sur une fine particularité de structure de l'epithélium, etc.: *A. I. B.*, LI. — **Goodale, H. D.**, '10. Some Results of Castration in Ducks: *B. B.*, XX. — '13. Castration in Relation to the Secondary Sexual Characters of Brown Leghorns: *A. N.*, XLVII. — '16. Gónadectomy in Relation to the Secondary Sexual Characters.of Some Domestic Birds: *P. C. I.*, CCXLIII. — **Goodrich, H. B.**, '16. (X). — '20. Rapidity of Activation in the Fertilization of *Nereis: B. B.*, XXXVIII. — **Goodsir, J.**, '45. Anatomical and Pathological Observations: *Edinburgh.* — **Goroschankin, J.**, '83. Zur Kenntniss der Corpuscula bei den Gymnospermen: *B. Z.*, LXI. — **Gould, H. N.**, '17. Studies on Sex in the Hermaphrodite Mollusc, *Crepidula plana*, I. — **Govaerts, P.**, '13. Recherches sur la structure de l'ovaire des insects: *A. B.*, XXVIII. — **Graham, M.**, '18. Centrosomes in Fertilization Stages of *Preissia: A. Bot.*, XXXII. — **Granata, L.**, '10. (VI). — **Gray, J.**, '13. The Effects .of Hypertonic Solutions upon the Fertilized Eggs of *Echinus: Q. J.*, LVIII. — '16. The electrical Conductivity of Echinoderm Eggs, etc.: *Phil. Trans.* 207 B. — '22. A critical Study of the Facts of Artificial Parthenogenesis, etc.: *Q. J.*, LXVI. — **Grégoire, V.**, '99. Les cinèses pollinques chez les Liliacées: *L. C.*, XVI. — '04. Le reduction numérique des chromosomes et les cinèses de maturation: *L. C.*, XXI. — '05, '10. (VI). — '06. (II, XI). — '07. La formation des gemini hétérotypiques dans les végétaux: *Ibid.*, XXIV. — '08. Theories courantes sur l'hérédité mendélienne: *Ann. Soc. Zool. Mal. Belgique*, XLII. — '09a. La reduction dans le *Zoögonus* et le " Primärtypus ": *L. C.*, XXV. — '09. Les phénomènes de l'étape synaptique, etc.: *L. C.*, XXV. — '11. Les recherches de Mendel et des mendélistes sur l'hérédité: *Rev. des Quest. Sci.*, Oct., '11, Apr., '12. — '12. Les phénomènes de la métaphase et de l'anaphase dans la caryocinèse somatique, etc.: *Ann. Soc. Sci. Bruxelles*, XXXIV. — '12. La vérité du schema hétéro-homéotypique: *C. R.*, 155. — '13. La télophase et la prophase dans la caryocinèse somatique: *Ibid.*, CLVI. — **Grégoire** et **Berghs**, '04. La figure achromatique dans le *Pellia: L. C.*, XXI. — **Grégoire** and **Wygaerts**, '03. (II). — **Gregory, R. P.**, '04. Spore Formation in leptosporangiate Ferns: *A. Bot.*, XVIII. — '11. On Gametic Coupling and Repulsion in *Primula: P. R. S.*, LXXXIV. — '11. Experiments with *Primula: J. G.*, I. — '12. The Chromosomes of a giant Form of *Primula: Proc. Cambridge Phil. Soc.*, XVI. — '14. On the Genetics of Tetraploid Plants in *Primula: P. R. S.*, LXXXVII. — **Grew, Nehemiah**, 1682. (Int.), — **Griffn, B. B.**, '99. Studies on the Maturation, Fertilization, and Cleavage of *Thalassema* and *Zirphœa: J. M.*, XV. — **Griggs, R. F.**, '09. Some Aspects of Amitosis in *Synchytrium: B. G.*, XLVII. — '12. The Development and Cytology of *Rhodochytrium: B. G.*, LIII. — **Grobben, C.**, '78. Beiträge sur Kenntniss der männlichen Geschlechtsorgane der Dekapoden: *Arb. Zool. Inst. Wien*, I. — **Gross, J.**, '01. Untersuchungen über das Ovarium der Hemiptera: *Z. W. Z.*, LXXIX. — '04. Die Spermatogenese von *Syromastes: Z. J.*, Anat. u. Ontog., XX. — '06. Die Spermatogenese von *Pyrrhocoris: Z. J.*, *Anat. Abt.*, XXIII. — '12. Heterochromosomen und Geschlechtsbestimmung bei

Insekten: *Z. J.*, *Allg. Teil.*, XXXII. — '16. Beobachtungen u. Versuche an lebenden Zellkerne: *A. Zf.*, XIV. — **Gruber, A.**, '84. Beiträge zur Kenntniss der Physiologie und Biologie der Protozoen: *Ber. Naturf. Ges. Freiburg*, I. — '85. Uber künstliche Teilung bei Infusorien: (VIII). — '93. Mikroscopische Vivisektion: *Ibid.*, VII, 1. — '97. Weitere Beobachtungen an vielkernigen Infusorien: *Ber. Naturf. Ges. Freiburg*, III. — **Gruber, K.**, '12. Biologische und experimentelle Untersuchungen an *Amoeba* (Lit).: *A. P.*, XXV. — **Guignard, L.**, '91. Nouvelles études sur la fécondation: *Ann. Sci. Nat. Bot.*, XIV. — '98. Les centres cinétiques chez les végétaux: *Ibid.* (VIII), V. Also *B. G.*, XXV. — '99. Sur les anthérozoides et la double copulation sexuelle chez les végétaux angiospermes: *C. R.*, CXXVIII. — '00. L'appareil sexuel et la double fécondation dans les Tulipes: *Ann. Sci. Nat. Bot.*, VIII, 11. — '01. La double fécondation chez les Ranonculacées: *Jour. Botanique*, XV. — '02. La double fécondation chez les *Solanées*: *Jour. Botanique*, XVI. — **Guilliermond, A.**, '06. Contribution a l'étude cytologique des Cyanophycées: *Revue de Botanique.* — '07. La cytologie des Bactéries: *Bull. Inst. Pasteur*, V. — '08. Contribution a l'étude cytologique des Bacilles endospores: *A. P.*, XII. — '09. Observations sur la cytologie d'un Bacille: *C. R.*, LXVII. — '10a. (VII). — '10b. A propos de la structure des Bacilles endospores: *A. P.*, XIX. — '11. Aperçu sur l'évolution nucleaire des ascomycetes et nouvelles observations sur les mitoses des asques: *Rev. Gen. Bot.*, XXIII. — '12a. Recherches cytologiques sur le mode le formation de l'amidon et sur les plastes végétaux: *A. A. M.*, XIV. — '12b. Sur le mode de formation du pigment dans la racine de carotte: *C. R.*, CLV. — '12c. Sur les mitochondries des organes sexuels des végétaux: *C. R.*, CLIV. — '13a. Sur les mitochondries des champignons: *C. R. S. B.*, LXXIV. — '13b. Sur la signification du chromatophore des algues: *C. R. S. B.*, LXXV. — '13c. Nouvelles remarques sur la signification des plastes de W. Schimper, etc.: *Ibid.* — '13d. Sur le rôle du chondriosome dans l'élaboration des produits de reserve des champignons: *C. R.*, CLVII. — '13e. Nouvelles recherches cytologiques sur la formation des pigments anthocyaniques: *Ibid.*, CLVII. — '13f. Nouvelles observations sur le chondriome des champignons: *Ibid.*, CLVI. — '13g. Sur la formation de l'anthocyane au sein des mitochondries: *Ibid.*, CLVI. — '13h. Sur l'étude vitale du chondriome de l'épiderme des pétales d'*Iris*, etc.: *C. R. S. B.*, LXXIV. — '14a. Nouvelles remarques sur les plastes végétaux: *A. A.*, XLVI. — '14b. (I, IX). — '14c. Bemerkungen über die Mitochondrien der vegetativen Zellen und ihre Verwandlung in Plastiden: *B. D. B. G.*, XXXII. — '15a. Nouvelles observations sur le chondriome des cellules épidermiques de la fleur d'Iris: *C. R. S. B.*, LXXVII. — '15b. Recherches sur le chondriome chez les champignons et les algues: *Rév. Gen. Bot.*, XXVII. — '17a. Sur la nature et le rôle des mitochondries des cellules végétales: *C. R. S. B.*, LXIX. — '17b. Observations vitales sur le chondriome de la fleur de Tulipe: *C. R.*, CLXIV. — '17d. Recherches sur l'origine des chromoplastes, etc.: *C. R.*, CLXIV. — '18. Sur l'origine mitochondriale des plastids: *C. R.*, CLXVII. — '19, '19a. (IX). — '20a. Sur l'évolution du chondriome dans la cellule végétale: *C. R.*, CLXX. — '20b. Sur les éléments figurés du cytoplasme: *C. R.*, CLXX. — '20c. Nouvelles recherches sur l'appareil vacuolaire dans les végétaux: *C. R.*, CLXXI. — **Gulick, A.**, '11. (X). — **Günthert, T.**, '10. Die Eibildung der Dytisciden: *Z. J.*, XXX. — **Gurwitsch, A.**, '00. Idiozom und Centralkörper im Ovarialeie der Säugethiere: *A. M. A.*, LVI. — '01. Der Haarbüschel der Epithelzellen, etc.: *A. M. A.*, LIX. — '04, '13. (I). — '08. Ueber Prämissen und anstossgebende Faktoren der Furchung und Zellvermehrung:

A. Zf., II. — '23. Die Natur des spezifischen Erregers der Zellteilung: *A. M. A.*, C. — **Gutherz, S.**, '07. Zur Kenntniss der Heterochromosomen: *A. M. A.*, LXIX. — '12. Ueber ein bemerkenwertes Strukturelement (Heterochromosom) in der Spermiogenese des Menschen: *Ibid.*, LXXIX, 2. — '22. Das Heterochromosomproblem bei den Vertebraten: *Ibid.*, LXXIX. — **Guyer, M. F.**, '00. Spermatogenesis of Normal and Hybrid Pigeons: *Bull. Univ. Cincinnati.* — '02. Hybridism and the Germ-cell: *Ibid.* XXI. — '03. The Germ-cell and the Results of Mendel: *Cincinnati Lancet-Clinic:* — '07. The Development of Unfertilized Frog's Eggs injected with Blood: *Sci.*, XXV. — '09a. The Spermatogenesis of the domestic Guinea: *A. A.*, XXIV. — '09b. The Spermatogenesis of the domestic Chicken: *Ibid.*, XXIV. — '11. (XIV). — '16. (X).

BIERENS DE HAAN, J. A., '13. Ueber bivalente Eier, etc.: *Z. A.*, XLII. — **Haberlandt, G.**, '87. (VIII). — '14. Physiological Plant Anatomy, 4th Ed. Trans. by Drummond. — **Haeckel, E.**, '66. Generelle Morphologie: *Jena.* — '76. The Perigenesis of Plastidules. — '91. Anthropogenie, 4th Ed.: Leipzig. — **Haecker, V.**, '90. Ueber die Reifungsvorgänge bei *Cyclops: Z. A.*, XIII. — '92. Die Eibildung bei *Cyclops* und *Canthocamptus: Z. J.*, V. — '92a. Die Furchung des Eies von *Aequorea: A. M. A.*, XL. — '92c. Die heterotypische Kerntheilung im Cyclus der generativen Zellen: *Ber. Naturf.Ges.Freiburg*, VI. — '93. (IV). — '95a. The Reduction of the Chromosomes in the Sexual Cells: *A. Bot.*, IX. — '95b. Die Vorstadien der Eireifung: *A. M. A.*, XLV. — '95c. Ueber die Selbständigkeit der väterlichen und mütterlichen Kernbestandteile, etc.: *A. M. A.*, XLVI. — '97a. Die Keimbahn von *Cyclops: A. M. A.*, XLIX. — '99. Die Reifungserscheinungen: *E. A. E.*, VIII. — '99, '11. (Int.). — '00. Mitosen im Gefolge amitosenähnlicher Vorgänge: *A. A.*, XVII. — '02. Ueber das Schicksal der elterlichen und grosselterlichen Kernanteile: *J. Z.*, XXXVII. — '04, '07, '10. (XII). — '12. (V). — '12. Allgemeine Vererbungslehre, 2te Aufl. — **Haldane, J. S.**, '17. Organism and Environment: *New Haven.* — **Hallez, P.**, '86, '87. (XIII). — **Halliburton, W. D.**, '16. (VIII). — **Hamburger, C.**, '04. Die Konjugation von *Paramoecium bursaria: A. P.*, IV. — **Hammar, J. A.**, '97. Ueber eine allgemein vorkommende primäre Protoplasmaverbindung zwischen den Blastomeren: *A. M. A.*, XLIX. — '00. Ist die Verbindung zwischen den Blastomeren wirklich protoplasmatisch, etc.: *A. M. A.*, L. — **Hammarsten, O.**, '09. (VIII). — **Hance, R. T.**, '17. The Fixation of mammalian Chromosomes: *A. R.*, XII. — '17b. Somatic Mitoses of the Mosquito: *J. M.*, XXVIII. — '17c, '18. (XI). — **Hanseman, D.**, '93. Spezificität, Altruismus und die Anaplasie der Zellen: Berlin. — **Hanstein, J.**, '80. (I). — **Hardy, W. B.**, '99. '13. (I). — '05. Colloidal Solution: *J. P.*, XXXIII. — **Hargitt, C. W.**, '04. The Early Development of *Pennaria: A.Entwm.*, XVIII. — **Hargitt, G. T.**, '09. Maturation, Fertilization, and Segmentation of *Pennaria*, etc.: *B. M. Z.*, LIII. — '13-'18. (IV). — **Harman, M. T.**, '13. Method of Cell-Division in the Sex Cells of *Taenia teniæformis: J. M.*, XXIV. — '15. Spermatogenesis in *Paratettix: Sci.*, XLI. — '20. Chromosome Studies in Tettigidae, II: *B. B.*, XXXVIII. — **Harms, W.**, '14. Experim. Untersuchungen über die innere Sekretion der Keimdrüsen, etc.: *Jena.* — '21. Untersuchungen über das Bidderschen Organ: *Z. Anat. u.Enw.*, LXII. — **Harper, E. H.**, '04. The Fertilization and Early Development of the Pigeons' egg: *A. J. A.*, III. — **Harper, R. A.**, '95. Beiträg zur Kenntniss der Kernteilung und Sporenbildung im Ascus: *B. D. B. G.*, XIII. — '96. Ueber das Verhalten der Kerne bei der Fruchtentwickelung einiger Ascomyceten: *J. W. B.*, XXIX. — '97. Kernteilung und freie Zellbildung im Ascus: *J. W. B.*, XXX. — '99. (II). — '00. Cell and Nuclear Division in *Fuligo: B. G.*, XXX. — '00, '10. (VII). — '02. Binucleate Cells in certain Hymenomycetes: *B. G.*, XXXIII. — '05. Sexual Reproduction and the Organization of the Nucleus in certain Mildews: *P. C. I.*, XXXVII. — '14. Cleavage in *Didymium melanospermum: A. J. B.*, I. — '18a, '18b. (XIII). — '19. (I). — **Harrison, R. G.**, '10. Outgrowth of the Nerve Fibre in Tissue-cultures: *J. E. Z.*, IX. — '12. Cultivation of Tissues in Extraneous Media, etc.: *A. R.*, VI. — **Harrison** and **Doncaster**, '14. (XI). — **Hartmann, F. A.**, '13. Variations in Size of Chromosomes: *B. B.*, XXIV. — **Hartmann, M.**, '04, '17, '21. (III). — '09, '13, '14, '18, '21. (VII). — '11. Die Konstitution der Protistenkerne und ihre Bedeutung für die Zellenlehre: *Fischer, Jena.* — '18. Theoretische Bedeutung und Terminologie der Vererbungserscheinungen bei haploiden Organismen: *Z. A. V.*, XX. — '21a. Practikum der Protozoologie, 4th Ed.: *Fischer, Jena.* — **Hartmann** und **Nägler**, '08. Copulation bei *Amoeba diploidea* mit Selbständigbleiben der Gametenkerne, etc.: *S.–B. Ges. Naturf. Freunde, Berlin.* — **Hartmann** and **Prowazek**, '07. (IX). — **Hartmann** and **Schilling**, '17. (VII). — **Hartog, M.**, '09. Mitokinetism in the mitotic Spindle and in the Polyasters: *A. Entwm.*, XXVII. — '10. Une force nouvelle, le Mitokinetisme: *C. R.*, CLI. — '13. (III). — '14. (II). — **Harvey (Browne), E. B.**, '16, '20. (XI). — '19. Mitotic Division of binucleate Cells: *B. B.*, XXXVII. — **Harvey, E. N.**, '10a. Methods of Artificial Parthenogenesis: *B. B.*, XVIII. — '10b. The Mechanism of Membrane-formation, etc.: *J. E. Z.*, VIII. — '14. Is the Fertilization-membrane . . . a Precipitation Membrane? *B. B.*, XXVII. — **Harvey, Wm.**, '51. (Int.). — **Hasper, M.**, '11. (IV). — **Hatschek, B.**, '87. Ueber die Bedeutung der geschlechtlichen Fortpflanzung: *Prager Med. Wochenschr.*, XLVI. — '88. Lehrbuch der Zoologie: — **Hatschek, E.**, '22. (VIII). — **Hayes** and **East**, '15. Further Experiments on Inheritance in Maize: *Conn. Agr. Exp. Sta. Bull.*, 188. — **Heath, H.**, '99. (XIII). — **Hegner, R. W.**, '08. An intra-nuclear mitotic Figure, etc.: *B. B.*, XIV. — '11. Germ-Cell Determinants and their Significance: *A. N.*, XLV. — '14a. Studies in Germ-cells, I and II: *J. M.*, XXV. — '14b, III: *A. A.*, XLVI. — '14c, '15. (IV). — '14d. The Origin and Early History of the Germ Cells in some Chrysomelid Beetles: *J. M.*, XX. — '19. (IX). — '20. The Relations between nuclear Number, Chromatin Mass, etc. . . . in *Arcella: J. E. Z.*, XXX. — **Heidenhain, M.**, '93. Ueber Kern und Protoplasma: *Festschr. z. 50-Jahr. Doctorjub. von v. Kölliker: Leipzig.* — '94. Neue Untersuchungen uber die Centralkörper, etc.: *A. M. A.*, XLIII. — '95. Cytomechanische Studien: *A. Entwm.*, I, 4. — '96. Ueber die Mikrocentren mehrkerniger Riesenzellen, etc.: *Morph. Arb.*, VII, 1. — '96. (II). — '99. Ueber die Struktur der Darmepithelzellen: *A. M. A.*, LIV. — '00. Die Centralkapseln und Pseudochromosomen in den Samenzellen von *Proteus*, etc.: *A. A.*, XVIII. — '01. Plasma und Zelle: *Jena.* — '02, '10. (VIII). — '07, '11. (Int.). — **Heidenhain** and **Cohn**, '97. Ueber die Mikrocentren in den Geweben des Vogelembryos, etc.: *Morph. Arb.*, VII. — **Heider, K.**, '00. (XIV). — **Heiderich, F.**, '10. Sichtbare Centrosomen in uberlebenden Zellen: *A. A.*, XXXVI. — **Heilborn, O.**, '21. Taxonomical and cytological studies on . . . *Carica: Ark. B.*, XVII. — '22. Die Chromosomenzahlen der Gattung *Carex: Svensk. Bot. Tidskr.* XVI. — **Heilbrunn, L. V.**, '15. Physical Changes in the Egg of Arbacia: *B. B.*, XXIX. — '20a. An Experimental Study of Cell-Division: *J. E. Z.*, XXX. — '20b. Studies in Artificial Parthenogenesis, III: *B. B.*, XXXVIII. — '21. Protoplasmic Viscosity Changes during Mitosis: *J. E. Z.*, XXXIV. — **Heitzmann, J.**, '73. Untersuchungen über das Protoplasma: *Sitz. d. k. Acad. Wiss. Wien.*, LXVII. — '83. Mikroscopische Morphologie des Thierkörpers im gesunden und kranken Zustande: *Wien.* — **Held, H.**, '12. Ueber den Vorgang der Befruchtung bei *Ascaris megalocephala*: *V. A. G.* — '16. (V). — **Hempelmann, F.**, '06. Eibildung, Eireifung und Befruchtung bei *Saccocirrus: Z. A.*, XXX. — Die Geschlechtsorgane und Zellen von *Saccocirrus: Z.*, LXVII. — **Henderson, L. J.**, '20. The Order of Nature: *Harvard Univ. Press, Cambridge.* — **Henderson, W. D.**, '07. Zur Kenntnis der Spermatogenese von *Dytiscus: Z. W. Z.*, LXXXVII. — **Henking, H.**, '91, '92. (VI). — **Henle, J.**, '41. (Int.). — **Henneguy, L. F.**, '98. (IX). — '03. (Int.). — '04. Les insectes: Paris. — '11. Sur la parthénogénèse expérimentale chez les amphibiens: *C. R.*, CLII. — **Hensen, V.**, '81. Physiologie der Zeugung: Hermann's Physiologie, VI. — **Herbst, C.** Experimentelle Untersuchungen über den Einfluss der veränderten chemischen Zusammensetzung des umgebenden Mediums, etc., I: *Z. W. Z.*, LV, '92; II, *M. Z. S.*, XI, '93a; III–VI, *A. Entwm.*, II, 4. — '94, '95. Ueber die Bedeutung der Reizphysiologie für die Kausale Auffassung von Vorgängen in der tierischen Ontogenese: *B. C.*, XIV, XV. — '93b. Ueber die künstliche Hervorufung von Dotter-membranen an unbefruchteten Seeigeleiern, etc.: *B. C.*, XIII. — '01. (XIV). — '04. Ueber die zur Entwicklung der Seeigel nothwendigen anorg. Stoffe, etc.: *A. Entwm.*, XVII. '06–'14. — (XII). Vererbungsstudien, I–X. (XII). — '12. (XIV). — **Herla, V.**, '95. Études des variations de la mitose chez l'*Ascaride megalocephale*: *A. B.*, XIII. — **Herlant, Maurice**, '11, '13, '19. (V). — '13. Le mechanisme de la parthénogénèse espérimentelle: *B. S. F. B.*, VII, 50. — '14. Sur le mécanisme de la première segmentation, etc.: *Ibid.*, XLVIII. — '17. Le mecanisme de la parthénogénèse expérimentale chez les Amphibiens et les Échinoderms: *Bull. Scient.*, VIII, 7. — **Herlitzka, A.**, '95. Contributo allo studio della capacità evolutiva dei due primi blastomeri nell' uovo di Tritoni: *A. Entwm.*, II. — '96. Sullo sviluppo di embrioni completi da blastomeri isolati di uova de Tritoni: *Ibid.*, IV. — **Hermann, F.**, '91. Beiträg zur Lehre von der Entstehung der karyokinetischen Spindel: *A. M. A.*, XXXVII. — '92. Struktur und Histiogenese der Spermatozoen: *E. A. E.*, II. — **Hertwig, Günther**, '11. Radiumbestrahlung unbefruchteter Froscheier und ihre Entwicklung mit normalen Samen: *A. M. A.*, LXXVII. — '12. Das Schicksal des mit Radium bestrahlen Spermachromatins im Seeigelei: *Ibid.*, LXXIX. — '13. (V). — '18. Kreuzungsversuche an Amphibien: *A. M. A.*, XCI. — '20. Das Schicksal des väterlichen Chromatins, etc.: *Ibid.*, *Festschr. f. O. Hertwig.* — '21. (X). — **Hertwig, O.**, '75, '77, '78. (Int., V). — '84, '93, '98, '06, '10, '17. (Int.). — '90. Experimentelle Studien am tierischen Ei: *J. Z.*, XVII. — '90. (VI). — '92. (XIV). — '92. Urmund und Spina Bifida: *A. M. A.*, XXXIX. — '93. Ueber den Werth der ersten Furchungszellen fur die Organbildung des Embryo: *A. M. A.*, XLII. — '94. Zeit und Streitfragen der Biologie: *Berlin.* — '98. Die Zelle und die Gewebe, II: *Jena.* — '00. Die Entwicklung der Biologie im 19 Jahrhundert: *Jena.* — '11. Radiumkrankheit tierischer Keimzellen: *A. M. A.*, LXXVII. — '12. Disharmonische Idioplasmaverbindungen und ihre Folgen: *Scientia*, XII. — '12, '20, '23. Allgemeine Biologie. 4te, 5te, 6te, Auflage (Int.). — '13. Versuche an *Tritoneiern* über die Einwirkung bestrahler Samenfäden auf die tierische Entwicklung: *A. M. A.*, LXXXII. — '17 (Int.). — **Hertwig, O. and R.**, '86. Experimentelle Untersuchungen über die Bedingungen der Bastardbefruchtung: *J. Z.*, XIX. — '87. (Int., II). — **Hertwig, P.**. '11. Durch Radiumbestrahlung her-

vorgerufene Veränderungen in den Kernteilungsfiguren der Eier von *Ascaris:*
A. M. A., LXXVII. — '13. Das Verhalten des mit Radium bestrahlten Sper-
machromatins in Froschei: *A. M. A.,* LXXXI. — '20. (V). — '20. Abweichende
Form der Parthenogenese bei einer Mutation von *Rhabdites: A. M. A.,* XCIV. —
'23. Bastardierungsversuche mit entkernten Amphibieneiern: *A. M. A.,* C. —
Hertwig, R., '84. Die Kerntheilung bei *Actinosphaerium Eichhorni: J. Z.,* XVII.
— '88. Ueber Kernstruktur und ihre Bedeutung fur Zellteilung und Befruchtung:
J. Z., IV. — '89, '14. (III). — '92. Ueber Befruchtung und Conjugation: *V. D.
Z. G., Berlin.* — '95. Ueber Centrosoma und Centralspindel: *S. B. M. P., Mün-
chen,* I. — '96. Ueber die Entwicklung des unbefruchteten Seeigeleies, etc.:
Festschr. f. Gegenbaur. — '97a. Ueber Karyokinese bei *Actinosphaerium: Ibid.,*
VIII. — '98. Ueber Kernteilung, Richtungskörperbildung und Befruchtung, von
Actinosphaerium: Ibid. (II), XIX. — '02. (VII). — '02. Ueber Wesen und
Bedeutung der Befruchtung: *S. B. Kgl. Bayer. Akad. Wiss. München,* XXXII. —
'03. Ueber Korrelation von Zell- und Kerngrösse, etc.: *B. C.,* XXIII. — '05.
Ueber das Problem der sexuellen Differenzierung: *V. D. Z. G.,* XV. — '06. (V). —
'06 u. '07. Weitere Untersuchungen uber das Sexualitätsproblem: *V. D. Z. G.*
— '08. (III, IX). — '12. (X). — '21. Das Sexualitätsproblem: *B. C.,* XLI.,
2. — **Heuser, F.,** '84. Beobachtungen über Zellkerntheilung: *B. C.,* XVII. —
Hewett, C. G., '06. The Cytological Aspects of Parthenogenesis in Insects:
Mem. and Pro. Manchester Lit. and Phil. Soc., L. — **Heymons, R.,** '93. (XIII). —
Hill, A. W., '00. Distribution and Character of Connecting Threads in the
Tissues of *Pinus,* etc.: *P. R. S.* — '01. The Histology of the Sieve-Tubes of
Pinus: A. Bot., XV. — **Hill, M. D.,** '95. Notes on the Fecundation of the Egg of
Sphaerechinus, etc.: *Q. J.,* XXXVIII. — **Hinderer, Th.,** '14. Ueber die Ver-
schiebung der Vererbungsrichtung unter dem Einfluss von Kohlensäure: *A.
Entwm.,* XXXVIII. — **Hindle, E.,** '11. A Cytological Study of Artificial Par-
thenogenesis in *Strongylocentrotus: A. Entwm.,* XXXI. — **Hirase, S.,** '94. Notes
on the Attraction-Spheres in the Pollen Cells of *Ginkgo: Bot. Mag. Tokyo,* VIII. —
'95, '98. Études sur la fécondation et l'embryogénie du *Ginkgo: Journ. Coll. Sci.
Imp. Univ. Tokio,* VIII, XII. — '18. Further Studies on the Fertilization and
Embryogeny in *Ginkgo biloba: Bot. Mag. Tokyo,* XXXII. — **Hirschler, J.,** '13.
Ueber die Plasmastrukturen in den Geschlechtszellen der Ascariden: *A. Zf.,* IX.
— '15. Ueber ein Verfahren zur gleichzeitigen Darstellung des Golgischen Ap-
parates und der Mitochondrien, etc.: *Z. Wiss. M. u. T.,* XXXII. — '18. (IV). —
His, W., '74. (XIV). — **Höber, R.,** '14. (VIII). — **Hof, A. C.,** '98. Histolo-
gische Studien an Vegetationspunkten: *B. C.,* LXXVI. — **Hofer, B.,** '89. Expe-
rimentelle Untersuchungen über den Einfluss des Kerns auf das Protoplasma:
J. Z., XXIV. — **Hoffman, R. W.,** '98. Ueber Zellplatten und Zellplattenrudi-
mente: *Z. W. Z.,* LXIII. — **Hofmeister, W.,** '49. Die Entstehung des Embryos
der Phanerogamen: — '58. Neuere Beobachtungen uber Embryobildung der
Phanerogamen: *J. W. B.,* I. — '67. (Int.). — **Hogben, L.,** '20a. Studies on
Synapsis, I, II: *P. R. S.,* XCI. — '20b. The Problem of Synapsis: *J. R. M.* — '21.
Studies on Synapsis (*Libellula*), III: *P. R. S.,* XCII. — **Hogue, J. M.,** '10. Ueber
die Wirkung der Centrifugalkraft auf die Eier von *Ascaris: A. Entwm.,* XXIX. —
Holmes, S., '99. '00. (XIII). — **Holmgren, E.,** '99. Zur Kenntniss der Spinal-
ganglionsellen von *Lophius piscatorius,* Lin.: *An. Hf.,* XII. — '03. Ueber die
" Saftkanälchen " der Leberzellen und der Epithelzellen der Nebenniere; *A. A.,*
XII. — **Holmgren, I.,** '19. Zytologische Studien über die Fortpflanzung bei

den Gattungen *Erigeron* und *Eupatorium: K. Svensk. Vet.-Akad. Handl.*, LIX. —
Holmgren, N., '02. Ueber den Bau der Hoden und die Spermatogenese von
Silpha carinata: A. A., XX. — **Holt, C. M.,** '17. Multiple Complexes in the
Alimentary tract of *Culex: J. M.*, XXIX. — **Hooke, R.,** '75. (Int.). — **Hooker,
D.,** '15. The Rôles of Nucleus and Cytoplasm in Melanin Elaboration: *A. R.*,
IX. — **Hopkins, F. G.,** '13. (VIII). — **Hovasse, R.,** '22. La régulation du
nombre des chromosomes, etc.: *C. R.*, CLXXIV. Also *B. B. F. B.*, LVI, 2. —
Hoven, H., 'ıoa, '11. (IX). — 'ıob. Du rôle du chondriome dans la sécrétion:
A. A., XXXVII. — **Hoy, W. E.,** '16. A Study of somatic Chromosomes: *B. B.*,
XXXI. — **Hoyt, W. D.,** '10. Alternation of Generations and Sexuality in *Dict-
yota: B. G.*, XLIX. — **Huie, L.,** '97. Changes in the Cell-organs of *Drosera* pro-
duced by Feeding with Egg-albumen:*Q. J.*, XXXIX. — **Hutchinson, A. N.,** '15.
Fertilization in *Abies: B. G.*, LX. — **Huxley, J. S.,** '20. Restitution-bodies and
free Tissue-cultures in *Sycon: Q. J.*, LXV. — **Huxley, T. H.,** '53. (Int.). — '68.
(I). — '78. (XIV). — **Hyde, I. H.,** '04. Differences in Electrical Potential in
developing Eggs: *A. J. P.*, XII. — **Hyman** and **Bellamy,** '22. The Correlation
between metabolic Gradients, Electrical Gradients and Galvanotaxis: *B. B.*,
XLIII.

IDE, M., '89. Nouvelles observations sur les cellules epithéliales: *L. C.*, V. —
Ikeno, S., '98. Untersuchungen uber die Entwicklung der Geschlechtsorgane,
etc., bei *Cycas: J. W. B.*, XXXVIII. — '98a. Zur Kenntniss des sogenannten
Centrosomähnlichen Körpers im Pollenschläuche der Cycaden: *Flora*, LXXXV,
1. — 'oi. Contribution a l'étude de la fécondation chez le *Ginkgo: Ann. Sci. Nat.
Bot.*, VIII, 13. — '03. Die Spermatogenese von *Marchantia: Beih. Bot. Centralb.*,
XVI. — '04. Blepharoplasten im Pflanzenreich: *Ibid.*, XXIV. — '06. Zur Frage
nach der Homologie der Blepharoplasten: *Flora*, XCVI. — **Ishikawa, C.,** '91.
On the Formation of Eggs in the Testis of *Gebia: Z. A.*, XIV. — '94. *Noctiluca
miliaris:* Its Division and Spore-formation: *Journ. College of Sc. Imp. Univ.
Japan*, VI. — '99. Further Observations on the Nuclear Division of *Noctiluca:
Ibid.*, XII, 4. — **Ishikawa, M.,** '11. Cytologische Studien über Dahlien: *Bot.
Mag. Tokyo.*, XXV. — '16. (XI). — **Issakowitsch,** '06. Geschlechtsbestim-
mende Ursachen bei den Daphniden: *A. M. A.*, LXIX.

JACOBS, M. H., '24. (VIII). — **Jaeger, F. M.,** '20. Lectures on the Principle of Symmetry: *Amsterdam.* — **Jahn, E.,** '11. Myxomycetenstudien. Der
Sexualakt: *B. D. B. G.*, XXIX. — **Janssens, F. A.,** 'oı, '05. (VI). — '04. Production artificielle de larves géantes, etc., dans l'*Arbacia: L. C.*, XXI. — '09, '19,
'24. (XII). — **Janssens** et **Dumez,** '03. (VI). — **Janssens** et **Willems,** '08.
La spermatogénèse l'*Alytes obstetricans: L. C.*, XXV. — '09. Spermatogénèse
dans les Batrachiens, IV: *Ibid.*, XXV. — **Jenkinson, J. W.,** '04. The Maturation and Fertilization of the Egg of the Axolotl: *Q. J.*, XLVIII. — '07, '09, '14,
'17. (XIV). — '11. On the Origin of the Polar and Bilateral Structure of the
Egg of the Sea-urchin: *A. Entwm.*, XXXII. — **Jennings, H. S.,** '96. (XIII). —
'08. Heredity, Variation and Evolution in the Protozoa: *Proc. Amer. Phil. Soc.*,
XLVII. — '09. Heredity and Variation in the simplest Organisms: *A. N.*, XLIII.
— '11. Assortive Mating, Variability and Inheritance of Size in the Conjugation
of *Paramecium: J. E. Z.*, XI. — '12, '13, '20. (III). — '18. Disproof of a certain
Type of Crossing-over between Chromosomes: *A. N.*, IIL. — '23. The numerical

Relations in Crossing-over, etc.: *P. G.*, VIII. — **Jennings** and **Hargitt,** '10. Characteristics of the diverse Races of *Paramecium: J. M.*, XXI. — **Jennings** and **Lashley,** '13. Biparental Inheritance and the Question of Sexuality in *Paramecium: J. E. Z.*, XIV. — **Jhering, H. v.,** '77. (IV). — **Johannsen, W.,** '09. Elemente der exakten Erblichkeitslehre: *Jena.* — '11. The Genotype Conception of Heredity: *A. N.*, XLV. — **Johnson, D. S.,** '00. On the Endosperm and Embryo of *Peperomia: B. G.*, '00. — '07. A New Type of Embryo Sac in *Peperomia: Johns Hopkins Univ. Circ.*, 1907. — '14. The History of the Discovery of Sex in Plants: *Sci.*, XXXIX. — **Johnson, H. H.,** '22. Peripheral Migration of a Centriole-Derivative in *Oecanthus: Sci.*, LVI. — **Jollos, V.,** '16. (III). — '21. (VII). — **Jones, Walter,** '14. (VIII). — **Jones, W. N.,** '18. On the Nature of Fertilization and Sex: *N. P.*, XVII. — **Jordan, H. E.,** '08. The Spermatogenesis of *Aplopus mayeri: P. C. I.*, 102. — '11. The Spermatogenesis of the Opossum, etc.: *A. Zf.*, VII. — '13. Amitosis in the Epididymis of the Mouse: *A. A.*, XLIII. — '14. Spermatogenesis in *Chrysemys* and *Cistudo: Sci. N. S.*, XXXIV. — **Jordan** and **Eycleshymer,** '94. The Cleavage of Amphibian Ova: *J. M.*, IX. — **Jordan** and **Ferguson,** '16. (I). — **Jörgenssen, M.,** '08. Untersuchungen über Eibildung bei *Nephelis*, etc.: *A. Zf.*, II. — '10a. Beitr. zur Kenntnis der Eibildung bei Schwämmen: *A. Zf.*, IV. — '10b. Zur Entw. des Eierstockeies von *Proteus: Festschrift R. Hertwig*, I. — '13a, '13b. (IV), — **Jost, L.,** '07. (I). — '13. Vorlesungen uber Pflanzenphysiologie. 3te Aufl.: *Fischer, Jena.* (English trans. of 1st ed. by Gibson, *Oxford.* '07). — **Juel, H. O.,** '97. Die Kerntheilungen in den Pollenmutterzellen, etc.: *J. W. B.*, XXX. — '98. Parthenogenesis bei *Antennaria: Bot. Centr.* LXXIV). — '00. Beiträge sur Kenntniss der Tetraden-teilung: *J. W. B.*, XXXV. — '00. Vergleichende Untersuchungen uber typische und parthenogenetische Fortpflanzung bei der Gattung *Antennaria: Handl. Svensk. Vet. Akad.*, XXXIII. — '04. Die Tetradenteilung in der Samenanlage von *Taraxacum: Ark. f. Bot.*, II. — '05. Die Tetradenteilung bei *Taraxacum* und anderen Cichoraceen: *Kgl. Svensk. Vet. Akad.*, XXXIX. — **Julin, J.,** '93a. Ovogénèse, spermatogénèse, et fécondation chez *Styleopsis: B. S. F. B.*, XXIV. — **Junker, H.,** '23. Cytologische Untersuchungen an . . . *Perla marginata: A. Zf.*, XVII. — **Just, E. E.,** '12. (XIV). — '15. Initiation of Development in *Nereis: B. B.*, XXVIII. — '19, '20, '23. (V). — '22a. The Effect of Sperm boiled, etc.: *Sci.*, LVI. — '22b. Initiation of Development in the Egg of *Arbacia*, I, II, III: *B. B.*, XLIII. —

KAHLE, W., '08. Die Paedogenese des Cecidomyiden: *Z.*, XXI. — **Kanitz, A.,** '09. '10. (VIII). — **Karsten, G.,** '96. Untersuchungen uber Diatomeen: *Flora*, LXXXII. — '00. Die Auxosporenbildung der Gattungen *Cocconeis, Surirella*, und *Cymatopleura: Ibid.*, LXXXVII. — '08. Die Entwicklung der Zygoten von *Spirogyra jugalis: Ibid.*, XCIX. — **Kassowitz, M.,** '99. Allgemeine Biologie: *Wien.* —**Kautzsch, G.,** '12, '13. Studien uber Entwicklungsanomalien bei *Ascaris*, I: *A. Zf.*, VIII; II, *A. Entwm.*, XXXV. — **Keeble, E.,** '12. Gigantism in *Primula: J. G.*, II. — **Keene, M. L.,** '14. Cytological Studies on the Zygospores of *Sporodinia: A. Bot.*, XXVIII. — '19. Studies of Zygospore Formation in *Phyoomyces: Trans. Wis. Acad. Sci.*, XIX. — **Kemnitz, G. A.,** '13. Eibildung, Eireifung, Samenreifung und Befruchtung von *Brachycoelium: A. Zf.*, X. — **Kemp, H. P.,** '10. On the Question of the Occurrence of " Heterotypical Reduction " in Somatic Cells: *A. Bot.*, XXIV. — **Keuten, J.,** '95. Die Kerntheilung von *Eu-*

glena: Z. W. Z., LX. — **Key, J. A.,** '16. On the Relation of Mitochondria to Zymogen Granules: *A. R.*, X. — **Kienitz-Gerloff, F.,** '91. Review and Bibliography of Researches on Protoplasmic Connections between adjacent Cells: *B. Z.*, XLIX. — **Kihara, H.,** '19a. Ueber cytologische Studien bei einigen Getreidearten, I: *Bot. Mag. Tokyo*, XXXII. — '19b, II: *Ibid.*, XXXIII. — '21. III: *Ibid.*, XXXV. — '24. (XI). — **Kihara** and **Ono,** '23. Chromosome Number and Sexes in *Rumex acetosa: Bot. Mag. Tokyo*, XXXVII. — '23. Cytological Studies on *Rumex: Bot. Mag. Tokyo*, XXXVII. — **King, H. D.,** '07. The Spermatogenesis of *Bufo: A. J. A.*, VII. — '08. The Oögenesis of *Bufo: J. M.*, XIX. — '08. The Structure and Development of Bidder's Organ in *Bufo: Ibid.*, XIX. — '10. Temperature as a Factor in the Determination of Sex in Amphibians: *B. B.*, XVIII. — '11. Studies on Sex-determination in Amphibians: *Ibid.*, XX. — '12. Dimorphism in the Spermatozoa of *Necturus: A. R.*, VI. — **King, Robt. L.,** '23. Heteromorphic homologous Chromosomes, etc.: *J. M.*, XXXVIII. — **King** and **Gatenby,** '23. The Golgi Bodies of a Coccidian: *Q. J.*, LXVII. — **Kingery, H. M.,** '14. So-called Parthenogenesis in the white Mouse: *B. B.*, XXVII. — '17, '18. Oögenesis in the white Mouse: *J. M.*, XXX. — **Kingsbury, B. F.,** '01. The Spermatogenesis of *Desmognathus: A. J. A.*, I. — '11. The Histological Demonstration of Lipoids: *A. R.*, V. — **Kingsbury** and **Hirsch,** '12. The Degeneration of the Secondary Spermatogonia of *Desmognathus: J. M.*, XXIII. — **Kirkham, W. B.,** '06. Maturation of the Mouse Egg: *B. B.*, XII. — '16. The Germ Cell Cycle in the Mouse: *A. R.*, X. — **Kite, G. L.,** '13a. (I). — '13b. The relative Permeability of . . . Animal and Plant cells: *B. B.*, XXV. — **Klebahn,** '90. Die Keimung von *Closterium* und *Cosmarium: J. W. B.*, XXII. — '92. Die Befruchtung von *Oedogonium: J. W. B.*, XXIV. — '96. Beiträge zur Kenntniss der Auxosporenbildung; I. *Rhopalodia: J. W. B.*, XXIX. — '02. Ein Ueberblick über die neue Diatomenliteratur: *A. P.*, I. — **Klebs, G.,** '81. Beiträge zur Kenntnis niederer Algenformen: *B. Z.* — '83. Ueber die Organization einiger Flagellaten-Gruppen, etc.: *Bot. Inst. Tubingen*, I, 1. — '84. Ueber die neueren Forschungen betreffs der Protoplasmaverbindungen: — '87. Ueber den Einfluss des Kerns in der Zelle: *B. C.*, VII. — '89. Zur Physiologie der Fortpflanzung: *B. C.* — '91. Uber die Bildung der Fortpflanzungszellen bei *Hydrodictyon: B. Z.*, XLIX. — '94. Ueber die Verhältnisse des männl. und weibl. Geschlechts in der Natur: *Jena.* — '95. Ueber einige Probleme der Physiol. der Fortpflanzung: *Jena.* — '96, '13, '17. (III). — '98. Alternation of Generations in the Thallophytes: *A. Bot.*, XII. — '99. (VII). — **Klein, E.,** '78-'79. (II). — '79. Ein Beitrag zur Kenntniss der Struktur des Zellkerns: *Centr. f. Med. Wiss. Berlin.* — **Kleinert, A.,** '09. Spermatogenese von *Helix: J. Z.*, XLV. — **Klinckowström, A. v.,** '97. Eireife und Befruchtung bei *Prostheceraeus: A. M. A.*, XLVIII. — **Kniep, H.,** '19a. Untersuchungen über den Antherenbrand (*Ustilago*), etc.: *Z. B.*, XI. — '19b. Ueber morphologische u. physiologische Geschlechtsdifferenzierung: *V. P. M. G.* — **von Knoche, E.,** '10. Experimentelle und andere Studien am Insektenovarium: *Z. A.*, XXXV. — **Kofoid, C. A.,** '95. (XIII). — '15. The Evolution of the Protozoan Nucleus and its extranuclear Connections: *Sci.*, XLII. — '21. A Critical Discussion of the Chromidial formation of Nuclei, etc.: *A. R.*, XX, 2. — '23. (III). — **Kofoid** and **Christiansen,** '15. On Binary and Multiple Fission in *Giardia: Univ. Cal. Pub.*, XVI. — **Kofoid** and **Swezy,** '20. On the Morphology and Mitosis of *Chilomastix: Ibid.*, XX. — '21. On the . . . Stages of *Councilmania*, etc.: *Ibid.*, XX. — **Koernicke, M.,** '04. (I). — '04, '05. (VI). — '06.

Zentrosomen bei Angiospermen? *Flora*, XCVI. — **Kohl, F. G.**, '03. Ueber die Organisation und Physiologie der Cyanophyzeenzelle und die mitotische Teilung ihres Kernes: *Jena.* — **Kohlbrugge, F.**, '10. Der Einfluss der Spermatoiden auf die Blastula: *A. M. A.*, LXXV. — **Kölliker, A. v.**, '41. Beiträge zur Kenntniss für Geschlechtsverhältnisse und Samenflüssigkeit wirbelloser Tiere: *Berlin.* — '44. Entwicklungsgeschichte der Cephalopoden: *Zurich.* — '95. (Int.). — '86. Das Karyoplasma und die Vererbung, etc.: *Z. W. Z.*, XLIV. — '89. Handbuch der Gewebelehre, 6th ed.: *Leipzig.* — '97. Die Energiden von Sachs, etc.: *V. P. M.G.*, *Würzburg*, XXXI. — **Koltzoff, N. K.**, '06, '09. (IV). — **Konapacki, M.**, '11. Ueber den Einfluss hypotonischen Lösungen auf befruchtete Echinideneier: *A. Zf.*, VII. — **Kopec, St.**, '11. Untersuchungen über Castration und Transplantation bei Schmetterlingen: *A. Entwm.*, XXXIII. — '13. Ueber die Unabhängigkeit der Ausbildung sekundärer Geschlechtscharaktere . . . bei Lepidopteren: *Z. A.*, XLIII. — **Kopsch, F.**, '02. Die Darstellung des Binnennetzes in Spinal-gangliunzellen, etc.: *Sitzb. d. k. preusse. Akad. d. Wiss.*, XL. — **Korff, K. v.**, '99. Zur Histogenese der Spermien von *Helix: A. M. A.*, LIV. — '01. Weitere Beobachtungen über das Vorkommen V-förmiger Central-korper: *A. A.*, XIX. — '02. (IV). — **Kornhauser, S. I.**, '14. A comparative Study of the Chromosomes in the Spermatogenesis of *Euchenopa*, etc.: *A. Zf.*, XII. — '15. A cytological Study of the semi-parasitic Copepod, *Hersilia*, etc.: *A. Zf.*, XIII. — **Korotneff, A.**, '09. Mitochondrien, Chondriomiten, und Faserepithel der Tricladen: *A. M. A.*, LXXIV. — **Korschelt, E.**, '82. Uber Bau und Entwicklung des *Dinophilus apatris: Z. W. Z.*, XXXVII. — '86. Ueber die Entstehung und Bedeutung der verschiedenen Elementen des Insektenovariums: *Z. W. Z.*, XLIII. — '89. (VIII). — '95. Ueber Kerntheilung, Eireifung und Befruchtung bei *Ophryotrocha: Z. W. Z.*, LX. — '97. Ueber den Bau der Kerne in den Spinndrüsen der Raupen: *Ibid.*, XLIX.—**Korschelt** and **Heider**, '02–'03. Lehrbuch der vergleichenden Entwicklungsgeschichte, Allgemeiner Theil: *Fischer, Jena.* — '02. Ei- und Eibildung: *Ibid.* — '02. Sperma und Spermatogenesis: *Ibid.* — '03. (V). — '13. (IV). — **Kossel, A.**, '91. Ueber die chemische Zusammensetzung der Zelle: *A. A. P.* — '93. Ueber die Nucleinsäure: *A. A. P.* — '96. Ueber die basischen Stoffe des Zellkernes: *Zeit. Phys. Chem.*, XXII. - '12. (VIII). — '21. Ueber die Beziehung der Biochemie zue den Morphologischen Wissenschaften: *Sitzb. Heidelberger Ak. Wiss.* — **Kostanecki, V. K.**, '97a. Ueber die Bedeutung der Polstrahlung, etc.: *A. M. A.*, LXIX. — '98. Die Befruchtung des Eies von *Myzostoma: A. M. A.*, LI. — '04. Cytologische Studien an künstlich sich entwickelnden Eiern von *Mactra: A. M. A.*, LXIV. — '08. Zur Morphologie der künstlichen parthenogenetischen Entwicklung bei *Mactra: Ibid.*, LXXII. — **Kostanecki** and **Siedlecki**, '97. Ueber das Verhältnis der Centrosomen zum Protoplasma: *A. M. A.*, XLVII. — **Kostanecki** et **Wierzeski**, '96. Ueber das Verhalten der sog. achromatischen Substanzen im befruchteten Ei: *A. M. A.*, XLVII. — **Kowalevsky, A.**, '71. (XIII). — **Kowalski, F.**, '04. Reconstitution du noyau et formation des chromosomes dans les cinèses somatiques de la larvae de Salamandre: — **Krimmel, O.**, '10. Chromosomenverhältnisse in generativen und somatischen Mitosen bei *Diaptomus*, etc.: *Z. A.*, XXXV. — **Krüger, Eva**, '13. Fortpflänzung und Keimzellenbildung von *Rhabditis aberrans: Z. W. Z.*, CV. — **Kuczynski, M. H.**, '17. Ueber die Teilung der Trypanosomenzelle, etc.: *A. P.*, XXXVIII. — **Kühn, A.**, '08. Die Entwicklung der Keimzellen in den parthenogenetischen Generationen der Cladoceren: *A. Zf.*, I. — '13. Die Sonderung der Keimesbezirke . . . von *Polyphemus pediculus: Z. J., (Anat.)*, XXXV. — '20. Untersuchungen zur kausalen Analyse der Zellteilung, I: *A. Entwm.*, XLVI. — **Kühne, W.**, '64. Untersuchungen über das Protoplasma und die Contractilität. — **Kupelweiser, H.**, '09. Entwicklungserregung bei Seeigeleiern durch Molluskensperma: *A. Entwm.*, XXVII. — '12. (V). — **Kupffer, C. v.**, '96. Ueber Energiden und paraplastische Bildungen: München. — **Kurssanow, L.**, '09. Beiträge zur Cytologie der Florideen: *Flora*, XCIX. — '11. Ueber Befruchtung, Reifung, und Keimung bei *Zygnema: Flora*, CIV. — **Kuschakewitsch, S.**, '10. Die Entwicklungsgeschichte der Keimdrüsen von *Rana: Festschr. f. R. Hertwig.* — '10. Zur Kenntniss der sogenannten " wurmförmigen " Spermien der Prosobanchien: *A. A.*, XXXVII. — '13. Studies über den Dimorphismus der männlichen Geschlechtselemente bei ben Prosobranchia: *A. Zf.*, X. — **Küster, E.**, '13. (I). — **Küster, W.**, '94. Die Oelkorper der Lebermoose und ihr Verhaltniss zu Elaioplasten: *Inaug. Dissert., Basel.* — **Küster** and **Bruel**, '15. (II). — **Kuwada, Y.**, '10. A Cytological Study of *Oryza: Bot. Mag. Tokyo*, XXXIX. — '19, '21. Die Chromosomenzahl von *Zea: J. S. C.*, XXXIX (Rev. in *A. N.*, LV). — **Kylin, H.**, '14. Studien über die Entwicklungsgeschichte von *Rhodomela: Svensk Botanisk Tidskr.* VIII. — '16. Die Entwicklungsgeschichte von *Griffithsia: Z. B.*, VIII. — '16. Ueber den Bau der Spermatozoiden der Fucaceen: *Ber. Bot. Ges.*, XXXIV. — '16. Ueber die Befruchtung und Reduktionsteilung bei *Nemalion: B. D.B.G.*, XXXIV. — '18. Studien uber die Entwicklungsgeschichte der Phaeophyceen: *Svensk. Bot. Tidskr.*, XII. —

LABBÉ, A., '04. La maturation des spermatides, etc. . . . chez les Crustaces decapodes: *A. Z. E.*, XI. — **Lacaze-Duthiers, H.**, '75. Sur la formation des monstres doubles chez les gasteropodes: *A. Z. E.*, IV. — '83. Étude sur l'embryogénie de Dentale: *Ann. Mus. d'Hist. Nat. de Marseille Zool.*, I, 7. — **Lagerberg, T.**, '06. Ueber die präsynaptische und synaptische Entwicklung der Kerne in den Embryosackmutterzellen von *Adoxa: Bot. Stud. Kjelmann, Upsala.* — '09. Studien über die Entwicklungsgeschichte und systematische Stellung von *Adoxa moschatellina, L.: Kgl. Svensk. Vet. Akad. Handl.*, XLIV. — **Laguesse, E.**, '11. Ergastoplasme et chondriome dans les cellules sécrétantes séreuses: *J. A.*, XXI. Bibl. — **Laibach, F.**, '07. Zur Frage nach der Individualität der Chromosomen im Pflanzenreich: *Beih. Bot. Cent.*, XXII. — **Lamb, A. B.**, '08. A new Explanation of the Mechanics of Mitosis: *J. E. Z.*, V. — **Lams, M. H.**, '07. Contribution a l'étude de la génèse du vitellus dans l'ovule des Amphibiens: *A. A. M.*, IX. — '08. Les divisions des spermatocytes chez la fourmi *(Camptonotus herculeanus): A. Zf.* I. — '09. Les globules polaires de l'œuf d'*Arion: A. Z. E.*, I. — '10. (IX). — '13. Étude de l'œuf de cobaye aux premiers stades de l'embryogénèse: *A. B.*, XXVIII. — **Lams** and **Doorme**, '08. Nouvelles recherches sur la maturation et la fécondation, etc.: *A. B.*, XXIII. — **Lang, A.**, '81. (XIII). — **Lang, W. H.**, '09. A Theory of Alternation of Generations in Archegoniate Plants: *N. P.*, VIII. — **Land, W. J. G.**, '00. Double Fertilization in Compositae: *B. G.*, XXX. — '07. Fertilization and Embryogeny of *Ephedra trifurca: B.G.*, XLIV. — **Landauer, W.**, '22. Untersuchungen über die Verschiebung der Vererbungsrichtung, etc.: *A. Entwm.*, LII. — **Lankester, E. Ray**, '77. Notes on Embryology and Classification: *Q. J.*, XVII. — **Laqueur, E.**, '09. Ueber Teilbildungen aus dem Froschei und ihre Postgeneration: *A. Entwm.*, XXVIII. — **Lauche, A.**, '13. Ueber pluripolare Mitosen in Hodenregeneraten von *Rana fusca· A. M. A.*, LXXXII. —

Lauterborn, R., '95. Kern- und Zellteilung von *Ceratium: Z. W. Z.,* XLIX. —
'96. Untersuchungen über Bau, Kernteilung, und Bewegung der Diatomen:
Leipzig. — **Lawson, A. A.,** '98. Some Observations on the Development of the
Karyokinetic Spindle in the Pollen Mother Cell of *Cobæa scandans: Proc.
Calif. Acad. Sci. Bot.,* III, 1. — '00, '03a. (II). — '03b. On the Relation of the
Nuclear Membrane to the Protoplast: *B. G.,* XXXV. — '04. The Gametophyte,
Archegonia, Fertilization and Embryo of *Sequoia: A. Bot.,* XVIII. — '04b. — The
Gametophyte, Fertilization and Embryo of *Cryptomeria: A. Bot.,* XVIII. — '07.
The Gametophytes . . . of *Cephalotaxus: A. Bot.,* XXI. — '11. Nuclear Osmosis
as a Factor in Mitosis: *Trans. Roy. Soc. Edinburgh,* XLVIII. — '11. The Phase of
the Nucleus known as Synapsis: *Ibid.,* — '12. A Study in Chromosome Reduc-
tion: *Ibid.,* XLVIII. — **Lebrun, H.,** '01. Les cinèses sexuelles des Anours: *L. C.,*
XVIII. — **Lécaillon, A.,** '10. La parthénogénèse chez les Oiseaux: *A. A. M.,* XII.
— **Leduc, St.,** '04. Production par diffusion des forces, des mouvements et des figures de la karyokinèse: *C. R. Ass. Adv. des Sciences.* — **Lee, A. Bolles,** '96. Sur le
Nebenkern, etc., chez *Helix: L. C.,* XI. — '97. Les cinèses spermatogénétiques
chez *Helix: L. C.,* XIII. — '11. Le réduction numérique et la conjugasion des
chromosomes chez l'escargot: *L. C.,* XXVII. — '13. La structure des chromosomes
et du noyau au repos chez *Paris: L. C.,* XXVIII. — '21. The Microtomist's
Vademecum, 8th ed., *London, Churchill.* — **Lefevre, G.,** '07. (V). — **Lefevre** and
McGill, '08. The Chromosomes of *Anasa* and *Anax: A. J. A.,* VIII. — **Legér, L.,**
'07. Le genre *Ophryocystis: A. P.,* VIII. — **Legér** et **Duboscq,** '09. Études sur
la sexualité chez les gregarines: *A. P.,* XVII. — **Lehman, O.,** '06. Fliessende
Kristalle und Organismen: *A. Entwm.,* XXI. — **Lenhossék, M. v.,** '95. Centrosom und Sphäre in den Spinalganglion des Frosches: *A. M. A.,* XLVI. — '98.
Untersuchungen über Spermatogenese: *A. M. A.,* LI. — '98. Ueber Flimmer-
zellen: *V. A. G., Kiel,* XII. — '99. Das Mikrocentrum der glatten Muskelzellen:
A. A., XVI. — **Lespeschkin, W. W.,** '11. Zur Kenntniss der chemischen Zusammensetzung der Plasmamembran: *B. D. B. G.,* XXIX. — **Leplat, G.,** '10. La
spermiogénèse chez le chat: *A. B.,* XXV. — '13. Les plastosomes des cellules
visuelles, etc.: *A. A.,* XLV. — **Lerat, P.,** '05. Les phénomènes de maturation
dans *Cyclops strenuus: L. C.,* XXII, 1. — **Levi, G.,** '05. Vergleichende Untersuchungen über die Grösse der Zellen: *V. A. G.,* XIX. — '05. Studi sulla grandezza
della cellule: *Arch. Ital. Anat. Embriol.,* V. — '11. Sulla presunta partecipazione
dei condriosomi alla differenziazione cellulare: *Ibid.,* X. — '12. I condriosomi delle
cellule secernenti: *A. A.,* XLII. — '13. Note citologiche sulle cellule somatiche
dell' ovaio dei Mammiferi: *A. Zf.,* XI. — '15–'16. Il comportamento dei condriosomi durante i piu precoci periodi, etc.: *A. Zf.,* XIV. — **Levi e Terni,** '11. Studi
sulla grandezza delle cellule: *Arch. Ital. Anat. e Embryol.,* X. — '11. Le variazioni
dell'indice plasmatico-nucleare, etc.: *Arch. Ital. Anat. e Emb.,* X. — **Levy, F.,** '15.
Ueber die Chromatinverhältnisse in der Spermatogenese von *Rana: A. M. A.,*
LXXXVI. — **Lewis, F. T.,** '23. (XIII). — **Lewis, I. M.,** '08. The Behavior of
the Chromosomes in *Pinus* and *Thuya: A. Bot.,* XXII. — **Lewis, J. F.,** '09. The
Life History of *Griffithsia hornetiana: A. Bot.,* XXIII. — '12. Alternation of
Generations in certain Floridiæ: *B. G.,* LIII. — **Lewis, M. R.,** '16. Sea Water
as a Medium for Tissue-Cultures: *A. R.,* X, 4. — '17. Development of Connective-
tissue Fibers in Tissue Cultures of Chick Embryos: *P. C. I., Cont. Embryol.,* XVII.
— **Lewis** and **Lewis,** '15. Mitochondria (and other cytoplasmic Inclusions) in
Tissue-Cultures: *A. J. A.,* XVII. — '17. The Duration of the Various Phases of

Mitosis in the Mesenchyme Cells of Tissue Cultures: *A. R.*, XIII. — '24. (I). —
Lewis and **Robertson**, '16. (II). The Mitochondria, etc., in *Chorthippus: B.
B.*, XXX. — **Lewitski, G.**, '10. Ueber die Chondriosomen in pflänzlichen
Zellen: *B. D. B. G.*, XXVIII. — '11. Die Chloroplastenanlagen in lebenden und
fixierten Zellen von *Elodea: Ibid.*, XXIX. — '14. Die Chondriosomen als Secret-
bildner bei den Pilzen: *Ibid.*, XXXI. — **Leydig, Fr.**, '54. (I). — '83. Untersuchungen zur Anatomie und Histologie der Thiere: *Bonn.* — '85. Zelle und
Gewebe, *Bonn.* — '89. Beiträge zur Kenntniss des thierischen Eies im unbefruchteten Zustande: *Zoöl. Jahrb. Anat. Ont.*, III. — **Lilienfeld, L.**, '93. Ueber die
Wahlverwandtschaft der Zellelemente zu Farbstoffen: *A. A. P.* — **Lillie, F. R.**,
'95, '99, '01. (XIII). — '96. On the smallest Parts of *Stentor* capable of Regeneration: *J. M.*, XII, 1. — '97. On the Origin of the Centres of the First Cleavage-
spindle in *Unio: Sci.*, V. — '98. Centrosome and Sphere in the Egg of *Unio:
Zool. Bull.*, I, 6. — '02. Differentiation without Cleavage in the Egg of the Annelid
Chaetopterus: A. Entwm., XIV. — '06. (XIV). — '08. A Contribution towards
an experimental Analysis of the Karyokinetic Figure: *Sci.*, XXVII. — '09a.
Polarity and Bilaterality of the Annelid Egg. Experiments with centrifugal Force:
B. B., XVI. — '09b. Karyokinetic Figures.of centrifuged Eggs: *B. B.*, XVIII. —
'11–'11. Studies of Fertilization. I–IV (Morphology). I, II, '12: *J. M.*, XXII;
III, IV, '12: *J. E. Z.*, XII. V–X (Physiology). V, VI, '13, '14: *J. E. Z.*, XIV, XVI;
VII, '15: *B. B.*, XXVIII; VIII, '21: *Ibid.*, XL; IX, X, '21a, '21b: *Ibid.*, XL, XLI. —
'12–'15. (V). — '16. The History of the Fertilization Problem: *Sci.*, XLIII. —
'16. The Theory of the Free-martin: *Sci.*, XLIII. — '17. Sex-determination and
Sex-differentiation in Mammals: *P. N. A.*, III. — '17. The Free-martin: *J. E. Z.*,
XXIII. — '19. (Int., V). — **Lillie** and **Just**, '24. (V). — **Lillie, R. S.**, '02.
On the oxidative Properties of the Cell-Nucleus: *A. J. P.*, VII. — '03, '05, '05–'11.
(II). — '08. Momentary Elevation of Temperature . . . producing artificial
Parthenogenesis in Star-fish Eggs, etc.: *J. E. Z.*, V. — '09, '18. (VIII). — '13.
The Rôle of Membranes in Cell-Processes: *S. M.*, Feb. — '13, '14. (I). — '15. On
the Conditions of Activation of Unfertilized Starfish Eggs, etc.: *B. B.*, XXVIII. —
'17. (V). — '22. (XIII). — '24. (VIII). — **Linville, H. R.**, '00. Maturation
and Fertilization in Pulmonate Gasteropods: *B. M. Z.*, XXV. — **Litardière, R.
de**, '12. Formation des chromosomes hétérotypiques chez le *Polypodium: C. R.*,
CLV. — '21. Recherches sur l'élément chromosomique, etc.: *L. C.*, XXI. —
Lloyd, F. E., '15. The Behavior of Protoplasm as a Colloidal Complex: *Yearbook
Carnegie Inst.*, XIV. — **Lock, R. H.**, '06. Recent Progress in the Study of Varia-
tion, Heredity, and Evolution: *London and N. Y.* — '07. On the Inheritance of
Certain Invisible Characters in Peas: *P. R. S.*, London, B 79. — '08. The Present
State of Knowledge of Heredity in *Pisum: Ann. Roy. Bot. Garden*, IV. — **Locy,
W. A.**, '15. (Int.). — **Loeb, J.**, '91–'92. Untersuchungen zur physiologischen
Morphologie. I. Heteromorphosis: *Würzburg*, '91. II. Organbildung und
Wachsthum: *Ibid.*, '92a, '92b. Experiments on Cleavage: *J. M.*, VII. — '93.
Some Facts and Principles of Physiological Morphology: *W. H. L.*, '93. — '94.
Ueber die Grenzen der Theilbarkeit der Eisubstanz: *A. Ph.*, LIX, 6, 7. — '95.
Ueber Kerntheilung ohne Zelltheilung: *A. Entwm.*, II. — '99. On the Nature of
the Process of Fertilization and the Artificial Production of Normal Larvae, etc.:
A. J. P., III, 3. — '01. Artificial Parthenogenesis in Annelids: *A. J. P.*, IV. — '10.
Ueber den autokatalytischen Charakter der Kernsynthese bei der Entwicklung:
B. C.. XXX. — '10. Heredity in Heterogeneous Hybrids: *J. M.*, XXIII. — '11.

Auf welche Weise rettet die Befruchtung das Leben des Eies: *A. Entwm.*, XXXI. — '12. The Mechanistic Conception of Life: *Chicago.* — '12, '13. (V). — '16a. The Sex of Parthenogenetic Frogs: *P. N. A.*, II. — '16b. (XIV). — '18. Further Experiments on the Sex of Parthenogenetic Frogs: *P. N. A.*, IV. — '18. (VIII). — '19. The Physiological Basis of Polarity, etc.: *J.G. P.*, I. — '21. Further Observations of the Production of Parthenogenetic Frogs: *J. G. P.*, III. — '22. Proteins and the Theory of Colloidal Behavior: *N. Y.* — **Loeb** and **Bancroft,** '13. The Sex of a Parthenogenetic Tadpole and Frog: *J. E. Z.*, XIV. — '13. Further Observations on Artificial Parthenogenesis in Frogs: *J. E. Z.*, XV. — **Loeb** and **Wasteneys,** '12. Die Oxydationsvorgänge im befruchteten und unbefruchteten Seesternei: *A. Entwm.*, XXXV. — **Loeb, L.,** '12. Growth of Tissues in Culture Media, etc.: *A. R.*, VI. — '15. Germ Cells and Somatic Cells: *A. N.*, XLIX. — **Lomen, F.,** '14. Der Hoden von *Culex: J. E. Z.*, LII. — **Lotsy, J. P.,** '05. Die X-Generation und die 2 X-Generation. Eine Arbeitshypothese: *B. C.*, XXV. — '07. Vorträge über botanische Stammesgeschichte, I: *Jena.* — '16. Evoluton by Means of Hybridization: *The Hague.* — **Löwschin, A. M.,** '13. Myelinformen und Chondriosomen: *B. D. B. G.*, XXXI. — '14. Vergleichende experimental-cytologische Untersuchungen über Mitochondrien, etc.: *B. D. B. G.*, XXXII. — **Loyez, M.,** '06. (IV). — '08. Les " noyaux de Blochmann " et la formation du vitellus chez les Hyménoptères: *C. R. Assoc. Anat.*, 10, *Marseilles.* — '09. Les premiers stades de la vitellogénèse chez quelques Tuniciers: *C. R. Assoc. Anat.* — '11. Sur la structure de l'oöcyte de la femme, etc.: *Ibid.* — **Lubosch, W.,** '02, '14. Ueber die Eireifung der Metazoen, etc.: *E. A. E.*, IX, XXI. — **Ludford** and **Gatenby,** '21. (II). — **Ludwig, H.,** '74. Ueber die Eibildung im Thierreiche: *Würzburg.* — **Luna, E.,** '13a. Lo sviluppo dei plastosomi negli anfibi: *A. A.*, XLV. — '13b. Sulla importanza dei condriosomi nella genesi delle miofibrille: *A. Zf.*, IX. — 13c. Ricerche sulla biologia dei condriosomi, condriosomi e pigmento retinico: *A. Zf.*, X. — **Lund, E. J.,** '23a. The normal electrical Polarity of *Obelia: J. E. Z.*, XXXVI. — '23b. Electrical Control of Organic Polarity in the Egg of *Fucus: B. G.*, LXXVI. — **Lundegårdh, H.,** '09. Ueber Reduktionsteilung in den Pollenmutterzellen einiger dikotylen Pflanzen: *Sv. Bot. Tids.*, III. — '10b. Ueber Kernteilung in den Wurzelspitzen von *Allium* und *Vicia: Svensk. Bot. Tidskr.*, IV. — '12a. (I). — '12b. (II). — '12c. Die Kernteilung bei höheren Organismen nach Untersuchungen an lebenden Material: *J. W. B.*, LI. — '12d. Das Caryotin im Ruhekern, etc.: *A. Zf.*, IX. — **Lutman, B. F.,** '11. Cell and Nuclear Division in *Closterium: B. G.*, LI. — **Lutz, A. M.,** '12, '16, '17. (XI). — **Lyon, E. P.,** '04. Rhythms of Susceptibility and of Carbon Dioxide Production in Cleavage: *A. J. P.*, XI. — '07. (XIV).

MAAS, P., '01. Experimentelle Untersuchungen über die Eifurchung: *S. G. M. P. München*, '01. — '03. (XIV). — **McAllister, F.,** '09. The Development of the Embryo Sac of *Smilacina: B. G.*, XLVIII. — '13. On the Cytology and Embryology of *Smilacina: Trans. Wis. Acad. Sci.*, XVII. — **Macallum, A. B.,** '91. Contribution to the Morphology and Physiology of the Cell: *Trans. Inst. Canad.*, 1, 2. — '95. On the Distribution of assimilated Iron Compounds, etc.: *Q. J.* — '04. Blood Salts same as Cambrian Sea: *Trans. Canad. Inst.* — '08. Die Methoden und Ergebnisse der Mikrochemie, etc.: *E. P.*, VII. — Oberflächenspannung und Lebenserscheinungen: *E. P.*, XI. — **Mac Bride** and **Jackson,** '15. Inheritance of Color in the Stick Insect, *Carassius: P. R. S.*, LXXXIX. — **McClendon, J. E.,**

'08. The Segmentation of Eggs of *Asterias* deprived of Chromatin: *A. Entwm.*, XXVI, 4. — '10a. Changes of Permeability of developing Eggs to Electrolytes: *A. J. P.*, XXVII. — '10b. Further Studies on the Gametogenesis of *Pandarus: A. Zf.*, V. — '10c. The Electric Charge on Colloids in living Tips of Plants: *A. Entwm.*, XXXI. — '10d. The Development of isolated Blastomeres of the Frog's Egg: *A. J. A.*, X. — '12. Artificial Parthenogenesis in Vertebrates: *A. J. P.*, XXIX. — '13. The Laws of Surface-Tension and their Applicability to Living Cells and Cell-Division: *A. Entwm.*, XXXVII, 2. — '17. Physical Chemistry of Vital Phenomena: *Princeton.* — '18. The Physical Chemistry of the Proteins: — **McClung, C. E.**, '99. A peculiar nuclear Element in male Reproductive Cells of Insects: *Zool. Bull.*, II. — '00. The Spermatocyte-Divisions of the Acrididae: *Kans. Univ. Quart.*, IX. — '01, '02a. (X). — '02b. The Spermatocyte Divisions of the Locustidae: *Kansas Univ. Sci. Bull.*, XIV. — '05, '08a, '17. (XI). — '08b. The Spermatogenesis of *Xiphidium: Kans. Univ. Sci. Bull.*, IV. — '14. (VI). — '24. (XII). — **Macdougal, D. T.**, '20. (XIII). — **Macdougal** and **Spoehr,** '20. (VIII). — **Mac Farland, F. M.**, '97. Celluläre Studien an Molluskeneiern: *Z. J.*, X. — **McGregor, J. H.**, '99. The Spermatogenesis of *Amphiuma: J. M.*, XV. *Suppl.* — **Mack, J. B.**, '14. A study of the Dimensions of the Chromosomes . . . of *Amblystoma: Kans. Univ. Sci. Bull.*, IX. — **Macklin, C. C.**, '16. (II). — **Maggi, L.**, '78. I plastiduli nei ciliate ed i plastiduli liberamente viventi: *Atti. Soc. Ital. Sc. Nat. Milano*, XXI. — **McGill, C.**, '06. The Behavior of the Nucleoli during Oögenesis, etc.: *Z. J.*, *Anat. Ontog.*, XXIII. — **McLean, R. C.**, '14. Amitosis in Parenchyma of Water Plants: *Proc. Camb. Phil. Soc.*, XVII. — **McMurrich, J. P.**, '86, '95. (XIII). — **Maier, H. W.**, '03. (IX). -- **Maire, R.**, '05. Recherches cytologiques sur quelques ascomycetes: *Ann. Mycol.*, III. — '11. La biologie des Uredinales: *P. R. B.*, IV. — **Malfatti, H.**, '91. Beiträge zur Kenntniss der Nucleine: *Zeit. Phys. Chem.*, XVI. — '91-'92. Zur Chemie der Zellkerne: *Ber. Naturwiss. Ver. zu Innsbrück.* — **Malone, J. Y.**, '18. Spermatogenesis of the Dog: *Trans. Am. Micr. Soc.*, XXXVII. — **Malpighi, M.**, 1675. (Int.). — **Malsen, H. v.**, '06. Geschlechtsbestimmende Einfluss und Eibildung des *Dinophilus: A. M. A.*, XLIX. — **Mann, G.**, '02, '06. (VIII). — **Marchal, É.**, '20. (XI). — **Marchal, Él.** et **Ém.**, '06, '07, '09. (VII). — '12, (XI). — **Marchal, P.**, '04. Recherches sur la biologie et la dévéloppement des Hyménoptères parasites, I: *A. Z. E.*, Sér. IV, II. — '13. Contribution à l'étude de la biologie des *Chermes: A. S. N., Zool.*, Sér. IX, XVIII. — **Marcus, H.**, '06. Ei und Samenreife bei *Ascaris canis: A. M. A.*, LXVIII. — **Maréchal, J.**, '04. (XI). — '05. Ueber die morphologische Entwicklung der Chromosomen im Teleostierei, usw.: *A. A.*, XXVI. — '06. (IV). — '07. (VI). — **Mark, E. L.**, '81. (Int.). — '90. Studies on *Lepidosteus: B. M. Z.*, XIX. — **Mark** and **Copeland,** '06. Some Stages in the Spermatogenesis of the Honey Bee: *Proc. Amer. Acad.*, XLII. — '07. Maturation Stages in the Spermatogenesis of *Vespa: Ibid.*, XLIII. — **Marshall, W. S.**, '07. Amitosis in the Malphighian Tubules of the Walking-Stick: *B. B.*, XIV. — '07. Contributions toward the Embryology and Anatomy of *Polistes: Z. W. Z.*, XXVI. — '07. Cellular elements in the Ovary of *Platyphylax: Ibid.* — **Marshall** and **Vorhies,** '06. Cytological Studies on the Spinning Glands of *Platyphylax: Int. Monatsch. Anat. u. Phy.*, XXIII. — **Martens, P.**, '22. Le cycle du chromosome somatique dans le *Paris quadrifolia: L. C.*, XXXII. — **Martin, F.**, '14. Zur Entwicklungsgeschichte des polyembryonalen *Ageniaspis (Encyrtus) fuscicollis: Z. W. Z.*, CX. — **Martins**

Mano, Th., '04. Nucleole et chromosomes: *L. C.*, XXII. — '09. La microsporogénèse dans le *Funkia: Broteria, Sér. Bot.*, VIII. — **Masing, E.,** '10. Ueber das Verhalten Nucleinsäure bei der Furchung des Seeigeleies: *A. Entwm.*, XXXI. — **Matala, J.,** '13. Der Kolloide Zustand der Materie: *Steinkopf, Dresden und Leipzig.* — **Mathews, A. P.,** '97a. Internal Secretions considered in Relation to Variation and Development: *Sci.*, V, 122. — '97b. Zur Chemie der Spermatozoa: *Zeit. Phys. Chem.*, XXIII, 4, 5. — '98. (VIII). — '99b. The Metabolism of the Pancreas Cell: *J. M.*, XV, Suppl. — '01. Artificial Parthenogenesis produced by mechanical Agitation: *A. J. P.*, VI. — '03. Electrical Polarity in Hydroids: *A. J. P.*, VIII. — '15a. A Theory of the Nature of Protoplasmic Respiration and Growth: *B. B.*, VIII. — '15b, '24. (VIII). — **Matschek, H.,** '09. Zur Kenntnis der Eireifung bei den Copepoden: *Z. A.*, XXXIV. — '10. (VI). — **Maupas, M.,** '88, '89, '91. (III). — '00. (X). — **Maurer, F.,** '15. (I). — **Mavor, J. W.,** '22. The Production of Non-Disjunction by X-rays: *Sci.*, LV. — **Maximow, A.,** '08. Ueber Amitose in den embryonalen Geweben bei Säugtieren: *A. A.*, XXXIII. — '13. Ueber Chondriosomen in lebenden Pflanzenzellen: *Ibid.*, XLIII. — '16b. Sur la structure des chondriosomes: *C. R. S. B.*, LXXIX. — **May** and **Walker,** '08. Note on the Multiplication and Migration of Nucleoli, etc.: *Q. J., Exp. Phys.*, I. — **Mayer, A.,** '08. Zur Kenntniss der Samenbildung bei *Ascaris: Z. J.*, XXV. — **Mayer, Rathery** and **Schaeffer,** '14. Les granulations ou mitochondries de la cellule hépatique: *Jour. Phys. Path. Gen.*, XVI. — **Maziarski, S.,** '13. Sur la persistance des résidus fusoriaux, etc.: *A. Zf.*, X. — **Mead, A. D.,** '95. Some Observations on the Maturation, and Fecundation in *Chaetopterus: J. M.*, X, 1. — '97. (XIII). — '97a. The Origin of the Egg-centrosomes: *J. M.*, XII. — '98a. (V). — '98b. The Rate of Cell-Division and the Function of the Centrosome: *W. H. L.* — **Medes, Grace,** '05. The Spermatogenesis of *Scutigera: B. B.*, IX. — **Meek, C. F. U.,** '11. The Spermatogenesis of *Stenobothrus: Jour. Linn. Soc.* (*Zool.*), XXXII. — '12a. A metrical Analysis of Chromosome Complexes, etc.: *P. T.*, B, CCIII. — '12b. The Correlation of somatic Characters and Chromatin Rod-lengths, etc.: *Jour. Linn. Soc.*, XXXII. — '13. The Problem of Mitosis: *Q. J.*, LVIII. — '14. The possible Connection between Spindle-length and Cell-Volume: *Proc. Zool. Soc. London.* — '20. A Further Study of Chromosome Dimensions: *P. R. S.*, B, XCI. — **Meisenheimer, J.,** '00. (XIII). — '08. Ueber den Zusammenhang von Geschlechtsdifferenzierung: *V. D. Z. G.* — '09, '12, '13. (X). — '21. Geschlecht und Geschlechter im Tierreich: *Jena.* — **Melin, E.,** '15. Die Sporogenese von *Sphagnum*, etc.: *Svensk. Bot. Tids.*, IX. — **Mendel, G.,** '65 ('66). Versuche über Pflanzenhybriden: *Reprinted in Flora*, LXXXIX. — **Mercier,** '07. Recherches sur les Bacterioides des Blattides: *A. P.*, IX. — **Mereschkowsky, C.,** '05. Ueber Natur und Ursprung der Chromatophoren im Pflanzenreiche: *B. C.* — **Merriman, M. L.,** '04. Vegetative Cell Division in *Allium: B. G.*, XXXVII. — '13. Nuclear Division in *Spirogyra: B. G.*, LVI. — **Metcalf, M. M.,** '15. Chromosomes in Protozoa: *Sci.*, XLII. — **Metschnikoff, E.,** '66. Embryologische Studien an Insecten: *Z. W. Z.*, XVI. — '86. Embryologische Studien an Medusen: *Wien.* — **Metz, C. W.,** '14. A preliminary Study of five different Types of Chromosome-groups in the Genus *Drosophila: J. E. Z.*, XVII. — '14, '16a, '16b. (XI). — '16. Pairing of Chromosomes in the Diptera: *Sci.*, XLIII. — '22. Association of Homologous chromosomes in tetraploid Cells of *Drosophila: B. B.*, XLIII. — '22. Chromosome Studies in the Diptera, IV. Incomplete Synapsis . . . in *Dasyllis: B. B.*, XLIII. — **Metz, Moses** and **Mason,** '23.

Genetic Studies on *Drosophila virilis: P. C. I.*, 328. — **Metz** and **Nonidez**, '21. '23. Spermatogenesis in *Asilus: J. E. Z.*, XXXII: *A. Zf.*, XVII. — **Meves, F.,** '91. Ueber amitotischen Kerntheilung in den Spermatogonien des Salamanders, etc.: *A. A.*, V. — '94. Ueber eine Metamorphose der Attractionsphäre in den Spermatogonien von *Salamandra: A. M. A.*, XLIV. — '96. Ueber die Entwicklung der männlichen Geschlechtszellen von *Salamandra: Ibid.*, XLVIII. — '96, '98. (II). — '97. Ueber Structur und Histogenese der Samenfäden von *Salamandra: A. M. A.*, L. — '97. Zur Struktur der Kerne in den Spinndrüsen der Raupen: *Ibid.*, XLVIII. — '97a. Ueber den Vorgang der Zelleinschnürung: *A. Entwm.*, V, 2. — '97b. Zelltheilung: *Merkel u. Bonnet, Erg.*, VI. — '97c. Ueber Centralkörper in männlichen Geschlechtszellen von Schmetterlingen: *A. A.*, XIV, 1. — '98. Zelltheilung: *E. A. E.*, VIII. — '98. Ueber das Verhalten der Centralkörper bei der Histogenese der Samenfäden von Mensch und Ratte: *V. A. G.*, XIV. — '99, '00, '01, '03. (IV). — '02. Ueber die Frage, ob die Centrosomen Boveri's als allgemeine und dauernde Zellorgane aufzufassen sind: *V. A. G.*, Halle. — '04. Ueber das Vorkommen von Mitochondrien bezw. Chondriomiten in Pflanzenzellen: *B. D. B. G.*, XX. — '04. Ueber Richtungskörperbildung im Hoden von Hymenopteren: *A. A.*, XXIV. — '07. Die Spermatocytenbildung bei der Honigbiene: *A. M. A.*, LXX. — '07a. Ueber Mitochondrien bezw. chondriokonten in den Zellen junger Embryonen: *A. A.*, XXXI. — '07b. Die Chondriokonten in ihrem Verhältnis zur Filarmasse Flemmings: *Ibid.*, XXXI. — '08. Die Chondriosomen als Träger erblicher Anlagen: *A. M. A.*, LXXII. — '08. Die Spermatocytenteilungen bei der Hornisse: *Ibid.*, LXXI. — '08. (VI). — '09. Ueber Neubildung quergestreifter Muskelfasern nach Beobachtungen am Hühnerembryo: *A. A.*, XXXIV. — '10a. Ueber Strukturen in den Zellen des embryonalen Stützgewebes, etc.: *A. M. A.*, LXXV. — '10b. Zur Einigung zwischen Fäden- und Granula-lehre des Protoplasma, etc.: *Ibid.*, LXXV. — '11. Chromosomenlängen bei *Salamandra*, etc.: *Ibid.*, LXXVII. — '11a. Gesammelte Studien an den roten Blutkörperchen der Amphibien: *Ibid.*, XXVIII. — '11, '14. (V). — '13. Ueber das Verhalten des plastomatischen Bestandteiles bei der befruchtung des Eies von *Phallusia: A. M. A.*, LXXXII. — '14. Was sind die Plastosomen? *A. A.*, LXXXV. — '15. Ueber Mitwirkung der Plastosomen bei der Befruchtung des Eies von *Filaria: A. M. A.*, LXXXVII. — '15a. Was sind die Plastosomen? II.: *Ibid.*, LXXXVII. — '15c. Ueber den Befruchtungsvorgang bei der Miesmuschel *(Mytilus): A. M. A.*, LXXXVII. — '16. (IX). — '17, '18a. (I). — '18b. Zur Kenntniss des Baues pflänzlicher Spermien: *A. M. A.*, XCI. — '18c. Ueber Umwandlung von Plastosomen in Sekretkügelchen, etc.: *Ibid.*, XC, 4. — **Meves, F.,** and **Duesberg, J.,** '08. Die Spermatocytenteilungen bei der Hornisse: *Ibid.*, LXXI. — **Meyer, A.,** '81. Ueber die Struktur der Stärkekörner: *B. Z.*, XXXIX. — '83a. Ueber Krystalloide der Trophoplasten und über die Chromoplasten der Angiospermen: *B. Z.*, XLI. — '95. Untersuchungen über die Stärkekörner: *Jena.* — '96. Die Plasmaverbindungen, etc.: *B. Z.*, XI, XII. — '04. Orientierende Untersuchungen über . . . Volutin: *B. Z.*, LXII. — '08. Der Zellkern der Bakterien: *Fischer, Jena.* — '12. (IX). — '16. Die Allinanten, etc.: *B. D. B. G.*, XXIV. — '20. (I). — **Meyer, O.,** '95. Cellular-Untersuchungen an Nematodeneiern: *J. Z.*, XXIX. — **De Meyer, J.,** '11. Observations et expériences relatives a l'action exercée par des extraits . . . sur les spermatozoides: *A. B.*, XXVI. — **Michaelis, L.,** '97. Die Befruchtung des Tritoneies: *A. M. A.*, XLVIII. — '99. Die vitale Färbung, eine Darstellungsmethode der Zellgranula: *Ibid.*, LV. —

'02. Einführung in die Farbstoffchemie fur Histologen: *Berlin, S. Karger.* — '10. Theorie der Färbung: Handbuch der Bioch., II, 1. — **Miehe, H.,** '23. (IX). — **Migula, W.,** '04. Der Bau der Bakterien: *Jena.* — **Mikosch,** '94. Ueber Struktur im pflänzlichen Protoplasma: *Verh. d. Ges. d. Naturf. u. Aertze.* — **Minchin, E. A.,** '12. (VII). — '15. (IX). — **Minot, C. S.,** '82. Theorie der Genoblasten: *B. C.,* XX. — '90. On certain Phenomena of Growing Old: *Proc. Amer. Ass'n. Adv. Sci.,* XXIX. — '91. Senescence and Rejuvenation: *J. P.,* XI, 2. — '92. Human Embryology: *New York.* — '95. Ueber die Vererbung und die Verjüngung: *B. C.,* XV. — '08, '13. (III). — **Mirande, M.,** '19. Sur le chondriome, les chloroplastes et les corpuscles nucleolaries du protoplasme des *Chara: C. R.,* CLXVIII. — **Miyake, K.,** '05. On the Centrosomes of Hepaticae: *Bot. Mag. Tokyo,* XIX. — '05. Ueber Reduktionsteilung in den Pollenmutterzellen einigen Monokotylen: *J. W. B.,* XLII. — '06. The Spermatozoid of *Ginkgo: Jour. Appl. Micr. and Lab. Methods,* V. — '10. The Development of the Gametophytes and Embryogeny in *Cunninghamia: Beih. Bot. Centr.,* XXVII. — **Moenkhaus, W. J.,** '04, '10. (XI). — **Mohl, H. v.,** '35, '37. Ueber die Vermehrung der Pflanzenzelle durch Theilung: *Dissert. Tübingen* 1835. *Flora.* — '46. Ueber die Saftbewegung im Innern der Zellen: *B. Z.* — '51. Grundzüge der Anatomie und Physiologie der vegetabilischen Zelle: *Engl. Trans.* by Henfrey, *London.* — **Mohr, Otto L.,** '14. (VI, X). — '16. (X). — **Mol, W. E. de,** '21. De l'existence der varietés hétéroploides de l' *Hyacinthus, etc.: Arch. Néerl. des Sci.,* III, b, IV. — **Moll, J. W.,** '93. Observations on Karyokinesis in *Spirogyra: Verh. Kon. Akad., Amsterdam,* IX. — **Molisch, H.,** '08. Ueber Ultramikroörganismen: *B. Z.,* LXVI. — '13. (VIII). — **Montgomery, T. H.,** '98a. The Spermatogenesis of *Pentatoma,* etc.: *Z. J.* — '98b. (I). — '01b. Further Studies on the Chromosomes of the Hemiptera-Heteroptera: *P. N. A.,* LIII. — '01, '06a. (XI). — '03. The heterotypical Maturation Mitosis in Amphibia, etc.: *B. B.,* IV, 5. — '04. (VI). — '05. The Spermatogenesis of *Syrbula* and *Lycosa,* etc.: *Proc. Acad. Nat. Sci. Phila.,* LVII. — '06. The Terminology of aberrant Chromosomes and their Behavior in certain Hemiptera: *Sci., n. s.,* XXIII. — '08. On the Morphological Difference of the Chromosomes in *Ascaris: A. Zf.,* II. — '10. On the dimegalous Sperm and Chromosomal Variation of *Euschistus,* etc.: *Ibid.,* V. — '11. Differentiation of the Human Cells of *Sertoli: B. B.,* XXI. — '11. The Spermatogenesis of an Hemipteron, *Euschistus: J. M.,* XXII, 3. — '12. Human Spermatogenesis: *Jour. Acad. Nat. Sci. Phila.,* XV. — '12. Complete Discharge of Mitochondria from the Spermatozoön of *Peripatus: B. B.,* XXII. — **Monti, R.,** '15. I condriosomi e gli apparati di Golgi nelle cellule nervose: *Arch. Ital. di Anat. e di Embriol.,* XIV. — **Moore, A. C.,** '05. Sporogenesis in *Pallavicinia: B. G.,* XL. — **Moore, B.,** '12. The Origin and Nature of Life: *N. Y. and London.* — **Moore, C. R.,** '16. On the Superposition of Fertilization and Parthenogenesis: *B. B.,* XXI. — '17. (V). — **Moore, J. E. S.,** '93. Mammalian Spermatogenesis: *A. A.,* VII. — '96. On the structural Changes in the reproductive Cells of Elasmobranchs: *Q. J.,* XXXVIII. — **Moore** and **Embleton,** '06. On the Synapsis in Amphibia: *P. R. S.,* LXXVII. — **Moore** and **Robinson,** '05. On the Behavior of the Nucleolus in the Spermatogenesis of *Periplaneta: Q. J.,* XLVIII. — **Moore** and **Walker,** '06. The Meiotic Process in the Mammalia: *Cancer Research Lab., Liverpool Univ.* — **Mordwilko, A.,** '07, '09. Beiträge zur Biologie der Pflanzenläuse: *B. C.,* XXVII, XXIX. — **Moreau, M. F.,** '14. Les mitochondries chez les Uredinées: *C. R. S. B.,* LXXVI. — '14. Le chondriosome et la division des mitochondries chez les *Vaucheria: Bul. Soc. Bot. France.*, LXI. — '14a. Sur la formation de corpuscles metachromatiques dans les mitochondries granuleuses: *C. R. S. B.*, LXXVII. — '15b. La division des mitochondries et ses rapports avec les phénomènes de secrétion: *Ibid.*, LXXVIII. — **Morgan, L. V.**, '22. Non-crisscross Inheritance in *Drosophila: B. B.*, XLII, 5. — **Morgan, T. H.**, '93a. Experimental Studies on Teleost Eggs: *A. A.*, VIII. — '93b. Experimental Studies on Echinoderm Eggs: *Ibid.*, IX. — '95a. (XIV). — '95b. Studies on the partial Larvae of *Sphaerechinus: A. Entwm.*, II. — '95c. A Study of Variation in Cleavage: *Ibid.*, II. — '96. The Number of Cells in Larvae from isolated Blastomeres of *Amphioxus: A. Entwm.*, III. — '96, '99. (IX). — '96. The Fertilization of nonnucleated Fragments of Echinoderm Eggs: *A. Entwm.*, III. — '99, '00, '08, '09, '10a, '17, '23. (XIV). — '00. Further Studies on the Action of Salt Solutions, etc.: *A. Entwm.*, X. — '01. Regeneration in Egg, Embryo, and Adult: *A. N.*, XXXV. — '01. Regeneration of Proportionate Structures in *Stentor: B. B.*, II. — '01. Regeneration: *Columbia Biol. Ser.*, VIII. — '03. Recent Theories in Regard to the Determination of Sex: *Pop. Sci. Monthly.* — '04. Relation between normal and abnormal Development of the Embryo of the Frog. III: *A. Entwm.*, XVIII. — '05a. Self-fertilization in *Ciona: B. B.*, VIII. — '05b. An Alternative Interpretation of gynandromorphous Insects: *Sci.*, XXI. — '06. The Influence of a strong centrifugal Force on the Frog's Egg: *A. Entwm.*, XXII. — '06. Male and female Eggs of the Phylloxerans of the Hickories: **B. B.**, X. — '07a. (III). — '07. The biological Signification and Control of Sex: *Sci.*, n. s., XXV. — '07b. The Cause of Gynandromorphism in Insects: *A. N.*, XLI. — '08. The Production of Two Kinds of Spermatozoa in *Phylloxerans: P. S. B. M.*, V. — '09. (X). — '09. Hybridology and Gynandromorphism: *A. N.*, XLIII. — '10. Chromosomes in the parthenogenetic and sexual Eggs of the Phylloxerans and Aphids: *P. S. B. M.*, VII. — '10. The Effect of Altering the Position of the Cleavage Planes, etc.: *A. Entwm.*, XXIX. — '10, '11, '19, '22. (XII). — '10. Experiments bearing on the Nature of the karyokinetic Figure: *P. S. B. M.*, VII. — '10. Sex-limited Inheritance in *Drosophila: Sci.*, XXXII. — '10b. The Method of Inheritance of Two Sex-limited Characters in the Same Animal: *P. S. B. M.*, VIII. — '11. The Application of the Conception of Pure Lines to Sex-limited Inheritance, etc.: *A. N.*, III. — '11a. An Attempt to analyze the Constitution of the Chromosomes on the Basis of sex-limited Inheritance in *Drosophila: J. E. Z.*, XI, 4. — '12. The Elimination of the Sex Chromosome from the Male-Producing Eggs of *Phylloxerans: J. E. Z.*, XII. — '13. Factors and Unit Characters in Mendelian Heredity: *A. N.*, XLVII. — '14. Sex-limited and Sex-linked Inheritance: *A. N.*, XLVIII. — '14. Chromosomes of the white Man and the Negro: *Sci.*, n. s., XXIX. — '14. Mosaics and Gynandromorphs in *Drosophila: P. S. B. M.*, XI. — '15a. The Constitution of the Hereditary Material: *Proc. Am. Phil. Soc.*, LIV. — '15b. Localization of the Hereditary Material in the Germ Cells: *P. N. A.*, I. — '15c. The Predetermination of Sex in *Phylloxerans* and *Aphids: J. E. Z.*, XIX, 3. — '23. The Bearing of Mendelism on the Origin of Species: *S. M.*, '23. Removal of the Block to Fertilization in *Ciona: P. N. A.*, IX. — '24. (XII). — **Morgan** and **Boring**, '03. The Relation of the first Plane of Cleavage and the grey Crescent, etc.: *A. Entwm.*, XVI. — **Morgan** and **Bridges**, '16. (XII). — '19. (X). — **Morgan, Bridges, Sturtevant**, '29. (XII). — **Morgan** and **Dimon**, '04. Physiological Polarity and Electrical Polarity in the Earthworm. *J. E. Z.*, I. — **Morgan** and **Goodale**, '12. Sex-linked Inheritance in Poultry: *Ann. N. Y. Acad. Sci.*, XXII. — **Morgan** and **Lyon,** '07. The Relation of the Substances of the Egg separated by a strong Centrifugal Force, etc.: *A. Entwm.,* XXIV. — **Morgan, Payne,** and **Browne,** '10. A Method to Test the Hypothesis of Selective Fertilization: *B. B.,* XVIII. — **Morgan** and **Spooner,** '09. (XIV). — **Morgan, Sturtevant, Bridges,** '21. (XII). — **Morgan, Sturtevant, Muller** and **Bridges,** '23. (XII). — **Morgan** and **Tsuda, U.,** '94. The Orientation of the Frog's Egg:*Q. J.,* XXXV. — **Moroff, Th.,** '09. Oögenetische Studien. I. Copepoden: *A. Zf.,* II. — **Morrill, C. V.,** '10. The Chromosomes in the Oögenesis, Fertilization and Cleavage of *Coreid Hemiptera: B. B.,* XIX, 2. — **Morris, Margaret,** '14. The Behavior of the Chromatin in Hybrids between *Fundulus* and *Ctenolabrus: J. E. Z.,* XVI. — '17. A Cytological Study of Parthenogenesis in *Cumingia: Ibid.,* XXII. — **Morse,** '09. The nuclear Components of the Sex Cells in four Species of Cockroaches: *A. Zf.,* III. — **Mottier, D. M.,** '97. Ueber das Verhalten der Kerne bei der Entwicklung des Embryosacs: *J. W. B.,* XXXI. — '97b. Beiträge zur Kenntniss der Kerntheilung in den Pollenmutterzellen, etc.: *Ibid.,* XXX. — '98. Das Centrosoma bei *Dictyota: B. D. B. G.,* XVI. — '98. Beiträge zur Kenntniss der Kerntheilung in den Pollenmutterzellen, etc.: *J. W. B.,* XXXI. — '98. Ueber das Verhalten der Kerne bei der Entwickelung des Embryosacks und die Vorgänge der Befruchtung: *J. W. B.,* XXXI. — '00. (II). — '03. The Behavior of the Chromosomes in the Spore-Mother-Cells of Higher Plants: *B. G.,* XXXV. — '04. The Development of the Spermatozoid of *Chara: A. Bot.,* XVIII. — '04. (V). — '05, '07, '09, '14. (VI). — '18. (IX). — '21. (I). — **Mottier** and **Nothnagel,** '13. The Development and Behavior of the Chromosomes in the First or heterotypic Mitosis of the Pollen Mother-Cells of *Allium: Bull. Torr. Bot. Club.* XL. — **Muckermann, H.,** '12. Zur Anordnung, Trennung und Polwanderung der Chromosomen in der Metaphase, etc.: *L. C.,* XXVIII. — **Müller, E.,** '96. (XIV). — **Müller, H.,** '03. Beiträg zur Embryonalentwicklung der *Ascaris: Z.,* XVII. — **Müller, H. A. Cl.,** '09. Ueber karyokinetische Bilder in den Wurzelspitzen von *Yucca: J. W. B.,* XLVII, 1. — '11. (II). — **Muller, H. J.,** '14, '16. (XII). — '20. Are the Factors of Heredity arranged in a Line? *A. N.,* LIV. — '22. Variations due to Change in the individual Gene: *A. N.,* LVI. — **Mülsow, K.,** '11. Chromosomenverhältnisse bei *Ancyracanthus: Z. A.,* XXXVIII. — '12. (X). — **Munson, J. P.,** '06. Spermatogenesis of the Butterfly, *Papilio: Proc. Boston Soc. Nat. Hist.,* XXXIII. — '12. A Comparative Study of the Structure and Origin of the Yolk Nucleus: *A. Zf.,* VIII. — **Murbeck,** '04. Parthenogenesis bei den Gattungen *Taraxacum* und *Hieracium: Bot. Not., Lund.* — **Murray, J. A.,** '98. Contributions to a Knowledge of the Nebenkern in the Spermatogenesis of Pulmonata: *Z. J.,* XI, 14. — **Murrill, W. A.,** '00. The Development of the Archegonium and Fertilization in the Hemlock Spruce: *A. Bot.,* XIV.

NABOURS, R. K., '14, '17. Studies of Inheritance and Evolution in Orthoptera. I, II, III: *J. G.,* III. — '19. Parthenogenesis and Crossing Over in the Grouse Locust *Apotettix: A. N.,* LIII. — **Nachtsheim, H.,** '13. (X, XII). — '14. Das Problem der Geschlechtsbestimmung bei *Dinophilus: Naturf. Ges. Freiburg,* XXI. — '15. Entstehen auch aus befruchteten Bieneiern Drohnen? *B. C.,* XXXV. — '19. (X). — '21. Sind haploid Organismen (Metazoen) lebensfähig? *B. C.,* XLI. — **Nagai, I.,** '15. On the Influence of Nutrition upon the Development of Sexual Organs in the Fern Prothallia: *J. Coll. Agr. Univ. Tokyo,* VI. — **Nägeli, C.,** '44. '46. Zellkerne, Zellbildung, und Zellwachsthum: *Z. W. B.,*

I, III. – '46. On the Utricular Structures in the Contents of Cells: Ray Society: — '84. (Int.) — **Nägeli** and **Schwenderer**, '67. Das Mikroscop: *Leipzig*. (See later editions) — **Nägler, K.**, '09. Entwicklungsgeschichtliche Studien über Amöben: *A. P.*, XV. — **Nakahara, W.**, '17. On the Physiology of the Nucleoli as seen in the Silk-gland of Certain Insects: *J. M.*, XXIX. — '17. Preliminary Note on the Nuclear Division in Adipose Cells of Insects: *A. R.*, XIII. — '18. Some Observations on the Growing Oöcytes of the Stonefly, etc.: *A. R.*, XV. — '18. Studies in Amitosis: Its Physiological Relations, etc.: *J. M.*, XXX. — '19. A Study of the Chromosomes in the Spermatogenesis of the Stonefly, etc.: *Ibid.*, XXXII. — '20. Side-to-side versus End-to-end Conjugation of Chromosomes in Relation to Crossing Over: *Sci.*, LII. — **Nakao, M.**, '11. Cytological Studies on the Nuclear Division of the Pollen Mother-cells of Some Cereals and Their Hybrids: *Jour. Coll. Agr. Tohoku Imp. Uni.*, V. — **Nassonov, D. N.**, '18. Recherches cytologiques sur les cellules végétales: *Arch. Russ. Anat. Histol. et Phys.*: II. — '23. Das Golgische Binnennetz, etc.: *A. M. A.*, XCVII. — '23b. Das Golgische Binnennetz, etc.: *Ibid.* C. — **Nathansohn A.**, '00. Physiologische Untersuchungen über amitotische Kernteilung: *J. W. B.*, XXXV. — **Nawaschin, M.**, '15. Haploide, Diploide, und Triploide Kerne von *Crepis virens*, Vill. (See Sakamura, '15, '20). — **Nawaschin, S.**, '99. Neue Beobachtungen über Befruchtung bei *Fritillaria* und *Lilium: Bot. Centr.*, LXXVII. — '09. Ueber das selbständige Bewegungsvermögen der Spermakerne bei einigen Angiospermen: *Oesterreich. Bot. Zeitschr.*, LIX. — '10. Näheres über die Bildung der Spermakerne bei *Lilium: Ann. Jard. Bot. Buit.*, XII. — **Nebeski, O.**, '80. Die Erzeugung von Eiern im Hoden von *Orchestia: Arb. Zool. int. Wien*, III. — **Nelson, J. A.**, '04. (XIII). — **Nemec, B.**, '97. Ueber die Struktur der Diplopodeneier: *A. A.*, XIII, 10, 11. — '99. Ueber die karyokinetische Kerntheilung in den Wurzelspitzen von *Allium: J. W. B.*, XXVIII, 2. — '03. (II). — '08. Ueber die Natur des Bakterienprotoplasten: *B. D. B. G.* — '10. (V). — '12. Ueber die Befruchtung bei *Gagea: Bull. Internat. Acad. Sci. Bohême.* I—XVII. — **Newell, Wilmon**, '14. Inheritance in the Honey Bee: *Sci., n. s.*, XLI. — **Newmann, H. H.**, '10. (XIV). — **Newman** and **Patterson**, '10. The Development of the nine-banded Armadillo: *J. M.*, XXI. — **Newport, G.**, '54. (XIII). — **Nichols, G. E.**, '10. A Morphological Study of *Juniperus: Beih. Bot. Centr.*, XXV. — '08. The Development of the Pollen of *Sarracenia: B. G.*, XLV. — **Newton, W. C. F.**, '24. Pairing and Segmentation in *Galtonia: A. B.*, XXXVIII. — **Nichols, M. L.**, '10. The Spermatogenesis of *Euchroma: B. B.*, XIX. — **Nicolas, A.**, '00. Contribution a l'étude de la fécondation chez l'orvet: *A. A. M.*, III. — '03. Nouvelles observations relatives a la fécondation chez l'orvet: *C. R. Soc. de biol. de Paris.* — **Niessing, C.**, '96. Die Betheiligung im Centralkörper und Sphäre um Aufbau des Samenfadens, etc.: *A. M. A.*, XLVIII. — **Noack, K. L.**, '21. Untersuchungen über die Individualität der Plastiden bei Phanerogamen: *Z. B.*, XIII. — **Noack, W.**, '01. Beiträge zur Entwicklungsgeschichte der Muscidae. *Z. W. Z.*, LXX. — **Noll, F.**, '07. Versuche über Geschlechtsbestimmung bei diözischen Pflanzen: *Sitzungber. d. Niederrhein. Ges. f. Natur- u. Heilkunde zu Bonn.* — **Nonidez, J. F.**, '20. Spermatogenesis of *Blaps*, etc.: *J. M.*, XXXIV. — **Nordenskiöld, E.**, '09. Zur Spermatogenese von *Ixodes: Z. A.*, XXXIV. — **Noren, C. O.**, '07. Zur Entwicklungsgeschichte des *Juniperus: Upsala Univ. Arsskrift.* — **Norman, W. W.**, '96. Segmentation of the Nucleus without segmentation of the Protoplasm: *A. Entwm.*, III. — **Nothnagel, M.**, '16. Reduction Divisions in the

Pollen Mother-cells of *Allium: B. G.,* LXI. — '18. Fecundation and Formation of the Primary Endosperm Nucleus in certain Liliaceae: *Ibid.,* LXVI. — **Nowikoff, M.,** '10. Zur Frage nach der Bedeutung der Amitose: *A. Zf.,* V. — **Nowlin, (W.) Nadine,** '08. The Chromosome Complex of *Melanoplus bivatattus: Kansas Univ. Sci. Bull.,* IV. — '06. Study of the Spermatogenesis of *Coptocycla: J. E. Z.,* III. — **Nussbaum, M.,** '80. Zur Differenzierung des Geschlechts im Tierreich: *A. M. A.,* XVIII. — '84a. Ueber Spontane und Künstliche Theilung von Infusorien: *Verh. d. naturf. preus. Rheinland.* — '84b. Ueber die Veränderungen der Geschlechtsproducte bis zur Eifurchung: *A. M. A.,* XXIII. — '86. Ueber die Teilbarkheit der lebendigen Materie, I: *Ibid.,* XXVI. — '94. Die mit der Entwicklung fortschreitende Differenzierung der Zellen: *B. C.,* XVI. — '97. Die Entstehung des Geschlechts bei *Hydatina: A. M. A.,* XLIX. **Nussbaum-Hilarowicz, J.,** '17. Ueber das Verhalten des Chondrioms während der Eibildung bei *Dytiscus: Z. W. Z.,* CXVII. — **Nuttall,** '04. (VIII).

OBST, P., '99. Untersuchungen über das Verhalten der Nucleolen, etc.: *Z. W. Z.,* LXVI, 2. — **Oehninger, M.,** '13. Ueber Kerngrössen bei Bienen: *V. P. M. G., Würzburg,* XLII. — **Oehlkers, F.,** '16. Beitrag zur Kenntniss der Kernteilung bei den Characeen: *B. D. B. G.,* XXXIV. — **Oes, A.,** '08. Ueber die Autolyse der Mitosen: *B. Z.* — '10. Neue Mitteilung über enzymatische Chromatolyse: *Z. B.,* II. — **Oettinger, R.,** '09. Samenreifung und Samenbildung bei *Pachyiulus: A. Zf.,* III, 4. — **Ogata, M.,** '83. Die Veränderung der Pancreaszellen bei der Secretion: *A. A. P. (Phys. Abt.).*—Oguma and Kihara, '23. Étude des chromosomes chez l'homme: *A. B.,* XXXIII.—Oguma and **Kihara,** '22. A preliminary Report on the Human Chromosomes: *Zool. Mag. Tokyo,* XXXIV, 401. — **Ohshima, Hiroshi,** '21. Inhibitory Effect of Dermal Secretion of the Sea-urchin upon Fertilizability of the Egg: *Sci.,* LIV. — **Okkelberg, P.,** '14. Volumetric Changes in the Egg of the Brook Lamprey, etc.: *B. B.,* XXVI. — '21. The early History of the Germ-cells in the Brook Lamprey: *J. M.,* XXXV. — **Olive, E. W.,** '05. Mitotic division of the Nuclei of the Cyanophyceae: *Beih. z. Biol. Zentralbl.* — '07. Cytological Studies on *Ceratomyxa: Trans. Wiss. Acad. Sci.,* XV. — **Oliver, J. R.,** '13. The Spermiogenesis of the Pribilof Fur Seal: *A. J. A.,* XIV. — **Oltmanns, F.,** '95. Ueber die Entwicklung der Sexualorgane bei *Vaucheria: Flora.* — '22, '23. (VII). — '13. Fortpflanzung der Gewächse, Algae: *H. Nw.,* IV. *Jena.* — **Oltmanns, Fischer, Winkler, Klebs, Korschelt,** and **others,** '13. Fortpflanzung: *H. Nw.,* IV, *Fischer, Jena.* — **Onions, G. W.,** '12, '14. South African " fertile Worker-bees ": *Ag. Journ. Union South Africa,* III and IV. — **Oppel, A.,** '91. Die Befruchtung des Reptilieneies: *A. A.,* VI. — **Orton, J. H.,** '09. On the Occurrence of Protandric Hermaphroditism in the Mollusc *Crepidula: P. R. S.,* LXXXI. — **Osawa, I.,** '12. Cytological and Experimental Studies in *Citrus: Jour. Coll. Agr. Imp. Uni., Tokyo,* IV. — '13. Studies on the Cytology of some Species of *Taraxacum: A. Zf.,* X. — '20. (XI). — **Osterhout, W. J. V.,** '97. (II). — '00. Befruchtung bei *Batrachospermum: Flora,* LXXXVII. – '17. The Rôle of the Nucleus in Oxidation: *Sci.,* XLVI. — '22. (III). — **Ostwald, W.,** '09. (VIII). — **Otte,** '07. Samenreifung und Samenbildung bei *Locusta: Z. J.,* XXIV. — **Overton, C. E..** '89. Beiträg zur Kenntniss der Gattung *Volvox: B. C.,* XXXIX. — '88. Ueber den Conjugationsvorgang bei *Spirogyra: B. D. B. G.,* VI. — '93. Ueber die Reduktion der Chromosomen in den Kernen der Pflanzen: *Vierteljahrschr. Naturf. Ges. Zürich,* XXXVIII. Also *A.*

Bot., VII. — **Overton, J. B.**, '02. Parthenogenesis in *Thalictrum: B. G.*, XXXIII. — '05. Ueber Reduktionsteilung in den Pollenmutterzellen einiger Dikotylen, etc.: *J. W. B.*, XLII. — '09. (XI). — '22. (II).

PACE, L., '07. Fertilization in *Cypripedium: B. G.*, XLIV. — '09. The Gametophyte of *Calopogon: B.G.*, XLVIII. — '10. Some Peculiar Fern Prothallia: *B. G.*, L. — '13. Apogamy in *Atamosco: Ibid.*, LVI. — **Packard, C.**, '18. The Effect of Radium Radiations on the Development of *Chaetopterus: B. B.*, XXXVI. — **Painter, T. S.**, '14. Spermatogenesis in Spiders: *Z. J., A. u. O.*, XXXVIII. — '18. Contributions to the Study of Cell Mechanics. II: *J. E. Z.*, XXIV. — '19. The Spermatogenesis of *Anolis: A. R.*, XVII. — '21. The Y-Chromosome in Mammals: *Sci., n. s.*, LIII. — '21, '22a, '23. (X). — '22. The Sex-chromosomes of the Monkey: *Sci.*, LVI. — '23b. The Sex Chromosomes of Monkeys: (In press). — '23b. The Fate of the Chromatin-nucleolus in the Opossum: (In press). — **Paladino, G.**, '90. I ponti intercellulari tra l'uovo ovarico e le cellule follicolari, etc.: *A. A.*, V. — **Palladin, V. I.**, '18. Plant Physiology: (*Eng. trans.*, *ed. by Livingston*). — **Pampaloni, L.**, '03. I fenomeni cariocinetici nelle cellule meristemali degli apici vegetativi de *Psilotum: Annali di Bot.*, I. — **Pantel** and **Sinéty**, '06. Les cellules de le lignée mâle chez le *Notonecta L.: L. C.*, XXIII. — '08. Sur l'apparition des mâles et d'hermaphrodites dans les pontes parthénogénétiques des Phasmes: *C. R.*, CXLVII. — **Papanicolaou, G.**, '10. Experimentelle Untersuchungen über die Fortpflanzungsverhältnisse der Daphniden: *B. C.*, XXX. — **Papanicolaou** and **Stockard**, '18. The Development of the Idiosome in the Germ-cells of the male Guinea-pig: *A. J. A.*, XXIV. — **Pappenheimer, A. M.**, '16. (IX). — **Parmenter, C. L.**, '19. Chromosome Number and Pairs in the somatic Mitoses of *Amblystoma: J. M.*, XXXIII, 1. — '20. The Chromosomes of parthenogenic Frogs: *J. G. P.*, XI, 3. — **Pascher, A.**, '16. Ueber die Kreuzung einzelliger haploiden Organismen, *Chlamydomonas: B. D.B.G.*, XXXIV. — **Patten, W.**, '85. The Embryology of *Patella: Arb. Zool. Inst. Wien*, VI, 2. — **Patterson, J. T.**, '08. Amitosis in the Pigeon's Egg: *A. A.*, XXXII. — '15. Observations on the Development of *Copidosoma: B. B.*, XXIX. — Studies on the Biology of *Paracopidosomopsis*, I, '17: *B.B.*, XXXII; II (with L. T. Porter): *Ibid.*, XXXIII; III, '17b: *Ibid.*; IV, '18: *Ibid.*, XXXV; V, '19: *J. H.*, X. — '21. The Development of *Paracopidosomopsis: J. M.*, XXXVI. — **Patterson** and **Porter**, '17. Studies on the Biology of *Paracopidosomopsis*, II: *B. B.*, XXXIII. — **Paulcke, W.**, '00. Ueber die Differenzierung der Zellelemente im Ovarium der Biener-Königin: *Z. J.*, XIV. — **Paulmier, F. C.**, '98. Chromatin Reduction in the Hemiptera: *A. A.*, XIV. — '99. The Spermatogenesis of *Anasa tristis: J. M.*, XV, Suppl. — **Payne, F.**, '08, '09. (X). — '10. The Chromosomes of *Acholla multispinosa: B. B.*, XVIII. — '12. A Further Study of the Chromosomes of the Reduviidae, etc.: *J. M.*, XXIII. — '12. The Chromosomes of *Gryllotalpa: A. Zf.*, IX. — '14. Chromosomal Variations and the Formation of the first Spermatocyte Chromosomes in . . . *Forficula: J. M.*, XXV. — '16. A Study of the Germ Cells of *Gryllotalpa: Ibid.*, XXVIII. — **Pearl, R.**, '21. The Biology of Death. II — The Conditions of Cellular Immortality: *S. M.*, XII. — '22. (III). — **Pensa, A.**, '12. Osservazioni di morfologia e biologia cellulare nei vegetali (mitocondri, cloroplasti): *A. Zf.*, VIII. — '13a. Condriosomi e pigmento antocianico nelle cellule vegetali: *A. A.*, XLV. — '13b. La struttura della cellula cartilaginea: *A. Zf.*, XI. — '14. Ancora a proposito de condriosomi e pigmento antocianico nelle cellule vegetali: *A. A.*, XLVI. — **Pentimalli, F.,** '09. Influenza della sorrente elettrica sulla dinamica del processo cariocinetica: *A. Entwm.*, XXVIII, 2, 3. — **Perroncito, A.,** '10. (IV). — **Peter, K.,** '99. Das Centrum fur die Flimmer- und Geisselbewegung: *A. A.*, XV, 14, 15. — **Petrunkewitsch, A.,** '01. Die Richtungskörper im befruchteten und unbefruchteten Bienenei: *Z. J., Abt. Anat.*, XIV. — '02. Die Reifung der partenog. Eier von *Artemia: A. A.*, XXI. — '03. Das Schicksal der Richtungskörper im Drohnenei: *Z. J.*, XVII. — '04. Künstliche Parthenogenesis: *Z. J.*, Suppl., VII. — **Pfeffer, W.,** '84. (V). — '96. Ueber den Einfluss des Zellkerns auf die Bildung der Zellhaut: — '09. Ueber die Erzeugung und die physiologische Bedeutung der Amitose: *Ber. Königl., Sachs., Ges. Wiss. Leipzig.* — '99. Bericht über amitotische Kerntheilung: *Ber. d. Math.-Phys. Kl. d. Klg. Sach. Ges. Wiss.* — **Pfitzner, W.,** '82. Ueber den feineren Bau der bei der Zelltheilung auffretenden fadenförmigen Differenzierungen des Zellkerns: *M. J.*, VII. — '83. Beiträge zur Lehre vom Baue des Zellkerns und seinen Theilungserscheinungen: *A. M. A.*, XXII. — **Pflüger, E.,** Versuche der Befruchtung uberreifer Eier: XXIX. '82. Ueber die geschlechtsbestimmenden Ursachen und die Geschlechtsverhältnisse der Frosche: *Ibid.*, XXIX. — '83. Ueber den Einfluss der Schwerkraft auf die Theilung der Zellen, I: *A. Ph.*, XXXI; II: *Ibid.*, XXXII. Abstract in *B. C.*, III, '84. — '84. Ueber die Einwirkung der Schwerkraft und anderer Bedingungen auf die Richtung der Zelltheilung: *A. Ph.*, XXXIV. — '89. Die allgemeinen Lebenserscheinungen: *Bonn.* — **Philips, O. P.,** '04. A comparative Study of the Cytology and Movements of the Cyanophyceae: *Contrib. Bot. Lab. Univ. Pa.*, II. — **Picard, M.,** '13. A Bibliography of Works on Meiosis and Somatic Mitosis in the Angiosperms: *Bull. Torr. Bot. Club.*, XL. — **Pinney, E.,** '08. Organization of the Chromosomes in *Phrynotettix: Kans. Univ. Sci. Bull.*, IV. — '18. A Study of the Relation of the Behavior of the Chromatin to Heredity and Development in Teleost Hybrids: *J. M.*, XXXI. — **Platner, G.,** '86a. Zur Bildung der Geschlechtsprodukte bei den Pulmonaten: *A. M. A.*, XXVI. — '86b. Ueber die Befruchtung von *Arion: Ibid.*, XXVII. — '89. Beiträge zur Kenntniss der Zelle und ihrer Theilung: *Ibid.*, XXXIII. — '89. (VI). — **Plough, H. H.,** '17. (XII). — **Poirault** and **Raciborski,** '96. Ueber konjugate Kerne und die konjugate Kerntheilung: *B. C.*, XVI, 1. — **Policard, A.,** '15. Chondriocontes et fibrilles plasmatiques dans les cellules du tube urinaire des Batraciens: *A. A.*, XLVII. — **Polowzow, W.,** '23. Wirkung der Alkoholnarkose auf . . . Seeigeleier: *A. M. A.*, XCVIII. — **Popoff, M.,** '07. Eibildung bei *Paludina*, etc.: *A. M. A.*, LXX. — '08. Ueber das Vorhandensein von Tetraden-Chromosomen in den Leberzellen von *Paludina: B. C.*, XXVIII, 17. — '08. Die Gametenbildung und Konjugation von *Carchesium: Z. W. Z.*, LXXXIX. — '08-'09. Experimentelle cytologische Studien: *A. Zf.*, I, III, IV. — '09. Ueber einige Ursache der physiologischen Depression der Zelle: *A. Zf.*, IV. — **Potts, F. A.,** '06. The Modification of the Sexual Characters of the Hermit Crab caused by the Parasite *Peltogaster: Q. J.*, L. — **Prandtl, H.,** '06. Die Konjugation von *Didinium: A. P.*, VII. — **Prankerd, T. L.,** '15. Notes on the Occurrence of Multinucleate Cells: *A. Bot.*, XXIX. — **Prantl, R.,** '81. Beobachtungen über die Ernährung der Farnprothallien und der Verteilung der Sexualorgane: *B. Z.*, XXXIX. — **Pratje, A.,** '20. (VIII). — **Pratt, B. H.,** and **Long, J. A.,** '17. The Period of Synapsis in the Egg of the White Rat: *J. M.*, XXIX. — **Prenant, A.,** '94. Sur le corpuscule central: *Bull. Soc. Sci., Nancy.* — '98-'99, '10, '11a, '13a. (IX). — '10. (II). — '11. (XII). — '13. Sur l'origine mitochondriale des grains de pigment: *C. R. S. B.*,

LXXIV. — **Prenant, Bouin, Maillard,** '04. (I). — **Preusse, F.,** '95. Ueber die amitotische Kerntheilung in den Ovarien der Hemipteren: *Z. W. Z.,* LIX, 2. — **Prévost** and **Dumas,** 1824. (Int.). — **Pringsheim, E. G.,** '13. Ueber Blaualgen: *Die Naturwissenschaften.* — **Pringsheim, N.,** '54. Untersuchungen über Bau und Bildung der Pflanzenzelle: Berlin. — '55. Ueber die Befruchtung und Keimung der Algen und das Wesen des Zeugungsaktes: *Monatsber. K. Akad. Wiss. Berlin,* I. — '58. Morphologie der Oedogonieen: *J. W. B.,* I. — '69. Ueber die Paarung von Schwärmsporen, die morphologische Grundform der Zeugung im Pflanzenreiche: *Monatschr. d. Kgl. Akad. d. Wissensch., Berlin.* — '78. Ueber Sprossung der Moosfrüchte und den Generationswechsel der Thallophyten: *J. W. B.,* XI. — **Prowazek, S.,** '02a. Spermatogenese der Weinbergschnecke, I: *Arb. Zool. Inst. Wien,* XIII. — '02b. Spermatogenese des Nashornkäfers (*Oryctes*): *Ibid.,* XIII. — '04. Untersuchungen über einige parasitische Flagellaten: *Arb. a. d. Kais. Gesundheitsamt.,* XXI. — **Prowazek** and **Nöller,** '20. (VII). — **Przibram, H.,** '08. (XIV). — **Punnett, R. C.,** '06. Sex-determination in *Hydatina,* etc.: *P. R. S.,* B, LXXVIII. — '09. On the Alleged Influence of Lecithin upon the Determination of Sex in Rabbits: *Proc. Camb. Phil. Soc.,* XV. — '11. Mendelism, 3rd ed.: New York. — '13, '17. Reduplication Series in Sweet Peas, I, II: *J. G.,* III and VI.

RABL, C., '79. (XIII). — '89. (XI). — '89b. Ueber die Prinzipien der Histologie; *Verh. Anat. Ges.,* III. — '89. (II). — '99. (IX). — '06. (Int., XIV). — '15. (Int.). — **Raffaele, F.,** '21. (XI). — **Rappeport, T.,** '15. Zur Spermatogenese der Süsswassertricladen: *A. Zf.,* XIV. — **Vom Rath, O.,** '92. Zur Kenntniss der Spermatogenese von *Gryllotalpa: A. M. A.,* XL. — '91. Ueber die Bedeutung der amitotischen Kerntheilung im Hoden: *Z. A.,* XIV. — '95. Neue Beiträge zur Frage der Chromatinreduction in der Samen- und Eireife: *A. M. A.,* XLVI. — '95b. Ueber den feineren Bau der Drüsenzellen des Kopfes von *Anilocra,* etc.: *Z. W. Z.,* LX, 1. — **Rauber, A.,** '83. Neue Grundlegungen zur Kentniss der Zelle: *M. J.,* VIII. — **Reed, G. B.,** '15. The Rôle of Oxidases in Respiration: *Jour. Biol. Chem.,* XXII. — **Reed, T.,** '14. The Nature of the Double Spireme in *Allium: A. Bot.,* XXVIII. — **Regaud, C.,** '09a. Attribution aux "formations mitochondriales" de la fonction générale d'extraction et de fixation électives, etc. *C. R. S. B.,* LXVI. — '09b. Sur les mitochondries des fibres musculaires du cœur: *C. R.,* CXLIX. — '09c. Participation du chondriomes a la formation des grains de sécrétion, etc.: *C. R. S. B.,* LXVI. — '10. (IV, IX). — '11. Les mitochondries, organites du protoplasma, etc.: *Revue de Medicin.* — **Regaud** and **Dubreuil,** '05. La constitution de la zone pellucida, etc.: *C. R. Ass. Anat., Geneva.* — **Regaud** and **Favre,** '12. Nouvelles recherches sur les formations mitochondriales de l'epiderme humain a l'état normal et pathologique: *C. R. S. B.,* LXVI. — **Regaud** and **Mawas,** '09a. Ergastoplasme et mitochondries dans les cellules de la glande sous-maxillaire: *C. R. S. B.,* LXVI. — '09b. Sur la structure du protoplasma: *C. R. Assoc. Anat.* — **Reichert, E. T.,** '14. The Germ-Plasm as a Stereochemic System: *Sci.,* XL. — **Reichert** and **Brown,** '09. (VIII). — **Reinke, Fr.,** '94. Zellstudien I: *A. M. A.,* XLVII. III: *Ibid.,* XLIV. — '00. Zum Beweis der trajektoriellen Natur der Plasmastrahlungen. Ein Beitrag zur Mechanik der Mitose: *A. Entwm.,* IX. — **Reinke, J.,** '01. Einleitung in die theoretische Biologie: Berlin. — **Remak, R.,** '41. Ueber Theilung rother Blutzellen beim Embryo: *Med. Ver. Zeit.* — '50–'55. (Int.). — '52. Ueber extracellulare Entstehung thierische Zellen und über Vermehrung derselben durch Theilung: *Müller's Archiv.* — **Renner, O.,** '14. Befruchtung und Embryobildung bei *Oenothera*, etc.: *Flora,* CVII. — '16. Zur Terminologie des pflänzlichen Generationswechsel: *B. C.,* XXXVI. — **Retzius, G.,** '89. Die Intercellularbrücken des Eierstockseies und der Follikelzellen, etc.: *V. A. G., Berlin.* — '02–'14. (IV). — '06. Ueber die Spermien der Fucaceen: *Ark. Bot.,* V; also *Biol. Unters.* N. P., XIII. — '12. Zur Kenntniss der Hüllen und besonders des Follikenepithels, etc.: *Biol. Unters.,* XVII. — '14. (I). — **Rhumbler, L.,** '93. Ueber Entstehung und Bedeutung der in den Kernen vieler Protozoen und im Keimbläschen von Metazoen vorkommenden Binnenkörper (Nucleolen): *Z. W. Z.,* LVI. — '96. Versuch einer mechanischen Erklärung der indirekten Zell- und Kerntheilung: *A. Entwm.,* III. — '97. Stemmen die Strahlen der Astrosphäre oder ziehen sie? *A. Entwm.,* IV. — '98. Die Mechanik der Zelldurchschnürung nach Meves' und nach meiner Auffassung: *A. Entwm.,* VII. — '99. Furchung des Ctenophoreneies nach Ziegler und deren Mechanik usw.: *A. Entwm.,* VIII. — '99. Mechanik der Abdruckung von Zelleinlagerungen, etc.: *A. Entwm.,* IX. — '99. Allgemeine Zellmechanik: *E. A. E.,* VIII. — '02. Zur Mechanik des Gastrulationsvorganges, etc.: *A. Entwm.,* XIV. — '03. (II). — '05. Aus dem Lückengebiet zwischen Organischer und Anorganischer Material: *E. A. E.,* XV. — '02, '14. (IX). — **Richards, A.,** '09, '11. (II). — '17. (XI). — **Richards** and **Thompson,** 21. The Migration of the Primary Sex-Cells of *Fundulus: B. B.,* XL. — **Richter, P.,** '13. Die Reinkultur und die durch sie erzeugten Fortschritte vornehmlich auf botanischen Gebiete: *P. R. B.* — **Riddle, O.,** '11. On the Formation, Significance and Chemistry of the White and Yellow Yolk of Ova: *J. M.,* XXII. — '12. Preliminary Chemical Studies on Male- and Female-Producing Eggs of Pigeons: *Sci.,* XXXV. — '14. The Determination of Sex and its Experimental Control: *Bull. Am. Acad. Med.,* XV. — '16a. (X). — '16b. Success in Controlling Sex: *J. H.,* VII. — '17. The Theory of Sex as Stated in Terms of Results of Studies on Pigeons: *Sci.,* XLVI. — '17. The Control of the Sex Ratio: *Jour. Wash. Acad. Sc.,* VII. — **Del Rio Hortega, P.,** '15. Estudios sobre el centrosoma de las celulas nerviosas, etc.: *Trab. Univ. Madrid,* XIII. — '17. Contribucion al conocimiento de las epiteliofibrillas: *Ibid.,* XV. — **Ritter, W. E.,** '19. (XIV). — **Rivett, M. F.,** '18. The Structure of the Cytoplasm in the Cells of *Alicularia: A. Bot.,* XXXII. — **Robert,** '02. (XIII). — **Robertson, T. B.,** '09a. The Proteins: *Univ. Calif. Publ. Phys.,* III, 16. — '09b. Note on the Chemical Mechanics of Cell-Division: *A. Entwm.,* XXVII. — '11. Further Remarks on the Chemical Mechanics of Cell Division: *Ibid.,* XXXII. — '13. Further Explanatory Remarks Concerning the Chemical Mechanics of Cell Division: *Ibid.,* XXXV. — '18. The Physical Chemistry of the Proteins: *New York.* — '20. Principles of Biochemistry: *Philadelphia and New York,* **Lee** and **Fibiger.**— '21. La base chimique de la croissance, etc.: *Scientia.,* March. — **Robertson, W. R. B.,** '08, '15, '16, '17. (XI). — '19. The Presence of a longitudinal Split in Chromosomes prior to their Union in Parasynapsis: *Abstract of Proc. Am. Soc. Zool.,* 1919. — **Rohde, E.,** '14. (I). — **Romeis, B.,** '13a. Ueber Plastosomen und andere Zellstrukturen in den Uterus, Darm- und Muskelzellen von *Ascaris: A. A.,* XLIV. — '13b. Beobachtungen über die Plastosomen von *Ascaris: A. M. A.,* LXXXI. — '13c. Das Verhalten der Plastosomen bei der Regeneration: *A. A.,* XLV. — **Romieu, M.,** '11. La spermiogénèse chez l'*Ascaris megalocephala: A. Zf.,* VI. — **Rosen, F.,** '96. Beiträge zur Kenntniss der Pflanzenzellen, III: *Beitr. z. Biol. der Pflanz.,* VII. — **Rosenberg, G.,**

'03. Das Verhalten der Chromosomen in einer hybriden Pflanze: *B. D. B. G.*, XXI.
— '04, '07, '09, '17. (XI). — '06. Ueber die Embryobildung in der Gattung
Hieracium: B. D. B. G., XXIV. — '07. Zur Kenntniss der praesynaptischen
Entwicklungsphasen der Reduktionsteilung: *Svenk. Bot. Tids.*, I. — '09. Ueber
die Chromosomenzahlen bei *Taraxacum* und *Rosa: Ibid.*, III. — '09a. Zur Kenntniss von den Tetradenteilung der Compositen: *Ibid.*, III. — '09b. Ueber den Bau
des Ruhekerns: *Ibid.*, III. — '18. Chromosomenzahlen und Chromosomendimen-
sionen in der Gattung *Crepis: Ark. B.*, XV. — '20. Weitere Untersuchungen
über die Chromosomenverhältnisse in *Crepis: Svensk. Bot. Tidskr.*, XIV. —
Roux, W., '83. (II, XI). — '83b. Ueber die Zeit der Bestimmung der Hauptrichtungen des Froschembryo: *Leipzig.* — '85, '87. (XIII). — '90. Die Ent-
wickelungsmechanik der Organismen: *Wien.* — '92, '93, '95, '03, '05. (XIV). —
'92. Ueber das Untwicklungsmechanische Vermögen jeder der Beiden ersten
Furchungzellen des Eies: *Verh. d. Anat. Ges. zu. Wien.* — '92a. Entwicklungsmechanik: *Merkel. u. Bonnet*, Erg., II. — '93b. Ueber die Spezification der Furchungzellen, etc.; B. C., XIII, — '94a. Ueber den " Cytotropismus " der Furchungzellen des Grasfrosches: *A. Entwm.*, I. — '94. Gesammelte Abhandlungen
über Entwicklungsmechanik: *Leipzig*, Engelmann. — '94b. Aufgabe der Entwicklungsmechanik, etc.: *A. Entwm.*, I. Trans. in *W. H. L.*, '94. — '95. Ueber
die verschiedene Entwicklung isolirter erster Blastomeren: *A. Entwm.*, I. — '97.
Für unser Program und seine Verwirklichung: *A. Entwm.*, V. — '02. Bemerkungen
über die Achsenbestimmung des Froschembryo und die Gastrulation des Fros-
cheies: *A. Entwm.*, XIV. — **Rubaschkin, W.,** '10. (IX). — '12. (IV). — **Rückert, J.,** '91. Zur Befruchtung des Selachiereies: *A. A.*, VI. — '92. Physiologische
Polyspermie bei meroblastischen Wirbeltiereiern: *A. A.*, VII. — '92a, '92b. (VI,
XII). — '93. (VI). — '94. Zur Eireifung der Copepoden: *E. A. E.*, *An. Hf.*,
IV. — '95a. Zur Kenntniss des Befruchtungsvorganges: *Sitzb. Bayer. Akad.
Wiss.*, XXVI, 1. — '95b. Zur Befruchtung von *Cyclops: A. A.*, X, 22. — '95c.
Ueber das Selbständigbleiben der väterlichen und mütterlichen Kernsubstanz
während der ersten Entwicklung des befruchteten *Cyclops-Eies: A. M. A.*, XLV,
3. — '99. Die erste Entwicklung des Eies der Elasmobranchier: *Festschrift für
C. von Kupffer.* — '10. Ueber Polyspermie: *A. A.*, XXXVII. — **Rudolph, K.,**
'12. Chondriosomen und Chromatophoren, etc.: *B. D. B. G.*, XXX. — **Ruhland,
W.,** '15. Zur Kritik der Lipoid- und Ultrafiltertheorie der Plasmahaut, usw.:
Biochem. Zeitschr., LIV. — **Russo, A.,** '12. Aumento dei granuli proplasmatici
nell' oöcite delle coniglia, etc.: *A. Zf.*, VIII. — **Ruzička, V.,** '09. Die Cytologie
der Sporenbildenden Bakterien und ihr Verhältnis zur Chromidienlehre: *Centr.
Bakt.*, II, XXIII.

SABASCHNIKOFF, M., '97. Beiträge zur Kenntniss der Chromatinreduktion in der Ovogenesis von *Ascaris: Bull. Soc. Nat. Moscow.*, I. **Sachs, J.,** '82.
(XIII). — '90. (Int.). — '92. Beiträge zur Zellentheorie: *Flora*, Heft I. — '93.
Stoff und Form der Pflanzenorgane: *Ges. Abh.*, II. — '93. Ueber einige Beziehungen der specifischen Grösse der Pflanzen zu ihrer Organization: *Flora*, LXXVII. —
'95. Weitere Betrachtungen über Energiden und Zellen: *Flora*, LXXXI. —
Saedeleer, A. de, '13. Contribution a l'étude de l'ovogénèse dans l'*Ascaris
megalocephala bivalens: L. C.*, XXVIII. — **Saguchi, S.,** '13. (I). — '15. Ueber
Sekretionserscheinungen, etc.: *Tokyo.* — '17. (IX). — '20. Studies on the
glandular Cells of the Frog's Pancreas: *A. J. A.*, XXVI. — **Sakamura, T.,** '14.

Ueber die Kernteilung bei *Vicia: Bot. Mag. Tokyo,* XXVIII. — '15. Ueber die Einschnürung der Chromosomen bei *Vicia faba L.: Ibid.,* XXIX. — '16. Ueber die Beeinflussung der Zell- und Kernteilung durch *Chloralisierung,* etc.: *Ibid.,* XXX. — '18. Kurze Mitteilung über die Chromosomenzahlen und die Verwandtschaftsverhältnisse der *Triticum-Arten: Ibid.* — '20. Experimentelle Studien über die Zell-und Kernteilung mit besonderer Rucksicht auf Form, Grösse und Zahl der Chromosomen: *Jour. Coll. Sci. Imp. Univ. Tolyo,* XXXIX. — **Sala, L.,** '95. Experimentelle Untersuchungen über die Reifung und Befruchtung der Eier bei *Ascaris megalocephala: A. M. A.,* XL. — **Samassa, P.,** '96. Studien über den Einfluss des Dotters auf die Gastrulation, etc.: *A. Entwm.,* II. — **Samssonow, N.,** '10. Ueber die Beziehungen der Filarmasse Flemmings zu den Fäden und Körnern Altmann's, etc.: *A. M. A.,* LXXV. — **Samuely, Fr.,** '09. Tierische Fermente: In *Handbuch der Biochemie* (Oppenheimer) I, Fischer, Jena. — **Sands, H. C.,** '07. Nuclear Structure and Spore-Formation in *Microsphaera: Trans. Wis. Acad. Sci.,* XV. — '22. Perigenesis: *Sci.,* LVI. - '23. (XI). — **Sapěhin, A. A.,** '11. Ueber das Verhalten der Plastiden im sporogonen Gewebe:*B. D. B. G.,* XXIX. — '13a. (IX). — '15. Untersuchungen über die Individualität der Plastide: *A. Zf.,* XIII. — **Santos, J. K.,** '23. Differentiation among Chromosomes in *Elodea: B. G.,* LXXV. — **Sarasin, P.,** '82. Entwicklungsgeschichte der *Bythinia tentaculata: Arb. Zoöl. Inst. Würzburg.* VI. — **Sargent, Ethel,** '95. Some Details of the first nuclear Division in the Pollen-mother-cells of *Lilium martagon: J. R. M.,* III. — '96. The Formation of the Sexual Nuclei in *Lilium Martagon: A. Bot.,* X. — '97. The Formation of the Sexual Nuclei in *Lilium,* II. Spermatogenesis: *A. Bot.,* XI. — **Sawyer, M. L.,** '17. Pollen Tube and Spermatogenesis in *Iris: B. G.,* LXIV. — **Sax, K.,** '16. Fertilization in *Fritillaria pudica: Bull. Torrey Bot. Club.,* XLIII. — '17. The Behavior of the Chromosomes in Fertilization: *G.,* III. — '22, '23. (XI). — **Schacke, M. A.,** '19. A Chromosome Difference between the Sexes of *Sphaerocarpus texanus: Sci.,* XLIV. — **Schaefer, F.,** '07. Spermatogenese von *Dytiscus: Z. J.,* XXIII. — **Schafer, E. A.,** '12. (Int.). — **Schaffer, J.,** '20. (I). — **Schaffner, J. H.,** '08. The Centrosomes of *Marchantia polymorpha: Ohio Nat.,* IX. — '09. The Reduction Division in the Microsporocytes of *Agave virginica: B. G.,* XLVII. — '22. (X). — **Schaudinn, F.,** '95. Ueber die Theilung von *Amoeba binucleata: Sitz. Ber. Ges. Naturf. Freunde, Berlin,* XCV. — '95c. Ueber das Centralkorn der Heliozoen: *V. D. Z. G.* — '96a. Ueber den Zeugungskreis von *Paramoeba Eilhardi: Sitz.- Ber. Akad. Wiss. Berlin,* Jan. 16. — '96b. Ueber die Copulation von *Actionophrys sol: Sitz. Ber. Akad. Wiss. Berlin,* Jan., 16. — '02. Beiträge zur Kenntniss der Bakterien und verwandten Organismen, I. *Bacillus Bütschlii,* n. sp.: *A. P.,* I. — '03. Untersuchungen über die Fortpflanzung einiger Rhizopoden: *Arb. Kaiserl. Gesundheitsamt,* XIX. — '05. Die Befruchtung der Protozoen: *V. D. Z. G.* — **Schaxel, J.,** '10. Die Beziehungen des Chromatins zum Cytoplasma, etc.: *Z. A.,* XXXVI. — '11a. (IX). — '11b. Das Verhalten des Chromatin bei der Eibildung einiger Hydrozoen:*Z. J.,* XXXI. — '12. (XIV). — **Schellenberg, A.,** '11. Ovogenese, Eireifung, und Befruchtung von *Fasciola hepatica: A. Zf.,* VI. — **Schepotieff, A.,** '11. Monerenstudien:*Z. J.* (Anat. Abth.), XXXII. — **Scherrer, A.,** '14. Untersuchungen über Bau und Vermehrung der Chromatophoren, etc.: *Flora,* CVII. — **Schewiakoff, W.,** '88. Ueber die karyokinetische Kerntheilung der *Euglypha alveolata: M. J.,* XIII. — '93. Ueber einen neuen Bakterienähnlichen Organismus: *Hab. Schrift.,* Heidelberg. — **Schiller, J.,** '09. Ueber künstliche Erzeugung "primitiver" Kernteilungsformen bei *Cyclops: A. Entwm.*, XXVII. — '09. Ueber die Entstehung der Plastiden aus dem Zellkern: *Oesterr. Bot. Zeitschr.* — **Schimper, A. F. W.**, '80,–'81. Untersuchungen über die *Entstehung der Stärkekörner: B. Z.*, XXXVIII. — '85. (I). — **Schittenhelm, A.**, '11. (VIII). — **Schittenhelm** and **Brahm**, '09. Nucleoproteide und ihre Spaltprodukte: Handbuch der Biochem: I. — **Schitz, V.**, '16. Sur la spermatogénèse chez *Columbella: A. Z. E.*, LVI. — **Schlater, G.**, '94. Zur Morphologie der Zelle: *A. M. A.*, XLIV, 2. — '11. Die Cellularpathologie und der gegerwartige Stand der Histologie: Fischer, Jena. — **Schleicher, W.**, '78. Die Knorpelzelltheilung, etc.: *Centr. med. Wiss. Berlin.* (Also *A. M. A.*, XVI, '79). — **Schleiden, M. J.**, '37. Einige Blicke aud die Entwicklungsgeschichte des vegetabilische Organismus bei den Phanerogamen: *Wiegmann's Archiv.*, I. — '38. (Int.). — **Schleip, W.**, '06. Die Entwicklung der Chromosomen im Ei von *Planaria: Z. J.*, XXIII. — '07. Die Samenreifung bei Planarien: *Z. J.*, XXIV. — '08. Die Richtungskörperbildung im Ei von *Formica: Zool. Jarb. Abt. Anat.*, XXVI. — '09. (VI). — '10. Die Reifung des Eies von *Rhodites*, etc.: *Ibid.*, V. — '11. Das Verhalten des Chromatin bei *Angiostomum (Rhabdonema) nigrovenosum: A. Zf.*, VII. — '12. (X). — '15. (III). — **Schmidt, E. W.**, '12. (I). — **Schmidt, W. J.**, '18. Die Chromatophoren der Reptilienhaut: *A. M. A.*, XC. — **Schmitz, Fr.**, '79. Untersuchungen über die Zellkerne der Thallophyten: *Verh. Naturhist. Ver. Preuss. Rheinl. u. Westfl.* — '82. Die Chromatophoren der Algen: *Bonn.* — **Schneider, A.**, '73. Untersuchungen über Platelminthen: *Jahr. d. Oberhess. Gesell. Natur-Heilkunde*, XIV. — '83. Das Ei und seine Befruchtung: *Breslau.* — **Schneider, H.**, '14. Ueber die Prophasen der ersten Reifeteilung in Pollenmutterzellen, etc.: *A. Zf.*, XII. — **Schneider, K. C.**, '02. (I). — '10. Chromosomengenese: *Festschrift R. Hertwig*, I. — **Schockaert, R.**, '01, '02. L'ovogénèse chez le *Thysanozoon*, I, II: *L. C.*, XVIII, XX. — **Schoenfeld, H.**, '01. (VI). — **Schönemund, E.**, '12. Zur Biologie und Morphologie einiger Perla-Arten: *Z. J. Anat.*, XXXIV. — **Schrader, F.**, '20. Sex Determination in the White Fly (*Trialeurodes*): *J. M.*, XXXIV. — '21. The Chromosomes of *Pseudococcus Nipae: B. B.*, XL. — '23. Haploidie bei einer Spinnmilbe: *A. M. A.*, XCVII. — '23. The Origin of the Mycetocytes in *Pseudococcus: B. B.*, XLV. — **Schreiner, A.** and **K. E.**, '04. Die Reifungsteilungen bei den Wirbeltieren: *A. A.*, XXIV. — '05. Ueber die Entwicklung der männlichen Geschlechtszellen von *Myxine glutinosa* (L.): *A. B.*, XXI. — '06a, '06b, '08. (VI). — '06. Die Reifung der Geschlechtszellen von *Ophryotrocha: A. A.*, XXIX. — '06c. Die Reifung der Geschlechtszellen von *Enteroxenos: Skrift. Vidensk. Christiania*, I. — '06d. Die Reifung der Geschlechtszellen von *Zoogonus mirus: Ibid.*, VIII. — '08. Zur Spermienbildung der Myxinoiden: *A. Zf.*, I. — **Schreiner, K. E.**, '12. Kurze Bemerkung zur Frage von der Bedeutung des Kerns, etc.: *B. C.*, XXXII. — '15. Ueber Kern- und Plasmaveränderungen in Fettzellen, etc.: *A. A.*, XLVIII. — '16, '18. Zur Kenntniss der Zellgranula, etc.: *A. M. A.*, LXXXIX; *Ibid.*, XCII. — **Schridde, H.**, '05. Die Körnelung der Plasmazellen: *An. Hf.*, 1 Abt., XXVIII. — '07. Myeloblasten, Lymphoblasten und lympoblastische Plasmazellen; *Ziegler's Beitr. z. path. Anat.*, XLI. — **Schuberg, A.**, '03. Untersuchungen über Zellverbindungen: *Z. W. Z.*, LXXIV. — **Schultze, Max**, '61. Ueber Muskelkörperchen und das was man eine Zelle zu nennen hat: *A. A. P.* — **Schultze, O.**, '87. Untersuchungen über die Reifung und Befruchtung des Amphibien-eies: *Z. W. Z.*, XLV. — '90. Ueber Zelltheilung: *S. B. P. M. G.*, Würzburg. — '94, '00. (XIII, XIV). — '95. Die künstliche Erzeugung von Doppelbildungen bei Froschlarven, etc.: *A. Entwm.*, I. — '03. Zur Frage, von den geschlechtsbildenden Ursachen: *A. M. A.*, LXIII. — '11b. Ueber die Genese der Granula in den Drüsen-Zellen: *A. A.*, XXXVIII. — '12. Ueber den direckten Zusammenhang am Muskelfibrillen und Sehnenfibrillen: *A. M. A.*, LXXIX. — **Schurhoff, P. N.,** '15. Amitosen von Riesenkernen im Endosperm von *Ranunculus acer: J. W. B.*, LV. — '18. Die Beziehungen des Kernkörperchens zu den Chromosomen und Spindel-fasern: *Flora*, CX. — '19. Das Verhalten des Kerns in den Knöllchenzellen von *Podocarpus: B. D. B. G.*, XXXVII. — **Schustow, L. v.,** '13a. Ueber Kernteilung in der Würzelspitze von *Allium Cepa: A. A.*, XLIII: *A. Zf.*, XI. — **Schwann, Th.,** '39. (Int.). — **Schwarz, Fr.,** '87. Die Morphologische und chemische Zusammensetzung des Protoplasmas: Breslau. (Rev. in Bot. Zeit. XLV). — **Schweigger-Seidel, O.,** '65. Ueber die Samenkörperchen und ihre Entwicklung: *A. M. A.*, I. — **Sedgwick, A.,** '85–'88. The Development of the Cape Species of *Peripatus*, I–VI: *Q. J.*, XXV–XXVIII. — '94. On the Inadequacy of the Cellular Theory of Development, etc.: *Q. J.*, XXXVII. — **Seeliger, O.,** '94. Giebt es geschlechtlicherzeugte Organismen ohne mütterliche Eigenschaften? *A. Entwm.*, I, 2. — **Seifriz, W.,** '18. Observations on the Structure of Protoplasm by the aid of Microdissection: *B. B.*, XXXIV. — '20. Viscosity values of Protoplasm as determined by Microdissection: *B. G.*, LXX. — '21. Observations on some Physical Properties of Protoplasm, etc.: *A. Bot.* — **Seiler, J.,** '14. Das Verhalten der Geschlechtschromosomen bei Lepidopteren: *A. Zv.*, XIII. — '17, '20, '21, '22, '23. (X). — **Seiler** and **Hanel,** '21. — Das verschiedene Verhalten der Chromosomen, etc., von *Lymantria monaca: Z. A. V.*, XXVII. — **Selenka, E.,** '83. Die Keimblätter der Echinodermen: *Studien über Entwick.*, II. *Wiesbaden.* — **Sertoli, E.,** '65. Dell' esistenza di particolari cellule ramificate dei canaliculi seminiferi del testiculo umano: *Il Morgagni.* — **Shackell, L. F.,** '11. Phosphorus Metabolism during early Cleavage of the Echinoderm Egg: *Sci.*, XXXIV, 878.— **Shaffer, E. L.,** '17. Mitochondria and other Cytoplasmic Structures in the Spermatogenesis of *Passalus: B. B.*, XXXII. — '20. The Germ-Cells of *Cicada: B. B.*, XXXVIII. — **Sharp, L. W.,** '11. The Embryo Sac of *Physostegia: B. G.*, LII. — '12b. The Orchid Embryo-Sac: *B. G.*, LIV. — '13, '20. (II). — '12a, '14, '20. (IV). — '14. Maturation in *Vicia: B. G.*, LVII. — '21. (I). — **Shattuck, C. H.,** '15. A Morphological Study of *Ulmus Americana: B. G.*, XL. — **Shaw, W. R.,** '98a. Ueber die Blepharoplasten bei *Onoclea* and *Marsilia: B. D. B. G.*, XVI, 7. — **Shearer, C.,** '12. The Problem of Sex Determination in *Dinophilus: Q. J.*, LVII. — **Shearer, C.,** and **Lloyd, D. J.,** '12. On Methods of Producing Artificial Parthenogenesis in *Echinus esculentus*, etc.: *Q. J.*, LVIII. — **Shearer, De Morgan** and **Fuchs,** '13. On the Experimental Hybridization of Echinoids: *P. T.*, CCIV, B. — **Sheppard, E. J.,** '13. The Structure of the Nucleus: *J. R. M.* — **Shull, A. F.,** '10, '11. (III). — '12. Studies in the Life Cycle of *Hydatina Senta*, III: *J. E. Z.*, XII. — '15. Inheritance in *Hydatina senta*, II: *J. E. Z.*, XVIII. — '21. Chromosomes and the Life Cycle of *Hydatina: B. B.*, XLI. — **Shull, G. H.,** '10. Inheritance of Sex in *Lychnis: B. G.*, XL. — '11. Reversible Sex-mutants in *Lychnis dioica: B. G.*, LII. — '14. (X). — **Siedlecki, M.,** '99. Étude cytologique et cycle évolutif de *Adelea: Ann. Inst. Pasteur*, XIII. — **Sijpkens, B.,** '04. Die Kernteilung bei *Fritillaria: Recueil des Trav. Bot. Néerlandais*, II, IV. — **Silvestri, F.,** '06–'08. Contribuzioni alla conoscenza biologica degli Imenotteri parasitici, 1–4: *Boll. Scuola Sup. Agric. Portici*, I–III. — '14. Prime fasi di sviluppo del *Copidosoma*, etc.: *A. A.*, XLVII. — **Simon, C. E.**, '23. The Filterable Viruses: *Phys. Rev.*, III. — **Sinéty, R. de**, 'o1. Recherches sur la biologie et l'anatomie des phasmes: *L. C.*, XIX. — **Sjövall, E.**, 'o6. (IV). — **Smallwood, W. M.**, 'o4. Maturation, Fertilization, etc. . . . of *Haminea: C. M. Z.*, XLV. — 'o5. Some Observations on the Chromosome Vesicles in the Maturation of Nudibranchs: *M. J.*, XXXIII. — **Smet, E. de**, '14. Chromosomes, prochromosomes, et nucléole dans quelques Dicotylées: *L. C.*, XXIX. — **Smith, Bertram, G.**, '12. The Embryology of *Cryptobranchus*, I: *J. M.*, XXIII. '19. The Individuality of the Germ-Nuclei during the Cleavage.of the Egg of *Cryptobranchus: B. B.*, XXXVII. — **Smith, E. A.**, '16. Spermatogensis of the Dragonfly *Sympetrum*, etc.: *B. B.*, XXXI. — **Smith, G.**, '10, '11, '10–'12. (X). — **Smith, R. W.**, '11. The tetra-nucleate Embryo-Sac of *Clintonia: B. G.*, LII. — **Snook, H. J.**, and **Long, J. A.**, '14. Parasynaptic Stages in the Testis of *Aneides lugubris: Univ. Calif. Publ.*, XV. — **Sobotta, J.**, '95. Die Befruchtung ond Furchung des Eies der Maus: *A. M. A.*, XLV. — '97. Die Reifung und Befruchtung des Eies von *Amphioxus: A. M. A.L.* — **Sokoloff, B.**, '23. Études sur la biologie des Protozoaires (Lit.): *A. B.*, XIII. — **Sokolow, I.**, '13. Ueber die Spermatogenese der Skorpione: *A. Zf.*, IX. — '24. (VIII). — **Sonnenbrodt**, 'o8. Wachstumsperiode der Oöcyte des Hühnes: *A. M. A.*, LXXII. — **Solger, B.**, '91. Die radiaren Strukturen der Zell-körper, etc.: *Berl. Klin. Wochenschr.*, XX. — **Spaeth, R. A.**, '16. (VIII). — Spallanzani, 1786. Experiences pour servir a l'histoire de la génération des animaux et des plantes: *Geneva.* — **Spek, J.**, '18a, 18b. (II). — **Spemann, H.**, 'o1–'o3. (XIV). — '14. Ueber verzögerte Kernversorgung von Keimteilen: *V. D. Z. G.* — '19. Experimentelle Forschungen zum Determinations- und Individualitätsproblem: *Die Naturwissenschaften*, VII, 32. — **Spencer, H.**, '66. Principles of Biology: *Am. Ed.* — **Spiro, K.**, 'o9. (VIII). — **Spitzer**, '97. Die Bedeutung gewisser Nucleoproteide für die oxydative Leistung der Zelle: *A. Ph.*, LXVII. — **Spitzchakoff, T.**, 'o9. Spermien und Spermiohistogenese bei *Cariden: A. Zf.*, III. — **Spooner, G. R.**, '10. Embryological Studies with the Centrifuge: *J. E. Z.*, X. — **Stauffacher, H.**, '94. Eibildung und Furchung bei *Cyclas: J. Z.*, XXVIII. — '10. Beiträge zur Kenntniss der Kernstrukturen: *Z. W. Z.*, XCV. — **Steil, W. N.**, '18. Studies of some new Cases of Apogamy in Ferns: *Bull. Torr. Bot. Club*, XLV. — '19a. Apogamy in *Nephrodium: A. Bot.*, XXXIII. — '19b. Apospory in *Pteris: B. G.*, LXVII. — **Stevens, F. L.**, '99. The Compound Oösphere of *Albugo bliti: B. G.*, XXVIII. — 'o1. Gametogenesis and Fertilization in *Albugo: B. G.*, XXXII. — **Stevens, N. M.**, 'o3. On the Ovogenesis and Spermatogenesis of *Sagitta: Z. J. (Anat.)*, XVIII. — 'o4. Further Studies on the Oogenesis of *Sagitta: Ibid.*, XXI. — 'o4. On the Germ Cells and the Embryology of *Planaria: Proc. Acad. Nat. Sci.*, *Phil.* — 'o5, 'o6, 'o9, '11. (X). — 'o8a. The Chromosomes in *Diabrotica*, etc.: *J. E. Z.*, V. — 'o8, '12b. (XI). — 'o9. The Effect of Ultraviolet Light upon the Developing Eggs of *Ascaris megaolcephala: A. Entwm.*, XXVII. — 'o9. An Unpaired Chromosome in the Aphids: *J. E. Z.*, VI. — '10. A Note on Reduction in the Maturation of male Eggs in Aphids: *B. B.*, XVIII. — '10. Further Studies on Reproduction in *Sagitta: J. M.*, XXI. — '10a. The Chromosomes in the Germ-cells of *Culex: J. E. Z.*, VIII. — '11a. Preliminary Note on Heterochromosomes in the Guinea-Pig: *B. B.*, XX. — '12. Supernumerary Chromosomes and Synapsis in *Ceuthophilus: B. B.*, XXII. — **Stieve, H.**, '20. '20a. (IV). — **Stockey, A. G.**, '18. Apogamy in the *Cyatheaceae: B. G.*, LXV. — **Stolc, A.**, '10. Ueber kernlose Individuen, etc. von *Amoeba: A Entwm.*, XXIX.

— **Stoll, N. R.,** '19. Sex-determination in the White Fly: *J. G.*, IV. — **Stomps, T. J.,** '10. (VI). — '11. Kernteilung und Synapsis bei *Spinacia: B. C.*, XXI. — '12. Mutation in *Oenothera biennis L.: B. C.*, XXXII. — '12. Die Entstehung von *Oenothera gigas: B. D. B. G.*, XXX. — '16. (XII). — '19. (XI). — **Stout, A. B.,** '12. (XI). — **Strasburger, E.,** '75, '80, '84, '07, '10. (Int.). — '77, '84, '09. (V). — '79. Die Angiospermen und die Gymnospermen: *Jena.* — '82. Ueber den Theilungsvorgang der Zellkerne, etc.: *A. M. A.*, XXI. — '82. Ueber den Bau und das Wachstum der Zellhäute: *Jena.* — '84a. Die Controversen der indirecten Zelltheilung: *A. M. A.*, XXIII. — '88. Ueber Kern- und Zellteilung im Pflanzenreich, nebst einem Anhang über Befruchtung: *Hist. Beitr.*, I. — '88, '95, '00. (II). — '89. Ueber das Wachsthum vegetabilischer Zellhäute: *Jena.* — '92. (IV). — '93a. (IX). — '93b. Ueber die Wirkungssphäre der Kerne und die Zellgrösse: *Fischer, Jena.* — '94. The Periodic Reduction of the Number of the Chromosomes, etc.: *A. Bot.*, VIII. — '97a. Kerntheilung und Befruchtung bei *Fucus: J. W. B.*, XXX. — '97c. Ueber Cytoplasmastrukturen, Kern- und Zelltheilung: *J. W. B.*, XXX. — '98, '03. (I). — '00. Versuche mit diözischen Pflanzen in Rücksicht auf Geschlechtsverteilung: *B. C.*, XX. — '01. Ueber Plasmaverbindungen pflänzlicher Zellen: *J. W. B.*, XXV. — '01. Ueber Befruchtung: *B. Z.*, LIX. — '04. Die Apogamie der *Eualchemillen: J. W. B.*, XLI. — '05. (VI). — '06. Zur Frage eines Generationswechsels bei Phaeophyceen: *B. Z.*, LXIV, 2. — '07, '08, '09, '10. (XI). — '07a. Apogamie bei *Marsilia: Flora,* XCVII. — '07b. (III). — '08a, b, '10. (XII). — '10. — '14. The Periodic Reduction of the Number of Chromosomes in the Life-History, etc.: *Ann. Bot.*, VII (see also *B. C.*, XIV). — **Strassen, O. L. zur,** '96. Embryonalentwicklung der *Ascaris meg.: A. Entwm.*, III. — '96. Riesenembryonen bei *Ascaris: B. C.*, XVI. — '98. (XIII). — '03. Ueber die Mechanik der Epithelbildung: *V. D. Z. G.* — '06. (XIII). — **Studnicka, F. K.,** '18. Die Reduktion und die Regeneration des Cytoplasmas, etc.: *Z. W. Z.*, CXVII, 4. — **Sturtevant, A. H.,** '13, '14, '15. (XII). — '15. No Crossing Over in the Female of the Silkworm Moth: *A. N.*, XLIX. — '17. Crossing over without Chiasmatype: *G.*, II. — '20. Intersexes in *Drosophila simulans: Sci.*, LI. — **Sturtevant, Bridges** and **Morgan,** '19. The Spatial Relations of Genes: *P. N. A.*, V. — **Sumner, F. B.,** '23. Size-Factors and Size-Inheritance: *P. N. A.*, IX. — **Süssenguth, K.,** '21. Bemerkungen zur meiotischen und somatischen Kerntheilung, etc.: *Flora,* XIV. — **Sutton, W. S.,** '00. The spermatogonial Divisions in *Brachystola magna: Kansas Univ. Quart.*, IX. — '02. On the Morphology of the Chromosome-group in *Brachystola magna: B. B.*, IV, 1. — '03. (XII). — **Suzuki, B.,** '98. Notiz über die Entstehung des Mittelstückes von Selachiern: *A. A.*, XV. — **Svedelius, N.,** '11. '15. (VII). — '14a. Ueber die Zystokarpienbildung bei *Delesseria: Ibid.*, VIII. — '14b. Ueber die Tetradenteilung en der vielkernigen Tetrasporangiumanlagen bei *Nitophyllum: B. D. B. G.*, XXXII. — '14b. Ueber Sporen an Geschlechtspflanzen von *Nitophyllum: B. D. B. G.*, XXII. — **Swarczewsky, B.,** '12. Zur Chromidienfrage, etc.: *B. C.*, XXXII. — '08. Ueber die Fortflanzungserscheinungen bei *Arcella: A. P.*, XII. — **Swezy, O.,** '16. (IX). — **Swift, C. H.,** '14. (IV). — '16. Two new Organs of the Plant Cell: *B. G.*, XXV. — **Swingle, W. W.,** '17. The Accessory Chromosome in a Frog, etc.: *Ibid.*, XXXII. — '18. The Effects of Inanition upon the Development of the Germglands, etc.: *J. E. Z.*, XXIV, 3. — '20. (IV). — '22. Is there a Transformation of Sex in Frogs? *J. E. Z.* — **Sykes, M. G.,** '08. Nuclear Division in *Funkia: A. Zf.*,

I. — '09. On the Nucleus of some unisexual Plants: *Ann. Bot.*, XXIII. — **Szuts, A. v.,** '15. Studien über die feinere Beschaffenheit, etc.: *A. Zf.*, XIII.

TÄCKHOLM, G., '14. Zur Kenntniss der Embryosackentwicklung von *Lopezia: Svensk. Bot. Tids.*, VIII. — '20. On the Cytology of the Genus *Rosa: Ibid.*, XIV, 2–3. — '22. (XI). — **Tahara, M.,** '10. Ueber die Kernteilung bei *Morus: Bot. Mag. Tokyo*, XXIV. — '15. Parthenogenesis in *Erigeron: Ibid.*, XXIV. — '15. Cytological Studies on *Chrysanthemum: Ibid.*, XXIX. — '21. Cytologische Studien an einigen Kompositen: *Jour. Coll. Sci. Imp. Univ. Tokyo*, V, 43. — **Tanaka, I.,** '13. A Study of Mendelian Factors in the Silkworm, *Bombyx: Jour. Coll. Agr., Tohoku Imp. Univ., Sapporo, Japan*, V. — '16. Genetic Studies on the Silkworm: *Ibid.*, VII. — **Tangl. E.,** '79. Ueber offene Communicationen zwischen den Zellen des Endosperms einiger Samen: *J. W. B.*, XII. — **Taylor, Monica,** '14. The Chromosome Complex of *Culex: Q. J.*, LX. — **Taylor, W. R.,** '20. A Morphological and Cytological Study of Reproduction in the Genus *Acer: Contrib. Bot. Lab. U. of Pa.*, V. — '22. Organization of herotypic Chromosomes: *Sci.*, XLVI. — '24. Chromosome Shape and Individuality (in *Gasteria*): *A. J. B.*, XI. — **Teichmann, E.,** '03. Ueber die Beziehung zwischen Astrosphären und Furchen: *A. Entwm.*, XVI, 2. — **Tellyesnickzy, K.,** '02. Zur Kritik der Kernstrukturen: *A. M. A.*, LX. — '05. Ruhekern and Mitose: *Ibid.*, LXVI. — '07. Die Entstehung der Chromosomen. Evolution oder Epigenesis? *Berlin, Wien.* — **Tennent, D. H.,** '08. The Chromosomes in cross-fertilized Echinoid Eggs: *B. B.*, XV. — '11. A Heterochromosome of Male Origin in Echinoids: *B. B.*, XXI. — '12. Studies in Cytology, I and II: *J. E. Z.*, XII. — **Terni, T.,** '14. Condriosomi, idiozoma e formazioni periidiozomiche nella spermatogenesi degli Anfibi: *A. Zf.*, XII. — **Thompson, D'Arcy W.,** '17. (XIII). — **Thompson, J. A.,** '08. Heredity: *London and New York.* — **Timberlake, H. G.,** '00. (II). — '02. Development and Structure of the Swarm-Spores of *Hydrodictyon: Trans. Wis. Acad. Sci.*, XIII. — **Tischler, G.,** '06. Ueber die Entwicklung des Pollens und der Tapetenzellen bei *Ribes-Hybriden: J. W. B.*, XLII. — '10, '15. (XI). — '18. Untersuchungen über den Riesenwuchs von *Phragmites: B. D. B. G.*, XXXVI. — '20. Ueber die sogenanannten "Erbsubstanzen" und ihre Lokalisation in der Pflanzenzelle: *B. C.*, XL. — '22. Allgemeine Pflanzencaryologie: *Handb. d. Pflanzenanat.* I, *Berlin.* — **Torrey, J. C.,** '03. (XIII). — **Townsend, C. O.,** '97. Der Einfluss des Zellkerns auf die Bildung der Zellhaut: *J. W. B.*, XXX. — **Toyama, K.,** '94. On the Spermatogenesis of the Silkworm: *Bull. Coll. Agric., Imp. Univ., Tokio.*, II. — **Treadwell, A. L.,** '01. (XIII). — **Tretjakoff, D.,** '04. Die Spermatogenese bei *Ascaris: A. M. A.*, LXV. — **Troland, L. T.,** '17. (IX). — **Tröndle, A.,** '11. Ueber die Reduktionsteilung in den Zygoten von *Spirogyra*, etc.: *Z. B.*, III. — '12. Der Nucleolus von *Spirogyra* und die Chromosomen höherer Pflanzen: *Z. B.* — **Trow, A. H.,** '95. The Karyology of *Saprolegnia: A. Bot.*, IX. — '16. A Criticism of the Hypothesis of Linkage and Crossing over: *J. G.*, V. — **Tschassownikoff, S.,** '14. Ueber Becher- und Flimmerepithelzellen, etc.: *A. M. A.*, LXXXIV. — **Tschermak, E. v.,** '08. Der moderne Stand des Vererbungsproblems: *Arch. Rass. und Gesell.*, V. — **Tschernoyarow, M.,** '14. Ueber die Chromosomenzahl in besonders beschaffene Chromosomen im Zellkerne von *Najas: B. D. B. G.*, XXXII. — **Twiss, W. C.,** '19. A Study of Plastids and Mitochondria in *Preissia* and Corn: *A. J. B.*, VI. — **Tyson, James,** '87. (Int.).

USSOW, M., '81. Untersuchungen über die Entwickelung der Cephalopoden: *A. B.*, II.

LA VALETTE ST. GEORGE, '65, '67. Ueber die Genese der Samenkörper, I and II: *A. M. A.*, I, III. — '76. Die Spermatogenese bei den Amphibien: *A. M. A.*, XII. — '78. Die Spermatogenese bei den Säugethieren und dem Menschen: *A. M. A.*, XV. — '85-'87. Spermatologische Beiträge, I–V: *A. M. A.*, XXV, XXVII, XXVIII and XXX. — '87. Zelltheilung und Samenbildung bei *Forficula: Festschrift f. v. Koelliker., Leipzig.* — **Van Bambeke, C.,** '93. Elimination d'éléments nucleaires dans l'œuf ovarien de *Scorpaena: A. B.*, XIII, 1. — '98. Recherches sur l'oöcyte de *Pholcus phalangioides: A. B.*, XV. — **Van Beneden, E.,** '70. Recherches sur la composition et la signification de l'œuf: *Mém. Cour. de l'Ac. Roy. de Belgique.* — '75. La maturation de l'œuf, la fécondation et les premières phases du développement embryonnaire des mammifères, etc.: *Bull. Ac. Roy. de Belgique*, XI. — '76. Recherches sur les Dicyémides: *Ibid.*, XLI, XLII. — '76. Contribution a l'histoire de la vésicule germinative et du premier noyau embryonnaire; *Ibid.*, XLI, also *Q. J.*, XVI. — '83, '84. (Int.). — **Van Beneden** and **Julin,** '81. Observations sur la maturation, la fécondation et la segmentation de l'œuf chez les Cheiroptères: *A. B.*, I. — '84a. (XIII). — '84b. La spermtogénèse chez *l'Ascaride mégalocéphale: B. A. B.*, 3me ser. VII. — **Van Beneden** et **Neyt,** '87. (V). — **Van Camp, G. M.,** '23. Le rôle du nucléole dans la caryocinèse somatique: *L. C.*, XXXIV. — **Van der Stricht, O.,** '92. Contribution a l'étude de la sphère attractive: *A. B.*, XII, 4. — '95a. La maturation et la fécondation de l'œuf d'*Amphioxus: B. A. B.*, XXX, 2. — '95b. De l'origine de la figure achromatique de l'ovule en mitose chez le *Thysanozoön: Verh. d. anat. Versamml. in Strasburg.* — '95c. Contributions a l'étude de la forme, de la structure et de la division du noyau: *B. A. B.*, XXIX. — '97. La formation des deux globules polaires, etc., dans l'œuf de *Thysanozoön: A. B.*, XV. — '98b. Contribution a l'étude du noyau vitellin de Balbiani: *V. A. G.*, XII. — '99. Étude de plusieurs anomalies interessante lors de la formation des globules polaires: *Livre Jubilaire dedié a Van Bambeke.* — '02. Les " pseudochromosomes " dans l'oöcyte de chauve-souris: *C. R. Assoc. Anat.* — '04. La couche vitellogène et les mitochondries de l'œuf des Mammifères: *V. A. G.* — '05. Structure de l'œuf ovarique de la femme: *B. A. B.* — '05. La structure de l'œuf de chauve-souris: *C. R. Assoc. Anat.* — '08. La structure de l'œuf de la chienne et la génèse du corps jaune: *Ibid.* — '09. La structure de l'œuf des Mammifères: *Mem. Acad. Royale de Belgique.* — '11. Vitellogénèse dans l'ovule de Chatte: *A. B.*, XXVI. — **Van Herwerden, M. A.,** '10. Ueber den Kernstructur in den Speicheldrüsen der *Chironumus* Larvae: *A. A.*, XXXVI. — '13. Ueber die Nucleasewirkung auf tierische Zellen: *A. Zf.*, X. — '16. La digestion de spermatozoides par la nuclease: *Arch. Néer. Phys.*, I. — '17. On the Nature and Significance of Volutin in Yeast Cells: *Proc. Kon. Akad. Wetensch. Amsterdam*, XX, 1. — **Van Leeuwen-Reijnvaan, D.,** '07. Ueber eine Zweifache Reduktion bei einigen *Polytrichum-Arten: Rec. Trav. Bot. Néerl.*, IV. — '08. Ueber die Spermatogenese der Moose: *B. D. B. G.*, XXVIa. — **Vejdovský, F.,** '81. Untersuchungen über die Anatomie, Physiologie und Entwicklung von *Sternaspia: Denkschr. d. Akad. Wien.*, XLIII. — '88-'92. (XIII). — '04. Ueber den Kern der Bakterien und seine Teilung: *Centr. Bakt.*, XI. — '07. (VI). — '11. Die Vererbungsträger: *Prag.* — '11-'12. (XI). — **Vejdovský** and **Mrázek,** '98. Centrosom und Periblast: *Sitzber. Böhm.*

Ges. Wiss. — '03. (II, V). — **Verworn, M.,** '88. Biologische Protisten-studien: *Z. W. Z.*, XLVI. — '91, '03, '09, '15. (VIII). — '95. Allgemeine Physiologie: *Jena.* — '13, '15. (I). — **Vialleton, L.,** '88. (XIII). — **Vines, S. H.,** '11. (V). — **Virchow, R.,** '55. Cellular-Pathologie: *Arch. Path. Anat. Phys.*, VIII, 1. — '58. (Int.). — **Voïnov, D. N.,** '03. Le spermatogénèse d'été chez le *Cybister: A. Z. E.*, I, 4th sér. — '14. Sur un nouveau mécanisme determinant le dimorphisme des éléments sexuels, etc.: *C. R. S. B.*, LXXVI. — '16. Recherches sur la spermatogénèse du *Gryllotalpa: A. Z. E.*, LIV. — '16. Sur une formation juxta-nucleaire dans les éléments sexuels du *Gryllotalpa*, etc.: *C. R. S. B.*, LXXIX. — '16. Sur l'existence d'une chondriodiérèse: *C. R. S. B.*, LXVIII. — **von Voss, H.,** '14. Cytologische Studien an *Mesostoma: A. Zf.*, XII. — **De Vries, H.,** '85. Plasmolytische Studien uber die Wand der Vacuolen: *J. W. B.*, XVI. — '89. (IX). — '03. Befruchtung und Bastardierung: *Leipzig.* (XII).

WAGER, H., '96. On the Structure and Reproduction of *Cystopus: A. Bot.*, X. — '03. The Cell-Structure of the Cyanophyceae: *P. R. S.* — '04. The Nucleolus and Nuclear Division in the Root Apex of *Phaseolus: A. Bot.*, XVIII. — **Wakker, J. H.,** '88. Studien über die Inhaltskörper der Pflanzenzelle: *J. W. B.*, XIX. — **Waldeyer, W.,** '70. (IV). — '88. (Int.). — '06. (IV). — **Walker, C. E.,** .07. The Essentials of Cytology: London. — '11. On Variation in Chromosomes: *A. Zf.*, VI. — **Walker, N.,** '13. On Abnormal Cell-Fusion in the Archegonium; and on Spermatogenesis in *Polytrichum: A. Bot.*, XXVII. — **Walker and Debaisieux,** '09. On the Behavior of the Nucleoli, etc.: *Proc. Roy. Soc. Med.* — **Walker and Tozer,** '09. (I). — **Wallace, L. B.,** '09. The Spermatogenesis of *Agalena: B. B.*, XVII. — **Wallin, I. E.,** '22, '23. — On the Nature of Mitochondria: *A. J. A.*, IV; *A. N.*, LVII. — '23a. The Mitochondria Problem: *A. N.*, LVII. — '23b. Symbionticism and Protaxis: *A. R.*, XXVI. — **Walter, H. E.,** '14. Genetics: New York. — **Walton, A. C.,** '18. The Oögenesis and Early Embryology of *Ascaris canis: J. M.*, XXX. — **Warburg, O.,** '08. Beobachtungen über die Oxidationsprozesse im Seeigelei: *Zeit. Physio. Chem.*, LVII. — '10. Ueber die Oxydationen in lebenden Zellen nach Versuchen am Seeigelei: *Zeitschr. phys. Chem.*, LXVI. — '13. (VIII). — '14. Beiträge zur Physiologie der Zelle, etc.: *E. P.*, XIV. — **Wasielewski, W. v.,** '02, '03. Theoretische u. experimentelle Beiträge zur Kenntniss der Amitose, I, II: *J. W. B.*, XXXVIII. — **Wassilieff, A.,** '07. Die Spermatogenese von *Blatta: A. M. A.*, LXX. — **Watasé, S.,** '90. (XIII). — '93a. (IX). — '97b. Homology of the Centrosome: *J. M.*, VIII, 2. — **Webber, H. J.,** '97b. The Development of the Antherozoids of *Zamia: B. G.*, XXIV. — '97c. Notes on the Fecundation of *Zamia* and the Pollen-tube Apparatus of *Gingko: B. G.*, XXIV, 4. — '00. Xenia . . . in Maize: *U. S. Dept. Agr., Bull.*, XXII. — '01. Spermatogenesis and Fecundation in *Zamia: U. S. Dept. Agr. Plt. Ind. Bull.*, II. — **Weigl, R.,** '12. Vorgleichend-zytologische Untersuchungen über den Golgi-Kopschschen Apparat, etc.: *Bull. Int. Acad. Sci. Cracovie*, LVII. — **Weinzieher, S.,** '14. — **Weismann, A.,** '81-'88, '04. (Int.). — '81-'83, '13. (III). — '82. Beiträge zur Kenntnis der ersten Entwicklungsvorgänge im Insektenei: Festschrift. — '83. Ueber Vererbung: *Jena.* — '83. Entstehung der Sexualzellen bei den Hydromedusen: *Fischer, Jena.* — '85. (V, XIV). — '87. Ueber die Zahl der Richtungskörper, etc.: *Jena.* — '91b. Amphimixis, oder die Vermischung der Individuen: *Fischer, Jena.* — '92b. Das Keimplasma: *Jena.* — '93. (XIV). — '94. Aeussere Einflüsse als Entwicklungsreize:

Jena. — '99. Regeneration: *Nat. Sci.*, XIV, 6. (See also *A. A.*, '99.) — **Welsford, E. J.**, '97. Fertilization in *Ascobolus: N. P.*, VI. — '14. The Genesis of the Male Nuclei in *Lilium: A. Bot.*, XXVIII. — '15. Nuclear Migration in *Phragmidium: A. Bot.*, XXIX. — **Wenck, W. v.**, '14. Entw. Untersuchungen an Tardigraden: *Z. J.*, XXXVII. — **Weniger, W.**, '18. Fertilization in *Lilium: B. G.*, LXVI. — **Wenrich, D. H.**, '15. Synapsis and the Individuality of the Chromosomes: *Sci.*, XLI. — '16, '17. (VI). — '21. The Structure and Division of *Trichomonas: J. M.*, XXXVI. — **Wenyon, C. M.**, '13. Observations on *Herpetomonas*, etc.: *A. P.*, XXXI. — **West, G. S.**, '16. (VII). — **West** and **Lechmere**, '15. On Chromatin Extrusion in Pollen Mother-cells of *Lilium: A. B.*, XXIX. — **Wetzel, G.**, '96. Beiträge sum Studium der künstlichen Doppelmissbildungen, etc.: *Inaug. Diss., Berlin.* — '04. Centrifugierversuche an unbefruchten Eiern von *Rana fusca: A. M. A.*, LXIII. — **Wheeler, W. M.**, '89. The Embryology of *Blatta* and *Doryphora: J. M.*, III. — '93. A Contribution to Insect-embryology: *Ibid.*, VIII, 1. — '95. The Behavior of the Centrosomes in the Fertilized Egg of *Myzostoma: Ibid.*, X. — '96. The Sexual Phases of *Myzostoma: M. Z. S.*, XII, 2. — '97. The Maturation, Fertilization and early Cleavage of *Myzostoma: A. B.*, XV. — '98. (Int.). — '03. (X). — **Wheldale, M.**, '16. The Anthocyanin Pigments of Plants: *Cambridge.* — **Whiting, P. W.**, '17. The Chromosomes of the common House-Mosquito, *Culex pipiens: J. M.*, XXVIII, 2. — '18. Sex-determination and Biology of a parasitic Wasp, etc.: *B. B.*, XXIV, 4. — '21. Studies on the Parasitic Wasp, *Hadrobracon: B. B.*, XLI. — '21. The Production of Mosaic Males . . . in Hymenoptera: *A. R.*, XX. — **Whitman, C. O.**, '78, 94a and b. (Int.). — '78, '87, '97. (XIII). — '87. (IX). — '88. '94. (XIV). — '93. The Inadequacy of the Cell-Theory of Development: *J. M.*, VIII. — **Whitney, D. D.**, '09. Observations on the Maturation Stages, etc. of *Hydatina: J. E. Z.*, VI. — '12. Reinvigoration Produced by Cross Fertilization in *Hydatina senta: Ibid.*, XII. — '14. (III). — '16. The Control of Sex by Food in Five Species of Rotifers: *Ibid.*, XX. — '17. The Relative Influence of Food and Oxygen in Controlling Sex in Rotifers: *Ibid.*, XXIV. — **Wiemann, H. L.**, '10. A Study of the Germ-Cells of *Leptinotarsa: J. M.*, XXI. — '17. The Chromosomes of Human Spermatocytes: *A. J. A.*, XXI. — **Wierzejski, A.**, '05. (XIII). — **Wiesner, J.**, '86. Untersuchungen über die Organization der vegetabilischen Zellhaut: *Sitzber. Akad. Wiss. Wien.* — '92. (IX). — **Wilcox, E. V.**, '01. Longitudinal and transverse Divisions of Chromosomes: *A. A.*, XIX. — **Wildman, E. E.**, '13. The Spermatogenesis of *Ascaris*, etc.: *J. M.*, XXIV. — **Wilke, G.**, '07. Die Spermatogenese von *Hydrometra: J. Z.*, XLII. — '13. Chromatinreifung und Mitochondrienkörper in der Spermatogenese von *Hydrometra: A. Zf.*, X. — **Will, L.**, '84. Ueber die Entstehung des Dotters, etc., Amphibien, Insecten: *Z. A.*, VII. — '86. Die Entstehung des Eies von *Colymbetes: Z. W. Z.*, XLIII. — '94. **Will, N.**, Ueber die Befruchtung bei *Nemalion: B. D. B. G.*, XII. — **Williams, C. L.**, '99. The Origin of the Karyokinetic Spindle in *Passiflora: Proc. Calif. Acad. Sci.*, III., Bot. I. — **Williams, J. L.**, '04. The Cytology of the Gametophyte Generation: *A. Bot.*, XVIII. — **Williams, L.**, '07. The Structure of Cilia, etc.: *A. N.*, XLI. — **Wilson, C. B.**, '99. The Habits and early Development of *Cerebratulus: Q. J.*, XLIII. — **Wilson, E. B.**, '84. The Development of *Renilla: P. T.*, CLXXIV. — '89. The Embryology of the Earthworm: *J. M.*, III. — '92, '98. (XIII). — '93. Amphioxus and the Mosaic Theory of Development: *J. M.*, VIII. Also *W. H. L.*, II. — '95. Archoplasm, Centrosome, and

Chromatin in the Sea-urchin Egg: *J. M.*, XI. — '96, '00, '09c. (Int.). — '96b, '03, '04a and b. (XIV). — '97. Centrosome and Middle-piece in the Fertilization of the Egg: *Sci.*, V, 114. — '99, '23. (I). — '01a. (V). — '01a·c. Experimental Studies in Cytology, I–III: *A. Entwm.*, XII, XIII. — '02. Mendel's Principles of Heredity and the Maturation of the Germ-Cells: *Sci.*, XVI. — '03a. Notes on Merogony and Regeneration in *Renilla: B. B.*, IV, 5. — '04a, '04b. (XIV). — '05a, b, '06, '09, '10, '11a, b, '12. (X, see also XII). — '05c. (X). — '09, '10. (XI, XII). — '09b. The female Chromosome-groups in *Syromastes* and *Pyrrhocoris: B. B.*, XVI, 4. — '09c. Photographic Illustrations . . . of the Chromosomes in Hemiptera (Abstract): *Proc. Seventh Internat. Zool. Congr.*, Boston, Aug., '07. — '09. Secondary Chromosome Couplings and the Sexual Relations in *Abraxas: Sci.*, XXIX. — '10. Note on the Chromosomes of *Nezara: Sci.*, XXXI. — '12. (VI). — '12a, '14. (XII). — '13. A Chromatoid Body simulating an Accessory Chromosome in *Pentatoma: B. B.*, XXIV. — '16. The Distribution of the Chondriosomes to the Spermatozoa of Scorpions: *P. N. A. S.*, II. — **Wilson** and **Leaming,** '95. Atlas of Fertilization: *New York.* — **Wilson** and **Mathews,** '95. (V). — **Wilson** and **Morgan,** '20. (XII). — **Wilson, H. V.,** '07. (XIII). — '10. Development of Sponges from Dissociated Tissue Cells: *Bull. Bureau Fisheries, Washington*, XXX. — **Wilson, M.,** '09. On Spore Formation, etc., in *Mnium: A. Bot.*, XXIII. — '11. Spermatogenesis in the Bryophyta: *Ibid.*, XXV. — **Winge, O.,** '14. The Pollination and Fertilization Process; etc.: *C. R. Trav. Lab. de Carlsberg*, II. — '17. (XI). — '19. On the Relation between Number of Chromosomes and Number of Types: *J. G.*, VIII. — '22. One-sided masculine and sex-linked Inheritance in *Lebistes: Ibid.*, XII. — '22. A peculiar mode of Inheritance and its Cytological Explanation: *Ibid.*, XII, 2. — '23. Crossing-over between the X- and the Y-chromosome in *Lebistes: J. G.*, XIII. — '23. (X). — **Winiwarter, H. de.,** '01. (VI). — '12. Études sur la spermatogénèse humaine, I, II: *A. B.*, XXVII. — '12. Observations cytologiques sur les cellules interstitielles du testicule humaine: *A. A.*, XLI. — '14. L'Hétérochromosomes chez le Chat: *Acad. Roy. de Belgique.* — '19. Les mitoses de l'épithélium séminal du chat: *A. B.*, XXX. — '21. La formule chromosomiale dans l'espèce humaine: *C. R. S. B.*, LXXXV., '21. (XII). — **Winiwarter** and **Sainmont, G.,** '09. (VI). — **Winkler, H.,** '01. Ueber Merogonie und Befruchtung: *J. W. B.*, XXXVI. — '04. Ueber Parthenogenesis bei *Wikstroemia: B. D. B. G.*, XXII. — '06. Ueber Parthenogenesis bei *Wikstroemia: Ann. Jard. Bot. Buit.*, V. — '08. (III, V). — '09, '16. (XI). — '13, '20. (V). — '13-'14. Die Chimärenforschung als Methode experimenteller Biologie: *V. P. W.* — '16. Ueber die experimentelle Erzeugung von Pflanzen mit abweichenden Chromosomenzahlen: *Zeitschr. f. Bot.*, VIII. — '21. Ueber die Entstehung von genotypischer Verschiedenheiten, etc.: *Leipzig.* — **Wisselingh, C.,** '14. On the Nucleolus and Karyokinesis in *Zygnema: Rec. Trav. Bot. Néer.*, II. — **Witschi, Emil,** '14a. Experimentelle Untersuchungen über die Entwicklungsgeschichte der Keimdrusen von *Rana: A. M. A.*, XXXV. — '14b. Studien über die Geschlechtsbestimmung bei Fröschen: *A. M. A.*, LXXXVI. '21. Development of Gonads and Transformation of Sex in Frogs: *A. N.*, LV. — '23. Ueber die genetische Konstitution der Froschzwitter: *B. C.*, XLIII. — **Wodsedalek, J. E.,** '13. Spermatogenesis of the Pig with special Reference to the Accessory Chromosomes: *B. B.*, XXV. — '14. Spermatogenesis of the Horse, etc.: *Ibid.*, XXVII, 6. — '16. Causes of Sterility in the Mule: *Ibid.*, XXX. — '20. Studies on the Cells of Cattle with special Reference to Sex-Determination:

Ibid., XXXVIII. — **Wolfe, J. J.**, '04. Cytological Studies on *Nemalion: A. Bot.*, XVIII. — '18. Alternation and Parthenogenesis in *Padina: J. Elisha Mitchell Sci. Soc.*, XXXIV. — **Wolff, C. F.**, 1759. (Int.). — **Wolff, Gustav**, '95. Die Regeneration der Urodelenlinse: *A. Entwm.*, I, 3. — **Woltereck, R.**, '98. Zur Bildung und Entwicklung des Ostracoden-Eies: *Z. W. Z.*, LIV. — '04. (XIII). — '08. Ueber Veränderungen der Sexualität bei Daphniden: *Internat. Zeitschr. Hydrobiol.*, IV.: *V. D. Z. G.* — '11. Ueber Veränderung der Sexualität bei Daphniden: *Internat. Revue. Hydrobiol.*, IV. — **Woodburn, W. L.**, '11. Spermatogenesis in certain Hepaticae: *A. Bot.*, XXV. — '13. Spermatogenesis in *Blasia: Ibid.*, XXVII. — '15. Spermatogenesis in *Mnium: Ibid.*, XXIX. — **Woodruff, L. L.**, '05, '08, '12, '14, '21. (III). — '11. Two thousand Generations of *Paramoecium: A. P.*, XXI. — '15. The Problem of Rejuvenescence in Protozoa: *Biochem. Bull.*, IV. — **Woodruff** and **Baitsell**, '11. (III). — **Woodruff** and **Erdmann**, '14. (III, VII). — **Woolery, R.**, '15. Meiotic Divisions in the Microspore Mother-Cells of *Smilacina: A. Bot.*, XXIX. — **Woolsey, C. I.**, '15. Linkage of Chromosomes, etc.: *B. B.*, XXVIII. — **Woronin, Helene W.**, '07. Apogamie und Aposporie bei einigen Farnen: *B. D. B. G.*, XXV.

YAMANOUCHI, S., '06. (VII). — '07. Apogamy in *Nephrodium: B. G.*, XLIV. — '08. Apogamy in *Nephrodium: Ibid.*, XLV. — '08. Spermatogenesis, Oögenesis, and Fertilization in *Nephrodium: Ibid.*, XLV. — '09. Mitosis in *Fucus: Ibid.*, XLVII. — '10. Chromosomes in *Osmunda: Ibid.*, XXIX. — '12. (VII). — **Yasui, K.**, '11. On the Life-History of *Salvinia: A. Bot.*, XXV. — **Yatsu, N.**, '04, '10a and b, '11, '12. (XIV). — '05. (IX). — '09. Observations on Ookinesis in *Cerebratulus: J. M.*, XX. — '10c. An experimental Study of the Cleavage of the Ctenophore Egg: *Proc. Int. Zool. Cong.: Boston.* — '13. Notes on the Spermatogenesis of the wild and the domesticated Silkworms: *Annot. Zoöl. Japon.*, VIII. — **Yocom, H. B.**, '17. Some Phases of Spermatogenesis in the Mouse: *Univ. Calif. Publ.*, XIV. — '23. The Occurrence of Telosynapsis in *Leptocoris; J. M.*, XXXVII. — **Young, R. T.**, '13. The Histogenesis of the Reproductive Organs of *Taenia pisiformis: Z. J.*, XXXV.

ZACHARIAS, E., '81-'93. Ueber die chemische Beschaffenheit des Zellkerns: *B. Z.*, XXXIX. — Ueber den Zellkern: *Ibid.*, XL. — Ueber Eiweiss, Nuclein, und Plastin: *Ibid.*, XLI. — Ueber den Nukleolus: *Ibid.*, XLIII. — Beiträge zur Kenntniss des Zellkerns und der Sexualzellen: *Ibid.*, XLV. — '85 Ueber die amöboiden Bewegungen der Spermatozoen von *Polyphemus pediculus: Z. W. Z.*, XLI. — Ueber Chromatophile: *B. D. B. G.*, XI. — '88. Ueber Kern und Zelltheilung: *Ibid.*, XLVI. — '93a. Ueber die chemische Beschaffenheit von Cytoplasma und Zellkern: *B. D. B. G.*, II, 5. — '93b. Ueber Chromatophilie: *Ibid.*, II, 5. — '94. Ueber Beziehungen des Zellenwachstums zur Beschaffenheit des Zellkerns: *Ibid.*, XII, 5. — '95. Ueber das Verhalten des Zellkerns in wachsenden Zellen: *Flora*, LXXXI. — '96. Ueber einige mikrochemische Untersuchungsmethoden: *B. D. B. G.*, XIV. — '98. Ueber Nachweis und Vorkommen von Nuclein: *Ibid.*, XVI, 7. — '07. (IX). — '10. (VIII). — '13. Die Chromatin-Diminution in den Furchungszellen von *Ascaris: A. A.*, XLIII. — **Zaleski, W.**, '11. Ueber die Rolle der Nucleoproteide in den Pflanzen: *B. D. B. G.* — **Zarnik, B.**, '11. Ueber den Chromosomencyclus bei Pteropoden: *V. D. Z. G.* — **Zawarzin, A.**, '09. Beobachtungen an dem Epithel der Dessemetschen Membran: *A.*

M. A., LXXIV. — **Zeleny, C.**, '04. (XIV). — '05. Compensatory Regulation: *J. E. Z.*, II. — **Zeleny** and **Faust**, '15. (X). — **Zeleny** and **Senay**, '15. (X). — **Ziegler, H. E.**, '87. Die Entstehung des Blutes bei Knochenfischenembryonen: *A. M. A.*, '89. Ueber die Ursachen der pathologischen Gewebsneubildungen: *Int. Beitr. zur wiss. Med. Festschrift, R. Virchow*, II. — '91. Die biologische Bedeutung der amitotischen Kerntheilung im Tierreich: *B. C.*, XI. — '94. Ueber das Verhalten der Kerne im Dotter der meroblastischen Wirbelthiere: *Ber. Naturf. Ges. Freiburg.* — '94. Ueber Furchung unter Pressung: *V. A. G.*, VIII. — '95. Untersuchungen über die ersten Entwicklungsvorgänge der Nematoden: *Z. W. Z.*, LX. — '95. Untersuchungen über die Zelltheilung: *V. D. Z. G.* — '96. Einige Betrachtungen zur Entwicklungsgeschichte der Echinodermen: *V. D. Z. G.* — '98. Experimentelle Studien über die Zelltheilung; I: *A. Entwm.*, VI, 2. — '98b. Die Furchungszellen von *Beröe: A. Entwm.*, VII. — **Zimmerman, A.**, '93. Beiträge sur Morphologie und Physiologie der Pflanzenzelle: *Tübingen.* — '94. Sammelreferate aus dem Gesammtgebiete der Zellenlehre: Bot. Centrb. Beihefte. — '96. Die Morphologie und Physiologie des pflänzlichen Zellkernes, etc.: *Jena.* — **Zimmerman, K. W.**, '93b. Studien über Pigmentsellen, etc.: *A. M. A.*, XLI. — '98. Beiträge zur Kenntniss einiger Drüsen und Epithelzellen: *A. M. A.*, LII. — **Zoja, R.**, '95a. Sullo sviluppo dei blastomeri isolate dalle uova di alcune meduse: *A. Entwm.*, I, II, IV. — '95b. Sulla independenza della cromatina paterna e materna nel nucleo delle cellule embrionali: *A. A.*, IX, 10. — '96. Untersuchungen über die Entwicklung der *Ascaris: A. M. A.*, XLVII. — **Zoja, F.** and **R.**, '91. Intorno ai plastiduli fuchsinofili (bioblastuli dell'Altmann): *Mem. Ist. Sc. Milano* XVI. — **Zukal, H.**, '96. Ueber den Bau der Cyanophyzeen und Bakterien: *B. D. B. G.* — **Zsigmondy, R.**, '20. (VIII). — **Zweiger, H.**, '07. Die Spermatogenese von *Forficula: Zeitsch. f. Naturwiss.*, XLII.

INDEX OF SUBJECTS

843; meiosis of, **844**; sterility, 844; of *Drosera, Triticum,* 846; *Papaver,* 846; *Œnothera,* 847; *Hieracium,* roses, 847; from giant eggs, 972; merogonic, 973.

Hydatina, parthenogenesis and sex, 229, 743; sexual eggs, dimegaly, 801 ff.

Hydrodictyon, 622, 1031.

Hydroides, reversal of symmetry, 1026.

Hymenoptera, parthenogenesis and sex, 467, **795**, 800, 869; hybrids, 929.

Idiochromatin, 328, 725, 726 ff.

Idioplasm, 722, **1037**; as chromatin, 1039.

Idiozome (idiosome), 30, 50, 259, **329**; and yolk-nucleus, 341; in sperm-formation, 329, 358, 361, 382.

Ids, 500.

Ilyanassa, experiments, 1063.

Individuality of chromosomes, **828**; general evidence, 830; sceptics, 833.

"Initial structure" of cytoplasm, 1110.

Inner cell-wall, 136.

Interkinesis, 28; meiotic, 532.

Internal reticular apparatus (see Golgi-apparatus), 48.

Interzonal fibers, 144.

Intracellular pangenesis (see De Vries), 1085.

Insects, promorphology of egg, 1020.

Intersexes, 808.

Inversion experiments, 1076.

Isoëtes, fertilization, 201, 406.

Isogamy, 256.

Isopods, metamerism, 1029.

Julus, sperms, 298.

Karyogamy, 250, 394; and the chromosomes, 426, 581.

Karyokinesis (see Mitosis), definition, 116; general account, **121** ff.

Karyokinetic axis, 157.

Karyolysis, 115.

Karyomeres, 133, **894.**

Karyomerites, 429.

Karyoplasm (nucleoplasm), 22.

Karyoplasmic ratio, 79, 101, **727**; and senescence, 236 ff.

Karyoplast, 37.

Karyosomes, 93; in Protista, **204.**

Karyospheres, 93, 353.

Karyotin, 90.

Kinetonucleus, 695, 736.

Kinoplasm, 72, 153, **723.**

Lamblia, 23.

Lamp-brush chromosomes, 350.

Lanice, experiments on, 1048.

Largus, meiosis, 556.

Larix, mitosis, 154.

Larval mesoblast, 1009.

Lata-types, in *Œnothera,* **944** ff.; in *Datura,* 945.

Leiotropic, 988.

Lepidoptera, sperms, 303; diminution, 326; chondriosomes, 359; sperm-formation, 374; acrosome, 381; sex-chromosomes, 784; parthenogenesis, 804.

Lepidosiren, conjugation and deconjugation, 564, 793; chromosomes, 905.

Lepisma, sperms, 296.

Leptisma, presynapsis, 562.

Leptonema, leptotene, 349, 539, 556.

Leptonene threads, number, 556.

Leptomonas, 590.

Leucocytes, 23; origin, 218; asters, 682.

Leucoplasts, 43.

Life-cycle, general, 226.

Lilium, fertilization, 453; tetrads, 518, 519.

Limax, spiral asters, 145; Golgi-bodies, 167; pronuclei, 426; asters, 681.

Limosphere, 391.

Linin, 88.

Linkage (chromosome), of sex-chromosomes, 779; of chromosomes, **879** ff.; *Hesperotettix,* 881; *Lymantria,* 883, 887.

Linkage (genetic), linkage-groups, 17, 927, 938; sex-linkage, **939** ff.

Litomastix, oösome, 321; polocytes, 495.

Living and lifeless matter, 58, 59.

Localization, 980, **1040**; and differentiation, 1083; and environment, 1117.

Localizing activities, **1094** ff.; rôle of the sperm in, 1102.

Locusta, tetrads, 554; X-chromosome, 760.

Loligo, cleavage, 996, 1001; ovum, 1020.

Loop-formation, theory of, 557.

Lygæus type, 764.

Lymantria, 961.

Lymnæa, Golgi-bodies, 51, 167, **714**; cleavage, 993.

Macrogametes, 584.

Macrogamy, 582.

Macromeres, 987, 1000.

Macromitosome, 372.

Macrosomes (megasomes), 68.

Mactra, artificial parthenogenesis, 477.